Series Editor – Julia Cameron

D0414290

The Glory of the Cross

The great crescendo of the gospel

JAMES PHILIP

Foreword by Sinclair B Ferguson

The Didasko Files

This growing series takes its name from the New Testament Greek verb *didasko*, meaning 'I teach'. We trust it will serve the world's Church by helping Christians to grow in their faith. The series was founded in 2007 by the International Fellowship of Evangelical Students (IFES), a global movement now in over 150 countries working to proclaim Christ in the world's universities. www.ifesworld.org

IFES plays an active role in The Lausanne Movement

Royalties from sales of this title have been given to the ministry of the Cornhill Training Course in Scotland.

This booklet, edited and expanded by kind permission, is based on sermons preached in Holyrood Abbey Church, Edinburgh, Scotland under the title 'The meaning of the death of Christ'.

All scripture quotations are taken from the New International Version.
© 1973, 1978, 1984 by the International Bible Society.

Designed by Chris Gander
Printed in Singapore by Excel Print Media

The Glory of the Cross

The great crescendo of the gospel

From time to time a publication appears, of modest size and author, its value greater than a whole bookshelf of contemporary bestsellers. *The Glory of the Cross* falls in this category.

Its theme is so profound that a lifetime devoted to its study could not exhaust it. It is, essentially, a simple theme, the story of the passion of Jesus of Nazareth. But it is more than a story; it is an explanation of what happened, and why – and, indeed, why it *needed* to happen.

The fine quality of James Philip's mind will immediately be obvious. But his writing is also full of pathos. He is at one with his subject, and has clearly been more deeply impacted by it than by anything else in the world.

Yet there is nothing sensational here, nothing esoteric. No hidden code is disclosed. But there is a spirit about these pages that makes the reader feel that they contain the deepest secret of all history. But how? And why? And what difference does it make? To discover that, you must read on.

I first heard James Philip when I was seventeen years and nine months old. The precision of the date in my memory is a measure of the impact he made upon me. My only regret in sounding a small fanfare for this wonderful little book is that you cannot share that experience in person. But these pages are the next best thing.

As you read them, slowly and thoughtfully, I hope you will begin to feel something of the same debt to their author that I have felt for more than four decades. And, as James Philip himself would wish, I hope that you will feel a far greater debt, of love and faith, to the Person about whom this is written. Read on, then, and discover the glory of the cross.

Sinclair B. Ferguson

Revd Prof Sinclair B Ferguson
First Presbyterian Reformed Church, Columbia, South Carolina

3

START HERE

The final 24 hours of the Lord Jesus's life on earth are a 'holy of holies' in scripture. The gospel writers give us detailed accounts of people who were with him at each stage, and of what was said. We also know from John's gospel how Christ prayed for us in the Garden of Gethsemane. What love! As we walk through these hours, we do so with a deep sense of awe and reverence.

This booklet is for everyone: for those who came to faith in Christ many years ago, and for those who found faith in him just recently. We will never exhaust the riches of his precious death, no matter how long we have been Christians. Lend it to friends; talk about it; but more importantly, let it lead you back into the scriptures - to reflect on the cross, and to rejoice in all that Christ's death achieved. Then it will have served its purpose.

We go first to the upper room where Jesus has gathered his disciples for their last meal together.

THE LAST SUPPER

Christ's disciples had been with him for three years, yet they still did not understand his mission - that he had been born to die. As they ate together on that Thursday evening, the eternal Son of God was able to show them why he had come, in terms they would eventually recognize.

The disciples knew their history, and celebrated the Passover every year; they had done so with Jesus at least twice already, but the

Christ's disciples still did not understand his mission

connection with his death had not dawned on them. Now, as Jesus knows his betrayal is only a few hours away, he holds up the Passover bread, and then the wine, and declares 'This is my body' and 'This is my blood'. He is saying, 'Look, *this* is what I mean. I have come to deliver you from slavery. Don't you understand?' It is no

THE PASSOVER STORY

n Exodus 12 we have the story of the Passover, which was to be celebrated with thankfulness and solemnity each year 'for the generations to come' (Exodus 12:14,42). The Israelites had lived in Egypt for 430 years, since Joseph had been appointed its governor (see Genesis chapters 41-47). Now they numbered around 600,000 men, besides women and children, and Pharaoh, king of Egypt, would not let them return home. Moses and Aaron had pleaded with him to let them go, but he refused. God sent plagues, but Pharaoh's heart remained hard. Now came the most painful plague of all: the death of every firstborn son and animal in every Egyptian household. The Lord would, however, 'pass over' the homes of the Israelite families.

In preparation for this plague, the Lord instructed Moses in detail. That month would become the first month of the Israelite year. On the tenth day each Israelite household was to select a one-year-old lamb (or kid) without defect; on the fourteenth day the animal would be slaughtered at twilight, roasted that evening, and eaten with bitter herbs and with bread made without yeast. All Israelites were to mark their homes by smearing the blood of these animals on the lintel and the doorposts. This is how the Israelite homes would be recognized and passed over, while the Egyptian firstborn sons and animals died.

In fear, Pharaoh now drove the Israelites out of Egypt. Their dramatic journey into Sinai is recorded in Exodus 12-14. They left Egypt not just as the Israelites, but as God's covenant people.

To understand the 'new Covenant' we must understand the first Covenant. For as we remember our Lord's death in the holy communion service, we find ourselves in a long trajectory of grace, reaching forward from ancient times – from the Israelites' exodus, and their delivery from slavery.

oincidence that Jesus's final meal with his disciples took place during he Jewish feast of the Passover.

mystery is not the same as mystification

As we celebrate the Lord's supper in our churches today, we look back to that Thursday evening in Jerusalem, and we look further back, as Jesus and his disciples did, to the events of the Passover. It is true that there is mystery here, but mystery is not the same as mystification. It is a mystery which is meant to be understood. It was God who arranged for the betrayal of Jesus to be on Passover night. [1]

The Israelites, brought out of bondage, were the people of God. That is the context in which God gives them the Ten Commandments, opening with the words, 'I am the Lord your God who brought you out of Egypt, out of the land of slavery. You shall have no other gods before me'. He was not just giving them laws to be obeyed, but establishing his covenant with them, the covenant described in the New Testament as 'the old covenant'.

As Christ holds up the bread and the wine, he is announcing a 'new covenant'. This new covenant is what lies behind the Apostle Paul's statement that 'if anyone is in Christ he is a new creation; the old has gone; the new has come' (2 Corinthians 5:17). Paul writes to the Christians in Ephesus, 'You who were once far away have been brought near through the blood of Christ' (Ephesians 2:13). To be 'brought near' is a technical phrase meaning to be brought into the covenant. This new covenant would also draw in those who were not Jews, but Gentiles, and in due time the gospel would spread to every continent. The fulfilment of that new covenant in our lives is described by Paul in one of the richest phrases in the New Testament, 'union with Christ'. [3] We have died with him and he lives in us by his Holy Spirit. By his death we are welcomed into fellowship and into friendship with the Son of God. [4]

The betrayal

Matthew, Mark and Luke all record the story of Judas's visit to the high priest to arrange to betray him. As Mary of Bethany anoints Christ's feet with expensive perfume that Thursday afternoon, Judas objects oudly that the money could have been given to the poor. But John notes that this was not because of his concern for the poor, but because he helped himself from the money bag which was entrusted to him. After witnessing this act of devotion from Mary, he went straight out to arrange the betrayal.

As we move to the upper room, the gospel writers give us a stark and dramatic contrast of two covenants; one between Christ and his disciples, and the other between Judas and the high priest. The Lord's supper is set in the context of unspeakable intrigue and betrayal. Or to put it the other way round, unspeakable betrayal is irradiated by the beauty of the new covenant.

On one level the story of the betrayal stands as a solemn warning, and as a reminder of the consequences of sin and of how far sin can go. Judas's life had been bright with promise. He was a disciple, an Apostle, in a position of responsibility. I wonder which disciple Judas walked with as they were sent out two by two, and what the two of them spoke about along the way?

None of his fellow disciples saw what was coming. We have no suggestion in the gospels that they nudged each other and nodded towards Judas when Christ predicted that one of them would betray him. On the contrary, they all asked, 'Is it I?'

the Lord's supper is set in the context of intrigue and betrayal

Judas had had his feet washed in the upper room by the eternal Son of God. Imagine Christ's eyes looking up at him, as he looked down in shame. John tells us that Jesus handed Judas a piece of bread, dipped in wine, before he left. This was a sign of honour, of love. How Christ yearned for this man. A love of money had overtaken him, and for all Jesus's teaching on money and possessions, his heart had remained hard, and now his avarice had gone to an unimaginable extreme. John tells us that as soon as Judas took the bread, Satan entered him (John 13:27). And then we read the fateful words: 'he went out. And it was night.'

THE GARDEN OF GETHSEMANE

Only a hard heart would be unmoved in thinking of the way the Lord Jesus wrestled in the Garden of Gethsemane till drops 'as of blood' fell from his brow. But if we reflect on those hours only in a devotional manner, we miss the point. We must probe the deep questions: 'Why did he suffer? What is the meaning of the agony?' As soon as we begin to explore the *why* question, we find new vistas. We see our own conversion to Christ in a new perspective – for we see it in the context of his plan for the whole world. As we do this, we find our love for him being given a firmer basis, a doctrinal foundation – building such a foundation for our faith is the best and truest way of keeping our love for him alive. [5]

Matthew, Mark and Luke all give a detailed account of Christ's agony in the Garden, but John does not even mention it. [6] Why not? Perhaps he did not feel it necessary. To John, the whole of our Lord's life on earth was suffering. Right from the beginning, his death on the cross was on his mind. For John it was humiliation and indeed agony that the Son of God should have condescended to become a man. Gethsemane was just one expression of that agony. Throughout his gospel John stresses the glory of the Son of God. To John all Christ's life on earth – including his suffering – is infused with his glory. [7] John's profound and wonderful perspective provides a key as we consider the cross.

John and Luke both emphasise that Jesus went into the Garden often. He was moving willingly towards his death and was not trying to hide; Judas would know exactly where to find him. [8] When he was ready to leave the Garden, he said 'Rise, let us go' not to escape his foes, but rather to *meet* them. He was on his way to die. His death was not something he suffered so much as something he accomplished. He chose when he would be betrayed, tried, and crucified. 'What you are about to do, do quickly', he said to Judas, as if to say 'This is the time which I have appointed for you to do your dire deed.'

to John all Christ's life on earth is infused with his glory

Christ's terrible temptation

As we know from Genesis 3, Adam sinned when he was tempted in the Garden of Eden. Christ is the 'second Adam', and he triumphed in the Garden of Gethsemane. He did not draw back from the suffering which awaited him, but like a King serving on the front line, he advanced to face the enemy. [9]

Adam was tempted in Eden; and Jesus was tempted in Gethsemane. It is important for us to grasp that Christ fought with temptation; it was a real issue for him. We are told by the writer to the Hebrews that he 'has been tempted in every way, just as we are – yet without sin'. [10] So there must have been the possibility for him of drawing back, and not dying for the sins of the world.

He had fought in the wilderness with temptation to Messiah-ship without a cross when Luke tells us 'the devil left him until an opportune time.' The devil was to return in all his terrible force in Gethsemane. [11] Sometimes the most intense temptation can come before the crisis that brings blessing, as we may know from our own experience; we see that happening here. [12]

Christ fought with temptation; it was a real issue for him

What was the cause of Christ's dreadful agony in the Garden? He did not fear physical death; not even the horrible death of crucifixion. Many believers have faced such death, calmly and fearlessly. The spiritual burden he carried - bearing the sin of the world - is what appalled his spirit. Christ's death would not symbolize, but actually *materialize* human guilt. This explains the intensity of his feelings and the words the gospel writers use to explain them - 'sorrowful and troubled', 'deeply distressed and troubled', 'overwhelmed with sorrow to the point of death'. [13]

The expression rendered 'deeply distressed and troubled' probably comes from a Greek root meaning 'away from home'. Certainly, for our

Lord Jesus, it was the beginning of the horror of great darkness that would end in his cry of sheer dereliction, 'My God, my God, why have you forsaken me?'

'May this cup be taken from me'

While in Gethsemane we see Christ shrinking from his suffering, but the Apostle John records him as saying, 'Shall I not drink the cup the Father has given me?' [14] He delighted to do the Father's will, yet he naturally shrank from the awful agony of separation from God.

There is no contradiction between Christ's desire to do his Father's will, while also shrinking from it.

In the book of Leviticus we read of the burnt offering (a 'sweet-savour offering' of an unblemished animal) presenting a beautiful aroma to the LORD. But there is also a 'sin offering', a different kind of sacrifice, where the animal's blood is shed to substitute for the taking of human life in punishment for sin. Here is the essence of atonement. All this foreshadows what now becomes real, and ultimate, in the offering *and* sacrifice of Christ himself. He offers to the Father a perfect life without blemish, in sheer devotion to the Father's will. And he becomes, in our place, the sacrifice for sin. This is the double truth captured in Thomas Binney's lovely hymn:

There is a way for man to rise
To that sublime abode:
An offering and a sacrifice,
A Holy Spirit's energies,
An advocate with God.

In the Garden he knew he had to accept his death, if atonement were to be made, yet as he is dying on the cross the following afternoon he cries out 'Why have you forsaken Me?' Christ's awareness of what was happening had become clouded. In the dereliction of being cut off from God, our Saviour had been cut off from light; here was the heart of his agony. To go through it knowing everything would turn out well would not have reached into the depths of our sinful nature; he had to forego that knowledge. For not only did he *bear* our sin for us, but he was *made sin* for us:

> God made him who had no sin to be sin for us, so that in him we might become the righteousness of God. (2 Corinthians 5:21)

Of all the descriptions of the Atonement in scripture, this is surely one of the most graphic. It comes at the close of perhaps the most profound exposition ever of suffering and glory in the whole of 2 Corinthians 4 & 5. It is just not possible to skate onto the next chapter without a deep sense of wonder at the depth of Christ's love.

Fierce, costly love

In Gethsemane Jesus turned to his disciples in his very human suffering seeking human solace. [15] As the Psalmist had written: 'Scorn has broken my heart and has left me helpless; I looked for sympathy, but there was none, for comforters, but I found none'. [16] How much the memory of Mary of Bethany's anointing must have meant to him. Evidently she understood. On Calvary as the Son of God lost the last consciousness of his Father's love and presence, our forgiveness would be won.

In the Lord's final words in the Garden he tells his disciples to sleep on, then seems immediately to ask them to wake up as it is time to leave. [17] We can assume that some hours passed in between; hours in which Christ sat watching over them as they slept. What a picture of love when he was in need. As the Psalmist wrote, 'He who watches over Israel will neither slumber nor sleep'. [18] It is a strangely peaceful scene as Christ thinks thoughts of love beyond human expression - fierce, costly love - revealing the longing heart of God. This is the message of Gethsemane. And this was the scene on which Judas arrived, accompanied by the Roman soldiers who would arrest Jesus.

how much the memory of Mary's anointing must have meant

JESUS ON TRIAL

Jesus was taken first to Ananias, father-in-law of Caiaphas the high priest, then to Caiaphas, then to Pilate the following morning. Pilate passed him on to Herod, and Herod back to Pilate for sentence. He was tried by both Church and State. The Jews wanted to crucify Jesus on religious grounds but they had no power, as a nation subject to Rome, to sentence anyone to death; only the Romans could do this, and in Roman law blasphemy was not an indictable offence. This is why the Jews had to charge him with treason as well as with blasphemy; to do this they cunningly portrayed his claim to be a king as an act of treason.

The trial was a shameful farce, unjust and illegal. It was hurried; it was held at the wrong time; it was unlawfully confirmed; and the chief priests and the whole Sanhedrin deliberately sought out witnesses to bring false evidence. But is this surprising? No true court of justice could have secured a conviction against the sinless Christ. Notice how God's sovereign purpose is serenely at work; he actually uses the designs of human evil to fulfil his wonderful eternal purpose in bringing salvation (Acts 4:27-28).

why not hire a hit man, or arrange a secret poisoning?

But why a trial at all? Was it only a pretext to get rid of Jesus? Why not hire a hit man, or arrange a secret poisoning? Surely this would have achieved the same result? But God decreed otherwise. As Christ stood on trial in our place, these particular charges had to be brought. In Revelation 20:11-15 we see the great white throne at the final judgment; here the books are opened. This is the trial which awaits all who have not put their trust in Jesus Christ, as their substitute and sin-bearer, all whose names are not written in the Lamb's Book of Life. The two charges against Christ, blasphemy and treason, are the very charges against the whole human race. In every sense, he stood in for us, and bore what was ours, and gave us what was his.

Jesus could have prayed to his Father and been lifted up into heaven by 'more than twelve legions of angels'. He could have, but he did not. Instead we see him silent, submitting to injustice without protest. He could have out-argued them in pleading his case. Yet, as a sheep before her shearers is silent, so he did not open his mouth. Jesus took on himself the guilt of the world's sin, and guilt silences us. He had nothing to say, because there is nothing to say before a holy God. He could have defended himself but he did not. He *chose* to be found guilty, to stand in for us. [19]

What a contrast with Paul's triumphant climax in Romans 8:31-38. Because of Christ's death and resurrection the Apostle can ask, 'If God is for us, who can be against us?' for 'Who will bring any charge against those whom God has chosen?' Who indeed, if the charges against us are laid on him? 'Who is he that condemns?' Who indeed, if Christ who died for us, and has been raised from the dead, is at the right hand of God, praying for us? This is why the Apostle Paul declares us 'more than conquerors' and why 'neither death nor life... nor anything in all creation will be able to separate us from the love of God that is in Christ Jesus our Lord.'

All four gospel writers record Pilate's words that he could find no charge against him. Yet emotion was running high in the crowd and a riot could break out if Christ were not found guilty.

Should Pilate let Christ go free? In his terrible dilemma he passed the decision to the crowd; they could choose between Christ and Barabbas, another man listed for crucifixion that day. Barabbas was a robber and an insurrectionist who had led a revolt against Rome, and was in prison awaiting execution. He knew he deserved to die. The crowd chose Barabbas, and Christ died in his place that afternoon, the just for the unjust. There is a kind of parable in the story of Barabbas. His name means literally 'son of his father'. He could be any one of us.

there is a kind of parable in the story of Barabbas

THE JUST FOR THE UNJUST

'Christ died for sins once for all, the righteous for the unrighteous, to bring you to God.' 1 Peter 3:18

This verse is the anchor to which Peter attaches most of his first letter, and it evidently occupies his thoughts.

We rightly speak of the love of God when we think of the gospel; it was God the Father's love that sent Christ to be the Saviour of the world, but it was ultimately justice that atoned for sin. This is Peter's point, and Paul, too, gives priority to it. Paul was proud of the gospel of Christ (Romans 1:16) not because it was an expression of the divine love - although that is certainly true - but because the righteousness of God is revealed in it. We see the same emphasis in John's writing. In his first letter he declared that 'God is faithful and just to forgive us our sins and to cleanse us from all un-righteousness.'

Priests and Prophets

We read at the opening of the letter to the Hebrews, 'In the past God spoke to our forefathers through the prophets at many times and in various ways, but in these last days he has spoken to us by his Son.' So there were different strands of revelation through the Old Testament, none complete in itself, but each pointing beyond itself, and finally culminating in Christ. This is how God gradually revealed himself to people.

there were different strands of revelation through the Old Testament

In the Old Testament we trace two great attempts at solving the problem of sin, both inspired by God, each complementary to the other, and both finding their fruition in Christ. These were the priestly system and prophetic ministry.

Priests: The Old Testament sacrificial system was elaborately intricate, but its message may be summed up like this:

Sacrifice is the remedy for sin, and 'without the shedding of blood there is no forgiveness' (Hebrews 9 :22). Christ's death fulfilled this sacrifice but more than that, he himself became our High Priest (Hebrews 2:17) so no more sacrifices would ever be needed.

Prophets: People multiplied their sacrifices, but their hearts remained far from God. And so God in his continuing mercy sent prophets, and the supreme note in prophetic preaching is ethical. The prophets called for a change of heart. 'What does the Lord require of you? To act justly, and to love mercy, and to walk humbly with your God' (Micah 6:8). But this is a counsel

the supreme note in prophetic preaching is ethical

of despair, for it is beyond our capability as sinners whose natural orientation, as we know all too well, is to pride and selfishness.

So where does this leave us with our natural inclination to sin? The priestly and the prophetic systems both offered only temporary solutions, interim answers to this problem. The blood of bulls and of goats could not take away sin. And prophetic witness could not produce in people's hearts what was demanded. There is only one effective solution. The wonderful good news of the gospel is that the prophetic and priestly systems are both fulfilled, and indeed meet, in Christ.

Micah's words may not be known by our unbelieving friends, neighbours or colleagues, nor may these people have any knowledge of the meaning of Christ's death, but they *will* be aware of having done wrong, and of having let others down; and they will sense a need for forgiveness. We are all people with a past, and that can bring regret, and even fear. How to repair the past is one of the great universal questions. Until our past is dealt with, there can be no possibility of a relationship with God. For all our longing, we ourselves cannot repair the past.

Longing to repair the past

The Persian mathematician and poet Omar Khayya'm, who lived a thousand years ago, wrote:

'The moving finger writes, and having writ moves on;
Nor all thy piety nor wit can lure it back to cancel half a line,
Nor all thy tears wash out a word of it.' [20]

This yearning is universal and has been a constant theme and thread of world literature down the centuries. The regrets and the 'if onlys' taunt us. We can put our past failures out of our minds, but if they are not repented of then eventually, maybe even years later, they return, and we find ourselves greatly troubled by them until we come to Christ in repentance and ask his forgiveness. Then we have peace. Deep down we know right from wrong.

Lady Macbeth desperately tries to wash the blood stain from her hands after the death of King Duncan, yet it will not disappear. 'Out, out damned spot. Out, I say!' we hear her cry, as she wanders around during the night. [21] She cannot escape her guilt through sleep; it engulfs her.

Briony longs that she could rewrite history

Briony Tallis in Ian McEwan's *Atonement* invested her life in trying to make good a foolish action at the age of thirteen. Her book, *Atonement*, took her fifty-nine years to complete. Now she has vascular dementia and is dying. Briony longs that she could rewrite history. (She does in a sense, but only as a novelist.) She wants to give a happy ending to her sister, who had died many years before; to give her sister the happy life which she had denied her. But Briony knows that writing a novel cannot achieve atonement. [22] Atonement can come only from beyond ourselves. Briony's shrewd perception, her gift in writing, and her imagination are all she has, and they are beginning to fail her.

Briony, Lady Macbeth, Omar: come with us into the gospel records. Hear Christ's call to all who are weary and burdened. 'I am gentle and humble in heart' says the Lord Jesus, 'and you will find rest for your souls'. [23]

God wants his picture back

The sacrificial system addressed the negative aspect of the problem, the penalty of sin; the prophetic system speaks of the positive, atoning element. Let us look at how these two work together. Suppose a painting is stolen from a private collection. The police track down the thief who is sent for trial, found guilty, and put in prison. The penalty is exacted for his crime. But this does not put matters right. The art collector says, 'I want my picture back'. And only when it is returned can the matter rest. For full atonement two things are involved: the punishment of the crime and the repair of the injury.

Christ paid the penalty for our sin, but God, as it were, wants *his* picture back - the image of himself in human beings, before that image became marred by sin. In Christ's life of grace and beauty, God had the picture returned. Full atonement.

This double aspect of Christ's atoning work is captured so memorably by the hymnwriter Philip Bliss:

Bearing shame and scoffing rude,
In my place condemned he stood,
Sealed my pardon with his blood...

Guilty vile and helpless we;
Spotless Lamb of God was he:
Full atonement – can it be?
Hallelujah, what a Saviour!

In Christ's cry from the cross, 'My God, my God, why have you forsaken me?' we see the biblical idea of substitution. There was no answer to that terrible cry; God was silent. Christ had been silent in his trial, having no defence to offer, with the weight of our sin on his shoulders. Now there is silence from heaven. There could be no answer from God; for that is what hell means. And in the terrible agony of that silence, atonement was made and our forgiveness was sealed in blood.

JUSTIFICATION AND SACRIFICE

We may not *feel* guilty but the Scriptures speak of our guilt before God as an objective reality (Romans 3:19, 20). Some people have less sensitive consciences than others, but how we feel does not change how God sees us.

Guilt is an objective reality. Justification, which deals with it, is also objective. It is something God does; it is a declaration God makes about us. It is, as the 17th century Shorter Catechism of the Church of Scotland says, 'an act of God's free grace, in which he, the Judge of all the earth, acquits the guilty sinner, and declares him to be righteous, and accepts him as righteous in his sight.' [24]

The Greek word translated 'justify' (*dikaioun*) means 'to count, or treat, as righteous', not to make righteous in any ethical sense. Justification is not something that is done *in* us, but something done *to* us and *for* us, and *outside* us. This is made possible only because of the death of Jesus Christ as our substitute, in our place.

> In the early chapters of Romans, Paul is comparing two scenarios. The first is a sombre and dark depiction of human beings; the image in which we were created has been marred; we are now a travesty, a caricature of what God had planned. But Jesus Christ as 'the second Adam' is all that we are not.
>
> Let's not miss the sheer drama of the comparison. On the one hand, we have 'the many' - humankind as a whole, in the first Adam - guilty before God; on the other hand we have, 'the One' who is perfect.

Christ came to substitute his humanity, in all its excellence and perfection, for our sinfulness. Nothing about us is acceptable to God. From our conception, we have all been sinners (see Psalms 51 and 139).

Christ identifies with us from that very point: he was conceived by the Holy Spirit and born for us; he was baptized for us; he was tempted for us; he lived for us; he stood trial for us, taking on himself the charges that were against us; he suffered and died for us, going into the outer darkness for our sakes; and he rose again for us. [25]

All his 'work' is imputed to us - counted as if it were ours - in his death on the cross, and our sin is counted as if it were his. It is this divine exchange that lies at the heart of the gospel, and makes it a gospel.

Charles Wesley's hymn 'And can it be' sums it up:

No condemnation now I dread;
Jesus, and all in him, is mine!
Alive in him, my living Head,
And clothed in righteousness divine,
Bold I approach the eternal throne,
And claim the crown, through Christ my own.

The prophet Zechariah gives a graphic picture of this great exchange in one of the earlier visions of his prophecy (Zechariah 3:1-5). Joshua the high priest appears before the angel of the Lord, with Satan ready to accuse him. The Lord rebukes Satan, and speaks of Joshua as a burning stick snatched from the fire. Zechariah continues:

> 'Now Joshua was dressed in filthy clothes as he stood before the angel. Then the angel said to those who were standing before him, "Take off his filthy clothes." Then he said to Joshua, "See, I have taken away your sin, and I will put rich garments on you." And I said, "Put a clean turban on his head." So they set a clean turban on his head, and clothed him while the angel of the LORD stood by.'

As we have already seen, the great themes of the gospel permeate the Scriptures and are threaded through them, each passage adding more light and texture. Martin Luther, reflecting on this theme in Romans wrote: 'I greatly longed to understand Paul's epistle to the Romans, but one expression stood in my way, namely "the

the great themes of the gospel permeate the Scriptures

righteousness of God". I took it to mean that God is righteous and deals righteously in punishing the unrighteous.' He goes on to explain how he suddenly realised the context of these words; that righteousness is a gift received by faith. The very words which had been so hard to understand now became 'inexpressibly sweet'. [26] Luther's discovery of the meaning of the Atonement sparked the sixteenth century Protestant Reformation.

The sacrifice itself

No metaphor is perfect. The law court metaphor is helpful in illustrating our needs, but it does not deal with God's 'needs'. And by its nature it has something impersonal about it. The human judge in any court of law, in his official capacity, is an impartial figure. His job is simply to administer justice, and to see it is administered fairly. He is not angry with the accused; the trial is all in a day's work. He can go home in the evening and forget about the whole thing. But God cannot forget. He cannot brush sin aside as if it had not happened. God has been made angry by sin, and this presents a serious problem.

God's anger is turned away by the sacrifice of Christ on the cross. This does not suggest, as some would have it, that God is a bloodthirsty, vengeful deity. [27] Nor does it contradict all we read of a loving God.

AN IMPORTANT DISTINCTION

The theological terms 'propitiation' and 'penal substitution' refer to the fact that Christ bore our punishment for us, in our place, to appease the wrath of God. This doctrine has come under attack at certain periods in church history, and again in recent years. Some Bible translators prefer to translate the Greek word *hilasmos* (used in 1 John 2:2 and 1 John 4:10) as 'expiation', which I believe is inadequate. Expiation emphasizes the payment of a penalty, but contains no sense of the need to appease a holy God.

The eternal God found his peace – his appeasement from righteous anger – at the cross. This is the meaning of the term 'propitiation'.

THE GREAT CRESCENDO

We are powerless to do anything about our sin. At infinite cost to himself, God in Christ took our punishment *in his own person*, in our place. 'This is love, not that we loved God, but that he loved us, and sent his Son to be the propitiation for our sins' (1 John 4:10). [28] What love!

As human anger is usually wrong, we tend to think that anger from God must also be wrong. But love and wrath are not contradictory. God does not stop loving us although he is angry with us for our sin, any more than a parent stops loving his child when the child has done wrong.

It is holiness, not punishment of sin, which pleases God. The seriousness of the situation, in God's sight, comes home to us when we consider his character. Let me quote again from the Shorter Catechism. The language may be old, but it is full of profound truth:

'God is a Spirit, infinite, eternal, unchangeable, in his being, wisdom, power, holiness, justice, goodness and truth. Justice and judgment are the habitation of his throne, clouds and darkness overshadow him. He is the Father of an infinite majesty; jealous, omnipotent, holy, terrible. He is of purer eyes than to behold evil, he cannot look on iniquity.'

So long as the relationship between humankind and God remains broken, there can be no thought of peace with God. Atonement comes only at the cross. To quote Horatius Bonar, a great Scottish hymnwriter:

I hear the words of love, I gaze upon the blood,
I see the mighty Sacrifice, And I have peace with God.

Let us pause here, or we may miss something. The precious blood of Christ brings peace not only to sinful, guilty human hearts, but also to the holy heart of God. As he gazes upon the blood, and sees the mighty Sacrifice, he too enters into peace.

let us pause here, or we may miss something

OUR WONDERFUL REDEMPTION

Let's now look at three pictures which show different aspects of God's plan of redemption.

the lost sheep is such a telling image

The *first* picture is that of finding the lost sheep in Luke 15:1-7. It is such a telling image. The shepherd loves each sheep so much that he will take the risk of leaving the ninety-nine to go in search of the one which is lost. But there is another vital aspect to the story. The lost sheep is powerless to find his way, and he needs the shepherd to come and look for him.

The *second* picture is that of defeating the enemy, in his struggle for power. Again, we cannot do anything ourselves. God, in Christ, delivers us, transferring us out of the kingdom of darkness and into the kingdom of his dear Son (Colossians 1:13, 2:11-15).

The *third* picture is that of our redemption. The same word 'redeem' was used in Israel's deliverance from Egypt. 'I am the LORD your God, who brought you out of Egypt, out of the land of slavery.' Christ's redeeming blood takes the place of the Passover lamb; it brings us into a new covenant relationship with God.

Paul expounds this new covenant in detail in Romans 6-8, three wonderfully rich chapters looking at the theme of our union with Christ in his death and resurrection.

Two kinds of faith

It is by faith alone that we receive God's grace in the gospel. This word is used in two ways. Propositional faith means to 'believe that he exists, and that he rewards those who earnestly seek him' (Hebrews 11:6). But to have faith in Christ also refers to our placing personal trust in him. The two complement each other, and neither can stand alone. When a person has only propositional faith without exercising a true and personal trust, there is a danger signal.

Justification, propitiation and redemption can hardly be separated in our experience, though we must distinguish them in thought. The verdict of guilty puts the criminal in prison; if he is acquitted, he is set free. But when we are acquitted in God's eyes (justified) through the blood of Christ (the propitiatory sacrifice) we are not simply declared righteous in an objective sense, but we are given power through the Holy Spirit of Christ living in us.

We cannot understand Paul's teaching on justification, propitiation and redemption if we do not grasp Paul's teaching on propositional truth. Something happened on the cross at Calvary; the possibility of a new relationship was established between the eternal creator God and human beings. That is objective fact; it does not rest on our spiritual experience. This is the truth on which our personal faith is grounded.

Faith as personal trust is prominent in Paul's thinking. He yearns that the early Christians be grounded thoroughly in doctrine because truth sets the heart on fire. His own love of the Saviour is clearly evident in his writing and in the way he prayed. He trusted Christ in a vital and intimate way, and he would have been very familiar with the Old Testament Hebrew words all rendered as 'trust' in the English versions. The most frequently-used are:

Paul's own love of the Saviour is evident in his writing and in the way he prayed

galal - to roll upon, in the sense of rolling a burden upon another

chul - to rely on, with the idea of trusting in the dark

chasah - to take refuge in

batach - to lean upon, in helplessness and weakness

Each carries a strong suggestion of helplessness; these words would have been at the forefront of Paul the pastor's thinking; they underlie all he taught in Romans about our helpless predicament.

faith is the gift of God to those who believe

We must also remember faith is the gift of God to those who believe, and that it comes through hearing the truth explained. [29] It is when people listen to the message of the gospel, and understand it, that they begin to make new discoveries about Christ, and glimpse something of his wonder and his greatness.

THE GLORY OF THE CROSS

Christ prayed for himself in the Garden: 'And now, Father, glorify me in your presence with the glory I had with you before the world began' (John 17:5). This Christ who lives in us by his Spirit is the glorified Christ, glorified through his death.

Only one response from us is possible, a response of worship. The chorus of Bob Kauflin's hymn uses the Apostle Paul's words (see Philippians 1:7-11) to express this.

And, oh, the glory of the cross
That you would send your Son for us;
I gladly count my life as loss
That I might come to know
The glory of, the glory of the cross. [30]

The cross and evangelism

The whole of 2 Corinthians 4 & 5 is one of the richest theological passages in the New Testament. It says so much about the gospel that it is difficult to know where to begin, and it is impossible to exhaust all its truth. We have looked at the narrative accounts of Christ's death in the gospels, and have traced back what we called 'the trajectory of grace' from the Passover. Now we look at the implications for ourselves

THE GREAT CRESCENDO

In that trajectory, as those who have died with Christ and been raised with him.

In 2 Corinthians 5 we see the love of Christ in the death that he died; the reconciliation achieved in that death; and how we become new creations when we hear and receive the great invitation. Then comes our wonderful commission by God himself to preach the reconciling word.

> The word 'reconciliation' is used five times in 2 Corinthians 5: twice of God's reconciling work in Christ, twice of the ministry he has committed to us, and once in the exhortation made in the gospel, 'Be reconciled to God'. Reconciliation is central to our message.

If we are gripped by the truth of the gospel, we find ourselves compelled to tell others. What a privilege beyond imagination that we should be Christ's ambassadors. Note the surprising contrast between 'we are ambassadors' and 'we implore you'. An ambassador stands upon his dignity, which rests on the reputation of the person he represents. Ambassadors would not normally 'implore'. But Paul is truly Christ's ambassador. He is preaching the gospel in the spirit of the gospel, and pleads with his readers to be reconciled to God. This is how we too are to exercise our role as ambassadors; and in this we too follow the example of Christ himself. For, as we have already reminded ourselves, the Lord says, 'Come to me', as he invites us to receive the gift of life. He is a humble God. [31]

ambassadors would not normally 'implore'

The verb used in some translations in 2 Corinthians 5:14 is not 'compels' (as in the NIV) but 'constrains'. Paul is using the metaphor of a horse. Christ's love 'held him in' in the way a rein 'holds in' a horse so that it can be given true direction under the skilful hand of its rider. This is how the horse is made to give of its very best. The rider brings out every latent power, drawing an unruly spirit under submission. So it is with Christ's followers. The constraint of divine love brings our *as the Apostle writes, his mind unerringly goes to the mystery of Christ's death*

thoughts and our energy into submission to Christ. And as the Apostle Paul writes, his mind unerringly goes to the mystery of Christ's death, to what was achieved on the cross, and to the miracle of the new creation. This is where the constraint of Christ's love led him! It was the same for all the apostles as they preached the risen and ascended Christ, and it should be the same for us. Such is the glory of the cross.

A close-up view of Calvary

The early Church was taught in detail about Christ's death; it remained its driving force and inspiration, as we see from New Testament writing. The writer to the Hebrews states that Christ 'tasted death for everyone'. He tasted not merely physical cessation of life, but death in its hideous intensity and power, such as no one has known or can know. [32]

Christ 'became obedient to death – even death on a cross!' (Philippians 2:8). As we have seen, our Lord chose to die, and that choice was in obedience to God's will. He remained silent when he could have confounded his accusers; he would not come down from the cross when he could have called on twelve legions of angels to deliver him. It was not the nails, but sheer love, and obedience to the Father's will, that kept him hanging there: love and obedience, in spite of temptations to take an easier way – even when his grasp of eternal reality became clouded.

This voluntary obedience gives the Atonement its moral value, and here we see Christ as the great example. 'Your attitude should be the same as Christ Jesus, who became obedient to death – even death on a cross.' [33]

Christ has 'destroyed death, and has brought life and immortality to light through the gospel' (2 Timothy 1:10). The word translated 'destroyed' means 'to bring to nothing'. The idea is that death has been overcome or vanquished through the gospel. Christ's death, then, was a victory over death.

Let us pause to look at this carefully.

Death is the great enemy to be dealt with; one could call it the 'sacrament' of sin. [34] Through Adam and Eve, death 'reigned' in human experience (Romans 5:14, 21). To establish instead a reign of grace and life, a battle with death would be needed.

Already Christ had had skirmishes with the power of death - in the raising of Jairus' daughter, the widow of Nain's son, and Lazarus. But now came the decisive battle. There was no other way for death to be dealt with decisively; Christ himself, the Prince and Lord of all life, needed to destroy it from the inside. This is the great crescendo of the gospel record. Jesus is Lord over disease, Lord over devils, Lord over nature and Lord of people like us - it was not possible that death should hold him!

Now we see, in stark simplicity, how the drama and mystery of Jesus's death is actually felt and experienced by those who were there at the time. The darkness which fell over the whole earth as he was dying was symbolic of the darkness that is outside the gates of God, and of the nameless horror of eternal loss.

this is the great crescendo of the gospel record

Matthew tells us that in the moment he died 'the curtain in the temple was torn in two, from the top to the bottom' (Matthew 27:51). The curtain separated the Holy Place in the temple from the holiest of all, the inmost sanctuary. [35] In Old Testament times, this was where the presence of the Lord dwelt. No one was allowed to enter apart from the high priest, and that only once a year, on the Day of Atonement, to make atonement for the sins of the people. The curtain was the 'sign' that there was no way into the divine presence. It was like the shut gate of the Garden of Eden. The way to God had been barred by sin. The torn curtain declared that Christ has opened up the way home to God.

it was an extraordinary time and something very extraordinary was taking place

Matthew goes on to describe how the earth shook, tombs broke open, and people of faith who had died were raised to life (Matthew 27:51ff). These verses are often taken as no more than a pious legend; people feel they cannot be true as these things could not have happened. But it was an extraordinary time and something very extraordinary was taking place. God was in Christ reconciling the world to himself - that is how big a thing was happening! Is it surprising that there should have been dislocations in the natural order? This moment is of cosmic importance.

Jesus was crucified because the rulers did not believe his claim to be the Son of God. This claim was clearly bandied about in the judgment hall and at Calvary, as Christ became the subject of mockery, and the soldiers joined in the general shouting of 'Hail, king of the Jews'. But then these hardened men had to take him and nail him to the cross. They had never seen such a prisoner, nor had they ever seen such a death as his, accompanied by such fearful signs.

John tells of the centurion in charge of the soldiers who crucified Jesus (John 27:54). Think of him: a Roman, perhaps a hardened soldier. That Friday started for him as just another day, but it ended very differently. When the centurion saw all this, he became convinced that Christ must be what he claimed to be. Spiritual light had dawned. His words give a foretaste of a great movement down the centuries and across the nations as people are drawn to faith, and say as he said: 'Truly this was the Son of God'.

The gospel transcends cultures and political divisions; it is for all, paying no regard to education or to wealth. What was true of the centurion that afternoon is also true of Joseph of Arimathea (Matthew 27:57-60). There could be no greater contrast between these two men:

THE GREAT CRESCENDO

one a rough soldier, the other a rich Pharisee and counsellor of the Jews - yet at the cross they are both on the same level, and both found salvation.

We are told that Joseph was Jesus' disciple, but John adds a significant comment in his record (John 19:38), 'but secretly, for fear of the Jews'. The cross drew him out into the open, to declare his allegiance. Nicodemus helped Joseph of Arimathea to wrap the Lord's body and lay him in the tomb. He had earlier come to seek out Jesus at night; now he too had been drawn into full and public commitment by the cross. He had not understood Christ's teaching when we meet him in John 3, but he was slowly drawn into the light as he continued his quest for truth (John 7:50,51). Now, at the cross, he takes a clear stand as Christ's disciple.

The cross will always divide. It is a stumbling block to the Jews. It raised scoffing among the Athenians gathered to listen to Paul at Mars Hill. But it must never be left out of our gospel message in the hope of making it more attractive. Without the cross there would be no gospel. Indeed as Christians we must all bear the mark of the cross in our lives as those who have died with Christ, and been raised with him to serve him in humility.

Christians have been helped in worship for three hundred years by singing Isaac Watts's searching hymn, 'When I survey the wondrous cross' and it brings our reflection to a fitting close. Here is the true perspective, the Apostle Paul's perspective. Let it be ours as the cross leaves its imprint on our lives and our ambitions, and on our fellowship with other Christians, and with the Saviour himself.

without the cross there would be no gospel

When I survey the wondrous cross
On which the Prince of Glory died,
My richest gain I count but loss
And pour contempt on all my pride.

Forbid it, Lord, that I should boast
Save in the cross of Christ my God;
The very things that charm me most –
I sacrifice them to his blood.

See from his head, his hands, his feet,
Sorrow and love from mingled down:
When did such love and sorrow meet,
Or thorns compose so rich a crown?

Were the whole realm of nature mine,
That were an offering far too small;
Love so amazing, so divine
Demands my soul, my life, my all.

Isaac Watts (1674-1748)

Hallelujah! What a Saviour!

FOR STUDY AND REFLECTION

◆ Take time for an unhurried read through the synoptic gospels, and then through John's gospel. The same Lord Jesus, his work finished, is now interceding for us in all our human struggles (Hebrews 4:14 - 5:9). What new things have you learned about his humanity as we have walked through his last day on earth?

◆ We don't know whether Barabbas was among the crowd that terrible Friday afternoon, but it is very possible he was there. I wonder if he came to faith as he reflected on Jesus dying - quite literally - in his place. We are told that one of the thieves found faith then (Luke 23:39-43). Sometimes we can dismiss people as not worth sharing the gospel with. What do we learn from Jesus's words to the thief?

◆ From Genesis 3 onwards, people have been searching for something to ease the conscience and give peace, something to deal with a guilty past. It's important to recognise that this searching in our hearts is God-given and God-inspired (Acts 17:26ff; Ecclesiastes 3:11); this should bring great confidence in sharing the gospel, and a sense of expectation as we do so. How can we help our friends, family, colleagues to find peace? What opportunities do books and films like *Atonement* and *The Kite Runner* give us?

◆ Read Romans 3:21-26. Here are all the great themes of the gospel in microcosm. The words righteousness, justification, propitiation, redemption and faith each have a specific and precise meaning, all contributing to the full picture. With the help of a Bible dictionary or, for example, J I Packer's 18 Words (Christian Focus Publications), trace these themes through Paul's letters to gain a good grasp of the rich meaning of each of them.

◆ 2 Corinthians 4 & 5 are filled with profound commentary on the theme of suffering and glory. Here the Apostle Paul opens out the wonder and mystery of God's plan for our salvation. Read the chapters slowly and let them seep into your thinking, and your praying. I never tire of their sheer depth and beauty. You may like to learn them by heart – then they can feed your thinking as you travel to work, or go for a walk, or do the gardening etc

◆ We are to remember Christ's death until he returns in glory. As we share bread and wine in church, we 'proclaim' his death (1 Corinthians 11:26), rehearsing God's promise to act justly to forgive our sins as we come in repentance (1 John 1:7,9). The Apostle Paul wrote movingly to the Galatians 'he loved me and gave himself for me' (Galatians 2:20). Take time to worship him quietly on your own for dying for you.

◆ What marks identify a growing Christian? Look at the recommended reading on 'union with Christ' (p38) and work through one of the books listed, or another which deals with this area. Our union with him is surely the richest aspect of the Christian life, and one which will always take us deeper, and higher, and onward.

1. It is worth giving time to a study of the Passover and its foreshadowing of the Cross. *The Cross of Christ* and *Pierced for our Transgressions* (see recommended reading p38) both address this in more detail than can be included here.

2. Note how Matthew and Mark record the Lord Jesus as saying that his blood was shed 'for many' (Matthew 26:28; Mark 14:24) and Luke 'for you' (Luke 22:20). He evidently said both. Even in the intimacy of the communion service as we remember Christ's death for our sakes, the Lord Jesus directs our eyes and our hearts to those who are not yet within the covenant. He is a missionary God.

3. The Apostle Paul described union with Christ very simply in Philippians 1:21: 'For to me, to live is Christ'. Our union with him is the essence of the Christian life. For further reading see p38.

4. See 1 John 1:3b; John 15:15

5. The Apostle Paul is a great model for us here. He has given us the basis for our New Testament theology, all written and preached with a passion for Christ, whom he loved dearly. He longed for Christians to understand what it means to 'live by faith in the Son of God'. Paul knew nothing of 'arid' doctrine. Doctrinal truth set his heart on fire.

6. The gospels of Matthew, Mark and Luke are often referred to as 'the synoptic gospels'. There is a sense in which they portray the life, death and resurrection of Christ from the same point of view; John brings a different perspective.

7. This makes sense of his choice to omit the account of Christ's transfiguration, found in all the synoptic gospels.

8. John 18:1-4; Luke 22:39

9. New Testament writers had a deep sense of symbolism. Gethsemane had earlier associations. In the story of the revolt of David's son Absalom (2 Samuel 15:30), David wept on Mount Olivet, the same place where his 'greater Son' now faced a greater revolt, that of the human race against the true and living God. David had company in his grief; Jesus was alone. 'Gethsemane' literally means 'an oil-press' or 'winepress', and in Jesus' day the Garden was a grove of olives with a winepress. The Gethsemane experience was for Christ the beginning of the action of the winepress of God. 'I have trodden the winepress alone; from the nations no-one was with me' (Isaiah 63:3). Even his inner circle, Peter, James and John, could not penetrate his awesome loneliness.

10. Hebrews 4:15

11. Luke 4:13. See also Peter's appeal in Matthew 16:22-23; Mark 8:31-33

12. The writer to the Hebrews (Hebrews 5:7-10) speaks of Christ praying with 'loud cries and tears'. This reference is clearly to Gethsemane. What was 'heard' (v7) was not 'May this cup be taken from me' - for that was not granted – but rather 'not as I will but as you will'. His cry was for strength to go through with what he knew to be the Father's will. And we see his prayer answered in the calm serenity which rested upon him right through to the crucifixion itself.

13. See Matthew 26:37-38; Mark 14:33-34

14. John 18:11

15. Matthew 26:40, 43

16. Psalm 69:20

17. Matthew 26:45-46

18. Psalm 121:4

19. See Matthew 26:53; Isaiah 53:7-12; Romans 3:19

20. Omar Khayya'm lived from 1048-1131. I quote from Edward Fitzgerald's 19th century translation of *The Ruba'iya't*.

21. Shakespeare's *Macbeth*. Act 5, Scene 1: lines 26-40

22. 'The problem these fifty-nine years has been this: how can a novelist achieve atonement, when, with her absolute power of deciding outcomes, she is also God? There is no one, no entity or higher form that she can appeal to, or be reconciled with, or that can forgive her. There is nothing outside her. In her imagination she has set the limits and the terms. No atonement for God, or novelists, even if they are atheists. It was always an impossible task, and that was precisely the point. The attempt was all.' Ian McEwan, *Atonement* p371

23. Matthew 11:28,29

24. The Shorter Catechism was drawn up in 1647, as a question-and-answer means of training church members in the Christian faith. It was one of the major documents to come out of the Reformation.

25. Christ knew us before even our conception, for we were chosen in him before the foundation of the world (see for example Ephesians 1). He is our Saviour in time and in eternity.

26. Martin Luther, *Preface to Latin Writings*, 1545, 34, p337

27. See Steve Jeffery, Mike Ovey, Andrew Sach: *Pierced for our Transgressions* (IVP 2007) for a full and helpful defence of this argument.

28. The NIV does not use the word 'propitiation' here, yet it is clear in the Greek.

29. Philippians 1:29; Romans 10:17

30. Bob Kauflin, 'The Glory of the Cross' from 'Songs of the Cross-Centered Life', Sovereign Grace Music, 2000

31. Lindsay Brown gives a wonderful contemporary example of Christ's humility in the opening chapter of *Shining Like Stars: the power of the gospel in the world's universities* (IVP). He reflects on the irony that 'the one in whom are hidden all the treasures of wisdom and knowledge' should be held in disregard or derision in the world's universities, the very places where wisdom and knowledge are deemed to be sought and taught. The university is arguably the most influential institution (in human terms) in any nation. Islam has a well-funded plan to place academics and administrators in strategic positions in academia, but in many of the world's universities the only ambassadors of the humble Christ are students, young in the faith, holding out the word of life to their friends and to faculty.

32. It is interesting to note the contrast of expressions used in the New Testament. Lazareth and Jairus' daughter are described as 'sleeping' but Jesus 'died'.

33. See Philippians 2:3-11

34. The reason that physical death is so sinister is because of the spiritual death which lies behind it.

35. According to the Roman historian Josephus, this curtain was gigantic, some 80 feet high. It was, he says, a 'Babylonian tapestry, with embroidery of blue and fine linen, of scarlet also and purple, wrought with marvellous skill. Nor was this mixture of materials without its mystic meaning: it typified the universe. Portrayed on this tapestry was a panorama of the entire heavens.' David Ulansey in the *Journal of Biblical Literature* 110:1 (Spring 1991) pp 123-25

Evangelicals Now

WE COVER THE WORLD IN 32 PAGES

How is the cause of Christ advancing? *Evangelicals Now* (widely known as *EN*), keeps Christians informed. It also acts as a resource to help readers to pray for the Church in every land.

Formed in 1986, *EN* seeks to be firm on essential truths, to promote evangelism, and to provide a forum where Christians can share ideas on a range of contemporary issues, within a biblical framework. This monthly interdenominational magazine is based in London.

EN is read in *Albania, Argentina, Australia, Austria, Belgium, Botswana, Brazil, Burkina Faso, Burma, Cameroon, Canada, Canary Islands, Chile, Czech Republic, Denmark, Ethiopia, Finland, France, Germany, Ghana, Greece, Hungary, India, Indonesia, Ireland, Italy, Hong Kong, Japan, Jordan, Kenya, Korea, Latvia, Madagascar, Malawi, Moldova, Morocco, Mozambique, Namibia, Nepal, Netherlands, New Zealand, Nigeria, Norway, Pakistan, Papua New Guinea, Peru, Philippines, Poland, Portugal, Romania, Russia, Rwanda, St Helena, Senegal, Singapore, South Africa, Spain, Sri Lanka, Sweden, Switzerland, Tanzania, Tchad, Thailand, Tunisia, UAE, UK, USA, Zambia and Zimbabwe.*

Evangelicals Now is known for its global news coverage, penetrating analysis, features, letters and book reviews. Downloads are free, or subscribe online to receive EN by post.

Editors: John Benton and Tim Thornborough

'The best Christian newspaper to come out of Britain'. Prof J I Packer

'EN shapes our minds and stimulates prayer. Well worth making it a monthy reading habit.' Christopher Ash, Proclamation Trust

'EN provides huge inspiration to pray for God's glory in all the earth.' Sharon James, author and conference speaker

www.e-n.org

The Lausanne Movement

THE WHOLE CHURCH TAKING THE WHOLE GOSPEL TO THE WHOLE WORLD

The Lord Jesus Christ, the eternal Son of God, gave his Church a command which he has never revoked: 'Go and make disciples of all nations.'

'We are,' as the Apostle Paul reminds the Christians in Corinth, 'Christ's ambassadors, as though God were making his appeal through us.'

The Lausanne Movement (also known as the Lausanne Committee on World Evangelization) unites evangelicals around the world in joyful submission to this command and calling. Our desire is to see Christians grow in their knowledge and love of God, and be better equipped to bring the presence of Christ into the professions, academia, family life and society – in all nations. Lausanne has a range of working groups and special interest committees which provide a place for theological and practical discussion, always with the end in view of stimulating more effective evangelism.

The movement, founded by Billy Graham, grew out of a global congress held in Lausanne, Switzerland in 1974. John Stott was the chief architect of the Lausanne Covenant, a major legacy of that congress. This document is widely-regarded as one of the most influential in modern church history. A second congress was held in 1989 in Manila, Philippines, where the Manila Manifesto reaffirmed the call of the Lausanne Covenant to 'Proclaim Christ until he comes'.

For news and reports of Cape Town 2010, The Third Lausanne Congress on World Evangelization, held with the participation of the World Evangelical Alliance, bookmark **www.lausanne.org**

MORE On our website you will find Lausanne's Occasional Papers. You can sign up to receive the monthly *Lausanne Connecting Point* enewsletter and find links to *LausanneWorldPulse.com*, a monthly online missions and evangelism magazine.
www.lausanne.org Email: info@lausanne.org

Also in this series

An Authentic Servant: the mark of a spiritual leader by Ajith Fernando
More Precious than Gold (McCheyne Reading Plan)
Light, Salt and the World of Business by Fred Catherwood
The Grace of Giving by John Stott
For the Lord we Love: Your study guide to The Lausanne Covenant
Further titles in preparation

Didasko File distributors

North America IBS-STL Distribution **www.stl-distribution.com**
Australia and New Zealand Word **www.word.au**
Singapore Armour Publishing **www.armourpublishing.com**
East Asia (not Singapore) OMF Literature Inc **www.omflit.com**
Europe 10ofthose.com **www.10ofthose.com**
Southern Africa Christian Book Discounters **www.christianbooks.co.za**
Rest of the world 10ofthose.com **www.10ofthose.com**

Recommended reading on the Cross

The Cross of Christ by John Stott (IVP)
Pierced for our Transgressions by Jeffery, Ovey, Sach (IVP)
Cross Examined by Mark Meynell (IVP)
The Gospel and the Achievement of the Cross by Mark Chan (Lausanne)
The cross-centered life by C J Mahaney (Multnomah)

Recommended reading on 'Union with Christ'

The Growing Christian by James Philip (Christian Focus Publications)
The Holy Spirit by Sinclair Ferguson (IVP)
Book III, *Institutes of the Christian Religion* by John Calvin (several)

Marks'

Basic Medical Biochemistry

A Clinical Approach

Fourth Edition

Michael Lieberman, PhD
Distinguished Teaching Professor
Department of Molecular Genetics, Biochemistry and Microbiology
University of Cincinnati College of Medicine
Cincinnati, Ohio

Allan Marks, MD
Associate Professor of Internal Medicine (Emeritus)
Department of Internal Medicine
Section of Endocrinology and Metabolism
Temple University School of Medicine
Philadelphia, Pennsylvania

Alisa Peet, MD
Associate Professor
Director, Internal Medicine Clerkship
Department of Internal Medicine
Section of General Internal Medicine
Temple University School of Medicine
Philadelphia, Pennsylvania

Illustrations by Matthew Chansky

 Wolters Kluwer | Lippincott Williams & Wilkins
Health
Philadelphia · Baltimore · New York · London
Buenos Aires · Hong Kong · Sydney · Tokyo

Acquisitions Editor: Susan Rhyner
Product Manager: Stacey Sebring
Marketing Manager: Joy Fisher-Williams
Vendor Manager: Bridgett Dougherty
Manufacturing Manager: Margie Orzech
Design Coordinator: Teresa Mallon
Compositor: Absolute Service, Inc.

351 West Camden Street   Two Commerce Square, 2001 Market Street
Baltimore, Maryland 21201 USA   Philadelphia, Pennsylvania 19103 USA

The publisher is not responsible (as a matter of product liability, negligence, or otherwise) for any injury resulting from any material contained herein. This publication contains information relating to general principles of medical care which should not be construed as specific instructions for individual patients. Manufacturers' product information and package inserts should be reviewed for current information, including contraindications, dosages, and precautions.

Printed in China

Library of Congress Cataloging-in-Publication Data

Lieberman, Michael, 1950-
  Marks' basic medical biochemistry : a clinical approach / Michael Lieberman, Allan Marks, Alisa Peet ; illustrations by Matthew Chansky. — 4th ed.
      p. ; cm.
  Basic medical biochemistry
  Includes bibliographical references and index.
  ISBN 978-1-45110-003-7 (pbk.)
  I. Marks, Allan D. II. Peet, Alisa. III. Title. IV. Title: Basic medical biochemistry.
  [DNLM: 1. Biochemistry. 2. Clinical Medicine. QU 4]

  612.1'111—dc23

                                                                              2011053244

The publishers have made every effort to trace copyright holders for borrowed material. If they have inadvertently overlooked any, they will be pleased to make the necessary arrangements at the first opportunity.

To purchase additional copies of this book, call our customer service department at (800) 638-3030 or fax orders to (301) 223-2320. For other book services, including chapter reprints and large quantity sales, ask for the Special Sales department.

For all other calls originating outside of the United States, please call (301) 223-2300.

Visit Lippincott Williams & Wilkins on the Internet: http://www.lww.com. Lippincott Williams & Wilkins customer service representatives are available from 8:30 AM to 6:30 PM, EST, Monday through Friday, for telephone access.

                                                                              06 07 08 10 9 8 7 6 5 4 3 2

Preface to the Fourth Edition

It has been 4 years since the third edition was completed. The third edition retained the major pedagogic tools of the first and second editions, whereas the text had been completely revised, and certain features updated from the first edition. The fourth edition has, based on extensive reviews by both faculty and students, enhanced the features of the third edition in the following ways:

1. A major effort for this edition has been to update the patient histories to better reflect changes in treatment options for the disorders presented in this text. Every patient history has been reviewed and updated, if needed, to reflect the standard of care in 2011.
2. The "methods" notes of the third edition have been expanded such that there is at least one such note per chapter. These notes allow students to understand how biochemistry is used as a foundation for many of the laboratory tests ordered during the diagnosis of a patient.
3. Biochemical comments in several chapters have been updated to reflect recent research, particularly as it applies to signaling, type 2 diabetes, and metabolic syndrome.
4. Every chapter now contains a Table, at the end of the chapter, summarizing the diseases discussed in the chapter.
5. All chapters were reviewed and updated, where appropriate. Errors found, or pointed out by observant readers, were corrected.
6. The online question bank has been expanded by 5 questions per chapter, bringing the total number of questions (and explanations) in that bank to 468. The text itself contains 245 questions and explanations for student review.
7. Chapter references are now only available as an online supplement to the text. The references, where appropriate, are linked to the original research article in PubMed.

In revising a text geared primarily toward medical students, the authors always struggle with new advances in biochemistry and whether such advances should be included in the text. In this text, the authors include only advances that will enable the student to better relate biochemistry to medicine, and future diagnostic tools. Although providing incomplete, but exciting, advances to graduate students is best for their education, medical students require a more directed approach, one that emphasizes how biochemistry is useful for the practice of medicine. This is a major goal of this book.

Any errors are the responsibility of the authors, and we would like to be notified when such errors are found.

We have retained the interesting names of the patients in this edition. The use of such names is meant as an educational tool and is not meant to be disrespectful to the patients or their conditions.

The accompanying website for this edition of *Marks' Basic Medical Biochemistry: A Clinical Approach* contains the aforementioned additional questions for review, patient summaries (complete stories of all the patients discussed in the text), and the references for each chapter.

HOW TO USE THIS BOOK

Icons identify the various components of the book: the patients who are presented at the start of each chapter; the clinical notes, methods notes, questions, and answers that appear in the margins; and the key concepts, clinical comments, and biochemical comments that are found at the end of each chapter.

Each chapter starts with an abstract that summarizes the information so that students can recognize the key words and concepts they are expected to learn. The next component of each chapter is "The Waiting Room," describing patients with complaints and detailing the events that led them to seek medical help.

 indicates a female patient

 indicates a male patient

 indicates a patient who is an infant or young child

As each chapter unfolds, icons appear in the margin, identifying information related to the material presented in the text:

 indicates a clinical note, usually related to the patients in "The Waiting Room" for that chapter. These notes explain signs or symptoms of a patient or give some other clinical information relevant to the text.

 indicates a methods note, which elaborates on how biochemistry is required to perform, and interpret, common laboratory tests.

Questions and answers also appear in the margin and should help to keep students thinking as they read the text:

 indicates a question

 indicates the answer to the question. The answer to a question is always located on the next page. If two questions appear on one page, the answers are given in order on the next page.

Each chapter ends with "Key Concepts," "Clinical Comments," and "Biochemical Comments":

The "Key Concepts" summarize the important take-home messages from the chapter.

 The "Clinical Comments" give additional clinical information, often describing the treatment plan and the outcome.

The "Biochemical Comments" add biochemical information that is not covered in the text or explore some facet of biochemistry in more detail or from another angle.

Finally, "Review Questions" are presented. These questions are written in a USMLE-like format and many of them have a clinical slant. Answers to the review questions, along with detailed explanations, are provided in the Appendix.

ACKNOWLEDGMENTS

The authors would like to thank Drs. Jerry Lingrel, Paul Rosevear, and Peter Stambrook for reviewing chapters as they were being revised. Their suggested revisions were thoughtful and improved the chapters they were reviewing. Matt Chansky, the illustrator, deserves a tremendous amount of credit for creating the new figures and revising existing figures. Stacey Sebring, our developmental editor, was very patient with the authors and was always there when needed. Her expertise and patience was greatly appreciated by the authors we worked through this revision. Susan Rhyner, our acquisitions editor, was also extremely supportive as the work was in progress. We would also like to acknowledge the initial contributions of Dawn Marks, whose vision of a textbook geared toward medical students led to the first edition of this book. Her vision is still applicable today.

Contents

Fuel Metabolism

I n order to survive, humans must meet two basic metabolic requirements: We must be able to synthesize everything our cells need that is not supplied by our diet, and we must be able to protect our internal environment from toxins and changing conditions in our external environment. In order to meet these requirements, we metabolize our dietary components through four basic types of pathways: fuel oxidative pathways, fuel storage and mobilization pathways, biosynthetic pathways, and detoxification or waste disposal pathways. Cooperation between tissues and responses to changes in our external environment are communicated through transport pathways and intercellular signaling pathways (Fig. I.1).

The foods in our diet are the fuels that supply us with energy in the form of calories. This energy is used for carrying out diverse functions such as moving, thinking, and reproducing. Thus, several of our metabolic pathways are *fuel oxidative pathways* that convert fuels into energy that can be used for biosynthetic and mechanical work. But what is the source of energy when we are not eating, such as between meals and while we sleep? How does a person on a hunger strike that you read about in the morning headlines survive so long? We have other metabolic pathways that are *fuel storage pathways*. The fuels that we store can be mobilized during periods when we are not eating or when we need increased energy for exercise.

Our diet also must contain the compounds we cannot synthesize, as well as all the basic building blocks for compounds we do synthesize in our *biosynthetic pathways*. For example, we have dietary requirements for some amino acids, but we can synthesize other amino acids from our fuels and a dietary nitrogen precursor. The compounds required in our diet for biosynthetic pathways include certain amino acids, vitamins, and essential fatty acids.

Detoxification pathways and *waste disposal pathways* are metabolic pathways devoted to removing toxins that can be present in our diets or in the air we breathe, introduced into our bodies as drugs, or generated internally from the metabolism of dietary components. Dietary components that have no value to the body and must be disposed of are called *xenobiotics*.

In general, biosynthetic pathways (including fuel storage) are referred to as *anabolic pathways*, that is, pathways that synthesize larger molecules from smaller components. The synthesis of proteins from amino acids is an example of an anabolic pathway. *Catabolic pathways* are those pathways that break down larger molecules into smaller components. Fuel oxidative pathways are examples of catabolic pathways.

In the human, the need for different cells to carry out different functions has resulted in cell and tissue specialization in metabolism. For example, our adipose tissue is a specialized site for the storage of fat and contains the metabolic pathways that allow it to carry out this function. However, adipose tissue is lacking many of the pathways that synthesize required compounds from dietary precursors. To enable our cells to cooperate in meeting our metabolic needs during changing conditions of diet, sleep, activity, and health, we need *transport pathways* into the blood and between tissues and *intercellular signaling pathways*. One means of communication is for *hormones* to carry signals to tissues about our dietary state.

Dietary
components

Fuels:
Carbohydrate
Fat
Protein

Vitamins
Minerals
H_2O

Xenobiotics

Digestion
absorption,
transport

Compounds
in cells

Biosynthetic
pathways

Fuel storage
pathways

Body
components

Fuel
stores

Detoxification
and waste
disposal
pathways

O_2

Fuel
oxidative
pathways

CO_2
H_2O

Energy

Waste
products

FIG. I.1. An overview of the general metabolic routes for dietary components in the body. The types of pathways are named in *red*.

For example, a message that we have just had a meal, carried by the hormone insulin, signals adipose tissue to store fat.

In the following section, we will provide an overview of various types of dietary components and examples of the pathways involved in using these components. We will describe the fuels in our diet, the compounds produced by their digestion, and the basic patterns of fuel metabolism in the tissues of our bodies. We will describe how these patterns change when we eat, when we fast for a short time, and when we starve for prolonged periods. Patients with medical problems that involve an inability to deal normally with fuels will be introduced. These patients will appear repeatedly throughout the book and will be joined by other patients as we delve deeper into biochemistry. In order for students to be able to remember the patients as they progress through the book, the patients have been given names that reflect their condition. This is not meant to demean the patient or the condition, but rather, to allow the student to better follow the progress of the patient throughout the book.

It is important to note that this section of the book contains an *overview* of basic metabolism, which allows patients to be presented at an elementary level and to whet the student's appetite for the biochemistry to come. Its goal is to enable the student to taste and preview what biochemistry is all about. It is not designed to be all-inclusive because all of these topics will be discussed in greater detail in Sections IV through VIII of the text. The next section of the text (Section II) begins with the basics of biochemistry and the relationship of basic chemistry to processes that occur in all living cells.

1 Metabolic Fuels and Dietary Components

Fuel Metabolism. We obtain our fuel primarily from **carbohydrates**, **fats**, and **proteins** in our diet. As we eat, our foodstuffs are **digested** and **absorbed**. The products of digestion circulate in the blood, enter various tissues, and are eventually taken up by cells and **oxidized** to produce **energy**. To completely convert our fuels to carbon dioxide (CO_2) and water (H_2O), molecular **oxygen** (O_2) is required. We breathe to obtain this oxygen and to eliminate the **carbon dioxide** that is produced by the oxidation of our foodstuffs.

Fuel Stores. Any dietary fuel that exceeds the body's immediate energy needs is stored, mainly as **triacylglycerol** (fat) in adipose tissue; as **glycogen** (carbohydrate) in muscle, liver, and other cells; and, to some extent, as **protein** in muscle. When we are fasting, between meals and overnight while we sleep, fuel is drawn from these stores and is oxidized to provide energy (Fig. 1.1).

Fuel Requirements. We require enough energy each day to drive the **basic functions** of our bodies and to support our **physical activity**. If we do not consume enough food each day to supply that much energy, the body's fuel stores supply the remainder, and we lose weight. Conversely, if we consume more food than required for the energy we expend, our body's fuel stores enlarge, and we gain weight.

Other Dietary Requirements. In addition to providing energy, the diet provides **precursors** for the **biosynthesis** of compounds necessary for cellular and tissue structure, function, and survival. Among these precursors are the **essential fatty acids** and essential **amino acids** (those that the body needs but cannot synthesize). The diet must also supply **vitamins**, **minerals**, and **water**.

Waste Disposal. Dietary components that we can use are referred to as nutrients. However, both the diet and the air we breathe contain **xenobiotic compounds**, compounds that have no use or value in the human body and may be toxic. These compounds are excreted in the urine and feces together with metabolic waste products.

Excess dietary fuel

Fed ↓

Fuel stores:
Fat
Glycogen
Protein

Fasting ↓

Oxidation

↘ ↓ ↓ ↙
◄ Energy ►
↗ ↑ ↑ ↖

FIG. 1.1. Fate of excess dietary fuel in fed and fasting states.

THE WAITING ROOM

Percy Veere is a 59-year-old school teacher who was in good health until his wife died suddenly. Since that time, he has experienced an increasing degree of fatigue and has lost interest in many of the activities he previously enjoyed. Shortly after his wife's death, one of his married children moved far from home. Since then, Mr. Veere has had little appetite for food. When a neighbor found Mr. Veere sleeping in his clothes, unkempt, and somewhat confused, she called an ambulance. Mr. Veere was admitted to the hospital psychiatric unit with a diagnosis of mental depression associated with dehydration and malnutrition.

Otto Shape is a 25-year-old medical student who was very athletic during high school and college but is now "out of shape." Since he started medical school, he has been gaining weight (at 5 ft 10 in tall, he currently weighs 187 lb). He has decided to consult a physician at the student health service before the problem becomes worse.

Ivan Applebod is a 56-year-old accountant who has been morbidly obese for several years. He exhibits a pattern of central obesity, referred to as an "apple shape," which is caused by excess adipose tissue being disproportionally deposited in the abdominal area. His major recreational activities are watching TV while drinking scotch and soda and doing occasional gardening. At a company picnic, he became very "winded" while playing baseball and decided it was time for a general physical examination. At the examination, he weighed 264 lb at 5 ft 10 in tall. His blood pressure was elevated, 155 mm Hg systolic (normal = 120 mm Hg or less, with prehypertensive defined as between 121 and 139), and 95 mm Hg diastolic (normal = 80 mm Hg or less, with prehypertensive defined as between 81 and 89).

Ann O'Rexia is a 23-year-old buyer for a woman's clothing store. Despite the fact that she is 5 ft 7 in tall and weighs 99 lb, she is convinced she is overweight. Two months ago, she started a daily exercise program that consists of 1 hour of jogging every morning and 1 hour of walking every evening. She also decided to consult a physician about a weight reduction diet.

I. DIETARY FUELS

The major fuels we obtain from our diet are carbohydrates, proteins, and fats. When these fuels are oxidized to CO_2 and H_2O in our cells, energy is released by the transfer of electrons to O_2. The energy from this oxidation process generates heat and adenosine triphosphate (ATP) (Fig. 1.2). Carbon dioxide travels in the blood to the lungs, where it is expired, and water is excreted in urine, sweat, and other secretions. Although the heat that is generated by fuel oxidation is used to maintain body temperature, the main purpose of fuel oxidation is to generate ATP. ATP provides the energy that drives most of the energy-consuming processes in the cell, including biosynthetic reactions, muscle contraction, and active transport across membranes. As these processes use energy, ATP is converted back to adenosine diphosphate (ADP) and inorganic phosphate (P_i). The generation and utilization of ATP is referred to as the *ATP–ADP cycle*.

The oxidation of fuels to generate ATP is called *respiration* (Fig. 1.3). Before oxidation, carbohydrates are converted principally to glucose, fat to fatty acids, and protein to amino acids. The pathways for oxidizing glucose, fatty acids, and

FIG. 1.2. The ATP–ADP cycle. The energy-generating pathways are shown in *red*; the energy-utilizing pathways in *blue*.

FIG. 1.3. Generation of adenosine ATP from fuel components during respiration. Glucose, fatty acids, and amino acids are oxidized to acetyl-CoA, a substrate for the tricarboxylic acid (TCA) cycle. In the TCA cycle, they are completely oxidized to CO_2. As fuels are oxidized, electrons (e^-) are transferred to O_2 by the electron-transport chain, and the energy is used to generate ATP.

FIG. 1.4. Structure of starch and glycogen. Starch, our major dietary carbohydrate, and glycogen, the body's storage form of glucose, have similar structures. They are polysaccharides (many sugar units) composed of glucose, which is a monosaccharide (one sugar unit). Dietary disaccharides are composed of two sugar units.

amino acids have many features in common. They first oxidize the fuels to acetyl coenzyme A (acetyl-CoA), a precursor of the tricarboxylic acid (TCA) cycle. The TCA cycle is a series of reactions that completes the oxidation of fuels to CO_2 (see Chapter 20). Electrons lost from the fuels during oxidative reactions are transferred to O_2 by a series of proteins in the electron-transport chain (see Chapter 21). The energy of electron transfer is used to convert ADP and P_i to ATP by a process known as *oxidative phosphorylation.*

Oxidative pathways are **catabolic**; that is, these pathways break molecules down. In contrast, **anabolic** pathways build molecules up from component pieces.

In discussions of metabolism and nutrition, energy is often expressed in units of calories. "Calorie" in this context really means kilocalorie (kcal). Calorie was originally spelled with a capital C, but the capitalization was dropped as the term became popular. Thus, a 1-cal soft drink actually has 1 cal (1 kcal) of energy. Energy is also expressed in joules. One kilocalorie equals 4.18 kilojoules (kJ). Physicians tend to use units of calories, in part, because that is what their patients use and understand. One kilocalorie of energy is the amount of energy required to raise the temperature of 1 L of water by 1°C.

A. Carbohydrates

The major carbohydrates in the human diet are starch, sucrose, lactose, fructose, and glucose. The *polysaccharide starch* is the storage form of carbohydrates in plants. Sucrose (table sugar) and lactose (milk sugar) are disaccharides, and fructose and glucose are monosaccharides. Digestion converts the larger carbohydrates to monosaccharides, which can be absorbed into the bloodstream. *Glucose*, a monosaccharide, is the predominant sugar in human blood (Fig. 1.4).

Oxidation of carbohydrates to CO_2 and H_2O in the body produces approximately 4 kcal/g (Table 1.1). In other words, every gram of carbohydrate we eat yields approximately 4 kcal of energy. Note that carbohydrate molecules contain a significant amount of oxygen and are already partially oxidized before they enter our bodies (see Fig. 1.4).

B. Proteins

Proteins are composed of amino acids that are joined to form linear chains (Fig. 1.5). In addition to carbon, hydrogen, and oxygen, proteins contain approximately 16%

Table 1.1   Caloric Content of Fuels

	kcal/g
Carbohydrate	4
Fat	9
Protein	4
Alcohol	7

Peptide bonds

Protein   Amino acid

FIG. 1.5.   General structure of proteins and amino acids. Each amino acid in this figure is indicated by a different color. R = side chain. Different amino acids have different side chains. For example, R_1 might be $-CH_3$; R_2, $-CH_2OH$; R_3, $-CH_2-COO^-$. In a protein, the amino acids are linked by peptide bonds.

nitrogen by weight. The digestive process breaks down proteins to their constituent amino acids, which enter the blood. The complete oxidation of proteins to CO_2, H_2O, and ammonium (NH_4^+) in the body yields approximately 4 kcal/g.

C. Fats

Fats are lipids composed of triacylglycerols (also called triglycerides). A triacylglycerol molecule contains three fatty acids esterified to one glycerol moiety (Fig. 1.6).

Fats contain much less oxygen than is contained in carbohydrates or proteins. Therefore, fats are more reduced and yield more energy when oxidized. The complete oxidation of triacylglycerols to CO_2 and H_2O in the body releases approximately 9 kcal/g, more than twice the energy yield from an equivalent amount of carbohydrate or protein.

 An analysis of **Ann O'Rexia's** diet showed she ate 100 g of carbohydrate, 20 g of protein, and 15 g of fat each day. Approximately how many calories did she consume per day?

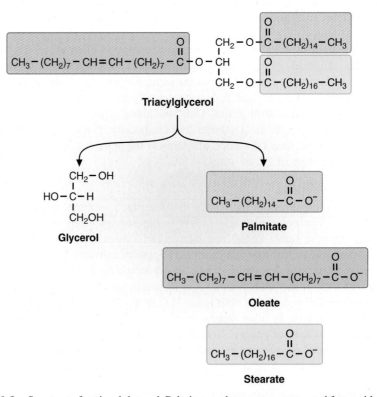

Triacylglycerol

Glycerol

Palmitate

Oleate

Stearate

FIG. 1.6.   Structure of a triacylglycerol. Palmitate and stearate are saturated fatty acids (i.e., they have no double bonds). Oleate is monounsaturated (one double bond). Polyunsaturated fatty acids have more than one double bond.

D. Alcohol

Many people used to believe that alcohol (ethanol, in the context of the diet) has no caloric content. In fact, ethanol (CH_3–CH_2–OH) is oxidized to CO_2 and H_2O in the body and yields approximately 7 kcal/g, which is more than carbohydrate or protein but less than fat.

II. BODY FUEL STORES

Although some of us may try, it is virtually impossible to eat constantly. Fortunately, we carry supplies of fuel within our bodies (Table 1.2), which are similar to the fuel supplies in the plants and animals we eat. These fuel stores are light in weight, large in quantity, and readily converted into oxidizable substances. Most of us are familiar with fat, our major fuel store, which is located in adipose tissue. Although fat is distributed throughout our bodies, it tends to increase in quantity in our hips and thighs and in our abdomens as we advance into middle age. In addition to our fat stores, we also have important, although much smaller, stores of carbohydrate in the form of glycogen located primarily in our liver and muscles. Glycogen consists of glucose residues joined together to form a large, branched polysaccharide (see Fig. 1.4). Body protein, particularly the protein of our large muscle masses, also serves to some extent as a fuel store, and we draw on it for energy when we fast.

A. Fat

Our major fuel store is adipose triacylglycerol (triglyceride), a lipid more commonly known as fat. The average 70-kg man has approximately 15 kg of stored triacylglycerol, which accounts for approximately 85% of his total stored calories (see Table 1.2).

Two characteristics make adipose triacylglycerol a very efficient fuel store: the fact that triacylglycerol contains more calories per gram than carbohydrate or protein (9 kcal/g vs. 4 kcal/g) and the fact that adipose tissue does not contain much water. Adipose tissue contains only about 15% water, compared to tissues such as muscle that contain about 80%. Thus, the 70-kg man with 15 kg of stored triacylglycerol has only about 18 kg of adipose tissue.

B. Glycogen

Our stores of glycogen in liver, muscle, and other cells are relatively small in quantity but perform important functions. Liver glycogen is used to maintain blood glucose levels between meals, which is necessary for optimal functioning of the nervous system. Thus, the size of this glycogen store fluctuates during the day; an average 70-kg man might have 200 g or more of liver glycogen after a meal but only 80 g after an overnight fast. Muscle glycogen supplies energy for muscle contraction during exercise. At rest, the 70-kg man has approximately 150 g of muscle glycogen. Almost all cells, including neurons, maintain a small emergency supply of glucose as glycogen.

It is not practical to store all of the energy in triacylglycerol as glycogen. Consider what would happen to a 70-kg man if the 135,000 kcal stored as triacylglycerols in his 18 kg of adipose tissue was stored instead as skeletal muscle glycogen. It would take approximately 34 kg of glycogen to store as many calories. Glycogen, because

Miss O'Rexia consumed

$100 \times 4 = 400$ kcal as carbohydrate
$20 \times 4 = 80$ kcal as protein
$15 \times 9 = 135$ kcal as fat
for a total of 615 kcal/day.

Ivan Applebod ate 585 g of carbohydrate, 150 g of protein, and 95 g of fat each day. In addition, he drank 45 g of alcohol daily. How many calories did he consume per day?

Table 1.2 Fuel Composition of the Average 70-kg Man[a] after an Overnight Fast

Fuel	Amount (kg)	Percentage of Total Stored Calories
Glycogen		
Muscle	0.15	0.4
Liver	0.08	0.2
Protein	6.0	14.4
Triglyceride	15.0	85.0

[a]In biochemistry and nutrition, the standard reference is often the 70-kg (154-lb) man. This standard was probably chosen because in the first half of the 20th century, when many nutritional studies were performed, young healthy medical and graduate students (who were mostly men) volunteered to serve as subjects for these experiments.

Mr. Applebod consumed

585 × 4 = 2,340 kcal as carbohydrate
150 × 4 = 600 kcal as protein
95 × 9 = 855 kcal as fat
45 × 7 = 315 kcal as alcohol

for a total of 4,110 kcal/day.

What are **Ivan Applebod's** and **Ann O'Rexia's** RMR? (Compare the method for a rough estimate to values obtained with equations in Table 1.4.)

Table 1.3 Factors Affecting BMR Expressed per Kilogram (kg) of Body Weight

Gender (males higher than females)
Body temperature (increased with fever)
Environmental temperature (increased in cold)
Thyroid status (increased in hyperthyroidism)
Pregnancy and lactation (increased)
Age (decreases with age)

it is a polar molecule with hydroxyl groups, binds approximately four times its weight as water, or 136 kg. Thus, his fuel stores would weigh 170 kg, as opposed to 18 kg when stored as triacylglycerol.

C. Protein

Protein serves many important roles in the body; unlike fat and glycogen, it is not solely a fuel store. Muscle protein is essential for body movement. Other proteins serve as enzymes (catalysts of biochemical reactions) or as structural components of cells and tissues. Only a limited amount of body protein can be degraded, approximately 6 kg in the average 70-kg man, before our body functions are compromised.

III. DAILY ENERGY EXPENDITURE

If we want to stay in energy balance, neither gaining nor losing weight, we must, on average, consume an amount of food equal to our daily energy expenditure (DEE). The DEE includes the energy to support our basal metabolism (basal metabolic rate [BMR] or resting metabolic rate [RMR]) and our physical activity, plus the energy required to process the food we eat (diet-induced thermogenesis [DIT]). Thus, the DEE, in kilocalories per day = RMR + the energy needed for physical activity + DIT.

A. Resting Metabolic Rate

The *resting metabolic rate* is a measure of the energy required to maintain life: the functioning of the lungs, kidneys, and brain; the pumping of the heart; the maintenance of ionic gradients across membranes; the reactions of biochemical pathways; and so forth. Another term used to describe basal metabolism is the *basal metabolic rate*. The BMR was originally defined as the energy expenditure of a person mentally and bodily at rest in a thermoneutral environment 12 to 18 hours after a meal. However, when a person is awakened and his or her heat production or oxygen consumption is measured, he or she is no longer sleeping or totally at mental rest, and his or her metabolic rate is called the *resting metabolic rate*. It is also sometimes called the *resting energy expenditure* (REE). The RMR and BMR differ very little in value.

The BMR, which is usually expressed in kilocalories per day, is affected by body size, age, sex, and other factors (Table 1.3). It is proportional to the amount of metabolically active tissue (including the major organs) and to the lean (or fat-free) body mass. Obviously, the amount of energy required for basal functions in a large person is greater than the amount required in a small person. However, the BMR is usually lower for women than for men of the same weight because women usually have more metabolically inactive adipose tissue. Body temperature also affects the BMR, which increases by 12% with each degree centigrade increase in body temperature (i.e., "feed a fever; starve a cold"). The ambient temperature affects the BMR, which increases slightly in colder climates as thermogenesis is activated. Excessive secretion of thyroid hormone (hyperthyroidism) causes the BMR to increase, whereas diminished secretion (hypothyroidism) causes it to decrease. The BMR increases during pregnancy and lactation. Growing children have a higher BMR per kilogram body weight than adults because a greater proportion of their bodies is composed of brain, muscle, and other more metabolically active tissues. The BMR declines in aging individuals because their metabolically active tissue is shrinking and body fat is increasing. In addition, large variations exist in BMR from one adult to another, determined by genetic factors.

A rough estimate of the BMR may be obtained by assuming it is 24 kcal/day/kg body weight and multiplying by the body weight. An easy way to remember this is 1 kcal/kg/hr. This estimate works best for young individuals who are near their ideal weight. More accurate methods for calculating the BMR use empirically derived equations for different gender and age groups (Table 1.4). Even these calculations do not take into account variation among individuals.

Table 1.4 Equation for Predicting BMR from Body Weight (W) in Kilograms (kg)

Males		Females	
Age Range (years)	**BMR (kcal/day)**	**Age Range (years)**	**BMR (kcal/day)**
0–3	60.9 W − 54	0–3	61.0 W − 51
3–10	22.7 W + 495	3–10	22.5 W + 499
10–18	17.5 W + 651	10–18	12.2 W + 746
18–30	15.3 W + 679	18–30	14.7 W + 496
30–60	11.6 W + 879	30–60	8.7 W + 829
>60	13.5 W + 487	>60	10.5 W + 596

From World Health Organization. *Energy and Protein Requirements: Report of a Joint FAO/WHO/UNU Expert Consultation.* Geneva, Switzerland: World Health Organization; 1987:71. Technical report series no. 724. See also Schofield WN. Predicting basal metabolic rate, new standards and review of previous work. *Hum Nutr Clin Nutr.* 1985;39(suppl 1):5–41.

B. Physical Activity

In addition to the RMR, the energy required for physical activity contributes to the DEE. The difference in physical activity between a student and a lumberjack is enormous, and a student who is relatively sedentary during the week may be much more active during the weekend. Table 1.5 gives factors for calculating the approximate energy expenditures associated with typical activities.

A rough estimate of the energy required per day for physical activity can be made by using a value of 30% of the RMR (per day) for a very sedentary person (such as a medical student who does little but study) and a value of 60% to 70% of the RMR (per day) for a person who engages in about 2 hours of moderate exercise per day (see Table 1.5). A value of 100% or more of the RMR is used for a person who does several hours of heavy exercise per day.

C. Diet-Induced Thermogenesis

Our DEE includes a component related to the intake of food known as *diet-induced thermogenesis* or the *thermic effect of food* (TEF). DIT was formerly called the *specific dynamic action* (SDA). After the ingestion of food, our metabolic rate increases because energy is required to digest, absorb, distribute, and store nutrients.

The energy required to process the types and quantities of food in the typical American diet is probably equal to approximately 10% of the kilocalories ingested. This amount is roughly equivalent to the error involved in rounding off the caloric content of carbohydrate, fat, and protein to 4, 9, and 4, respectively. Therefore,

Table 1.5 Typical Activities with Corresponding Hourly Activity Factors[a]

Activity Category	Hourly Activity Factor (for Time in Activity)
Resting: sleeping, reclining	1.0
Very light: seated and standing activities, driving, laboratory work, typing, sewing, ironing, cooking, playing cards, playing a musical instrument	1.5
Light: walking on a level surface at 2.5–3 mph, garage work, electrical trades, carpentry, restaurant trades, house cleaning, golf, sailing, table tennis	2.5
Moderate: walking 3.5–4 mph, weeding and hoeing, carrying loads, cycling, skiing, tennis, dancing	5.0
Heavy: walking uphill with a load, tree felling, heavy manual digging, mountain climbing, basketball, football, soccer	7.0

[a]The hourly activity factor is multiplied by the BMR (RMR) per hour times the number of hours engaged in the activity to give the caloric expenditure for that activity. If this is done for all of the hours in a day, the sum over 24 hours will approximately equal the daily energy expenditure.
Reprinted with permission from National Research Council. *Recommended Dietary Allowances.* 10th ed. Washington, DC: National Academy Press; 1989.

Mr. Applebod weighs 264 lb or 120 kg (264 lb divided by 2.2 lb/kg). His estimated RMR = 24 kcal/kg/day × 120 kg = 2,880 kcal/day. His RMR calculated from Table 1.4 is only 2,271 kcal (11.6 W + 879 = (11.6 × 120) + 879). **Miss O'Rexia** weighs 99 lb or 45 kg (99 lb divided by 2.2 lb/kg). Her estimated RMR = 24 kcal/kg/day × 45 kg = 1,080 kcal/day. Her RMR from Table 1.4 is very close to this value (14.7 W + 496 = 1,157 kcal/day). Thus, the rough estimate does not work well for obese patients because a disproportionately larger proportion of their body weight is relatively inactive metabolically.

Registered dieticians use extensive tables for calculating energy requirements, based on height, weight, age, and activity level. A more accurate calculation is based on the fat-free mass (FFM), which is equal to the total body mass minus the mass of the person's adipose tissue. With FFM, the BMR is calculated using the equation BMR = 186 + FFM × 23.6 kcal/kg/day. This formula eliminates differences between sexes and between aged versus young individuals that are attributable to differences in relative adiposity. However, determining FFM is relatively cumbersome—one technique requires weighing the patient under water and measuring the residual lung volume.

Indirect calorimetry, a technique that measures O_2 consumption and CO_2 production, can be used when more accurate determinations are required for hospitalized patients. A portable indirect calorimeter is used to measure oxygen consumption and the *respiratory quotient* (RQ), which is the ratio of O_2 consumed to CO_2 produced. The RQ is 1.00 for individuals oxidizing carbohydrates, 0.83 for protein, and 0.71 for fat. From these values, the DEE can be determined.

A simplified method to measure the DEE also uses indirect calorimetry, but only measures oxygen production. Because the oxidation of nutrients requires molecular oxygen, through the measurement of the volume of total inspired and expired air, and the amount of oxygen in that air, a very good estimate of the BMR can be determined. The device required for this method is less cumbersome than the device that measures both oxygen and carbon dioxide consumption, and it is easier to use.

Based on the activities listed in Table 1.5, the average US citizen is rather sedentary. Sedentary habits correlate strongly with risk for cardiovascular disease, so it is not surprising that cardiovascular disease is the major cause of death in this country.

What are reasonable estimates for **Ivan Applebod's** and **Ann O'Rexia's** DEE?

Are **Ivan Applebod** and **Ann O'Rexia** in a healthy weight range?

DIT is often ignored and calculations are based simply on the RMR and the energy required for physical activity.

D. Calculations of Daily Energy Expenditure

The total DEE is usually calculated as the sum of the RMR (in kilocalories per day) plus the energy required for the amount of time spent in each of the various types of physical activity (see Table 1.5). An approximate value for the DEE can be determined from the RMR and the appropriate percentage of the RMR required for physical activity (given previously). For example, a very sedentary medical student would have a DEE equal to the RMR plus 30% of the RMR (or 1.3 × RMR), and an active person's daily expenditure could be two times the RMR.

E. Healthy Body Weight

Ideally, we should strive to maintain a weight consistent with good health. Overweight people are frequently defined as more than 20% above their ideal weight. But what is the ideal weight? The body mass index (BMI), calculated as weight per height^2 (kg/m^2), is currently the preferred method for determining whether a person's weight is in the healthy range. This formula, in the English system, is (weight [in pounds] × 704)/height^2 (with height in inches).

In general, adults with BMI values below 18.5 are considered underweight. Those with BMIs between 18.5 and 24.9 are considered to be in the healthy weight range, between 25 and 29.9 are in the overweight or preobese range, and above 30 are in the obese range. Morbid obesity is defined as a BMI of 40 or greater.

F. Weight Gain and Loss

To maintain our body weight, we must stay in caloric balance. We are in caloric balance if the kilocalories in the food we eat equal our DEE. If we eat less food than we require for our DEE, our body fuel stores supply the additional calories, and we lose weight. Conversely, if we eat more food than we require for our energy needs, the excess fuel is stored (mainly in our adipose tissue), and we gain weight.

When we draw on our adipose tissue to meet our energy needs, we lose approximately 1 lb whenever we expend approximately 3,500 kcal more than we consume. In other words, if we eat 1,000 kcal less than we expend per day, we will lose about 2 lb/week. Because the average individual's food intake is only about 2,000 to 3,000 kcal/day, eating one-third to one-half the normal amount will cause a person to lose weight rather slowly. Fad diets that promise a loss of weight much more rapid than this have no scientific merit. In fact, the rapid initial weight loss the fad dieter typically experiences is attributable largely to loss of body water. This loss of water occurs in part because muscle tissue protein and liver glycogen are degraded rapidly to supply energy during the early phase of the diet. When muscle tissue (which is approximately 80% water) and glycogen (approximately 70% water) are broken down, this water is excreted from the body.

IV. DIETARY REQUIREMENTS

In addition to supplying us with fuel and with general-purpose building blocks for biosynthesis, our diet also provides us with specific nutrients that we need to remain healthy. We must have a regular supply of vitamins and minerals and of the essential fatty acids and essential amino acids. "Essential" means that they are essential in the diet; the body cannot synthesize these compounds from other molecules and therefore must obtain them from the diet. Nutrients that the body requires in the diet only under certain conditions are called *conditionally essential*.

The Recommended Dietary Allowance (RDA) and the Adequate Intake (AI) provide quantitative estimates of nutrient requirements. The RDA for a nutrient is the average daily dietary intake level necessary to meet the requirement of nearly all (97% to 98%) healthy individuals in a particular gender and life stage group.

Life stage group is a certain age range or physiologic status (i.e., pregnancy or lactation). The RDA is intended to serve as a goal for intake by individuals. The AI is a recommended intake value that is used when not enough data are available to establish an RDA.

A. Carbohydrates

No specific carbohydrates have been identified as dietary requirements. Carbohydrates can be synthesized from amino acids, and we can convert one type of carbohydrate to another. However, health problems are associated with the complete elimination of carbohydrate from the diet, partly because a low-carbohydrate diet must contain higher amounts of fat to provide us with the energy we need. High-fat diets are associated with obesity, atherosclerosis, and other health problems.

B. Essential Fatty Acids

Although most lipids required for cell structure, fuel storage, or hormone synthesis can be synthesized from carbohydrates or proteins, we need a minimal level of certain dietary lipids for optimal health. These lipids, known as *essential fatty acids*, are required in our diet because we cannot synthesize fatty acids with these particular arrangements of double bonds. The essential fatty acids, α-linoleic and α-linolenic acid, are supplied by dietary plant oils, and eicosapentaenoic acid (EPA) and docosahexaenoic acid (DHA) are supplied in fish oils. They are the precursors of the eicosanoids (a set of hormone-like molecules that are secreted by cells in small quantities and have numerous important effects on neighboring cells). The eicosanoids include the prostaglandins, thromboxanes, leukotrienes, and other related compounds.

C. Protein

The RDA for protein is approximately 0.8 g high-quality protein per kilogram of ideal body weight, or approximately 60 g/day for men and 50 g/day for women. "High-quality" protein contains all of the essential amino acids in adequate amounts. Proteins of animal origin (milk, egg, and meat proteins) are high quality. The proteins in plant foods are generally of lower quality, which means they are low in one or more of the essential amino acids. Vegetarians may obtain adequate amounts of the essential amino acids by eating mixtures of vegetables that complement each other in terms of their amino acid composition.

1. ESSENTIAL AMINO ACIDS

Different amino acids are used in the body as precursors for the synthesis of proteins and other nitrogen-containing compounds. Of the 20 amino acids commonly required in the body for synthesis of protein and other compounds, 9 amino acids are essential in the diet of an adult human because they cannot be synthesized in the body. These are lysine, isoleucine, leucine, threonine, valine, tryptophan, phenylalanine, methionine, and histidine.

Certain amino acids are conditionally essential, that is, required in the diet only under certain conditions. Children and pregnant women have a high rate of protein synthesis to support growth and require some arginine in the diet, although it can be synthesized in the body. Histidine is essential in the diet of the adult in very small quantities because adults efficiently recycle histidine. The increased requirement of children and pregnant women for histidine is therefore much larger than their increased requirement of other essential amino acids. Tyrosine and cysteine are considered conditionally essential. Tyrosine is synthesized from phenylalanine, and it is required in the diet if phenylalanine intake is inadequate, or if an individual is congenitally deficient in an enzyme required to convert phenylalanine to tyrosine (the congenital disease phenylketonuria). Cysteine is synthesized by using sulfur from methionine, and it also may be required in the diet under certain conditions.

Mr. Applebod's BMR is 2,271 kcal/day. He is sedentary, so he only requires approximately 30% more calories for his physical activity. Therefore, his daily expenditure is approximately 2,271 + (0.3 × 2,271) or 1.3 × 2,271 or 2,952 kcal/day. **Miss O'Rexia's** BMR is 1,157 kcal/day. She performs 2 hours of moderate exercise per day (jogging and walking), so she requires approximately 65% more calories for her physical activity. Therefore, her daily expenditure is approximately 1,157 + (0.65 × 1,157) or 1.65 × 1,157 or 1,909 kcal/day.

Ivan Applebod's weight is classified as obese. His BMI is (264 lb × 704)/(70 in)^2 = 37.9. **Ann O'Rexia** is underweight. Her BMI is (99 lb × 704)/(67 in)^2 = 15.5.

To evaluate a patient's weight, physicians need standards of obesity applicable in a genetically heterogeneous population. Life insurance industry statistics have been used to develop tables giving the weight ranges, based on gender, height, and body frame size, that are associated with the greatest longevity, such as the Metropolitan Height and Weight Tables. However, these tables are considered inadequate for several reasons (e.g., they reflect data from upper-middle-class white groups). The BMI is the classification that is currently used clinically. It is based on two simple measurements, height without shoes and weight with minimal clothing.

Patients can be shown their BMI in a nomogram and need not use calculations. The healthy weight range coincides with the mortality data derived from life insurance tables. The BMI also shows a good correlation with independent measures of body fat. The major weakness of the use of the BMI is that some very muscular individuals may be classified as obese when they are not. Other measurements to estimate body fat and other body compartments, such as weighing individuals under water, are more difficult, expensive, and time consuming and have generally been confined to research purposes.

If patients are above or below ideal weight (such as **Ivan Applebod** or **Ann O'Rexia**), the physician, often in consultation with a registered dietician, prescribes a diet designed to bring the weight into the ideal range.

2. NITROGEN BALANCE

The proteins in the body undergo constant turnover; that is, they are constantly being degraded to amino acids and resynthesized. When a protein is degraded, its amino acids are released into the pool of free amino acids in the body. The amino acids from dietary proteins also enter this pool. Free amino acids can have one of three fates: They are used to make proteins; they serve as precursors for the synthesis of essential nitrogen-containing compounds (e.g., heme, DNA, RNA); or they are oxidized as fuel to yield energy. When amino acids are oxidized, their nitrogen atoms are excreted in the urine principally in the form of urea. The urine also contains smaller amounts of other nitrogenous excretory products (uric acid, creatinine, and ammonium ion) derived from the degradation of amino acids and compounds synthesized from amino acids. Some nitrogen is also lost in sweat, feces, and cells that slough off.

Nitrogen balance is the difference between the amount of nitrogen taken into the body each day (mainly in the form of dietary protein) and the amount of nitrogen in compounds lost (Table 1.6). If more nitrogen is ingested than excreted, a person is said to be in positive nitrogen balance. Positive nitrogen balance occurs in growing individuals (e.g., children, adolescents, pregnant women) who are synthesizing more protein than they are breaking down. Conversely, if less nitrogen is ingested than excreted, a person is said to be in negative nitrogen balance. A negative nitrogen balance develops in a person who is eating either too little protein or protein that is deficient in one or more of the essential amino acids. Amino acids are continuously being mobilized from body proteins. If the diet is lacking an essential amino acid or if the intake of protein is too low, new protein cannot be synthesized, and the unused amino acids will be degraded, with the nitrogen appearing in the urine. If a negative nitrogen balance persists for too long, bodily function will be impaired by the net loss of critical proteins. In contrast, healthy adults are in nitrogen balance (neither positive nor negative), and the amount of nitrogen consumed in the diet equals its loss in urine, sweat, feces, and other excretions.

D. Vitamins

Vitamins (Latin *vita*, life) are a diverse group of organic molecules required in very small quantities in the diet for health, growth, and survival. The absence of a vitamin from the diet or an inadequate intake results in characteristic deficiency signs and, ultimately, death. Table 1.7 lists the signs and symptoms of deficiency for each vitamin, its RDA or AI for young adults, and common food sources. The amount of each vitamin required in the diet is small (in the microgram or milligram range) compared with essential amino acid requirements (in the gram range). The vitamins are often divided into two classes: water-soluble vitamins and fat-soluble vitamins. This classification has little relationship to their function but is related to the absorption and transport of fat-soluble vitamins with lipids.

Most vitamins are used for the synthesis of coenzymes, complex organic molecules that assist enzymes in catalyzing biochemical reactions, and the deficiency symptoms reflect an inability of cells to carry out certain reactions. However, some vitamins also act as hormones. We will consider the roles played by individual vitamins as we progress through the subsequent chapters of this text.

Although the RDA or AI for each vitamin varies with age and sex, the difference is usually not very large once adolescence is reached. For example, the RDA for riboflavin is 0.9 mg/day for males between 9 and 13 years of age, 1.3 mg/day

Table 1.6 Nitrogen Balance[a]

Positive nitrogen balance	Growth (e.g., childhood, pregnancy)	Dietary N > Excreted N
Nitrogen balance	Normal healthy adult	Dietary N = Excreted N
Negative nitrogen balance	Dietary deficiency of total protein or amino acids: catabolic stress	Dietary N < Excreted N

[a]N refers to nitrogen.

Table 1.7 Vitamins

Vitamin	Dietary Reference Intakes (DRI) Females (F) Males (M) (18–30 yrs old)	Some Common Food Sources	Consequences of Deficiency (Names of Deficiency Diseases Are in Bold)
Water-soluble vitamins			
Vitamin C	**RDA** F: 75 mg M: 90 mg **UL**: 2 g	Citrus fruits; potatoes; peppers, broccoli, spinach; strawberries	**Scurvy:** defective collagen formation leading to subcutaneous hemorrhage, aching bones, joints, and muscle in adults, rigid position and pain in infants
Thiamin	**RDA** F: 1.1 mg M: 1.2 mg	Enriched cereals and breads; unrefined grains; pork; legumes, seeds, nuts	**Beriberi:** (wet) edema; anorexia, weight loss; apathy, decrease in short-term memory, confusion; irritability; muscle weakness; an enlarged heart
Riboflavin	**RDA** F: 1.1 mg M: 1.3 mg	Dairy products; fortified cereals; meats, poultry, fish; legumes	**Ariboflavinosis:** Sore throat, hyperemia, edema of oral mucosal membranes; cheilosis, angular stomatitis; glossitis, magenta tongue; seborrheic dermatitis; normochromic normocytic anemia
Niacin[a]	**RDA** F: 14 mg NEQ M: 16 mg NEQ **UL**: 35 mg	Meat: chicken, beef, fish; enriched cereals or whole grains; most foods	**Pellagra:** Pigmented rash in areas exposed to sunlight; vomiting; constipation or diarrhea; bright red tongue; neurologic symptoms
Vitamin B$_6$ (pyridoxine)	**RDA** F: 1.3 mg M: 1.3 mg **UL**: 100 mg	Chicken, fish, pork; eggs; fortified cereals, unmilled rice, oats; starchy vegetables; noncitrus fruits; peanuts, walnuts	Seborrheic dermatitis; microcytic anemia; epileptiform convulsions; depression and confusion
Folate	**RDA** F: 400 μg M: 400 μg **UL**: 1,000 μg	Citrus fruits; dark green vegetables; fortified cereals and breads; legumes	Impaired cell division and growth; **megaloblastic anemia**; neural tube defects
Vitamin B$_{12}$	**RDA** F: 2.4 μg M: 2.4 μg	Animal products[b]	**Megaloblastic anemia**; neurologic symptoms
Biotin	**AI** F: 30 μg M: 30 μg	Liver Egg yolk	Conjunctivitis; central nervous system abnormalities; glossitis; alopecia; dry, scaly dermatitis
Pantothenic acid	**AI** F: 5 mg M: 5 mg	Wide distribution in foods, especially animal tissues; whole grain cereals; legumes	Irritability and restlessness; fatigue, apathy, malaise; gastrointestinal symptoms; neurologic symptoms
Choline	**AI** F: 425 mg M: 550 mg **UL**: 3.5 g	Milk; liver; eggs; peanuts	Liver damage
Fat-soluble vitamins			
Vitamin A	**RDA** F: 700 μg M: 900 μg **UL**: 3,000 μg	Carrots; dark green and leafy vegetables; sweet potatoes and squash; broccoli	Night blindness; **xerophthalmia**; keratinization of epithelium in GI, respiratory and genitourinary tract, skin becomes dry and scaly
Vitamin K	**RDA** F: 90 μg M: 120 μg	Green leafy vegetables; cabbage family (brassica); bacterial flora of intestine	Defective blood coagulation; hemorrhagic anemia of the newborn

(continued)

Q: Are **Ivan Applebod** and **Ann O'Rexia** gaining or losing weight?

Malnutrition, the absence of an adequate intake of nutrients, occurs in the United States principally among children of families with incomes below the poverty level, the elderly, individuals whose diet is influenced by alcohol and drug usage, and those who make poor food choices. More than 13 million children in the United States live in families with incomes below the poverty level. Of these, approximately 10% have clinical malnutrition, most often anemia resulting from inadequate iron intake. A larger percentage have mild protein and energy malnutrition and exhibit growth retardation, sometimes as a result of parental neglect. Childhood malnutrition may also lead to learning failure and chronic illness later in life. A weight-for-age measurement is one of the best indicators of childhood malnourishment because it is easy to measure, and weight is one of the first parameters to change during malnutrition.

The term *kwashiorkor* refers to a disease originally seen in African children suffering from a protein deficiency (although overall caloric intake may be normal). It is characterized by marked hypoalbuminemia (low levels of albumin in the blood), anemia, edema (buildup of fluids in the interstitial spaces), pot belly, loss of hair, and other signs of tissue injury. The term *marasmus* is used for prolonged protein and calorie malnutrition, particularly in young children. Children with marasmus usually do not develop edema. The term *protein-calorie malnutrition* can be used to describe both disorders.

Mr. Applebod expends about 2,952 kcal/day and consumes 4,110 kcal. By this calculation, he consumes 1,158 more kcal than he expends each day and is gaining weight. **Miss O'Rexia** expends 1,909 kcal/day while she consumes only 615 kcal. Therefore, she expends 1,294 more kcal/day than she consumes, so she is losing weight.

Multiple vitamin deficiencies accompanying malnutrition are far more common in the United States than the characteristic deficiency diseases associated with diets lacking just one vitamin, because we generally eat a variety of foods. The characteristic deficiency diseases arising from single vitamin deficiencies were often identified and described in humans through observations of populations consuming a restricted diet because that was all that was available. For example, thiamine deficiency was discovered by a physician in Java, who related the symptoms of beriberi to diets composed principally of polished rice. Today, single vitamin deficiencies usually occur as a result of conditions that interfere with the uptake or utilization of a vitamin or as a result of poor food choices or a lack of variety in the diet. For example, peripheral neuropathy associated with vitamin E deficiency can occur in children with fat malabsorption, and alcohol consumption can result in beriberi. Vegans, individuals who consume diets lacking all animal products, can develop deficiencies in vitamin B$_{12}$.

Table 1.7   Vitamins *(continued)*

Vitamin	Dietary Reference Intakes (DRI) Females (F) Males (M) (18–30 yrs old)	Some Common Food Sources	Consequences of Deficiency (Names of Deficiency Diseases Are in Bold)
Vitamin D	**AI**[c] F: 5 μg M: 5 μg **UL:** 50 μg	Fortified milk; exposure of skin to sunlight	**Rickets** (in children); inadequate bone mineralization (osteomalacia)
Vitamin E	**RDA** F: 15 mg M: 15 mg **UL:** 1 g	Vegetable oils, margarine; wheat germ; nuts; green leafy vegetables	Muscular dystrophy, neurologic abnormalities

RDA, Recommended Dietary Allowance; AI, Adequate Intake; UL, Tolerable Upper Intake Level.
[a]NEQ = niacin equivalents. Niacin can be synthesized in the human from tryptophan, and this term takes into account a conversion factor for dietary tryptophan.
[b]Vitamin B$_{12}$ is found only in animal products.
[c]Dietary requirement assumes the absence of sunlight.
Information for this table is from Food and Nutrition Board, Institute of Medicine. *Dietary Reference Intakes for Thiamin, Riboflavin, Niacin, Vitamin B$_6$, Folate, Vitamin B$_{12}$, Pantothenic Acid, Biotin, and Choline* (1998); *Dietary Reference Intakes for Vitamin C, Vitamin E, Selenium, and Carotenoids* (2000); *Dietary Reference Intakes for Calcium, Phosphorus, Magnesium, Vitamin D, and Fluoride* (1997); *Dietary Reference Intakes for Vitamin A, Vitamin K, Arsenic, Boron, Chromium, Copper, Iodine, Iron, Manganese, Molybdenum, Nickel, Silicon, Vanadium, and Zinc* (2001). Washington, DC: National Academy Press. This information can also be obtained via the Web, at http://fnic.nal.usda.gov/, and click on Dietary Guidance, then Dietary Reference Intakes, and then DRI tables.

for males 19 to 30 years of age, still 1.3 mg/day for males older than 70 years, and 1.1 mg/day for females aged 19 to 30 years. The largest requirements occur during lactation (1.6 mg/day).

Vitamins, by definition, cannot be synthesized in the body, or are synthesized from a very specific dietary precursor in insufficient amounts. For example, we can synthesize the vitamin niacin from the essential amino acid tryptophan, but not in sufficient quantities to meet our needs. Niacin is therefore still classified as a vitamin.

Excessive intake of many vitamins, both fat-soluble and water-soluble, may cause deleterious effects. For example, high doses of vitamin A, a fat-soluble vitamin, can cause desquamation of the skin and birth defects. High doses of vitamin C cause diarrhea and gastrointestinal disturbances. One of the Dietary Reference Intakes is the Tolerable Upper Intake Level (UL), which is the highest level of daily nutrient intake that is likely to pose no risk of adverse effects to almost all individuals in the general population. As intake increases above the UL, the risk of adverse effects increases. Table 1.7 includes the ULs for vitamins known to pose a risk at high levels. Intake above the UL occurs most often with dietary or pharmacologic supplements of single vitamins and not from foods.

E. Minerals

Many minerals are required in the diet. They are generally divided into the classifications of electrolytes (inorganic ions that are dissolved in the fluid compartments of the body), minerals (required in relatively large quantities), trace minerals (required in smaller quantities), and ultratrace minerals (Table 1.8).

Sodium (Na$^+$), potassium (K$^+$), and chloride (Cl$^-$) are the major electrolytes (ions) in the body. They establish ion gradients across membranes, maintain water balance, and neutralize positive and negative charges on proteins and other molecules.

Calcium and phosphorus serve as structural components of bones and teeth and are thus required in relatively large quantities. Calcium (Ca^{2+}) plays many other roles in the body; for example, it is involved in hormone action and blood clotting. Phosphorus is required for the formation of ATP and of phosphorylated intermediates in metabolism. Magnesium activates many enzymes and also forms a complex

Table 1.8   Minerals Required in the Diet

Electrolytes	Minerals	Trace Minerals	Ultratrace or Trace Minerals[a]
Sodium	Calcium	Iodine	Manganese
Potassium	Phosphorus	Selenium	Fluoride
Chloride	Magnesium	Copper	Chromium
	Iron	Zinc	Molybdenum
	Sulfur		

[a]These minerals can be classified as trace or as ultratrace.

with ATP. Iron is a particularly important mineral because it functions as a component of hemoglobin (the oxygen-carrying protein in the blood) and is part of many enzymes. Other minerals, such as zinc or molybdenum, are required in very small quantities (trace or ultratrace amounts).

Sulfur is ingested principally in the amino acids cysteine and methionine. It is found in connective tissue, particularly in cartilage and skin. It has important functions in metabolism, which we will describe when we consider the action of coenzyme A (CoA), a compound used to activate carboxylic acids. Sulfur is excreted in the urine as sulfate.

Minerals, like vitamins, have adverse effects if ingested in excessive amounts. Problems associated with dietary excesses or deficiencies of minerals are described in subsequent chapters in conjunction with their normal metabolic functions.

F. Water

Water constitutes one-half to four-fifths of the weight of the human body. The intake of water required per day depends on the balance between the amount produced by body metabolism and the amount lost through the skin, through expired air, and in the urine and feces.

V. DIETARY GUIDELINES

Dietary guidelines or goals are recommendations for food choices that can reduce the risk of developing chronic or degenerative diseases while maintaining an adequate intake of nutrients. Many studies have shown an association between diet and exercise and decreased risk of certain diseases, including hypertension, atherosclerosis, stroke, diabetes, certain types of cancer, and osteoarthritis. Thus, the American Heart Institute and the American Cancer Institute, as well as several other groups, have developed dietary and exercise recommendations to decrease the risk of these diseases. The *Dietary Guidelines for Americans* (2010), prepared under the authority of the U.S. Department of Agriculture (USDA) Center for Nutrition Policy and Promotion, merges many of these recommendations, which are revised every 5 years (you can view these at the Web site listed in the references). Recommended servings of different food groups can be customized for individuals by going to the USDA MyPlate Web site (see references). Issues of special concern for physicians who advise patients include the following:

A. General Recommendations

• Aim for a healthy weight and be physically active each day. For maintenance of a healthy weight, caloric intake should balance caloric expenditure. Accumulate at least 30 minutes of moderate physical activity (such as walking 2 miles) daily. A regular exercise program helps in achieving and maintaining ideal weight, cardiovascular fitness, and strength.
• Choose foods in the proportions recommended by your personalized Plan from MyPlate, including a variety of grains and a variety of fruits and vegetables daily.
• Keep food safe to eat. For example, refrigerate leftovers promptly.

In the hospital, it was learned that **Mr. Percy Veere** had lost 32 lb in the 8 months since his last visit to his family physician. On admission, his hemoglobin (the iron-containing compound in the blood, which carries O_2 from the lungs to the tissues) was 10.7 g/dL (reference range, males = 12 to 15.5 g/dL), his serum ferritin was 4 ng/mL (reference range, males = 40 to 200 ng/mL), and other hematologic indices that reflect nutritional status were also abnormal. These values are indicative of an iron deficiency anemia. His serum folic acid level was 0.9 ng/mL (reference range = 3 to 20 ng/dL), indicating a low intake of this vitamin. His vitamin B_{12} level was 190 pg/mL (reference range = 180 to 914 pg/mL). A low blood vitamin B_{12} level can be caused by decreased intake, absorption, or transport, but it takes a long time to develop. His serum albumin was 3.2 g/dL (reference range = 3.5 to 5.0 g/dL), which is an indicator of protein malnutrition or liver disease.

A dietary deficiency of calcium can lead to *osteoporosis* and *osteomalacia*, a disorder in which bones are insufficiently mineralized and consequently are fragile and easily fractured. Osteoporosis is a particularly common problem among elderly women. Deficiency of phosphorus results in bone loss along with weakness, anorexia, malaise, and pain. Iron deficiencies lead to *anemia*, a decrease in the concentration of hemoglobin in the blood.

Q: Which foods would provide **Percy Veere** with good sources of folate and vitamin B_{12}?

Folate is found in fruits and vegetables: citrus fruits (e.g., oranges), green leafy vegetables (e.g., spinach, broccoli), fortified cereals, and legumes (e.g., peas) (see Table 1.7). Conversely, vitamin B_{12} is found only in foods of animal origin, including meats, eggs, and milk.

Cholesterol is obtained from the diet and synthesized in most cells of the body. It is a component of cell membranes and the precursor of steroid hormones and of the bile salts used for fat absorption. High concentrations of cholesterol in the blood, particularly the cholesterol in lipoprotein particles called low-density lipoproteins (LDL), contribute to the formation of atherosclerotic plaques inside the lumen of arterial vessels, particularly in the heart and brain. These plaques (fatty deposits on arterial walls) can obstruct blood flow to these vital organs causing heart attacks and strokes. A high content of saturated fat in the diet tends to increase circulatory levels of LDL cholesterol and contributes to the development of atherosclerosis.

The high intake of sodium and chloride (in table salt) of the average American diet appears to be related to the development of hypertension (high blood pressure) in individuals who are genetically predisposed to this disorder.

B. Vegetables, Fruits, and Grains

- Diets rich in vegetables, fruits, and grain products should be chosen. Four and one-half cups of vegetables and fruits should be eaten each day, particularly green and yellow vegetables and citrus fruits. Three or more ounce-equivalents of whole grain products should be eaten per day (starches and other complex carbohydrates, in the form of breads, fortified cereals, rice, and pasta). In addition to energy, vegetables, fruits, and grains supply vitamins, minerals, protective substances (such as carotenoids), and fiber. Fiber, the indigestible part of plant food, has various beneficial effects, including relief of constipation.
- The consumption of refined sugar in foods and beverages should be reduced to below the American norm. Refined sugar has no nutritional value other than its caloric content, and it promotes tooth decay.

C. Fats

- Fat intake should be reduced. Fat should account for no more than 35% of total dietary calories (but >20%), and saturated fatty acids should account for 10% or less. Fats derived from fish, nuts, and vegetables, which are primarily polyunsaturated and monosaturated fatty acids, are preferred. Foods high in saturated fat, which should be limited, include cheese, whole milk, butter, regular ice cream, and many cuts of beef. *Trans*-fatty acids, such as the partially hydrogenated vegetable oils used in margarine, should also be avoided.
- Cholesterol intake should be <300 mg/day in subjects without atherosclerotic disease and <200 mg/day in those with established atherosclerosis.

D. Proteins

- Based on the year 2000 report, and still present in the 2010 report, protein intake for adults should be approximately 0.8 g/kg ideal body weight per day. The protein should be of high quality and should be obtained from sources low in saturated fat (e.g., fish, lean poultry, dry beans). Vegetarians should eat a mixture of vegetable proteins that ensures the intake of adequate amounts of the essential amino acids.

E. Alcohol

- Alcohol consumption should not exceed moderate drinking. Moderation is defined as no more than one drink per day for women and no more than two drinks per day for men. A drink is defined as 1 regular beer, 5 oz of wine (a little over 0.5 cup), or 1.5 oz of an 80-proof liquor, such as whiskey. Pregnant women should drink no alcohol. The ingestion of alcohol by pregnant women can result in fetal alcohol syndrome (FAS), which is marked by prenatal and postnatal growth deficiency; developmental delay; and craniofacial, limb, and cardiovascular defects.

F. Vitamins and Minerals

- Sodium intake should be decreased in most individuals. Sodium is usually consumed as salt, NaCl. Less than 2.3 g of sodium should be consumed daily, which is about 4.5 g, or 1 tbsp, of salt.
- Many of the required vitamins and minerals can be obtained from eating a variety of fruits, vegetables, and grains (particularly whole grains). However, calcium and iron are required in relatively high amounts. Low-fat or nonfat dairy products and dark green leafy vegetables provide good sources of calcium. Lean meats, shellfish, poultry, dark meat, cooked dry beans, and some green leafy vegetables provide good sources of iron. Vitamin B_{12} is found only in animal sources.

- Dietary supplementation in excess of the recommended amounts (e.g., megavitamin regimens) should be avoided.
- Fluoride should be present in the diet, at least during the years of tooth formation, as a protection against dental caries.

VI. XENOBIOTICS

In addition to nutrients, our diet also contains a large number of chemicals called *xenobiotics*, which have no nutritional value, are of no use in the body, and can be harmful if consumed in excessive amounts. These compounds occur naturally in foods, can enter the food chain as contaminants, or can be deliberately introduced as food additives.

Dietary guidelines of the American Cancer Society and the American Institute for Cancer Research make recommendations relevant to the ingestion of xenobiotic compounds, particularly carcinogens. The dietary advice that we eat a variety of food helps to protect us against the ingestion of a toxic level of any one xenobiotic compound. It is also suggested that we reduce consumption of salt-cured, smoked, and charred foods, which contain chemicals that can contribute to the development of cancer. Other guidelines encourage the ingestion of fruits and vegetables that contain protective chemicals called antioxidants.

The prevalence of obesity in the US population is increasing. In 1962, 12.8% of the population had a BMI ≥30 and therefore were clinically obese. That number increased to 14.5% by 1980 and to 22.5% by 1998. An additional 30% were pre-obese in 1998 (BMI = 25.0 to 29.9). In 2009, 26.7% of adults had a BMI ≥30. It is apparent, therefore, that more than 50% of the population is currently overweight, that is, obese or preobese.

Increased weight increases cardiovascular risk factors, including hypertension, diabetes mellitus, and alterations in blood lipid levels. It also increases the risk of respiratory problems, gallbladder disease, and certain types of cancer.

CLINICAL COMMENTS

Otto Shape. **Otto Shape** sought help in reducing his weight of 187 lb (BMI of 27) to his previous level of 154 lb (BMI of 22, in the middle of the healthy range). **Otto Shape** was 5 ft 10 in tall, and he calculated that his maximum healthy weight was 173 lb. He planned on becoming a family physician, and he knew that he would be better able to counsel patients in healthy behaviors involving diet and exercise if he practiced them himself. With this information and assurances from the physician that he was otherwise in good health, Otto embarked on a weight loss program. One of his strategies involved recording all the food he ate and the portions. To analyze his diet for calories, saturated fat, and nutrients, he used the personalized MyPlate Plan (see references), available online from the USDA Food and Nutrition Information Center.

Ivan Applebod. **Ivan Applebod** weighed 264 lb and was 5 ft 10 in tall with a heavy skeletal frame. For a male of these proportions, a BMI of 18.5 to 24.9 would correspond to a weight between 129 lb and 173 lb. He is currently almost 100 lb overweight, and his BMI of 37.9 is in the obese range.

Mr. Applebod's physician cautioned him that exogenous obesity (caused by overeating) represents a risk factor for atherosclerotic vascular disease, particularly when the distribution of fat is primarily "central" or in the abdominal region (apple shape, in contrast to the pear shape, which results from adipose tissue deposited in the buttocks and hips). In addition, obesity may lead to other cardiovascular risk factors such as hypertension (high blood pressure), hyperlipidemia (high blood lipid levels), and type 2 diabetes mellitus (characterized by hyperglycemia). He already has elevated blood pressure. Furthermore, his total serum cholesterol level was 296 mg/dL, well above the desired normal value (200 mg/dL).

Mr. Applebod was referred to the hospital's weight reduction center, where a team of physicians, dieticians, and psychologists could assist him in reaching his ideal weight range.

Ann O'Rexia. Because of her history and physical examination, **Ann O'Rexia** was diagnosed as having early *anorexia nervosa*, a behavioral disorder that involves both emotional and nutritional disturbances. Miss

O'Rexia was referred to a psychiatrist with special interest in anorexia nervosa, and a program of psychotherapy and behavior modification was initiated.

Percy Veere. Percy Veere weighed 125 lb and was 5 ft 11 in tall (without shoes) with a medium frame. His BMI was 17.5, which is significantly underweight. At the time his wife died, he weighed 147 lb. For his height, a BMI in the healthy weight range corresponds to weights between 132 lb and 178 lb.

Mr. Veere's malnourished state was reflected in his admission laboratory profile. The results of hematologic studies were consistent with an iron deficiency anemia complicated by low levels of folic acid and vitamin B_{12}, two vitamins that can affect the development of normal red blood cells. His low serum albumin level was caused by insufficient protein intake and a shortage of essential amino acids, which result in a reduced ability to synthesize body proteins. The psychiatrist requested a consultation with a hospital dietician to evaluate the extent of Mr. Veere's *marasmus* (malnutrition caused by a deficiency of both protein and total calories) as well as his vitamin and mineral deficiencies.

BIOCHEMICAL COMMENTS

Dietary Reference Intakes. DRIs are quantitative estimates of nutrient intakes that can be used in evaluating and planning diets for healthy people. They are prepared by the Standing Committee on the Scientific Evaluation of DRIs of the Food and Nutrition Board, Institute of Medicine, and the National Academy of Science, with active input of Health Canada. The four reference intake values are the Recommended Dietary Allowance (RDA), the Estimated Average Requirement (EAR), the Adequate Intake (AI), and the Tolerable Upper Intake Level (UL). For each vitamin, the committee has reviewed available literature on studies with humans and established criteria for AI, such as prevention of certain deficiency symptoms, prevention of developmental abnormalities, or decreased risk of chronic degenerative disease. The criteria are not always the same for each life stage group. A requirement is defined as the lowest continuing intake level of a nutrient able to satisfy these criteria. The EAR is the daily intake value that is estimated to meet the requirement in half of the apparently healthy individuals in a life stage or gender group. The RDA is the EAR plus two standard deviations of the mean, which is the amount that should satisfy the requirement in 97% to 98% of the population. The AI level instead of an RDA is set for nutrients when there is not enough data to determine the EAR.

The UL refers to the highest level of daily nutrient intake consumed over time that is likely to pose no risks of adverse effects for almost all healthy individuals in the general population. Adverse effects are defined as any significant alteration in the structure or function of the human organism. The UL does not mean that most individuals who consume more than the UL will suffer adverse health effects, but that the risk of adverse effects increases as intake increases above the UL.

An example of the difference between the AI and the EAR is provided by riboflavin. Very few data exist on the nutrient requirements of very young infants. However, human milk is the sole recommended food for the first 4 to 6 months, so the AI of the vitamin riboflavin for this life stage group is based on the amount in breast milk consumed by healthy full-term infants. Conversely, the riboflavin EAR for adults is based on several studies in humans relating dietary intake of riboflavin to biochemical markers of riboflavin status and development of clinical deficiency symptoms.

Table 1.9   Diseases Discussed in Chapter 1

Disorder or Condition	Genetic or Environmental	Comments
Depression	Both	Diagnosed by behavioral changes, can be treated with a variety of pharmacologic agents and counseling therapy
Obesity	Both	Long-term effects of obesity affect cardiovascular system and may lead to metabolic syndrome
Anorexia	Environmental	Self-induced reduction of food intake, distorted body image, considered at least in part a psychiatric disorder
Kwashiorkor	Environmental	Protein and mineral deficiency yet normal amount of calories in the diet. Leads to marked hypoalbumin-emia, anemia, edema, pot belly, loss of hair, and other indications of tissue injury
Marasmus	Environmental	Prolonged calorie and protein malnutrition
Osteoporosis/ osteomalacia	Environmental	Calcium-deficient diet leading to insufficient mineralization of the bones, which produces fragile and easily broken bones.

Diseases that may have a genetic component are indicated as genetic; disorders caused by environmental factors (with or without genetic influences) are indicated as environmental.

Key Concepts

- Fuel is provided in the form of carbohydrates, fats, and proteins in our diet.
- Energy is obtained from the fuel by oxidizing it to carbon dioxide and water.
- Unused fuel can be stored as triacylglycerol (fat) or glycogen (carbohydrate) within the body.
- Weight gain or loss is a balance between the energy consumed in our diet and the energy required each day to drive the basic functions of our body and our physical activity. The daily energy expenditure (DEE) is the amount of fuel consumed in a 24-hour period.
- The resting metabolic rate (RMR) is a measure of the energy required to maintain nonexercise bodily functions such as respiration, contraction of the heart muscle, biosynthetic processes, and establishment of ion gradients across neuronal membranes.
- The DEE is determined by the RMR and the individual's activity level while awake.
- The body mass index (BMI) is a rough measure of determining an ideal weight for an individual, and whether a person is underweight or overweight.
- In addition to nutrients, the diet provides vitamins, minerals, essential fatty acids, and amino acids.
- The Recommended Dietary Allowance (RDA) and the Adequate Intake (AI) provide quantitative estimates of nutrient requirements.
- The Tolerable Upper Intake Level (UL) indicates the highest level of daily nutrient uptake that is likely to pose no risk of adverse effects.
- A summary of the diseases/disorders discussed in this chapter are presented in Table 1.9.

REVIEW QUESTIONS—CHAPTER 1

Directions: For each question that follows, select the single best answer.

1. In the process of respiration, fuels most often undergo which one of the following fates?

    A. They are stored as triacylglycerols.

    B. They are oxidized to generate ATP.

    C. They release energy principally as heat.

    D. They combine with CO_2 and H_2O and are stored.

    E. They combine with other dietary components in anabolic pathways.

2. Mrs. Jones is a sedentary 83-year-old woman who is 5 ft 4 in tall and weighs 125 lb. She has been at this weight for about a year. She says that a typical diet for her includes a breakfast of toast (white bread, no butter), a boiled egg, and coffee with cream. For lunch, she often has a cheese sandwich (white bread) and a glass of whole milk. For supper, she prefers cream of chicken soup and a slice of frosted cake. Mrs. Jones' diet is most likely to be inadequate in which one of the following?

    A. Vitamin C

    B. Protein

    C. Calcium

D. Vitamin B$_{12}$

E. Calories

3. The resting metabolic rate is best explained by which one of the following statements?

A. It is equivalent to the caloric requirement of our major organs and resting muscle.

B. It is generally higher per kilogram body weight in women than in men.

C. It is generally lower per kilogram body weight in children than adults.

D. It is decreased in a cold environment.

E. It is approximately equivalent to the daily energy expenditure.

4. The RDA is best described by which one of the following?

A. The average amount of a nutrient required each day to maintain normal function in 50% of the US population.

B. The average amount of a nutrient ingested daily by 50% of the US population.

C. The minimum amount of a nutrient ingested daily that prevents deficiency symptoms.

D. A reasonable dietary goal for the intake of a nutrient by a healthy individual.

E. It is based principally on data obtained with laboratory animals.

5. A 35-year-old sedentary male patient weighing 120 kg was experiencing angina (chest pain) and other signs of coronary artery disease. His physician, in consultation with a registered dietician, conducted a 3-day dietary recall. The patient consumed an average of 585 g of carbohydrate, 150 g of protein, and 95 g of fat each day. In addition, he drank 45 g of alcohol. The patient's diet is best described by which one of the following?

A. He consumed between 2,500 and 3,000 kcal/day.

B. He had a fat intake within the range recommended in current dietary guidelines (i.e., year 2010).

C. He consumed 50% of his calories as alcohol.

D. He was deficient in protein intake.

E. He was in negative caloric balance.

2 The Fed or Absorptive State

The Fed State. *During a **meal**, we ingest carbohydrates, lipids, and proteins, which are subsequently **digested** and **absorbed**. Some of this food is **oxidized** to meet the immediate **energy** needs of the body. The amount consumed in **excess** of the body's energy needs is transported to the **fuel depots**, where it is stored. During the period from the start of absorption until absorption is completed, we are in the **fed** or absorptive state. Whether a fuel is oxidized or stored in the fed state is determined principally by the concentration of two **endocrine hormones** in the blood: **insulin** and **glucagon**.*

    Fate of Carbohydrates. *Dietary carbohydrates are digested to monosaccharides, which are absorbed into the blood. The major monosaccharide in the blood is **glucose** (Fig. 2.1). After a meal, glucose is **oxidized** by various tissues for energy, enters biosynthetic pathways, and is **stored** as **glycogen**, mainly in the liver and muscles. Glucose is the major biosynthetic precursor in the body, and the carbon skeletons of most of the compounds we synthesize can be synthesized from glucose. Glucose is also converted to **triacylglycerols**. The liver packages triacylglycerols, made from glucose or from fatty acids obtained from the blood, into **very low-density lipoproteins (VLDL)** and releases them into the blood. The fatty acids of the VLDL are stored mainly as triacylglycerols in adipose tissue, but some may be used to meet the energy needs of cells.*

    Fate of Proteins. *Dietary proteins are digested to **amino acids**, which are absorbed into the blood. In cells, the amino acids are converted to **proteins** or used to make various **nitrogen-containing compounds** such as neurotransmitters and heme. The carbon skeleton may also be **oxidized** for energy directly, or be converted to glucose.*

    Fate of Fats. *Triacylglycerols are the major lipids in the diet. They are digested to fatty acids and 2-monoacylglycerols, which are resynthesized into **triacylglycerols** in intestinal epithelial cells, packaged in **chylomicrons** and secreted by way of the lymph into the blood. The **fatty acids** of the chylomicron triacylglycerols are stored mainly as triacylglycerols in **adipose** cells. They are subsequently oxidized for energy or used in biosynthetic pathways, such as synthesis of membrane lipids.*

FIG. 2.1. Major fate of fuels in the fed state. *TG*, triacylglycerol.

The body can make fatty acids from a caloric excess of carbohydrate and protein. These fatty acids, together with the fatty acids of chylomicrons (derived from dietary fat), are deposited in adipose tissue as triacylglycerols. Thus, **Ivan Applebod's** increased adipose tissue is coming from his intake of all fuels in excess of his caloric need.

THE WAITING ROOM

Ivan Applebod returned to his doctor for a second visit. His initial efforts to lose weight had failed dismally. In fact, he now weighed 270 lb, an increase of 6 lb since his first visit 2 months ago (see Chapter 1). He reported that the recent death of his 45-year-old brother from a heart attack had made him realize that he must pay more attention to his health. Because Mr. Applebod's brother had a history of hypercholesterolemia and because his serum total cholesterol had been significantly elevated (296 mg/dL) at his first visit, his blood lipid profile was determined, his blood glucose level was measured, and several other blood tests were ordered. (The *blood lipid profile* is a test that measures the content of the various triacylglycerol- and cholesterol-containing particles in the blood.) His blood pressure was 162 mm Hg systolic and 98 mm Hg diastolic or 162/98 mm Hg (normal = <120/80 mm Hg, with prehypertension 120 to 139/80 to 89 mm Hg and hypertension defined as >140/90 mm Hg). His waist circumference was 48 in (healthy values for men, <40 in; for women, <35 in).

I. DIGESTION AND ABSORPTION

A. Carbohydrates

Dietary carbohydrates are converted to monosaccharides. *Starch*, a polymer of glucose, is the major carbohydrate of the diet. It is digested by the enzyme salivary α-amylase and then by pancreatic α-amylase, which acts in the small intestine. *Enzymes* are proteins that catalyze biochemical reactions (usually, they increase the speed at which the reactions occur). Disaccharides, trisaccharides, and oligosaccharides (*disaccharide* refers to two linked sugars; a *trisaccharide* to three linked sugars, and an *oligosaccharide* to *N*-linked sugars) produced by these α-amylases are cleaved to glucose by digestive enzymes located on the surface of the brush border of the intestinal epithelial cells. Dietary disaccharides also are cleaved by enzymes in this brush border. Sucrase converts the disaccharide sucrose (table sugar) to glucose and fructose, and lactase converts the disaccharide lactose (milk sugar) to glucose and galactose. Monosaccharides produced by digestion and dietary monosaccharides are absorbed by the intestinal epithelial cells and released into the hepatic portal vein, which carries them to the liver.

B. Proteins

Proteins contain amino acids that are linked through peptide bonds (see Chapter 1). Dipeptides contain two amino acids, tripeptides contain three amino acids, and so on. Dietary proteins are cleaved to amino acids by enzymes known as *proteases* (Fig. 2.2, circle 3), which cleave the peptide bond between amino acids (see Fig. 1.5). Pepsin acts in the stomach, and the proteolytic enzymes produced by the pancreas (trypsin, chymotrypsin, elastase, and the carboxypeptidases) act in the lumen of the small intestine. Aminopeptidases, dipeptidases, and tripeptidases associated with the intestinal epithelial cells complete the conversion of dietary proteins to amino acids, which are absorbed into the intestinal epithelial cells and released into the hepatic portal vein.

C. Fats

The digestion of fats is more complex than that of carbohydrates or proteins because fats are not very soluble in water. The triacylglycerols of the diet are emulsified in the intestine by bile salts, which are synthesized in the liver and stored in the gallbladder. The enzyme pancreatic lipase converts the triacylglycerols in the lumen of

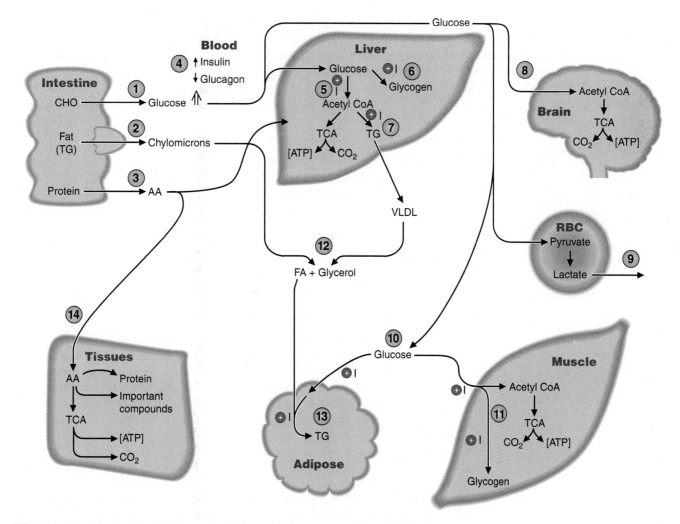

FIG. 2.2. The fed state. The circled numbers indicate the approximate order in which the processes occur. *TG*, triacylglycerols; *FA*, fatty acid; *AA*, amino acid; *RBC*, red blood cell; *VLDL*, very low-density lipoprotein; *I*, insulin; ⊕, stimulated by.

the intestine to fatty acids and 2-monoacylglycerols (glycerol with a fatty acid ester-ified at carbon 2), which interact with bile salts to form tiny microdroplets called *micelles*. The fatty acids and 2-monoacylglycerols are absorbed from these micelles into the intestinal epithelial cells, where they are resynthesized into triacylglycerols. The triacylglycerols are packaged with proteins, phospholipids, cholesterol, and other compounds into the lipoprotein complexes known as *chylomicrons*, which are secreted into the lymph and ultimately enter the bloodstream (see Fig. 2.2, circle 2). Fats must be transported in the blood bound to protein or in lipoprotein complexes because they are insoluble in water. Thus, both triacylglycerols and cholesterol are found in lipoprotein complexes.

II. CHANGES IN HORMONE LEVELS AFTER A MEAL

After a typical high-carbohydrate meal, the pancreas is stimulated to release the hormone insulin, and release of the hormone glucagon is inhibited (see Fig. 2.2, circle 4). Endocrine hormones are released from endocrine glands, such as the pancreas, in response to a specific stimulus. They travel in the blood, carrying messages between tissues concerning the overall physiologic state of the body. At their target tissues, they adjust the rate of various metabolic pathways to meet the changing conditions. The endocrine hormone insulin, which is secreted from

The laboratory studies ordered at the time of his second office visit show that **Ivan Applebod** has *hyperglycemia*, an elevation of blood glucose greater than normal values. At the time of this visit, his blood glucose, determined after an overnight fast, was 162 mg/dL (normal is 80 to 100 mg/dL). Because this blood glucose measurement was significantly above normal, the fasting blood glucose levels were tested the next day, with a result of 170 mg/dL. This led to a diagnosis of type 2 diabetes mellitus, formerly known as *non–insulin-dependent diabetes mellitus* (NIDDM). In this disease, liver, muscle, and adipose tissue are relatively resistant to the action of insulin in promoting glucose uptake into cells and storage as glycogen and triacylglycerols. Therefore, more glucose remains in his blood.

the β-cells of the pancreas in response to a high-carbohydrate meal, carries the message that dietary glucose is available and can be used and stored. The release of another hormone, glucagon, from the α-cells of the pancreas is suppressed by glucose and insulin. Glucagon carries the message that glucose must be generated from endogenous fuel stores. The subsequent changes in circulating hormone levels cause changes in the body's metabolic patterns, involving several different tissues and metabolic pathways.

III. FATE OF GLUCOSE AFTER A MEAL
A. Conversion to Glycogen, Triacylglycerols, and Carbon Dioxide in the Liver

Because glucose leaves the intestine via the hepatic portal vein, the liver is the first organ it passes through. The liver extracts a portion of this glucose from the blood. Some of the glucose that enters hepatocytes (liver cells) is oxidized in adenosine triphosphate (ATP)-generating pathways to meet the immediate energy needs of these cells, and the remainder is converted to glycogen and triacylglycerols or used for biosynthetic reactions. In the liver, insulin promotes the uptake of glucose by increasing its use as a fuel and its storage as glycogen and triacylglycerols (see Fig. 2.2, circles 5, 6, and 7).

As glucose is being oxidized to CO_2, it is first oxidized to pyruvate in the pathway of glycolysis. Pyruvate is then oxidized to acetyl coenzyme A (acetyl-CoA). The acetyl group enters the tricarboxylic acid (TCA) cycle, where it is completely oxidized to CO_2. Energy from the oxidative reactions is used to generate ATP. The ATP that is generated is used for anabolic and other energy-requiring processes in the cell. Coenzyme A (CoA), which makes the acetyl group more reactive, is a cofactor derived from the vitamin pantothenate.

Liver glycogen stores reach a maximum of approximately 200 to 300 g after a high-carbohydrate meal, whereas the body's fat stores are relatively limitless. As the glycogen stores begin to fill, the liver also begins converting some of the excess glucose it receives to triacylglycerols. Both the glycerol and the fatty acid moieties of the triacylglycerols can be synthesized from glucose. The fatty acids are also obtained preformed from the blood. The liver does not store triacylglycerols, however, but packages them along with proteins, phospholipids, and cholesterol into the lipoprotein complexes known as *very low-density lipoproteins* (VLDL), which are secreted into the bloodstream. Some of the fatty acids from the VLDL are taken up by tissues for their immediate energy needs, but most are stored in adipose tissue as triacylglycerols.

B. Glucose Metabolism in Other Tissues

The glucose from the intestine that is not metabolized by the liver travels in the blood to the peripheral tissues (most other tissues), where it can be oxidized for energy. Glucose is the one fuel that can be used by all tissues. Many tissues store small amounts of glucose as glycogen. Muscle has relatively large glycogen stores.

Insulin greatly stimulates the transport of glucose into the two tissues that have the largest mass in the body: muscle and adipose tissue. It has much smaller effects on the transport of glucose into other tissues.

Fuel metabolism is often discussed as though the body consisted only of brain, skeletal and cardiac muscle, liver, adipose tissue, red blood cells, kidney, and intestinal epithelial cells ("the gut"). These are the dominant tissues in terms of overall fuel economy, and they are the tissues we describe most often. Of course, all tissues require fuels for energy, and many have a very specific fuel requirement.

1. BRAIN AND OTHER NEURAL TISSUES

The brain and other neural tissues are very dependent on glucose for their energy needs. They generally oxidize glucose, via glycolysis and the TCA cycle, completely to CO_2 and H_2O, generating ATP (see Fig. 2.2, circle 8). Except under conditions of starvation, glucose is their only major fuel. Glucose is also a major precursor of neurotransmitters, the chemicals that convey electrical impulses (as ion gradients) between neurons. If our blood glucose drops much lower than normal levels, we become dizzy and light-headed. If blood glucose continues to drop, we become comatose and, ultimately, die. Under normal, nonstarving conditions, the brain and the rest of the nervous system require roughly 150 g of glucose each day.

2. RED BLOOD CELLS

Glucose is the only fuel used by red blood cells because they lack mitochondria. Fatty acid oxidation, amino acid oxidation, TCA cycle, electron-transport chain, and oxidative phosphorylation (ATP generation that is dependent on oxygen and the electron-transport chain) occur principally in the mitochondria. Glucose, in contrast, generates ATP from anaerobic glycolysis in the cytosol and, thus, red blood cells obtain all their energy by this process. In anaerobic glycolysis, the pyruvate formed from glucose is converted to lactate and then released into the blood (see Fig. 2.2, circle 9).

Without glucose, red blood cells could not survive. Red blood cells carry O_2 from the lungs to the tissues. Without red blood cells, most of the tissues of the body would suffer from a lack of energy because they require O_2 to completely convert their fuels to CO_2 and H_2O.

3. MUSCLE

Exercising skeletal muscles can use glucose from the blood or from their own glycogen stores, converting glucose to lactate through glycolysis or oxidizing it completely to CO_2 and H_2O. Muscle also uses other fuels from the blood such as fatty acids (Fig. 2.3). After a meal, glucose is used by muscle to replenish the glycogen

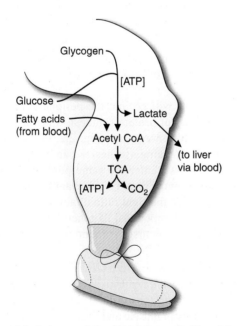

FIG. 2.3. Oxidation of fuels in exercising skeletal muscle. Exercising muscle uses more energy than resting muscle, and, therefore, fuel utilization is increased to supply more ATP.

stores that were depleted during exercise. Glucose is transported into muscle cells and converted to glycogen by processes that are stimulated by insulin.

4. ADIPOSE TISSUE

Insulin stimulates the transport of glucose into adipose cells as well as into muscle cells. Adipocytes oxidize glucose for energy, and they also use glucose as the source of the glycerol moiety of the triacylglycerols they store (see Fig. 2.2, circle 10).

IV. FATE OF LIPOPROTEINS IN THE FED STATE

Two types of lipoproteins, chylomicrons and VLDL, are produced in the fed state. The major function of these lipoproteins is to provide a blood transport system for triacylglycerols, which are very insoluble in water. However, these lipoproteins also contain the lipid cholesterol, which is also somewhat insoluble in water. The triacylglycerols of chylomicrons are formed in intestinal epithelial cells from the products of digestion of dietary triacylglycerols. The triacylglycerols of VLDL are synthesized in the liver.

When these lipoproteins pass through blood vessels in adipose tissue, their triacylglycerols are degraded to fatty acids and glycerol (see Fig. 2.2, circle 12). The fatty acids enter the adipose cells and combine with a glycerol moiety that is produced from blood glucose. The resulting triacylglycerols are stored as large fat droplets in the adipose cells. The remnants of the chylomicrons are cleared from the blood by the liver. The remnants of the VLDL can be cleared by the liver, or they can form a low-density lipoprotein (LDL), which is cleared by the liver or by peripheral cells.

Most of us have not even begun to reach the limits of our capacity to store triacylglycerols in adipose tissue. The ability of humans to store fat appears to be limited only by the amount of tissue we can carry without overloading the heart.

V. FATE OF AMINO ACIDS IN THE FED STATE

The amino acids derived from dietary proteins travel from the intestine to the liver in the hepatic portal vein (see Fig. 2.2, circle 3). The liver uses amino acids for the synthesis of serum proteins as well as its own proteins, and for the biosynthesis of nitrogen-containing compounds that need amino acid precursors, such as the nonessential amino acids, heme, hormones, neurotransmitters, and purine and pyrimidine bases (e.g., adenine and cytosine in DNA). The liver also may oxidize the amino acids or convert them to glucose or ketone bodies and dispose of the nitrogen as the nontoxic compound urea.

Many of the amino acids will go into the peripheral circulation, where they can be used by other tissues for protein synthesis and various biosynthetic pathways, or can be oxidized for energy (see Fig. 2.2, circle 14). Proteins undergo turnover; they are constantly being synthesized and degraded. The amino acids released by protein breakdown enter the same pool of free amino acids in the blood as the amino acids from the diet. This free amino acid pool in the blood can be used by all cells to provide the right ratio of amino acids for protein synthesis or for biosynthesis of other compounds. In general, each individual biosynthetic pathway using an amino acid precursor is found in only a few tissues in the body.

VI. SUMMARY OF THE FED (ABSORPTIVE) STATE

After a meal, the fuels that we eat are oxidized to meet our immediate energy needs. Glucose is the major fuel for most tissues. Excess glucose and other fuels are stored as glycogen mainly in muscle and liver, and as triacylglycerols in adipose tissue. Amino acids from dietary proteins are converted to body proteins or oxidized as fuels.

Ivan Applebod's total cholesterol level is now 315 mg/dL, slightly higher than his previous level of 296 mg/dL. (The currently recommended level for total serum cholesterol is 200 mg/dL or less.) His triacylglycerol level is 250 mg/dL (normal is between 60 and 150 mg/dL). These lipid levels clearly indicate that Mr. Applebod has a hyperlipidemia (a high level of lipoproteins in the blood) and therefore is at risk for the future development of atherosclerosis and its consequences, such as heart attacks and strokes.

CLINICAL COMMENTS

Ivan Applebod. Mr. Applebod was advised that his obesity represents a risk factor for future heart attacks and strokes. He was told that his body has to maintain a larger volume of circulating blood to service his extra fat tissue. This expanded blood volume not only contributes to his elevated blood pressure (itself a risk factor for vascular disease), but also puts an increased workload on his heart. This increased load will cause his heart muscle to thicken and eventually to fail.

Mr. Applebod's increasing adipose mass has also contributed to his development of type 2 diabetes mellitus, which is characterized by hyperglycemia (high blood glucose levels). The mechanism behind this breakdown in his ability to maintain normal levels of blood glucose is, at least in part, a resistance by his triacylglycerol-rich adipose cells to the action of insulin.

In addition to diabetes mellitus, Mr. Applebod has a hyperlipidemia (high blood lipid level—elevated cholesterol and triacylglycerols), another risk factor for cardiovascular disease. A genetic basis for Mr. Applebod's disorder is inferred from a positive family history of hypercholesterolemia and premature coronary artery disease in his brother.

At this point, the first therapeutic step should be nonpharmacologic. Mr. Applebod's obesity should be treated with caloric restriction and a carefully monitored program of exercise. A reduction of dietary fat and sodium would be advised in an effort to correct his hyperlipidemia and his hypertension, respectively. He should also monitor his carbohydrate intake because of his type 2 diabetes.

BIOCHEMICAL COMMENTS

Anthropometric Measurements. Anthropometry uses measurements of body parameters to monitor normal growth and nutritional health in well-nourished individuals, and to detect nutritional inadequacies or excesses. In adults, the measurements most commonly used are height, weight, triceps skinfold thickness (SFT), arm muscle circumference (AMC), and waist circumference. In infants and young children, length and head circumference are also measured.

Weight and Height. Weight should be measured by using a calibrated beam or lever balance-type scale, and the patient should be in a gown or in underwear. Height for adults should be measured while the patient stands against a straight surface, without shoes, with the heels together, and with the head erect and level. The weight and height are used in calculation of the body mass index (BMI).

Skinfold Thickness. More than half of the fat in the body is deposited in subcutaneous tissue under the skin, and the percentage increases with increasing weight. To provide an estimate of the amount of body fat, a standardized caliper is used to pinch a fold of the skin, usually in more than one site (e.g., the biceps, triceps, subscapular and suprailiac areas). Obesity by this physical anthropometric technique is defined as a fatfold thickness greater than the 85th percentile for young adults, that is, 18.6 mm for males and 25.1 mm for females.

Midarm Anthropometry. The AMC, also called the mid-upper arm muscle circumference (MUAMC), reflects both caloric adequacy and muscle mass and can serve as a general index of marasmic-type malnutrition. The arm circumference is measured at the midpoint of the left upper arm by a flexible fiberglass-type tape. The AMC can be calculated from a formula that subtracts a factor related to the SFT from the arm circumference:

$$\text{MUAMC (cm)} = \text{arm circumference (cm)} - (3.14 \times \text{SFT [mm]})/10$$

where MUAMC is the mid-upper arm muscle circumference in centimeters, and SFT is the skinfold thickness, expressed in millimeters.

Ivan Applebod's waist circumference indicates that he has the android pattern of obesity (apple shape). Fat stores are distributed in the body in two different patterns: android and gynecoid. After puberty, men tend to store fat in and on their abdomens and upper body (an android pattern), whereas women tend to store fat around their breasts, hips, and thighs (a gynecoid pattern). Thus, the typical overweight male tends to have more of an apple shape than the typical overweight woman, who is more pear-shaped. Abdominal fat carries a greater risk of hypertension, cardiovascular disease, hyperinsulinemia, diabetes mellitus, gallbladder disease, stroke, and cancer of the breast and endometrium. It also carries a greater risk of overall mortality. Because more men than women have the android distribution, they are more at risk for most of these conditions. However, women who deposit their excess fat in a more android manner have a greater risk than women whose fat distribution is more gynecoid.

Upper-body fat deposition tends to occur more by hypertrophy of the existing cells, whereas lower-body fat deposition is by differentiation of new fat cells (hyperplasia). This may partly explain why many women with lower-body obesity have difficulty losing weight.

The constellation of symptoms exhibited by Mr. Applebod—abdominal obesity, hyperglycemia, hyperlipidemia, and high blood pressure—can all be related to the disorder known as metabolic syndrome or "syndrome X." We will discuss more aspects of metabolic syndrome as Mr. Applebod's case progresses.

M To obtain reliable measures of SFT, procedures are carefully defined. For example, in the triceps measurement, a fold of skin in the posterior aspect of the nondominant arm midway between shoulder and elbow is grasped gently and pulled away from the underlying muscle. The SFT reading is taken at a precise time, 2 to 3 seconds after applying the caliper, because the caliper compresses the skin. Even when these procedures are performed by trained dieticians, reliable measurements are difficult to obtain.

The waist-to-hip ratio has been used instead of the waist circumference as a measure of abdominal obesity in an attempt to correct for differences between individuals with respect to body type or bone structure. In this measurement, the waist circumference is divided by the hip circumference (measured at the iliac crest). The average waist-to-hip ratio for men is 0.93 (with a range of 0.75 to 1.10), and the average for women is 0.83 (with a range of 0.70 to 1.00). However, the waist circumference may actually correlate better with intra-abdominal fat and the associated risk factors than the waist-to-hip ratio.

Table 2.1   Diseases Discussed in Chapter 2

Disorder or Condition	Genetic or Environmental	Comments
Hypercholesterolemia	Both	Elevated cholesterol caused by mutation within a specific protein, or excessive cholesterol intake
Hyperglycemia	Both	High blood glucose levels caused by either mutations in specific proteins, or tissue resistance to insulin
Hyperlipidemia	Both	High levels of blood lipids, may be caused by mutations in specific proteins, or ingestion of high-fat diets

MUAMC values can be compared with reference graphs available for both sexes and all ages. Protein-calorie malnutrition and negative nitrogen balance induce muscle wasting and decrease muscle circumference.

Waist Circumference. The waist circumference is another anthropometric measurement that serves as an indicator of body composition but is used as a measure of obesity and body fat distribution (the "apple shape"), not malnutrition. It is the distance around the natural waist of a standing individual (at the umbilicus). A high-risk waistline is larger than 35 in (88 cm) for women and larger than 40 in (102 cm) for men.

Key Concepts

- During a meal, we ingest carbohydrate, lipids, and proteins.
- Two endocrine hormones—insulin and glucagon—primarily regulate fuel storage and retrieval.
- The predominant carbohydrate in the blood is glucose. Blood glucose levels regulate the release of insulin and glucagon from the pancreas.
- Under the influence of insulin (fed state), glucose can be used as a fuel and also as a precursor for storage via conversion to glycogen or triacylglycerol.
- Insulin stimulates the uptake of glucose into adipose and muscle cells.
- Triacylglycerol obtained from the diet is released into circulation in the form of chylomicrons. Triacylglycerol synthesized from glucose in the liver is released as VLDL. Adipose tissue is the storage site for triacylglycerol.
- Brain and red blood cells use glucose as their primary energy source under normal conditions.
- Amino acids obtained from the diet are used for the biosynthesis of proteins and nitrogen-containing molecules and as an energy source.
- Diseases discussed in this chapter are summarized in Table 2.1.

REVIEW QUESTIONS—CHAPTER 2

1. During digestion of a mixed meal, which one of the following is most likely to occur?
    A. Starch and other polysaccharides are transported to the liver.
    B. Proteins are converted to dipeptides, which enter the blood.
    C. Dietary triacylglycerols are transported in the portal vein to the liver.
    D. Monosaccharides are transported to adipose tissue via the lymphatic system.
    E. Glucose levels increase in the blood.

2. After digestion of a high-carbohydrate meal, which one of the following is most likely to occur?
    A. Glucagon is released from the pancreas.
    B. Insulin stimulates the transport of glucose into the brain.
    C. Liver and skeletal muscle use glucose as their major fuel.
    D. Skeletal muscles convert glucose to fatty acids.
    E. Red blood cells oxidize glucose to CO_2.

3. Insulin release in the fed state will lead to which of the following metabolic changes?

	Increased Glucose Transport by Muscle	VLDL Synthesis by the Liver	Fatty Acid Synthesis in Fat Cells	Glycogen Synthesis in the Liver
A	Yes	Yes	Yes	No
B	Yes	No	Yes	No
C	Yes	Yes	No	Yes
D	No	No	Yes	Yes
E	No	Yes	Yes	Yes
F	No	Yes	No	Yes

4. Elevated levels of chylomicrons were measured in the blood of a patient. A dietary therapy, which decreased which one of the following answer choices would be most helpful in lowering chylomicron levels?

   A. Overall calories
   B. Fat
   C. Cholesterol
   D. Starch
   E. Sugar

5. A male patient exhibited a BMI of 33 kg/m^2 and a waist circumference of 47 in. What dietary therapy would you consider most helpful?

   A. Decreased intake of total calories, because all fuels can be converted to adipose tissue triacylglycerols.
   B. The same amount of total calories, but substitution of carbohydrate calories for fat calories.
   C. The same amount of total calories, but substitution of protein calories for fat calories.
   D. A pure-fat diet, because only fatty acids synthesized by the liver can be deposited as adipose triacylglycerols.
   E. A limited food diet, such as the ice cream and sherry diet.

3 Fasting

The Fasting State. Fasting begins approximately 2 to 4 hours after a meal, when blood glucose levels return to basal levels, and continues until blood glucose levels begin to rise after the start of the next meal. Within about 1 hour after a meal, blood glucose levels begin to fall. Consequently, **insulin** levels decline and **glucagon** levels rise. These changes in hormone levels trigger the **release of fuels** from the body stores. **Liver glycogen** is degraded by the process of **glycogenolysis**, which supplies glucose to the blood. **Adipose triacylglycerols** are **mobilized** by the process of **lipolysis**, which releases fatty acids and glycerol into the blood. Use of **fatty acids** as a fuel increases with the length of the fast; they are the **major fuel** oxidized during overnight fasting.

Fuel Oxidation. During fasting, glucose continues to be **oxidized** by **glucose-dependent tissues** such as the brain and red blood cells, and **fatty acids** are oxidized by tissues such as muscle and liver. Muscle and most other tissues oxidize fatty acids completely to CO_2 and H_2O. However, the **liver** partially oxidizes fatty acids to smaller molecules called **ketone bodies**, which are released into the blood. Muscle, kidney, and certain other tissues derive energy from completely oxidizing ketone bodies in the tricarboxylic acid (TCA) cycle.

Maintenance of Blood Glucose. As fasting progresses, the **liver produces glucose** not only by **glycogenolysis** (the release of glucose from glycogen), but also by a second process called **gluconeogenesis** (the synthesis of glucose from noncarbohydrate compounds). The major **sources of carbon** for gluconeogenesis are **lactate**, **glycerol**, and **amino acids**. When the carbons of the amino acids are converted to glucose by the liver, their **nitrogen** is converted to **urea**.

Starvation. When we fast for 3 or more days, we are in the starved state. **Muscle** continues to burn fatty acids but **decreases** its use of **ketone bodies**. As a result, the concentration of ketone bodies rises in the blood to a level at which the **brain** begins to **oxidize** them for energy. The brain then needs less glucose, so the liver decreases its rate of gluconeogenesis. Consequently, less **protein** in muscle and other tissues is degraded to supply amino acids for gluconeogenesis. Protein sparing preserves vital functions for as long as possible. Because of these changes in the fuel use patterns of various tissues, humans can survive for extended periods without ingesting food.

THE WAITING ROOM

 Percy Veere had been admitted to the hospital with a diagnosis of mental depression associated with malnutrition (see Chapter 1). At the time of admission, his body weight of 125 lb gave him a body mass index (BMI) of 17.5 (healthy range, 18.5 to 24.9). His serum albumin was 10% below the low end of the normal range, and he exhibited signs of iron and vitamin deficiencies.

Additional tests were made to help evaluate Mr. Veere's degree of malnutrition and his progress toward recovery. His arm circumference and triceps skinfold were measured, and his mid-upper arm muscle circumference (MUAMC) was calculated (see Chapter 2, Anthropometric Measurements). His serum prealbumin as well as his serum albumin were measured. Fasting blood glucose and serum ketone body concentration were determined on blood samples drawn the next day before breakfast. A 24-hour urine specimen was collected to determine ketone body excretion and creatinine excretion for calculation of the creatinine–height index (CHI), a measure of protein depletion from skeletal muscle.

 Percy Veere has grade I protein-calorie malnutrition. At his height of 71 in, his body weight would have to be >132 lb to achieve a BMI of >18.5. **Ann O'Rexia** has grade III malnutrition. At 67 in, she needs a body weight that is >118 lb to achieve a BMI of 18.5. Degrees of protein-calorie malnutrition (marasmus) are classified as types I, II, and III according to BMI. Type I refers to a BMI in the 17.0 to 18.4 range, type II to a BMI in the 16.0 to 16.9 range, and type III is designated for a BMI of <16.0.

 Ann O'Rexia was receiving psychological counseling for anorexia nervosa, but with little success (see Chapter 1). She saw her gynecologist because she had not had a menstrual period for 5 months. She also complained of becoming easily fatigued. The physician recognized that Ann's body weight of 85 lb was now <65% of her ideal weight, and he calculated that her BMI was now 13.3. The physician recommended immediate hospitalization. The admission diagnosis was severe malnutrition (grade III protein-calorie malnutrition) secondary to anorexia nervosa. Clinical findings included decreased body core temperature, blood pressure, and pulse (adaptive responses to malnutrition). Her physician ordered measurements of blood glucose and ketone body levels and made a spot check for ketone bodies in the urine as well as ordering tests to assess the functioning of her heart and kidneys.

 Creatinine is usually released from the muscles at a constant rate, and it is proportional to muscle mass. The creatinine is removed from the circulation by the kidneys and appears in the urine. Thus, elevated creatinine in the blood relates to impaired renal function. To measure creatinine in biologic specimens, the Jaffé reaction is used. Creatinine is reacted with picric acid in an alkaline solution to form a red-orange product, which can be quantitated via spectrophotometry. To increase specificity, a kinetic Jaffé reaction is run, and the rate of formation of the product is determined. Creatinine can be measured in plasma, serum, and urine.

I. THE FASTING STATE

Blood glucose levels peak approximately 1 hour after eating and then decrease as tissues oxidize glucose or convert it to storage forms of fuel. By 2 hours after a meal, the level returns to the fasting range (between 80 and 100 mg/dL). This decrease in blood glucose causes the pancreas to decrease its secretion of insulin, and the serum insulin level decreases. The liver responds to this hormonal signal by starting to degrade its glycogen stores and release glucose into the blood.

If we eat another meal within a few hours, we return to the fed state. However, if we continue to fast for a 12-hour period, we enter the basal state (also known as the postabsorptive state). A person is generally considered to be in the basal state after an overnight fast, when no food has been eaten since dinner the previous evening. By this time, the serum insulin level is low and glucagon is rising. Figure 3.1 illustrates the main features of the basal state.

A. Blood Glucose and the Role of the Liver during Fasting

The liver maintains blood glucose levels during fasting, and its role is thus critical. Glucose is the major fuel for tissues such as the brain and neural tissue and the sole fuel for red blood cells. Most neurons lack enzymes required for oxidation of fatty acids, but they can use ketone bodies to a limited extent. Red blood cells lack mitochondria, which contain the enzymes of fatty acid and ketone body oxidation,

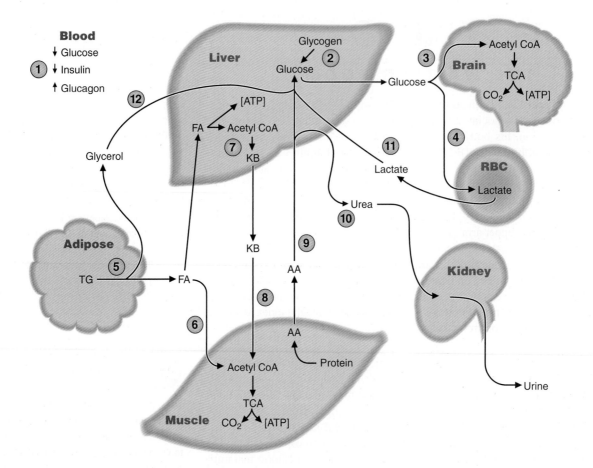

FIG. 3.1. Basal state. This state occurs after an overnight (12-hour) fast. The circled numbers serve as a guide indicating the approximate order in which the processes begin to occur. *KB*, ketone bodies; other abbreviations are defined in Figure 2.2.

Urea

FIG. 3.2. The structure of urea, the highly soluble nitrogen disposal molecule.

and can use only glucose as a fuel. Therefore, it is imperative that blood glucose not decrease too rapidly nor fall too low.

Initially, liver glycogen stores are degraded to supply glucose to the blood, but these stores are limited. This pathway is known as *glycogenolysis* (the lysis, or splitting of glycogen to form glucose subunits). Although liver glycogen levels may increase to 200 to 300 g after a meal, only approximately 80 g remain after an overnight fast. Fortunately, the liver has another mechanism for producing blood glucose, known as *gluconeogenesis*. Gluconeogenesis means formation (genesis) of new (neo) glucose, and, by definition, converts new (noncarbohydrate) precursors to glucose. In gluconeogenesis, lactate, glycerol, and amino acids are used as carbon sources to synthesize glucose. As fasting continues, gluconeogenesis progressively adds to the glucose produced by glycogenolysis in the liver.

Lactate is a product of glycolysis in red blood cells and exercising muscle; *glycerol* is obtained from lipolysis of adipose triacylglycerols; and *amino acids* are generated by the breakdown of protein. Because our muscle mass is so large, most of the amino acid is supplied from degradation of muscle protein. These compounds travel in the blood to the liver, where they are converted to glucose by gluconeogenesis. Because the nitrogen of the amino acids can form ammonia, which is toxic to the body, the liver converts this nitrogen to urea. Urea has two amino groups for just one carbon (Fig. 3.2). It is a very soluble, nontoxic compound that can be readily excreted by the kidneys and thus is an efficient means for disposing of excess ammonia.

As fasting progresses, gluconeogenesis becomes increasingly more important as a source of blood glucose. After a day or so of fasting, liver glycogen stores are depleted, and gluconeogenesis is the only source of blood glucose.

B. Role of Adipose Tissue during Fasting

Adipose triacylglycerols are the major source of energy during fasting. They supply fatty acids, which are quantitatively the major fuel for the human body. Fatty acids are oxidized not only directly by various tissues of the body; they are also partially oxidized in the liver to four-carbon products called *ketone bodies*. Ketone bodies are subsequently oxidized as a fuel by other tissues.

As blood insulin levels decrease and blood glucagon levels rise, adipose triacylglycerols are mobilized by a process known as *lipolysis* (lysis of triacylglycerol). They are converted to fatty acids and glycerol, which enter the blood.

It is important to realize that most fatty acids cannot provide carbon for gluconeogenesis. Thus, of the vast store of food energy in adipose tissue triacylglycerols, only the small glycerol portion travels to the liver to enter the gluconeogenic pathway.

Fatty acids serve as a fuel for muscle, kidney, and most other tissues. They are oxidized to acetyl coenzyme A (acetyl-CoA), and subsequently to CO_2 and H_2O in the tricarboxylic acid (TCA) cycle, producing energy in the form of adenosine triphosphate (ATP). In addition to the ATP required to maintain cellular integrity, muscle uses ATP for contraction, and the kidney uses it for urinary transport processes.

Most of the fatty acids that enter the liver are converted to ketone bodies rather than being completely oxidized to CO_2. The process of conversion of fatty acids to acetyl-CoA produces a considerable amount of energy (ATP), which drives the reactions of the liver under these conditions. The acetyl-CoA is converted to the ketone bodies acetoacetate and β-hydroxybutyrate, which are released into the blood (Fig. 3.3).

The liver lacks an enzyme required for ketone body oxidation. Nevertheless, ketone bodies can be further oxidized by most other cells with mitochondria, such as muscle and kidney. In these tissues, acetoacetate and β-hydroxybutyrate are converted to acetyl-CoA and then oxidized in the TCA cycle, with subsequent generation of ATP.

C. Summary of the Metabolic Changes during a Brief Fast

In the initial stages of fasting, stored fuels are used for energy (see Fig. 3.1). The liver plays a key role by maintaining blood glucose levels in the range of 80 to 100 mg/dL, first by glycogenolysis (Fig. 3.1, circle 2) and subsequently by gluconeogenesis (Fig. 3.1, circles 9, 11, and 12). Lactate, glycerol, and amino acids serve as carbon sources for gluconeogenesis. Amino acids are supplied by muscle (via *proteolysis*, lysis of proteins to individual amino acids). Their nitrogen is converted in the liver to urea (Fig. 3.1, circle 10), which is excreted by the kidneys.

Fatty acids, which are released from adipose tissue by the process of lipolysis (Fig. 3.1, circle 5), serve as the body's major fuel during fasting. The liver oxidizes most of its fatty acids only partially, converting them to ketone bodies (Fig. 3.1, circle 7), which are released into the blood. Thus, during the initial stages of fasting, blood levels of fatty acids and ketone bodies begin to increase. Muscle uses fatty acids, ketone bodies (Fig. 3.1, circles 6 and 8), and (when exercising and while supplies last) glucose from muscle glycogen. Many other tissues use either fatty acids or ketone bodies. However, red blood cells, the brain, and other neural tissues use mainly glucose (Fig. 3.1, circles 3 and 4). The metabolic capacities of different tissues with respect to pathways of fuel metabolism are summarized in Table 3.1.

Percy Veere had not eaten much on his first day of hospitalization. His fasting blood glucose determined on the morning of his second day of hospitalization was 72 mg/dL (normal, overnight fasting = 80 to 100 mg/dL). Thus, in spite of his malnutrition and his overnight fast, his blood glucose was being maintained at nearly normal levels through gluconeogenesis using amino acid precursors. If his blood glucose had decreased to <50 to 60 mg/dL during fasting, his brain would have been unable to absorb glucose fast enough to obtain the glucose needed for energy and neurotransmitter synthesis, resulting in coma and eventual death. Although many other tissues, such as red blood cells, are also totally or partially dependent on glucose for energy, they are able to function at lower concentrations of blood glucose than the brain.

On his second day of hospitalization, **Percy Veere's** serum ketone body level was 110 μM. (Normal value after a 12-hour fast is approximately 70 μM.) No ketone bodies were detectable in his urine. At this stage of protein-calorie malnutrition, Mr. Veere still has remaining fat stores. After 12 hours of fasting, most of his tissues are using fatty acids as a major fuel, and the liver is beginning to produce ketone bodies from fatty acids. As these ketone bodies increase in the blood, their use as a fuel will increase.

β-Hydroxybutyrate

Acetoacetate

$$CH_3 - \overset{\overset{\displaystyle O}{\|}}{C} - CH_3$$

Acetone

FIG. 3.3. The ketone bodies β-hydroxybutyrate, acetoacetate, and acetone. β-hydroxybutyrate and acetoacetate are formed in the liver. Acetone is produced by nonenzymatic decarboxylation of acetoacetate. However, acetone is expired in the breath and is not metabolized to a significant extent in the body, whereas β-hydroxybutyrate and acetoacetate are used by muscle and the nervous system as an energy source.

Table 3.1   Metabolic Capacities of Various Tissues

Process	Liver	Adipose Tissue	Kidney Cortex	Muscle	Brain	Red Blood Cells
TCA cycle (acetyl-CoA → CO_2 + H_2O)	+++	++	+++	+++	+++	- -
β-Oxidation of fatty acids	+++	- -	++	+++	- -	- -
Ketone body formation	+++	- -	+	- -	- -	- -
Ketone body utilization	- -	+	+	+++	+++ (Prolonged starvation)	- -
Glycolysis (glucose → CO_2 + H_2O)	+++	++	++	+++	+++	- -
Lactate production (glucose → lactate)	+	+	- -	+++ (Exercise)	+	+++
Glycogen metabolism (synthesis and degradation)	+++	+	+	+++	+	- -
Gluconeogenesis (lactate, amino acids, glycerol → glucose)	+++	- -	+	- -	- -	- -
Urea cycle (ammonia → urea)	+++	- -	- -	- -	- -	- -
Lipogenesis (glucose → fatty acids)	+++	+	- -	- -	- -	- -

TCA, tricarboxylic acid; acetyl-CoA, acetyl coenzyme A.
++ indicates use of the fuel; +++ is maximal use, whereas + is minimal use. - - indicates no use of the fuel.

The liver synthesizes several serum proteins and releases them into the blood. These proteins decrease in the blood during protein malnutrition. Two of these serum proteins, albumin and prealbumin (a liver-derived protein that transports thyroid hormone), are often measured to assess the state of protein malnutrition. Serum albumin is the traditional standard of protein malnutrition. Neither measurement is specific for protein malnutrition. Serum albumin and prealbumin levels decrease with hepatic disease (although prealbumin levels are less affected by liver disease than albumin levels), certain renal diseases, surgery, and several other conditions in addition to protein malnutrition. **Percy Veere's** values were below the normal range for both of these proteins, indicating that his muscle mass was unable to supply sufficient amino acids to sustain both gluconeogenesis and the synthesis of serum proteins by the liver.

Ann O'Rexia's admission laboratory studies showed a blood glucose level of 65 mg/dL (normal fasting blood glucose = 80 to 100 mg/dL). Her serum ketone body concentration was 4,200 μM (normal = ~70 μM). The Ketostix (Bayer Diagnostics, Mishawaka, Indiana) urine test was moderately positive, indicating that ketone bodies were present in the urine. In her starved state, ketone body use by her brain was helping to conserve protein in her muscles and vital organs.

II.   METABOLIC CHANGES DURING PROLONGED FASTING

If the pattern of fuel utilization that occurs during a brief fast were to persist for an extended period, the body's protein would be quite rapidly consumed to the point at which critical functions would be compromised. Fortunately, metabolic changes occur during prolonged fasting that conserve (spare) muscle protein by causing muscle protein turnover to decrease. Figure 3.4 shows the main features of metabolism during prolonged fasting (starvation).

A.   Role of Liver during Prolonged Fasting

After 3 to 5 days of fasting, when the body enters the starved state, muscle decreases its use of ketone bodies and depends mainly on fatty acids for its fuel. The liver, however, continues to convert fatty acids to ketone bodies. The result is that the concentration of ketone bodies rises in the blood (Fig. 3.5). The brain begins to take up these ketone bodies from the blood and oxidizes them for energy. Therefore, the brain needs less glucose than it did after an overnight fast (Table 3.2).

Glucose is still required, however, as an energy source for red blood cells, and the brain continues to use a limited amount of glucose, which it oxidizes for energy and uses as a source of carbon for the synthesis of neurotransmitters. Overall, however, glucose is "spared" (conserved). Less glucose is used by the body and, therefore, the liver needs to produce less glucose per hour during prolonged fasting than during shorter periods of fasting.

Because the stores of glycogen in the liver are depleted by approximately 30 hours of fasting, gluconeogenesis is the only process by which the liver can supply glucose to the blood if fasting continues. The amino acid pool, produced by the breakdown of protein, continues to serve as a major source of carbon for gluconeogenesis. A fraction of this amino acid pool is also used for biosynthetic functions (e.g., synthesis of heme and neurotransmitters) and new protein synthesis, processes that must continue during fasting. However, as a result of the decreased rate of gluconeogenesis during prolonged fasting, protein is "spared"; less protein is degraded to supply amino acids for gluconeogenesis.

While converting amino acid carbon to glucose in gluconeogenesis, the liver also converts the nitrogen of these amino acids to urea. Consequently, because glucose production decreases during prolonged fasting compared with early fasting, urea production also decreases (Fig. 3.6).

B.   Role of Adipose Tissue during Prolonged Fasting

During prolonged fasting, adipose tissue continues to break down its triacylglycerol stores, providing fatty acids and glycerol to the blood. These fatty acids serve as the major source of fuel for the body. The glycerol is converted to glucose, whereas the fatty

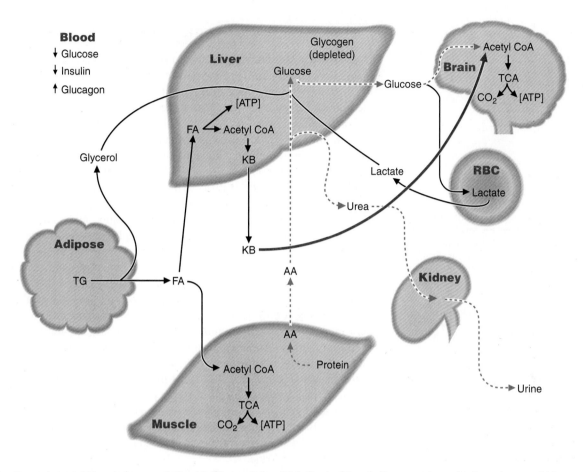

FIG. 3.4. Starved state. Abbreviations are defined in Figures 2.2 and 3.1. *Dashed lines* indicate processes that have decreased (the use of amino acids as a gluconeogenic precursor), and the *red solid line* indicates a process that has increased relative to the fasting state (the use of ketone bodies by the brain as a major energy source).

acids are oxidized to CO_2 and H_2O by tissues such as muscle. In the liver, fatty acids are converted to ketone bodies that are oxidized by many tissues including the brain.

Several factors determine how long we can fast and still survive. The amount of adipose tissue is one factor, because adipose tissue supplies the body with its major source of fuel. However, body protein levels can also determine the length of time we can fast. Glucose is still used during prolonged fasting (starvation), but in significantly reduced amounts. Although we degrade protein to supply amino acids for gluconeogenesis at a slower rate during starvation than during the first days of a fast, we are still losing protein that serves vital functions for our tissues. Protein can become so depleted that the heart, kidney, and other vital tissues stop functioning, or we can develop an infection and not have adequate reserves to mount an immune response. In addition to fuel problems, we are also deprived of the vitamin and mineral precursors of coenzymes and other compounds necessary for tissue function. Because of either a lack of ATP or a decreased intake of electrolytes, the electrolyte composition of the blood or cells could become incompatible with life. Ultimately, we die of starvation.

 Death by starvation occurs with loss of roughly 40% of body weight, when approximately 30% to 50% of body protein has been lost, or 70% to 95% of body fat stores. Generally, this occurs at body mass indices (BMIs) of approximately 13 for men and 11 for women.

Table 3.2   Metabolic Changes during Prolonged Fasting Compared with Fasting for 24 Hours

Muscle use of ketone bodies	Decreases
Brain use of ketone bodies	Increases
Brain use of glucose	Decreases
Liver gluconeogenesis	Decreases
Muscle protein degradation	Decreases
Liver production of urea	Decreases

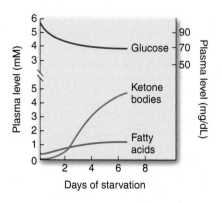

FIG. 3.5. Changes in the concentration of fuels in the blood during prolonged fasting.

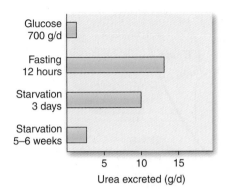

FIG. 3.6. Changes in urea excretion during fasting. Urea production is very low in a person who is consuming only glucose. It increases during fasting as muscle protein is broken down to supply amino acids for gluconeogenesis. However, as fasting progresses, urea synthesis decreases. Because the brain meets some of its energy needs by oxidizing ketone bodies after 3 to 5 days of fasting, gluconeogenesis decreases, sparing protein in muscle and other tissues.

Creatinine–height index. The most widely used biochemical marker for estimating body muscle mass is the 24-hour urinary creatinine excretion. Creatinine is a degradation product formed in active muscle at a constant rate, in proportion to the amount of muscle tissue present in a patient. In a protein-malnourished individual, urinary creatinine will decrease in proportion to the decrease in muscle mass. To assess depletion of muscle mass, creatinine excreted is expressed relative to the height, the CHI. The amount of creatinine (in milligrams) excreted by the subject in 24 hours is divided by the amount of creatinine excreted by a normal, healthy subject of the same height and sex. The resulting ratio is multiplied by 100 to express it as a percentage. **Percy Veere's** CHI was 85% (80% to 90% of normal indicates a mild deficit; 60% to 80% of normal indicates a moderate deficit; and <60% of normal indicates a severe deficit of muscle mass).

Percy Veere. As a result of his severely suppressed appetite for food, **Percy Veere** developed a mild degree (type I) of protein-calorie malnutrition. When prolonged, this type of protein malnutrition can cause changes in the villi of the small intestine that reduce its absorptive capacity for what little food is ingested.

Despite his insufficient intake of dietary carbohydrates, Mr. Veere's blood glucose level was 72 mg/dL, close to the lower limit (80 mg/dL) of the normal range for a well-nourished, healthy person after a 12-hour fast. This is the finding you would expect; it reflects the liver's capacity to maintain adequate levels of blood glucose by means of gluconeogenesis, even during prolonged and moderately severe caloric restriction. Amino acids from degradation of protein, principally in skeletal muscle, supply most of the precursors for gluconeogenesis.

Percy Veere had several indicators of his protein malnutrition: His serum albumin and prealbumin levels were below normal; his mid-upper arm muscle circumference (MUAMC) was at the 12th percentile; and his creatinine–height index (CHI) was at 85%. The low levels of serum proteins reflect a low dietary protein intake and possibly diminished capacity to absorb dietary amino acids. Consequently, amino acids were being mobilized from degradation of protein in muscle and other tissues to supply precursors for new protein synthesis as well as gluconeogenesis. The result was a loss of muscle mass, indicated by the MUAMC and the CHI, and decreased levels of serum proteins.

Fatty acids mobilized from adipose tissue are the major source of energy for most tissues. Because Percy was eating, and not in total starvation, his ketone bodies were only moderately elevated in the blood (110 μM vs. normal of 70 μM) and did not appear in the urine.

After several psychological counseling sessions, and the promise of an extended visit from his grandchild, Mr. Veere resumed his normal eating pattern.

Ann O'Rexia. Ann O'Rexia has *anorexia nervosa*, a chronic disabling disease in which poorly understood psychological and biologic factors lead to disturbances in the patient's body image. These patients typically pursue thinness in spite of the presence of severe emaciation and a "skeletal appearance." They generally have an intense fear of being overweight and deny the seriousness of their low body weight.

Amenorrhea (lack of menses) usually develops during anorexia nervosa and other conditions when a woman's body fat content falls to approximately 22% of her total body weight. The immediate cause of amenorrhea is a reduced production of the gonadotropic protein hormones (luteinizing hormone and follicle-stimulating hormone) by the anterior pituitary; the connection between this hormonal change and body fat content is not yet understood.

Ms. O'Rexia is suffering from the consequences of prolonged and severe protein and caloric restriction. Fatty acids, released from adipose tissue by lipolysis, are being converted to ketone bodies in the liver, and the level of ketone bodies in the blood is extremely elevated (4,200 μM vs. normal of 70 μM). The fact that her kidneys are excreting ketone bodies is reflected in the moderately positive urine test for ketone bodies noted on admission.

Although Ms. O'Rexia's blood glucose is below the normal fasting range (65 mg/dL vs. normal of 80 mg/dL), she is experiencing only a moderate degree of hypoglycemia (low blood glucose) despite her severe, near-starvation diet. Her blood glucose level reflects the ability of the brain to use ketone bodies as a fuel when they are elevated in the blood, thereby decreasing the amount of glucose that must be synthesized from amino acids provided by protein degradation.

Ms. O'Rexia's body mass index (BMI) showed that she was close to death through starvation (grade III protein-calorie malnutrition). She was therefore hospitalized and placed on enteral nutrition (nutrients provided through tube feeding). The general therapeutic plan, outlined in Chapter 1, of nutritional restitution and identification and treatment of those emotional factors leading to the patient's anorectic behavior was continued. She was coaxed into eating small amounts of food while hospitalized.

BIOCHEMICAL COMMENTS

 Clinical Use of Metabolite Measurements in Blood and Urine. When a patient develops a metabolic problem, it is difficult to examine cells to determine the cause. To obtain tissue for metabolic studies, biopsies must be performed. These procedures can be difficult, dangerous, or even impossible, depending on the tissue. Cost is an additional problem. However, both blood and urine can be obtained readily from patients, and measurements of substances in the blood and urine can help in diagnosing a patient's problem. Concentrations of substances that are higher or lower than normal indicate which tissues are malfunctioning. For example, if blood urea nitrogen (BUN) levels are low, a problem centered in the liver might be suspected because urea is produced in the liver. Conversely, high blood levels of urea suggest that the kidney is not excreting this compound normally. Decreased urinary and blood levels of creatinine indicate diminished production of creatinine by skeletal muscle. However, high blood creatinine levels could indicate an inability of the kidney to excrete creatinine, resulting from renal disease. If high levels of ketone bodies are found in the blood or urine, the patient's metabolic pattern is that of the starved state. If the high levels of ketone bodies are coupled with elevated levels of blood glucose, the problem is most likely a deficiency of insulin; that is, the patient probably has type 1, formerly called insulin-dependent diabetes mellitus. Without insulin, fuels are mobilized from tissues rather than being stored.

These relatively easy and inexpensive tests on blood and urine can be used to determine which tissues need to be studied more extensively to diagnose and treat the patient's problem. A solid understanding of fuel metabolism helps in the interpretation of these simple tests.

Key Concepts

- During fasting, when blood glucose levels drop, glucagon is released from the α-cells of the pancreas. Glucagon signals the liver to use its shared carbohydrate to release glucose into the circulation, primarily for use by the brain and red blood cell.
- After fasting for about 3 days, the liver releases ketone bodies (derived from fat oxidation) as an alternative fuel supply for the brain. Liver glycogen stores are depleted and gluconeogenesis provides glucose to the body.
- Glucagon also signals the fat cell to degrade triacylglycerol, supplying the body with fatty acids for energy and glycerol for gluconeogenesis.
- The substrates for liver gluconeogenesis are lactate (from the red blood cells), amino acids (from muscle protein degradation), and glycerol.
- In prolonged starvation, the brain can adapt to using ketone bodies for energy, which reduces the body's demand for glucose. This reduces the rate of muscle protein degradation to provide precursors for gluconeogenesis and allows extended survival times under starvation conditions.
- The major disease discussed in this chapter is summarized in Table 3.3.

Table 3.3   A Summary of the Major Disorder Discussed in Chapter 3

Disorder or Condition	Genetic or Environmental	Comments
Malnutrition	Both	Reduced nutrient uptake, may be caused by genetic mutation in specific proteins or dietary habit. May lead to increased ketone body production and reduced liver protein synthesis.

You will need some information from Chapters 1 and 2, as well as Chapter 3, to answer these questions.

1. By 24 hours after a meal, which one of the following is most likely to occur?

   A. Gluconeogenesis in the liver will be the major source of blood glucose.
   B. Muscle glycogenolysis provides glucose to the blood.
   C. Muscles convert amino acids to blood glucose.
   D. Fatty acids released from adipose tissue provide carbon for synthesis of glucose.
   E. Ketone bodies provide carbon for gluconeogenesis.

2. A physician is treating a type 1 diabetic patient who has neglected to take his or her insulin for 5 days. The patient demonstrates elevated blood glucose and ketone body levels. Ketone bodies are elevated due to which one of the following?

   A. Elevated glucose levels
   B. Reduced BUN
   C. Decreased fatty acid release from the adipocyte
   D. Inhibition of liver oxidation of ketone bodies
   E. Reduced muscle utilization of fatty acids

3. In a well-nourished individual, as the length of fasting increases from overnight to 1 week, which one of the following is most likely to occur?

   A. Blood glucose levels decrease by approximately 50%.
   B. Red blood cells switch to using ketone bodies.
   C. Muscles decrease their use of ketone bodies, which increase in the blood.

   D. The brain begins to use fatty acids as a major fuel.
   E. Adipose tissue triacylglycerols are nearly depleted.

4. A hospitalized patient had low levels of serum albumin and high levels of blood ammonia. His CHI was 98%. His BMI was 20.5. BUN was not elevated, consistent with normal kidney function. The diagnosis most consistent with these finding is which one of the following?

   A. A loss of hepatic function (e.g., alcohol-induced cirrhosis)
   B. Anorexia nervosa
   C. Kwashiorkor (protein malnutrition)
   D. Marasmus (protein-calorie malnutrition)
   E. Decreased absorption of amino acids by intestinal epithelial cells (e.g., celiac disease)

5. **Otto Shape**, an overweight medical student (see Chapter 1), discovered that he could not exercise enough during his summer clerkship rotations to lose 2 to 3 lb/wk. He decided to lose weight by eating only 300 kcal/day of a dietary supplement that provided half the calories as carbohydrate and half as protein. In addition, he consumed a multivitamin supplement. During the first 3 days on this diet, which statement best represents the state of Otto's metabolism?

   A. His protein intake met the RDA for protein.
   B. His carbohydrate intake met the fuel needs of his brain.
   C. Both his adipose mass and his muscle mass decreased.
   D. He remained in nitrogen balance.
   E. He developed severe hypoglycemia.

SECTION TWO

Chemical and Biologic Foundations of Biochemistry

The discipline of biochemistry developed because chemists began to study the molecules of cells, tissues, and body fluids, and physicians began to look for the molecular basis of various diseases. Today, the practice of medicine depends on understanding the roles and interactions of the enormous number of different chemicals that enable our bodies to function. The task is less overwhelming if one knows the properties, nomenclature, and functions of classes of compounds such as carbohydrates and enzymes. The intent of this section is to review some of this information in a context relevant to medicine. Students enter medical school with different scientific backgrounds, and some of the information in this section will therefore be familiar to many students.

We begin by discussing the relationship of metabolic acids and buffers to blood pH in Chapter 4. Chapter 5 focuses on the nomenclature, structure, and some of the properties of the major classes of compounds found in the human body. The structure of a molecule determines its function and its fate, and the common name of a compound can often tell you something about its structure.

Proteins are linear chains of amino acids that fold into complex three-dimensional structures. They function in the maintenance of cellular and tissue structure and the transport and movement of molecules. Some proteins are enzymes, which are catalysts that enormously increase the rate of chemical reactions in the body. Chapters 6 and 7 describe the amino acids and their interactions within proteins that provide proteins with a flexible and functional three-dimensional structure. Chapters 8 and 9 describe the properties, functions, and regulation of enzymes.

Our proteins and other compounds function within a specialized environment defined by their location in cells or body fluids. Their ability to function partially depends on membranes that restrict the free movement of molecules. Chapter 10 includes a brief review of the components of cells, their organization into subcellular organelles, and the manner in which various types of molecules move into cells and between compartments within a cell.

In a complex organism such as a human, different cell types carry out different functions. This specialization of function requires cells to communicate with each other. One of the ways they communicate is through the secretion of chemical messengers that carry a signal to another cell. In Chapter 11, we consider some of the principles of cell signaling and describe some of the chemical messenger systems.

Both in this book and in medical practice, you will need to interconvert different units used for the weight and size of compounds and for their concentration in blood and other fluids. Table II.1 provides definitions of some of the units used for these interconversions.

The nomenclature used to describe patients may include the name of a class of compounds. For example, a patient with diabetes mellitus who has hyperglycemia has hyper (high) concentrations of carbohydrates (glyc) in her blood (emia).

From a biochemist's point of view, most metabolic diseases are caused by enzymes and other proteins that malfunction, and the pharmacologic drugs used to treat these diseases correct that malfunction. For example, individuals with atherosclerosis who have elevated blood cholesterol levels are treated with a drug that inhibits an enzyme in the pathway for cholesterol synthesis. Even a bacterial infection can be considered a disease of protein function, if one considers the bacterial toxins that are proteins, the enzymes in our cells affected by these toxins, and the proteins involved in the immune response when we try to destroy these bacteria.

 Di Abietes had an elevated blood glucose level of 684 mg/dL. What is the molar concentration of glucose in Di's blood? (Hint: The molecular weight of glucose [$C_6H_{12}O_6$] is 180 g/mol.)

Milligrams per deciliter (mg/dL) is the common way clinicians in the United States express blood glucose concentration. A concentration of 684 mg/dL is 684 mg per 100 mL of blood, or 6,480 mg/L, or 6.48 g/L. If 6.84 g/L is divided by 180 g/mol, one obtains a value of 0.038 mol/L, which is 0.038 M, or 38 mM.

Table II.1 Common Units Expressed in Equivalent Ways

1 M	1 mol/L	Molecular Weight in g/L
1 mM	1 millimol/L	10^{-3} mol/L
1 μM	1 micromol/L	10^{-6} mol/L
1 nM	1 nanomol/L	10^{-9} mol/L
1 mL	1 milliliter	10^{-3} L
1 mg%	1 mg/100 mL	10^{-3} g/100 mL
1 mg/dL	1 mg/100 mL	10^{-3} g/100 mL
1 mEq/L	1 milliequivalent/L	mM × valence of ion
1 kg	1,000 g	2.2 lb
1 cm	10^{-2} m	0.394 in

4 Water, Acids, Bases, and Buffers

Approximately 60% of our body is water. It acts as a solvent for the substances we need, such as K^+, glucose, adenosine triphosphate (ATP), and proteins. It is important for the transport of molecules and heat. Many of the compounds produced in the body and dissolved in water contain chemical groups that act as acids or bases, releasing or accepting hydrogen ions. The hydrogen ion content and the amount of body water are controlled to maintain a constant environment for the cells called homeostasis (same state) (Fig. 4.1). Significant deviations from a constant environment such as acidosis or dehydration may be life threatening. This chapter describes the role of water in the body and the buffer systems used by the body to protect itself from acids and bases produced from metabolism.

Water. *Water is distributed between intracellular and extracellular compartments, the latter comprising interstitial fluids, blood, and lymph. Because water is a **dipolar molecule** with an uneven distribution of electrons between the hydrogen and oxygen atoms, it forms hydrogen bonds with other polar molecules and acts as a **solvent**.*

The pH of Water. *Water **dissociates** to a slight extent to form **hydrogen** (H^+) and hydroxyl (OH^-) ions. The concentration of hydrogen ions determines the acidity of the solution, which is expressed in terms of **pH**. The pH of a solution is the negative log of its hydrogen ion concentration.*

Acids and Bases. *An **acid** is a substance that can **release hydrogen ions** (protons), and a **base** is a substance that can **accept hydrogen ions**. When dissolved in water, almost all the molecules of a **strong acid** dissociate and release their hydrogen ions, but only a small percentage of the total molecules of a weak acid dissociate. A **weak acid** has a characteristic **dissociation constant, K_a**. The relationship between the pH of a solution, the K_a of an acid, and the extent of its dissociation are given by the **Henderson-Hasselbalch equation**.*

Buffers. *A buffer is a mixture of an **undissociated acid** and its **conjugate base** (the form of the acid that has lost its proton). It causes a solution to resist changes in pH when either H^+ or OH^- is added. A buffer has its greatest buffering capacity in the pH range near its **pK_a** (the negative log of its K_a). Two factors determine the effectiveness of a buffer: its pKa relative to the pH of the solution and its concentration.*

Metabolic Acids and Bases. *Normal metabolism generates CO_2, **metabolic acids** (e.g., **lactic acid** and **ketone bodies**), and **inorganic acids** (e.g., **sulfuric acid**). The major source of acid is CO_2, which reacts with water to produce **carbonic acid**. To maintain the pH of body fluids in a range compatible with life, the body has **buffers** such as **bicarbonate**, **phosphate**, and **hemoglobin** (see Fig. 4.1). Ultimately, **respiratory mechanisms** remove carbonic acid through the **expiration of CO_2**, and the **kidneys excrete acid** as **ammonium ion** (NH_4^+) and other ions.*

FIG. 4.1. Maintenance of body pH. The body produces approximately 13 to 22 mol/day of acid from normal metabolism. The body protects itself against this acidity by buffers that maintain a neutral pH and by the expiration of CO_2 through the lungs and the excretion of NH_4^+ and other ions through the kidneys.

THE WAITING ROOM

Dianne (Di) Abietes has a keto-acidosis. When the amount of insulin she injects is inadequate, she remains in a condition similar to a fasting state even though she ingests food (see Chapters 2 and 3). Her liver continues to metabolize fatty acids to the ketone bodies acetoacetic acid and β-hydroxybutyric acid. These compounds are weak acids that dissociate to produce anions (acetoacetate and β-hydroxybutyrate, respectively) and hydrogen ions, thereby lowering her blood and cellular pH below the normal range. Because the dissociation of the ketone bodies is causing the acidosis, it is classified as a ketoacidosis.

Dianne (Di) Abietes is a 26-year-old woman who was diagnosed with type 1 diabetes mellitus at the age of 12 years. She has an absolute insulin deficiency resulting from autoimmune destruction of the β cells of her pancreas. As a result, she depends on daily injections of insulin to prevent severe elevations of glucose and ketone bodies in her blood.

When Di Abietes could not be aroused from an afternoon nap, her roommate called an ambulance, and Di was brought to the emergency room of the hospital in a coma. Her roommate reported that Di had been feeling nauseated and drowsy and had been vomiting for 24 hours. Di is clinically dehydrated, and her blood pressure is low. Her respirations are deep and rapid, and her pulse rate is rapid. Her breath has the "fruity" odor of acetone.

Blood samples are drawn for measurement of her arterial blood pH, arterial partial pressure of carbon dioxide ($Paco_2$), serum glucose, and serum bicarbonate (HCO_3^-). In addition, serum and urine are tested for the presence of ketone bodies, and Di is treated with intravenous normal saline and insulin. The laboratory reports that her blood pH is 7.08 (reference range = 7.36 to 7.44), and that ketone bodies are present in both her blood and urine. Her blood glucose level is 648 mg/dL (reference range = 80 to 100 mg/dL after an overnight fast, and no higher than 200 mg/dL in a casual glucose sample taken without regard to the time of a last meal).

Blood gas analyzers are used to measure Po_2 and Pco_2. The basic mechanism whereby these analyzers work is through the use of specific gas-permeable membranes. For oxygen, a Clark electrode is used; oxygen diffuses through a membrane specific for oxygen permeability, and once oxygen passes through the membrane, it diffuses to the cathode. When oxygen reaches the cathode, electrons are attracted from the anode, thereby reducing the oxygen to water. Because it requires four electrons to reduce molecular oxygen (forming two molecules of water), measurement of the current flow can quantitate the amount of oxygen that has reached the cathode. Pco_2 is determined using a Severinghaus electrode, which consists of an outer gas permeable membrane, specific for CO_2, and a bicarbonate buffer within the electrode. Once the CO_2 crosses the membrane, the gas interacts with bicarbonate, altering the equilibrium among CO_2, carbonic acid, and bicarbonate. This alters the pH in direct proportion to the amount of CO_2 gas that has entered the electrode, and the change in pH can be used to calculate the Pco_2. Improved manufacturing techniques have allowed microelectrodes, and tiny circuit boards, to be used in these machines, thereby greatly increasing their portability.

Dennis "the Menace" Veere, aged 3 years, was brought to the emergency department by his grandfather, **Percy Veere**. While Dennis was visiting his grandfather, he climbed up on a chair and took a half-full, 500-tablet bottle of 325-mg aspirin (acetylsalicylic acid) tablets from the kitchen counter. Mr. Veere discovered Dennis with a mouthful of aspirin, which he removed, but he could not tell how many tablets Dennis had already swallowed. When they arrived at the emergency room, the child appeared bright and alert, but Mr. Veere was hyperventilating.

I. WATER

Water is the solvent of life. It bathes our cells, dissolves and transports compounds in the blood, provides a medium for movement of molecules into and throughout cellular compartments, separates charged molecules, dissipates heat, and participates in chemical reactions. Most compounds in the body, including proteins, must interact with an aqueous medium in order to function. In spite of the variation in the amount of water we ingest each day and produce from metabolism, our body maintains a nearly constant amount of water that is approximately 60% of our body weight (Fig. 4.2).

A. Fluid Compartments in the Body

Total body water is roughly 50% to 60% of body weight in adults and 75% of body weight in children. Because fat has relatively little water associated with it, obese people tend to have a lower percentage of body water than thin people, women tend to have a lower percentage than men, and older people have a lower percentage than younger people.

Approximately 60% of the total body water is intracellular and 40% extracellular (see Fig. 4.2). The extracellular water includes the fluid in plasma (blood after the cells have been removed) and interstitial water (the fluid in the tissue spaces, lying between cells). Transcellular water is a small, specialized portion of extracellular water that includes gastrointestinal secretions, urine, sweat, and fluid that has leaked through capillary walls because of such processes as increased hydrostatic pressure or inflammation.

B. Hydrogen Bonds in Water

The dipolar nature of the water (H_2O) molecule allows it to form hydrogen bonds, a property that is responsible for the role of water as a solvent. In H_2O, the oxygen atom has two unshared electrons that form an electron-dense cloud around it. This cloud lies above and below the plane formed by the water molecule (Fig. 4.3). In the covalent bond formed between the hydrogen and oxygen atoms, the shared electrons are attracted toward the oxygen atom, thus giving the oxygen atom a partial negative charge and the hydrogen atom a partial positive charge. As a result, the oxygen side of the molecule is much more electronegative than the hydrogen side, and the molecule is dipolar.

Both the hydrogen and oxygen atoms of the water molecule form hydrogen bonds and participate in hydration shells. A hydrogen bond is a weak noncovalent interaction between the hydrogen of one molecule and the more electronegative atom of an acceptor molecule. The oxygen of water can form hydrogen bonds with two other water molecules, so that each water molecule is hydrogen-bonded to approximately four close neighboring water molecules in a fluid three-dimensional lattice (see Fig. 4.3).

1. WATER AS A SOLVENT

Polar organic molecules and inorganic salts can readily dissolve in water because water also forms hydrogen bonds and electrostatic interactions with these molecules. Organic molecules containing a high proportion of electronegative atoms (generally oxygen or nitrogen) are soluble in water because these atoms participate in hydrogen bonding with water molecules (Fig. 4.4A). Chloride (Cl^-), bicarbonate (HCO_3^-), and other anions are surrounded by a hydration shell of water molecules arranged with their hydrogen atoms closest to the anion. In a similar fashion, the oxygen atom of water molecules interacts with inorganic cations such as Na^+ and K^+ to surround them with a hydration shell (see Fig. 4.4B).

Although hydrogen bonds are strong enough to dissolve polar molecules in water and to separate charges, they are weak enough to allow movement of water and solutes. The strength of the hydrogen bond between two water molecules is only approximately 4 kcal, roughly 1/20th of the strength of the covalent O–H bond in the water molecule. Thus, the extensive water lattice is dynamic and has many strained bonds that are continuously breaking and re-forming. The average hydrogen bond between water molecules lasts only about 10 picoseconds (1 picosecond is 10^{-12} second), and each water molecule in the hydration shell of an ion stays for only 2.4 nanoseconds (1 nanosecond $= 10^{-9}$ second). As a result, hydrogen bonds between water molecules and polar solutes continuously dissociate and re-form, thereby permitting solutes to move through water and water to pass through channels in cellular membranes.

2. WATER AND THERMAL REGULATION

The structure of water also allows it to resist temperature change. Its heat of fusion is high, so a large drop in temperature is needed to convert liquid water to the solid state of ice. The thermal conductivity of water is also high, thereby facilitating heat dissipation from high energy-using areas such as the brain into the blood and the total body water pool. Its heat capacity and heat of vaporization are remarkably high; as liquid water is converted to a gas and evaporates from the skin, we feel a cooling effect. Water responds to the input of heat by decreasing the extent of hydrogen bonding and to cooling by increasing the bonding between water molecules.

FIG. 4.2. Fluid compartments in the body based on an average 70-kg man.

FIG. 4.3. Hydrogen bonds between water molecules. The oxygen atoms are shown in *black*.

FIG. 4.4. **A.** Hydrogen bonds between water and polar molecules. *R* denotes additional atoms. **B.** Hydration shells surrounding anions and cations.

In the emergency room, **Dianne (Di) Abietes** was rehydrated with intravenous saline, which is a solution of 0.9% NaCl. Why was saline used instead of water?

Dianne (Di) Abietes has an osmotic diuresis. Because her blood levels of glucose and ketone bodies are so high, these compounds are passing from the blood into the glomerular filtrate in the kidneys and then into the urine. As a consequence of the high osmolality of the glomerular filtrate, much more water is being excreted in the urine than usual. Thus, Di has polyuria (increased urine volume). As a result of water lost from the blood into the urine, water passes from inside cells into the interstitial space and into the blood, resulting in an intracellular dehydration. The dehydrated cells in the brain are unable to carry out their normal functions. As a result, Di is in a coma.

$$H_2O \rightleftharpoons H^+ + OH^-$$

FIG. 4.5. Dissociation of water.

Table 4.1   Distribution of Ions in Body Fluids

	ECF^a (mmol/L)	ICF (mmol/L)
Cations		
Na^+	145	12
K^+	4	150
Anions		
Cl^-	105	5
HCO_3^-	25	12
Inorganic phosphate	2	100

ECF, extracellular fluid; *ICF*, intracellular fluid.
*a*The content of inorganic ions is very similar in plasma and interstitial fluid, the two components of the ECF.

C. Electrolytes

Both extracellular fluid (ECF) and intracellular fluid (ICF) contain *electrolytes*, a general term applied to bicarbonate and inorganic anions and cations. The electrolytes are unevenly distributed between compartments; Na^+ and Cl^- are the major electrolytes in the ECF (plasma and interstitial fluid), and K^+ and phosphates such as HPO_4^{2-} are the major electrolytes in cells (Table 4.1). This distribution is maintained principally by energy-requiring transporters that pump Na^+ out of cells in exchange for K^+ (see Chapter 10).

D. Osmolality and Water Movement

Water distributes between the different fluid compartments according to the concentration of solutes, or osmolality, of each compartment. The osmolality of a fluid is proportional to the total concentration of all dissolved molecules, including ions, organic metabolites, and proteins, and is usually expressed as milliosmoles (mOsm) per kilogram water. The semipermeable cellular membrane that separates the extracellular and intracellular compartments contains several ion channels through which water can move freely, but other molecules cannot. Likewise, water can move freely through the capillaries separating the interstitial fluid and the plasma. As a result, water will move from a compartment with a low concentration of solutes (lower osmolality) to one with a higher concentration to achieve an equal osmolality on both sides of the membrane. The force it would take to keep the same amount of water on both sides of the membrane is called the *osmotic pressure*.

As water is lost from one fluid compartment, it is replaced with water from another compartment to maintain a nearly constant osmolality. The blood contains a high content of dissolved negatively charged proteins and the electrolytes needed to balance these charges. As water is passed from the blood into the urine to balance the excretion of ions, the blood volume is repleted with water from interstitial fluid. When the osmolality of the blood and interstitial fluid is too high, water moves out of the cells. The loss of cellular water also can occur in hyperglycemia because the high concentration of glucose increases the osmolality of the blood.

II. ACIDS AND BASES

Acids are compounds that donate a hydrogen ion (H^+) to a solution, and bases are compounds (such as the OH^- ion) that accept hydrogen ions. Water itself dissociates to a slight extent, generating hydrogen ions (H^+), which are also called *protons*, and hydroxide ions (OH^-) (Fig. 4.5). The hydrogen ions are extensively hydrated in water to form species such as H_3O^+, but nevertheless are usually represented as simply H^+. Water itself is neutral, neither acidic nor basic.

A. The pH of Water

The extent of dissociation by water molecules into H^+ and OH^- is very slight, and the hydrogen ion concentration of pure water is only 0.0000001 M, or 10^{-7} mol/L. The concentration of hydrogen ions in a solution is usually denoted by the term *pH*, which is the negative $\log_{10}$ of the hydrogen ion concentration expressed in moles per liter (mol/L) (Equation 4.1). Therefore, the pH of pure water is 7.

Equation 4.1. Definition of pH.
$$pH = -\log[H^+]$$

The dissociation constant for water, K_d, expresses the relationship between the hydrogen ion concentration $[H^+]$, the hydroxide ion concentration $[OH^-]$, and the concentration of water $[H_2O]$ at equilibrium (Equation 4.2). Because water dissociates to such a small extent, $[H_2O]$ is essentially constant at 55.5 M. Multiplication of the K_d for water (approximately 1.8×10^{-16} M) by 55.5 M gives a value of approximately 10^{-14} (M)^2, which is called the *ion product of water* (K_w) (Equation 4.3). Because K_w, the product of $[H^+]$ and $[OH^-]$, is always constant, a decrease of $[H^+]$ must be accompanied by a proportionate increase of $[OH^-]$.

Equation 4.2. Dissociation of water.
$$K_d = \frac{[H^+][OH^-]}{[H_2O]}$$

Equation 4.3. Ion product of water.
$$K_w = [H^+][OH^-] = 1 \times 10^{-14}$$

A pH of 7 is termed *neutral* because $[H^+]$ and $[OH^-]$ are equal. Acidic solutions have a greater hydrogen ion concentration and a lower hydroxide ion concentration than pure water (pH <7.0), and basic solutions have a lower hydrogen ion concentration and a greater hydroxide ion concentration (pH >7.0).

B. Strong and Weak Acids

During metabolism, the body produces several acids that increase the hydrogen ion concentration of the blood or other body fluids and tend to lower the pH (Table 4.2). These metabolically important acids can be classified as weak acids or strong acids by their degree of dissociation into a hydrogen ion and a base (the anion component). Inorganic acids such as sulfuric acid (H_2SO_4) and hydrochloric acid (HCl) are strong acids that dissociate completely in solution (Fig. 4.6). Organic acids containing carboxylic acid groups (e.g., the ketone bodies acetoacetic acid and β-hydroxybutyric acid) are weak acids that dissociate to only a limited extent in water. In general, a weak acid (HA), called the *conjugate acid*, dissociates into a hydrogen ion and an anionic component (A^-), called the

 A 0.9% NaCl is 0.9 g NaCl/100 mL, equivalent to 9 g/L. NaCl has a molecular weight of 58 g/mol, so the concentration of NaCl in isotonic saline is 0.155 M, or 155 mM. If all of the NaCl were dissociated into Na^+ and Cl^- ions, the osmolality would be 310 mOsm/kg water. Because NaCl is not completely dissociated and some of the hydration shells surround undissociated NaCl molecules, the osmolality of isotonic saline is approximately 290 mOsm/kg H_2O. The osmolality of plasma, interstitial fluids, and ICF is also approximately 290 mOsm/kg water, so no large shifts of water or swelling occur when isotonic saline is given intravenously.

Table 4.2 Acids in the Blood of a Healthy Individual

Acid	Anion	pK$_a$	Major Sources
Strong acid			
Sulfuric acid (H_2SO_4)	Sulfate (SO_4^{2-})	Completely dissociated	Dietary sulfate and S-containing amino acids
Weak acid			
Carbonic acid (R–COOH)	Bicarbonate (R–COO$^-$)	3.80	CO_2 from TCA cycle
Lactic acid (R–COOH)	Lactate (R–COO$^-$)	3.73	Anaerobic glycolysis
Pyruvic acid (R–COOH)	Pyruvate (R–COO$^-$)	2.39	Glycolysis
Citric acid (R–3COOH)	Citrate (R–3COO$^-$)	3.13; 4.76; 6.40	TCA cycle and diet (e.g., citrus fruits)
Acetoacetic acid (R–COOH)	Acetoacetate (R–COO$^-$)	3.62	Fatty acid oxidation to ketone bodies
β-Hydroxybutyric acid (R–COOH)	β-Hydroxybutyrate (R–COO$^-$)	4.41	Fatty acid oxidation to ketone bodies
Acetic acid (R–COOH)	Acetate (R–COO$^-$)	4.76	Ethanol metabolism
Dihydrogen phosphate ($H_2PO_4^-$)	Monohydrogen phosphate (HPO_4^{2-})	6.80	Dietary organic phosphates
Ammonium ion (NH_4^+)	Ammonia (NH_3)	9.25	Dietary nitrogen-containing compounds

Dennis Veere has ingested an unknown number of acetylsalicylic acid (aspirin) tablets. Acetylsalicylic acid is rapidly converted to salicylic acid in the body. The initial effect of aspirin is to produce a respiratory alkalosis caused by a stimulation of the "metabolic" central respiratory control center in the medulla. This increases the rate of breathing and the expiration of CO_2. This is followed by a complex metabolic acidosis caused partly by the dissociation of salicylic acid (salicylic acid ↔ salicylate⁻ + H⁺, pK_a = ~3.5).

Acetylsalicylate

Salicylate also interferes with mitochondrial ATP production, resulting in increased generation of CO_2 and accumulation of lactate and other organic acids in the blood. Subsequently, salicylate may impair renal function, resulting in the accumulation of strong acids of metabolic origin, such as sulfuric acid and phosphoric acid. Usually, children who ingest toxic amounts of aspirin are acidotic by the time they arrive in the emergency room.

The laboratory reported that **Dianne (Di) Abietes's** blood pH was 7.08 (reference range = 7.37 to 7.43). What was the [H⁺] in her blood compared with the concentration at a normal pH of 7.4?

FIG. 4.6. Dissociation of acids. Sulfuric acid is a strong acid that dissociates into H⁺ ions and sulfate. The ketone bodies acetoacetic acid and β-hydroxybutyric acid are weak acids that partially dissociate into H⁺ and their conjugate bases.

conjugate base. The name of an undissociated acid usually ends in "-ic acid" (e.g., acetoacetic acid), and the name of the dissociated anionic component ends in "-ate" (e.g., acetoacetate).

The tendency of the acid (HA) to dissociate and donate a hydrogen ion to solution is denoted by its K_a, the equilibrium constant for dissociation of a weak acid (Equation 4.4). The higher the K_a, the greater is the tendency to dissociate a proton.

Equation 4.4. The K_a of an acid.

For the reaction,

$$HA \leftrightarrow A^- + H^+$$
$$K_a = \frac{[H^+][A^-]}{[HA]}$$

In the Henderson-Hasselbalch equation, the formula for the dissociation constant of a weak acid is converted to a convenient logarithmic equation (Equation 4.5). The term pK_a represents the negative log of K_a. If the pK_a for a weak acid is known, this equation can be used to calculate the ratio of the unprotonated to the protonated form at any pH. From this equation, you can see that a weak acid is 50% dissociated at a pH equal to its pK_a.

Equation 4.5. The Henderson-Hasselbalch equation.

For the weak acid HA,

$$pH = pK_a + \log\frac{[A^-]}{[HA]}$$

Most of the metabolic carboxylic acids have a pK_a between 2 and 5, depending on the other groups on the molecule (see Table 4.2). The pK_a reflects the strength of an acid. Acids with a pK_a of 2 are stronger acids than those with a pK_a of 5 because, at any pH, a greater proportion is dissociated.

III. BUFFERS

Buffers, which consist of a weak acid and its conjugate base, cause a solution to resist changes in pH when hydrogen ions or hydroxide ions are added. In Figure 4.7, the pH of a solution of the weak acid acetic acid is graphed as a function of the amount of OH⁻ that has been added. The OH⁻ is expressed as equivalents of total acetic acid present in the dissociated and undissociated forms.

FIG. 4.7. Titration curve for acetic acid.

At the midpoint of this curve, 0.5 equivalents of OH⁻ have been added and half of the conjugate acid has dissociated, so [A⁻] equals [HA]. This midpoint is expressed in the Henderson-Hasselbalch equation as the pK_a, defined as the pH at which 50% dissociation occurs. As you add more OH⁻ ions and move to the right on the curve, more of the conjugate acid molecules (HA) dissociate to generate H⁺ ions, which combine with the added OH⁻ ions to form water. Consequently, only a small increase in pH results. If you add hydrogen ions to the buffer at its pK_a (moving to the left of the midpoint in Fig. 4.7), conjugate base molecules (A⁻) combine with the added hydrogen ions to form HA, and almost no decrease in pH occurs.

As can be seen from Figure 4.7, a buffer can only compensate for an influx or removal of hydrogen ions within approximately 1 pH unit of its pK_a. As the pH of a buffered solution changes from the pK_a to 1 pH unit below the pK_a, the ratio of [A⁻] to HA changes from 1:1 to 1:10. If more hydrogen ions were added, the pH would fall rapidly because relatively little conjugate base remains. Likewise, at 1 pH unit above the pK_a of a buffer, relatively little undissociated acid remains. More concentrated buffers are more effective simply because they contain a greater total number of buffer molecules per unit volume that can dissociate or recombine with hydrogen ions.

IV. METABOLIC ACIDS AND BUFFERS

An average rate of metabolic activity produces roughly 22,000 milliequivalents (mEq) of acid per day. If all of this acid were dissolved at one time in unbuffered body fluids, their pH would be <1. However, the pH of the blood is normally maintained between 7.36 and 7.44, and intracellular pH at approximately 7.1 (between 6.9 and 7.4). The widest range of extracellular pH over which the metabolic functions of the liver, the beating of the heart, and conduction of neural impulses can be maintained is 6.8 to 7.8. Thus, until the acid produced from metabolism can be excreted as CO_2 in expired air and as ions in the urine, it needs to be buffered in the body fluids. The major buffer systems in the body are the bicarbonate–carbonic acid buffer system, which operates principally in ECF; the hemoglobin buffer system in red blood cells; the phosphate buffer system in all types of cells; and the protein buffer system of cells and plasma.

A: From inspection, you can tell that her [H⁺] is greater than normal, but less than 10 times higher. A 10-fold change in [H⁺] changes the pH by 1 unit. For Di, the pH of 7.08 = −log[H⁺], and therefore her [H⁺] is 1 × 10⁻⁷·⁰⁸. To calculate her [H⁺], express −7.08 as −8 + 0.92. The antilog to the base 10 of 0.92 is 8.3. Thus, her [H⁺] is 8.3 × 10⁻⁸ compared with 4.0 × 10⁻⁸ at pH 7.4, or slightly more than double the normal value.

FIG. 4.8. Bicarbonate buffer system.

A. The Bicarbonate Buffer System

The major source of metabolic acid in the body is the gas CO_2, produced principally from fuel oxidation in the tricarboxylic acid (TCA) cycle. Under normal metabolic conditions, the body generates more than 13 mol of CO_2 per day (approximately 0.5 to 1 kg). CO_2 dissolves in water and reacts with water to produce carbonic acid, H_2CO_3, a reaction that is accelerated by the enzyme carbonic anhydrase (Fig. 4.8). Carbonic acid is a weak acid that partially dissociates into H^+ and bicarbonate anion, HCO_3^-.

Carbonic acid is both the major acid produced by the body and its own buffer. The pK_a of carbonic acid itself is only 3.8, so at the blood pH of 7.4, it is almost completely dissociated and theoretically unable to buffer and generate bicarbonate. However, carbonic acid can be replenished from CO_2 in body fluids and air because the concentration of dissolved CO_2 in body fluids is approximately 400 times greater than that of carbonic acid. As base is added and H^+ is removed, H_2CO_3 dissociates into hydrogen and bicarbonate ions, and dissolved CO_2 reacts with H_2O to replenish the H_2CO_3 (see Fig. 4.8). Dissolved CO_2 is in equilibrium with the CO_2 in air in the alveoli of the lungs, and thus the availability of CO_2 can be increased or decreased by an adjustment in the rate of breathing and the amount of CO_2 expired. The pK_a for the bicarbonate buffer system in the body thus combines K_h (the hydration constant for the reaction of water and CO_2 to form H_2CO_3) with the chemical pK_a to obtain a modified version of the Henderson-Hasselbalch equation (Equation 4.6). To use the terms for blood components measured in the emergency room, the dissolved CO_2 is expressed as a fraction of the partial pressure of CO_2 in arterial blood, $Paco_2$. The pK_a for dissociation of bicarbonate anion (HCO_3^-) into H^+ and carbonate (CO_3^{2+}) is 9.8; therefore, only trace amounts of carbonate exist in body fluids.

Equation 4.6. The Henderson-Hasselbalch equation for the bicarbonate buffer system.

$$pH = pK_a + \log\frac{[HCO_3^-]}{[H_2CO_3]}$$

The $pK_a = 3.5$, so

$$pH = 3.5 + \log\frac{[HCO_3^-]}{[H_2CO_3]}$$

$[H_2CO_3]$ is best estimated as $[CO_2]_d/400$, where $[CO_2]_d$ is the concentration of dissolved CO_2, so substituting this value for $[H_2CO_3]$ we get

$$pH = 3.5 + \log 400 + \log\frac{[HCO_3^-]}{[CO_2]_d}$$

or

$$pH = 6.1 + \log\frac{[HCO_3^-]}{[CO_2]_d}$$

Because only 3% of the gaseous CO_2 is dissolved, $[CO_2]_d = 0.03\ Paco_2$, so

$$pH = 6.1 + \log\frac{[HCO_3^-]}{0.03\ Paco_2}$$

The HCO_3^- is expressed as milliequivalents per milliliter (mEq/ml), and $Paco_2$ as millimeters of mercury (mm Hg).

B. Bicarbonate and Hemoglobin in Red Blood Cells

The bicarbonate buffer system and hemoglobin in red blood cells cooperate in buffering the blood and transporting CO_2 to the lungs. Most of the CO_2 produced from tissue metabolism in the TCA cycle diffuses into the interstitial fluid and the blood plasma and then into red blood cells (Fig. 4.9, circle 1). Although no carbonic anhydrase can be found in blood plasma or interstitial fluid, the red blood cells contain high amounts of this enzyme, and CO_2 is rapidly converted to carbonic acid (H_2CO_3) within these cells (circle 2). As

The partial pressure of CO_2 ($Paco_2$) in **Dianne (Di) Abietes's** arterial blood was 28 mm Hg (reference range = 37 to 43 mm Hg), and her serum bicarbonate level was 8 mEq/L (reference range = 24 to 28 mEq/L). Elevated levels of ketone bodies had produced a ketoacidosis, and Di was exhaling increased amounts of CO_2 by breathing deeply and frequently (Kussmaul breathing) to compensate. Why does this occur? Ketone bodies are weak acids that partially dissociate, increasing H^+ levels in the blood and the interstitial fluid surrounding the "metabolic" respiratory center in the medulla that controls the rate of breathing. As a result of the decrease in pH, her respiratory rate increased, causing a fall in the $Paco_2$. As bicarbonate and increased protons combined to form carbonic acid and produce more CO_2, her bicarbonate concentration decreased ($HCO_3^- + H^+ \rightarrow H_2CO_3 \rightarrow CO_2 + H_2O$). As shown by Di's low arterial blood pH of 7.08, the Kussmaul breathing was unable to fully compensate for the high rate of acidic ketone body production.

FIG. 4.9. Buffering systems of the body. CO_2 produced from cellular metabolism is converted to bicarbonate and H^+ in the red blood cells. Within the red blood cells, the H^+ is buffered by hemoglobin (Hb) and phosphate (HPO_4^{2-}) (*circles 4 and 6*). The bicarbonate is transported into the blood to buffer H^+ generated by the production of other metabolic acids, such as the ketone body acetoacetic acid (*circle 5*). Other proteins (Pr) also serve as intracellular buffers. See the text for more details.

the carbonic acid dissociates (circle 3), the H^+ released is also buffered by combination with hemoglobin (Hb, circle 4). The side chain of the amino acid histidine in hemoglobin has a pK_a of 6.7 and is thus able to accept a proton. The bicarbonate anion is transported out of the red blood cells into the blood in exchange for chloride anions, and thus bicarbonate is relatively high in the plasma (circle 5) (see Table 4.1).

As the red blood cells approach the lungs, the direction of the equilibrium reverses. CO_2 is released from the red blood cells, causing more carbonic acid to dissociate into CO_2 and water and more hydrogen ions to combine with bicarbonate. Hemoglobin loses some of its hydrogen ions, a feature that allows it to bind oxygen more readily (see Chapters 7 and 44). Thus, the bicarbonate buffer system is intimately linked to the delivery of oxygen to tissues.

The respiratory center within the hypothalamus, which controls the rate of breathing, is sensitive to changes in pH. As the pH falls, individuals breathe more rapidly and expire more CO_2. As the pH rises, they breathe more shallowly. Thus, the rate of breathing contributes to regulation of pH through its effects on the dissolved CO_2 content of the blood.

Bicarbonate and carbonic acid, which diffuse through the capillary wall from the blood into interstitial fluid, provide a major buffer for both plasma and interstitial fluid. However, blood differs from interstitial fluid in that the blood contains a high content of extracellular proteins, such as albumin, which contribute to its buffering capacity through amino acid side chains that are able to accept and release protons. The protein content of interstitial fluid is too low to serve as an effective buffer.

C. Intracellular pH

Phosphate anions and proteins are the major buffers involved in maintaining a constant pH of ICFs. The inorganic phosphate anion $H_2PO_4^-$ dissociates to generate H^+ and the conjugate base, HPO_4^{2-} with a pK_a of 7.2 (see Fig. 4.9, circle 6). Thus, phosphate anions play a major role as an intracellular buffer in the red blood cell and in other types of cells, where their concentration is much higher than in blood and interstitial fluid (see Table 4.1, ECF). Organic phosphate anions such as glucose 6-phosphate and ATP also act as buffers. ICF contains a high content of proteins that contain histidine and other amino acids that can accept protons in a fashion similar to hemoglobin (see Fig. 4.9, circle 7).

The transport of hydrogen ions out of the cell is also important for maintenance of a constant intracellular pH. Metabolism produces several other acids

 Both **Dianne (Di) Abietes** and **Percy Veere** were hyperventilating when they arrived at the emergency room: Ms. Abietes in response to her primary metabolic acidosis and Mr. Veere in response to anxiety. Hyperventilation raised blood pH in both cases: In Ms. Abietes's case, it partially countered the acidosis, and in Mr. Veere's case, it produced a respiratory alkalosis (abnormally high arterial blood pH).

in addition to CO_2. For example, the metabolic acids acetoacetic acid and β-hydroxybutyric acid are produced from fatty acid oxidation to ketone bodies in the liver, and lactic acid is produced by glycolysis in muscle and other tissues. The pK_a for most metabolic carboxylic acids is <5, so these acids are completely dissociated at the pH of blood and cellular fluid. Metabolic anions are transported out of the cell together with H^+ (see Fig. 4.9, circle 8). If the cell becomes too acidic, more H^+ is transported out in exchange for Na^+ ions by a different transporter. If the cell becomes too alkaline, more bicarbonate is transported out in exchange for Cl^- ions.

D. Urinary Hydrogen, Ammonium, and Phosphate Ions

The nonvolatile acid that is produced from body metabolism cannot be excreted as expired CO_2 and is excreted in the urine. Most of the nonvolatile acid hydrogen ion is excreted as undissociated acid that generally buffers the urinary pH between 5.5 and 7.0. A pH of 5.0 is the minimum urinary pH. The acid secretion includes inorganic acids such as phosphate and ammonium ions, as well as uric acid, dicarboxylic acids, and TCA such as citric acid (see Table 4.2). One of the major sources of nonvolatile acid in the body is sulfuric acid (H_2SO_4). Sulfuric acid is generated from the sulfate-containing compounds ingested in foods and from metabolism of the sulfur-containing amino acids, cysteine, and methionine. It is a strong acid that is dissociated into H^+ and sulfate anion (SO_4^-) in the blood and urine (see Fig. 4.6). Urinary excretion of $H_2PO_4^-$ helps to remove acid. To maintain metabolic homeostasis, we must excrete the same amount of phosphate in the urine that we ingest with food as phosphate anions or organic phosphates such as phospholipids. Whether the phosphate is present in the urine as $H_2PO_4^-$ or $HPO4^-$ depends on the urinary pH and the pH of the blood.

Ammonium ions are major contributors to buffering urinary pH, but not blood pH. Ammonia (NH_3) is a base that combines with protons to produce ammonium (NH_4^+) ions ($NH_3 + H^+ \leftrightarrow NH_4^+$), a reaction that occurs with a pK_a of 9.25. Ammonia is produced from amino acid catabolism or absorbed through the intestine and is kept at very low concentrations in the blood because it is toxic to neural tissues. Cells in the kidney generate NH_4^+ and excrete it into the urine in proportion to the acidity (proton concentration) of the blood. As the renal tubular cells transport H^+ into the urine, they return bicarbonate anions to the blood.

E. Hydrochloric Acid

Hydrochloric acid (HCl), also called gastric acid, is secreted by parietal cells of the stomach into the stomach lumen, where the strong acidity denatures ingested proteins so they can be degraded by digestive enzymes. When the stomach contents are released into the lumen of the small intestine, gastric acid is neutralized by bicarbonate secreted from pancreatic cells and by cells in the intestinal lining.

Q: Ammonium ions are acids that dissociate to form the conjugate base, ammonia, and hydrogen ions. What is the form present in blood? In urine?

CLINICAL COMMENTS

Dianne (Di) Abietes. Di Abietes has type 1 diabetes mellitus (formerly called juvenile or insulin-dependent diabetes mellitus [IDDM]). She maintains her insulin level through several subcutaneous (under the skin) injections of insulin throughout the day. If her blood insulin levels fall too low, free fatty acids leave her adipocytes (fat cells) and are converted by the liver to the ketone bodies acetoacetic acid and β-hydroxybutyric acid. As these acids accumulate in the blood, a metabolic acidosis known as *diabetic ketoacidosis* (DKA) develops. Until insulin is administered to reverse this trend, several compensatory mechanisms operate to minimize the extent of the acidosis. One of these mechanisms is a stimulation of the respiratory center in the hypothalamus induced by the acidosis, which leads to deeper and more frequent respiration (Kussmaul respiration). CO_2 is expired more rapidly than normal, and the blood pH rises. The results of the laboratory studies performed on **Di Abietes** in the emergency room were consistent with a moderately severe DKA. Her arterial blood pH and serum bicarbonate were low, and ketone bodies were present in her blood and urine (normally, ketone bodies are not present in the urine). In addition, her serum glucose level was 648 mg/dL (reference range = 80 to 110 mg/dL fasting and no higher than 200 mg/dL in a random glucose sample). Her hyperglycemia, which induces an osmotic diuresis, contributed to her dehydration and the hyperosmolality of her body fluids.

Treatment was initiated with intravenous saline solutions to replace fluids lost with the osmotic diuresis and hyperventilation. The osmotic diuresis resulted from increased urinary water volume to dilute the large amounts of glucose and ketone bodies excreted in the urine. Hyperventilation increased the water of respiration lost with expired air. A loading dose of regular insulin was given as an intravenous bolus, followed by additional insulin given as an intravenous continuous drip. The patient's metabolic response to the treatment was monitored closely.

 Dennis Veere. Dennis remained alert in the emergency room. While awaiting the report of his initial serum salicylate level, his stomach was lavaged, and several white tablets were found in the stomach aspirate. He was examined repeatedly and showed none of the early symptoms of salicylate toxicity, such as respiratory stimulation, upper abdominal distress, nausea, or change in mental status.

His serum salicylate level was reported as 92 μg/mL (the usual level in an adult receiving a therapeutic dosage of 2 to 4 g/day is 120 to 350 μg/mL, and a level of 1,000 μg/mL is considered potentially lethal). He was admitted for overnight observation and continued to do well. A serum salicylate level the following morning was 24 μg/mL. He was discharged later that day.

 Percy Veere. At the emergency room, Mr. Veere complained of light-headedness and "pins and needles" (paresthesias) in his hands and around his lips. These symptoms resulted from an increase in respiratory drive mediated in this case through the "behavioral" rather than the "metabolic" central respiratory control system (as seen in **Di Abietes** when she was in diabetic ketoacidosis). The behavioral system was activated in Mr. Veere's case by his anxiety over his grandson's potential poisoning. His alveolar hyperventilation caused Mr. Veere's $Paco_2$ to decrease below the normal range of 37 to 43 mm Hg. The alkalemia caused his neurologic symptoms. After being reassured that his grandson would be fine, Mr. Veere was asked to breathe slowly into a small paper bag placed around his nose and mouth, allowing him to reinhale the CO_2 being exhaled through hyperventilation. Within 20 minutes, his symptoms disappeared.

 The pK_a for dissociation of ammonium ions is 9.25. Thus, the undissociated conjugate acid form, NH_4^+, predominates at the physiologic pH of 7.4 and urinary pH of 5.5 to 7.0. Ammonia is an unusual conjugate base because it is not an anion.

 Diabetes mellitus is diagnosed by the concentration of plasma glucose (plasma is blood from which the red blood cells have been removed by centrifugation). Because plasma glucose normally increases after a meal, the normal reference ranges and the diagnostic level are defined relative to the time of consumption of food, or to consumption of a specified amount of glucose during an oral glucose tolerance test. After an overnight fast, values for the fasting plasma glucose <100 mg/dL are considered normal, and values >126 mg/dL define diabetes mellitus. Fasting plasma glucose values ≥100 and <126 mg/dL define an intermediate condition termed *impaired fasting glucose*. Normal random plasma glucose levels (random is defined as any time of day without regard to the time since a last meal) should not be >200 mg/dL. A 2-hour postprandial (after a meal or after an oral glucose load) plasma glucose level between 140 and 199 mg/dL defines a condition known as *impaired glucose tolerance*. A level >200 mg/dL defines "overt" diabetes mellitus. Diabetes mellitus is also diagnosed by measuring the hemoglobin A_{1c} (HbA1c) values, which is a measure of glycosylated hemoglobin in the red blood cells. This is a nonenzymatic reaction that is dependent on glucose concentration, so as the glucose concentration increases, the levels of HbA1c increase. Normal levels of HbA1c are 4% to 6% of total hemoglobin, and a value of >6.5% HbA1c defines diabetes mellitus.

BIOCHEMICAL COMMENTS

Body Water and Dehydration. Dehydration, or loss of water, occurs when salt and water intake is less than the combined rates of renal plus extrarenal volume loss (Fig. 4.10). In a true hypovolemic state, total body water, functional extracellular fluid (ECF) volume, and intracellular fluid (ICF) volume are decreased. One of the causes of hypovolemia is an intake of water that is inadequate to resupply the daily excretion volume (maintenance of fluid homeostasis). The amount of water lost by the kidneys is

FIG. 4.10. Body fluid homeostasis (constant body water balance). Intake is influenced by availability of fluids and food, thirst, hunger, and the ability to swallow. The rates of breathing and evaporation and urinary volume influence water loss. The body adjusts the volume of urinary excretion to compensate for variations in other types of water loss and for variations in intake. The hormones aldosterone and antidiuretic hormone (ADH) help to monitor blood volume and osmolality through mechanisms that regulate thirst as well as sodium and water balance.

determined by the amount of water necessary to dilute the ions, acids, and other solutes excreted. Both urinary solute excretion and water loss in expired air, which amount to almost 400 mL/day, occur during fasting as well as during periods of normal food intake. Thus, people who are lost in the desert or shipwrecked continue to lose water in air and urine, in addition to their water loss through the skin and sweat glands. Comatose patients and patients who are debilitated and unable to swallow also continue to lose water and become dehydrated. Anorexia (loss of appetite), such as **Percy Veere** experienced during his depression (see Chapters 1 and 3), can result in dehydration because food intake is normally a source of fluid. Cerebral injuries that cause a loss of thirst response also can lead to dehydration.

Dehydration also can occur secondary to excessive water loss through the kidneys, lungs, and skin. Excessive renal loss could be the result of impaired kidney function or impaired response by the hormones that regulate water balance (e.g., antidiuretic hormone [ADH] and aldosterone). However, in individuals such as **Di Abietes** who have normal kidney function, dehydration can occur as a response to water dilution of the high concentrations of ketone bodies, glucose, and other solutes excreted in the urine (osmotic diuresis). If the urinary water loss is associated with an acidosis, hyperventilation occurs, increasing the amount of water lost in expired air. Water loss in expired air (pulmonary water loss) could occur also as a result of a tracheotomy or cerebral injury. An excessive loss of water and electrolytes through the skin can result from extensive burns.

Gastrointestinal water losses also can result in dehydration. We secrete approximately 8 to 10 L of fluid per day into our intestinal lumen. Normally, more than 90% of this fluid is reabsorbed in the intestines. The percentage reabsorbed can be decreased by vomiting, diarrhea, tube drainage of gastric contents, or loss of water into tissues around the gut via bowel fistulas.

Key Concepts

- Approximately 60% of our body weight is water.
- Water is distributed between intracellular and extracellular (interstitial fluids, blood, lymph) compartments.
- Because water is a dipolar molecule with an uneven distribution of electrons between the hydrogen and oxygen atoms, it forms hydrogen bonds with other polar molecules and acts as a solvent.
- Many of the compounds produced in the body and dissolved in water contain chemical groups that act as acids or bases, releasing or accepting hydrogen ions.
- The hydrogen ion content and the amount of body water are controlled to maintain homeostasis, a constant environment for our cells.
- The pH of a solution is the negative log of its hydrogen ion concentration.
- Acids release hydrogen ions; bases accept hydrogen ions.
- Strong acids dissociate completely in water, whereas only a small percentage of the total molecules of a weak acid dissociate.
- The dissociation constant of a weak acid is designated as K_a.
- The Henderson-Hasselbalch equation defines the relationship between the pH of a solution, the K_a of the acid, and the extent of acid dissociation.
- A buffer, a mixture of an undissociated acid and its conjugate base, resists changes in pH when either H^+ or OH^- is added.
- Buffers work best within a range of 1 pH unit either above or below the pK_a of the buffer, where the pK_a is the negative log of the K_a.
- Normal metabolism generates metabolic acids (lactate, ketone bodies), inorganic acids (sulfuric acid, hydrochloric acid), and carbon dioxide.
- Carbon dioxide reacts with water to form carbonic acid, which will dissociate to form bicarbonate and a proton.
- Physiologic buffers include bicarbonate, phosphate, and the protein hemoglobin.
- Diseases discussed in this chapter are described in Table 4.3.

Table 4.3   Diseases Associated with Chapter 4

Disorder or Condition	Genetic or Environmental	Comments
Type 1 diabetes	Both	Lack of insulin production leads to type 1 diabetes. One consequence of untreated type 1 diabetes is ketoacidosis (elevated levels of ketone bodies in the blood).
Salicylate overdose	Environmental	Complex effects on respiratory center and basic metabolism, causing alterations in acid/base management, among other effects. Leads to impaired renal function.
Hyperventilation	Environmental	Complex effects on respiratory center and acid/base management. Leads to a respiratory alkalosis.

REVIEW QUESTIONS—CHAPTER 4

1. A decrease of blood pH from 7.5 to 6.5 would be accompanied by which of the following changes in ion concentration?

    A. A 10-fold increase in hydrogen ion concentration
    B. A 10-fold increase in hydroxyl ion concentration
    C. An increase in hydrogen ion concentration by a factor of 7.5/6.5
    D. A decrease in hydrogen ion concentration by a factor of 6.5/7.5
    E. A shift in concentration of buffer anions, with no change in hydrogen ion concentration

2. Consider a biochemical reaction that is taking place in a 0.1 M buffer. The initial pH is 7.4, and the pK_a of the buffer is 7.2. If, in a final reaction volume of 1.0 mL, 10 μmol of protons are generated, what would be the final pH of the solution?

    A. 7.59
    B. 7.25
    C. 7.22
    D. 7.20
    E. 7.15

3. A patient with an enteropathy (intestinal disease) produced large amounts of ammonia (NH_3) from bacterial overgrowth in the intestine. The ammonia was absorbed through the intestine into the portal vein, and entered the circulation. Which of the following is a likely consequence of his ammonia absorption?

    A. A decrease of blood pH
    B. Conversion of ammonia to ammonium ion in the blood

    C. A decreased concentration of bicarbonate in the blood
    D. Kussmaul respiration
    E. Increased expiration of CO_2

4. Which of the following physiologic/pathologic conditions is most likely to result in an alkalosis, provided the body could not fully compensate?

    A. Production of lactic acid by muscles during exercise
    B. Production of ketone bodies by a patient with diabetes mellitus
    C. Repeated vomiting of stomach contents, including HCl
    D. Diarrhea with loss of the bicarbonate anions secreted into the intestine
    E. An infection resulting in a fever and hypercatabolism

5. Laboratory tests on the urine of a patient identified the presence of methylmalonate ($^-OOC–CH(CH_3)–COO^-$). Methylmalonate is best described as which one of the following?

    A. A strong acid
    B. The conjugate base of a weak acid
    C. It is 100% dissociated at its pK_a.
    D. It is 50% dissociated at the pH of the blood.
    E. It is a major intracellular buffer.

5 Structures of the Major Compounds of the Body

CH₃CH₂OH ethanol

CH₃OH methanol

The names of chemical groups are often incorporated into the common name of a compound and denote important differences in chemical structure. For example, in the name "ethanol," the "eth-" denotes the ethyl group (CH_3CH_2—), the "-ol" denotes the alcohol group (OH), and the "an" denotes the single bonds between the carbon atoms. Methanol contains a methyl group (CH_3) instead of the ethyl group. Methanol (also called wood alcohol) is much more toxic to humans than ethanol, the alcohol in alcoholic beverages. Ingestion of methanol results in visual disturbances, bradycardia, coma, and seizures.

The body contains compounds of great structural diversity, ranging from relatively simple sugars and amino acids to enormously complex polymers such as proteins and nucleic acids. Many of these compounds have common structural features related to their names, their solubility in water, the pathways in which they participate, or their physiologic function. Thus, learning the terminology used to describe individual compounds and classes of compounds can greatly facilitate learning biochemistry.

In this chapter, we describe the major classes of carbohydrates and lipids and some of the classes of nitrogen-containing compounds. The structures of amino acids, proteins, nucleic acids, and vitamins are covered in more detail in subsequent chapters.

Functional Groups of Molecules. *Organic molecules are composed principally of carbon and hydrogen. However, their unique characteristics are related to structures termed functional groups that involve **oxygen**, **nitrogen**, **phosphorus**, or **sulfur**.*

Carbohydrates. *Carbohydrates, commonly known as sugars, can be classified by their carbonyl group (**aldo** or **keto sugars**), the number of carbons they contain (e.g., pentoses, hexoses), or the positions of the hydroxyl groups on their asymmetric carbon atoms (**D-** or **L-sugars**, **stereoisomers**, or **epimers**). They can also be categorized according to their substituents (e.g., **amino sugars**), or the number of monosaccharides (such as glucose) joined through **glycosidic bonds** (**disaccharides**, **oligosaccharides**, and **polysaccharides**). **Glycoproteins** and **proteoglycans** have sugars attached to their protein components.*

Lipids. *Lipids are a group of structurally diverse compounds defined by their **hydrophobicity**; they are not very soluble in water. The major lipids of the human body are the **fatty acids**, which are esterified to **glycerol** to form **triacylglycerols** (triglycerides) or **phosphoacylglycerols** (phosphoglycerides). In the **sphingolipids**, a fatty acid is attached to sphingosine, which is derived from serine and another fatty acid. **Glycolipids** contain sugars attached to a lipid hydroxyl group. Specific **polyunsaturated fatty acids** are precursors of **eicosanoids**. The lipid **cholesterol** is a component of membranes, and the precursor of other compounds that contain the steroid nucleus, such as the **bile salts** and **steroid hormones**. Cholesterol is one of the compounds synthesized from a five-carbon precursor called the **isoprene** unit.*

Nitrogen-Containing Compounds. *Nitrogen in **amino groups** or **heterocyclic ring** structures often carries a positive charge at neutral pH. **Amino acids** contain a carboxyl group, an amino group, and one or more additional carbons. **Purines**, **pyrimidines**, and **pyridines** have heterocyclic nitrogen-containing ring structures. **Nucleosides** comprise one of these ring structures attached to a sugar. The addition of a phosphate produces a **nucleotide**.*

THE WAITING ROOM

 Di Abietes recovered from her bout of diabetic ketoacidosis and was discharged from the hospital (see Chapter 4). She has returned for a follow-up visit as an outpatient. She reports that she has been compliant with her recommended diet and that she faithfully gives herself insulin by subcutaneous injection usually four times daily. She self-monitors her blood glucose levels at least four times a day and reports the results to her physician.

Lotta Topaigne is a 54-year-old woman who came to her physician's office complaining of a severe throbbing pain in the right great toe that began 8 hours earlier. The toe has suffered no trauma but appears red and swollen. It is warmer than the surrounding tissue and is exquisitely tender to even light pressure. Ms. Topaigne is unable to voluntarily flex or extend the joints of the digit, and passive motion of the joints causes great pain.

 Di Abietes had a metabolic acidosis resulting from increased hepatic production of ketone bodies. Her response to therapy was followed with screening tests for ketone bodies in her urine that employed a paper strip containing nitroprusside, a compound that reacts with keto groups. Her blood glucose was measured with an enzymatic assay that is specific for the sugar D-glucose and will not react with other sugars.

I. FUNCTIONAL GROUPS ON BIOLOGIC COMPOUNDS

A. Biologic Compounds

The organic molecules of the body consist principally of carbon, hydrogen, oxygen, nitrogen, sulfur, and phosphorus joined by covalent bonds. The key element is carbon, which forms four covalent bonds with other atoms. Carbon atoms are joined through double or single bonds to form the carbon backbone for structures of varying size and complexity (Fig. 5.1). Groups containing one, two, three, four, and five carbons plus hydrogen are referred to as methyl, ethyl, propionyl, butyl, and pentanyl groups, respectively. If the carbon chain is branched, the prefix "iso-" is used. If the compound contains a double bond, "ene" is sometimes incorporated into the name. Carbon structures that are straight or branched with single or double bonds, but do not contain a ring, are called *aliphatic*.

Carbon-containing rings are found in several biologic compounds. One of the most common is the six-membered carbon-containing benzene ring, sometimes called a phenyl group (see Fig. 5.1B). This ring has three double bonds, but the electrons are shared equally by all six carbons and delocalized in planes above and below the ring. Compounds containing the benzene ring, or a similar ring structure with benzenelike properties, are called *aromatic*.

B. Functional Groups

Biochemical molecules are defined both by their carbon skeleton and by structures called *functional groups* that usually involve bonds between carbon and oxygen, carbon and nitrogen, carbon and sulfur, or carbon and phosphate groups (Fig. 5.2). In carbon–carbon and carbon–hydrogen bonds, the electrons are shared equally between atoms, and the bonds are nonpolar and relatively unreactive. In carbon–oxygen and carbon–nitrogen bonds, the electrons are shared unequally, and the bonds are polar and more reactive. Thus, the properties of the functional groups usually determine the types of reactions that occur and the physiologic role of the molecule.

Functional group names are often incorporated into the common name of a compound. For example, a ket**one** might have a name that ends in "-one," such as acet**one**, and the name of a compound that contains a hydroxyl (alcoh**ol** or OH group) might end in "-ol" (e.g., ethan**ol**). The acyl group is the portion of the molecule that provides the carbonyl (—C=O) group in an ester or amide linkage. It is denoted in a name by an "-yl" ending. For example, the fat stores of the body

A

Aliphatic isopentenyl group

B

Aromatic phenyl group

FIG. 5.1. Examples of aliphatic and aromatic compounds. **A.** An **isoprene** group, which is an aliphatic group. The "iso-" prefix denotes branching, and the "-ene" denotes a double bond. **B.** A benzene ring (or phenyl group), which is an aromatic group.

 The ketone bodies synthesized in the liver are β-hydroxybutyrate and acetoacetate. A third ketone body, acetone, is formed by the nonenzymatic decarboxylation of acetoacetate (see Fig. 3.3). Acetone is volatile and accounts for the sweet mousy odor in the breath of patients such as **Di Abietes** when they have a ketoacidosis. What functional groups are present in each of these ketone bodies?

FIG. 5.2. Major types of functional groups found in biochemical compounds of the human body.

 β-Hydroxybutyrate and acetoacetate are carboxylates (dissociated carboxylic acids). Acetoacetate and acetone contain keto/ketone groups. Because β-hydroxybutyrate contains an alcohol (hydroxyl) group and not a keto group, the general name of ketone bodies for these compounds is really a misnomer.

 Which compound is glycerol, and which is glyceraldehyde?

 Judging from the structures of the ketone bodies shown in Figure 3.3, which compound is more oxidized, β-hydroxybutyrate or acetoacetate? Which is more reduced?

are triacylglycerols. Three acyl (fatty acid) groups are esterified to glycerol, a compound that contains three alcohol groups. In the remainder of this chapter, we will set in bold the portions of names of compounds that refer to a class of compounds or a structural feature.

1. OXIDIZED AND REDUCED GROUPS

The carbon–carbon and carbon–oxygen groups are described as "oxidized" or "reduced" according to the number of electrons around the carbon atom. *Oxidation* is the loss of electrons and results in the loss of hydrogen atoms together with one or two electrons, or the gain of an oxygen atom or hydroxyl group. *Reduction* is the gain of electrons and results in the gain of hydrogen atoms or loss of an oxygen atom. Thus, the carbon becomes progressively more oxidized (and less reduced) as we go from an alcohol to an aldehyde or a ketone to a carboxyl group (see Fig. 5.2). Carbon–carbon double bonds are more oxidized (and less reduced) than carbon–carbon single bonds.

2. GROUPS THAT CARRY A CHARGE

Acidic groups contain a proton that can dissociate, usually leaving the remainder of the molecule as an anion with a negative charge (see Chapter 4). In biomolecules, the major anionic substituents are carboxylate groups, phosphate groups, or sulfate groups (the "-ate" suffix denotes a negative charge) (Fig. 5.3). Phosphate groups attached to metabolites are often abbreviated as P with a circle around it, or just as "P," as in glucose 6-**P**.

Compounds that contain nitrogen are usually basic and can acquire a positive charge (Fig. 5.4). Nitrogen has five electrons in its valence shell. If only three of these electrons form covalent bonds with other atoms, the nitrogen has no charge. If the remaining two electrons form a bond with a hydrogen ion or a carbon atom, the nitrogen carries a positive charge. Amines consist of nitrogen attached through single bonds to hydrogen atoms and to one or more carbon atoms. Primary amines, such as dopamine, have one carbon–nitrogen bond. These amines are weak acids with a pK_a of approximately 9, so that at pH 7.4 they carry a positive charge. Secondary, tertiary, and quarternary amines have two, three, and four nitrogen–carbon bonds, respectively (see Fig. 5.4).

C. Polarity of Bonds and Partial Charges

Polar bonds are covalent bonds in which the electron cloud is more dense around one atom (the atom with the greater electronegativity) than the other. Oxygen is more electronegative than carbon, and a carbon–oxygen bond is therefore polar, with the oxygen atom carrying a partial negative charge and the carbon atom carrying a partial positive charge (Fig. 5.5). In nonpolar carbon–carbon bonds and carbon–hydrogen bonds, the two electrons in the covalent bond are shared almost equally. Nitrogen, when it has only three covalent bonds, also carries a partial negative charge relative to carbon, and the carbon–nitrogen bond is polarized. Sulfur can carry a slight partial negative charge.

1. SOLUBILITY

Water is a dipolar molecule in which the oxygen atom carries a partial negative charge and the hydrogen atoms carry partial positive charges (see Chapter 4). For molecules to be soluble in water, they must contain charged or polar groups that can associate with the partial positive and negative charges of water. Thus, the solubility of organic molecules in water is determined by both the proportion of polar to nonpolar groups attached to the carbon–hydrogen skeleton and to their relative positions in the molecule. Polar groups or molecules are called *hydrophilic* (water loving), and nonpolar groups or molecules are hydrophobic (water fearing). Sugars such as glucose 6-phosphate, for example, contain so many polar groups that they are very hydrophilic and almost infinitely water-soluble (Fig. 5.6). The water molecules interacting with a polar or ionic compound form a hydration shell around the compound, which includes hydrogen bonds and/or ionic interactions between water and the compound.

Compounds that have large nonpolar regions are relatively water-insoluble. They tend to cluster together in an aqueous environment and form weak associations through van der Waals interactions and hydrophobic interactions. Hydrophobic compounds are essentially pushed together (the hydrophobic effect) as the water molecules maximize the number of energetically favorable hydrogen bonds they can form with each other in the water lattice. Thus, lipids form droplets or separate layers in an aqueous environment (e.g., vegetable oils in a salad dressing).

2. REACTIVITY

Another consequence of bond polarity is that atoms that carry a partial (or full) negative charge are attracted to atoms that carry a partial (or full) positive charge and vice versa. These partial or full charges dictate the course of biochemical reactions, which follow the same principles of electrophilic and nucleophilic attack that are characteristic of organic reactions in general. The partial positive charge on the carboxyl carbon attracts more negatively charged groups and accounts for many of the reactions of carboxylic acids. An ester is formed when a carboxylic acid and an alcohol combine, splitting out water (Fig. 5.7). Similarly, a thioester is formed when an acid combines with a sulfhydryl group, and an amide is formed when an acid combines with an amine. Similar reactions result in the formation of a phosphoester from phosphoric acid and an alcohol and in the formation of an anhydride from two acids.

D. Nomenclature

Biochemists use two systems for the identification of the carbons in a chain. In the first system, the carbons in a compound are numbered, starting with the carbon in the most oxidized group (e.g., the carboxyl group). In the second system, the carbons are given Greek letters, starting with the carbon next to the most oxidized group. Hence, the compound shown in Figure 5.8 is known as 3-hydroxybutyrate or β-hydroxybutyrate.

Compound A contains three **alcohol** groups and is called glycer**ol**. Compound B contains an **aldehyde** group and is called glycer**aldehyde**.

Acetoacetate is more oxidized than β-hydroxybutyrate. The carbon in the keto group contains one less hydrogen than the carbon to which the –OH group is attached. It has lost an electron.

Carboxylate group

Phosphate group

Sulfate group

FIG. 5.3. Examples of anions formed by dissociation of acidic groups. At physiologic pH, carboxylic acids, phosphoric acid, and sulfuric acid are dissociated into hydrogen ions and negatively charged anions.

Dopamine (a primary amine)

Choline (a quaternary amine)

FIG. 5.4. Examples of amines. At physiologic pH, many amines carry positive charges.

FIG. 5.5. Partial charges on carbon–oxygen, carbon–nitrogen, and carbon–sulfur bonds.

Glucose 6-phosphate

FIG. 5.6. Glucose 6-phosphate, a very polar and water-soluble molecule.

FIG. 5.7. Formation of esters, thioesters, amides, phosphoesters, and anhydrides.

FIG. 5.8. Two systems for identifying the carbon atoms in a compound. This compound is called 3-hydroxybutyrate or β-hydroxybutyrate.

Ketose

Fructose

FIG. 5.9. Fructose is a ketohexose.

II. CARBOHYDRATES

A. Monosaccharides

Simple monosaccharides consist of a linear chain of three or more carbon atoms, one of which forms a carbonyl group through a double bond with oxygen (Fig. 5.9). The other carbons of an unmodified monosaccharide contain hydroxyl groups, resulting in the general formula for an unmodified sugar of $C_nH_{2n}O_n$. The suffix "-ose" is used in the names of sugars. If the carbonyl group is an aldehyde, the sugar is an aldose; if the carbonyl group is a ketone, the sugar is a ketose. Monosaccharides are also classified according to their number of carbons: Sugars containing three, four, five, six, and seven carbons are called trioses, tetroses, pentoses, hexoses, and heptoses, respectively. Fructose is therefore a ketohexose (see Fig. 5.9), and glucose is an aldohexose (see Fig. 5.6).

1. D- AND L-SUGARS

A carbon atom that contains four different chemical groups forms an asymmetric (or chiral) center (Fig. 5.10A). The groups attached to the asymmetric carbon atom can be arranged to form two different isomers that are mirror images of each other and not superimposable. Monosaccharide stereoisomers are designated D or L based on whether the position of the hydroxyl group farthest from the carbonyl carbon matches D- or L-glyceraldehyde (see Fig. 5.10B). Such mirror image compounds are known as *enantiomers*. Although a more sophisticated system of nomenclature using the designations (R) and (S) is generally used to describe the positions of groups on complex molecules such as drugs, the D and L designations are still used in medicine for describing sugars and amino acids. Because glucose (the major sugar in human blood) and most other sugars in human tissues belong to the D series, sugars are assumed to be D unless L is specifically added to the name.

2. STEREOISOMERS AND EPIMERS

Stereoisomers have the same chemical formula but differ in the position of the hydroxyl group on one or more of their asymmetric carbons (Fig. 5.11). A sugar with n asymmetric centers has 2^n stereoisomers unless it has a plane of symmetry. Epimers are stereoisomers that differ in the position of the hydroxyl group at only one of their asymmetric carbons. D-glucose and D-galactose are epimers of each other, differing only at position 4, and can be interconverted in human cells by enzymes called *epimerases*. D-mannose and D-glucose are also epimers of each other, differing only at position 2.

3. RING STRUCTURES

Monosaccharides exist in solution mainly as ring structures in which the carbonyl (aldehyde or ketone) group has reacted with a hydroxyl group in the same molecule to form a five- or six-membered ring (Fig. 5.12). The oxygen that was on the hydroxyl group is now part of the ring, and the original carbonyl carbon, which now contains an —OH group, has become the anomeric carbon atom. A hydroxyl group on the anomeric carbon drawn down below the ring is in the α position; drawn up above the ring, it is in the β position. In the actual three-dimensional structure, the ring is not planar but usually takes a "chair" conformation in which the hydroxyl groups are located at a maximal distance from each other.

In solution, the hydroxyl group on the anomeric carbon spontaneously (nonenzymatically) changes from the α to the β position through a process called *mutarotation*. When the ring opens, the straight-chain aldehyde or ketone is formed. When the ring closes, the hydroxyl group may be in either the α or the β position (Fig. 5.13). This process occurs more rapidly in the presence of cellular enzymes called *mutarotases*. However, if the anomeric carbon forms a bond with another molecule, that bond is fixed in the α or β position, and the sugar cannot mutarotate. Enzymes are specific for α or β bonds between sugars and other molecules and react with only one type.

4. SUBSTITUTED SUGARS

Sugars frequently contain phosphate groups, amino groups, sulfate groups, or *N*-acetyl groups. Most of the free monosaccharides within cells are phosphorylated at their terminal carbons, which prevents their transport out of the cell

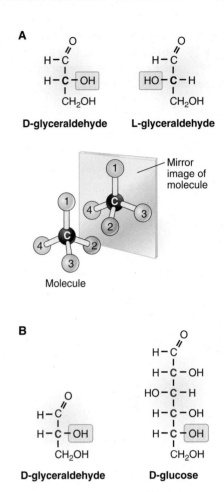

A

D-glyceraldehyde   **L-glyceraldehyde**

Mirror image of molecule

Molecule

B

D-glyceraldehyde   **D-glucose**

FIG. 5.10. **A.** D- and L-glyceraldehyde. The carbon in the center contains four different substituent groups arranged around it in a tetrahedron. A different arrangement creates an isomer that is a nonsuperimposable mirror image. If you rotate the mirror image structure so that groups 1 and 2 align, group 3 will be in the position of group 4, and group 4 will be in position 3. **B.** D-glyceraldehyde and D-glucose. These sugars have the same configuration at the asymmetric carbon atom farthest from the carbonyl group. Both belong to the D series. Asymmetric carbons are shown in *red*.

The stereospecificity of D-glucose is still frequently denoted in medicine by the use of its old name, dextrose. A solution used for intravenous infusions in patients is a 5% (5 g/100 mL) solution of dextrose.

Are D-mannose and D-galactose stereoisomers? Are they epimers of each other? (See Fig. 5.11.)

D-glucose   **D-mannose**   **D-galactose**

FIG. 5.11. Examples of stereoisomers. These compounds have the same chemical formula ($C_6H_{12}O_6$) but differ in the positions of the hydroxyl groups on their asymmetric carbons (in *red*).

They are stereoisomers but not epimers of each other. They have the same chemical formula but differ in the position of two hydroxyl groups.

FIG. 5.12. Pyranose and furanose rings formed from glucose and fructose. The anomeric carbons are highlighted.

(see glucose 6-phosphate in Fig. 5.6). Amino sugars such as galacto**samine** and gluco**samine** contain an amino group instead of a hydroxyl group on one of the carbon atoms, usually carbon 2 (Fig. 5.14). Frequently, this amino group has been acetylated to form an *N*-acetylated sugar. In complex molecules termed *proteoglycan*s, many of the *N*-acetylated sugars also contain negatively charged sulfate groups attached to a hydroxyl group on the sugar.

5. OXIDIZED AND REDUCED SUGARS

Sugars can be oxidized at the aldehyde carbon to form an acid. Technically, the compound is no longer a sugar, and the ending on its name is changed from "-ose" to "-onic acid" or "-onate" (e.g., gluc**onic** acid, Fig. 5.15). If the carbon containing the terminal hydroxyl group is oxidized, the sugar is called a *uronic acid* (e.g., gluc**uronic** acid).

If the aldehyde of a sugar is reduced, all of the carbon atoms contain alcohol (hydroxyl) groups, and the sugar is a poly**ol** (e.g., sorbit**ol**) (see Fig. 5.15). If one of the hydroxyl groups of a sugar is reduced so that the carbon contains only hydrogen, the sugar is a deoxysugar, such as the **deoxy**ribose in DNA.

FIG. 5.13. Mutarotation of glucose in solution, with percentages of each form at equilibrium.

FIG. 5.14. An *N*-acetylated amino sugar. The "*N*-" denotes the amino group to which the acetyl group is attached, as shown in the *colored box.*

Proteoglycans contain many long unbranched polysaccharide chains attached to a core protein. The polysaccharide chains, called *glycosaminoglycans*, are composed of repeating disaccharide units containing oxidized acid sugars (such as glucuronic acid), sulfated sugars, and *N*-acetylated amino sugars. The large number of negative charges causes the glycosaminoglycan chains to radiate out from the protein so that the overall structure resembles a bottle brush. The proteoglycans are essential parts of the extracellular matrix, aqueous humor of the eye, secretions of mucus-producing cells, and cartilage and are described in further detail in Chapter 49.

B. Glycosides

1. *N*- AND *O*-GLYCOSIDIC BONDS

The hydroxyl group on the anomeric carbon of a monosaccharide can react with an —OH or an —NH group of another compound to form a glyc**osidic** bond. The linkage may be either α or β, depending on the position of the atom attached to the anomeric carbon of the sugar. *N*-glycosidic bonds are found in nucle**osides** and nucle**otides**. For example, in the adenosine moiety of adenosine triphosphate (ATP), the nitrogenous base adenine is linked to the sugar ribose through a β-*N*-glycosidic bond (Fig. 5.16). In contrast, *O*-glycosidic bonds, such as those found in lactose, join sugars to each other or attach sugars to the hydroxyl group of an amino acid on a protein.

2. DISACCHARIDES, OLIGOSACCHARIDES, AND POLYSACCHARIDES

A disaccharide contains two monosaccharides joined by an *O*-glycosidic bond. Lactose, which is the sugar in milk, consists of galactose and glucose linked through a $\beta(1{\to}4)$ bond formed between the β–OH group of the anomeric carbon of galactose and the hydroxyl group on carbon 4 of glucose (see Fig. 5.16). Oligosaccharides contain from 3 to roughly 12 monosaccharides linked together. They are often found attached through *N*- or *O*-glycosidic bonds to proteins to form **glyco**proteins (see Chapter 6). Polysaccharides contain tens to thousands of monosaccharides joined by glycosidic bonds to form linear chains or branched structures. Amylopectin (a form of starch) and glycogen (the storage form of glucose in human cells) are branched polymers of glucosyl residues linked through $\alpha(1{\to}4)$ and $\alpha(1{\to}6)$ bonds.

III. LIPIDS

A. Fatty Acids

Fatty acids are usually straight aliphatic chains with a methyl group at one end (called the ω-carbon) and a carboxyl group at the other end (Fig. 5.17A). Most fatty acids in the human have an even number of carbon atoms, usually between 16 and 20. Saturated fatty acids have single bonds between the carbons in the chain, and unsaturated fatty acids contain one or more double bonds. The most common saturated fatty acids present in the cell are palmitic acid (C16) and stearic acid (C18). Although these two fatty acids are generally called by their common names, shorter fatty acids are often called by the Latin word for the number of carbons, such as octanoic acid (8 carbons) and decanoic acid (10 carbons).

The melting point of a fatty acid increases with chain length and decreases with the degree of unsaturation. Thus, fatty acids with many double bonds, such as those in vegetable oils, are liquid at room temperature; and saturated fatty acids, such as those in butterfat, are solids. Lipids with lower melting points are more fluid at body temperature and contribute to the fluidity of our cellular membranes.

Monounsaturated fatty acids contain one double bond, and polyunsaturated fatty acids contain two or more double bonds (see Fig. 5.17). The position of a double bond is designated by the number of the carbon in the double bond that is closest to the carboxyl group. For example, oleic acid, which contains 18 carbons and a double bond between positions 9 and 10, is designated 18:1, Δ^9. The number 18 denotes the number of carbon atoms, 1 (one) denotes the number of double bonds, and Δ^9 denotes the position of the double bond between the 9th and 10th carbon atoms.

Oxidized Sugars

β-D-glucuronate

D-gluconate

Reduced Sugars

D-sorbitol

Deoxyribose

FIG. 5.15. Oxidized and reduced sugars. The affected group is shown in the *colored box*. Gluconic acid (D-gluconate) is formed by oxidation of the glucose aldehyde carbon. Glucuronic acid is formed by oxidation of the glucose terminal —OH group. Sorbitol, a sugar alcohol, is formed by reduction of the glucose aldehyde group. Deoxyribose is formed by reduction of ribose.

 Palmitoleic acid, oleic acid, and arachidonic acid are the most common unsaturated fatty acids in the cell. Palmitoleic acid is a 16:1, Δ^9 fatty acid. How would you name it as an ω fatty acid?

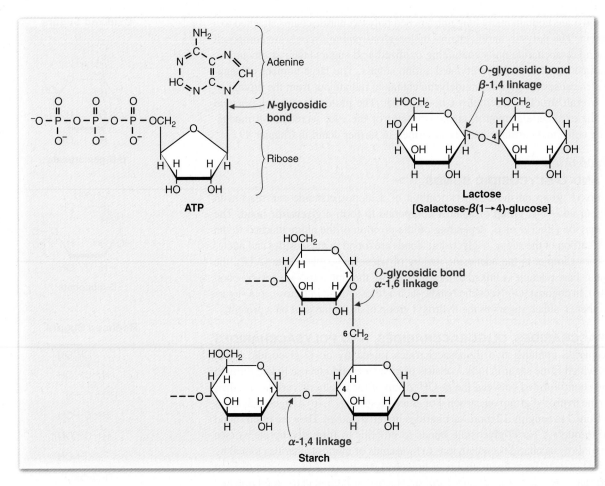

FIG. 5.16. *N-* and *O*-glycosidic bonds. Adenosine triphosphate (ATP) contains a β, *N*-glycosidic bond. Lactose contains an *O*-glycosidic β(1→4) bond. Starch contains α-1,4 and α-1,6 *O*-glycosidic bonds. The glycosidic bonds are shown in *red*.

 Palmitoleic acid is an ω7 fatty acid. It has one double bond between the 9th and 10th carbons. It has 16 carbons, like palmitic acid, so the double bond must be at the 7th carbon from the ω end.

 Trans-fatty acids (partially hydrogenated fat) were used by restaurants as an oil that had a longer shelf life than polyunsaturated fatty acids. Nevertheless, the presence of trans fat in food has been linked to an increased risk of heart disease. Many cities have now banned the use of *trans*-fatty acids in restaurant cooking.

Oleic acid can also be designated 18:1(9), without the Δ. Fatty acids are also classified by the distance of the double bond closest to the ω end (the methyl group at the end farthest from the carboxyl group). Thus, oleic acid is an ω9 fatty acid, and linolenic acid is an ω3 fatty acid. *Arachidonic acid*, a polyunsaturated fatty acid with 20 carbons and 4 double bonds, is an ω6 fatty acid that is completely described as 20:4, $\Delta^{5,8,11,14}$. The eicosanoids are a group of hormonelike compounds produced by many cells in the body. They are derived from polyunsaturated fatty acids such as arachidonic acid that contain 20 carbons (eicosa) and have 3, 4, or 5 double bonds. The prostaglandins, thromboxanes, and leukotrienes belong to this group of compounds.

The double bonds in most naturally occurring fatty acids are in the *cis* configuration (Fig. 5.17B). The designation *cis* means that the hydrogens are on the same side of the double bond and the acyl chains are on the other side. In *trans*-fatty acids, the acyl chains are on opposite sides of the double bond. Margarine and the fat used in preparing French fries are probably the major sources of *trans*-fatty acids found in humans. *Trans*-fatty acids are produced by the chemical hydrogenation of polyunsaturated fatty acids in vegetable oils and are not a natural food product.

B. Acylglycerols

An **acyl**glycerol comprises glycerol with one or more fatty acids (the **acyl** group) attached through ester linkages (Fig. 5.18). Monoacylglycerols, diacylglycerols, and triacylglycerols contain one, two, or three fatty acids esterified to glycerol, respectively. Tri**acyl**glycer**ol**s rarely contain the same fatty acid at all three positions and

FIG. 5.17. **A.** Saturated fatty acids and unsaturated fatty acids. In stearic acid, the saturated fatty acid at the top of the figure, all the atoms are shown. A more common way of depicting the same structure is shown below. The carbons are either numbered starting with the carboxyl group or given Greek letters starting with the carbon next to the carboxyl group. The methyl (or ω) carbon at the end of the chain is always called the ω-carbon, regardless of the chain length. The symbol 18:0 refers to the number of carbon atoms (18) and the number of double bonds (0). In the unsaturated fatty acids shown, not all of the carbons are numbered, but note that the double bonds are *cis* and spaced at three-carbon intervals. Both ω3 and ω6 fatty acids are required in the diet. **B.** *Cis* and *trans* double bonds in fatty acid side chains. Note that the *cis* double bond causes the chain to bend.

are therefore called *mixed triacylglycerols*. Unsaturated fatty acids, when present, are most often esterified to carbon 2. In the three-dimensional configuration of glycerol, carbons 1 and 3 are not identical, and enzymes are specific for one or the other carbon.

C. Phosphoacylglycerols

Phosphoacylglycerols contain fatty acids esterified to positions 1 and 2 of glycerol and a phosphate (alone or with a substituent) attached to carbon 3. If only a phosphate group is attached to carbon 3, the compound is **phospha**tidic acid (Fig. 5.19). Phosphatidic acid is a precursor for the synthesis of the other phosphoacylglycerols.

Phosphatidylchol**ine** is one of the major phosphoacylglycerols found in membranes (see Fig. 5.19). The am**ine** is positively charged at neutral pH, and the phosphate is negatively charged. Thus, the molecule is amphipathic; it contains large polar and nonpolar regions. Phosphatidylcholine is also called *lecithin*. Removal of a fatty acyl group from a phosphoacylglycerol leads to a lyso-lipid; for example, removing the fatty acyl group from lecithin forms lysolecithin.

Triacyl-*sn*-glycerol

FIG. 5.18. A triacylglycerol. Note that carbons 1 and 3 of the glycerol moiety are not identical. The broad end of each arrowhead is closer to the reader than the narrow, pointed end.

Phosphatidylcholine   **Phosphatidic acid**

FIG. 5.19.   Phosphoacylglycerols. Phospholipids found in membranes, such as phosphatidylcholine, have a polar group attached to the phosphate.

FIG. 5.20. Sphingolipids, derivatives of ceramide. The structure of ceramide is shown at the bottom of the figure. The portion of ceramide shown in *red* is sphingosine. The —NH and —OH were contributed by serine. Different groups are added to the hydroxyl group of ceramide to form sphingomyelin, galactocerebrosides, and gangliosides. *NANA*, *N*-acetylneuraminic acid, also called *sialic acid*; *Glc*, glucose; *Gal*, galactose; *GalNAc*, *N*-acetylgalactosamine.

D. Sphingolipids

Sphingolipids do not have a glycerol backbone; they are formed from sphingosine (Fig. 5.20). Sphing**osine** is derived from ser**ine** and a specific fatty acid, palmitate. Cer**amides** are **amides** formed from sphingosine by attaching a fatty acid to the amino group. Various sphingolipids are then formed by attaching different groups to the hydroxyl group on ceramide. As reflected in the names for cerebr**osides** and gangli**osides**, these sphingolipids contain sugars attached to the hydroxyl group of ceramide through glycosidic bonds. They are glycolipids (more specifically, glyco-sphingolipids). *Sphingomyelin*, which contains a phosphorylcholine group attached to ceramide, is a component of cell membranes and the myelin sheath around neurons.

E. Steroids

Steroids contain a four-ring structure called the *steroid nucleus* (Fig. 5.21). *Cholesterol* is the steroid precursor in human cells from which all of the steroid hormones are synthesized by modifications to the ring or C-20 side chain. Although cholesterol is not very water-soluble, it is converted to amphipathic water-soluble bile salts such as cholic acid. Bile salts line the surfaces of lipid droplets called *micelles* in the lumen of the intestine, where they keep the droplets emulsified in the aqueous environment.

Cholesterol is one of the compounds synthesized in the human from branched five-carbon units with one double bond called an *isoprenyl unit* (see Fig. 5.1A). Isoprenyl units are combined in long chains to form other structures, such as the side chains of coenzyme Q in humans and vitamin A in plants. Isoprene units form polymers to generate gerenyl groups (10 carbons) and farnesyl groups (15 carbons) (see Chapter 34). The gerenyl and farnesyl groups, due to their highly hydrophobic nature, are often covalently attached to proteins to allow the proteins to associate with cellular membranes.

IV. NITROGEN-CONTAINING COMPOUNDS

Nitrogen, as described in Section I.B.2, is an electronegative atom with two unshared electrons in its outer valence shell. At neutral pH, the nitrogen in amino groups is usually bonded to four other atoms and carries a positive charge. However, the presence of a nitrogen atom in an organic compound will increase its solubility in water, whether the nitrogen is charged or uncharged.

A. Amino Acids

Amino acids are compounds that contain an amino group and a carboxylic acid group. In proteins, the amino acids are always L-α-amino acids (the amino group is attached to the α carbon in the L-configuration) (Fig. 5.22). These same amino acids also serve as precursors of nitrogen-containing compounds in the body, such as phosphatidylcholine (see Fig. 5.19) and are the basis of most human amino acid metabolism. However, our metabolic reactions occasionally produce an amino acid that has a β- or γ-amino group, such as the neurotransmitter γ-aminobutyric acid (see Fig. 5.22). Nevertheless, only L-α-amino acids are incorporated into

FIG. 5.21. Cholesterol and its derivatives. The steroid nucleus is shown in the *green box.* The bile salt, cholic acid, and the steroid hormone 17β-estradiol are derived from cholesterol and contain the steroid ring structure.

proteins. Although D-amino acids are not usually incorporated into proteins in living organisms, they serve many other functions in bacteria, such as synthesis of cross-links in cell walls.

B. Nitrogen-Containing Ring Structures

1. PURINES, PYRIMIDINES, AND PYRIDINES

Nitrogen is also a component of ring structures referred to as heterocyclic rings or nitrogenous bases. The three most common types of nitrogen-containing rings in the body are pur**ines** (e.g., aden**ine**), pyrimid**ines** (e.g., thym**ine**), and pyrid**ines** (e.g., the vitamins nicoti**nic** acid, also called niacin, and pyridox**ine**, also called vitamin B$_6$) (Fig. 5.23). The suffix "-ine" denotes the presence of nitrogen (am**ine**) in the ring. The pyrimidine uracil is an exception to this general type of nomenclature. The utility of these nitrogen-containing ring structures lies in the ability of the nitrogen to form hydrogen bonds and to accept and donate electrons while still part of the ring. In contrast, the unsubstituted aromatic benzene ring, in which electrons are distributed equally among all six carbons (see Fig. 5.1), is nonpolar, hydrophobic, and relatively unreactive.

2. NUCLEOSIDES AND NUCLEOTIDES

Nitrogenous bases form nucleosides and nucleotides. A nucleoside consists of a nitrogenous base joined to a sugar, usually ribose or deoxyribose, through an *N*-glycosidic bond (see Fig. 5.16). If phosphate groups are attached to the sugar, the compound becomes a nucleotide. In the name of the nucleotide ATP, the addition of the ribose is indicated by the name change from adenine to aden**osine** (for the gly-**cosidic** bond). Monophosphate, diphosphate, or triphosphate is added to the name to indicate the presence of one, two, or three phosphate groups in the nucleotide. The structures of the nucleotides that serve as precursors of DNA and RNA are discussed in more detail in Section 3 of Chapter 12.

 What structural features account for the differences in the solubility of chole**sterol**, estra**diol**, and chol**ic** **acid** in the body? (See Fig. 5.21.)

Lotta Topaigne's gout is caused by depositions of monosodium urate crystals in the joint of her big toe. At a blood pH of 7.4, all of the uric acid has dissociated a proton to form urate, which is not very water-soluble and forms crystals of the Na$^+$ salt. In the more acidic urine generated by the kidney, the acidic form, uric acid, may precipitate to form kidney stones.

FIG. 5.22. The structure of the α-amino acid alanine (both the D- and L-configuration), and the γ-amino acid γ-aminobutyrate.

Purines

Adenine (A)

Guanine (G)

 Pyrimidine

Thymine (T)

 Pyridine

Nicotinic acid

FIG. 5.23. The nitrogenous bases.

 Cholesterol is composed almost entirely of —CH$_2$ groups and is therefore water-insoluble. Estradiol is likewise relatively water-insoluble. However, cholic acid contains a hydrophilic carboxyl group and three hydroxyl groups. As shown by the *dashed lines*, the three hydroxyl groups all lie on one side of the molecule, thus creating a hydrophilic surface.

 Compounds that cannot be oxidized as fuels in the human are often excreted in the urine. Chemical modifications often occur in the liver, kidney, or other tissues that inactivate or detoxify the chemicals, make them more water-soluble, or otherwise target such molecules for excretion. Uric acid, the basis of **Lotta Topaigne's** pain, is excreted in the urine (see Fig. 5.24). Judging from the similarity in structure, do you think it is derived from the degradation of purines, pyrimidines, or pyridines?

 Free radicals are not just esoteric reactants; they are the agents of cell death and destruction. They are involved in all chronic disease states (e.g., coronary artery disease, diabetes mellitus, arthritis, and emphysema) as well as acute injury (e.g., radiation, strokes, myocardial infarction, and spinal cord injury). Through free radical defense mechanisms in our cells, we can often restrict the damage attributed to the "normal" aging process.

3. TAUTOMERS

In many of the nitrogen-containing rings, the hydrogen can shift to produce a tautomer, a compound in which the hydrogen and double bonds have changed position (i.e., —N=C—OH → —NH—C=O) (Fig. 5.24). Tautomers are considered the same compound, and the structure may be represented either way. Generally, one tautomeric form is more reactive than the other. For example, in the two tautomeric forms of uric acid, a proton can dissociate from the enol form to produce urate.

V. FREE RADICALS

Radicals are compounds that have a single electron, usually in an outer orbital. Free radicals are radicals that exist independently in solution or in a lipid environment. Although many enzymes generate radicals as intermediates in reactions, these are not usually released into the cell to become free radicals.

Many of the compounds in the body are capable of being converted to free radicals by natural events that remove one of their electrons, or by radiation. Radiation, for example, dissociates water into the hydrogen atom and the hydroxyl radical:

$$H_2O \leftrightarrow H\bullet + OH\bullet$$

In contrast, water normally dissociates into a proton and the negatively charged hydroxyl ion. The hydroxyl radical forms organic radicals by taking one electron (as H•) from a compound such as an unsaturated membrane lipid, which then has a single unpaired electron and is a new radical.

Compounds that are radicals may be written with, or without, the radical showing. For example, nitrogen dioxide—a potent, reactive, toxic radical present in smog and cigarette smoke—may be designated in medical and lay literature as NO_2 rather than $NO_2\bullet$. *Superoxide*, a radical produced in the cell and that is the source of much destruction, is correctly written as the superoxide anion, O_2^-. However, to emphasize its free radical nature, the same compound is sometimes written as $O_2^-\bullet$. If a compound is designated as a radical in the medical literature, you can be certain that it is a reactive radical, and that its radical nature is important for the pathophysiology under discussion. Reactive oxygen and nitrogen-containing free radicals are discussed in more detail in Chapter 24.

Uric acid
(keto form)

pK 5.4

H$^+$

Uric acid
(enol form)

Urate

FIG. 5.24. Tautomers of uric acid. The tautomeric form affects the reactivity. The enol form dissociates a proton to form urate.

CLINICAL COMMENTS

Dianne Abietes. The severity of clinical signs and symptoms in patients with diabetic ketoacidosis (DKA), such as **Di Abietes**, is correlated directly with the concentration of ketone bodies in the blood. Direct quantitative methods for measuring acetoacetate and β-hydroxybutyrate are not routinely available. As a result, clinicians usually rely on semiquantitative reagent strips (Ketostix; Bayer Diagnostics, Mishawaka, Indiana) or tablets (Acetest; Bayer Diagnostics, Mishawaka, Indiana) to estimate the level of acetoacetate in the blood and the urine. The nitroprusside on the strips and in the tablets reacts with acetoacetate and to a lesser degree with acetone (both of which have ketone groups) but does not react with β-hydroxybutyrate (which does not have a ketone group). β-Hydroxybutyrate is the predominant ketone body present in the blood of a patient in DKA, and its concentration could decline at a disproportionately rapid rate compared with that of acetoacetate and acetone. Therefore, tests employing the nitroprusside reaction to monitor the success of therapy in such a patient may be misleading.

In contrast to the difficulty of ketone body measurements, diabetic patients can self-monitor blood glucose levels at home, thereby markedly decreasing the time and expense of the many blood glucose determinations they need. Blood obtained from a finger prick is placed on the pad of a plastic strip. The strip has been impregnated with an enzyme (usually the bacterial enzyme glucose oxidase) that specifically converts the glucose in the blood to an oxidized (gluconate) and a reduced compound (hydrogen peroxide, H_2O_2). The H_2O_2 reacts with a dye to produce a color. The intensity of the color, which is directly proportionate to the concentration of glucose in the patient's blood, is read on an instrument called a *blood glucose monitor*.

Lotta Topaigne. Ms. Topaigne has acute gouty arthritis (podagra) involving her right great toe. Polarized light microscopy of the fluid aspirated from the joint space showed crystals of monosodium urate phagocytosed by white blood cells. The presence of the relatively insoluble urate crystals within the joint space activates an inflammatory cascade leading to the classic components of joint inflammation (pain, redness, warmth, swelling, and limitation of joint motion).

Uric acid contains two rings and is similar to the purines adenine and guanine (adenine is shown in Fig. 5.23). In fact, it is the urinary excretion product formed from the oxidation of these two purine bases. It is not very soluble in water, particularly if the pH is near the pK_a of its acidic —OH group. If it is present in excess amounts, sodium urate tends to precipitate in joints, causing the severe pain of gout experienced by **Ms. Topaigne**.

The reducing sugar test. The reducing sugar test was used for detection of sugar in the urine long before specific enzymatic assays for glucose and galactose became available. In this test, the aldehyde group of sugar is oxidized as it donates electrons to copper; the copper becomes reduced and produces a blue color. In alkaline solution, keto sugars (e.g., fructose) also react in this test because they form tautomers that are aldehydes. Ring structures of sugars also react but only if the ring can open (i.e., it is not attached to another compound through a glycosidic bond). Until a specific test for fructose becomes available, a congenital disease resulting in the presence of fructose in the urine is indicated by a positive reducing sugar test and negative results in the specific enzymatic assays for glucose or galactose.

BIOCHEMICAL COMMENTS

Chlorinated Aromatic Hydrocarbon Environmental Toxins. As a result of human endeavor, toxic compounds containing chlorinated benzene rings have been widely distributed in the environment. The pesticide DDT (dichloro-diphenyl-trichloroethane) and the class of chemicals called *dioxins* provide examples of chlorinated aromatic hydrocarbons and structurally related compounds that are very hydrophobic and poorly biodegraded (Fig. 5.25). As a consequence of their persistence and lipophilicity, these chemicals are concentrated in the adipose tissue of fish, fish-eating birds, and carnivorous mammals, including humans.

DDT, a chlorinated biphenyl, was widely used in the United States as an herbicide between the 1940s and 1960s (see Fig. 5.25). Although it has not been used in this country since 1972, the chlorinated benzene rings are resistant to biodegradation, and US soil and water are still contaminated with small amounts. DDT is still used in other parts of the world. Because this highly lipophilic molecule is stored in the fat of animals, organisms accumulate progressively greater amounts of DDT at each successive stage of the food chain. Fish-eating birds, one of the organisms at the top of the food chain, have declined in population because of the effect of DDT on the thickness of their eggshells. DDT is not nearly as toxic in the human, although long-term exposure or exposure to high doses may cause reversible neurologic symptoms, hepatotoxic effects, or cancer.

DDT

Chlorodibenzo-*p*-dioxin

FIG. 5.25. Environmental toxins. Dichloro-diphenyl-trichloroethane (DDT) is a member of a class of aromatic hydrocarbons that contains two chlorinated benzene (phenyl) rings joined by a chlorinated ethane molecule. Chlorodibenzo-*p*-dioxins (CDDs) are a related class of more than 75 chlorinated hydrocarbons that all contain a dibenzo-*p*-dioxin (DD) molecule comprising two benzene rings joined via two oxygen bridges at adjacent carbons on each of the benzene rings. The compound 2,3,7,8-tetrachlorodibenzo-*p*-dioxin, shown previously, is one of the most toxic and the most extensively studied. Chlorinated dibenzofurans (CDFs) are structurally and toxicologically related.

 The accumulation of DDT in adipose tissue may be protective in the human because it decreases the amount of DDT available to pass through nonpolar lipid membranes to reach neurons in the brain or pass through placental membranes to reach the fetus. Eventually, we convert DDT to more polar metabolites that are excreted in the urine. However, some may pass with lipid into the breast milk of nursing mothers.

 Most of what is known about the toxicity of dioxins in the human comes from individuals exposed incidentally or chronically to higher levels (e.g., industrial accidents or presence in areas sprayed with Agent Orange or other herbicides contaminated with dioxins). The lowest-dose effects are probably associated with thymic atrophy and decreased immune response, chloracne and related skin lesions, and neoplasia (cancer). Dioxins can cross into the placenta to cause developmental and reproductive effects, decreased prenatal growth, and prenatal mortality.

Dioxins, specifically chlorodibenzo-*p*-dioxins (CDDs), constitute another class of environmental toxins that are currently of great concern (see Fig. 5.25). They have been measured at what is termed background levels in the blood, adipose tissue, and breast milk of all humans tested. CDDs are formed as a by-product during the production of other chlorinated compounds and herbicides, and from the chlorine bleaching process used by pulp and paper mills. They are released during the incineration of industrial, municipal, and domestic waste and during the combustion of fossil fuels and are found in cigarette smoke and the exhaust from engines, which burn gasoline and diesel fuels. They can also be formed from the combustion of organic matter during forest fires. They enter the atmosphere as particulate matter, are vaporized, and can spread large distances to enter soil and water.

As humans at the top of the food chain, we have acquired our background levels of dioxins principally through the consumption of food, primarily meat, dairy products, and fish. Once in the human body, dioxins are stored in human fat and adipose tissue and have an average half-life of approximately 5 to 15 years. They are unreactive, poorly degraded, and not readily converted to more water-soluble compounds that can be excreted in the urine. They are slowly excreted in the bile and feces, and together with lipids enter the breast milk of nursing mothers.

Key Concepts

- Carbohydrates, commonly known as sugars, can be classified by several criteria:
  - Type of carbonyl group (aldo or keto sugars)
  - Number of carbons (pentoses [five carbons], hexoses [six carbons])
  - Positions of hydroxyl groups on asymmetric carbon atoms (D- or L-configuration, stereoisomers, epimers)
  - Substituents (amino sugars)
  - Number of monosaccharides joined through glycosidic bonds (disaccharides, oligosaccharides, polysaccharides)
- Lipids are structurally diverse compounds that are not very soluble in water (i.e., they are hydrophobic).
  - The major lipids are fatty acids.
  - Triacylglycerol (triglycerides) consist of three fatty acids esterified to the carbohydrate glycerol.
  - Phosphoacylglycerols (phosphoglycerides or phospholipids) are similar to triacylglycerol but contain a phosphate in place of a fatty acid.
  - Sphingolipids are built on sphingosine.
  - Cholesterol is a component of membranes and a precursor for molecules that contain the steroid nucleus, such as bile salts and steroid hormones.
- Nitrogen is found in various compounds in addition to amino sugars.
  - Amino acids and heterocyclic rings contain nitrogens, which carry a positive charge at neutral pH.
  - Amino acids contain a carboxyl group, an amino group, and a side chain attached to a central carbon.
  - Proteins consist of a linear chain of amino acids.
  - Purines, pyrimidines, and pyridines have heterocyclic nitrogen-containing ring structures.
  - Nucleosides consist of a heterocyclic ring attached to a sugar.
  - A nucleoside plus phosphate is a nucleotide.
- Glycoproteins and proteoglycans have sugars attached to protein components.
- Diseases discussed in this chapter are summarized in Table 5.1.

Table 5.1   Diseases Discussed in Chapter 5

Disorder or Condition	*Genetic or Environmental*	*Comments*
Gout	Both	May be due to mutations in specific proteins, or dietary habits. Leads to a buildup of uric acid in the blood.
Type 1 diabetes	Both	Appropriate management of type 1 diabetes requires insulin injections and frequent monitoring of blood glucose levels throughout the day. Without such careful monitoring, ketone bodies may be produced inappropriately.

REVIEW QUESTIONS—CHAPTER 5

Select the single best answer for each of the following questions. Base your answers on your knowledge of nomenclature. You need not recognize any of the structures shown to answer the questions.

1. Which of the following is a universal characteristic of water-soluble organic compounds?

    A. They are composed of carbon and hydrogen atoms.
    B. They must contain a group that has a full negative charge.
    C. They must contain a group that has a full positive charge.
    D. They contain polar groups that can hydrogen bond with water.
    E. They contain aromatic groups.

2. A patient was admitted to the hospital emergency room in a coma. Laboratory tests found high levels of the compound shown below in her blood:

    $$CH_2OH—CH_2—CH_2—COO^-$$

    On the basis of its structure (and your knowledge of the nomenclature of functional groups), you identify the compound as which one of the following?

    A. Methanol (wood alcohol)
    B. Ethanol (alcohol)
    C. Ethylene glycol (antifreeze)
    D. β-Hydroxybutyrate (a ketone body)
    E. γ-Hydroxybutyrate (the "date rape" drug)

3. A patient was diagnosed with a deficiency of the lysosomal enzyme α-glycosidase. The name of the deficient enzyme suggests that it hydrolyzes a glycosidic bond, which is best described as a bond formed via which of the following?

    A. Through multiple hydrogen bonds between two sugar molecules
    B. Between the anomeric carbon of a sugar and an O—H (or N) of another molecule
    C. Between two anomeric carbons in polysaccharides
    D. Internal bond formation between the anomeric carbon of a monosaccharide and its own fifth carbon hydroxyl group
    E. Between the carbon containing the aldol or keto group and the α-carbon of the sugar

4. A patient was diagnosed with a hypertriglyceridemia. This condition is named for the high blood levels of lipids composed of which one of the following?

    A. Three fatty acyl groups attached to a glycerol backbone
    B. A glycerol lipid containing a phosphorylcholine group
    C. A sphingolipid containing three fatty acyl groups
    D. Three glycerol moieties attached to a fatty acid
    E. Three glyceraldehyde moieties attached to a fatty acid

5. A patient was diagnosed with one of the types of sphingolipidoses, which are congenital diseases involving the inability to degrade sphingolipids. All sphingolipids have in common which one of the following?

    A. A glycerol backbone
    B. Ceramide
    C. Phosphorylcholine
    D. N-acetylneuraminic acid (NANA)
    E. A steroid ring structure to which sphingosine is attached

6 Amino Acids in Proteins

 The *genetic code* is the sequence of three bases (nucleotides) in DNA that contains the information for the linear sequence of amino acids in a polypeptide chain (its primary structure). A *gene* is the portion of DNA that encodes a functional product, such as a polypeptide chain. *Mutations,* which are changes in the nucleotides in a gene, result in a change in the products of that gene that may be inherited. The inherited disease sickle cell anemia, for example, is caused by a mutation in the gene that encodes one of the subunits of hemoglobin. *Hemoglobin* is the protein present in red blood cells that reversibly binds O_2 and transports it to tissues. The adult hemoglobin (HbA) protein comprises four polypeptide chains, 2α and 2β. The α and β subunits differ in primary structure (i.e., they have different sequences of amino acids and are encoded by different genes). Sickle cell anemia is caused by a single nucleotide mutation in DNA that changes just one amino acid in the hemoglobin β-chains from a glutamic acid to a valine.

Proteins have many functions in the body. They serve as transporters of hydrophobic compounds in the blood, as cell adhesion molecules that attach cells to each other and to the extracellular matrix, as hormones that carry signals from one group of cells to another, as ion channels through lipid membranes, and as enzymes that increase the rate of biochemical reactions. The unique characteristics of a protein are dictated by its linear sequence of amino acids, termed its **primary structure**. The primary structure of a protein determines how it can fold and how it interacts with other molecules in the cell to perform its function. The primary structures of all of the diverse human proteins are synthesized from 20 amino acids arranged in a linear sequence determined by the genetic code.

General Properties of Amino Acids. *Each of the amino acids used for protein synthesis has the same general structure (Fig. 6.1A). It contains a **carboxylic acid** group, an **amino group** attached to the α-**carbon** in an **L-configuration**, a **hydrogen atom**, and a chemical group called a **side chain** that is different for each amino acid. In solution, at physiologic pH, the free amino acids exist as **zwitterions**, ions in which the amino group is positively charged, and the carboxylate group is negatively charged (see Fig. 6.1B). In proteins, these amino acids are joined into linear polymers called **polypeptide chains** through **peptide bonds** between the carboxylic acid group of one amino acid and the amino group of the next amino acid.*

Classification of Amino Acids According to Chemical Properties of the Side Chains. *The chemical properties of the side chain determine the types of bonds and interactions each amino acid in a polypeptide chain can make with other molecules. Thus, amino acids are often grouped by polarity of the side chain (**charged**, **nonpolar hydrophobic**, or **uncharged polar**) or by structural features (**aliphatic**, **cyclic**, or **aromatic**). The side chains of the **nonpolar hydrophobic** amino acids (alanine, valine, leucine, isoleucine, phenylalanine, and methionine) cluster together to exclude water in the **hydrophobic effect**. The **uncharged polar** amino acids (serine, threonine, tyrosine, asparagine, and glutamine) participate in **hydrogen bonding**.*

*Cysteine, which contains a sulfhydryl group, forms **disulfide bonds**. The negatively charged **acidic** amino acids (aspartate and glutamate) form **ionic** (**electrostatic**) **bonds** with positively charged molecules, such as the **basic** amino acids (lysine, arginine, and histidine). The charge on the amino acid at a particular pH is determined by the pK_a of each group that has a dissociable proton.*

Amino Acid Substitutions in the Primary Structure. *Mutations in the genetic code result in proteins with an altered **primary structure**. Mutations resulting in single amino acid substitutions can affect the functioning of a protein or can confer an advantage specific to a tissue or a set of circumstances. Many proteins, such as **hemoglobin**, exist in the human population as **polymorphisms** (genetically determined variations in primary structure).*

*Within the same individual, the primary structure of many proteins varies with the stage of development and is present in **fetal** and **adult isoforms**, such as fetal hemoglobin (HbF) and adult hemoglobin (HbA). The primary structure of some proteins, such as **creatine kinase** (CK), can also vary between* *tissues (**tissue-specific isozymes**) or between intracellular locations in the same tissue. **Electrophoretic separation** of tissue-specific isozymes has been useful in medicine as a means of identifying the tissue site of injury.*

*   **Modified Amino Acids.** In addition to the amino acids encoded by DNA that form the primary structure of proteins, many proteins contain specific amino acids that have been modified by **phosphorylation**, **oxidation**, **carboxylation**, or other reactions. When these reactions are enzyme-catalyzed, they are referred to as **posttranslational modifications**.*

THE WAITING ROOM

 Will Sichel is a 17-year-old boy who came to the hospital emergency room with severe pain in his lower back, abdomen, and legs, which began after a 2-day history of nausea and vomiting caused by gastroenteritis. He was diagnosed as having sickle cell disease at the age of 3 years and had been admitted to the hospital on numerous occasions for similar vaso-occlusive sickle cell crises.

On admission, the patient's hemoglobin level in peripheral venous blood was 7.8 g/dL (reference range = 12 to 16 g/dL). The hematocrit or packed cell volume (the percentage of the total volume of blood made up of red blood cells) was 23.4% (reference range = 41% to 53%). His serum total bilirubin level (a pigment derived from hemoglobin degradation) was 2.3 mg/dL (reference range = 0.2 to 1.0 mg/dL). A radiograph of his abdomen showed radiopaque stones in his gallbladder. With chronic hemolysis (red blood cell destruction), the amount of heme degraded to bilirubin is increased. These stones are the result of the chronic excretion of excessive amounts of bilirubin from the liver into the bile, leading to bilirubinate crystal deposition in the gallbladder lumen.

 Cal Kulis is an 18-year-old boy who was brought to the hospital by his mother because of the sudden onset of severe pain in his left flank, radiating around his left side toward his pubic area. His urine was reddish-brown in color, and a urinalysis showed the presence of many red blood cells. When his urine was acidified with acetic acid, clusters of flat hexagonal transparent crystals of cystine were noted. A radiograph of his abdomen showed radiopaque calculi (stones) in both kidneys. There was no family history of kidney stone disease.

 Di Abietes, who has type 1 diabetes mellitus, was giving herself subcutaneous injections of insulin (regular/NPH beef insulin) several times daily after her disease was first diagnosed (see Chapters 4 and 5). Subsequently, her physician switched her to synthetic human insulin. At this visit, her physician changed her insulin therapy and wrote a prescription for Humalog mix 75/25 (Eli Lilly, Indianapolis, Indiana), a mixture of Humalog in protamine suspension and unbound Humalog insulin (25%).

Ann Jeina is a 54-year-old woman who is 68 in tall and weighs 198 lb. She has a history of high blood pressure and elevated serum cholesterol levels. After a heated argument with a neighbor, Mrs. Jeina experienced a "tight pressurelike band of pain" across her chest, associated with shortness of breath, sweating, and a sense of light-headedness.

After 5 hours of intermittent chest pain, she went to the hospital emergency department, where her electrocardiogram showed changes consistent with an acute infarction

A

Amino group   Carboxyl group

$$H_3N^+ - \overset{\displaystyle COO^-}{\underset{\displaystyle R}{\overset{|}{\underset{|}{C}}}} - H \quad \alpha\text{-Carbon}$$

Side chain

B

$$H_3\overset{+}{N} - \overset{\displaystyle COOH}{\underset{\displaystyle R}{\overset{|}{\underset{|}{C}}}} - H$$

pK ~ 2 ↕ H+

$$H_3\overset{+}{N} - \overset{\displaystyle COO^-}{\underset{\displaystyle R}{\overset{|}{\underset{|}{C}}}} - H$$

pK ~ 9–10 ↕ H+

$$H_2N - \overset{\displaystyle COO^-}{\underset{\displaystyle R}{\overset{|}{\underset{|}{C}}}} - H$$

FIG. 6.1. **A.** General structure of the amino acids found in proteins. **B.** Dissociation of the α-carboxyl and α-amino groups of amino acids. At physiologic pH (~7), a form in which both the α-carboxyl and α-amino groups are charged predominates. Some amino acids also have ionizable groups on their side chains.

 The term *calculus* is used to describe any abnormal concretion (concrete-like precipitate) of mineral salts. These almost always form within the cavity of a hollow organ, such as the kidney (kidney or renal stones) or the lumen of a duct (e.g., common bile duct stones).

 The term *angina* describes a crushing or compressive pain. The term *angina pectoris* is used when this pain is located in the center of the chest or pectoral region, often radiating to the neck or arms. The most common mechanism for the latter symptom is a decreased supply of oxygen to the heart muscle caused by atherosclerotic coronary artery disease, which results in obstruction of the vessels that supply arterial blood to cardiac muscle.

of the anterior wall of her heart. She was admitted to the cardiac care unit. Blood was sent to the laboratory for various tests, including the total creatine kinase (CK) level, cardiac troponin T (TnT), and the MB ("muscle–brain") fraction of CK in the blood.

I. GENERAL STRUCTURE OF THE AMINO ACIDS

Twenty different amino acids are commonly found in proteins. They are all α-amino acids, amino acids in which the amino group is attached to the α-carbon (the carbon atom next to the carboxylate group) (see Fig. 6.1A). The α-carbon has two additional substituents: a hydrogen atom and an additional chemical group called a *side chain* (–R). The side chain is different for each amino acid.

At a physiologic pH of 7.4, the amino group on these amino acids carries a positive charge and the carboxylic acid group is negatively charged (see Fig. 6.1B). The pK_a of the primary carboxylic acid groups for all of the amino acids is approximately 2 (1.8 to 2.4). At pH values much lower than the pK_a (higher hydrogen ion concentrations), all of the carboxylic acid groups are protonated. At the pK_a, 50% of the molecules are dissociated into carboxylate anions and protons, and at a pH of 7.4, more than 99% of the molecules are dissociated (see Chapter 4). The pK_a for all of the α-amino groups is approximately 9.5 (8.8 to 11.0), so that at the lower pH of 7.4, most of the amino groups are fully protonated and carry a positive charge. The form of an amino acid that has both a positive and a negative charge is called a *zwitterion*. Because these charged chemical groups can form hydrogen bonds with water molecules, all of these amino acids are water-soluble at physiologic pH.

In all of the amino acids except glycine, the α-carbon is an asymmetric carbon atom that has four different substituents and can exist in either the D- or L-configuration (Fig. 6.2). The amino acids in mammalian proteins are all L-amino acids represented with the amino group to the left if the carboxyl group is at the top of the structure. These same amino acids serve as precursors of nitrogen-containing compounds that are synthesized in the body, and thus human amino acid metabolism is also centered on L-amino acids. The amino acid glycine is neither D nor L because the α-carbon atom contains two hydrogen atoms.

Bilirubin is a degradation product of hemoglobin, and its levels are elevated in **Will Sichel**. Bilirubin can be present in serum either conjugated to glucuronic acid (which is determined by the direct measurement) or free (which is very hydrophobic, and is determined by the indirect measurement). Measurement of bilirubin in serum is dependent on the reaction of bilirubin with a diazotized sulfonic acid, which generates, after appropriate treatments, a blue azobilirubin. The intensity of the blue color can be determined spectrophotometrically at 600 nm. Total bilirubin is measured in the presence of caffeine-benzoate, which separates the hydrophobic nonconjugated bilirubin from its binding partners. A second measurement is done in the absence of caffeine-benzoate, which will only determine the conjugated, soluble forms of bilirubin (the direct measurement). Unconjugated bilirubin is then calculated by determining the difference in values obtained in the presence and absence of caffeine-benzoate (the indirect measurement). Recently, a transcutaneous device has been developed to determine bilirubin levels in newborns. The instrument is pressed against the infant's forehead, and light at various wavelengths is transmitted through the forehead, generating a reflective multiwavelength spectrum. Analysis of the spectrum allows the instrument to determine the levels of bilirubin, hemoglobin, and melanin in the infant's skin.

FIG. 6.2. L- and D-amino acids. The L-forms are the only ones found in human proteins. Bonds coming out of the paper are shown by *black arrows*; those going in, by *shaded arrows*. The α-amino groups and H atoms come toward the reader, and the α-carboxyl and side chains go away. The L- and D-forms are mirror images that cannot be superimposed by rotating the molecule. The reference for the L- and D-forms is the stereoisomers of glyceraldehyde (see Fig. 5.10A).

The chemical properties of the amino acids give each protein its unique characteristics. Proteins are composed of one or more linear polypeptide chains containing hundreds of amino acids. The sequence of amino acids, termed the *primary structure*, is determined by the genetic code for the protein. In the polypeptide chains, amino acids are joined through peptide bonds between the carboxylic acid of one amino acid and the amino group of the adjacent amino acid (Fig. 6.3, see also Fig. 1.5). Thus, the amino group, the α-carbon, and the carboxyl groups form the peptide backbone, and the side chains of the amino acids extend outward from this backbone. The side chains interact with the peptide backbone of other regions of the chain or with the side chains of other amino acids in the protein to form hydrophobic regions, electrostatic bonds, hydrogen bonds, or disulfide bonds. These interactions dictate the folding pattern of the molecule. The three-dimensional folding of the protein forms distinct regions called *binding sites* that are lined with amino acid side chains that interact specifically with another molecule termed a *ligand* (such as the heme in hemoglobin). Thus, the chemical properties of the side chains determine how the protein folds, how it binds specific ligands, and how it interacts with its environment (such as the aqueous medium of the cytoplasm).

FIG. 6.3. Peptide bonds. Amino acids in a polypeptide chain are joined through peptide bonds between the carboxyl group of one amino acid and the amino group of the next amino acid in the sequence.

II. CLASSIFICATION OF AMINO ACID SIDE CHAINS

In Figure 6.4, the 20 amino acids used for protein synthesis are grouped into different classifications according to the polarity and structural features of the side chains. These groupings can be helpful in describing common functional roles or metabolic pathways of the amino acids. However, some amino acid side chains fit into several different classifications and are therefore grouped differently in different textbooks. Two of the characteristics of the side chain that are useful for classification are its pK_a and its hydropathic index, shown in Table 6.1. The *hydropathic index* is a scale used to denote the hydrophobicity of the side chain; the more positive the hydropathic index, the greater is the tendency to cluster with other nonpolar molecules and exclude water in the hydrophobic effect. The more negative the hydropathic index of an amino acid, the more hydrophilic is its side chain.

The names of the different amino acids have been given three-letter and one-letter abbreviations (see Fig. 6.4). The three-letter abbreviations use the first two letters in the name plus the third letter of the name or the letter of a characteristic sound, such as "trp" for tryptophan. The one-letter abbreviations use the first letter of the name of the most frequent amino acid in proteins (such as an "A" for alanine). If the first letter has already been assigned, the letter of a characteristic sound is used (such as an "R" for arginine). Single-letter abbreviations are usually used to denote the amino acids in a polypeptide sequence.

A. Nonpolar, Aliphatic Amino Acids

Glycine is the simplest amino acid, and it really does not fit well into any classification because its side chain is just a hydrogen atom. Alanine and the branched-chain amino acids (valine, leucine, and isoleucine) have bulky, nonpolar, aliphatic side chains. The high degree of hydrophobicity of the branched-chain amino acid side chains is denoted by their high hydropathic index (see Table 6.1). Electrons are shared equally between the carbon and hydrogen atoms in these side chains, so that they cannot hydrogen bond with water. Within proteins, these amino acid side chains will cluster together to form hydrophobic cores. Their association is also promoted by van der Waals forces between the positively charged nucleus of one atom and the electron cloud of another. This force is effective over short distances when many atoms pack closely together.

The roles of proline and glycine in amino acid structure differ from those of the nonpolar amino acids. The amino acid proline contains a ring involving its α-carbon and its α-amino group, which are part of the peptide backbone. This rigid ring causes a kink in the peptide backbone that prevents it from forming its usual configuration. Because the side chain of glycine is so small compared with that of other amino acids,

The proteolytic digestive enzyme chymotrypsin cleaves the peptide bonds formed by the carboxyl groups of large, bulky uncharged amino acids. Which amino acids fall into this category?

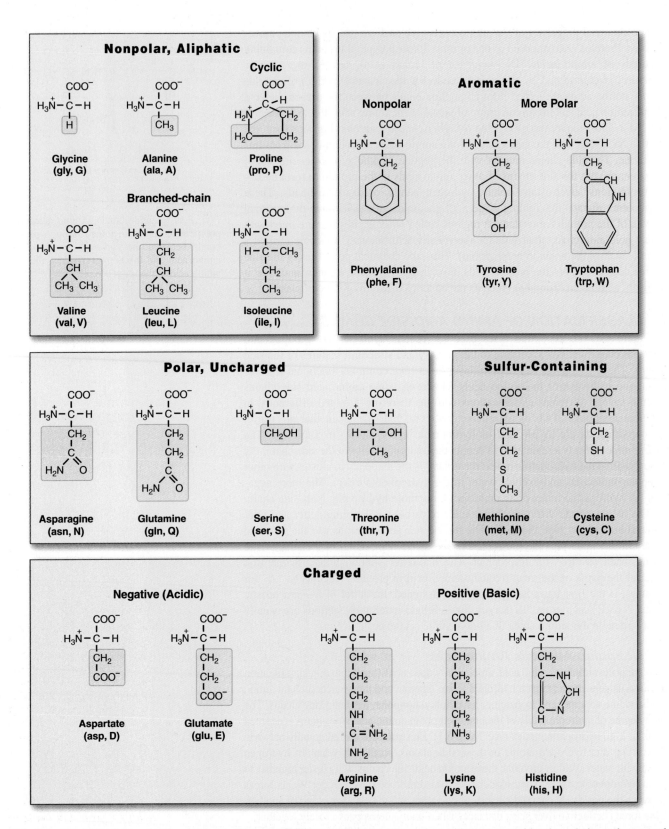

FIG. 6.4.   The side chains of the amino acids. The side chains are highlighted. The amino acids are grouped by the polarity and structural features of their side chains. These groupings are not absolute, however. Tyrosine and tryptophan, often listed with the nonpolar amino acids, are more polar than other aromatic amino acids because of their phenolic and indole rings, respectively. The single- and three-letter codes are also indicated for each amino acid.

Table 6.1   Properties of the Common Amino Acids

Amino Acid	pK_{a1}[a] (Carboxyl)	pK_{a2} (Amino)	pK_{aR} (R group)	Hydropathy Index[b]
Nonpolar aliphatic				
Glycine	2.4	9.8		−0.4
Proline	2.0	11.0		−1.6
Alanine	2.3	9.7		1.8
Leucine	2.4	9.6		3.8
Valine	2.3	9.6		4.2
Isoleucine	2.4	9.7		4.5
Aromatic				
Phenylalanine	1.8	9.1		2.8
Tyrosine	2.2	9.1	10.5	−1.3
Tryptophan	2.4	9.4		−0.9
Polar uncharged				
Threonine	2.1	9.6	13.6	−0.7
Serine	2.2	9.2	13.6	−0.8
Asparagine	2.0	8.8		−3.5
Glutamine	2.2	9.1		−3.5
Sulfur-containing				
Cysteine	2.0	10.3	8.4	2.5
Methionine	2.3	9.2		1.9
Charged negative				
Aspartate	1.9	9.6	3.9	−3.5
Glutamate	2.2	9.7	4.1	−3.5
Charged positive				
Histidine	1.8	9.3	6.0	−3.2
Lysine	2.2	9.0	10.5	−3.9
Arginine	2.2	9.0	12.5	−4.5
Average	2.2	9.5		

[a]When these amino acids reside in proteins, the pK_a for the side chains may vary to some extent from the value for the free amino acid, depending on the local environment of the amino acid in the three-dimensional structure of the protein.
[b]The hydropathy index is a measure of the hydrophobicity of the amino acid (the higher the number, the more hydrophobic).
Values based on Kyte J, Doolittle RF. A simple method for displaying the hydropathic character of a protein. *J Mol Biol.* 1982;157(1):105–132.

it causes the least amount of steric hindrance in a protein (i.e., it does not significantly impinge on the space occupied by other atoms or chemical groups). Therefore, glycine is often found in bends or in the tightly packed chains of fibrous proteins.

B. Aromatic Amino Acids

The aromatic amino acids have been grouped together because they all contain ring structures with similar properties, but their polarities differ a great deal. The aromatic ring is a six-membered carbon–hydrogen ring with three conjugated double bonds (the benzene ring or phenyl group). The substituents on this ring determine whether the amino acid side chain engages in polar or hydrophobic interactions. In the amino acid phenylalanine, the ring contains no substituents, and the electrons are shared equally between the carbons in the ring, resulting in a very nonpolar hydrophobic structure in which the rings can stack on each other (Fig. 6.5). In tyrosine, a hydroxyl group on the phenyl ring engages in hydrogen bonds, and the side chain is therefore more polar and more hydrophilic. The more complex ring structure in tryptophan is an indole ring with nitrogen that can engage in hydrogen bonds. Tryptophan is therefore also more polar than phenylalanine.

C. Aliphatic, Polar, Uncharged Amino Acids

Amino acids with side chains that contain an amide group (asparagine and glutamine) or a hydroxyl group (serine and threonine) can be classified as aliphatic,

Chymotrypsin's highest activity is toward peptide bonds formed by the carboxyl groups of aromatic amino acids (phenylalanine, tyrosine, tryptophan). The side chains of these amino acids are all large and uncharged. One of the chymotrypsin isozymes also exhibits activity toward leucine and methionine, which are similar in polarity.

A. Hydrophobic interaction

B. Hydrogen bonds

FIG. 6.5. Hydrophobic and hydrogen bonds. **A.** Strong hydrophobic interactions occur with the stacking of aromatic groups in phenylalanine side chains. **B.** Examples of hydrogen bonds in which a hydrogen atom is shared by a nitrogen in the peptide backbone and an oxygen atom in an amino acid side chain or between an oxygen in the peptide backbone and an oxygen in an amino acid side chain.

Will Sichel has sickle cell anemia caused by a point mutation in his DNA that changes the sixth amino acid in the β-globin chain of hemoglobin from glutamate to valine. What difference would you expect to find in the chemical bonds formed by these two amino acids?

Glutamate carries a negative charge on its side chain at physiologic pH and thus can engage in ionic bonds or hydrogen bonds with water or other side chains. Valine is a hydrophobic amino acid and therefore tends to interact with other hydrophobic side chains to exclude water.

FIG. 6.6. A disulfide bond. Covalent disulfide bonds may be formed between two molecules of cysteine or between two cysteine residues in a protein. The disulfide compound is called cystine. The hydrogens of the cysteine sulfhydryl groups are removed during oxidation.

 Cal Kulis passed a renal stone shortly after admission, which immediately relieved his pain. Its major component was identified as cystine. Normally, amino acids are filtered by glomerular capillaries into the tubular urine but are almost entirely reabsorbed from this fluid back into the blood via transport proteins in the proximal tubular cells. **Cal Kulis** has cystinuria, an inherited amino acid substitution in the transport protein that reabsorbs cystine, arginine, and lysine. Therefore, his urine contained high amounts of these amino acids. Cystine, which is less soluble than other amino acids, precipitates in the urine to form renal stones (calculi).

polar, uncharged amino acids. Asparagine and glutamine are amides of the amino acids aspartate and glutamate. The hydroxyl groups and the amide groups in the side chains allow these amino acids to form hydrogen bonds with water, with each other and the peptide backbone, or with other polar compounds in the binding sites of the proteins (see Fig. 6.5). As a consequence of their hydrophilicity, these amino acids are frequently found on the surface of water-soluble globular proteins. Cysteine, which is sometimes included in this class of amino acids, has been separated into the class of sulfur-containing amino acids.

D. Sulfur-Containing Amino Acids

Both cysteine and methionine contain sulfur. The side chain of cysteine contains a sulfhydryl group that has a pK_a of approximately 8.4 for dissociation of its hydrogen, so cysteine is predominantly undissociated and uncharged at the physiologic pH of 7.4. The free cysteine molecule in solution can form a covalent disulfide bond with another cysteine molecule through spontaneous (nonenzymatic) oxidation of their sulfhydryl groups. The resultant amino acid, cystine, is present in blood and tissues and is not very water-soluble. In proteins, the formation of a cystine disulfide bond between two appropriately positioned cysteine sulfhydryl groups often plays an important role in holding two polypeptide chains or two different regions of a chain together (Fig. 6.6). *Methionine*, although it contains a sulfur group, is a nonpolar amino acid with a large bulky side chain that is hydrophobic. It does not contain a sulfhydryl group and cannot form disulfide bonds. Its important and central role in metabolism is related to its ability, when appropriately activated, to transfer the methyl group attached to the sulfur atom to other compounds.

E. The Acidic and Basic Amino Acids

The amino acids aspartate and glutamate have carboxylic acid groups that carry a negative charge at physiologic pH (see Fig. 6.4). The basic amino acids histidine, lysine, and arginine have side chains containing nitrogen that can be protonated and positively charged at physiologic and lower pH values. Histidine has a nitrogen-containing imidazole ring for a side chain; lysine has a primary amino group on the ε-carbon (from the sequence α, β, γ, δ, ε); and arginine has a guanidinium group.

The positive charge on the basic amino acids enables them to form ionic bonds (electrostatic bonds) with negatively charged groups, such as the side chains of acidic amino acids or the phosphate groups of coenzymes (Fig. 6.7). In addition, lysine and arginine side chains often form ionic bonds with negatively charged compounds bound to the protein binding sites, such as the phosphate groups in adenosine triphosphate (ATP). The acidic and basic amino acid side chains also participate in hydrogen bonding and the formation of salt bridges (such as the binding of an inorganic ion such as Na^+ between two partially or fully negatively charged groups).

The charge on these amino acids at physiologic pH is a function of their pK_a for dissociation of protons from the α-carboxylic acid groups, the α-amino groups, and the side chains. The titration curve of histidine illustrates the changes in amino acid structure that occurs as the pH of the solution is changed from <1 to 14 by the addition of hydroxide ions (Fig. 6.8). At low pH, all groups carry protons; amino groups have a positive charge, and carboxylic acid groups have zero charge. As the pH is increased by the addition of alkali (OH^-), the proton dissociates from the carboxylic acid group, and its charge changes from zero to negative one with a pK_a of approximately 2, the pH at which 50% of the protons have dissociated.

The histidine side chain is an imidazole ring with a pK_a of approximately 6 that changes from a predominantly protonated positively charged ring to an uncharged ring at this pH. The amino group on the α-carbon titrates at a much higher pH (between 9 and 10), and the charge changes from positive one to zero as the pH rises. The pH at which the net charge on the molecules in solution is zero is called the *isoelectric point* (pI). At this pH, the molecules will not migrate in an electric field toward either a positive pole (cathode) or a negative pole (anode), because the number of negative charges on each molecule is equal to the number of positive charges.

Amino acid side chains change from uncharged to negatively charged, or positively charged to uncharged as they release protons (Fig. 6.9). The acidic amino acids lose a proton from their carboxylic acid side chains at a pH of roughly 4 and are thus negatively charged at pH 7.4. Cysteine and tyrosine lose protons at their pK_a (~8.4 and 10.5, respectively), so their side chains are uncharged at physiologic pH. Histidine, lysine, and arginine side chains change from positively charged to neutral at their pK_a. The side chains of the two basic amino acids, arginine and lysine, have pK_a values >10, so the positively charged form always predominates at physiologic pH. The side chain of histidine (pK_a ~ 6.0) dissociates near physiologic pH, so only a portion of the histidine side chains carry a positive charge (see Fig. 6.8).

In proteins, only the amino acid side chains, the amino group at the amino terminal, and the carboxyl group at the carboxyl terminal have dissociable protons. All of the other carboxylic acid and amino groups on the α-carbons are joined in peptide bonds that have no dissociable protons. The amino acid side chains might have very different pK_a values than those of the free amino acids if they are involved in hydrogen or ionic bonds with other amino acid side chains. The pK_a of the imidazole group of histidine, for example, is often shifted to a higher value between 6 and 7 so that it adds and releases a proton in the physiologic pH range.

Electrophoresis is a technique used to separate proteins on the basis of charge that has been extremely useful in medicine to identify proteins with different amino acid compositions. The net charge on a protein at a certain pH is a summation of all of the positive and negative charges on all of the ionizable amino acid side chains plus the N-terminal amino and C-terminal carboxyl groups. Theoretically, the net

FIG. 6.7. Electrostatic interaction between the positively charged side chain of lysine and the negatively charged side chain of aspartate.

Q: Is the substitution of a glutamate for a valine in sickle cell hemoglobin a conservative replacement? What about the substitution of an aspartate for a glutamate?

FIG. 6.8. Titration curve of histidine. The ionic species that predominates in each region is shown below the graph. *pI* is the isoelectric point (the pH at which there is no net charge on the molecule).

FIG. 6.9. Dissociation of the side chains of the amino acids. As the pH increases, the charge on the side chain goes from 0 to − or from + to 0. The pK_a is the pH at which half the molecules of an amino acid in solution have side chains that are charged. Half are uncharged.

 A: The substitution of a glutamate for a valine is a nonconservative replacement because a negatively charged amino acid is substituted for a hydrophobic branched-chain aliphatic amino acid. However, the substitution of an aspartate for a glutamate is a conservative replacement because the two amino acids have the same polarity and nearly the same size.

charge of a protein at any pH could be determined from its amino acid composition by calculating the concentration of positively and negatively charged groups from the Henderson-Hasselbalch equation (see Chapter 4). However, hydrogen bonds and ionic bonds between amino acid side chains in the protein, which can alter pK_a values, make this calculation unrealistic.

III. VARIATIONS IN PRIMARY STRUCTURE

The primary structure of a protein is its linear sequence of amino acids. Although almost every amino acid in the primary structure of a protein contributes to its conformation (three-dimensional structure), the primary structure of a protein can vary to some degree among species. Even within the human species, the amino acid sequence of a normal functional protein can vary somewhat among individuals, tissues of the same individual, and the stage of development. These variations in the primary structure of a functional protein are tolerated if they are confined to noncritical regions (called variant regions), if they are conservative substitutions (replace one amino acid with one of similar structure), or if they confer an advantage. If many different amino acid residues are tolerated at a position, the region is called *hypervariable*. In contrast, the regions that form binding sites or are critical for forming a functional three-dimensional structure are usually invariant regions that have exactly the same amino acid sequence from individual to individual, tissue to tissue, or species to species.

A. Polymorphism in Protein Structure

Within the human population, the primary structure of a protein may vary slightly among individuals. The variations generally arise from mutations in DNA that are passed to the next generation. The mutations can result from the substitution of one base for another in the DNA sequence of nucleotides (a point mutation), from deletion or insertions of bases into DNA, or from larger changes (see Chapter 14). For many alleles, the variation has a distinct phenotypic consequence that contributes to our individual characteristics, produces an obvious dysfunction (a congenital or inherited disease), or increases susceptibility to certain diseases. A defective protein may differ from the most common allele by as little as a single amino acid that is a nonconservative substitution (replacement of one amino acid with another of a different polarity or very different size) in an invariant region. Such mutations might affect the ability of the protein to carry out its function, catalyze a particular reaction, reach the appropriate site in a cell, or be degraded. For other proteins, the variations appear to have no significance.

Variants of an allele that occur with a significant frequency in the population are referred to as *polymorphisms*. Thus far in studies of the human genome almost one-third of the genetic loci appear to be polymorphic. When a particular variation of an allele, or polymorphism, increases in the general population to a frequency of >1%, it is considered stable. The sickle cell allele is an example of a point mutation that is stable in the human population. Its persistence is probably attributable to selective pressure for the heterozygous mutant phenotype, which confers some protection against malaria.

B. Protein Families and Superfamilies

A homologous family of proteins is composed of proteins related to the same ancestral protein. Groups of proteins with similar, but not identical, structure and function that have evolved from the same gene after the gene was duplicated are called *paralogs* and are considered members of the same protein family. Once a gene has duplicated, one gene can continue to perform the original function, and the second copy can mutate into a protein with another function or another type of regulation. This process is called *divergent evolution*. Very large families of homologous proteins are called a *superfamily*, which is subdivided by name into families of proteins with the most similarity in structure.

The paralogs of a protein family are considered different proteins and have different names because they have different functions. They are all present in the same individual. Myoglobin and the different chains of hemoglobin, for example, are paralogs and members of the same globin family that have similar, but not identical, structures and functions. *Myoglobin*, an intracellular heme

 For the most part, human chromosomes occur as homologous pairs, with each member of a pair containing the same genetic information. One member of the pair is inherited from the mother and one from the father. Genes are arranged linearly along each chromosome. A genetic locus is a specific position or location on a chromosome. Alleles are alternative versions of a gene at a given locus. For each locus (site), we have two alleles of each gene, one from our mother and one from our father. If both alleles of a gene are identical, the individual is homozygous for this gene; if the alleles are different, he or she is heterozygous for this gene. **Will Sichel** has two identical alleles for the sickle variant of the β-globin gene that results in substitution of a valine for a glutamate residue at the sixth position of the β-globin chain. He is therefore homozygous and has sickle cell anemia. Individuals with one normal gene and one sickle cell allele are heterozygous. They are carriers of the disease and have sickle cell trait.

 Will Sichel's hemoglobin, sickle hemoglobin (HbS), comprises two normal α-chains and two β-globin chains with the sickle cell variant $(\alpha_2\beta_2{}^S)$. The change in amino acid composition from a glutamate to a valine in the β-chain allows HbS to be separated from normal adult hemoglobin (HbA, or $\alpha_2\beta_2{}^A$) by electrophoresis. In electrophoresis, an aliquot of blood or other solution containing proteins is applied to a support, such as paper or a gel. When an electrical field is applied, proteins migrate a distance toward the anode (negative pole) or cathode (positive pole) that reflects small differences in their net charge. Electrophoresis of **Will Sichel's** blood shows that he is homozygous for the sickle cell variant, HbS, and has increased amounts of fetal hemoglobin (HbF). Individuals with sickle cell trait are heterozygous and have both HbA and HbS, plus small amounts of HbF $(\alpha_2\gamma_2)$.

In heterozygous individuals with sickle cell trait, the sickle cell allele provides some protection against malaria. Malaria is caused by the parasite *Plasmodium falciparum*, which spends part of its life cycle in red blood cells. The infected red blood cells of individuals with normal hemoglobin (HbA) develop protrusions that attach to the lining of capillaries. This attachment occludes the vessels and prevents oxygen from reaching cells in the affected region, resulting in cell death. In heterozygous individuals, HbS in infected cells aggregates into long fibers that cause the cell to become distorted. These distorted cells containing the malarial parasite are preferentially recognized by the spleen and are rapidly destroyed, thus ending the life of the parasite.

In **Will Sichel** and other homozygous individuals with sickle cell anemia, the red blood cells sickle more frequently, especially under conditions of low oxygen tension (see Chapter 7). The result is a vaso-occlusive crisis in which the sickled cells clog capillaries and prevent oxygen from reaching cells (ischemia), thereby causing pain. The enhanced destruction of the sickled cells by the spleen results in anemia. Consequently, the sickle cell allele is of little advantage to homozygous individuals.

Because heterozygous individuals occur more frequently in a population than homozygous individuals, a selective advantage in a heterozygous state can outweigh a disadvantage in a homozygous state, causing the mutation to become a stable polymorphism in a population. As a consequence, the frequency of sickle cell anemia in parts of equatorial Africa in which malaria was endemic in the past is 1 in 25 births. Migration from Africa accounts for the high frequency of sickle cell anemia among blacks in the United States, which is approximately 1/400 at birth.

	1	5	10	15
Myoglobin	gly-----leu-ser-asp-gly-glu-trp-gln-leu-val-leu-asn-val-trp-gly-lys-val-
β-chain hemoglobin	val-his-leu-thr-pro-glu-glu-lys-ser-ala-val-thr-ala-leu-trp-gly-lys-val-
α-chain hemoglobin	val-----leu-ser-pro-ala-asp-lys-thr-asn-val-lys-ala-ala-trp-gly-lys-val-
ζ-chain hemoglobin	met-ser-leu-thr-lys-thr-glu-arg-thr-ile-ile-val-ser-met-trp-ala-lys-ile-
γ-chain hemoglobin	met-gly-his-phe-thr-glu-glu-asp-lys-ala-thr-ile-thr-ser-leu-trp-gly-lys-val-

FIG. 6.10. The primary structures of a region in human globin proteins. To compare the primary structure of two homologous polypeptide chains, the sequences are written left to right from the amino terminal to the carboxyl terminal. The sequences are aligned with computer programs that maximize the identity of amino acids and minimize the differences caused by segments that are present in one protein and not in the other. Gaps in the structure, indicated with *dashes*, are introduced to maximize the alignment between proteins in structure comparisons. They are assumed to coincide with mutations that caused a deletion. Regions of sequence similarity (identity and conservative substitution) are indicated by *colored bars*. Within these regions are smaller regions of invariant residues that are exactly the same from protein to protein. Myoglobin is a single polypeptide chain. The α- and β-chains are part of adult hemoglobin (HbA) ($\alpha_2\beta_2$). The ζ-chain is part of embryonic hemoglobin ($\zeta_2\varepsilon_2$). The γ-chain is part of fetal hemoglobin (HbF), $\alpha_2\gamma_2$.

protein present in most cells that stores and transports O_2 to mitochondria, is a single polypeptide chain containing one heme oxygen-binding site. In contrast, hemoglobin is composed of four globin chains, each with a heme oxygen-binding site that is present in red blood cells; hemoglobin transports O_2 from the lungs to tissues. The gene for myoglobin is assumed to have evolved from gene duplication of the α-chain for hemoglobin, which evolved from duplication of the β-chain. Figure 6.10 compares a region of the structure of myoglobin and the α- and β-chains of hemoglobin. Among these three proteins, only 15 invariant (identical) residues are present, but many of the other amino acid residues are conservative substitutions.

C. Tissue and Developmental Variations in Protein Structure

Within the same individual, different isoforms or isozymes of a protein may be synthesized during different stages of fetal and embryonic development, may be present in different tissues, or may reside in different intracellular locations. Isoforms of a protein all have the same function. If they are isozymes (isoforms of enzymes), they catalyze the same reactions. However, isoforms have somewhat different properties and amino acid structure.

1. DEVELOPMENTAL VARIATION

Hemoglobin isoforms provide an example of variation during development. Hemoglobin is expressed as the fetal isozyme (HbF) during the last trimester of pregnancy until after birth, when it is replaced with adult hemoglobin (HbA). HbF is composed of two hemoglobin α and two hemoglobin γ polypeptide chains, in contrast to HbA, which has two α- and two β-chains. During the embryonic stages of development, chains with a different amino acid composition, the embryonic ε- and ζ-chains, are produced (see Fig. 6.10). These differences are believed to arise evolutionarily from mutation of a duplicated α gene to produce ζ, and mutation of a duplicate α gene to produce ε. The fetal and embryonic forms of hemoglobin have a much higher affinity for O_2 than the adult forms and thus confer an advantage at the low O_2 tensions to which the fetus is exposed. At different stages of development, the globin genes specific for that stage are expressed and translated. (This is discussed in more detail in Section VI, Chapter 44.)

2. TISSUE-SPECIFIC ISOFORMS

Proteins that differ somewhat in primary structure and properties from tissue to tissue, but that retain essentially the same function, are called *tissue-specific isoforms* or *isozymes*. The enzyme creatine kinase (CK) is an example of a protein that exists as tissue-specific isozymes, each composed of two subunits with 60% to 72% sequence homology. The M form is produced in skeletal muscle, and the B polypeptide chains are produced in the brain. Because the protein comprises two subunits, skeletal muscle, therefore, produces a CK-MM, and the brain produces a BB form. The heart produces both types of chains and therefore forms a heterodimer, MB, as well as the homodimers. Two more CK isozymes are found in mitochondria, a heart mitochondrial CK and the "universal" isoform found in other tissues. (In general, most proteins that are present in both the mitochondria and cytosol will be present as different isoforms.) The advantage conferred on different tissues by having their own isoform of CK is unknown. However, tissue-specific isozymes such as CK-MB are useful in diagnosing sites of tissue injury and cell death.

The structure of proteins involved in the response to hormones has been studied in greater depth than many other types of proteins, and most of these proteins are present as several tissue-specific isoforms that help different tissues respond differently to the same hormone. One of these proteins present in cell membranes is *adenylyl cyclase*, an enzyme that catalyzes the synthesis of intracellular 3′,5′-cyclic adenosine monophosphate (cAMP) (Fig. 6.11). In human tissues, at least nine different isoforms of adenylyl cyclase are coded by different genes in different tissues. Although they have an overall sequence homology of 50%, the two intracellular regions involved in the synthesis of cAMP are an invariant consensus sequence with a 93% identity. The different isoforms help cells respond differently to the same hormone.

D. Species Variations in the Primary Structure of Insulin

Species variations in primary structure are also important in medicine, as illustrated by the comparison of human, beef, and pork insulin. Insulin is one of the hormones that is highly conserved between species, with very few amino acid substitutions and none in the regions that affect activity. *Insulin* is a polypeptide hormone of 51 amino acids that is composed of two polypeptide chains (Fig. 6.12). It is synthesized as a single polypeptide chain but is cleaved in three places before secretion to

 A myocardial infarction (heart attack) is caused by an atheromatous obstruction or a severe spasm in a coronary artery that prevents the flow of blood to an area of heart muscle. Thus, heart cells in this region suffer from a lack of oxygen and blood-borne fuel. Because the cells cannot generate ATP, the membranes become damaged, and enzymes leak from the cells into the blood.

Creatine kinase (CK or CPK) is one of these enzymes. The protein is composed of two subunits, which may be either of the muscle (M) or the brain (B) type. The MB form, containing one M and one B subunit, is found primarily in cardiac muscle. It can be separated electrophoretically from other CK isozymes and the amount in the blood used to determine if a myocardial infarction has occurred. On admission to the hospital, **Ann Jeina's** total CK was 182 U/L (reference range = 38 to 174 U/L). Her MB fraction was 6.8% (reference range = 5% or less of the total CK). Although these values are only slightly elevated, they are typical of the phase immediately following a myocardial infarction. Additional information was provided by myoglobin and troponin T (TnT) measurements.

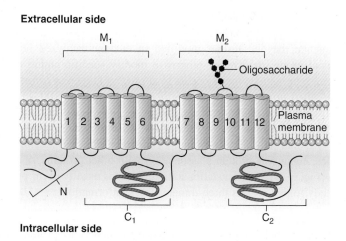

Extracellular side

Intracellular side

FIG. 6.11. Invariant regions in the isoforms of adenylyl cyclase. The invariant regions are on the cytosolic side of the membrane in the C1 and C2 loops shown in *red*. These amino acid residues participate in the catalytic function of the enzyme, synthesis of 3′,5′-cyclic adenosine monophosphate (cAMP). The protein also has several helical regions that span the membrane (M1 helices and M2 helices), represented as *tubes*. An oligosaccharide chain is attached to an extracellular domain. N is the amino terminus. (From Taussig R, Gilman AG. Mammalian membrane-bound adenylyl cyclases. *J Biol Chem.* 1995;270[1]:1–4.)

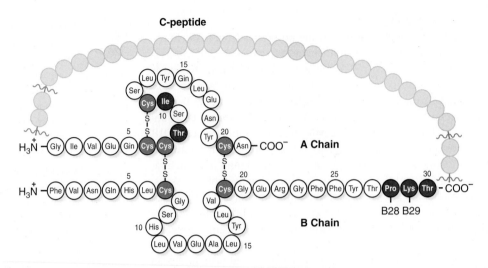

FIG. 6.12. The primary structure of human insulin. The substituted amino acids in bovine (beef) and porcine (pork) insulin are shown in *red*. Threonine 30 at the carboxy terminal of the B chain is replaced by alanine in both beef and pork insulin. In beef insulin, threonine 8 on the A chain is also replaced with alanine, and isoleucine 10 with valine. The cysteine residues, which form the disulfide bonds (shown in *blue*) holding the chains together, are invariant. In the bioengineered insulin Humalog (lispro insulin), the position of proline at B28 and lysine at B29 is switched. Insulin is synthesized as a longer precursor molecule, proinsulin, which is one polypeptide chain. Proinsulin is converted to insulin by proteolytic cleavage of certain peptide bonds (*squiggly lines* in the figure). The cleavage removes a few amino acids and the 31-amino acid C-peptide that connects the A and B chains. The active insulin molecule, thus, has two nonidentical chains.

 Although bovine (beef) insulin is identical to human insulin in those amino acid residues essential for activity, the amino acid residues that are in the variable regions can act as antigens and stimulate the formation of antibodies against bovine insulin. Consequently, recombinant DNA techniques have been used for the synthesis of insulin, identical in structure to native insulin, such as Humulin (intermediate-acting insulin) (see Chapter 17 for information on recombinant DNA technology.) Although **Di Abietes** had not yet experienced an allergic response to her beef insulin, the cost of Humulin is now sufficiently low that most patients have been changed from beef insulin to the synthetic forms of human insulin.

form the C-peptide and the active insulin molecule containing the A and B chains. The folding of the A and B chains into the correct three-dimensional structure is promoted by the presence of one intrachain and two interchain disulfide bonds formed by cysteine residues. The invariant residues consist of the cysteine residues engaged in disulfide bonds and the residues that form the surface of the insulin molecule that binds to the insulin receptor. The amino acid substitutions in bovine and porcine insulin (shown in red in Fig. 6.12) are not in amino acids that affect its activity. Consequently, bovine and pork insulin were used for many years for the treatment of diabetes mellitus. However, even with only a few different amino acids, some patients developed an immune response to these insulins.

IV. MODIFIED AMINO ACIDS

After synthesis of a protein has been completed, a few amino acid residues in the primary sequence may be further modified in enzyme-catalyzed reactions that add a chemical group, oxidize, or otherwise modify specific amino acids in the protein. Because protein synthesis occurs by a process known as *translation*, these changes are called *posttranslational modification*. More than 100 different posttranslationally modified amino acid residues have been found in human proteins. These modifications change the structure of one or more specific amino acids on a protein in a way that may serve a regulatory function, target or anchor the protein in membranes, enhance a protein's association with other proteins, or target it for degradation (Fig. 6.13). Posttranslational modifications usually occur once the protein has already folded into its three-dimensional conformation.

A. Glycosylation

Oligosaccharides (small carbohydrate chains) are bound to proteins by either *N*-linkages or *O*-linkages (see Fig. 6.13). *N*-linked oligosaccharides are found attached to cell surface proteins, where they protect the cell from proteolysis or an immune attack. In contrast, an *O*-glycosidic link is a common way of attaching oligosaccharides to the serine or threonine hydroxyl groups in secreted proteins. The intracellular polysaccharide glycogen is attached to a protein through an *O*-glycosidic linkage to a tyrosine. Adenylyl cyclase is an example of an enzyme

Carbohydrate addition

O-glycosylation: OH of ser, thr, tyr,

N-glycosylation: NH₂ of asn

Lipid addition

Palmitoylation: Internal SH of cys

Myristoylation: NH of N-terminal gly

Prenylation: SH of cys

Regulation

Phosphorylation: OH of ser, thr, tyr

Acetylation: NH₂ of lys, N-terminus

ADP-ribosylation: N of arg, gln; S of cys

Modified amino acids

Oxidation: pro, lys

Carboxylation: glu

4-Hydroxyproline

γ-Carboxyglutamate residue

FIG. 6.13. Posttranslational modifications of amino acids in proteins. Some of the common amino acid modifications and the sites of attachment are illustrated. The added group is shown in *red*. Because these modifications are enzyme-catalyzed, only a specific amino acid in the primary sequence is altered. R–O– represents additional carbohydrates attached to the first carbohydrate. In *N*-glycosylation, the attached sugar is usually *N*-acetylglucosamine (*N*-Ac).

that is posttranslationally modified (see Fig. 6.13). It has an oligosaccharide chain attached to the external portion of the protein.

B. Fatty Acylation or Prenylation

Many membrane proteins contain a covalently attached lipid group that interacts hydrophobically with lipids in the membrane. Palmitoyl groups (C16) are often attached to plasma membrane proteins, and the myristoyl group (C14) is often attached to proteins in the lipid membranes of intracellular vesicles (see Fig. 6.13). The farnesyl group (C15) and the geranylgeranyl group (C20) are synthesized from the five-carbon isoprene unit (isopentenyl pyrophosphate, see Fig. 5.1A) and are therefore called *isoprenoids*. These are attached in thioether linkage to a specific cysteine residue of certain membrane proteins, particularly proteins involved in regulation.

C. Regulatory Modifications

Several pathogenic bacteria produce bacterial toxins that are ADP-ribosyl transferases (NAD^+-glycohydrolases). These enzymes hydrolyze the *N*-glycosidic bond of NAD^+ and transfer the ADP-ribose portion to a specific amino acid residue on a protein in the affected human cell. Cholera AB toxin, a pertussis toxin, and a diptheria toxin are all ADP-ribosyl transferases.

Phosphorylation, acetylation, and adenosine diphosphate (ADP)-ribosylation of specific amino acid residues in a polypeptide can alter bonding by that residue and change the activity of the protein (see Fig. 6.13). Phosphorylation of an –OH group on serine, threonine, or tyrosine by a protein kinase (an enzyme that transfers a phosphate group from ATP to a protein) introduces a large, bulky, negatively charged group that can alter the activity of a protein. Some of the isozymes of adenylyl cyclase contain serine residues on the intracellular portion of the protein that can be phosphorylated by a protein kinase. Reversible acetylation occurring on lysine residues of histone proteins in the chromosome changes their interaction with the negatively charged phosphate groups of DNA. ADP-ribosylation is the transfer of an ADP-ribose from NAD^+ to an arginine, glutamine, or a cysteine residue on a target protein in the membrane (primarily in leukocytes, skeletal muscles, brain, and testes). This modification may regulate the activity of these proteins.

D. Other Amino Acid Posttranslational Modifications

Several other posttranslational modifications of amino acid side chains alter the activity of the protein in the cell (see Fig. 6.13). Carboxylation of the γ-carbon of glutamate (carbon 4) in certain blood-clotting proteins is important for attaching the clot to a surface. Calcium ions mediate this attachment by binding to the two negatively charged carboxyl groups of γ-glutamate and two additional negatively charged groups provided by phospholipids in the cell membrane. Collagen, an abundant fibrous extracellular protein, contains the oxidized amino acid hydroxyproline. The addition of the hydroxyl group to the proline side chain provides an extra polar group that can engage in hydrogen bonding between the polypeptide strands of the fibrous protein.

E. Selenocysteine

$$HSe-CH_2-CH-COO^-$$
$$\overset{|}{{}^+NH_3}$$

Selenocysteine

FIG. 6.14. Selenocysteine.

The unusual amino acid *selenocysteine* is found in a few enzymes and is required for their activity (Fig. 6.14). Its synthesis is not a posttranslational modification, however, but a modification to serine that occurs while serine is bound to a unique tRNA (see Chapter 15). The selenocysteine is then inserted into the protein as it is being synthesized.

CLINICAL COMMENTS

Will Sichel. Will Sichel was treated for 3 days with parenteral (intravascular) narcotics, hydration, and nasal inhalation of oxygen for his vaso-occlusive crisis. The diffuse severe pains of sickle cell crises result from occlusion of small vessels in various tissues, thereby causing damage to cells from ischemia (low blood flow) or hypoxia (low levels of oxygen). Vaso-occlusion occurs when sickle hemoglobin (HbS) molecules in red blood cells polymerize in the lumen of capillaries, where the partial pressure of O_2 (Po_2) is low. This polymerization causes the red blood cells to change from a biconcave disc to a sickle shape that cannot deform to pass through the narrow capillary lumen. The cells aggregate in the capillaries and occlude blood flow.

Will's acute symptoms gradually subsided. Had his severe pain persisted, partial-exchange blood transfusions would have been considered, because no other effective therapy is currently available. Patients with sickle cell anemia experience sickle cell crises periodically, and Will's physician urged him to seek medical help whenever symptoms reappeared. Once stabilized, Will was treated with hydroxyurea therapy, which increases the production and concentration of fetal hemoglobin (HbF) in red blood cells. As HbF molecules do not participate in sickling, increasing their levels within the red blood cells decreases the frequency of painful sickle cell crises.

 Cal Kulis. **Mr. Kulis** has cystinuria, a relatively rare disorder, with a prevalence that ranges between 1 in 2,500 and 1 in 15,000 births, depending on the population studied. It is a genetically determined disease with a complex recessive mode of inheritance resulting from allelic mutations. These mutations lead to a reduction in the activity of renal tubular cell transport proteins that normally carry cystine from the tubular lumen into the renal tubular cells. The transport of the basic amino acids (lysine, arginine, and ornithine, an amino acid found in the urea cycle but not in proteins) is also often compromised, and they appear in the urine.

Because cystine is produced by oxidation of cysteine, conservative treatment of cystinuria includes decreasing the amount of cysteine within the body and, hence, the amount of cystine eventually filtered by the kidneys. Reduction of cysteine levels is accomplished by restricting dietary methionine, which contributes its sulfur to the pathway for cysteine formation. To increase the amount of cystine that remains in solution, the volume of fluid ingested daily is increased. Crystallization of cystine is further prevented by chronically alkalinizing the urine. Finally, drugs may be administered to enhance the conversion of urinary cystine to more soluble compounds. If these conservative measures fail to prevent continued cystine stone formation, existing stones may be removed by a surgical technique that involves sonic fracture of the stones. The fragmented stones may then pass spontaneously or may be more easily extracted surgically because of their smaller size.

 Di Abietes. **Di Abietes's** treatment was first changed to multiple daily injections of Humulin instead of beef insulin. Humulin is now mass-produced by recombinant DNA techniques that insert the human DNA sequences for the insulin A and B chains into the *Escherichia coli* or yeast genome (see Chapter 17). The insulin chains that are produced are then extracted from the media and treated to form the appropriate disulfide bonds between the chains. Because costs have fallen for production of the synthetic human insulins, they have replaced pork insulin and the highly antigenic beef insulin.

Di's physician then recommended that she also take Humalog, an insulin preparation containing lispro, an ultrafast-acting bioengineered insulin analog in which lysine at position B29 has been moved to B28 and proline at B28 has been moved to B29 (hence, lispro) (see Fig. 6.12). With lispro, Di will be able to time her injections of this rapidly acting insulin minutes before her consumption of carbohydrate-containing meals, rather than having to remember to give herself an insulin injection 1 hour before a meal. Di is now taking one long-acting insulin shot a day (lantus), and three Humalog shots prior to meals each day.

 The switch in position of amino acids in lispro does not affect the action of this synthetic insulin on cells because it is not in a critical invariant region, but it does affect the ability of insulin to bind zinc. Normally, human insulin is secreted from the pancreas as a zinc hexamer in which six insulin molecules are bound to the zinc atom. When zinc insulin is injected, the binding to zinc slows the absorption from the subcutaneous (under the skin) injection site. Lispro cannot bind zinc to form a hexamer, and thus it is absorbed much more quickly than other insulins.

 Ann Jeina. **Mrs. Jeina** continued to be monitored in the cardiac care unit. At admission, her blood creatine kinase (CK) levels were elevated (182 U/L compared with a reference range of 38 to 174 U/L), and the muscle–brain (MB) fraction was high at 6.8% of the total (reference = <5% of the total). Her total CK continued to rise (228 U/L 12 hours after admission

**Creatine kinase
isozymes in blood**

Normal

Patient 24 hours after
myocardial infarction

FIG. 6.15. Electrophoretic separation of serum creatine kinase (CK) enzymes from a normal healthy adult and from a patient who had a myocardial infarction 24 hours previously. CK catalyzes the reversible transfer of a phosphate from ATP to creatine to form phosphocreatine and ADP. The reaction is an important part of energy metabolism in heart muscle, skeletal muscle, and brain. Three different forms of the dimer exist: BB (or CK-1) found in brain, MB (or CK-2) found only in heart (indicated in *red*), and MM (or CK-3), found only in skeletal and heart muscle.

and 266 U/L at 24 hours), as did her MB fraction (8% at 12 hours and 10.8% at 24 hours). Within 2 hours of the onset of an acute myocardial infarction, the MB form of CK begins leaking from heart cells that were injured by the ischemic process. These rising serum levels of the MB fraction (and, therefore, of the total CK) reach their peak 12 to 36 hours later and usually return to normal within 3 to 5 days from the onset of the infarction (Fig. 6.15). In addition to the CK measurements, her blood was also analyzed for myoglobin and the heart isoform of troponin T (TnT), a protein involved in muscle contraction (see Chapter 7).

BIOCHEMICAL COMMENTS

Enzyme and Protein Databases. Large databases of protein structure have been assembled to collate data from various laboratories around the world. The National Library of Medicine maintains a Web site, PubMed, which catalogs the medical literature, and a search engine that allows you to search for reference articles by topic or author (www.ncbi.nlm.nih.gov/pubmed). From the menu, you can enter a protein database or a structure database directly. These databases are linked, so you can type in the name of a protein, such as human hemoglobin chain A, obtain a list of contributors to sequence data, and retrieve a complete amino acid sequence for many proteins. You can link to PubMed to find recent articles about the protein, or you can link to the structure database. A program called Cn3D can be downloaded from this site that allows you to view three-dimensional versions of the protein structures.

These databases are only a few of more than 500 biologic databases that have been assembled to collate and exchange biologic information in the areas of DNA, RNA, genomics, gene mapping, and protein structure. The first issue of the *Journal of Nucleic Acid Research* each year provides a description of currently available biologic databases. Their goal is to provide information that can relate a particular DNA sequence or mutation to the protein involved, to its function, and to the pathologic consequences of a particular amino acid substitution, by comparing proteins that have similar functional elements.

Will these databases be of any use to the practicing physician or to the practice-oriented medical student? Very few students will ever want to do protein modeling. However, students and physicians may wish to use the literature search in PubMed as part of their approach to evidence-based medicine. They also may wish to use it to track definitions or fundamental knowledge about particular topics. Thus, a move has begun to link biomedical and basic science textbooks to PubMed.

Key Concepts

- A protein's unique characteristics, including its three-dimensional folded structure, are dictated by its linear sequence of amino acids, termed its primary structure.
- The primary structures of all of the diverse human proteins are synthesized from 20 amino acids arranged in a linear sequence determined by the genetic code.
- Each three-base (nucleotide) sequence within the coding region of a gene (the genetic code) specifies which amino acid should be present in a protein. The genetic code is discussed further in Chapter 12.
- All amino acids contain a central α-carbon joined to a carboxylic acid group, an amino group, a hydrogen, and a side chain, which varies among the 20 different amino acids.
- At physiologic pH, the amino acids are zwitterions; the amino group is positively charged, and the carboxylate is negatively charged.
- In proteins, amino acids are joined into linear polymers called *polypeptide chains* via peptide bonds, which are formed between the carboxylic acid of one amino acid and the amino group of the next amino acid.
- Amino acid side chains can be classified either by polarity (charged, nonpolar hydrophobic, or uncharged polar) or structural features (aliphatic, cyclic, or aromatic).
- Depending on their side-chain characteristics, certain amino acids cluster together to exclude water (hydrophobic effect), whereas others participate in hydrogen bonding. Cysteine can form disulfide bonds, whereas charged amino acids can form ionic bonds.

Table 6.2   Diseases Discussed in Chapter 6

Disorder or Condition	Genetic or Environmental	Comments
Sickle cell anemia	Genetic	Single amino acid replacement at the sixth position of the β-chain of hemoglobin, leading to an E6V alteration (instead of glutamic acid at position 6, a valine is in its place).
Cystinuria	Genetic	Inability to appropriately transport cystine, leading to its accumulation in the kidney and the formation of kidney stones.
Type 1 diabetes	Both	Understanding the structure of insulin, and how it is absorbed at injection sites, allows various forms of insulin to be synthesized that are either rapidly or slowly absorbed. This provides type 1 diabetic patients with a variety of treatment options.
Myocardial infarction	Both	Primarily environmental factors, which can be exacerbated by genetic conditions. The release of heart-specific isozymes into the circulation is diagnostic for a heart attack.

- Amino acids in proteins can be modified by phosphorylation, carboxylation, or other reactions after the protein is synthesized (posttranslational modifications).
- Alterations in the genetic code may lead to mutations in the protein's primary structure, which can affect the protein's function.
- Proteins with the same function but different primary structures (isoforms and isozymes) can exist in different tissues or during different phases of development.
- Diseases discussed in this chapter are summarized in Table 6.2.

REVIEW QUESTIONS—CHAPTER 6

1. In a polypeptide at physiologic pH, hydrogen bonding may occur between which of the following?

   A. The side chains of a leucine residue and a lysine residue
   B. The side chains of an aspartyl residue and a glutamyl residue
   C. The terminal α-amino group and the terminal α-carboxyl group
   D. The amide group in the peptide bond and an aspartyl side chain
   E. The –SH groups of two cysteine residues

2. Which of the following shows the linear sequence of atoms joined by covalent bonds in a peptide backbone?

   A. –N–C–C–N–C–C–N–C–C
   B. –N–C–O–N–C–O–N–C–O–
   C. –N–C–C–O–N–C–C–O–N–C–C–O–
   D. –N–H–C–C–N–H–C–C–N–H–C–C–
   E. –N–H–C–O–H–N–H–C–O–H–N–H–C–C–

3. **Di Abietes's** different preparations of insulin contain some insulin complexed with protamine that is absorbed slowly after injection. Protamine is a protein preparation from rainbow trout sperm containing arginine-rich peptides that bind insulin. Which of the following provides the best explanation for complex formation between protamine and insulin?

   A. Arginine is a basic amino acid that binds to negatively charged amino acid side chains in insulin.

   B. Arginine is a basic amino acid that binds to the α-carboxylic acid groups at the N-terminals of insulin chains.
   C. Arginine is a large bulky hydrophobic amino acid that complexes with leucine and phenylalanine in insulin.
   D. Arginine forms disulfide bonds with the cysteine residues that hold the A and B chains together.
   E. Arginine has a side chain that forms peptide bonds with the carboxyl terminals of the insulin chains.

4. Protein kinases phosphorylate proteins only at certain hydroxyl groups on amino acid side chains. Which of the following groups of amino acids all contain side-chain hydroxyl groups?

   A. Aspartate, glutamate, and serine
   B. Serine, threonine, and tyrosine
   C. Threonine, phenylalanine, and arginine
   D. Lysine, arginine, and proline
   E. Alanine, asparagine, and serine

5. A protein's activity is altered when a particular serine side chain is phosphorylated. Which of the following amino acid substitutions at this position could lead to a permanent alteration in normal enzyme activity?

   A. S → E
   B. S → T
   C. S → Y
   D. S → K
   E. S → L

Structure–Function Relationships in Proteins

Diseases can be caused by changes in protein structure that affect the protein's ability to bind other molecules and carry out its function. They can be caused also by conformational changes in proteins that affect their solubility and degradability. In amyloidosis/AL, immunoglobulin chains form an insoluble protein aggregate called *amyloid* in organs and tissues. Alzheimer disease and familial amyloid polyneuropathy are neurodegenerative diseases characterized by the deposition of amyloid. Prion diseases result from misfolding and aggregation of a normal cellular protein. Even in sickle cell anemia, the mutation in hemoglobin principally affects the quaternary structure of hemoglobin and its solubility, and not its ability to bind oxygen.

A multitude of different proteins can be formed from only 20 common amino acids because these amino acids can be linked together in an enormous variety of sequences determined by the genetic code. The sequence of amino acids and its primary structure determines the way a protein folds into a unique three-dimensional structure, which is its native conformation. Once it is folded, the three-dimensional structure of a protein forms binding sites for other molecules, thereby dictating the function of the protein in the body. In addition to creating binding sites, a protein must fold in such a way that it is flexible, stable, able to function in the correct site in the cell, and capable of being degraded by cellular enzymes.

*Levels of Protein Structure. Protein structure is described in terms of four different levels: primary, secondary, tertiary, and quaternary (Fig. 7.1). The **primary structure** of a protein is the linear sequence of amino acids in the polypeptide chain. The **secondary structure** consists of local regions of polypeptide chains formed into structures that are stabilized by a repeating pattern of hydrogen bonds, such as the regular structures called α-helices and β-sheets. The **rigidity of the peptide backbone** determines the types of secondary structure that can occur. The **tertiary structure** involves folding of the secondary structural elements into an overall three-dimensional conformation. In **globular proteins** such as **myoglobin**, the tertiary structure generally forms a densely packed **hydrophobic core** with polar amino acid side chains on the outside. Some proteins exhibit **quaternary structure**, the combination of two or more **subunits**, each composed of a polypeptide chain.*

*Domains and Folds. The tertiary structure of a globular protein can be made up of structural **domains**, regions of structure that fold independently. Multiple domains can be linked together to form a functional protein. Within a domain, a combination of secondary structural elements forms a fold, such as the **nucleotide-binding fold** or an **actin fold**. Folds are defined by their similarity in several different proteins.*

*Quaternary Structure. Assembly of globular polypeptide subunits into a multisubunit complex can provide the opportunity for **cooperative binding** of ligands (e.g., oxygen [O₂] binding to hemoglobin), form **binding sites** for complex molecules (e.g., antigen binding to immunoglobulin), and increase **stability** of the protein. The polypeptide chains of **fibrous proteins** such as **collagen** are aligned along an axis, have repeating elements, and are extensively linked to each other through hydrogen and covalent bonds.*

*Ligand Binding. Proteins form binding sites for specific molecules, called **ligands** (e.g., adenosine triphosphate [ATP] or O₂), or for another protein. The affinity of a binding site for its ligand is characterized quantitatively by an **association** or **affinity constant (K_a)** (or its dissociation constant [K_d], in which $K_d = 1/K_a$).*

*Folding of Proteins. The primary structure of a protein dictates the way that it folds into its tertiary structure, which is a **stable conformation** that is identical to the shape of other molecules of the same protein (i.e., its **native***

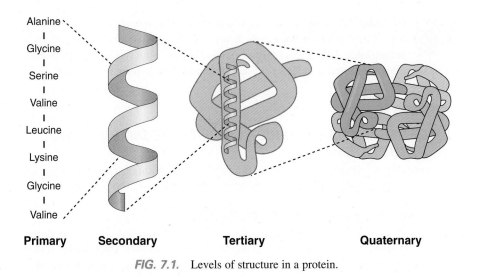

Alanine
|
Glycine
|
Serine
|
Valine
|
Leucine
|
Lysine
|
Glycine
|
Valine

Primary   **Secondary**   **Tertiary**   **Quaternary**

FIG. 7.1.   Levels of structure in a protein.

conformation). ***Chaperonins*** *act as templates to overcome the kinetic and thermodynamic barrier to reaching a stable conformation.* ***Prion proteins*** *cause neurodegenerative diseases by acting as a template for misfolding. Heat, acid, and other agents cause proteins to* ***denature***, *that is, to unfold or refold and lose their native three-dimensional conformation.*

THE WAITING ROOM

 Will Sichel, who has sickle cell anemia, was readmitted to the hospital with symptoms indicating that he was experiencing another sickle cell crisis (see Chapter 6).

Anne Jeina is a 54-year-old woman who arrived in the hospital 4 days ago, approximately 5 hours after she began to feel chest pain (see Chapter 6). In the emergency room, the physician had drawn blood for the measurement of myoglobin; creatine kinase, muscle–brain fraction (CK-MB); and cardiac troponin T (cTnT) subunit. The results from these tests had supported the diagnosis of an acute myocardial infarction (MI), and Mrs. Jeina was hospitalized.

 Amy Lloyd is a 62-year-old woman who presented with weakness, fatigue, an enlarged tongue (macroglossia), and edema. She had signs and symptoms of cardiac failure, including electrocardiographic abnormalities. Initial laboratory studies showed a serum creatinine of 1.9 mg/dL (reference range [females] = 0.5 to 1.1 mg/dL), indicating mild renal failure. A urinalysis indicated a moderate proteinuria and numerous white blood cells in the urinary sediment. She was subsequently diagnosed with amyloidosis/AL secondary to a plasma cell dyscrasia. *Amyloidosis* is a term that encompasses many diseases sharing a common feature, the extracellular deposition of pathologic insoluble fibrillar proteins called *amyloid*, in organs and tissues. In **Amy Lloyd's** disease, amyloidosis/AL, the amyloid is derived from immunoglobulin light chains (AL-5 amyloidosis, light-chain-related).

 The simplest test for detecting protein in the urine is the use of specific reagent test strips. The strips are coated with tetrabromophenol blue, buffered at pH 3.0. With protein, the indicator dye is no longer as responsive to changes in pH unlike in the absence of protein. A yellow color indicates that protein is not detectable; as protein levels increase, the yellow color changes, going to green, then bluish green. This is a useful qualitative test (which detects primarily serum albumin), but to be more quantitative, different dyes, which react specifically with particular amino acid side chains, are used. Different tests are required to detect the presence of a specific protein in the urine or sera, and these will be discussed in subsequent chapters.

Di Abietes returned to her physician's office for a routine visit to monitor her treatment (see Chapters 4, 5, and 6). Her physician drew blood for a hemoglobin A1C (HbA1c) (pronounced hemoglobin A-1-c) determination. The laboratory reported a value of 8.5%, compared with a normal reference range of 5.8% to 7.2%.

I.   GENERAL CHARACTERISTICS OF THREE-DIMENSIONAL STRUCTURE

The overall conformation of a protein, the particular position of the amino acid side chains in three-dimensional space, determines the function of the protein.

A.   Descriptions of Protein Structure

Proteins are generally grouped into major structural classifications: globular proteins, fibrous proteins, and transmembrane proteins. *Globular proteins* are usually soluble in aqueous medium and resemble irregular balls. The *fibrous proteins* are geometrically linear, arranged around a single axis, and have a repeating unit structure. Another general classification, *transmembrane proteins*, consists of proteins that have one or more regions aligned to cross the lipid membrane (see Fig. 6.11). DNA-binding proteins, although a member of the globular protein family, are sometimes classified separately, and are considered in Chapter 16.

The structure of proteins is often described according to levels called primary, secondary, tertiary, and quaternary structure (see Fig. 7.1). The *primary structure* is the linear sequence of amino acid residues joined through peptide bonds to form a polypeptide chain. The *secondary structure* refers to recurring structures (such as the regular structure of the α-helix) that form in short localized regions of the polypeptide chain. The overall three-dimensional conformation of a protein is its *tertiary structure*. The *quaternary structure* is the association of polypeptide subunits in a geometrically specific manner. The forces involved in a protein folding into its final conformation are primarily noncovalent interactions. These interactions include the attraction between positively and negatively charged molecules (ionic interactions), the hydrophobic effect, hydrogen bonding, and van der Waals interactions (the nonspecific attraction between closely packed atoms).

B.   Requirements of the Three-Dimensional Structure

The overall three-dimensional structure of a protein must meet certain requirements to enable the protein to function in the cell or extracellular medium of the body. The first requirement is the creation of a binding site that is specific for just one molecule, or a group of molecules with similar structural properties. The specific binding sites of a protein usually define its biologic functions. The three-dimensional structure must exhibit the degrees of flexibility and rigidity required to carry out its specific function. Some rigidity is essential for the creation of binding sites and for a stable structure (i.e., a protein that is excessively flexible could be dysfunctional). However, an appropriate degree of flexibility and mobility in structure enables the protein to fold as it is synthesized, and to adapt as it binds other proteins and small molecules. The three-dimensional structure must have an external surface that is appropriate for its environment (e.g., cytoplasmic proteins need to have polar amino acids on the surface to remain soluble in an aqueous environment). In addition, the conformation must also be stable, with little tendency to undergo refolding into a form that cannot fulfill its function or that precipitates in the cell. Finally, the protein must have a structure that can be degraded when it is damaged or no longer needed in the cell. Almost every region in the sequence of amino acids, the primary structure, participates in fulfilling one or more of these requirements through the chemical properties of the peptide bonds and the individual amino acid side chains.

FIG. 7.2. The peptide backbone. Because of the resonance nature of the peptide bond, the C and N of the peptide bonds form a series of rigid planes. Rotation within allowed torsion angles can occur around the bonds attached to the α-carbon. The side chains are *trans* to each other, and alternate above and below the peptide chain. The actual peptide bond is a hybrid between the resonance forms shown, resulting in a partial negative charge on the carbonyl oxygen, a partial positive charge on the nitrogen, and partial double-bond character for the peptide bond itself.

II. THE THREE-DIMENSIONAL STRUCTURE OF THE PEPTIDE BACKBONE

The amino acids in a polypeptide chain are joined sequentially by peptide bonds between the carboxyl group of one amino acid and the amide group of the next amino acid in the sequence (Fig. 7.2). Usually, the peptide bond assumes a *trans* configuration in which successive α-carbons and their R groups are located on opposite sides of the peptide bond.

The polypeptide backbone can bend in a very restricted way. The peptide bond itself is a hybrid of two resonance structures, one of which has double-bond character, so that the carboxyl and amide groups that form the bond must remain planar (see Fig. 7.2). As a consequence, the peptide backbone consists of a sequence of rigid planes formed by the peptide groups (see Fig. 7.2). However, rotation within certain allowed angles (torsion angles) can occur around the bond between the α-carbon and the α-amino group and around the bond between the α-carbon and the carbonyl group. This rotation is subject to steric constraints that maximize the distance between atoms in the different amino acid side chains and prohibit torsion (rotation) angles that place the side-chain atoms too close to each other. These folding constraints, which depend on the specific amino acids present, limit the secondary and tertiary structures that can be formed from the polypeptide chain.

III. SECONDARY STRUCTURE

Regions within polypeptide chains form recurring, localized structures known as secondary structures. The two regular secondary structures called the α-*helix* and the β-*sheet* contain repeating elements formed by hydrogen bonding between atoms of the peptide bonds. Other regions of the polypeptide chain form irregular, nonrepetitive secondary structures such as loops and coils.

A. The α-Helix

The α-helix is a common secondary structural element of globular proteins, membrane-spanning domains, and DNA-binding proteins. It has a rigid, stable conformation that maximizes hydrogen bonding while maintaining the allowed rotation angles of the polypeptide backbone. The peptide backbone of the α-helix is formed by hydrogen bonds between each carbonyl oxygen atom and the amide hydrogen (N–H) of an amino acid residue located four residues farther down the chain (Fig. 7.3). Thus, each peptide bond is connected by hydrogen bonds to the peptide bond four amino acid residues ahead of it and four amino acid residues behind it in the amino acid sequence. The core of the helix is tightly packed, thereby maximizing association energies between atoms. The *trans* side chains of the amino acids project backward and outward from the helix, thereby avoiding steric hindrance with the polypeptide backbone and with each other (Fig. 7.4). It is important to note that proline, because its nitrogen is part of its cyclic structure, cannot form the appropriate bond angles to fit within an α-helix. Thus, proline is known as a "helix breaker" and is not found in α-helical regions of proteins.

B. β-Sheets

β-*Sheets* are a second type of regular secondary structure that maximizes hydrogen bonding between the peptide backbones while maintaining the allowed torsion angles. In β-sheets, the hydrogen bonding usually occurs between regions of separate neighboring polypeptide strands aligned parallel to each other (Fig. 7.5A). Thus, the carbonyl oxygen of one peptide bond is hydrogen-bonded to the nitrogen of a peptide bond on an adjacent strand. (This pattern contrasts with the α-helix, in which the peptide backbone hydrogen bonds are located within the same strand.) Optimal hydrogen bonding occurs when the sheet is bent (pleated) to form β-pleated sheets.

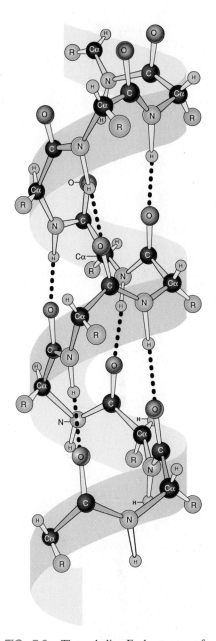

FIG. 7.3. The α-helix. Each oxygen of a carbonyl group of a peptide bond forms a hydrogen bond (indicated by the *black dots*) with the hydrogen atom attached to a nitrogen atom in a peptide bond four amino acids farther along the chain. The result is a highly compact and rigid structure.

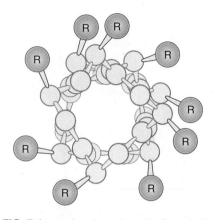

FIG. 7.4.   A view down the axis of an α-helix. The side chains (R) jut out from the helix. Steric hindrance occurs if they come within their van der Waals radii of each other and a stable helix cannot form.

The β-pleated sheet is described as parallel if the polypeptide strands run in the same direction (as defined by their amino and carboxy terminals), and antiparallel if they run in opposite directions. Antiparallel strands are often the same polypeptide chain folded back on itself, with simple hairpin turns or long runs of polypeptide chain connecting the strands. The amino acid side chains of each polypeptide strand alternate between extending above and below the plane of the β-sheet (see Fig. 7.5). Parallel sheets tend to have hydrophobic residues on both sides of the sheets; antiparallel sheets usually have a hydrophobic side and a hydrophilic side. Frequently, sheets twist in one direction. The hydrogen-bonding pattern is slightly different depending on whether one examines a parallel or antiparallel β-sheet (see Fig. 7.5B). In an antiparallel sheet, the atoms involved in hydrogen bonding are directly opposite to each other; in a parallel β-sheet, the atoms involved in the hydrogen bonding are slightly skewed from one another, such that one amino acid is hydrogen-bonded to two others in the opposite strand.

C. Nonrepetitive Secondary Structures

α-Helices and β-pleated sheets are patterns of regular structure with a repeating element—the ordered formation of hydrogen bonds. In contrast, bends, loops, and turns are irregular secondary structures that do not have a repeating element of hydrogen bond formation. They are characterized by an abrupt change of direction and are often found on the protein surface. For example, β-turns are short regions that usually involve four successive amino acid residues. They often connect strands of antiparallel β-sheets (Fig. 7.6). The surface of large globular proteins usually has at least one omega loop: a structure with a neck like the capital Greek letter omega (Ω).

FIG. 7.5.   **A.** A β-pleated sheet. In this case, the chains are oriented in opposite directions (antiparallel). The *large arrows* show the direction of the carboxy terminal. The amino acid side chains (R) in one strand are *trans* to each other, and alternate above and below the plane of the sheet, which can have a hydrophobic face and a polar face that engages in hydrogen bonding. **B.** Hydrogen-bonding pattern with parallel β-strands.

D. Patterns of Secondary Structure

Figure 7.7 is a three-dimensional drawing of a globular domain in the soluble enzyme lactate dehydrogenase (LDH). It illustrates the combination of secondary structural elements to form patterns. This LDH domain is typical of globular proteins, which average approximately 31% α-helical structure and approximately 28% β-pleated sheets (with a wide range of variation). The helices of globular domains have an average span of approximately 12 residues, corresponding to approximately three to four helical turns, although many are much longer. The β-sheets, represented in diagrams by an arrow for each strand, are an average of six residues long and six strands wide (2 to 15 strands). Like the β-sheet in the LDH domain, they generally twist to the right rather than lie flat (see Fig. 7.7). Most globular domains, such as this LDH domain, also contain motifs. *Motifs* are relatively small arrangements of secondary structure that are recognized in many different proteins; for example, certain of the β-strands are connected with α-helices to form the $\beta\alpha\,\beta\alpha\,\beta$ structural motif.

The remaining polypeptide segments connecting the helices and β-sheets are said to have a coil or loop conformation (see Fig. 7.7). Although some of the connecting segments recognized in many proteins have been given names (like the Ω-loops), other segments such as those in this LDH domain appear disordered or irregular. These nonregular regions, generally called *coils*, should never be referred to as "random coils." They are neither truly disordered nor random; they are stabilized through specific hydrogen bonds dictated by the primary sequence of the protein and do not vary from one molecule of the protein to another of the same protein.

The irregular coils, loops, and other segments are usually more flexible than the relatively rigid helices and β-pleated sheets. They often form hinge regions that allow segments of the polypeptide chain to move as a compound binds or to move as the protein folds around another molecule.

IV. TERTIARY STRUCTURE

The tertiary structure of a protein is the folding pattern of the secondary structural elements into a three-dimensional conformation, as shown for the LDH domain in Figure 7.7. As illustrated with examples in the following text, this three-dimensional structure is designed to serve all aspects of the protein's function. It creates specific and flexible binding sites for ligands (the compounds that bind), illustrated with actin and myoglobin. The tertiary structure also maintains residues on the surface appropriate for the protein's cellular location, polar residues for cytosolic proteins, and hydrophobic residues for transmembrane proteins (illustrated with the β_2-adrenergic receptor). Flexibility is one of the most important features of protein structure. Although every portion of every amino acid in a protein is engaged in bonding to the rest of the protein, to water, or to a ligand, proteins do not have rigid structures. The three-dimensional structure is flexible and dynamic, with rapidly fluctuating movement in the exact position of amino acid side chains and domains. These fluctuations are like wiggling or shaking that can occur without unfolding. They allow ions and water to diffuse through the structure and provide alternative conformations for ligand binding. The forces that maintain tertiary structure are hydrogen bonds, ionic bonds, van der Waals interactions, the hydrophobic effect, and disulfide bond formation.

A. Domains in the Tertiary Structure

The tertiary structure of large complex proteins is often described in terms of physically independent regions called *structural domains*. You can usually identify domains from visual examination of a three-dimensional figure of a protein, such as the three-dimensional figure of G-actin shown in Figure 7.8. Each domain is formed from a continuous sequence of amino acids in the polypeptide chain that are

FIG. 7.6. β-Turn. The four amino acid residues that form the β-turn (also called a hairpin loop) are held together by hydrogen bonds, which make this an extremely stable structure. The C α-carbons of the amino acids are numbered in the figure.

 A renal biopsy used in the diagnosis of **Amy Lloyd's** disease showed amorphous deposits in the glomeruli. When stained with Congo red dye, these deposits appeared red with ordinary light microscopy and exhibited apple-green fluorescence when viewed in polarized light. This staining is characteristic of the amyloid fibril structure, which is composed of repeated β-sheets aligned orthogonally (perpendicular) to the axis of the fiber.

Several diseases involve deposition of a characteristic amyloid fiber. However, in each of these diseases, the amyloid is derived from a different protein that has changed its conformation (three-dimensional structure) to that of the amyloid repeated β-sheet structure. Once amyloid deposition begins, it seems to proceed rapidly as if the fibril itself were promoting formation and deposition of more fibrils (a phenomenon called "seeding"). The different clinical presentations in each of these diseases result from differences in the function of the native protein and the site of amyloid deposition.

Lactate dehydrogenase domain 1

FIG. 7.7. Ribbon drawing showing the arrangement of secondary structures into a three-dimensional pattern in domain 1 of LDH. The individual polypeptide strands in the six-stranded β-sheet are shown with *arrows*. Different strands are connected by helices and by nonrepetitive structures (turns, coils, and loops). This domain is the nucleotide-binding fold. NAD⁺ is bound to a site created by the helices (upper left of figure). (Modified from Richardson JS. The anatomy and taxonomy of protein structure. *Adv Protein Chem.* 1981;34:167.)

folded into a three-dimensional structure independently of the rest of the protein, and two domains are connected through a simpler structure such as a loop (e.g., the hinge region on Fig. 7.8). The structural features of each domain can be discussed independently of another domain in the same protein, and the structural features of one domain may not match that of other domains in the same protein.

B. Folds in Globular Proteins

Folds are relatively large patterns of three-dimensional structure that have been recognized in many proteins, including proteins from different branches of the phylogenetic tree. A characteristic activity is associated with each fold, such as adenosine triphosphate (ATP) binding and hydrolysis (the actin fold) or NAD⁺ binding (the nucleotide-binding fold). Examples of these folding patterns are discussed in the following text.

1.   THE ACTIN FOLD

In the three-dimensional drawing of G-actin shown in Figure 7.8, all four subdomains contribute to a folding pattern called the *actin fold*, named for the first protein in which it was described. ATP is bound into the middle of the cleft of the actin fold by amino acid residues contributed by domains on both sides; thus, ATP binding promotes a conformational change that closes the cleft. Once it is bound, ATP is cleaved to adenosine diphosphate (ADP) and phosphate.

The actin fold is found in proteins as diverse as actin, which polymerizes to form the cytoskeleton; heat-shock protein 70 (hsp70), which uses ATP energy in changing the conformation of other proteins; and hexokinase, which catalyzes phosphorylation of glucose (see Chapter 8 for further discussion of hexokinase). Although these proteins have very little sequence identity, three-dimensional drawings of their actin folds are almost superimposable. The amount of sequence identity they

FIG. 7.8. G-actin. ATP binds in the center of the cleft. The two domains that form the cleft are further subdivided into subdomains 1 to 4. The overall structure is found in many ATP-binding proteins and is called the actin fold. The conformations of the regions shown in *green* are nearly superimposable among the proteins that contain the actin fold. (From Kabsch W, Holmes KC. The actin fold. *FASEB J.* 1995;9:167–174.)

do have is consistent with their membership in the same fold family and establishes that they are all homologs of the same ancestral protein. In all of these proteins, ATP binding results in large conformational changes that contribute to the function of the protein.

2. THE NUCLEOTIDE-BINDING FOLD

A fold also can be formed by one domain. In the example of secondary structures provided by LDH (see Fig. 7.7), domain 1 alone forms the nucleotide-binding fold. This fold is a binding site for NAD^+ or, in other proteins, molecules with a generally similar structure (e.g., riboflavin). However, many proteins that bind NAD^+ or $NADP^+$ contain a very different fold from a separate fold family. These two different NAD^+-binding folds arise from different ancestral lines and have different structures, but they have similar properties and function. They are believed to be the product of convergent evolution.

C. The Solubility of Globular Proteins in an Aqueous Environment

Most globular proteins are soluble in the cell. In general, the core of a globular domain has a high content of amino acids with nonpolar side chains (Val, Leu, Ile, Met, and Phe), out of contact with the aqueous medium (the hydrophobic effect). This hydrophobic core is densely packed to maximize attractive van der Waals forces, which exert themselves over short distances. The charged polar amino acid side chains (Arg, His, Lys, Asp, and Glu) are generally located on the surface of the protein, where they form ion pairs (salt bridges, ionic interactions) or are in contact with aqueous solvent. Charged side chains often bind inorganic ions (e.g., K^+, PO_4^{3-}, or Cl^-) to decrease repulsion between like charges. When charged amino acids are located on the interior, they are generally involved in forming specific binding sites. The polar uncharged amino acid side chains of Ser, Thr, Asn, Gln, Tyr, and Trp are also usually found on the surface of the protein, but they may occur in the interior, hydrogen-bonded to other side chains. Cystine disulfide bonds (the bond formed by two cysteine sulfhydryl groups) are also sometimes involved in the formation of tertiary structure.

D. Tertiary Structure of Transmembrane Proteins

Transmembrane proteins, such as the β_2-adrenergic receptor, contain membrane-spanning domains and intracellular and extracellular domains on either side of the membrane (Fig. 7.9). Many ion channel proteins, transport proteins, neurotransmitter receptors, and hormone receptors contain similar membrane-spanning segments that are α-helices with hydrophobic residues exposed to the lipid bilayer. These rigid helices are connected by loops containing hydrophilic amino acid side chains that extend into the aqueous medium on both sides of the membrane. In the β_2-adrenergic receptor, the helices clump together so that the extracellular loops form a surface that acts as a binding site for the hormone adrenaline (epinephrine)—our fight-or-flight hormone. The binding site is sometimes referred to as a binding domain (a functional domain), even though it is not formed from a continuous segment of the polypeptide chain. Once adrenaline binds to the receptor, a conformational change in the arrangement of rigid helical structures is transmitted to the intracellular domains that form a binding site for another signaling protein, a heterotrimeric G protein (a guanosine triphosphate [GTP]-binding protein composed of three different subunits, which is described further in Chapter 11). Thus, receptors require both rigidity and flexibility to transmit signals across the cell membrane.

As discussed in Chapter 6, transmembrane proteins usually have several post-translational modifications that provide additional chemical groups to fulfill requirements of the three-dimensional structure. As shown in Figure 7.9 (and see Fig. 6.13),

FIG. 7.9. β_2-Adrenergic receptor. The receptor has seven α-helical domains that span the membrane and is therefore a member of the hepta-helical class of receptors. **A.** The transmembrane domains are drawn in an extended form. The amino terminus (residues 1 through 34) extends out of the membrane and has branched high-mannose oligosaccharides linked through *N*-glycosidic bonds to the amide of asparagine. Part of the receptor is anchored in the lipid plasma membrane by a palmitoyl group (shown as a *squiggle*) that forms a thioester with the $-SH$ residue of a cysteine. The $-COOH$ terminus, which extends into the cytoplasm, has several serine and threonine phosphorylation sites (shown as *red circles*). **B.** The seven transmembrane helices (shown as *tubes*) form a cylindrical structure. Loops connecting helices form the hormone-binding site on the external side of the plasma membrane, and a binding site for a G protein is on the intracellular side.

the amino terminus of the β_2-adrenergic receptor (residues 1 to 34) extends out of the membrane and has branched high-mannose oligosaccharides linked through *N*-glycosidic bonds to the amide of asparagines. Part of the receptor is anchored in the lipid plasma membrane by a palmitoyl group that forms a thioester with the $-SH$ residue of a cysteine. The $-COOH$ terminus, which extends into the cytoplasm, has several serine and threonine phosphorylation sites (shown as red circles) that regulate receptor activity.

V. QUATERNARY STRUCTURE

The quaternary structure of a protein refers to the association of individual polypeptide chain subunits in a geometrically and stoichiometrically specific manner. Many proteins function in the cell as dimers, tetramers, or oligomers, proteins in which two, four, or more subunits, respectively, have combined to make one functional protein. The subunits of a particular protein always combine in the same number and in the same way, because the binding between the subunits is dictated by the tertiary structure, which is dictated by the primary structure, which is determined by the genetic code.

Several different terms are used to describe subunit structure. The prefixes "homo-" and "hetero-" are used to describe identical or different subunits, respectively, of two, three, or four subunit proteins (e.g., heterotrimeric G proteins have three different subunits). A *protomer* is the unit structure within a protein composed of multiple, nonidentical subunits. For example, adult hemoglobin consists of two α- and two β-chains, and is a tetramer ($\alpha_2 \beta_2$). One α-β pair can be considered a protomer. In contrast, F-actin is an oligomer, a multisubunit protein composed of identical G-actin subunits. "Multimer" is sometimes used as a more generic term to designate a complex with many subunits of more than one type.

The contact regions between the subunits of globular proteins resemble the interior of a single subunit protein; they contain closely packed nonpolar side chains, hydrogen bonds involving the polypeptide backbones and their side chains, and occasional ionic bonds or salt bridges. The subunits of globular proteins are rarely held together by interchain disulfide bonds, and never by other covalent bonds. In contrast, fibrous and other structural proteins may be extensively linked to other proteins through covalent bonds.

Assembly into a multisubunit structure increases the stability of a protein. The increase in size increases the number of possible interactions between amino acid residues and, therefore, makes it more difficult for a protein to unfold and refold. As a result, many soluble proteins are composed of two or four identical or nearly identical subunits with an average size of approximately 200 amino acids.

A multisubunit structure has many advantages besides increased stability. It may enable the protein to exhibit cooperativity between subunits in binding ligands (illustrated later with hemoglobin) or to form binding sites with a high affinity for large molecules (illustrated with antigen binding to the immunoglobulin molecule, immunoglobulin G [IgG]). An additional advantage of a multisubunit structure is that the different subunits can have different activities and cooperate in a common function. Examples of enzymes that have regulatory subunits or exist as multiprotein complexes are provided in Chapter 9.

VI. QUANTITATION OF LIGAND BINDING

In the examples of tertiary structure that we have discussed, the folding of a protein created a three-dimensional binding site for a ligand (NAD^+ for the LDH domain 1, ATP for hexokinase, or adrenaline for the β_2-adrenergic receptor). The binding affinity of a protein for a ligand is described quantitatively by its association constant, K_a, which is the equilibrium constant for the binding reaction of a ligand (L) with a protein (P) (Eq. 7.1).

Equation 7.1. The association constant (K_a) for a binding site on a protein.
Consider a reaction in which a ligand (L) binds to a protein (P) to form a ligand–protein complex (LP) with a rate constant of k_1. LP dissociates with a rate constant of k_2:

$$L + P \underset{k_2}{\overset{k_1}{\rightleftharpoons}} LP$$

then,

$$K_{eq} = \frac{k_1}{k_2} = \frac{[LP]}{[L][P]} = K_a = \frac{1}{K_d}$$

The equilibrium constant (K_{eq}) is equal to the association constant (K_a) or $1/K_d$, the dissociation constant. Unless otherwise given, the concentrations of L, P, and LP are expressed as mol/L, and K_a has the units of $(mol/L)^{-1}$.

K_a is equal to the rate constant (k_1) for association of the ligand with its binding site divided by the rate constant (k_2) for dissociation of the LP. K_d, the dissociation constant for ligand–protein binding, is the reciprocal of K_a. The tighter the binding of the ligand to the protein, the higher is the K_a and the lower is the K_d. The K_a is useful for comparing proteins produced by different alleles, or for describing the affinity of a receptor for different drugs.

VII. STRUCTURE–FUNCTION RELATIONSHIPS IN MYOGLOBIN AND HEMOGLOBIN

Myoglobin and hemoglobin are two oxygen-binding proteins with very similar primary structures (Fig. 7.10). However, *myoglobin* is a globular protein composed of a single polypeptide chain that has one O_2-binding site. *Hemoglobin* is a tetramer composed of two different types of subunits (2α- and 2β-polypeptide chains, referred to as two $\alpha\beta$-protomers). Each subunit has a strong sequence homology to myoglobin and contains an O_2-binding site. A comparison between myoglobin and hemoglobin illustrates some of the advantages of a multisubunit quaternary structure.

 Insulin is composed of two nonidentical polypeptide chains attached to each other through disulfide bonds between the chains (see Chapter 6, Fig. 6.12). The subunits of globular proteins are generally not held together by disulfide bonds, but regions of the same chain may be connected by disulfide bonds that form as the chain folds. Insulin actually fits this generalization because it is synthesized as a single polypeptide chain, which forms the disulfide bonds. Subsequently, a proteolytic enzyme in the secretory vesicles clips the polypeptide chain into two nonidentical subunits. Generally, each subunit of most protomers and oligomers is synthesized as a separate polypeptide chain. In fibrous proteins, which have a regular, sometimes repeating sequence of amino acids, interchain and intrachain covalent binding serves different functions. In collagen, for example, extensive interchain binding provides great tensile strength. Collagen is discussed in more detail in Chapter 49.

 Two different ligands (A and B) bind to the same receptor on the cell surface. The K_d for ligand A is 10^{-7}M; for ligand B it is 10^{-9}M. Which ligand has the higher affinity for the receptor?

FIG. 7.10. Myoglobin and hemoglobin. Myoglobin (**A**) consists of a single polypeptide chain, which is similar in structure to the α- and β-subunits of hemoglobin (**B**). In all of the subunits, heme is tightly bound in a hydrophobic binding pocket. The proximal histidine extends down from a helix to bind to the Fe atom. The oxygen binds between the distal histidine and the heme. Panel **C** displays the quaternary structure of hemoglobin (which consists of two α- and two β-subunits). (From Frescht A. *Structure and Mechanism in Protein Science*. New York, NY: WH Freeman; 1999. Used with permission.)

 The association constant (K_a) is equal to the reciprocal of the dissociation constant (K_d). The K_a for ligand A is $10^7 M^{-1}$, whereas for ligand B it is $10^9 M^{-1}$. Ligand B has the higher affinity for the receptor, by 100-fold as compared to ligand A.

The tetrameric structure of hemoglobin facilitates saturation with O_2 in the lungs and release of O_2 as it travels through the capillary beds (Fig. 7.11). When the amount of oxygen bound to myoglobin or hemoglobin is plotted against the partial pressure of oxygen (P_{O_2}), a hyperbolic curve is obtained for myoglobin, whereas that for hemoglobin is sigmoidal. These curves show that when the P_{O_2} is high, as in the lungs, both myoglobin and hemoglobin are saturated with oxygen. However, at the lower levels of P_{O_2} in oxygen-using tissues, hemoglobin cannot bind oxygen as well as myoglobin (i.e., its percentage saturation is much lower). Myoglobin, which is present in heart and skeletal muscle, can bind the O_2 released by hemoglobin, which it stores to meet the demands of contraction. As O_2 is used in the muscle cell for generation of ATP during contraction, it is released from myoglobin and picked up by *cytochrome oxidase* (a heme-containing enzyme in the electron-transport chain that has an even higher affinity for oxygen than myoglobin).

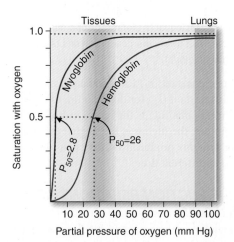

FIG. 7.11. Oxygen saturation curves for myoglobin and hemoglobin. Note that the curve for myoglobin is hyperbolic, whereas that for hemoglobin is sigmoidal. The effect of the tetrameric structure is to inhibit O_2 binding at low O_2 concentrations. P_{50} is the partial pressure of O_2 (P_{O_2}) at which the protein is half-saturated with O_2. P_{50} for myoglobin is 2.8 torrs, and that for hemoglobin is 26 torrs, where 1 torr is equal to 1 mm Hg.

Heme

FIG. 7.12. Heme. The Fe is bound to four nitrogen atoms in the center of the heme porphyrin ring. Methyl (M, $-CH_3$), vinyl (V, $-CH = CH_2$), and propionate (P, $-CH_2CH_3COO^-$) side chains extend out from the four pyrrole rings that constitute the porphyrin ring.

A. Oxygen Binding and Heme

The tertiary structure of myoglobin consists of eight α-helices connected by short coils, a structure that is known as the *globin fold* (see Fig. 7.10). This structure is unusual for a globular protein in that it has no β-sheets. The helices create a hydrophobic O_2-binding pocket, containing tightly bound heme with an iron atom (Fe^{2+}) in its center.

Heme consists of a planar porphyrin ring composed of four pyrrole rings linked by methylene bridges that lie with their nitrogen atoms in the center, binding an Fe^{2+} atom (Fig. 7.12). Negatively charged propionate groups on the porphyrin ring interact with arginine and histidine side chains from the hemoglobin, and the hydrophobic methyl and vinyl groups that extend out from the porphyrin ring interact with hydrophobic amino acid side chains from hemoglobin, positioning the heme group within the protein. All together, there are approximately 16 different interactions between myoglobin amino acids and different groups in the porphyrin ring.

Organic ligands that are tightly bound, such as the heme of myoglobin, are called *prosthetic groups*. A protein with its attached prosthetic group is called a *holoprotein*; without the prosthetic group, it is called an *apoprotein*. The tightly bound prosthetic group is an intrinsic part of the protein and does not dissociate until the protein is degraded.

Within the binding pocket of myoglobin, O_2 binds directly to the Fe^{2+} atom on one side of the planar porphyrin ring (Fig. 7.13A). The Fe^{2+} atom is able

 Myoglobin is readily released from skeletal muscle or cardiac tissue when the cell is damaged. It has a small molecular weight (17,000 kDa), and is not complexed to other proteins in the cell. *Da* is the abbreviation for the dalton, which is a unit of mass approximately equal to one H atom. Thus, a molecular weight of 17,000 kDa is equal to approximately 17,000 g/mol. Large injuries to skeletal muscle that result from physical crushing or lack of ATP production result in cellular swelling and the release of myoglobin and other proteins into the blood. Myoglobin passes into the urine (myoglobinuria) and turns the urine red because the heme (which is red) remains covalently attached to the protein. During an acute MI, myoglobin is one of the first proteins released into the blood from damaged cardiac tissue; however, the amount released is not high enough to cause myoglobinuria. Laboratory measurements of serum myoglobin were used in the past for early diagnosis in patients, such as **Ann Jeina**. Because myoglobin is not present in skeletal muscle and the heart as tissue-specific isozymes, and the amount released from the heart is much smaller than the amount that can be released from a large skeletal muscle injury, myoglobin measurements are not specific for an MI. Because of the lack of specificity in myoglobin measurements, the cardiac markers of choice for detection of MIs are the heart isozyme of the troponins (I and/or T), and creatine kinase (CK).

FIG. 7.13. Oxygen binding to the Fe^{2+} of heme in hemoglobin. **A.** A histidine residue called the proximal histidine binds to the Fe^{2+} on one side of the porphyrin ring; O_2 binds to Fe^{2+} on the other side. **B.** O_2 binding causes a conformational change that pulls the Fe^{2+} back into the plane of the ring. As the proximal histidine moves, it moves the helix that contains it.

Sickle cell anemia is really a disease caused by the wrong quaternary structure. The painful vaso-occlusive crises experienced by **Will Sichel** are caused by the polymerization of sickle cell hemoglobin (HbS) molecules into long fibers that distort the shape of the red blood cells into sickle cells. The substitution of a hydrophobic valine for a glutamate in the β_2 chain creates a hydrophobic knob on the surface of deoxygenated hemoglobin that fits into a hydrophobic binding pocket on the β_1 subunit of a different hemoglobin molecule. A third hemoglobin molecule, which binds to the first and second hemoglobin molecules through aligned polar interactions, binds a fourth hemoglobin molecule through its valine knob. Thus, the polymerization continues until long fibers are formed.

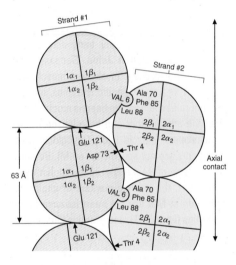

Polymerization of the hemoglobin molecules highly depends on the concentration of HbS and is promoted by the conformation of the deoxygenated molecules. At 100% oxygen saturation, even high concentrations of HbS will not polymerize. A red blood cell spends the longest amount of time at the lower oxygen concentrations of the venous capillary bed, where polymerization is most likely initiated.

to chelate six different ligands; four of the ligand positions are in a plane and taken by the central nitrogens in the planar porphyrin ring. Two ligand positions are perpendicular to this plane. One of these positions is taken by the nitrogen atom on a histidine—called the *proximal histidine*—which extends down from a myoglobin helix. The other position is taken by O_2, carbon monoxide (CO), or remains empty.

The proximal histidine of myoglobin and hemoglobin is sterically repelled by the heme porphyrin ring. Thus, when the histidine binds to the Fe^{2+} in the middle of the ring, it pulls the Fe^{2+} above the plane of the ring (see Fig. 7.13A). When oxygen binds on the other side of the ring, it pulls the Fe^{2+} back into the plane of the ring (see Fig. 7.13B). The pull of O_2 binding moves the proximal histidine toward the porphyrin ring, which moves the helix containing the proximal histidine. This conformational change has no effect on the function of myoglobin. However, in hemoglobin, the movement of one helix leads to the movement of other helices in that subunit, including one in a corner of the subunit that is in contact with a different subunit through ionic interactions (salt bridges). The loss of these salt bridges then induces conformational changes in all other subunits, and all four subunits may change in a concerted manner from their original conformation to a new conformation (see Biochemical Comments).

B. Cooperativity of O_2 Binding in Hemoglobin

The cooperativity in oxygen binding in hemoglobin comes from conformational changes in tertiary structure that take place when O_2 binds (Fig. 7.14). The conformational change of hemoglobin is usually described as changing from a *T* (tense) state with low affinity for O_2 to an *R* (relaxed) state with a high affinity for O_2. Breaking the salt bridges in the contacts between subunits is an energy-requiring process and, consequently, the binding rate for the first oxygen is very low. When the next oxygen binds, many of the hemoglobin molecules containing one O_2 will already have all four subunits in the R state; therefore, the rate of binding is much higher. With two O_2 molecules bound, an even higher percentage of the hemoglobin molecules will have all four subunits in the R state. This phenomenon, known as *positive cooperativity*, is responsible for the sigmoidal oxygen saturation curve of hemoglobin (see Fig. 7.11). Other factors that alter oxygen binding to hemoglobin are discussed in Chapter 44.

VIII. STRUCTURE–FUNCTION RELATIONSHIPS IN IMMUNOGLOBULINS

The *immunoglobulins* (or antibodies) are one line of defense against invasion of the body by foreign organisms. In this capacity, they function by binding to ligands called *antigens* on the invading organisms, thereby initiating the process by which these organisms are inactivated or destroyed.

Immunoglobulins all have a similar structure; each antibody molecule contains two identical small polypeptide chains (the light or L chains) and two identical large polypeptide chains (the heavy or H chains) (Fig. 7.15). The chains are joined to each other by disulfide bonds.

The body has five major classes of immunoglobulins. The most abundant immunoglobulin in human blood is the γ-globulins, which belong to the IgG class. The γ-globulins have approximately 220 amino acids in their light chains and 440 in their heavy chains. Like most serum proteins, they have attached oligosaccharides that participate in targeting the protein for clearance from the blood. Both the light and heavy chains consist of domains known as the *immunoglobulin fold*, which is a collapsed number of β-sheets, known as a β-barrel (Fig. 7.16).

Both the light and heavy chains contain regions termed as *variable* (V) and *constant* (C) regions. The variable regions of the L and H chains (V_L and V_H,

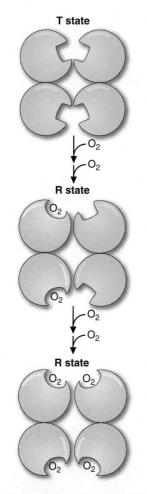

FIG. 7.14. Equilibria for binding of O_2 molecules to hemoglobin according to the concerted model of Monod, Wyman, and Changeux. Hemoglobin exists in two alternate conformations, the T (tense) state with a low affinity for O_2, and the R (relaxed) state with a higher affinity. In the T subunits, the binding sites are hindered, and in the R state, the binding sites are open. Each successive addition of O_2 shifts the equilibrium further toward the R state. Because the conformation of all the subunits can change when O_2 binds to one subunit, O_2 binding is said to follow the concerted model. Most of the molecules change to the R state when two O_2 molecules have bound.

respectively) interact to produce a single antigen-binding site at each branch of the Y-shaped molecule. Each population (clone) of B cells produces an antibody with a different amino acid composition in the variable region that is complementary to the structure of the antigen that elicits the response. The K_d of antibodies for their specific antigens is extremely small and varies from approximately 10^{-7} to 10^{-11} M. The antigen thus binds very tightly with almost no tendency to dissociate and can be removed from circulation as the antigen–antibody complex is ingested by macrophages. The constant domains that form the Fc part of the antibody are important for binding of the antigen–antibody complex to phagocytic cells for clearance and for other aspects of the immune response.

IX. PROTEIN FOLDING

Although the peptide bonds in a protein are rigid, flexibility around the other bonds in the peptide backbone allows an enormous number of possible conformations for each protein. However, every molecule of the same protein folds

Amy Lloyd's serum protein electrophoresis indicated a sharp narrow peak or homogeneous "spike" in the characteristic γ-globulin zone known as an *M protein* (monoclonal-protein) component. A narrow peak or spike in electrophoresis, which separates proteins according to charge distribution of the side chains, suggests an elevation of proteins with a similar or identical structure. Subsequently, it was shown that Amy Lloyd's immunoglobulin M-component was composed of a single homogeneous type of immunoglobulin (just one amino acid sequence in the N-terminal variable region). Thus, the M protein was produced by a single clone of antibody-secreting cells (cells that all arose from proliferation of one cell) in the bone marrow (called *plasma cell dyscrasia*).

In amyloidosis/AL, amyloid is formed from degradation products of the λ- or κ-light chains that deposit most frequently in the extracellular matrix of the kidney and the heart, but also may deposit in the tongue. In other types of amyloidosis, the amyloid arises from other proteins and deposits in a characteristic organ. For example, the amyloid associated with chronic inflammatory conditions, such as rheumatoid arthritis, is derived from the serum protein called *serum amyloid A* that is produced by the liver in response to inflammation. It deposits most frequently in the kidney.

The treatment of AL is multifactorial and only partially successful. Initially, alkylating agents were used to reduce the synthesis of immunoglobulin light chains by plasma cells, but were found to be too toxic for routine use. The most efficacious approach involves the use of stem cell transplantation in concert with immunosuppression. If the patient is not a candidate for transplantation, then drugs such as melphalan (an antineoplastic agent) and dexamethasone (a steroid) can be used.

Renal transplantation and cardiac transplantation have been performed in patients with renal and cardiac amyloidosis, respectively, with some success.

FIG. 7.15. Structure of immunoglobulins. **A.** Each IgG molecule contains two light (L) and two heavy (H) chains joined by disulfide bonds. Each light chain contains two domains: a variable domain (V_L) and a region of constant amino acid sequence (C_L). Each heavy chain has four domains: one variable domain (V_H) and three constant domains (C_H). The conformation of the constant domain contains the β-sheets that are called the immunoglobulin fold. The variable domains are specific for the antigen that is bound, whereas the constant regions are the same for all antibody molecules of a given class. Carbohydrate ($-CHO$) is bound as indicated within the constant region of the heavy chains. The hinge region allows flexibility when the molecule binds antigen. **B.** In the space-filling model, the light chains are light in color and the heavy chains are two different shades of orange. (Modified from Silverton EW, Navia MA, Davies DR, et al. Three-dimensional structure of an intact human immunoglobulin. *Proc Natl Acad Sci U S A.* 1977;11:5142.)

V$_L$ domain

C$_L$ domain

FIG. 7.16. Structure of the V$_L$ and C$_L$ domains of IgG. Layers of antiparallel β-sheets are stacked in these domains, which has been referred to as collapsed β-barrels (one can envision a hollow space between the β-sheets, which define the barrel). The antigen binds between the V$_H$ and V$_L$ immunoglobulin folds, and *not* in the barrel. The C$_L$ domain is also called the immunoglobulin fold. (Top modified from Richardson JS. The anatomy and taxonomy of protein structure. *Adv Protein Chem*. 1981;34:167; bottom reprinted in part with permission from Edmundson AB, Ely KR, Abola EE, et al. Rational allomerism and divergent evolution of domains in immunoglobulin light chains. *Biochemistry*. 1975;14:3954. Copyright 1975 American Chemical Society.)

 The tight binding affinity of immunoglobulins for their specific antigen makes them useful for the measurement of small amounts of other compounds in various radioimmunoassays. The principle of the radioimmunoassay is that the immunoglobulin will specifically bind the compound being measured, and an additional component of the system that is labeled with a radioactive chemical will bind the immunoglobulin. The complex is then separated from the solution and the bound radioactivity is measured. The different isozymes of creatine kinase (CK) and troponin T (TnT) used to track **Ann Jeina's** MI are measured with a type of radioimmunoassay by using antibodies specific for each isozyme. This method is much faster than the laborious separation of isozymes by electrophoresis. Radioimmunoassays are also useful for measuring the small amounts of hormones present in the blood for diagnosis of endocrine diseases.

into the same stable three-dimensional structure. This shape is known as the *native conformation.*

A. Primary Structure Determines Folding

The primary structure of a protein determines its three-dimensional conformation. More specifically, the sequence of amino acid side chains dictates the fold pattern of the three-dimensional structure and the assembly of subunits into quaternary structure. Under certain conditions, denatured proteins can refold into their native conformation, regaining their original function. Proteins can be denatured with organic molecules such as urea that disrupt hydrogen-bonding patterns (both of the protein and of water) and convert the protein to a soluble random coil. Many simple single-subunit proteins such as ribonuclease that are denatured in this way refold spontaneously into their native conformation if they are carefully brought back to physiologic conditions. Even complex multisubunit proteins containing bound cofactors can sometimes renature spontaneously under the right conditions. Thus, the primary structure essentially specifies the folding pattern. Very little difference is seen in the energy state of the native state and several other stable conformations that a protein might assume. If misfolded proteins do not precipitate into aggregates, they can be degraded in the cell by proteolytic reactions, or even refolded.

In the cell, not all proteins fold into their native conformation on their own. As the protein folds and refolds while it is searching for its native low-energy

 Treatment of mature insulin (see Fig. 6.12) with denaturing agents, followed by renaturation, does not restore mature insulin activity (a result distinct from which occurred when the experiment was done with ribonuclease). Why does renaturation of denatured mature insulin not result in restoration of biological activity?

Recall, the primary structure of a protein dictates the folding pattern of the protein. The primary structure of mature insulin is different than that of its precursor—preproinsulin. Proinsulin forms the three-dimensional structure, and then the C-peptide is removed from the protein by proteolytic cleavage, thereby altering the primary structure of the protein. This change in primary structure (the loss of the C-peptide) does not allow the denatured mature insulin to refold into an active conformation.

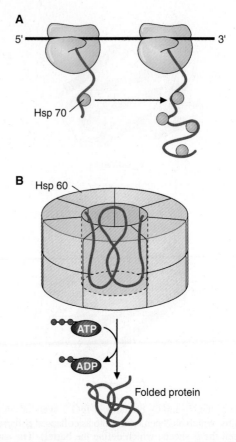

FIG. 7.17. Role of heat-shock proteins in folding. **A.** The hsp70 family of proteins prevents folding of the nascent chain and promote unfolding. The ATPase domain of the protein has the actin fold. This figure depicts the synthesis of protein from ribosomes bound to mRNA in the cytoplasm (see Chapter 15). **B.** The hsp60 class of protein has a barrel shape into which the protein fits. It acts as a template, binding and rebinding portions of the unfolded protein until folding is completed. It hydrolyzes many ATP bonds (generating ADP) to provide energy for the process.

state, it passes through many high-energy conformations that slow the process (called *kinetic barriers*). These kinetic barriers can be overcome by heat-shock proteins, which use energy provided by ATP hydrolysis to assist in the folding process (Fig. 7.17). Heat-shock proteins were named because their synthesis in bacteria increased when the temperature was raised suddenly. They are present in human cells as different families of proteins with different activities. For example, the hsp70 proteins bind to nascent polypeptide chains as their synthesis is being completed to keep the uncompleted chains from folding prematurely. They also unfold proteins before their insertion through the membrane of mitochondria and other organelles. The multisubunit barrel-shaped hsp60 family of proteins is called *chaperonins*. The unfolded protein fits into the barrel cavity that excludes water and serves as a template for the folding process. The hydrolysis of several ATP molecules is used to overcome the energy barriers to reaching the native conformation.

A *cis–trans* isomerase and a protein disulfide isomerase also participate in folding. The *cis–trans* isomerase converts a *trans* peptide bond preceding a proline into the *cis* conformation, which is well suited for making hairpin turns. The protein disulfide isomerase breaks and reforms disulfide bonds between the –SH groups of two cysteine residues in transient structures formed during the folding process. After the protein has folded, cysteine–SH groups in close contact in the tertiary structure can react to form the final disulfide bonds.

B. Protein Denaturation

1. DENATURATION THROUGH NONENZYMATIC MODIFICATION OF PROTEINS

Amino acids on proteins can undergo a wide range of chemical modifications that are not catalyzed by enzymes, such as nonenzymatic glycosylation or oxidation. Such modifications lead to a loss of function and denaturation of the protein, sometimes to a form that cannot be degraded in the cell. In nonenzymatic glycosylation, glucose that is present in blood, or in interstitial or intracellular fluid, binds to an exposed amino group on a protein (Fig. 7.18). The two-step process forms an irreversibly glycosylated protein. Proteins that turn over very slowly in the body, such as collagen or hemoglobin, exist with a significant fraction present in the glycosylated form. Because the reaction is nonenzymatic, the rate of glycosylation is proportionate to the concentration of glucose present, and individuals with hyperglycemia have much higher levels of glycosylated proteins than individuals with normal blood glucose levels. Collagen and other glycosylated proteins in tissues are further modified by nonenzymatic oxidation and form additional cross-links. The net result is the formation of large protein aggregates referred to as *advanced glycosylation end products* (AGEs). AGE is a particularly meaningful acronym because AGEs accumulate with age, even in individuals with normal blood glucose levels.

2. PROTEIN DENATURATION BY TEMPERATURE, PH, AND SOLVENT

Proteins can be denatured by changes—pH, temperature, or solvent—that disrupt ionic, hydrogen, and hydrophobic bonds. At a low pH, ionic bonds and hydrogen bonds formed by carboxylate groups would be disrupted; at a very alkaline pH, hydrogen and ionic bonds formed by the basic amino acids would be disrupted. Thus, the pH of the body must be maintained within a range compatible with three-dimensional structure.

Physiologically, proteins are denatured by the gastric juice of the stomach, which has a pH of 1 to 2. Although this pH cannot break peptide bonds, disruption of the native conformation makes the protein a better substrate for digestive enzymes. Temperature increases vibrational and rotational energies in the bonds, thereby affecting the energy balance that goes into making a stable three-dimensional conformation. Thermal denaturation is often illustrated by the process of cooking an egg. With heat, the protein albumin converts from its native translucent state to a denatured white precipitate. Protein precipitates can sometimes be dissolved by amphipathic agents such as urea, guanidine hydrochloride (HCl), or sodium dodecylsulfate (SDS) that form extensive hydrogen bonds and hydrophobic interactions with the protein.

Hydrophobic molecules can also denature proteins by disturbing hydrophobic interactions in the protein. For example, long-chain fatty acids can inhibit many enzyme-catalyzed reactions by binding nonspecifically to hydrophobic pockets in proteins and disrupting hydrophobic interactions. Thus, long-chain fatty acids and other highly hydrophobic molecules have their own binding proteins in the cell.

3. PROTEIN MISFOLDING AND PRIONS

Prion proteins are believed to cause a neurodegenerative disease by acting as a template to misfold other cellular prion proteins into a form that cannot be degraded. The word "prion" stands for proteinaceous infectious agent. The prion diseases can be acquired either through infection (mad cow disease) or from sporadic or inherited mutations (e.g., Creutzfeldt-Jakob disease [CJD]). Although the infectious prion diseases represent a small proportion of human cases, their link to mad cow disease in the United Kingdom (new-variant CJD), to growth-hormone inoculations in the United States and France (iatrogenic or "doctor-induced" CJD), and to ritualistic cannibalism in the Fore tribespeople (Kuru) have received the most publicity.

FIG. 7.18. Nonenzymatic glycosylation of hemoglobin. Glucose forms a Schiff base with the N-terminal amino group of the protein, which rearranges to form a stable glycosylated product. Similar nonenzymatic glycosylation reactions occur on other proteins. Four minor components of adult hemoglobin (HbA) result from posttranslational, nonenzymatic glycosylation of different amino acid residues (HbA1a1, HbA1a2, HbA1b1, and HbA1c). In HbA1c, the fraction that is usually measured, the glycosylation occurs on an N-terminal valine.

Di Abietes's physician used her glycosylated hemoglobin levels, specifically the HbA1c fraction, to determine whether she had sustained hyperglycemia over a long period. The rate of irreversible nonenzymatic glycosylation of hemoglobin and other proteins is directly proportional to the glucose concentration to which they are exposed over the last 4 months. The danger of sustained hyperglycemia is that, over time, many proteins become glycosylated and subsequently oxidized, affecting their solubility and ability to function. The glycosylation of collagen in the heart, for example, is believed to result in a cardiomyopathy in patients with chronic uncontrolled diabetes mellitus. In contrast, glycosylation of hemoglobin has little effect on its function.

Prion diseases are categorized as transmissible spongiform encephalopathies, which are neurodegenerative diseases characterized by spongiform degeneration and astrocytic gliosis in the central nervous system. Frequently, protein aggregates and amyloid plaques are seen. These aggregates are resistant to proteolytic degradation.

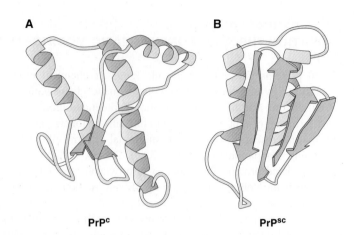

FIG. 7.19. The conformation of PrP^c (normal) and PrP^{sc} (disease form). The prion proteins have two domains: an N-terminal region that binds four Cu^{2+} per chain, and a C-terminal region. In PrP^c, the C-terminal regions contain three substantial helices and two three-residue β-strands joined by two to three hydrogen bonds (approximately 40% α-helix and almost no β-sheet structure). It exists as a monomer. In PrP^{sc}, the C-terminal region is folded into an extensive β-sheet. The overall structure is approximately 40% to 50% β-sheet and 20% to 30% α-helices. This conformation promotes aggregation.

Familial prion diseases are caused by point mutations in the gene encoding the Pr protein (point mutations are changes in one base in the DNA nucleotide sequence). The diseases have various names related to the different mutations and the clinical syndrome (e.g., Gerstmann-Straussler-Scheinker disease and familial Creutzfeldt-Jakob disease [fCJD]). fCJD arises from an inherited mutation and has an autosomal dominant pedigree. It typically presents in the fourth decade of life. The mutation lowers the energy required for the protein to fold into the PrP^{Sc} conformation, thereby the conversion occurs more readily. It is estimated that the rate of generating prion disease by refolding of PrP^c in the normal cell is approximately 3,000 to 4,000 years. Lowering of the activation energy for refolding by mutation presumably decreases this time to the observed 30- to 40-year prodromal period. Sporadic CJD may arise from somatic cell mutation or rare spontaneous refolding that initiates a cascade of refolding into the PrP^{Sc} conformation. The sporadic form of the disease accounts for 85% of all cases of CJD.

The prion protein is normally found in the brain and is encoded by a gene that is a normal component of the human genome. The disease-causing form of the prion protein has the same amino acid composition but is folded into a different conformation that aggregates into multimeric protein complexes resistant to proteolytic degradation (Fig. 7.19). The normal conformation of the prion protein has been designated PrP^c and the disease-causing form as PrP^{Sc} (sc for the prion disease scrapies in sheep). Although PrP^{Sc} and PrP^c have the same amino acid composition, the PrP^{Sc} conformer is substantially enriched in β-sheet structure compared with the normal PrP^c conformer, which has little or no β-sheet structure and is approximately 40% α-helix. This difference favors the aggregation of PrP^{Sc} into multimeric complexes. These two conformations presumably have similar energy levels. Fortunately, spontaneous refolding of PrP proteins into the PrP^{Sc} conformation is prevented by a large activation energy barrier that makes this conversion extremely slow. Thus, very few molecules of PrP^{Sc} are normally formed during a lifetime.

The infectious disease occurs with the ingestion of PrP^{Sc} dimers in which the prion protein is already folded into the high β-structure. These PrP^{Sc} proteins are thought to act as a template to lower the activation energy barrier for the conformational change, causing native proteins to refold into the PrP^{Sc} conformation much more rapidly (much like the role of chaperonins). The refolding initiates a cascade as each new PrP^{Sc} formed acts as a template for the refolding of other molecules. As the number of PrP^{Sc} molecules increases in the cell, they aggregate into a multimeric assembly that is resistant to proteolytic digestion. Once an aggregate begins to form, the concentration of free PrP^{Sc} decreases, thereby shifting the equilibrium between PrP and PrP^{Sc} to produce more PrP^{Sc}. This leads to further aggregate formation through the shift in equilibrium.

CLINICAL COMMENTS

Will Sichel. Will Sichel continued to experience severe low back and lower extremity pain for many hours after admission. The diffuse pains of sickle cell crises are believed to result from occlusion of small vessels in various tissues, which deprives cells of oxygen and cause, ischemic or anoxic damage to the tissues. In a sickle cell crisis, long hemoglobin polymers form, causing the red blood cells to become distorted and change from a biconcave disc to an irregular shape, such as a sickle (for which the disease was named) or a stellate structure (Fig. 7.20). The aggregating hemoglobin polymers damage the cellular membrane and promote aggregation of membrane proteins, increased permeability of the cell, and dehydration. Surface charge and antigens of red blood cells are carried on the transmembrane proteins glycophorin and band 3 (the erythrocyte anion-exchange channel, see Chapter 10). Hemoglobin S binds tightly to the cytoplasmic portion of band 3, contributing to further polymer aggregation and uneven distribution of negative charge on the sickle cell surface. As a result, the affected cells adhere to endothelial cells in capillaries, occluding the vessel and decreasing blood flow to the distal tissues. The subsequent hypoxia in these tissues causes cellular damage, severe ischemic pain, and even death.

The sickled cells are sequestered and destroyed mainly by phagocytic cells, particularly those in the spleen. An anemia results as the number of circulating red blood cells decreases and bilirubin levels rise in the blood as hemoglobin is degraded.

After a few days of treatment, Will's crisis was resolved. In the future, should Will suffer a cerebrovascular accident as a consequence of vascular occlusion or have recurrent life-threatening episodes, a course of long-term maintenance blood transfusions to prevent repeated sickle crises may be indicated. Iron chelation would have to accompany such a program to prevent or delay the development of iron overload. Although a few individuals with this disease have survived into the sixth decade, mean survival is probably into the fourth decade. Death usually results from renal failure or cardiopulmonary disease.

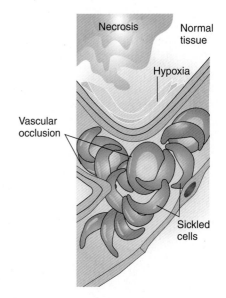

FIG. 7.20. Sickled red blood cells occlude a blood vessel, causing hypoxia (low O_2 in cells) and necrosis (cell death).

Anne Jeina. Mrs. Jeina's diagnosis of an acute MI was based partly on measurements of creatine kinase, muscle–brain fraction (CK-MB); myoglobin; and cardiac troponin T (cTnT) (the cardiac isozyme of troponin T, a subunit of the regulatory protein troponin). Early diagnosis is critical for a decision on the type of therapeutic intervention to be used. Of these proteins, myoglobin appears in the blood most rapidly. However, its levels are relatively nonspecific for cardiac injury because the amino acid sequences of cardiac and skeletal muscle myoglobins are identical. Myoglobin measurements do have a very high negative predictive value within the 2- to 6-hour period after the onset of symptoms (i.e., if myoglobin is not elevated, an MI did not occur). In contrast, serum cTnT is a relatively late but highly specific marker of myocardial injury. It is typically detected in an acute MI within 3 to 5 hours after onset of symptoms, positive in most cases within 8 hours, and approaches 100% sensitivity at 10 to 12 hours. It remains elevated for 5 to 10 days.

Mrs. Jeina stayed in the hospital until she had been free of chest pain for 5 days. She was discharged on a low-fat diet and was asked to participate in the hospital's cardiac rehabilitation program for patients recovering from a recent heart attack. Her physician scheduled her for regular examinations.

Amy Lloyd. Amy Lloyd has amyloidosis/AL, which is characterized by deposition of amyloid fibers derived principally from the variable region of λ- or κ-immunoglobulin light chains. Increased amounts of the fragments of the light chains called *Bence-Jones proteins* appeared in her urine. Fibril deposition in the extracellular matrix of her kidney glomeruli has resulted in mild renal failure. Deposition of amyloid in the extracellular matrix of her heart muscle resulted in the cardiac arrhythmia seen on an electrocardiogram. In addition to other signs of right-sided heart failure, she had peripheral edema. The loss of weight may have been caused by infiltrations of amyloid in the gastrointestinal tract or by constipation and diarrhea resulting from involvement of the autonomic nervous system. Treatment may be directed against the plasma cell proliferation

Troponin is a heterotrimeric protein involved in the regulation of striated and cardiac muscle contraction. Most troponin in the cell is bound to the actin–tropomyosin complex in the muscle fibril. The three subunits of troponin consist of troponin C, troponin T, and troponin I, each with a specific function in the regulatory process. Troponin T and troponin I exist as different isoforms in cardiac and skeletal muscle (sequences with a different amino acid composition), thus allowing the development of specific antibodies against each form. As a consequence, either cardiac troponin T or cardiac troponin I may be rapidly measured in blood samples by immunoassay with a good degree of specificity.

and against the symptomatic results of organ dysfunction, and is only partially successful. Initially, alkylating agents were used to reduce the synthesis of immunoglobulin light chains by plasma cells but were found to be too toxic for routine use. The most efficacious approach involves the use of stem cell transplantation in concert with immunosuppression. If the patient is not a candidate for transplantation, then drugs such as melphalan (an antineoplastic agent) and dexamethasone (a steroid) can be used. Renal transplantation and cardiac transplantation have been performed in patients with renal and cardiac AL, respectively, with some success.

During Amy's evaluation, she developed a cardiac arrhythmia that was refractory to treatment. The extensive amyloid deposits in her heart had disrupted the flow of electrical impulses in the conduction system of the heart, ultimately resulting in cardiac arrest. On autopsy, amyloid deposits were found within the heart, tongue, liver, adipose tissue, and every organ examined except the central nervous system, which is protected by the blood–brain barrier.

Dianne Abietes. Di Abietes's HbA1c of 8.5% was greater than the normal range (5.8% to 7.2% of total hemoglobin), and her physician decided to slightly alter her insulin treatment plan. *Glycosylation* is a nonenzymatic reaction that occurs with a rate directly proportionate to the concentration of glucose in the blood. In the normal range of blood glucose concentrations (approximately 80 to 140 mg/dL, depending on time after a meal), 4% to 6% of the hemoglobin is glycosylated to form HbA1c. Hemoglobin turns over in the blood as red blood cells are phagocytosed and their hemoglobin degraded and new red blood cells are derived from reticulocytes. The average life span of a red blood cell is 120 days. Thus, the extent of hemoglobin glycosylation is a direct reflection of the average serum glucose concentration to which the cell has been exposed during its 120-day life span. Di's elevated HbA1c indicates that, on average, her blood glucose levels have been elevated more than the preceding 6 weeks to 4 months. An increase of her insulin dosage would decrease the severity of her hyperglycemia and would, over time, decrease her HbA1c level as well. There will also be a slightly increased risk of hypoglycemic events.

BIOCHEMICAL COMMENTS

The Basics of Hemoglobin Cooperativity. Using X-ray diffraction to study both the oxygenated and deoxygenated forms of hemoglobin, it is now possible to describe the change in conformation at the molecular level when oxygen binds to hemoglobin. We will present a simplistic approach here, looking at interactions that the β-subunit experiences and having oxygen bind initially to one of the two β-subunits in the hemoglobin tetramer. All of the subunits of hemoglobin contain eight helices (labeled A through H), with A representing the helix at the amino-terminal end. The deoxygenated form of hemoglobin is stabilized by the following interactions, which are also depicted in Figure 7.21:

1. Asp 94 (of the F helix of the β-chain), through its carboxylate side chain, forms a salt bridge (ionic interaction) with the charged imidazole group of His 146, which is the carboxy-terminal amino acid in the β-chain.
2. The carbonyl carbon of Val 98 forms a hydrogen bond with the tyrosine hydroxyl group at position 145 (the next-to-last amino acid in the β-chain). The effect of these first two interactions is to position helices F and H in close proximity to each other.
3. The free carboxylate group of His 146 (of the β-chain) forms a salt bridge with the ε-amino group of the side chain of Lys 40 of the corresponding α-chain. This salt bridge allows communication between these two subunits, and places the β-chain H helix close to the α-subunit.

A. No oxygen

B. Plus oxygen

FIG. 7.21.   Molecular changes that occur when oxygen binds to hemoglobin. See the text for details. **A.** Interactions in the absence of oxygen. **B.** The loss of stabilizing interactions when oxygen binds.

In the β-chain, the proximal His 92 (the eighth amino acid of the F helix, F8) forms a coordinate covalent bond with the iron in heme, and in so doing, pulls the iron slightly out of the plane of the heme ring. These interactions are all occurring in the deoxygenated state.

So what happens when oxygen binds to a β-subunit? Oxygen binds to the iron in a bent conformation. The binding event triggers the movement of the iron into the plane of the heme ring. Because the iron is also covalently linked to histidine F8, the entire F helix and the FG corner (where the F and G helices meet) also move.

1. Asp 94 is in the F helix. Because it is moved (because of the movement of the F helix), it can no longer form a salt bridge with the imidazole of His 146, which weakens the interactions between the F and H helices.
2. Valine 98 is in the FG corner of the β-subunit, so as that moves, the hydrogen bond formed between Val 98 and Tyr 145 (at the end of the H helix) is also broken.
3. Caused in part by the loss of interactions between the F and H helices, the H helix moves, and in so doing, breaks the ionic interaction between His 146 and Lys 40 of the α-subunit. This, along with other changes, leads to a rotation of one $\alpha\beta$-dimer relative to the other $\alpha\beta$-dimer, and will allow oxygen to bind more readily to the other subunits.

The disruption of the bonds listed earlier has to occur for oxygen to bind. This is why it takes a high concentration of oxygen to get the first oxygen bound to hemoglobin. At low oxygen levels, the oxygen can dissociate from the iron, which allows the T form to re-form, and allow the salt bridges and hydrogen bonds, which stabilize the deoxygenated form, to re-form. If the oxygen concentration is high, such that the iron is continuously occupied with oxygen, the events described earlier are more likely to occur, and the oxygenation of hemoglobin will occur.

Key Concepts

- There are four levels of protein structure:
  - The primary structure (linear sequence of amino acids within the protein)
  - The secondary structure (a regular, repeating pattern of hydrogen bonds that stabilize a particular structure)
  - The tertiary structure (the folding of the secondary structure elements into a three-dimensional conformation)
  - The quaternary structure (the association of subunits within a protein)
- The primary structure of a protein determines the way a protein folds into a unique three-dimensional structure, called its native conformation.
- When globular proteins fold, the tertiary structure generally forms a densely packed hydrophobic core with polar amino acid side chains on the outside, facing the aqueous environment.
- The tertiary structure of a protein consists of one or more structural domains, which may be similar between different proteins, and perform similar functions for the different proteins.
- Certain structural domains are binding sites for specific molecules, called *ligands*, or for other proteins.
- The affinity of a binding site for its ligand is characterized quantitatively by an association or affinity constant, K_a (or dissociation constant, K_d).
- Protein denaturation is the loss of tertiary (and/or secondary) structure within a protein, which can be caused by heat, acid, or other agents that interfere with hydrogen bonding, and usually causes a decrease in solubility (precipitation).
- Diseases discussed in this chapter are summarized in Table 7.1.

Table 7.1   Diseases Discussed in Chapter 7

Disorder or Condition	Genetic or Environmental	Comments
Myocardial infarction	Both	Specific heart proteins analyzed include myoglobin (not heart-specific), creatine kinase MB (heart-specific isozyme), and cardiac troponin (cTn) (cardiac-specific isozyme). Myoglobin is the least specific marker, whereas cTn is the most specific marker for evidence of heart muscle damage.
Amyloidosis	Both	A generic name for the extracellular deposition of pathologic insoluble proteins called amyloid, which are located in organs and tissues. In this chapter, the amyloid is derived from the immunoglobulin light chain. In this disorder, the amyloid will accumulate in the kidney and heart, leading to renal and cardiac-related symptoms.
Sickle cell disease	Genetic	Hemoglobin S polymerization under deoxygenated conditions as a result of hydrophobic interactions caused by the valine in position 6 of the β-chain, instead of glutamic acid. This leads to alterations in red blood cell shape, which causes occluded capillaries. The lack of blood flow through the capillaries will lead to hypoxia and tissue damage, which generates some of the pain endured during a sickle cell crisis.
Diabetes, types 1 and 2	Both	The use of glycosylated hemoglobin (HbA1c) to determine glycemic control in the diabetic patient. HbA1c is generated by the nonenzymatic glycosylation of hemoglobin. The extent of this reaction depends on the glucose levels in the circulation. The higher the blood glucose levels, the greater the extent of glycosylation.
Prion diseases	Both	Protein aggregation diseases because of altered tertiary structure for proteins with the same, or slightly altered, primary structure. The aggregates that form precipitate in the brain, leading to eventual neural degeneration and loss of function.

1. Which of the following characterize α-helix regions of proteins?

   A. They all have the same primary structure.
   B. They are formed principally by hydrogen bonds between a carbonyl oxygen atom in one peptide bond and the amide hydrogen from a different peptide bond.
   C. They are formed principally by hydrogen bonds between a carbonyl atom in one peptide bond and the hydrogen atoms on the side chain of another amino acid.
   D. They are formed by hydrogen bonding between two adjacent amino acids in the primary sequence.
   E. They require a high content of proline and glycine.

2. Which of the following is a characteristic of globular proteins?

   A. Hydrophilic amino acids tend to be on the inside.
   B. Hydrophobic amino acids tend to be on the outside.
   C. Tertiary structure is formed by hydrophobic and electrostatic interactions between amino acid side chains and by hydrogen bonds between peptide bonds.
   D. Secondary structures are formed principally by hydrophobic interactions between amino acids.
   E. Covalent disulfide bonds are necessary to hold the protein in a rigid conformation.

3. A protein has one transmembrane domain composed entirely of α-helical secondary structure. Which of the following amino acids would you expect to find in the transmembrane domain?

   A. Proline
   B. Glutamate
   C. Lysine
   D. Leucine
   E. Arginine

4. Autopsies of patients with Alzheimer disease show protein aggregates called *neurofibrillary tangles* and *neuritic plaques* in various regions of the brain. These plaques exhibit the characteristic staining of amyloid. Which of the following structural features is the most likely characteristic of at least one protein in these plaques?

   A. A high content of β-pleated sheet structure
   B. A high content of α-helical structure
   C. A high content of random coils
   D. Disulfide bond cross-links between polypeptide chains
   E. A low-energy native conformation

5. While studying a novel pathway in a remote species of bacteria, you discover a new globular protein that phosphorylates a substrate, using ATP as the phosphate donor. Which of the following structures most likely contains this protein?

   A. An actin fold
   B. An immunoglobulin fold
   C. A nucleotide-binding fold
   D. A globin fold
   E. A β-barrel

**After 1 year
in the absence of enzyme**

8 ft

12 ft

12 ft

**After 1 second
with one molecule of enzyme**

8 ft

12 ft

12 ft

FIG. 8.1. Catalytic power of enzymes. Many enzymes increase the rate of a chemical reaction by a factor of 10^{11} or higher. To appreciate an increase in reaction rate by this order of magnitude, consider a room-sized box of golf balls that "react" by releasing energy and turning brown. The 12 ft $\times$ 12 ft $\times$ 8 ft box contains 380,000 golf balls. If the rate of the reaction in the absence of enzyme were 100 golf balls per year, the presence of 1 molecule of enzyme would turn the entire box of golf balls brown in 1 second (assuming a 10^{11} increase in reaction rate).

*Enzymes are proteins that act as **catalysts**, compounds that increase the rate of chemical reactions (Fig. 8.1). Enzyme catalysts bind reactants (substrates), convert them to products, and release the products. Although enzymes may be modified during their participation in this reaction sequence, they return to their original form at the end. In addition to increasing the speed of reactions, enzymes provide a means for regulating the rate of metabolic pathways in the body. This chapter describes the properties of enzymes that allow them to function as catalysts. The next chapter explains the mechanisms of enzyme regulation.*

*   **Enzyme-Binding Sites.** An enzyme binds the **substrates** of the reaction and converts them to **products**. The substrates are bound to specific **substrate-binding sites** on the enzyme through interactions with the amino acid residues of the enzyme. The spatial geometry required for all the interactions between the substrate and the enzyme makes each enzyme **selective for** its **substrates** and ensures that only **specific products** are formed.*

*   **Active Catalytic Sites.** The substrate-binding sites overlap in the **active catalytic site** of the enzyme, the region of the enzyme where the reaction occurs. Within the catalytic site, **functional groups** provided by **coenzymes, tightly bound metals**, and, of course, **amino acid residues** of the enzyme participate in catalysis.*

*   **Activation Energy and the Transition State.** The functional groups in the catalytic site of the enzyme activate the substrate and decrease the energy needed to form the high-energy intermediate stage of the reaction known as the **transition-state complex**. Some of the catalytic strategies employed by enzymes, such as **general acid–base catalysis**, formation of **covalent intermediates**, and **stabilization of the transition state**, are illustrated by **chymotrypsin**.*

*   **pH and Temperature Profiles.** Enzymes have a functional pH range determined by the **pK_a** of the functional groups in the active site and the interactions required for three-dimensional structure. Increases of temperature, which do not lead to protein denaturation, increase the reaction rate.*

*   **Mechanism-Based Inhibitors.** The effectiveness of many **drugs** and **toxins** depends on their ability to inhibit an enzyme. The strongest inhibitors are **covalent inhibitors**, compounds that form covalent bonds with a reactive group in the enzyme active site, or **transition-state analogs** that mimic the transition-state complex.*

*   **Enzyme Names.** Most enzyme names end in "-ase." Enzymes usually have both a common name and a systematic classification that includes a name and an Enzyme Commission (EC) number.*

THE WAITING ROOM

A year after recovering from salicylate poisoning (see Chapter 4), **Dennis "the Menace" Veere** was playing in his grandfather's basement. Dennis drank an unknown amount of the insecticide malathion, which is sometimes used for killing fruit flies and other insects (Fig. 8.2). Sometime later, when he was not feeling well, Dennis told his grandfather what he had done. Mr. Veere retrieved the bottle and rushed Dennis to the emergency room of the local hospital. On the way, Dennis vomited repeatedly and complained of abdominal cramps. At the hospital, he began salivating and had an uncontrollable defecation.

In the emergency room, physicians passed a nasogastric tube for stomach lavage, started intravenous fluids, and recorded vital signs. Dennis's pulse rate was 48 beats/minute (slow), and his blood pressure was 78/48 mm Hg (low). The physicians noted involuntary twitching of the muscles in his extremities.

Lotta Topaigne was diagnosed with acute gouty arthritis involving her right great toe (see Chapter 5). The presence of insoluble urate crystals within the joint space confirmed the diagnosis. Several weeks after her acute gout attack subsided, Ms. Topaigne was started on allopurinol therapy in an oral dose of 150 mg twice per day.

Al Martini, a 44-year-old man who has been an alcoholic for the past 5 years, had a markedly diminished appetite for food. One weekend, he became unusually irritable and confused after drinking two-fifths of scotch and eating very little. His landlady convinced him to visit his doctor. Physical examination indicated a heart rate of 104 beats/minute. His blood pressure was slightly low, and he was in early congestive heart failure. He was poorly oriented to time, place, and person.

FIG. 8.2. Organophosphorous compounds. Malathion and parathion are organophosphorous insecticides. Nausea, coma, convulsions, respiratory failure, and death have resulted from the use of parathion by farmers who have gotten it on their skin. Malathion is similar in structure to parathion but is not nearly as toxic. The nerve gas sarin, another organophosphorus compound, was used in a terrorist attack in a Japanese subway.

I. THE ENZYME-CATALYZED REACTION

Enzymes, in general, provide speed, specificity, and regulatory control to reactions in the body. Enzymes are usually proteins that act as catalysts, compounds that increase the rate of chemical reactions. Enzyme-catalyzed reactions have three basic steps:

1. Binding of substrate (a reactant): $E + S \leftrightarrow ES$
2. Conversion of bound substrate to bound product: $ES \leftrightarrow EP$
3. Release of product: $EP \leftrightarrow E + P$

An enzyme binds the substrates of the reaction it catalyzes and brings them together at the right orientation to react. The enzyme then participates in the making and breaking of bonds required for product formation, releases the products, and returns to its original state once the reaction is completed.

Enzymes do not invent new reactions; they simply make reactions occur faster. The catalytic power of an enzyme (the rate of the catalyzed reaction divided by the rate of the uncatalyzed reaction) is usually in the range of 10^6 to 10^{14}. Without the catalytic power of enzymes, reactions such as those involved in nerve conduction, heart contraction, and digestion of food would occur too slowly for life to exist.

Each enzyme usually catalyzes a specific biochemical reaction. The ability of an enzyme to select just one substrate and distinguish this substrate from a group of very similar compounds is referred to as *specificity* (Fig. 8.3). The enzyme converts

Most, if not all, of the tissues and organs in the body are adversely affected by chronic ingestion of excessive amounts of alcohol, including the liver, pancreas, heart, reproductive organs, central nervous system, and the fetus. Some of the effects of alcohol ingestion, such as the psychotropic effects on the brain or inhibition of vitamin transport, are direct effects caused by ethanol itself. However, many of the acute and chronic pathophysiologic effects of alcohol relate to the pathways of ethanol metabolism (see Chapter 25).

FIG. 8.3. Reaction catalyzed by glucokinase, an example of enzyme reaction specificity. Glucokinase catalyzes the transfer of a phosphate from adenosine triphosphate (ATP) to carbon 6 of glucose. It cannot rapidly transfer a phosphate from other nucleotides to glucose, or from ATP to closely related sugars such as galactose, or from ATP to any other carbon on glucose. The only products formed are glucose 6-phosphate and adenosine diphosphate (ADP).

this substrate to just one product. The specificity, as well as the speed, of enzyme-catalyzed reactions results from the unique sequence of specific amino acids that form the three-dimensional structure of the enzyme.

A. The Active Site

To catalyze a chemical reaction, the enzyme forms an enzyme–substrate complex in its active catalytic site (Fig. 8.4). The active site is usually a cleft or crevice in the enzyme formed by one or more regions of the polypeptide chain. Within the active site, cofactors and functional groups from the polypeptide chain participate in transforming the bound substrate molecules into products.

Initially, the substrate molecules bind to their substrate-binding sites, also called the substrate recognition sites (see Fig. 8.4B). The three-dimensional arrangement of binding sites in a crevice of the enzyme allows the reacting portions of the substrates to approach each other from the appropriate angles. The proximity of the bound substrate molecules and their precise orientation toward each other contribute to the catalytic power of the enzyme.

The active site also contains functional groups that participate directly in the reaction (see Fig. 8.4C). The functional groups are donated by the polypeptide chain or by bound cofactors (metals or complex organic molecules called *coenzymes*). As the substrate binds, it induces conformational changes in the enzyme that promote further interactions between the substrate molecules and the enzyme functional groups. (For example, a coenzyme might form a covalent intermediate with the substrate, or an amino acid side chain might abstract a proton from the reacting substrate.) The activated substrates and the enzyme form a *transition-state complex*, an unstable high-energy complex with a strained electronic configuration that is intermediate between substrate and product. Additional bonds with the enzyme stabilize the transition-state complex and decrease the energy required for its formation.

The transition-state complex decomposes to products, which dissociate from the enzyme (see Fig. 8.4D). The enzyme generally returns to its original form. The free enzyme then binds another set of substrates and repeats the process.

FIG. 8.4. Reaction in the enzyme active catalytic site. **A.** The enzyme contains an active catalytic site, shown in *dark red*, with a region or domain where the substrate binds. The active site also may contain cofactors, nonprotein components that assist in catalysis. **B.** The substrate forms bonds with amino acid residues in the substrate-binding site. Substrate binding induces a conformational change in the active site. **C.** Functional groups of amino acid residues and cofactors in the active site participate in forming the transition-state complex, which is stabilized by additional noncovalent bonds with the enzyme, shown in *red*. **D.** Because the products of the reaction dissociate, the enzyme returns to its original conformation.

B. *Substrate-Binding Sites*

Enzyme specificity (the enzyme's ability to react with just one substrate) results from the three-dimensional arrangement of specific amino acid residues in the enzyme that form binding sites for the substrates and activate the substrates during the course of the reaction. The "lock-and-key" and the "induced-fit" models for substrate binding describe two aspects of the binding interaction between the enzyme and substrate.

1. LOCK-AND-KEY MODEL FOR SUBSTRATE BINDING

The substrate-binding site contains amino acid residues arranged in a complementary three-dimensional surface that "recognizes" the substrate and binds it through multiple hydrophobic interactions, electrostatic interactions, or hydrogen bonds (Fig. 8.5). The amino acid residues that bind the substrate can come from very different parts of the linear amino acid sequence of the enzyme, as seen in glucokinase. The binding of compounds with a structure that differs from the substrate even to a small degree may be prevented by steric hindrance and charge repulsion. In the lock-and-key model, the complementarity between the substrate and its binding site is compared to that of a key fitting into a rigid lock.

2. INDUCED-FIT MODEL FOR SUBSTRATE BINDING

Complementarity between the substrate and the binding site is only part of the picture. As the substrate binds, enzymes undergo a conformational change ("induced fit") that repositions the side chains of the amino acids in the active site and increases the number of binding interactions (see Fig. 8.4). The induced-fit model for substrate binding recognizes that the substrate-binding site is not a rigid "lock" but rather a dynamic surface created by the flexible overall three-dimensional structure of the enzyme.

FIG. 8.5.   Glucose-binding site in glucokinase. **A.** Glucose, shown in *red*, is held in its binding site by multiple hydrogen bonds between each hydroxyl group and polar amino acids from different regions of the enzyme amino acid sequence in the actin fold (see Chapter 7). The position of the amino acid residue in the linear sequence is given by its number. The multiple interactions enable glucose to induce large conformational changes in the enzyme (induced fit). (Modified from Pilkis SJ, Weber IT, Harisson RW, et al. Glucokinase: structural analysis of a protein involved in susceptibility to diabetes. *J Biol Chem.* 1994;269:21925–21928.) **B.** Enzyme specificity is illustrated by the comparison of galactose and glucose. Galactose differs from glucose only in the position of the –OH group, shown in *red*. However, it is not phosphorylated at a significant rate by the enzyme. Cells therefore require a separate galactokinase for the metabolism of galactose.

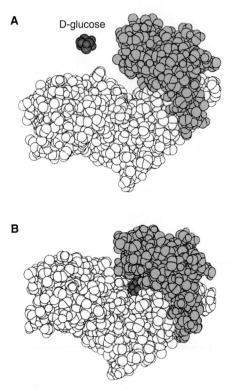

A D-glucose

B

FIG. 8.6. Conformational change resulting from the binding of glucose to hexokinase. (The figure is actually yeast hexokinase, which is more similar to human glucokinase than it is to the other human hexokinase isozymes.) The shaded and unshaded areas show the two domains (four subdomains) that form the actin fold with its adenosine triphosphate (ATP)-binding cleft. **A.** Free enzyme. **B.** With glucose bound, the cleft closes, forming the ATP-binding site. The closure of the cleft when glucose binds to hexokinase (or human glucokinase) is one of the largest "induced fits" known. The combination of secondary structures in the actin fold that give hexokinase the flexibility required for this shift are discussed in Chapter 7, Section IV.B.1, "The Actin Fold." (From Bennett WS, Steitz TA. Structure of a complex between yeast hexokinase A and glucose. II. Detailed comparisons of conformation and active site configuration with the native hexokinase B monomer and dimer. *J Mol Biol.* 1980;140:211–230.)

The function of the conformational change induced by substrate binding, the induced fit, is usually to reposition functional groups in the active site in a way that promotes the reaction, improves the binding site of a cosubstrate, or activates an adjacent subunit through cooperativity. For example, consider the large conformational changes that occur in the actin fold of glucokinase when glucose binds. The induced fit involves changes in the conformation of the whole enzyme that close the cleft of the fold, thereby improving the binding site for adenosine triphosphate (ATP) and excluding water (which might interfere with the reaction) from the active site (Fig. 8.6). Thus, the multiple interactions between the substrate and the enzyme in the catalytic site serve both for substrate recognition and for initiating the next stage of the reaction—formation of the transition-state complex.

C. The Transition-State Complex

For a reaction to occur, the substrates undergoing the reaction need to be activated. If the energy levels of a substrate are plotted as the substrate is progressively converted to product, the curve will show a maximum energy level that is higher than that of either the substrate or the product (Fig. 8.7). This high energy level occurs at the transition state. For some enzyme-catalyzed reactions, the transition state is a condition in which bonds in the substrate are maximally strained. For other enzyme-catalyzed reactions, the electronic configuration of the substrate becomes very strained and unstable as it enters the transition state. The highest energy level corresponds to the most unstable substrate configuration, and the condition in which the changing substrate molecule is most tightly bound to participating functional groups in the enzyme. The difference in energy between the substrate and the transition-state complex is called the *activation energy*.

According to transition-state theory, the overall rate of the reaction is determined by the number of molecules acquiring the activation energy necessary to form the transition-state complex. Enzymes increase the rate of the reaction by decreasing this activation energy. They use various catalytic strategies, such as electronic stabilization of the transition-state complex or acid–base catalysis, to obtain this decrease.

Once the transition-state complex is formed, it can collapse back to substrates or decompose to form products. The enzyme does not change the initial energy level of the substrates or the final energy level of the products.

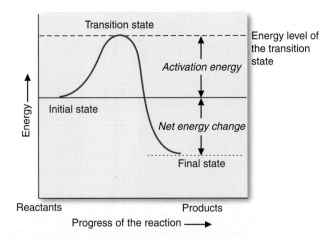

FIG. 8.7. Energy diagram showing the energy levels of the substrates as they progress toward products in the absence of enzyme. The substrates must pass through the high-energy transition state during the reaction. Although a favorable loss of energy occurs during the reaction, the rate of the reaction is slowed by the energy barrier to form the transition state. The energy barrier is referred to as the activation energy.

Because the transition-state complex binds more tightly to the enzyme than does the substrate, compounds that resemble its electronic and three-dimensional surface (transition-state analogs) are more potent inhibitors of an enzyme than are substrate analogs. Consequently, a drug developed as a transition-state analog would be highly specific for the enzyme it is designed to inhibit. Nevertheless, transition-state analogs are highly unstable when they are not bound to the enzyme, and would have great difficulty making it from the digestive tract or injection site to the site of action. Some of the approaches in drug design that are being used to deal with the instability problem include designing drugs that are almost transition-state analogs but have a stable modification, designing a prodrug that is converted to a transition-state analog at the site of action, and using the transition-state analog to design a complementary antibody.

If the structure of a transition state can be modeled, it can be used as an antigen for the production of *abzymes* (catalytic antibodies). These antibodies have an arrangement of amino acid side chains in their variable regions that is similar to the active site of the enzyme in the transition state. Consequently, they can act as artificial enzymes. For example, abzymes have been developed against analogs of the transition-state complex of cocaine esterase, the enzyme that degrades cocaine in the body. These abzymes have esterase activity, and monthly injections of the abzyme drug can be used to rapidly destroy cocaine in the blood, thereby decreasing the dependence of addicted individuals. (See Chapter 7 for antibody structure.)

II. CATALYTIC MECHANISM OF CHYMOTRYPSIN

The enzyme chymotrypsin provides a good example of the strategies and amino acid side chains used by enzymes to lower the amount of activation energy required. *Chymotrypsin* is a digestive enzyme released into the intestine that catalyzes the hydrolysis of specific peptide bonds in denatured proteins. *Hydrolysis* is the use of water to lyse (break) a bond. Chymotrypsin is a member of the serine protease superfamily, enzymes that use a serine in the active site to form a covalent intermediate during proteolysis (the hydrolysis of a peptide bond in a protein). In the overall hydrolysis reaction, an OH^- from water is added to the carbonyl carbon of the peptide bond, and an H^+ to the N, thereby cleaving the bond (Fig. 8.8). The bond that is cleaved is called the *scissile bond*.

A. The Reaction in the Absence of Enzyme

In the reaction carried out in the absence of enzyme, the negatively charged hydroxyl group of water attacks the carbonyl carbon, which carries a partial positive charge. An unstable oxyanion tetrahedral transition-state complex is formed in which the oxygen atom carries a full negative charge. The rate of the chemical reaction in the absence of chymotrypsin is slow because there are too few OH^- molecules in H_2O with enough energy to form the transition-state complex and too few OH^- molecules colliding with the substrate at the right orientation.

B. Catalytic Strategies in the Reaction Catalyzed by Chymotrypsin

In the reaction catalyzed by chymotrypsin, the same oxyanion intermediate is formed by using the hydroxyl group of a serine residue for the attack instead of a free hydroxyl anion. The rate of the chymotrypsin-catalyzed reaction is faster because functional groups in the enzyme active site activate the attacking hydroxyl group, stabilize the oxyanion transition-state complexes, form a covalent intermediate, and destabilize the leaving group. The reaction takes place in two stages: (1) cleavage of the peptide bond in the denatured substrate protein and formation of a covalent acyl–enzyme intermediate (Fig. 8.9, steps 1 through 5), and (2) hydrolysis of the acyl–enzyme intermediate to release the remaining portion of the

FIG. 8.8. Chymotrypsin hydrolyzes certain peptide bonds in proteins. The scissile bond is shown in *red*. The carbonyl carbon, which carries a partial positive charge, is attacked by a hydroxyl group from water. An unstable tetrahedral oxyanion intermediate is formed, which is the transition-state complex. As the electrons return to the carbonyl carbon, it becomes a carboxylic acid, and the remaining proton from water adds to the leaving group to form an amine.

1. Substrate binding

2. Histidine activates serine for nucleophilic attack

3. The oxyanion tetrahedral intermediate is stabilized by hydrogen bonds

4. Cleavage of the peptide bond

5. The covalent acyl–enzyme intermediate

6. Water attacks the carbonyl carbon

7. Second oxyanion tetrahedral intermediate

8. Acid catalysis breaks the acyl–enzyme covalent bond

9. The product is free to dissociate

substrate protein (see Fig. 8.9, steps 6 through 9). The names of the catalytic strategies employed in the various steps are in italics in the following paragraphs.

1. SPECIFICITY OF BINDING TO CHYMOTRYPSIN

Chymotrypsin hydrolyzes the peptide bond on the carbonyl side of a phenylalanine, tyrosine, or tryptophan in a denatured protein. The substrate recognition site consists of a hydrophobic binding pocket that holds the hydrophobic amino acid contributing the carbonyl group of the scissile bond (see Fig. 8.9, step 1). The substrate protein must be denatured to fit into the pocket and be held rigidly in place by glycines in the enzyme peptide backbone. Scissile-bond specificity is also provided by the subsequent steps of the reaction, such as moving serine 195 into attacking position (*proximity* and *orientation*).

2. FORMATION OF THE ACYL–ENZYME INTERMEDIATE IN CHYMOTRYPSIN

In the first stage of the reaction, the peptide bond of the denatured protein substrate is cleaved as an active-site serine hydroxyl group attacks the carbonyl carbon of the scissile bond (*nucleophilic catalysis—a nucleophile is a chemical group that is attracted to the positively charged nucleus*) (see Fig. 8.9, step 2). Aspartate and histidine cooperate in converting this hydroxyl group (with a partial negative charge on the oxygen) into a better nucleophilic attacking group by giving it a more negative charge. An active-site histidine acts as a base and abstracts a proton from the serine hydroxyl (*acid–base catalysis*). The protonated histidine is stabilized by the negative charge of a nearby aspartate. This step is necessary because the "normal" pK for the serine hydroxyl group is very high; at physiologic pH, conditions within the enzyme structure must be established that aid in removal of the proton and stabilization of the resulting oxygen anion.

The aspartate–histidine–serine combination, referred to as the *catalytic triad*, is an example of cooperative interactions between amino acid residues in the active site. The strong nucleophilic attacking group created by this charge-relay system has the same general effect on reaction rate as increasing the concentration of hydroxyl ions available for collision in the uncatalyzed reaction. This same combination of active-site residues is found in many serine proteases, particularly those proteins involved in protein digestion and blood clotting (see Chapter 44).

In the next step of the reaction sequence, an oxyanion tetrahedral transition-state complex is formed that is stabilized by hydrogen bonds with –NH groups in the peptide backbone (see Fig. 8.9, step 3). The original view of the way enzymes form transition-state complexes was that they stretched the bonds or distorted the bond angles of the reacting substrates. Nevertheless, most transition-state complexes, such as the oxyanion tetrahedral complex, are better described as showing "electronic strain," an electrostatic surface that would be highly improbable if it

Q: In the stomach, gastric acid decreases the pH to 1 to 2 in order to denature proteins through disruption of hydrogen bonding. The protease in the stomach, pepsin, is a member of the aspartate protease superfamily, enzymes that use two aspartate residues in the active site for acid–base catalysis of the peptide bond. Why can they not use histidine like chymotrypsin?

FIG. 8.9. Catalytic mechanism of chymotrypsin. The substrate (a denatured protein) is in the *shaded area.* **1.** As the substrate protein binds to the active site, serine 195 and histidine (his 57) are moved closer together and at the right orientation for the nitrogen electrons on histidine to attract the hydrogen of serine. Without this change of conformation on substrate binding, the catalytic triad cannot form. **2.** Histidine serves as a general base catalyst because it abstracts a proton from the serine, increasing the nucleophilicity of the serine-oxygen, which attacks the carbonyl carbon. **3.** The electrons of the carbonyl group form the oxyanion tetrahedral intermediate. The oxyanion is stabilized by the N–H groups of serine 195 and glycine in the chymotrypsin peptide backbone. **4.** The amide nitrogen in the peptide bond is stabilized by interaction with the histidine proton. Here, the histidine acts as a general acid catalyst. Because the electrons of the carbon–nitrogen peptide bond withdraw into the nitrogen, the electrons of the carboxyanion return to the substrate carbonyl carbon, resulting in cleavage of the peptide bond. **5.** The cleavage of the peptide bond results in formation of the covalent acyl–enzyme intermediate, and the amide half of the cleaved protein dissociates. **6.** The nucleophilic attack by H_2O on the carbonyl carbon is activated by histidine, whose nitrogen electrons attract a proton from water. **7.** The second tetrahedral oxyanion intermediate (the transition-state complex) is formed. It is again stabilized by hydrogen bonds with the peptide backbone bonds of glycine and serine. **8.** Because the histidine proton is donated to the electrons of the bond between the serine oxygen and the substrate carbonyl group, the electrons from the oxyanion return to the substrate carbon to form the carboxylic acid, and the acyl–enzyme bond is broken. **9.** The enzyme, as it releases substrate, returns to its original state.

To participate in general acid–base catalysis, the amino acid side chain must be able to extract a proton at one stage of the reaction and donate it back at another. Histidine (pK_a 6.0) would be protonated at this low pH and could not extract a proton from a potential nucleophile. However, aspartic acid, with a pK_a of about 2, can release protons at a pH of 2. The two aspartates work together to activate water through the removal of a proton to form the hydroxyl nucleophile.

were not stabilized by bonds with functional groups on the enzyme. *Stabilization of the transition-state complex* lowers its energy level and increases the number of molecules that reach this energy level.

Subsequently, the serine in the active site forms a full covalent bond with the carbon of the carbonyl group as the peptide bond is cleaved (*covalent catalysis*). The formation of a stable covalent intermediate is a catalytic strategy employed by many enzymes and often involves serine or cysteine residues. The covalent intermediate is subsequently hydrolyzed (*acid–base catalysis*). The dissociating products of an enzyme-catalyzed reaction are often "destabilized" by some degree of charge repulsion in the active site. In the case of chymotrypsin, the amino group formed after peptide-bond cleavage is destabilized or "uncomfortable" in the presence of the active-site histidine (*destabilization of developing product*).

3. HYDROLYSIS OF THE ACYL–CHYMOTRYPSIN INTERMEDIATE

The next sequence of events hydrolyzes the acyl–enzyme intermediate to release the bound carbonyl-side peptide (see Fig. 8.9, steps 6 through 9). The active-site histidine activates water to form an OH$^-$ for a nucleophilic attack, resulting in a second oxyanion transition-state complex. When the histidine adds the proton back to serine, the reaction is complete, and the product dissociates.

C. Energy Diagram in the Presence of Chymotrypsin

The number of steps in real enzymatic reactions results in a "multibump" energy diagram (Fig. 8.10). At the initial stage of the reaction, a dip occurs because energy is provided by formation of the initial multiple weak bonds between the substrate and enzyme. As the reaction progresses, the curve rises because additional energy is required for formation of the transition-state complex. This

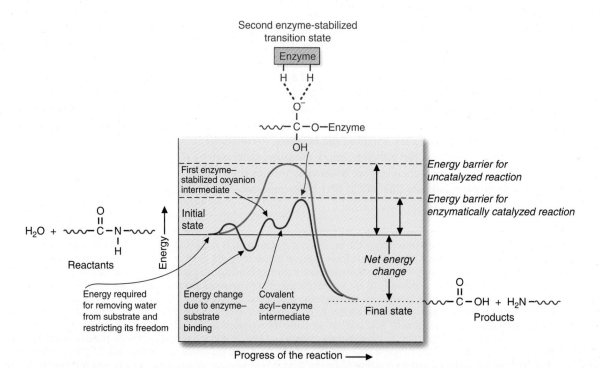

FIG. 8.10. A postulated energy diagram for the reaction catalyzed by chymotrypsin. In the presence of enzyme (*red*); in the absence of enzyme (*blue*). The energy barrier to the transition state is lowered in the enzyme-catalyzed reaction by the formation of additional bonds between the substrate and enzyme in the transition-state complex. The energy is provided by substrate binding to the enzyme. The enzyme does not, however, change the energy levels of the substrate or product.

energy is provided by the subsequent steps in the reaction, replacing the initial weak bonds with progressively tighter bonds. Semistable covalent intermediates of the reaction have lower energy levels than do the transition-state complexes and are present in the reaction diagram as dips in the energy curve. The final transition-state complex has the highest energy level in the reaction and is therefore the most unstable state. It can collapse back to substrates or decompose to form products.

III. FUNCTIONAL GROUPS IN CATALYSIS

The catalytic strategies employed by chymotrypsin to increase the reaction rate are common to many enzymes. One of these catalytic strategies, proximity and orientation, is an intrinsic feature of substrate binding and part of the catalytic mechanism of all enzymes. All enzymes also stabilize the transition state by electrostatic interactions, but not all enzymes form covalent intermediates.

Great variety occurs in the functional groups employed by different enzymes to carry out these catalytic strategies. Some enzymes, such as chymotrypsin, rely on amino acid residues within the active site. Other enzymes increase their repertoire by employing cofactors (nonprotein compounds that participate in the catalytic process) to provide a functional group with the right size, shape, and properties. They are generally divided into three categories: coenzymes, metal ions (e.g., Fe^{2+}, Mg^{2+}, or Zn^{2+}), and metallocoenzymes (similar to the Fe^{2+}-heme in hemoglobin, see Chapter 7).

A. Functional Groups on Amino Acid Side Chains

Almost all of the polar amino acids participate directly in catalysis in one or more enzymes (Table 8.1). Serine, cysteine, lysine, and histidine can participate in covalent catalysis. Histidine, because it has a pK_a that can donate and accept a proton at neutral pH, often participates in acid–base catalysis. Most of the polar amino acid side chains are nucleophilic and participate in nucleophilic catalysis by stabilizing more positively charged groups that develop during the reaction.

B. Coenzymes in Catalysis

Coenzymes (cofactors) are complex nonprotein organic molecules that participate in catalysis by providing functional groups, much like the amino acid side chains. In the human, they are usually (but not always) synthesized from vitamins. Each coenzyme is involved in catalyzing a specific type of reaction for a class of substrates with certain structural features. Coenzymes can be divided into two general classes: activation-transfer coenzymes and oxidation–reduction coenzymes.

Because most vitamins function as coenzymes, the symptoms of vitamin deficiencies reflect the loss of specific enzyme activities that depend on the coenzyme form of the vitamin. Thus, drugs and toxins that inhibit proteins required for coenzyme synthesis (e.g., vitamin transport proteins or biosynthetic enzymes) can cause the symptoms of a vitamin deficiency. This type of deficiency is called a *functional deficiency*, whereas an inadequate intake is called a *dietary deficiency*.

Most coenzymes are tightly bound to their enzymes and do not dissociate during the course of the reaction. However, a functional or dietary vitamin deficiency that decreases the level of a coenzyme will result in the presence of the apoenzyme in cells (an enzyme devoid of cofactor).

Ethanol is an "antivitamin" that decreases the cellular content of almost every coenzyme. For example, ethanol inhibits the absorption of thiamine, and acetaldehyde produced from ethanol oxidation displaces pyridoxal phosphate from its protein-binding sites, thereby accelerating its degradation.

Table 8.1   Some Functional Groups in the Active Site

Function of Amino Acid	Enzyme Example
Covalent intermediates	
Cysteine–SH	Glyceraldehyde 3–phosphate dehydrogenase
Serine–OH	Acetylcholinesterase
Lysine–NH₂	Aldolase
Histidine–NH	Phosphoglucomutase
Acid–base catalysis	
Histidine–NH	Chymotrypsin
Aspartate–COOH	Pepsin
Stabilization of anion formed during the reaction	
Peptide backbone–NH	Chymotrypsin
Arginine–NH	Carboxypeptidase A
Serine–OH	Alcohol dehydrogenase
Stabilization of cation formed during the reaction	
Aspartate–COO⁻	Lysozyme

Q: Although coenzymes look as though they should be able to catalyze reactions autonomously (on their own), they have almost no catalytic power when not bound to the enzyme. Why?

1. ACTIVATION-TRANSFER COENZYMES

The activation-transfer coenzymes usually participate directly in catalysis by forming a covalent bond with a portion of the substrate; the tightly held substrate moiety is then activated for transfer, addition of water, or some other reaction. The portion of the coenzyme that forms a covalent bond with the substrate is its functional group. A separate portion of the coenzyme binds tightly to the enzyme.

Thiamine pyrophosphate provides a good illustration of the manner in which coenzymes participate in catalysis (Fig. 8.11). It is synthesized in human cells from the vitamin thiamine by the addition of a pyrophosphate. This pyrophosphate provides negatively charged oxygen atoms that chelate Mg^{2+}, which then binds tightly to the enzyme. The functional group that extends into the active site is the reactive carbon atom with a dissociable proton (see Fig. 8.11). In all of the enzymes that use thiamine pyrophosphate, this reactive thiamine carbon forms a covalent bond with a substrate keto group while cleaving the adjacent carbon–carbon bond. However, each thiamine-containing enzyme catalyzes the cleavage of a different substrate (or group of substrates with very closely related structures).

FIG. 8.11. The role of the functional group of thiamine pyrophosphate (the reactive carbon shown in *red*) in formation of a covalent intermediate. **A.** A base on the enzyme (*B*) abstracts a proton from thiamine, creating a carbanion (general acid–base catalysis). **B.** The carbanion is a strong nucleophile and attacks the partially positively charged keto group on the substrate. **C.** A covalent intermediate is formed, which, after decarboxylation, is stabilized by resonance forms. The uncharged intermediate is the stabilized transition-state complex.

Coenzymes have very little activity in the absence of the enzyme and very little specificity. The enzyme provides specificity, proximity, and orientation in the substrate recognition site, as well as other functional groups for stabilization of the transition state, acid–base catalysis, and so on. For example, thiamine is made into a better nucleophilic attacking group by a basic amino acid residue in the enzyme that removes the dissociable proton (EnzB in Fig. 8.11), thereby generating a negatively charged thiamine carbon anion. Later in the reaction, the enzyme returns the proton.

Coenzyme A (CoA), biotin, and pyridoxal phosphate are also activation-transfer coenzymes synthesized from vitamins. CoA (CoASH), which is synthesized from the vitamin pantothenate, contains an adenosine $3',5'$-bisphosphate that binds reversibly, but tightly, to a site on an enzyme (Fig. 8.12A). Its functional group, a sulfhydryl group at the other end of the molecule, is a nucleophile that always attacks carbonyl groups and forms acyl thioesters (in fact, the "A" in CoA stands for the *a*cyl group that becomes attached). Most coenzymes, such as functional groups on the enzyme amino acids, are regenerated during the course of the reaction. However, CoASH and a few of the oxidation–reduction coenzymes are transformed during the reaction into products that dissociate from the enzyme at the end of the reaction (e.g., CoASH is converted to an acyl-CoA derivative, and nicotinamide adenine dinucleotide [NAD^+] is reduced to NADH). These dissociating coenzymes are nonetheless classified as coenzymes rather than substrates because they are common to so many reactions, the original form is regenerated by subsequent reactions in a metabolic pathway, they are synthesized from vitamins, and the amount of coenzyme in the cell is nearly constant.

Biotin, which does not contain a phosphate group, is covalently bonded to a lysine in enzymes called *carboxylases* (see Fig. 8.12B). Its functional group is a nitrogen atom that covalently binds a CO_2 group in an energy-requiring reaction. This bound CO_2 group is activated for addition to another molecule. In the human, biotin functions only in carboxylation reactions.

Pyridoxal phosphate is synthesized from the vitamin pyridoxine, which is also called vitamin B_6 (see Fig. 8.12C). The reactive aldehyde group usually functions in enzyme-catalyzed reactions by forming a covalent bond with the amino groups on amino acids. The positively charged ring nitrogen withdraws electrons from a bond in the bound amino acid, resulting in cleavage of that bond. The enzyme participates by removing protons from the substrate and by keeping the amino acid and the pyridoxal group in a single plane to facilitate shuttling of electrons.

These coenzymes illustrate three features all activation-transfer coenzymes have in common: (1) a specific chemical group involved in binding to the enzyme, (2) a separate and different functional or reactive group that participates directly in the catalysis of one type of reaction by forming a covalent bond with the substrate, and (3) dependence on the enzyme for additional specificity of substrate and additional catalytic power.

2. OXIDATION–REDUCTION COENZYMES

A large number of coenzymes are involved in oxidation–reduction reactions catalyzed by enzymes categorized as *oxidoreductases*. When a compound is oxidized, it loses electrons. As a result, the oxidized carbon has fewer H atoms or gains an O atom. The reduction of a compound is the gain of electrons, which shows in its structure as the gain of H or loss of O. Some coenzymes, such as NAD^+ and flavin adenine dinucleotide (FAD), can transfer electrons together with hydrogen and have unique roles in the generation of ATP from the oxidation of fuels. Other oxidation–reduction coenzymes work with metals to transfer single electrons to oxygen. Vitamin E and vitamin C (ascorbic acid) are oxidation–reduction coenzymes that can act as antioxidants and protect against oxygen free radical injury. The different functions of oxidation–reduction coenzymes in metabolic pathways are explained in Chapters 19 through 22. A subclass of oxidoreductases is given the

A: For a substrate to react with a coenzyme, it must collide with a coenzyme at exactly the right angle. The probability of the substrate and coenzyme in free solution colliding in exactly the right place at the exactly right angle is very small. In addition to providing this proximity and orientation, enzymes contribute in other ways, such as activating the coenzyme by extracting a proton (e.g., thiamine pyrophosphate and coenzyme A) or polarizing the substrate to make it more susceptible to nucleophilic attack.

Many alcoholics like **Al Martini** develop thiamine deficiency because alcohol inhibits the transport of thiamine through the intestinal mucosal cells. In the body, thiamine is converted to thiamine pyrophosphate (TPP). TPP acts as a coenzyme in the decarboxylation of α-keto acids such as pyruvate and α-ketoglutarate (see Fig. 8.11) and in the utilization of pentose phosphates in the pentose phosphate pathway. As a result of thiamine deficiency, the oxidation of α-keto acids is impaired. Dysfunction occurs in the central and peripheral nervous system, the cardiovascular system, and other organs.

A. CoASH

Adenosine 3',5'-bisphosphate

B. Biotin

The biotin–lysine (biocytin) complex

C. Pyridoxal phosphate (PLP)

FIG. 8.12. Activation-transfer coenzymes. **A.** Coenzyme A (CoA or CoASH) and phosphopantetheine are synthesized from the vitamin pantothenate (pantothenic acid). The active sulfhydryl group, shown in *red*, binds to acyl groups (e.g., acetyl, succinyl, or fatty acyl) to form thioesters. **B.** Biotin activates and transfers CO_2 to compounds in carboxylation reactions. The reactive *N* is shown in *red*. Biotin is covalently attached to a lysine residue in the carboxylase enzyme. **C.** Reactive sites of pyridoxal phosphate. The functional group of pyridoxal phosphate is a reactive aldehyde (shown in the *yellow box*) that forms a covalent intermediate with amino groups of amino acids (a Schiff base). The positively charged pyridine ring is a strong electron-withdrawing group that can pull electrons into it (electrophilic catalysis).

name *dehydrogenases* because they transfer hydrogen (hydrogen atoms or hydride ions) from the substrate to an electron-accepting coenzyme such as NAD^+.

Oxidation–reduction coenzymes follow the same principles as activation-transfer coenzymes, except that they do not form covalent bonds with the substrate. Each coenzyme has a unique functional group that accepts and donates electrons and is specific for the form of electrons it transfers (e.g., hydride ions, hydrogen atoms, oxygen). A different portion of the coenzyme binds the enzyme. Like activation-transfer coenzymes, oxidation–reduction coenzymes are not good catalysts without participation from amino acid side chains on the enzyme.

The enzyme lactate dehydrogenase, which catalyzes the transfer of electrons from lactate to NAD^+, illustrates these principles (Fig. 8.13). The coenzyme NAD^+ is synthesized from the vitamin niacin (which forms the nicotinamide ring) and from ATP (which contributes an adenosine monophosphate [AMP]). The adenosine diphosphate (ADP) portion of the molecule binds tightly to the enzyme and causes conformational changes in the enzyme. The functional group of NAD^+ is the carbon on the nicotinamide ring opposite the positively charged nitrogen. This carbon atom accepts the hydride ion (a hydrogen atom that has two electrons) transferred from a specific carbon atom on the substrate. The H^+ from the substrate alcohol (–OH) group then dissociates, and a keto group (C=O) is formed. One of the roles

In humans, most of ingested ethanol is oxidized to acetaldehyde in the liver by alcohol dehydrogenase (ADH):

$$Ethanol + NAD^+ \leftrightarrow acetaldehyde + NADH + H^+$$

ADH is active as a dimer, with an active site containing zinc present in each subunit. The human has at least seven genes that encode isozymes of ADH, each with a slightly different range of specificities for the alcohols it oxidizes.

The acetaldehyde produced from ethanol is highly reactive, toxic, and immunogenic. In **Al Martini** and other patients with chronic alcoholism, acetaldehyde is responsible for much of the liver injury associated with chronic alcoholism.

FIG. 8.13. The coenzyme NAD^+ accepting a hydride ion, shown in *red*, from lactate. NAD^+-dependent dehydrogenases catalyze the transfer of a hydride ion (H^-) from a carbon to NAD^+ in oxidation reactions such as the oxidation of alcohols to ketones or aldehydes to acids. The positively charged pyridine ring nitrogen of NAD^+ increases the electrophilicity of the carbon opposite it in the ring. This carbon then accepts the negatively charged hydride ion. The proton from the alcohol group is released into water. $NADP^+$ functions by the same mechanism, but it is usually involved in pathways of reductive synthesis.

of the enzyme is to contribute a histidine nitrogen that can bind the dissociable proton on lactate, thereby making it easier for NAD^+ to pull off the other hydrogen with both electrons. Finally, NADH dissociates.

C. Metal Ions in Catalysis

Metal ions, which have a positive charge, contribute to the catalytic process by acting as electrophiles (electron-attracting groups). They assist in binding of the substrate, or they stabilize developing anions in the reaction. They can also accept and donate electrons in oxidation–reduction reactions.

The ability of certain metals to bind multiple ligands in their coordination sphere enables them to participate in binding substrates or coenzymes to enzymes. For example, Mg^{2+} plays a role in the binding of the negatively charged phosphate groups of thiamine pyrophosphate to anionic or basic amino acids in the enzyme (see Fig. 8.11). The phosphate groups of ATP are usually bound to enzymes through Mg^{2+} chelation.

The metals of some enzymes bind anionic substrates or intermediates of the reaction to alter their charge distribution, thereby contributing to catalytic power. The enzyme alcohol dehydrogenase (ADH), which transfers electrons from ethanol to NAD^+ to generate acetaldehyde and NADH, illustrates this role (Fig. 8.14). In the active site of ADH, an activated serine pulls a proton off the ethanol –OH group, leaving a negative charge on the oxygen that is stabilized by zinc. This electronic configuration allows the transfer of a hydride ion to NAD^+. Zinc is essentially fulfilling the same function in ADH that histidine fulfills in lactate dehydrogenase.

D. Noncatalytic Roles of Cofactors

Cofactors sometimes play a noncatalytic structural role in certain enzymes, binding different regions of the enzyme together to form the tertiary structure. They can also serve as substrates that are cleaved during the reaction.

IV. OPTIMAL pH AND TEMPERATURE

If the activity of most enzymes is plotted as a function of the pH of the reaction, an increase of reaction rate is usually observed as the pH goes from a very acidic level to the physiologic range; a decrease of reaction rate occurs as the pH goes from the

In the clinical laboratory, ethanol (in serum) is usually analyzed by coupling its oxidation to the formation of NADH using the enzyme alcohol dehydrogenase. NAD^+ has a low extinction coefficient at 340 nm; NADH has a much higher one. Thus, the increase in absorbance at 340 nm that occurs during the reaction indicates how much NADH was produced, which is directly proportional to the ethanol concentration in the serum. These reactions have been fully automated for the clinical lab.

FIG. 8.14.   Liver alcohol dehydrogenase (ADH) catalyzes the oxidation of ethanol (shown in *red*) to acetaldehyde. The active site of liver ADH contains a bound zinc atom, a serine side chain –OH, and histidine nitrogen that participate in the reaction. The histidine pulls an H+ off the active site serine, which pulls the H+ off of the substrate –OH group, leaving the oxygen with a negative charge that is stabilized by zinc.

physiologic range to a very basic range (Fig. 8.15). The shape of this curve in the acid region usually reflects the ionization of specific functional groups in the active site (or in the substrate) by the increase of pH, and the more general formation of hydrogen bonds important for the overall conformation of the enzyme. The loss of activity on the basic side usually reflects the inappropriate ionization of amino acid residues in the enzyme.

Most human enzymes function optimally at a temperature of approximately 37°C. An increase of temperature from 0° to 37°C increases the rate of the reaction by increasing the vibrational energy of the substrates. The maximum activity for most human enzymes occurs near 37°C because denaturation (loss of secondary and tertiary structure) occurs at higher temperatures.

V. MECHANISM-BASED INHIBITORS

Inhibitors are compounds that decrease the rate of an enzymatic reaction. Mechanism-based inhibitors mimic or participate in an intermediate step of the catalytic reaction. The term includes transition state analogs (see Section I.C) and compounds that can react irreversibly with functional groups in the active site.

A. Covalent Inhibitors

Covalent inhibitors form covalent or extremely tight bonds with functional groups in the active catalytic site. These functional groups are activated by their interactions with other amino acid residues and are therefore far more likely to be targeted by drugs and toxins than amino acid residues outside the active site.

The lethal compound *diisopropylphosphofluoridate* (diisopropylfluorophosphate [DFP]) is an organophosphorus compound that served as a prototype for the development of the nerve gas sarin and other organophosphorus toxins such as the insecticides malathion and parathion (Fig. 8.16). DFP exerts its toxic effect by forming a covalent intermediate in the active site of acetylcholinesterase, thereby preventing the enzyme from degrading the neurotransmitter acetylcholine. Once the covalent bond is formed, the inhibition by DFP is essentially irreversible, and activity can only be recovered as new enzyme is synthesized. DFP also inhibits many other enzymes that use serine for hydrolytic cleavage (such as the serine proteases), but the inhibition is not as lethal.

Aspirin (acetylsalicylic acid) provides an example of a pharmacologic drug that exerts its effect through the covalent acetylation of an active site serine in the enzyme prostaglandin endoperoxide synthase (cyclooxygenase). Aspirin resembles a portion of the prostaglandin precursor that is a physiologic substrate for the enzyme.

B. Transition-State Analogs and Compounds that Resemble Intermediate Stages of the Reaction

Transition-state analogs are extremely potent and specific inhibitors of enzymes because they bind more tightly to the enzyme than do substrates or products. Drugs cannot be designed that precisely mimic the transition state because of its highly unstable structure. However, substrates undergo progressive changes in their overall electrostatic structure during the formation of a transition-state complex, and effective drugs often resemble an intermediate stage of the reaction more closely than they resemble the substrate. Medical literature often refers to such compounds as substrate analogs, even though they bind more tightly than substrates.

1. PENICILLIN

The antibiotic penicillin is a transition-state analog that binds very tightly to glycopeptidyl transferase, an enzyme required by bacteria for synthesis of the cell wall (Fig. 8.17). Glycopeptidyl transferase catalyzes a partial reaction with penicillin

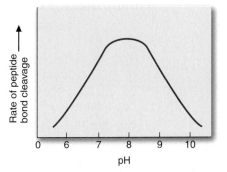

FIG. 8.15. pH profile of an enzyme. The rate of the reaction increases as the pH increases from 6 to 7.4. The exact shape of the curve depends on the protonation state of active-site amino acid residues or on the hydrogen bonding required for maintenance of three-dimensional structure in the enzyme. For the enzyme shown in the figure, the increase of reaction rate corresponds to deprotonation of the active-site histidine. At a pH >8.5, deprotonation of an amino-terminal $-NH_3^+$ alters the conformation at the active site and the activity decreases. Other enzymes might have a lower pH maximum, a broader peak, or retain their activity in the basic side of the curve.

The symptoms experienced by **Dennis Veere** resulted from inhibition of acetylcholinesterase. Acetylcholinesterase cleaves the neurotransmitter acetylcholine to acetate and choline in the postsynaptic terminal, thereby terminating the transmission of the neural signal (see Fig. 8.16). Malathion is metabolized in the liver to a toxic derivative (malaoxon) that binds to the active-site serine in acetylcholinesterase and other enzymes, an action similar to that of diisopropylfluorophosphate. As a result, acetylcholine accumulates and overstimulates the autonomic nervous system (the involuntary nervous system, including the heart, blood vessels, and glands), thereby accounting for Dennis's vomiting, abdominal cramps, salivation, and sweating. Acetylcholine is also a neurotransmitter for the somatic motor nervous system, where its accumulation resulted in Dennis's involuntary muscle twitching (muscle fasciculations).

A. Normal reaction of acetylcholinesterase

B. Reaction with organophosphorus inhibitors

FIG. 8.16.   **A.** Acetylcholinesterase normally catalyzes inactivation of the neurotransmitter acetylcholine in a hydrolysis reaction. The active-site serine forms a covalent intermediate with a portion of the substrate during the course of the reaction. **B.** Diisopropylphosphofluoridate (DFP), the ancestor of current organophosphorus nerve gases and pesticides, inactivates acetylcholinesterase by forming a covalent complex with the active-site serine that cannot be hydrolyzed by water. The result is that the enzyme cannot carry out its normal reaction, and acetylcholine accumulates.

FIG. 8.17.   The antibiotic penicillin inhibits the bacterial enzyme glycopeptide transpeptidase. The transpeptidase is a serine protease involved in cross-linking components of bacterial cell walls and is essential for bacterial growth and survival. It normally cleaves the peptide bond between two D-alanine residues in a polypeptide. Penicillin contains a strained peptide bond within the β-lactam ring that resembles the transition state of the normal cleavage reaction, and thus penicillin binds very readily in the enzyme active site. As the bacterial enzyme attempts to cleave this penicillin peptide bond, penicillin becomes irreversibly covalently attached to the enzyme's active-site serine, thereby inactivating the enzyme.

that covalently attaches penicillin to its own active-site serine. The reaction is favored by the strong resemblance between the peptide bond in the β-lactam ring of penicillin and the transition-state complex of the natural transpeptidation reaction. Active-site inhibitors such as penicillin that undergo partial reaction to form irreversible inhibitors in the active site are sometimes termed *suicide inhibitors*.

2. ALLOPURINOL

Allopurinol, a drug used to treat gout, decreases urate production by inhibiting xanthine oxidase. This inhibition provides an example of an enzyme that commits suicide by converting a drug to a transition-state analog. The normal physiologic function of xanthine oxidase is the oxidation of hypoxanthine to xanthine and xanthine to uric acid (urate) in the pathway for degradation of purines (Fig. 8.18). The enzyme contains a molybdenum–sulfide (Mo-S) complex that binds the substrates and transfers the electrons required for the oxidation reactions. Xanthine oxidase oxidizes the drug allopurinol to oxypurinol, a compound that binds very tightly to a molybdenum–sulfide complex in the active site. As a result, the enzyme has committed suicide and is unable to carry out its normal function—the generation of uric acid (urate).

Lotta Topaigne is being treated with allopurinol for gout, which is caused by an accumulation of sodium urate crystals in joints and joint fluid, particularly in the ankle and great toe. Allopurinol is a suicide inhibitor of the enzyme xanthine oxidase, which is involved in the degradation of purine nucleotides adenosine monophosphate (AMP) and guanosine monophosphate (GMP) to uric acid (urate). Although hypoxanthine levels increase in the presence of allopurinol, hypoxanthine does not participate in urate crystal formation and precipitation at this concentration. It is excreted in the urine.

FIG. 8.18. Allopurinol is a suicide inhibitor of xanthine oxidase. **A.** Xanthine oxidase catalyzes the oxidation of hypoxanthine to xanthine and xanthine to uric acid (urate) in the pathway for degradation of purine nucleotides. **B.** The oxidations are performed by a molybdenum–oxo–sulfide coordination complex in the active site that complexes with the group being oxidized. Oxygen is donated from water. The enzyme can work either as an oxidase (O_2 accepts the $2e-$ and is reduced to H_2O_2) or as a dehydrogenase (NAD^+ accepts the $2e-$ and is reduced to NADH). The figure only indicates that $2e-$ is generated during the course of the reaction. **C.** Xanthine oxidase is able to perform the first oxidation step and convert allopurinol to alloxanthine (oxypurinol). As a result, the enzyme has committed suicide; the oxypurinol remains bound in the molybdenum coordination sphere, where it prevents the next step of the reaction. The portion of the purine ring in *green* indicates the major structural difference between hypoxanthine, xanthine, and allopurinol.

C. Heavy Metals

Heavy-metal toxicity is caused by tight binding of a metal such as mercury (Hg), lead (Pb), aluminum (Al), or iron (Fe) to a functional group in an enzyme. Heavy metals are relatively nonspecific for the enzymes they inhibit, particularly if the metal is associated with high-dose toxicity. Mercury, for example, binds to so many enzymes, often at reactive sulfhydryl groups in the active site, that it has been difficult to determine which of the inhibited enzymes is responsible for mercury toxicity. Lead provides an example of a metal that inhibits through replacing the normal functional metal in an enzyme, such as calcium, iron, or zinc. Its developmental and neurologic toxicity may be caused by its ability to replace Ca^{2+} in several regulatory proteins that are important in the central nervous system and other tissues.

CLINICAL COMMENTS

 Dennis Veere. Dennis Veere survived his malathion intoxication because he had ingested only a small amount of the chemical, vomited shortly after the agent was ingested, and was treated rapidly in the emergency room. Lethal doses of oral malathion are estimated at 1 g/kg of body weight for humans. Once it has been ingested, the liver converts malathion to the toxic reactive compound, malaoxon, by replacing the sulfur with oxygen. Malaoxon then binds to the active site of acetylcholinesterase and reacts to form the covalent intermediate. Unlike the complex formed between diisopropylfluorophosphate and acetylcholinesterase, this initial acylenzyme intermediate is reversible. However, with time, the enzyme-inhibitor complex "ages" (dealkylation of the inhibitor and enzyme modification) to form an irreversible complex. Emergency room physicians used the drug pralidoxime (an oxime) to reactivate the acetylcholinesterase in Dennis before the aged complex formed. They also used intravenous atropine, an anticholinergic (antimuscarinic) agent, to antagonize the action of the excessive amounts of acetylcholine accumulating in cholinergic receptors throughout his body.

After several days of intravenous therapy, the signs and symptoms of acetylcholine excess abated, and therapy was slowly withdrawn. Dennis made an uneventful recovery.

 Lotta Topaigne. Within several days of starting allopurinol therapy, Ms. Topaigne's serum uric acid level began to decrease. Several weeks later, the level in her blood was normal. Nevertheless, while Lotta was adapting to allopurinol therapy, she experienced a mild gout attack, which was treated with a low dose of colchicine (see Chapter 10).

 Al Martini. Al Martini was admitted to the hospital after intravenous thiamine was initiated at a dose of 100 mg/day (compared with an RDA of 1.4 mg/day). His congestive heart failure was believed to be the result, in part, of the cardiomyopathy (heart muscle dysfunction) of acute thiamine deficiency known as *beriberi heart disease*. This nutritional cardiac disorder and the peripheral nerve dysfunction usually respond to thiamine replacement. However, an alcoholic cardiomyopathy can also occur in well-nourished patients with adequate thiamine levels. Exactly how ethanol, or its toxic metabolite acetaldehyde, causes alcoholic cardiomyopathy in the absence of thiamine deficiency is unknown.

At low concentrations of ethanol, liver alcohol dehydrogenase is the major route of ethanol oxidation to acetaldehyde, a highly toxic chemical. Acetaldehyde not only damages the liver, it can enter the blood and potentially damage the heart and other tissues. At low ethanol intakes, much of the acetaldehyde produced is safely oxidized to acetate in the liver by acetaldehyde dehydrogenases.

BIOCHEMICAL COMMENTS

Basic Reactions and Classes of Enzymes. In the following chapters, students will be introduced to various reaction pathways and enzyme names. Although it may seem that the number of reactions is infinite, many of these reactions are similar and occur frequently in different pathways.

Recognition of the type of reaction can aid in remembering the pathways and enzyme names, thereby reducing the amount of memorization required. You may wish to use this section for reference as you go through your first biochemical pathways.

The Enzyme Commission (EC) has divided the basic reaction types and the enzymes catalyzing them into six broad-numbered classes: (1) oxidoreductases, (2) transferases, (3) hydrolases, (4) lyases, (5) isomerases, and (6) ligases. Each broad class of enzymes includes subsets of enzymes with a systematic name and a common name (e.g., dehydrogenases and kinases). For example, glucokinase (common name) has the systematic name ATP: D-hexose 6-phosphotransferase, and its EC number is EC 2.7.1.2. The first "2" refers to the general class (transferase) of enzyme, followed by a period. The "7" refers to the specific number of subclasses within the transferase family of enzymes (in this case, the class that transfers a phosphate). The "1" denotes transfer to an alcohol receptor, and the final "2" yields a specific enzyme number for glucokinase.

Oxidoreductases. Oxidation–reduction reactions are very common in biochemical pathways and are catalyzed by a broad class of enzymes called *oxidoreductases*. Whenever an oxidation–reduction reaction occurs, at least one substrate gains electrons and becomes reduced, and another substrate loses electrons and becomes oxidized. One subset of reactions is catalyzed by dehydrogenases, which accept and donate electrons in the form of hydride ions (H^-) or hydrogen atoms. Usually, an electron-transferring coenzyme, such as NAD^+/NADH, acts as an electron donor or acceptor (e.g., see Figs. 8.13 and 8.14).

In another subset of reactions, O_2 donates either one or both of its oxygen atoms to an acceptor (e.g., see xanthine oxidase, Fig. 8.18). When this occurs, O_2 becomes reduced, and an electron donor is oxidized. Enzymes participating in reactions with O_2 are called *hydroxylases* and *oxidases* when one oxygen atom is incorporated into a substrate and the other oxygen atom into water, or both atoms are incorporated into water. They are called *oxygenases* when both atoms of oxygen are incorporated into the acceptor. Most hydroxylases and oxidases require metal ions, such as Fe^{2+}, for electron transfer.

Transferases. Transferases catalyze group transfer reactions—the transfer of a functional group from one molecule to another. If the transferred group is a high-energy phosphate (as shown in Fig. 8.3), the enzyme is a kinase; if the transferred group is a carbohydrate residue, the enzyme is a glycosyltransferase; and if it is a fatty acyl group, the enzyme is an acyltransferase. A common feature of these reactions is that the group being transferred exists as a good leaving group on the donor molecule.

Another subset of group transfer reactions consists of transaminations (Fig. 8.19A). In this type of reaction, the nitrogen group from an amino acid is donated to an α-keto acid, forming a new amino acid and the α-keto acid corresponding to the donor amino acid. Enzymes that catalyze this last type of reaction are called *transaminases* or *aminotransferases*. The coenzyme pyridoxal phosphate is required for all transaminases (see Fig. 8.12C).

When the physiologically important aspect of the reaction is the compound synthesized, the transferase may be called a *synthase*. For example, the enzyme commonly called *glycogen synthase* transfers a glucosyl residue from UDP-glucose to the end of a glycogen molecule. Its systematic name is UDP-glucose-glycogen glycosyltransferase.

Hydrolases. In hydrolysis reactions, C–O, C–N, or C–S bonds are cleaved by the addition of H_2O in the form of OH^- and H^+ to the atoms forming the bond (see, e.g., Fig. 8.8). The enzyme class names specify the group being cleaved (e.g., the enzyme commonly named chymotrypsin is a protease, a hydrolase that cleaves peptide bonds in proteins).

FIG. 8.19. **A.** An example of a group transfer reaction—a transamination. Pyridoxal phosphate (PLP) on aspartate aminotransferase transfers an amino group from aspartate to the α-keto acid (α-ketoglutarate) to form a new amino acid (glutamate). The enzyme was formerly called *glutamate-oxaloacetate transaminase*. **B.** An example of a lyase. Aldolases catalyze carbon–carbon bond cleavage in reactions that are usually reversible. In glycolysis, the enzyme fructose 1,6-bisphosphate aldolase cleaves a carbon–carbon bond in fructose 1,6-bisphosphate. Aldolases have a lysine ε-amino group in the active site that participates in the reaction. **C.** An example of an isomerase. Isomerases rearrange atoms within a molecule. In the pathway of glycolysis, triose phosphate isomerase converts dihydroxyacetone phosphate to glyceraldehyde 3-phosphate by rearranging hydrogen atoms. No other substrates or products of the reaction exist.

Lyases. The lyase class of enzymes consists of a diverse group of enzymes that cleave C–C, C–O, and C–N bonds by means other than hydrolysis or oxidation. Some of the enzymes that catalyze C–C bond cleavage are called aldolases, decarboxylases (when carbon dioxide is released from a substrate), and thiolases (when the sulfur-containing nucleophile of cysteine or CoASH is used to break a carbon–carbon bond) (see Fig. 8.19B). The structures amenable to carbon–carbon bond cleavage usually require a carbonyl carbon that can act as an electron sink to stabilize the carbanion formed transiently when the carbon–carbon bond breaks.

This broad class of enzymes also includes dehydratases and many synthases. Dehydratases remove the elements of water from two adjacent carbon–carbon bonds to form a double bond. Certain enzymes in this group, such as certain group transferases, are commonly called synthases when the physiologically important direction of the reaction favors the formation of a carbon–carbon bond (e.g., citrate synthase).

 Isomerases. Many biochemical reactions simply rearrange the existing atoms of a molecule, that is, create isomers of the starting material (see Fig. 8.19C). Enzymes that rearrange the bond structure of a compound are called *isomerases*, whereas enzymes that catalyze movement of a phosphate from one atom to another are called *mutases*.

Ligases. Ligases synthesize C–C, C–S, C–O, and C–N bonds in reactions coupled to the cleavage of a high-energy phosphate bond in ATP or another nucleotide. Carboxylases, for example, add CO_2 to another compound in a reaction that requires ATP cleavage to provide energy (see Fig. 8.12B). Most carboxylases require the coenzyme biotin. Other ligases are named *synthetases* (e.g., fatty acyl CoA synthetase). Synthetases differ from the synthases mentioned under "Lyases" and "Transferases" in that synthetases derive the energy for new bond formation from cleavage of high-energy phosphate bonds, and synthases use a different source of energy.

Key Concepts

- Enzymes are proteins that act as catalysts—molecules that can accelerate the rate of a reaction.
- Enzymes are specific for various substrates due to the selective nature of the binding sites on the enzyme.
- The catalytic (active) site is the portion of the enzyme molecule at which the reaction occurs.
- Enzymes accelerate reaction rates by decreasing the amount of energy required to reach a high-energy intermediate stage of the reaction known as the transition-state complex. This is referred to as lowering the energy of activation.
- Enzymes use functional groups at the active site provided by coenzymes, metals, or amino acid residues to perform catalysis.
- Enzymes use general acid–base catalysis, formation of covalent intermediates, and transition-state stabilization as various mechanisms to accelerate reaction rates.
- Many drugs and toxins act by inhibiting enzymes.
- Enzymes can be regulated to control reaction rates through various mechanisms.
- Diseases discussed in this chapter are summarized in Table 8.2.

Table 8.2   Diseases Discussed in Chapter 8

Disorder or Condition	Genetic or Environmental	Comments
Malathion poisoning	Environmental	Inhibition of acetylcholinesterase at neuromuscular junctions, leading to acetylcholine accumulation at the junction and overstimulation of the autonomic nervous system.
Gout	Both	Accumulation of uric acid in blood, leading to precipitation in joints and severe pain and discomfort.
Thiamin deficiency (beriberi heart disease)	Environmental	Leads to lack of energy production due to reduced activity of key enzymes, and can lead to the Wernicke-Korsakoff syndrome. Brought about by alcoholism, as manifest by a poor diet, and ethanol inhibition of thiamine transport through the intestinal mucosa.

REVIEW QUESTIONS—CHAPTER 8

The following questions cover material from Chapters 6 and 7 as well as Chapter 8 (including Biochemical Comments).

1. A patient was born with a congenital mutation in an enzyme that severely affected its ability to bind an activation-transfer coenzyme. As a consequence, which one of the following is most likely to occur?

   A. The enzyme will be unable to bind the substrate of the reaction.
   B. The enzyme will be unable to form the transition-state complex.
   C. The enzyme will normally use a different activation-transfer coenzyme.
   D. The enzyme will normally substitute the functional group of an active-site amino acid residue for the coenzyme.
   E. The reaction may be carried out by the free coenzyme, provided the diet carries an adequate amount of its vitamin precursor.

2. An individual had a congenital mutation in glucokinase in which a proline was substituted for a leucine on a surface helix far from the active site but within the hinge region of the actin fold. This mutation would be expected to have which one of the following effects?

   A. It would have no effect on the rate of the reaction because it is not in the active site.
   B. It would have no effect on the rate of the reaction because proline and leucine are both nonpolar amino acids.
   C. It would have no effect on the number of substrate molecules reaching the transition state.
   D. It would probably affect the binding of ATP or a subsequent step in the reaction sequence.
   E. It would probably cause the reaction to proceed through an alternate mechanism.

3. Lysozyme is an enzyme that cleaves glycosidic linkages in bacterial cell walls. The pH optimum of the purified enzyme is 5.2. There are two acidic residues at the active site of lysozyme (E35 and D52) that are required for enzyme activity. The pK_a of E35 is 5.9, whereas the pK_a of D52 is 4.5. What are the primary ionization

states of these two residues at the pH optimum of the enzyme?

   A. E35 is protonated, D52 is ionized.
   B. E35 is protonated, D52 is protonated.
   C. E35 is ionized, D52 is protonated.
   D. E35 is ionized, D52 is ionized.
   E. This cannot be determined from the information provided.

Questions 4 and 5 refer to the following reaction:

4. The type of reaction shown fits into which of the following classifications?

   A. Group transfer
   B. Isomerization
   C. Carbon–carbon bond breaking
   D. Carbon–carbon bond formation
   E. Oxidation–reduction

5. The type of enzyme that catalyzes this reaction is which one of the following?

   A. Kinase
   B. Dehydrogenase
   C. Glycosyltransferase
   D. Transaminase
   E. Isomerase

9 Regulation of Enzymes

In the human body, thousands of diverse enzymes are regulated to fulfill their individual functions without waste of dietary components. Thus, with changes in our physiologic state, time of eating, environment, diet, or age, the rates of some enzymes must increase and those of others decrease. In this chapter, we describe the mechanisms for regulating enzyme activity and the strategies employed to regulate the metabolic pathways in which they reside.

Regulation Matches Function. Changes in the rate of a metabolic pathway occur because at least one enzyme in that pathway, the regulatory enzyme, has been activated or inhibited, or the amount of enzyme has increased or decreased. Regulatory enzymes usually catalyze the rate-limiting, or slowest, step in the pathway, so that increasing or decreasing their rate changes the rate of the entire pathway (Fig. 9.1). The mechanisms used to regulate the rate-limiting enzyme in a pathway reflect the function of the pathway.

Substrate Concentration. The rate of all enzymes depends on substrate concentration. Enzymes exhibit **saturation kinetics**; their rate increases with increasing substrate concentration [S], but it reaches a maximum velocity (V_{max}) when the enzyme is saturated with substrate. For many enzymes, the **Michaelis-Menten equation** describes the relationship among v_i (the initial velocity of a reaction), [S], V_{max}, and the K_m (the substrate concentration at which $v_i = \frac{1}{2}V_{max}$).

Reversible Inhibition. Enzymes are reversibly inhibited by **structural analogs** and **products**. These inhibitors are classified as **competitive**, **noncompetitive**, or **uncompetitive**, depending on their effect on formation of the **enzyme–substrate complex**.

Allosteric Enzymes. Allosteric **activators** or **inhibitors** are compounds that bind at sites other than the active catalytic site and regulate the enzyme through **conformational changes** that affect the catalytic site.

Covalent Modification. Enzyme activity also may be regulated by a covalent modification, such as **phosphorylation** of a serine, threonine, or tyrosine residue by a **protein kinase**.

Protein–Protein Interactions. Enzyme activity can be modulated through the reversible binding of a **modulator protein**, such as Ca^{2+} **calmodulin**. **Monomeric G proteins** (guanosine triphosphate [GTP]-binding proteins) activate target proteins through reversible binding.

Zymogen Cleavage. Some enzymes are synthesized as inactive precursors, called zymogens, which are activated by **proteolysis** (e.g., the digestive enzyme chymotrypsin).

Changes in Enzyme Concentration. The concentration of an enzyme can be regulated by changes in the rate of enzyme synthesis (e.g., induction of gene transcription) or the rate of degradation.

FIG. 9.1. The flux of substrates down a metabolic pathway is analogous to cars traveling down a highway. The rate-limiting enzyme is the portion of the highway that is narrowed to one lane by a highway barrier. This single portion of the highway limits the rate at which cars can arrive at their final destination miles later. Cars will back up before the barrier (similar to the increase in concentration of a precursor when a rate-limiting enzyme is inhibited). Some cars may exit and take an alternate route (similar to precursors entering another metabolic pathway). Moving the barrier just a little to open an additional lane is like activating a rate-limiting enzyme: It increases flow through the entire length of the pathway.

> *Regulation of Metabolic Pathways. The regulatory mechanisms for the rate-limiting enzyme of a pathway always reflect the **function of the pathway in a particular tissue**. In **feedback regulation**, the end product of a pathway directly or indirectly controls its own rate of synthesis; in **feed-forward regulation**, the substrate controls the rate of the pathway. **Biosynthetic** and **degradative** pathways are controlled through different but **complementary regulation**. Pathways are also regulated through **compartmentation** of enzymes unique to specific pathways.*

When **Al Martini** was stopped by police, he was required to take a Breathalyzer test. The Breathalyzer analyzes ethanol levels in expired air (assuming a ratio of 1 part ethanol in expired air to 2,000 parts ethanol in the blood). Once the sample enters the Breathalyzer, it is reacted with sulfuric acid, silver nitrate, and potassium dichromate. If ethanol is present, it will react with the potassium dichromate to form potassium sulfate, chromium sulfate, acetic acid, and water. Potassium dichromate generates a reddish brown color, whereas chromium sulfate is light green. In the Breathalyzer device, the reacted sample is compared with a nonreacted sample, and the difference in light absorption (due to the different colors) is converted to an electrical current. The extent of current generated will lead to a determination of blood alcohol level (i.e., if there is no ethanol in the sample, no current will be generated). Other forms of gaseous ethanol determination use infrared spectroscopy or a fuel cell.

Al Martini was not able to clear his blood ethanol rapidly enough to stay within the legal limit for driving. Ethanol is cleared from the blood at about 0.5 oz/h (15 mg/dL/h). Liver metabolism accounts for more than 90% of ethanol clearance from the blood. The major route of ethanol metabolism in the liver is the enzyme liver alcohol dehydrogenase (ADH), which oxidizes ethanol to acetaldehyde with generation of NADH.

Ethanol + NAD$^+$ →
acetaldehyde + NADH + H$^+$

The multienzyme complex MEOS (**m**icrosomal **e**thanol **o**xidizing **s**ystem), which is also called cytochrome P450-2E1, provides an additional route for ethanol oxidation to acetaldehyde in the liver.

THE WAITING ROOM

Al Martini is a 44-year-old man who has been an alcoholic for the past 5 years. He was recently admitted to the hospital for congestive heart failure (see Chapter 8). After being released from the hospital, he continued to drink. One night, he arrived at a friend's house at 7:00 P.M. Between his arrival and 11:00 P.M., he drank four beers and five martinis (for a total ethanol consumption of 9.5 oz). His friends encouraged him to stay an additional hour and drink coffee to sober up. Nevertheless, he ran his car off the road on his way home. He was taken to the emergency room of the local hospital and arrested for driving under the influence of alcohol. His blood alcohol concentration at the time of his arrest was 240 mg/dL, compared with the legal limit of ethanol for driving of 80 mg/dL.

Ann O'Rexia, a 23-year-old woman, 5 ft 7 in tall, is being treated for anorexia nervosa (see Chapters 1 through 3). She has been gaining weight and is now back to 99 lb from a low of 85 lb. Her blood glucose is still below normal (fasting blood glucose of 72 mg/dL, compared with a normal range of 80 to 100 mg/dL). She complains to her physician that she feels tired when she jogs, and she is concerned that the "extra weight" she has gained is slowing her down.

I. GENERAL OVERVIEW

Although the regulation of metabolic pathways is an exceedingly complex subject, dealt within most of the subsequent chapters of this text, several common themes are involved. Physiologic regulation of a metabolic pathway depends on the ability to alter flux through the pathway by activating the enzyme catalyzing the rate-limiting step in the pathway (see Fig. 9.1). The type of regulation employed always reflects the function of the pathway and the need for that pathway in a particular tissue or cell type. Pathways that produce a necessary product are usually feedback-regulated through a mechanism that involves concentration of product (e.g., allosteric inhibition or induction/repression of enzyme synthesis), either directly or indirectly. The concentration of the product signals when enough of the product has been synthesized. Storage and toxic disposal pathways are usually regulated directly or indirectly through a feed-forward mechanism that reflects the availability of precursor. Regulatory enzymes are often tissue-specific isozymes whose properties reflect the different functions of a pathway in particular tissues. Pathways are also regulated through compartmentation, collection of enzymes with a common function within a particular organelle or at a specific site in the cell.

The mechanisms employed to regulate enzymes have been organized into three general categories: regulation by compounds that bind reversibly in the active site (including the dependence of velocity on substrate concentration and product levels); regulation by changing the conformation of the active site (including allosteric regulators, covalent modification, protein–protein interactions, and zymogen cleavage); and regulation by changing the concentration of enzyme (enzyme synthesis and degradation). We will generally be using the pathways of fuel oxidation to illustrate the role of various mechanisms of enzyme regulation in metabolic pathways (see Chapters 1 through 3 for a general overview of these pathways).

II. REGULATION BY SUBSTRATE AND PRODUCT CONCENTRATION

A. Velocity and Substrate Concentration

The velocity of all enzymes is dependent on the concentration of substrate. This dependence is reflected in conditions such as starvation, in which several pathways are deprived of substrate. In contrast, storage pathways (e.g., glucose conversion to glycogen in the liver) and toxic waste disposal pathways (e.g., the urea cycle, which prevents NH_4^+ toxicity by converting NH_4^+ to urea) are normally regulated to speed up when more substrate is available. In the following sections, we use the Michaelis-Menten equation to describe the response of an enzyme to changes in substrate concentration, and we use glucokinase to illustrate the role of substrate supply in regulating enzyme activity.

1. THE MICHAELIS-MENTEN EQUATION

The equations of enzyme kinetics provide a quantitative way of describing the dependence of enzyme rate on substrate concentration. The simplest of these equations, the Michaelis-Menten equation, relates the initial velocity (v_i) to the concentration of substrate [S] and the two parameters K_m and V_{max} (Equation 9.1). The V_{max} of the enzyme is the maximal velocity that can be achieved at an infinite concentration of substrate, and the K_m of the enzyme for a substrate is the concentration of substrate required to reach $\frac{1}{2}V_{max}$. The Michaelis-Menten model of enzyme kinetics applies to a simple reaction in which the enzyme and substrate form an enzyme–substrate complex (ES) that can dissociate back to the free enzyme and substrate. The initial velocity of product formation, v_i, is proportional to the concentration of [ES]. As substrate concentration is increased, the concentration of ES increases, and the reaction rate increases proportionately. The total amount of enzyme present is represented by E_t.

Equation 9.1. The Michaelis-Menten equation.

For the reaction,

$$E + S \underset{k_2}{\overset{k_1}{\rightleftharpoons}} ES \overset{k_3}{\longrightarrow} E + P$$

the Michaelis-Menten equation is given by

$$v_i = \frac{V_{max}[S]}{K_m + [S]}$$

where $K_m = (k_2 + k_3)/k_1$ and $V_{max} = k_3 [E_t]$.

The graph of the Michaelis-Menten equation (v_i as a function of substrate concentration) is a rectangular hyperbola that approaches a finite limit, V_{max}, as the fraction of total enzyme present as ES increases (Fig. 9.2). At a hypothetical infinitely high substrate concentration, all of the enzyme molecules contain bound substrate, and the reaction rate is at V_{max}. The approach to the finite limit of V_{max} is called *saturation kinetics* because velocity cannot increase any further once the enzyme is saturated with substrate. Saturation kinetics is a characteristic property of all rate processes that depend on the binding of a compound to a protein.

One of the fuels used by **Ann O'Rexia's** skeletal muscles for jogging is glucose, which is converted to glucose 6-phosphate (glucose 6-P) by the enzymes hexokinase (HK) and glucokinase (GK). Glucose 6-P is metabolized in the pathway of glycolysis to generate adenosine triphosphate (ATP). This pathway is feedback-regulated, so that as her muscles use ATP, the rate of glycolysis will increase to generate more ATP.

When she is resting, her muscles and liver will convert glucose 6-P to glycogen (a fuel storage pathway, shown in *red*). Glycogen synthesis is feed-forward–regulated by the supply of glucose and by insulin and other hormones that signal glucose availability. Glycogenolysis (glycogen degradation) is activated during exercise to supply additional glucose 6-P for glycolysis. Unless Ann consumes sufficient calories, her glycogen stores will not be replenished after exercise, and she will tire easily.

FIG. 9.2. A graph of the Michaelis-Menten equation. V_{max} (*solid red line*) is the initial velocity extrapolated to infinite [S]. K_m (*dotted red line*) is the concentration of S at which $v_i = V_{max}/2$.

Patients with maturity-onset diabetes of the young (MODY) have a rare genetic form of diabetes mellitus in which the amount of insulin being secreted from the pancreas is too low, resulting in hyperglycemia. One class of MODY is caused by mutations in the gene for pancreatic glucokinase (a closely related isozyme of liver glucokinase) that affect its kinetic properties (K_m or V_{max}). Glucokinase is part of the mechanism that controls release of insulin from the pancreas. Decreased glucokinase activity results in lower insulin secretion for a given blood glucose level.

As **Ann O'Rexia** eats a high-carbohydrate meal, her blood glucose will rise to approximately 20 mM in the portal vein, and much of the glucose from her carbohydrate meal will enter the liver. How will the activity of glucokinase in the liver change as glucose is increased from 4 mM to 20 mM? (Hint: Calculate v_i as a fraction of V_{max} for both conditions, using a K_m for glucose of 5 mM and the Michaelis-Menten equation).

FIG. 9.3. A comparison between hexokinase I and glucokinase. The initial velocity (v_i) as a fraction of V_{max} is graphed as a function of glucose concentration. The plot for glucokinase (*heavy blue line*) is slightly sigmoidal (S-shaped), possibly because the rate of an intermediate step in the reaction is so slow that the enzyme does not follow Michaelis-Menten kinetics. The *dashed blue line* has been derived from the Michaelis-Menten equation fitted to the data for concentrations of glucose >5 mM. For S-shaped curves, the concentration of substrate required to reach half V_{max}, or half-saturation, is sometimes called the $S_{0.5}$ or $K_{0.5}$ rather than K_m. At $v_i/V_{max} = 0.5$, for glucokinase, the K_m is 5 mM and the $S_{0.5}$ is 6.7 mM.

The K_m of the enzyme for a substrate is defined as the concentration of substrate at which v_i equals $\frac{1}{2}V_{max}$. The velocity of an enzyme is most sensitive to changes in substrate concentration over a concentration range below its K_m (see Fig. 9.2). At substrate concentrations less than one-tenth of the K_m, a doubling of substrate concentration nearly doubles the velocity of the reaction; at substrate concentrations 10 times the K_m, doubling the substrate concentration has little effect on the velocity.

The K_m of an enzyme for a substrate is related to the dissociation constant, K_d, which is the rate of substrate release divided by the rate of substrate binding (k_2/k_1). For example, a genetic mutation that decreases the rate of substrate binding to the enzyme decreases the affinity of the enzyme for the substrate and increases the K_d and K_m of the enzyme for that substrate. The higher the K_m, the higher is the substrate concentration required to reach $\frac{1}{2}V_{max}$.

2. HEXOKINASE ISOZYMES HAVE DIFFERENT K_m VALUES FOR GLUCOSE

A comparison between the isozymes of hexokinase found in red blood cells and in the liver illustrates the significance of the K_m of an enzyme for its substrate. Hexokinase catalyzes the first step in glucose metabolism in most cells: the transfer of a phosphate from adenosine triphosphate (ATP) to glucose to form glucose 6-phosphate. Glucose 6-phosphate may then be metabolized in glycolysis, which generates energy in the form of ATP, or it can be converted to glycogen, a storage polymer of glucose. Hexokinase I, the isozyme in red blood cells (erythrocytes), has a K_m for glucose of approximately 0.05 mM (Fig. 9.3). The isozyme of hexokinase, called *glucokinase*, which is found in the liver and pancreas, has a much higher K_m of approximately 5 to 6 mM. The red blood cell is totally dependent on glucose metabolism to meet its needs for ATP. At the low K_m of the erythrocyte hexokinase, blood glucose could fall drastically below its normal fasting level of approximately 5 mM, and the red blood cell could still phosphorylate glucose at rates near V_{max}. The liver, however, stores large amounts of "excess" glucose as glycogen or converts it to fat. Because glucokinase has a K_m of approximately 5 mM, the rate of glucose phosphorylation in the liver will tend to increase as blood glucose increases after a high-carbohydrate meal and decreases as blood glucose levels fall. The high K_m of hepatic glucokinase, thus, promotes the storage of glucose as liver glycogen or as fat, but only when glucose is in excess supply.

3. VELOCITY AND ENZYME CONCENTRATION

The rate of a reaction is directly proportional to the concentration of enzyme; if you double the amount of enzyme, you will double the amount of product produced per minute, whether you are at low or at saturating concentrations of substrate. This important relationship between velocity and enzyme concentration is not immediately apparent in the Michaelis-Menten equation because the concentration of total enzyme present (E_t) has been incorporated into the term V_{max} (i.e., V_{max} is equal to the rate constant k_3 times E_t). However, V_{max} is most often expressed as product produced per minute per milligram of enzyme and is meant to reflect a property of the enzyme that is not dependent on its concentration.

4. MULTISUBSTRATE REACTIONS

Most enzymes have more than one substrate, and the substrate-binding sites overlap in the catalytic (active) site. When an enzyme has more than one substrate, the sequence of substrate binding and product release affect the rate equation. As a consequence, an apparent value of K_m ($K_{m,app}$) depends on the concentration of cosubstrate or product present.

5. RATES OF ENZYME-CATALYZED REACTIONS IN THE CELL

Equations for the initial velocity of an enzyme-catalyzed reaction such as the Michaelis-Menten equation can provide useful parameters for describing or comparing enzymes. However, many multisubstrate enzymes, such as glucokinase, have kinetic patterns that do not fit the Michaelis-Menten model (or do so under nonphysiologic conditions). The Michaelis-Menten model is also inapplicable to enzymes present in a higher concentration than their substrates. Nonetheless, the term K_m is still used for these enzymes to describe the approximate concentration of substrate at which velocity equals $\frac{1}{2}V_{max}$.

B. Reversible Inhibition within the Active Site

One of the ways of altering enzyme activity is through compounds binding in the active site. If these compounds are not part of the normal reaction, they inhibit the enzyme. An *inhibitor of an enzyme* is defined as a compound that decreases the velocity of the reaction by binding to the enzyme. It is a reversible inhibitor if it is not covalently bound to the enzyme and can dissociate at a significant rate. Reversible inhibitors are generally classified as competitive, noncompetitive, or uncompetitive with respect to their relationship to a substrate of the enzyme. In most reactions, the products of the reaction are reversible inhibitors of the enzyme that produces them.

1. COMPETITIVE INHIBITION

A competitive inhibitor "competes" with a substrate for binding at the enzyme's substrate-recognition site and therefore is usually a close structural analog of the substrate (Fig. 9.4A). An increase of substrate concentration can overcome competitive inhibition; when the substrate concentration is increased to a sufficiently high level, the substrate-binding sites are occupied by substrate and inhibitor molecules cannot bind. Competitive inhibitors, therefore, increase the apparent K_m of the enzyme ($K_{m,app}$) because they raise the concentration of substrate necessary to saturate the enzyme. They have no effect on V_{max}.

2. NONCOMPETITIVE AND UNCOMPETITIVE INHIBITION

If an inhibitor does not compete with a substrate for its binding site, the inhibitor is either a noncompetitive or an uncompetitive inhibitor with respect to that particular substrate (see Fig. 9.4B). Uncompetitive inhibition is almost never encountered in medicine and will not be discussed further. To illustrate noncompetitive inhibition, consider a multisubstrate reaction in which substrates A and B react to form a product. An inhibitor (NI) that is a structural analog of substrate B would fit into substrate B's binding site, but the inhibitor would be a noncompetitive inhibitor with regard to the other substrate, substrate A. An increase of A will not prevent the inhibitor from binding to substrate B's binding site. The inhibitor, in effect, lowers the concentration of the active enzyme and therefore changes the V_{max} of the enzyme. If the inhibitor has absolutely no effect on the binding of substrate A, it will not change the K_m for A (a pure noncompetitive inhibitor).

Some inhibitors, such as metals, might not bind at either substrate-recognition site. In this case, the inhibitor would be noncompetitive with respect to both substrates.

3. SIMPLE PRODUCT INHIBITION IN METABOLIC PATHWAYS

All products are reversible inhibitors of the enzymes that produce them and may be competitive or noncompetitive relative to a particular substrate. Simple product inhibition, a decrease in the rate of an enzyme caused by the accumulation of its own product, plays an important role in metabolic pathways: It prevents one enzyme in a sequence of reactions from generating a product faster than it can be used by the next enzyme in that sequence. As an example, product inhibition of hexokinase by glucose 6-phosphate conserves blood glucose for tissues that need it. Tissues take up glucose from the blood and phosphorylate it to glucose 6-phosphate, which can then enter several different pathways (including glycolysis and glycogen

Glucokinase, which has a high K_m for glucose, phosphorylates glucose to glucose 6-phosphate about twice as fast after a carbohydrate meal as during fasting. Substitute the values for S and K_m into the Michaelis-Menten equation. The initial velocity will be 0.44 times V_{max} when blood glucose is at 4 mM and about 0.80 times V_{max} when blood glucose is at 20 mM. In the liver, glucose 6-phosphate is a precursor for both glycogen and fat synthesis. Thus, these storage pathways are partially regulated through a direct effect of substrate supply. They are also partially regulated through an increase of insulin and a decrease of glucagon, two hormones that signal the supply of dietary fuel.

The liver alcohol dehydrogenase that is most active in oxidizing ethanol has a very low K_m for ethanol, approximately 0.04 mM, and is at more than 99% of its V_{max} at the legal limit of blood alcohol concentration for driving (80 mg/dL or about 17 mM). In contrast, the microsomal ethanol oxidizing system (MEOS) isozyme that is most active toward ethanol has a K_m of approximately 11 mM. Thus, MEOS makes a greater contribution to ethanol oxidation and clearance from the blood at higher ethanol levels than at lower ones. Liver damage such as cirrhosis results partly from toxic by-products of ethanol oxidation generated by MEOS. **Al Martini**, who has a blood alcohol level of 240 mg/dL (approximately 52 mM), is drinking enough to potentially cause liver damage, as well as his car accident and arrest for driving under the influence of alcohol. The various isozymes and polymorphisms of alcohol dehydrogenase and MEOS are discussed in more detail in Chapter 25.

Some of **Al Martini's** problems have arisen from product inhibition of liver alcohol dehydrogenase by NADH. As ethanol is oxidized in liver cells, NAD^+ is reduced to NADH and the $NADH/NAD^+$ ratio rises. NADH is an inhibitor of alcohol dehydrogenase, competitive with respect to NAD^+, so the increased $NADH/NAD^+$ ratio slows the rate of ethanol oxidation and ethanol clearance from the blood.

NADH is also a product inhibitor of enzymes in the pathway that oxidizes fatty acids. Consequently, these fatty acids accumulate in the liver, eventually contributing to the alcoholic fatty liver.

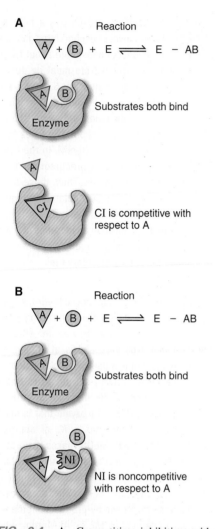

FIG. 9.4. **A.** Competitive inhibition with respect to substrate *A*. *A* and *B* are substrates for the reaction that forms the enzyme–substrate complex (*E–AB*). The enzyme has separate binding sites for each substrate, which overlap in the active site. The competitive inhibitor (*CI*) competes for the binding site of *A*, the substrate it most closely resembles. **B.** *NI* is a noncompetitive inhibitor with respect to substrate *A*. *A* can still bind to its binding site in the presence of *NI*. However, *NI* is competitive with respect to *B* because it binds to the B-binding site. In contrast, an inhibitor that is uncompetitive with respect to *A* might also resemble *B*, but it could bind to the *B* site only after *A* is bound.

synthesis). As these pathways become more active, glucose-6-phosphate concentration decreases, and the rate of hexokinase increases. When these pathways are less active, glucose-6-phosphate concentration increases, hexokinase is inhibited, and glucose remains in the blood for other tissues.

III. REGULATION THROUGH CONFORMATIONAL CHANGES

In substrate response and product inhibition, the rate of the enzyme is affected principally by the binding of a substrate or a product within the catalytic site. Most rate-limiting enzymes are also controlled through regulatory mechanisms that change the conformation of the enzyme in a way that affects the catalytic site. These regulatory mechanisms include (1) allosteric activation and inhibition; (2) phosphorylation or other covalent modification; (3) protein–protein interactions between regulatory and catalytic subunits or between two proteins; and (4) proteolytic cleavage. These types of regulation can rapidly change an enzyme from an inactive form to a fully active conformation.

In the following sections, we describe the general characteristics of these regulatory mechanisms and illustrate the first three with glycogen phosphorylase, glycogen phosphorylase kinase, and protein kinase A.

A. Conformational Changes in Allosteric Enzymes

Allosteric activators and inhibitors (allosteric effectors) are compounds that bind to the allosteric site (a site separate from the catalytic site) and cause a conformational change that affects the affinity of the enzyme for the substrate. Usually, an allosteric enzyme has multiple interacting subunits that can exist in active and inactive conformations, and the allosteric effector promotes or hinders conversion from one conformation to another.

1. COOPERATIVITY IN SUBSTRATE BINDING TO ALLOSTERIC ENZYMES

Allosteric enzymes usually contain two or more subunits and exhibit positive cooperativity; the binding of substrate to one subunit facilitates the binding of substrate to another subunit (Fig. 9.5). The first substrate molecule has difficulty in binding to the enzyme because all of the subunits are in the conformation with a low affinity for substrate (the taut "T" conformation) (see oxygen binding to hemoglobin in Chapter 7, Section VII.B). The first substrate molecule to bind changes its own subunit and at least one adjacent subunit to the high-affinity conformation (the relaxed "R" state). In the example of the tetramer hemoglobin, discussed in Chapter 7, the change in one subunit facilitated changes in all four subunits, and the molecule generally changed to the new conformation in a concerted fashion. However, most allosteric enzymes follow a more stepwise (sequential) progression through intermediate stages (see Fig. 9.5).

2. ALLOSTERIC ACTIVATORS AND INHIBITORS

Allosteric enzymes bind activators at the allosteric site, a site that is physically separate from the catalytic site. The binding of an allosteric activator changes the conformation of the catalytic site in a way that increases the affinity of the enzyme for the substrate.

In general, activators of allosteric enzymes bind more tightly to the high-affinity R state of the enzyme than the T state (i.e., the allosteric site is open only in the R enzyme) (Fig. 9.6). Thus, the activators increase the amount of enzyme in the active state, thereby facilitating substrate binding in their own and other subunits. In contrast, allosteric inhibitors bind more tightly to the T state, so either substrate concentration or activator concentration must be increased to overcome the effects of the allosteric inhibitor. Allosteric inhibitors might have their own binding site on the enzyme, or they might compete with the substrate at the active site and prevent cooperativity. Thus, the term *allosteric inhibitor* is more generally applied to any inhibitor of an allosteric enzyme.

In the absence of activator, a plot of velocity versus substrate concentration for an allosteric enzyme usually results in a sigmoid or S-shaped curve (rather than the rectangular hyperbola of Michaelis-Menten enzymes) as the successive binding of substrate molecules activates additional subunits (see Fig. 9.6). In plots of velocity versus substrate concentration, the effect of an allosteric activator generally makes the sigmoidal S-shaped curve more like the rectangular hyperbola, with a substantial decrease in the $S_{0.5}$ (K_m) of the enzyme, because the activator changes all of the subunits to the high-affinity state. Such allosteric effectors are "*K* effectors"; they change the K_m but not the V_{max} of the enzyme. An allosteric inhibitor makes it more difficult for substrate or activators to convert the subunits to the most active conformation, and therefore inhibitors generally shift the curve to the right, either increasing the $S_{0.5}$ alone or increasing it together with a decrease in the V_{max}.

Some of the rate-limiting enzymes in the pathways of fuel oxidation (e.g., muscle glycogen phosphorylase in glycogenolysis, phosphofructokinase-1 in glycolysis, and isocitrate dehydrogenase in the tricarboxylic acid [TCA] cycle) are allosteric enzymes regulated by changes in the concentration of adenosine

FIG. 9.5. A sequential model for an allosteric enzyme. The sequential model is actually the preferred path from the T_0 (taut, with 0 substrate bound) low-affinity conformation to the R_4 (relaxed, with four substrate molecules bound) conformation, taken from an array of all possible equilibrium conformations that differ by the conformation of only one subunit. The final result is a stepwise path in which intermediate conformations exist, and subunits may change conformations independently, depending on their geometric relationship to the subunits already containing bound substrate.

A model of an allosteric enzyme

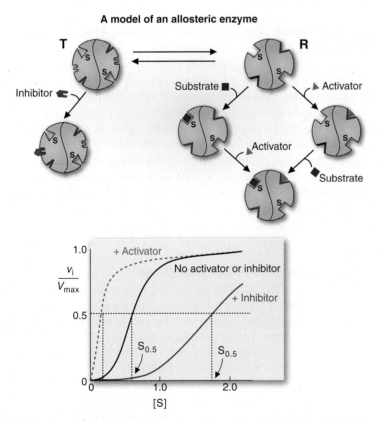

FIG. 9.6. Activators and inhibitors of an allosteric enzyme (simplified model). This enzyme has two identical subunits, each containing three binding sites: one for the substrate (*S*), one for the allosteric activator (*green triangle*), and one for the allosteric inhibitor (*two-pronged red shape*). The enzyme has two conformations: a relaxed active conformation (*R*) and an inactive conformation (*T*). The activator binds only to its activator site when the enzyme is in the R configuration. The inhibitor-binding site is open only when the enzyme is in the T state.

A plot of velocity (v_i/V_{max}) versus substrate concentration reveals that binding of the substrate at its binding site stabilizes the active conformation so that the second substrate binds more readily, resulting in an S (sigmoidal)-shaped curve. The graph of v_i/V_{max} becomes hyperbolic in the presence of activator (which stabilizes the high-affinity R form), and more sigmoidal with a higher $S_{0.5}$ in the presence of inhibitor (which stabilizes the low-affinity form).

diphosphate (ADP) or adenosine monophosphate (AMP), which are allosteric activators. The function of fuel oxidation pathways is the generation of ATP. When the concentration of ATP in a muscle cell begins to decrease, ADP and AMP increase; ADP activates isocitrate dehydrogenase, and AMP activates glycogen phosphorylase and phosphofructokinase-1. The response is very fast, and small changes in the concentration of activator can cause large changes in the rate of the reaction.

3. ALLOSTERIC ENZYMES IN METABOLIC PATHWAYS

Regulation of enzymes by allosteric effectors provides several advantages over other methods of regulation. Allosteric inhibitors usually have a much stronger effect on enzyme velocity than competitive and noncompetitive inhibitors in the active catalytic site. Because allosteric effectors do not occupy the catalytic site, they may function as activators. Thus, allosteric enzymes are not limited to regulation through inhibition. Furthermore, the allosteric effector need not bear any resemblance to substrate or product of the enzyme. Finally, the effect of an allosteric effector is rapid, occurring as soon as its concentration changes in the cell. These features of allosteric enzymes are often essential for feedback regulation of metabolic pathways by end products of the pathway or by signal molecules that coordinate multiple pathways.

B. Conformational Changes from Covalent Modification

1. PHOSPHORYLATION

The activity of many enzymes is regulated through phosphorylation by a protein kinase or dephosphorylation by a protein phosphatase (Fig. 9.7). Serine/threonine protein kinases transfer a phosphate from ATP to the hydroxyl group of a specific serine (and sometimes threonine) on the target enzyme; tyrosine kinases transfer a phosphate to the hydroxyl group of a specific tyrosine residue. Phosphate is a bulky, negatively charged residue that interacts with other nearby amino acid residues of the protein to create a conformational change at the catalytic site. The conformational change is caused by alterations in ionic interactions and/or hydrogen bond patterns due to the presence of the phosphate group. The conformational change makes certain enzymes more active and other enzymes less active. The effect is reversed by a specific protein phosphatase that removes the phosphate by hydrolysis.

2. MUSCLE GLYCOGEN PHOSPHORYLASE

Muscle glycogen phosphorylase, the rate-limiting enzyme in the pathway of glycogen degradation, degrades glycogen to glucose 1-phosphate. It is regulated by the allosteric activator AMP, which increases in the cell as ATP is used for muscular contraction (Fig. 9.8). Thus, a rapid increase in the rate of glycogen degradation to glucose 1-phosphate is achieved when an increase of AMP signals that more fuel is needed for ATP generation in the glycolytic pathway.

Glycogen phosphorylase also can be activated through phosphorylation by glycogen phosphorylase kinase. Either phosphorylation or AMP binding can change the enzyme to the same fully active conformation. The phosphate is removed by protein phosphatase-1. Glycogen phosphorylase kinase links the activation of muscle glycogen phosphorylase to changes in the level of the hormone adrenaline in the blood. It is regulated through phosphorylation by protein kinase A and by activation of Ca^{2+}-calmodulin (a modulator protein) during contraction.

3. PROTEIN KINASE A

Some protein kinases, called dedicated protein kinases, are tightly bound to a single protein and regulate only the protein to which they are tightly bound. However,

Protein with serine side chain

ATP

Phosphorylated protein

FIG. 9.7. Protein kinases and protein phosphatases.

When **Ann O'Rexia** begins to jog, adenosine monophosphate (AMP) activates her muscle glycogen phosphorylase, which degrades glycogen to glucose 1-phosphate. This compound is converted to glucose 6-phosphate, which feeds into the glycolytic pathway to generate ATP for muscle contraction. As she continues to jog, her adrenaline (epinephrine) levels rise, producing the signal that activates glycogen phosphorylase kinase. This enzyme phosphorylates glycogen phosphorylase, causing it to become even more active than with AMP alone (see Fig. 9.8).

FIG. 9.8. Activation of muscle glycogen phosphorylase by AMP and by phosphorylation. Muscle glycogen phosphorylase is composed of two identical subunits. The substrate-binding sites in the active catalytic site are denoted by *S*. AMP binds to the allosteric site, a site separate from the active catalytic site. Glycogen phosphorylase kinase can transfer a phosphate from ATP to one serine residue in each subunit. Either phosphorylation or binding of AMP causes a change in the active site that increases the activity of the enzyme. The first event at one subunit facilitates the subsequent events that convert the enzyme to the fully active form.

other protein kinases and protein phosphatases simultaneously regulate several rate-limiting enzymes in a cell to achieve a coordinated response. For example, protein kinase A, a serine/threonine protein kinase, phosphorylates several enzymes that regulate different metabolic pathways. One of these enzymes is glycogen phosphorylase kinase (see Fig. 9.8).

Protein kinase A provides a means for hormones to control metabolic pathways. Adrenaline and many other hormones increase the intracellular concentration of the allosteric regulator 3′,5′-cyclic AMP (cAMP), which is referred to as a *hormonal second messenger* (Fig. 9.9A). cAMP binds to regulatory subunits of protein kinase A, which dissociate and release the activated catalytic subunits (see Fig. 9.9B). Dissociation of inhibitory regulatory subunits is a common theme in enzyme regulation. The active catalytic subunits phosphorylate glycogen phosphorylase and other enzymes at serine residues.

In the example shown in Figure 9.8, adrenaline (epinephrine) indirectly increases cAMP, which activates protein kinase A, which phosphorylates and activates glycogen phosphorylase kinase, which phosphorylates and activates glycogen phosphorylase. The sequence of events in which one kinase phosphorylates another kinase is called a *phosphorylation cascade*. Because each stage of the phosphorylation cascade is associated with one enzyme molecule activating many enzyme molecules, the initial activating event is greatly amplified.

FIG. 9.9. **A.** Structure of cAMP (3′,5′-cyclic AMP). The phosphate group is attached to hydroxyl groups on both the third (3′) and fifth (5′) carbons of ribose, forming a cyclic molecule. **B.** Protein kinase A. When the regulatory subunits (*R*) of protein kinase A bind the allosteric activator, cAMP, they dissociate from the enzyme, thereby releasing active catalytic subunits (*C*).

4. OTHER COVALENT MODIFICATIONS
Several proteins are modified covalently by the addition of groups such as acetyl, ADP-ribose, or lipid moieties (see Chapter 6). These modifications may activate or inhibit the enzyme directly. However, they also may modify the ability of the enzyme to interact with other proteins or to reach its correct location in the cell.

C. Conformational Changes from Protein–Protein Interactions
Changes in the conformation of the active site also can be regulated by direct protein–protein interaction. This type of regulation is illustrated by Ca^{2+}-calmodulin and small (monomeric) G proteins.

← Flexible region between domains

FIG. 9.10. Calcium-calmodulin has four binding sites for calcium (shown in green). Each calcium forms a multiligand coordination sphere by simultaneously binding several amino acid residues on calmodulin. Thus, calmodulin can create large conformational changes in proteins to which it is bound when calcium binds. Calmodulin has a flexible region in the middle connecting the two domains.

1. THE CALCIUM-CALMODULIN FAMILY OF MODULATOR PROTEINS

Modulator proteins bind to other proteins and regulate their activity by causing a conformational change at the catalytic site or by blocking the catalytic site (steric hindrance). They are protein allosteric effectors that can either activate or inhibit the enzyme or protein to which they bind.

Ca^{2+}-calmodulin is an example of a dissociable modulator protein that binds to several different proteins and regulates their function. It also exists in the cytosol and functions as a Ca^{2+}-binding protein (Fig. 9.10). The center of the symmetric molecule is a hinge region that bends as Ca^{2+}-calmodulin folds over the protein it is regulating.

One of the enzymes activated by Ca^{2+}-calmodulin is muscle glycogen phosphorylase kinase (see Fig. 9.8), which is also activated by protein kinase A. When a neural impulse triggers Ca^{2+} release from the sarcoplasmic reticulum, Ca^{2+} binds to the calmodulin subunit of muscle glycogen phosphorylase kinase, which undergoes a conformational change. This conformational change leads to the activation of glycogen phosphorylase kinase, which then phosphorylates glycogen phosphorylase, ultimately increasing the generation of ATP to supply energy for muscle contraction. Simultaneously, Ca^{2+} binds to troponin C, a member of the Ca^{2+}-calmodulin superfamily that serves as a nondissociable regulatory subunit of troponin, a regulator of muscle contraction. Calcium binding to troponin prepares the muscle for contraction. Thus, the supply of energy for contraction is activated simultaneously with the contraction machinery.

2. SMALL (MONOMERIC) G PROTEINS REGULATE THROUGH CONFORMATIONAL CHANGES

The masters of regulation through reversible protein association in the cell are the monomeric G proteins, small single-subunit proteins that bind and hydrolyze guanosine triphosphate (GTP). GTP is a purine nucleotide that, like ATP, contains high-energy phosphoanhydride bonds that release energy when hydrolyzed. When G proteins bind GTP, their conformation changes so that they can bind to a target protein, which is then either activated or inhibited in carrying out its function (Fig. 9.11, step 1).

G proteins are said to possess an internal clock because they are GTPases that slowly hydrolyze their own bound GTP to GDP and phosphate. As they hydrolyze GTP, their conformation changes and the complex they have formed with the target protein disassembles (see Fig. 9.11, step 2). The bound GDP on the inactive G protein is eventually replaced by GTP, and the process can begin again (see Fig. 9.11, step 3).

The activity of many G proteins is regulated by accessory proteins (GAPs [*G*TPase-*a*ctivating *p*roteins], GEFs [*g*uanine nucleotide *e*xchange *f*actors], and GDIs [*G*DP *d*issociation *i*nhibitors]), which may, in turn, be regulated by allosteric effectors. GAPs increase the rate of GTP hydrolysis by the G protein, and therefore the rate of dissociation of the G protein–target protein complex (see Fig. 9.11, step 2). When a GEF protein binds to a G protein, it increases the rate of GTP exchange for a bound GDP, and therefore activates the G protein (see Fig. 9.11, step 3). GDI proteins bind to the GDP–G protein complex and inhibit dissociation of GDP, thereby keeping the G protein inactive.

The Ras superfamily of small G proteins is divided into five families: Ras, Rho, Arf, Rab, and Ran. These monomeric G proteins play major roles in the regulation of cell growth, morphogenesis, cell motility, axonal guidance, cytokinesis, and trafficking through the Golgi, nucleus, and endosomes. They are generally bound to a lipid membrane through a lipid anchor such as a myristoyl group or farnesyl group and regulate the assembly and activity of protein complexes at these sites. The functions of some of these G proteins will be discussed further in Chapters 10 and 11.

D. Proteolytic Cleavage

Although many enzymes undergo some cleavage during synthesis, others enter lysosomes, secretory vesicles, or are secreted as proenzymes, which are precursor proteins that must undergo proteolytic cleavage to become fully functional. Unlike most other forms of regulation, proteolytic cleavage is irreversible.

The precursor proteins of proteases (enzymes that cleave specific peptide bonds) are called *zymogens*. To denote the inactive zymogen form of an enzyme, the name is modified by addition of the suffix "-ogen" or the prefix "pro-." The synthesis of zymogens as inactive precursors prevents them from cleaving proteins prematurely at their sites of synthesis or secretion. Chymotrypsinogen, for example, is stored in vesicles within pancreatic cells until it is secreted into ducts leading to the intestinal lumen. In the digestive tract, chymotrypsinogen is converted to chymotrypsin by the proteolytic enzyme trypsin, which cleaves off a small peptide from the N-terminal region (and two internal peptides). This cleavage activates chymotrypsin by causing a conformational change in the spacing of amino acid residues around the binding site for the denatured protein substrate and around the catalytic site.

Most of the proteases involved in blood clotting are zymogens, such as fibrinogen and prothrombin, which circulate in blood in the inactive form. They are cleaved to the active form (fibrin and thrombin, respectively) by other proteases, which have been activated by their attachment to the site of injury in a blood vessel wall. Thus, clots form at the site of injury and not randomly in the circulation.

IV. REGULATION THROUGH CHANGES IN AMOUNT OF ENZYME

Tissues continuously adjust the rate at which different proteins are synthesized to vary the amount of different enzymes present. The expression for V_{max} in the Michaelis-Menten equation incorporates the concept that the rate of a reaction is proportional to the amount of enzyme present. Thus, the maximal capacity of a tissue can change with increased protein synthesis or with increased protein degradation.

A. Regulated Enzyme Synthesis

Protein synthesis begins with the process of gene transcription, transcribing the genetic code for that protein from DNA into messenger RNA. The code in messenger RNA is then translated into the primary amino acid sequence of the protein. Generally, the rate of enzyme synthesis is regulated by increasing or decreasing the rate of gene transcription, processes that are generally referred to as *induction* (increase) and *repression* (decrease). However, the rate of enzyme synthesis is sometimes regulated through stabilization of the messenger RNA. (These processes are covered in Section III of the text). Compared with the more immediate types of regulation discussed earlier, regulation by means of induction/repression of enzyme synthesis is usually slow in humans, occurring over hours to days.

B. Regulated Protein Degradation

The content of an enzyme in the cell can be altered through selective regulated degradation as well as through regulated synthesis. Although all proteins in the cell can be degraded with a characteristic half-life within lysosomes, protein degradation via two specialized systems, proteosomes and caspases, is highly selective and regulated. During fasting or infective stress, protein degradation in skeletal muscle is activated to increase the supply of amino acids in the blood for gluconeogenesis, or for the synthesis of antibodies and other components of the immune response. Under these conditions, synthesis of ubiquitin, a protein that targets proteins for degradation in proteosomes, is increased by the steroid hormone cortisol. Protein degradation is discussed in more detail in Chapter 37.

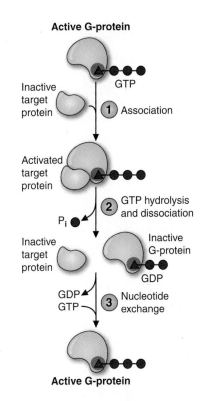

FIG. 9.11. Monomeric G proteins. Step 1: When GTP is bound, the conformation of the G protein allows it to bind target proteins, which are then activated (as shown) or inhibited. Step 2: The G protein hydrolyzes a phosphate from GTP to form guanosine diphosphate (GDP), which changes the G protein conformation and causes it to dissociate from the target protein. Step 3: GDP is exchanged for GTP, which reactivates the G protein.

 The maximal capacity of MEOS (cytochrome P450-2E1) is increased in the liver with continued ingestion of ethanol through a mechanism involving induction of gene transcription. Thus, **Al Martini** has a higher capacity to oxidize ethanol to acetaldehyde than a naive drinker (a person not previously subjected to alcohol). Nevertheless, the persistence of his elevated blood alcohol level shows that he has saturated his capacity for ethanol oxidation (V-maxed out). Once his enzymes are operating near V_{max}, any additional ethanol he drinks will not appreciably increase the rate of ethanol clearance from his blood.

V. REGULATION OF METABOLIC PATHWAYS

The different means of regulating enzyme activity we have described are used to control metabolic pathways, cellular events, and physiologic processes to match the body's requirements. Although many metabolic pathways are present in the body, a few common themes or principles are involved in their regulation. Of course, the overriding principle is that regulation of a pathway matches its *function*.

A. Principles of Pathway Regulation

Metabolic pathways are a series of sequential reactions in which the product of one reaction is the substrate of the next reaction (Fig. 9.12). Each step or reaction is usually catalyzed by a separate enzyme. The enzymes of a pathway have a common function—conversion of substrate to the final end products of the pathway. A pathway also may have a branch point at which an intermediate becomes the precursor for another pathway.

1. REGULATION OCCURS AT THE RATE-LIMITING STEP

Pathways are principally regulated at one key enzyme, the regulatory enzyme, which catalyzes the rate-limiting step in the pathway. This is the slowest step and is usually not readily reversible. Thus, changes in the rate-limiting step can influence flux through the rest of the pathway (see Fig. 9.1). The rate-limiting step is usually the first committed step in a pathway, or a reaction that is related to, or influenced by, the first committed step. Additional regulated enzymes occur after each metabolic branch point to direct flow into the branch (e.g., in Fig. 9.12, feedback inhibition of enzyme 2 results in accumulation of B, which enzyme 5 then uses for synthesis of compound G). Inhibition of the rate-limiting enzyme in a pathway usually leads to accumulation of the pathway precursor.

2. FEEDBACK REGULATION

Feedback regulation refers to a situation in which the end product of a pathway controls its own rate of synthesis (see Fig. 9.12). Feedback regulation usually involves allosteric regulation of the rate-limiting enzyme by the end product of a pathway (or a compound that reflects changes in the concentration of the end product). The end product of a pathway may also control its own synthesis by inducing or repressing the gene for transcription of the rate-limiting enzyme in the pathway. This type of regulation is much slower to respond to changing conditions than allosteric regulation.

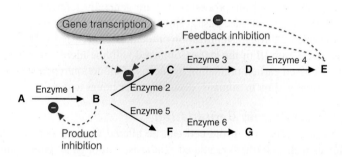

FIG. 9.12.   A common pattern for feedback inhibition of metabolic pathways. The letters represent compounds formed from different enzymes in the reaction pathway. *Compound B is* at a metabolic branch point: It can go down one pathway to *E* or down an alternate pathway to *G*. The end product of the pathway, *E*, might control its own synthesis by allosterically inhibiting *enzyme 2*, the first committed step of the pathway, or by inhibiting transcription of the gene for *enzyme 2*. As a result of the feedback inhibition, *B* accumulates and more *B* enters the pathway for conversion to *G*, which could be a storage pathway or a disposal pathway. In this hypothetical pathway, *B* is a product inhibitor of *enzyme 1*, competitive with respect to *A*. *Precursor A* might induce the synthesis of *enzyme 1*, which would allow more *A* to go to *G*.

3. FEED-FORWARD REGULATION

Certain pathways, such as those involved in the disposal of toxic compounds, are feed-forward–regulated. Feed-forward regulation may occur through an increased supply of substrate to an enzyme with a high K_m, allosteric activation of a rate-limiting enzyme through a compound related to substrate supply, substrate-related induction of gene transcription (e.g., induction of cytochrome P450-2E1 by ethanol), or increased concentration of a hormone that stimulates a storage pathway by controlling enzyme phosphorylation state.

4. TISSUE ISOZYMES OF REGULATORY PROTEINS

The human body is composed of several different cell types that perform specific functions unique to that cell type and synthesize only the proteins consistent with their functions. Because regulation matches function, regulatory enzymes of pathways usually exist as tissue-specific isozymes, with somewhat different regulatory properties unique to their function in different cell types. For example, hexokinase and glucokinase are tissue-specific isozymes with different kinetic properties. These different isozymes arose through gene duplication. Glucokinase, the low-affinity enzyme found in liver, is a single polypeptide chain with a molecular weight of 55 kDa that contains one active catalytic site. The hexokinases found in erythrocytes, skeletal muscles, and most other tissues are 110 kDa and are essentially two mutated glucokinase molecules synthesized as one polypeptide chain. However, only one catalytic site is functional. All of the tissue-specific hexokinases except glucokinase have a K_m for glucose that is <0.2 mM.

5. COUNTERREGULATION OF OPPOSING PATHWAYS

A pathway for the synthesis of a compound usually has one or more enzymatic steps that differ from the pathway for degradation of that compound. A biosynthetic pathway can therefore have a different regulatory enzyme than the opposing degradative pathway, and one pathway can be activated while the other is inhibited (e.g., glycogen synthesis is activated while glycogen degradation is inhibited).

6. SUBSTRATE CHANNELING THROUGH COMPARTMENTATION

In the cell, compartmentation of enzymes into multienzyme complexes or organelles provides a means of regulation, either because the compartment provides unique conditions or because it limits or channels access of the enzymes to substrates. Enzymes or pathways with a common function are often assembled into organelles. For example, enzymes of the TCA cycle are all located within the mitochondrion. The enzymes catalyze sequential reactions, and the product of one reaction is the substrate for the next reaction. The concentration of the pathway intermediates remains much higher within the mitochondrion than in the surrounding cellular cytoplasm.

Another type of compartmentation involves the assembly of enzymes that catalyze sequential reactions into multienzyme complexes so that intermediates of the pathway can be transferred directly from the active site on one enzyme to the active site on another enzyme, thereby preventing loss of energy and information. One example of this is the MEOS, which is composed of two different subunits with different enzyme activities. One subunit transfers electrons from NADPH to a cytochrome Fe-heme group on the second subunit, which then transfers the electrons to O_2.

7. LEVELS OF COMPLEXITY

You may have noticed by now that regulation of metabolic pathways in humans is exceedingly complex; this might be called the second principle of metabolic regulation. As you study different pathways in subsequent chapters, it may help to develop diagrams such as Figure 9.12 to keep track of the function and rationale behind different regulatory interactions.

When **Ann O'Rexia** jogs, the increased use of ATP for muscle contraction results in an increase of AMP, which allosterically activates both the allosteric enzyme phosphofructokinase-1, the rate-limiting enzyme of glycolysis, and glycogen phosphorylase, the rate-limiting enzyme of glycogenolysis. This is an example of feedback regulation by the ATP/AMP ratio. Unfortunately, her low caloric consumption has not allowed feed-forward activation of the rate-limiting enzymes in her fuel storage pathways, and she has very low glycogen stores. Consequently, she has inadequate fuel stores to supply the increased energy demands of exercise.

The hormone epinephrine (released during stress and exercise) and glucagon (released during fasting) activate the synthesis of cyclic-adenosine monophosphate (cAMP) in several tissues. cAMP activates protein kinase A. Because protein kinase A is able to phosphorylate key regulatory enzymes in many pathways, these pathways can be regulated coordinately. In muscle, for example, glycogen degradation is activated while glycogen synthesis is inhibited. At the same time, fatty-acid release from adipose tissue is activated to provide more fuel for muscle. The regulation of glycolysis, glycogen metabolism, and other pathways of metabolism is much more complex than we have illustrated here and is discussed in many subsequent chapters of this text.

CLINICAL COMMENTS

Al Martini. In the emergency room, **Al Martini** was evaluated for head injuries. From the physical examination and blood alcohol levels, it was determined that his mental state resulted from his alcohol consumption. Although his chronic ethanol consumption had increased his level of microsomal ethanol oxidizing system (MEOS) (and therefore the rate of ethanol oxidation in his liver), his excessive drinking resulted in a blood alcohol level higher than the legal limit of 80 mg/dL. He suffered bruises and contusions but was otherwise uninjured. He left in the custody of the police officer.

Ann O'Rexia. Ann O'Rexia's physician explained that she had inadequate fuel stores for her exercise program. To jog, her muscles require an increased rate of fuel oxidation to generate the adenosine triphosphate (ATP) for muscle contraction. The fuels used by muscles for exercise include glucose from muscle glycogen, fatty acids from adipose-tissue triacylglycerols, and blood glucose supplied by liver glycogen. These fuel stores were depleted during her prolonged bout of starvation. In addition, starvation resulted in the loss of muscle mass as muscle protein was degraded to supply amino acids for other processes, including gluconeogenesis (the synthesis of glucose from amino acids and other noncarbohydrate precursors). Therefore, Ann will need to increase her caloric consumption to rebuild her fuel stores. Her physician helped her calculate the additional amount of calories her jogging program will need, and they discussed which foods she would eat to meet these increased caloric requirements. He also helped her visualize the increase of weight as an increase in strength.

BIOCHEMICAL COMMENTS

The Lineweaver-Burk Transformation. The K_m and V_{max} for an enzyme can be visually determined from a plot of $1/v_i$ versus $1/S$, called a Lineweaver-Burk or a double-reciprocal plot. The reciprocal of both sides of the Michaelis-Menten equation generates an equation that has the form of a straight line, $y = mx + b$ (Fig. 9.13). K_m and V_{max} are equal to the reciprocals of the intercepts on the abscissa and ordinate, respectively. Although double-reciprocal plots are often used to illustrate certain features of enzyme

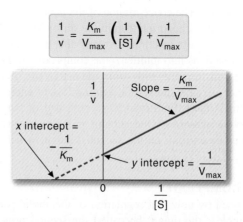

$$\frac{1}{v} = \frac{K_m}{V_{max}}\left(\frac{1}{[S]}\right) + \frac{1}{V_{max}}$$

FIG. 9.13. The Lineweaver-Burk transformation (shown in the *green box*) for the Michaelis-Menten equation converts it to a straight line of the form $y = mx + b$. When $[S]$ is infinite, $1/[S] = 0$, and the line crosses the ordinate (y axis) at $1/v = 1/V_{max}$. The slope of the line is K_m/V_{max}. Where the line intersects the abscissa (x axis), $1/[S] = -1/K_m$.

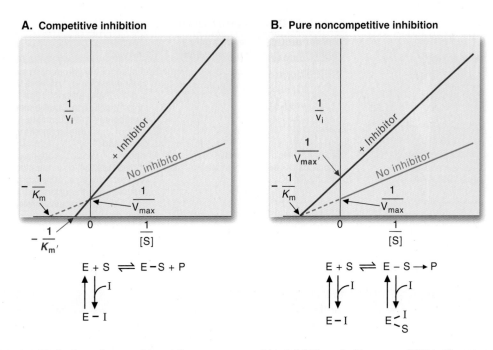

FIG. 9.14. Lineweaver-Burk plots of competitive and pure noncompetitive inhibition. **A.** $1/v_i$ versus $1/[S]$ in the presence of a competitive inhibitor. The competitive inhibitor alters the intersection on the abscissa. The new intersection is $1/K_{m,app}$ (also called $1/K_m'$). A competitive inhibitor does not affect V_{max}. **B.** $1/v_i$ versus $1/[S]$ in the presence of a pure noncompetitive inhibitor. The noncompetitive inhibitor alters the intersection on the ordinate, $1/V_{max,app}$ or $1/V_{max}'$, but does not affect $1/K_m$. A pure noncompetitive inhibitor binds to E and ES with the same affinity. If the inhibitor has different affinities for E and ES, the lines will intersect above or below the abscissa, and the noncompetitive inhibitor will change both the K_m' and the V_m'.

reactions, they are not used directly for the determination of K_m and V_{max} values by researchers.

Lineweaver-Burk plots provide a good illustration of competitive inhibition and pure noncompetitive inhibition (Fig. 9.14). In competitive inhibition, plots of $1/v$ versus $1/[S]$ at a series of inhibitor concentrations intersect on the ordinate. Thus, at infinite substrate concentration, or $1/[S] = 0$, there is no effect of the inhibitor. In pure noncompetitive inhibition, the inhibitor decreases the velocity even when $[S]$ has been extrapolated to an infinite concentration. However, if the inhibitor has no effect on the binding of the substrate, the K_m is the same for every concentration of inhibitor, and the lines intersect on the abscissa.

Key Concepts

- Enzyme activity is regulated to reflect the physiologic state of the organism.
- The rate of an enzyme-catalyzed reaction depends on substrate concentration and can be represented mathematically by the Michaelis-Menten equation.
- Allosteric activators or inhibitors are compounds that bind at sites other than the active catalytic site and regulate the enzyme through conformational changes that affect the catalytic site.
- Several different mechanisms are available to regulate enzyme activity. These include the following:
  - Feedback inhibition, which often occurs at the first committed step of a metabolic pathway
  - Covalent modification of an amino acid residue (or residues) within the protein
  - Interactions with modulator proteins, which, when bound to the enzyme, alter the conformation of the enzyme and hence activity
  - Altering the primary structure of the protein via proteolysis
  - Increasing or decreasing the amount of enzyme available in the cell via alterations in the rate or synthesis of degradation of the enzyme
- Metabolic pathways are frequently regulated at the slowest, or rate-limiting, step of the pathway.
- Diseases discussed in this chapter are summarized in Table 9.1.

Table 9.1   Diseases Discussed in Chapter 9

Disorder or Condition	Genetic or Environmental	Comments
Alcoholism	Both	Both alcohol dehydrogenase and the microsomal ethanol oxidizing system (MEOS) are active in detoxifying ethanol. High NADH can inhibit alcohol dehydrogenase, allowing toxic metabolites to accumulate.
Anorexia	Both	Effects of malnutrition on energy production was discussed.
Maturity onset diabetes of the young (MODY)	Genetic	Mutations in various proteins can lead to this form of diabetes, which is manifest by hyperglycemia, without, however, other complications associated with either type 1 or 2 diabetes. Specifically, mutations in pancreatic glucokinase were discussed.

REVIEW QUESTIONS—CHAPTER 9

1. Which of the following describes a characteristic feature of an enzyme that obeys Michaelis-Menten kinetics?

    A. The enzyme velocity is at one-half the maximal rate when 100% of the enzyme molecules contain bound substrate.

    B. The enzyme velocity is at one-half the maximal rate when 50% of the enzyme molecules contain bound substrate.

    C. The enzyme velocity is at its maximal rate when 50% of the enzyme molecules contain bound substrate.

    D. The enzyme velocity is at its maximal rate when all of the substrate molecules in solution are bound by the enzyme.

    E. The velocity of the reaction is independent of the concentration of enzyme.

2. The pancreatic glucokinase of a patient with MODY had a mutation replacing a leucine with a proline. The result was that the K_m for glucose was decreased from a normal value of 6 mM to a value of 2.2 mM, and the V_{max} was changed from 93 U/mg protein to 0.2 U/mg protein. Which of the following best describes the patient's glucokinase compared with the normal enzyme?

    A. The patient's enzyme requires a lower concentration of glucose to reach $\frac{1}{2}V_{max}$.

    B. The patient's enzyme is faster than the normal enzyme at concentrations of glucose <2.2 mM.

    C. The patient's enzyme is faster than the normal enzyme at concentrations of glucose >2.2 mM.

    D. At near-saturating glucose concentration, the patient would need 90 to 100 times more enzyme than normal to achieve normal rates of glucose phosphorylation.

    E. As blood glucose levels increase after a meal from a fasting value of 5 mM to 10 mM, the rate of the patient's enzyme will increase more than the rate of the normal enzyme.

3. Methanol (CH_3OH) is converted by alcohol dehydrogenases to formaldehyde (CH_2O), a compound that is highly toxic to humans. Patients who have ingested toxic levels of methanol are sometimes treated with ethanol (CH_3CH_2OH) to inhibit methanol oxidation by alcohol dehydrogenase. Which of the following statements provides the best rationale for this treatment?

    A. Ethanol is a structural analog of methanol and might therefore be an effective noncompetitive inhibitor.

    B. Ethanol is a structural analog of methanol that can be expected to compete with methanol for its binding site on the enzyme.

    C. Ethanol can be expected to alter the V_{max} of alcohol dehydrogenase for the oxidation of methanol to formaldehyde.

    D. Ethanol is an effective inhibitor of methanol oxidation regardless of the concentration of methanol.

    E. Ethanol can be expected to inhibit the enzyme by binding to the formaldehyde-binding site on the enzyme, even though it cannot bind at the substrate-binding site for methanol.

4. An allosteric enzyme has the following kinetic properties: a V_{max} of 25 U/mg enzyme, and a $K_{m,app}$ of 1.0 mM. These

kinetic parameters were then measured in the presence of an allosteric activator. Which one of the following would best describe the findings of that experiment?

- A. A V_{max} of 25 U/mg enzyme, and a $K_{m,app}$ of 0.2 mM.
- B. A V_{max} of 15 U/mg enzyme, with a $K_{m,app}$ of 2.0 mM.
- C. A V_{max} of 25 U/mg enzyme, with a $K_{m,app}$ of 2.0 mM.
- D. A V_{max} of 50 U/mg enzyme, with a $K_{m,app}$ of 5.0 mM.
- E. A V_{max} of 50 U/mg enzyme, with a $K_{m,app}$ of 10.0 mM.

5. A rate-limiting enzyme catalyzes the first step in the conversion of a toxic metabolite to a urinary excretion product. Which of the following mechanisms for regulating this enzyme would provide the most protection to the body?

- A. The product of the pathway should be an allosteric inhibitor of the rate-limiting enzyme.
- B. The product of the pathway should act through gene transcription to decrease synthesis of the enzyme.
- C. The toxin should act through gene transcription to increase synthesis of the enzyme.
- D. The enzyme should have a high K_m for the toxin.
- E. The toxin allosterically activates the last enzyme in the pathway.

10 Relationship between Cell Biology and Biochemistry

The basic unit of a living organism is the cell. In humans, each tissue is composed of a variety of cell types, which differ from those cell types in other tissues. The diversity of cell types serves the function of the tissue and organs in which they reside, and each cell type has unique structural features that reflect its role. In spite of their diversity in structure, human cell types have certain architectural features in common, such as the plasma membrane, membranes around the nucleus and organelles, and a cytoskeleton (Fig. 10.1). In this chapter, we review some of the chemical characteristics of these common features, the functions of organelles, and the transport systems for compounds into cells and between organelles.

*Plasma Membrane. The cell membrane consists of a **lipid bilayer** that serves as a selective barrier; it restricts the entry and exit of compounds. Within the plasma membrane, different **integral membrane proteins** facilitate the **transport** of compounds by **energy-requiring active transport**, **facilitated diffusion**, or by forming **pores** or **gated channels**. The plasma membrane is supported by a **membrane skeleton** composed of proteins.*

*Organelles and Cytoplasmic Membrane Systems. Most organelles within the cell are compartments surrounded by a membrane system that restricts exchange of compounds and information with other compartments (see Fig. 10.1). In general, each organelle has unique functions that are served by the enzymes and other compounds it contains, or the environment it maintains. **Lysosomes** contain **hydrolytic enzymes** that degrade proteins and other large molecules. The **nucleus** contains the genetic material and carries out **gene replication** and **transcription** of **DNA**, the first step of protein synthesis. The last phase of protein synthesis occurs on **ribosomes**. For certain proteins, the ribosomes become attached to the complex membrane system called the **endoplasmic reticulum** (ER); for other proteins, synthesis is completed on ribosomes that remain in the cytoplasm. The **ER** is also involved in lipid synthesis and transport of molecules to the Golgi. The **Golgi** forms vesicles for transport of molecules to the plasma membrane and other membrane systems and for secretion. **Mitochondria** are organelles committed to **fuel oxidation** and **adenosine triphosphate** (ATP) **generation**. **Peroxisomes** contain many enzymes that use or produce **hydrogen peroxide**. The **cytosol** is the intracellular compartment free of organelles and membrane systems.*

*Cytoskeleton. The **cytoskeleton** is a flexible fibrous protein support system that maintains the geometry of the cell, fixes the position of organelles, and moves compounds within the cell. The cytoskeleton also facilitates movement of the cell itself. It is composed primarily of **actin microfilaments**, **intermediate filaments** (IFs), **tubulin microtubules**, and their attached proteins.*

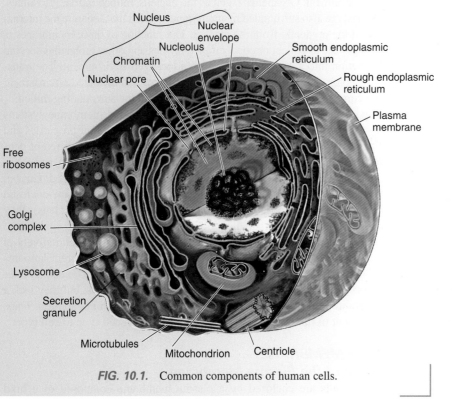

Nucleus
Nuclear envelope
Nucleolus
Chromatin
Nuclear pore
Smooth endoplasmic reticulum
Rough endoplasmic reticulum
Plasma membrane
Free ribosomes
Golgi complex
Lysosome
Secretion granule
Microtubules
Mitochondrion
Centriole

FIG. 10.1. Common components of human cells.

THE WAITING ROOM

Al Martini had been drinking heavily when he drove his car off the road and was taken to the hospital emergency room (see Chapters 8 and 9). Although he suffered only minor injuries, his driving license was suspended.

Two years after **Dennis "the Menace" Veere** recovered from his malathion poisoning, he visited his grandfather, **Percy Veere**. Mr. Veere took Dennis with him to a picnic at the shore, where they ate steamed crabs. Later that night, Dennis experienced episodes of vomiting and watery diarrhea, and Mr. Veere rushed him to the hospital emergency room. Dennis's hands and feet were cold; he appeared severely dehydrated, and he was approaching hypovolemic shock (a severe drop in blood pressure related to fluid losses). He was diagnosed with cholera, caused by the bacteria *Vibrio cholerae*.

Before **Lotta Topaigne** was treated with allopurinol (see Chapter 8), her physician administered colchicine (acetyltrimethylcolchicinic acid) for the acute attack of gout affecting her great toe. After taking two doses of colchicine divided over 1 hour (1.2 mg for the first dose, followed 1 hour later by 0.6 mg), the throbbing pain in her toe had abated significantly. The redness and swelling also seemed to have lessened slightly.

I. COMPARTMENTATION IN CELLS

Membranes are lipid structures that separate the contents of the compartment they surround from its environment. An outer plasma membrane separates the cell from

Vibrio cholerae epidemics are associated with unsanitary conditions affecting the drinking water supply and are rare in the United States. However, these bacteria grow well under the alkaline conditions found in seawater and attach to chitin in shellfish. Thus, sporadic cases occur in the southeast United States associated with the ingestion of contaminated shellfish.

Uric acid levels in blood or urine can be determined enzymatically through the use of the enzyme uricase, which converts uric acid (plus oxygen) to allantoin and hydrogen peroxide. Uricase is found in lower primates but not in humans. Uric acid has a strong light absorbance at 293 nm, whereas allantoin does not. Therefore, measurement of the decrease in absorbance at 293 nm after treating an unknown sample with uricase can allow determination of uric acid levels. Because the presence of proteins can reduce the sensitivity of this method, an alternative method is to determine the amount of hydrogen peroxide formed during the course of the reaction. In most cases, the enzymes peroxidase or catalase is used, and the enzymatic products are coupled to a chemical indicator reaction (a color change). One can determine the extent of color change during the reaction, which is proportional to the hydrogen peroxide concentration, which is the same as the concentration of uric acid in the sample.

Bacteria are single cells surrounded by a cell membrane and a cell wall exterior to the membrane. They are prokaryotes, which do not contain nuclei or other organelles (i.e., membrane-surrounded subcellular structures) found in eukaryotic cells. Nonetheless, bacteria carry out many similar metabolic pathways, with the enzymes located in either the intracellular compartment or the cell membrane.

The *Vibrio cholerae* responsible for **Dennis Veere's** cholera are gram-negative bacteria. Their plasma membrane is surrounded by a thin cell wall composed of a protein–polysaccharide structure called *peptidoglycan* and an outer membrane. In contrast, gram-positive bacteria have a plasma membrane and a thick peptidoglycan cell wall that retains the Gram stain. *V. cholerae* grow best not only under aerobic conditions, but also under low-oxygen conditions. They possess enzymes similar to those in human cells for glycolysis, the tricarboxylic acid (TCA) cycle, and oxidative phosphorylation. They have a low tolerance for acid, which partially accounts for their presence in slightly basic seawater and shellfish.

the external environment. Organelles (such as the nucleus, mitochondria, lysosomes, and peroxisomes) are also surrounded by membrane systems that separate the internal compartment of the organelle from the cytosol. The function of these membranes is to allow the organelle to collect or concentrate enzymes and other molecules serving a common function into a compartment within a localized environment. The transporters and receptors in each membrane system control this localized environment and facilitate communication of the cell or organelle with the surrounding milieu.

The following sections describe the various organelles and membrane systems found in most human cells and outline the relationship between their properties and function. Each organelle contains different enzymes and carries out different general functions. For example, the nucleus contains the enzymes for DNA and RNA synthesis. The cells of humans and other animals are eukaryotes (*eu*, good; *karyon*, nucleus) because the genetic material is organized into a membrane-enclosed nucleus. In contrast, bacteria are prokaryotes (*pro*, before; *karyon*, nucleus); they do not contain nuclei or other organelles found in eukaryotic cells.

Not all cells in the human are alike. Different cell types differ quantitatively in their organelle content, and their organelles may contain vastly different amounts of a particular enzyme, *consistent with the function of the cell*. For example, liver mitochondria contain a key enzyme for synthesizing ketone bodies, but they lack a key enzyme required for their use. The reverse is true in muscle mitochondria. Thus, the enzyme content of the organelles varies somewhat from cell type to cell type.

II. PLASMA MEMBRANE
A. Structure of the Plasma Membrane
All mammalian cells are enclosed by a plasma membrane composed of a lipid bilayer (two layers) containing embedded proteins (Fig. 10.2). The membranes are continuous and sealed so that the hydrophobic lipid bilayer selectively restricts the exchange of polar compounds between the external mileau and the intracellular compartment. The membrane is sometimes referred to as a *fluid mosaic* because it consists of a mosaic of proteins and lipid molecules that can, for the most part, move laterally in the plane of the membrane. The proteins are classified as *integral proteins*, which span the cell membrane, or *peripheral proteins*, which are attached to the membrane surface through electrostatic bonds to lipids or integral proteins.

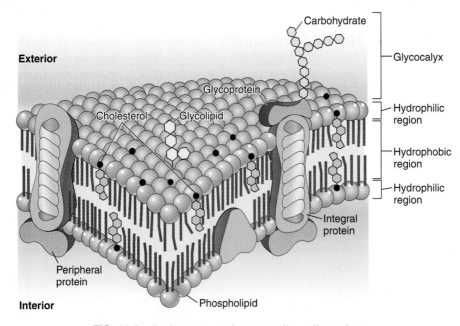

FIG. 10.2.   Basic structure of a mammalian cell membrane.

Many of the proteins and lipids on the external leaflet of the plasma membrane contain covalently bound carbohydrate chains and therefore are glycoproteins and glycolipids. This layer of carbohydrate on the outer surface of the cell is called the *glycocalyx*. The variable carbohydrate components of the glycolipids on the cell surface function, in part, as cell recognition markers for small molecules or other cells.

1.   LIPIDS IN THE PLASMA MEMBRANE

Each layer of the plasma membrane lipid bilayer is formed primarily by phospholipids, which are arranged with their hydrophilic head groups facing the aqueous medium and their fatty acyl tails forming a hydrophobic membrane core (see Fig. 10.2). The principal phospholipids in the membrane are the glycerol lipids phosphatidylcholine, phosphatidylethanolamine, and phosphatidylserine, and the sphingosine-based sphingomyelin (Fig. 10.3). Sphingosine also forms the base for the *glycosphingolipids*, which are membrane-anchored lipids with carbohydrates attached. The lipid composition varies among different cell types, with phosphatidylcholine being the major plasma membrane phospholipid in most cell types and glycosphingolipids being the most variable.

The lipid composition of the bilayer is asymmetric, with a higher content of phosphatidylcholine and sphingomyelin in the outer leaflet and a higher content of phosphatidylserine and phosphatidylethanolamine in the inner leaflet. Phosphatidylinositol, which can function in the transfer of information from hormones and neurotransmitters across the cell membrane (see Chapter 11), is also

 One of the bacterial toxins secreted by *Clostridium perfringens*, the bacteria that cause gas gangrene, is a lipase that hydrolyzes phosphocholine from phosphatidylcholine and from sphingomyelin. The resulting lysis (breakage) of the cell membrane releases intracellular contents that provide the bacteria with nutrients for rapid growth. These bacteria are strict anaerobes and grow only in the absence of oxygen. As their toxins lyse membranes in the endothelial cells of blood vessels, the capillaries are destroyed, and the bacteria are protected from oxygen transported by the red blood cells. They are also protected from antibiotics and components of the immune system carried in the blood.

FIG. 10.3.   Common phospholipids in the mammalian cell membrane. **A.** Phosphatidylcholine (a glycerol-based lipid) and sphingomyelin (a sphingosine-based lipid). Note the similarity in structures. **B.** Different head groups for the phospholipids. These head groups replace the choline in phosphatidylcholine and form, respectively, phosphatidylethanolamine, phosphatidylserine, and phosphatidylinositol.

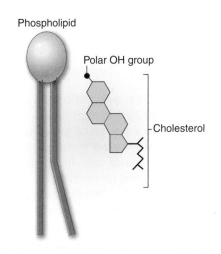

Phospholipid

Polar OH group

Cholesterol

FIG. 10.4. Cholesterol in the plasma membrane. The polar hydroxyl group of cholesterol is oriented toward the surface. The hydrocarbon tail and the steroid nucleus (*orange*) lie in the hydrophobic core. A *cis* double bond in the fatty acyl chain of a phospholipid bends the chain to create a hydrophobic binding site for cholesterol.

Al Martini is suffering from both short-term and long-term effects of ethanol on his central nervous system. Data support the theory that the short-term effects of ethanol on the brain arise partly from an increase in membrane fluidity caused when ethanol intercalates between the membrane lipids. The changes in membrane fluidity may affect proteins that span the membrane (integral proteins), such as ion channels and receptors for neurotransmitters involved in conducting the nerve impulse.

only found in the inner leaflet. Phosphatidylserine contains a net negative charge that contributes to the membrane potential and may be important for binding positively charged molecules within the cell.

Cholesterol, which is interspersed between the phospholipids, maintains membrane fluidity. In the glycerol-based phospholipids, unsaturated fatty acid chains bent into the *cis* conformation form a pocket for cholesterol, which binds with its hydroxyl group in the external hydrophilic region of the membrane and its hydrophobic steroid nucleus in the hydrophobic membrane core (Fig. 10.4). The presence of cholesterol and the *cis* unsaturated fatty acids in the membrane prevent the hydrophobic chains from packing too closely together. As a consequence, lipid and protein molecules that are not bound to external or internal structural proteins can rotate and move laterally in the plane of the leaflet. This movement enables the plasma membrane to partition between daughter cells during cell division, to deform as cells pass through capillaries, and to form and fuse with vesicle membranes. The fluidity of the membrane is partially determined by the unsaturated fatty acid content of the diet.

The composition of the membrane is dynamic. Sections of membrane form buds that pinch off into vesicles, and membrane vesicles formed in the Golgi and elsewhere bring new and recycled components back to the membrane. Individual fatty acyl chains turn over as they are hydrolyzed from the lipids and replaced, and enzymes called *flipases* transfer lipids between leaflets.

2. PROTEINS IN THE PLASMA MEMBRANE

The integral membrane proteins contain transmembrane domains with hydrophobic amino acid side chains that interact with the hydrophobic portions of the lipids to seal the membrane (see Fig. 10.2). Hydrophilic regions of the proteins protrude into either the extracellular milieu or the cytoplasm. These proteins function primarily as channels or transporters for the movement of compounds across the membrane, as receptors for the binding of hormones and neurotransmitters, or as structural proteins (Fig. 10.5).

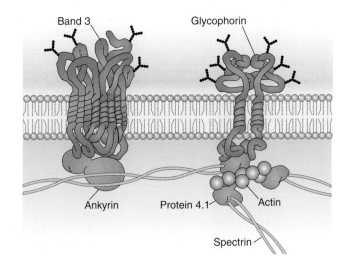

FIG. 10.5. Proteins in the red blood cell membrane. The proteins named *Band 3* (the bicarbonate–chloride exchange transporter) and glycophorin (provides an external negative charge that repels other cells) both contain nonpolar α-helical segments spanning the lipid bilayer. These proteins contain a large number of polar and charged hydrophilic amino acids in the intracellular and extracellular domains. On the inside of the cell, they are attached to peripheral proteins constituting the inner membrane skeleton. Band 3 is connected to spectrin filaments via the protein ankyrin. Glycophorin is connected to short actin filaments and spectrin via protein 4.1.

Peripheral membrane proteins, which were originally defined as those proteins that can be released from the membrane by ionic solvents, are bound through weak electrostatic interactions with the polar head groups of lipids or with integral proteins. One of the best characterized classes of peripheral proteins is the spectrin family of proteins, which are bound to the intracellular membrane surface and provide mechanical support for the membrane. Spectrin is bound to actin, which together form a structure that is called the *inner membrane skeleton* or the *cortical skeleton* (see Fig. 10.5).

A third classification of membrane proteins consists of lipid-anchored proteins bound to the inner or outer surface of the membrane. The *glycophosphatidylinositol glycan* (GPI) anchor is a covalently attached lipid that anchors proteins to the external surface of the membrane (Fig. 10.6). Several proteins involved in hormonal regulation are anchored to the internal surface of the membrane through palmityl (C16) or myristyl (C14) fatty acyl groups or through geranylgeranyl (C20) or farnesyl (C15) isoprenyl groups (see Fig. 6.13). However, many integral proteins also contain attached lipid groups to increase their stability in the membrane.

3. THE GLYCOCALYX OF THE PLASMA MEMBRANE

Some of the proteins and lipids on the external surface of the membrane contain short chains of carbohydrates (oligosaccharides) that extend into the aqueous medium. Carbohydrates constitute 2% to 10% of the weight of plasma membranes. This hydrophilic carbohydrate layer, called the *glycocalyx*, protects the cell from digestion and restricts the uptake of hydrophobic compounds.

The glycoproteins generally contain branched oligosaccharide chains of approximately 15 sugar residues that are attached through *N*-glycosidic bonds to the amide nitrogen of an asparagine side chain (*N*-glycosidic linkage) or through a glycosidic bond to the oxygen of serine (*O*-glycoproteins). The membrane glycolipids are usually galactosides or cerebrosides. Specific carbohydrate chains on the glycolipids serve as cell-recognition molecules (see Chapter 5 for structures of these compounds).

B. Transport of Molecules across the Plasma Membrane

Membranes form hydrophobic barriers around cells to control the internal environment by restricting the entry and exit of molecules. As a consequence, cells require transport systems to permit entry of small polar compounds that they need (e.g., glucose) to concentrate compounds inside the cell (e.g., K^+) and to expel other compounds (e.g., Ca^{2+} and Na^+). The transport systems for small organic molecules and inorganic ions fall into four categories: simple diffusion through the lipid bilayer, facilitative diffusion, gated channels, and active transport pumps (Fig. 10.7). These transport mechanisms are classified as passive if energy is not required or active if energy is required. The energy is often provided by the hydrolysis of adenosine triphosphate (ATP).

In addition to these mechanisms for the transport of small individual molecules, cells engage in a process called *endocytosis*. The plasma membrane extends or invaginates to surround a particle, a foreign cell, or extracellular fluid, which then closes into a vesicle that is released into the cytoplasm (see Fig. 10.7).

1. SIMPLE DIFFUSION

Gases such as oxygen and carbon dioxide and lipid-soluble substances (such as steroid hormones) can cross membranes by simple diffusion (see Fig. 10.7). In simple diffusion (free diffusion), molecules move by engaging in random collisions with other like molecules. There is a net movement from a region of high concentration to a region of low concentration because molecules keep bumping into each other where their concentration is highest. Energy is not required for diffusion, and compounds that are uncharged eventually reach the same concentrations on both sides of the membrane.

 All cells contain an inner membrane skeleton of spectrin-like proteins. Red blood cell spectrin was the first member of the spectrin family to be described. The protein *dystrophin*, present in skeletal muscle cells, is a member of the spectrin family. Genetic defects in the dystrophin gene are responsible for Duchenne and Becker muscular dystrophies.

 The prion protein, present in neuronal membranes, provides an example of a protein attached to the membrane through a GPI anchor. This is the protein that develops an altered pathogenic conformation in both mad cow disease and Creutzfeldt-Jakob disease (see Section IX.B.3, Chapter 7).

FIG. 10.6. An example of a GPI anchor. The carboxy terminus of the protein is attached to phosphoethanolamine, which is bound to a branched oligosaccharide that is attached to the inositol portion of phosphatidylinositol. The hydrophobic fatty acyl chains of the phosphatidylinositol portion are bound in the hydrophobic core of the membrane.

FIG. 10.7. Common types of transport mechanisms for human cells. The electrochemical gradient consists of the concentration gradient of the compound and the distribution of charge on the membrane, which affects the transport of charged ions such as Cl^-. Both protein amino acid residues and lipid polar head groups contribute to the net negative charge on the inside of the membrane. Generally, the diffusion of uncharged molecules (passive transport) is net movement from a region of high concentration to a region of low concentration, and active transport (energy requiring) is net movement from a region of low concentration to one of high concentration.

 The A, B, and O blood groups are determined by the carbohydrate composition of the glycolipids on the cell surface. These glycolipids may also serve as binding sites for viruses and bacterial toxins before penetrating the cell. For example, the cholera AB toxin (which is affecting **Dennis Veere**) binds to GM₁-gangliosides on the surface of the intestinal epithelial cells. The toxin is then endocytosed in caveolae (invaginations or "caves" that can form in specific regions of the membrane). Once inside the cell, the toxin will alter normal cellular metabolism.

 Dennis Veere has become dehydrated because he has lost so much water through vomiting and diarrhea (see Chapter 4). Cholera toxin increases the efflux of sodium and chloride ions from his intestinal mucosal cells into the intestinal lumen. The increase of water in his stools results from the passive transfer of water from inside the cell and body fluids, where it is in high concentration (i.e., intracellular Na^+ and Cl^- concentrations are low), to the intestinal lumen and bowel, where water is in lower concentration (relative to high Na^+ and Cl^-). The watery diarrhea is also high in K^+ ions and bicarbonate. All of the signs and symptoms of cholera generally derive from this fluid loss.

Water is considered to diffuse through membranes by nonspecific movement through ion channels, pores, or around proteins embedded in the lipids. Certain cells (e.g., renal tubule cells) also contain large protein pores, called *aquaporins*, which permit a high rate of water flow from a region of a high water concentration (low solute concentration) to one of low water concentration (high solute concentration).

2. FACILITATIVE DIFFUSION THROUGH BINDING TO TRANSPORTER PROTEINS

Facilitative diffusion requires that the transported molecule bind to a specific carrier or transport protein in the membrane (Fig. 10.8A). The transporter protein then undergoes a conformational change that allows the transported molecule to be released on the other side of the membrane. Although the transported molecules are bound to proteins, the transport process is still classified as diffusion because energy is not required, and the compound equilibrates (achieves a balance of concentration and charge) on both sides of the membrane.

Transporter proteins, like enzymes, exhibit saturation kinetics; when all the binding sites on the transporter proteins in the membrane are occupied, the system is saturated and the rate of transport reaches a plateau (the maximum velocity). By analogy to enzymes, the concentration of a transported compound required to reach half the maximum velocity is often called the K_m (see Fig. 10.8B). Facilitative transporters are similar to enzymes with respect to two additional features: They are relatively specific for the compounds they bind, and they can be inhibited by compounds that block their binding sites or change their conformation.

3. GATED CHANNELS IN PLASMA MEMBRANES

In the case of gated channels, transmembrane proteins form a pore for ions that is either opened or closed in response to a stimulus. These stimuli can be voltage changes across the membrane (voltage-gated channels), the binding of a compound (ligand-gated channels), or a regulatory change in the intracellular domain (phosphorylation-gated and pressure-gated channels). For example, the conduction of a nerve impulse along an axon depends on the passive flux of Na^+ ions through a voltage-gated channel that is opened by depolarization of the membrane.

A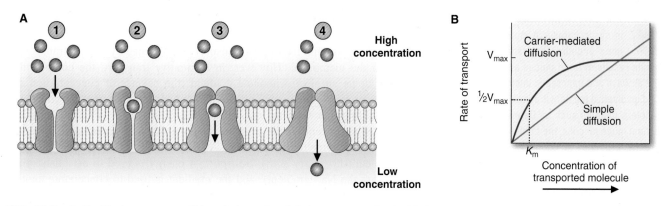

High concentration

Low concentration

B

FIG. 10.8. **A.** Facilitative transport. Although the molecule being transported must bind to the protein transporter, the mechanism is passive diffusion, and the molecule moves from a region of high concentration to one of low concentration. *Passive* refers to the lack of an energy requirement for the transport. **B.** Saturation kinetics of transporter proteins. When a compound must bind to a protein to be transported across a membrane, the velocity of transport depends on the amount of compound bound. It reaches a maximum rate when the compound's concentration is raised so high that all of the transporter-binding sites are occupied. The curve is a rectangular hyperbola that approaches V_{max} at infinite substrate concentration, identical to that of Michaelis-Menten enzymes. The K_m of transport is the concentration of compound required for $1/2V_{max}$. In contrast, simple diffusion of a compound does not require its binding to a protein, and the rate of transport increases linearly with increasing concentration of the compound.

Cystic *f*ibrosis *t*ransmembrane conductance *r*egulator (CFTR) is a chloride channel that provides an example of a ligand-gated channel regulated through phosphorylation (phosphorylation-gated channels) (Fig. 10.9). CFTR is a member of the *ABC* (adenine nucleotide–binding cassette or ATP-binding cassette) superfamily of transport proteins. It has two transmembrane domains that form a closed channel, each connected to an ATP-binding site, and a regulatory domain that sits in front of the channel. When the regulatory domain is phosphorylated by a kinase, its conformation changes and it moves away from the ATP-binding domains. As ATP binds and is hydrolyzed, the transmembrane domains change conformation and open the channel, and chloride ions diffuse through. As the conformation reverts back to its original form, the channel closes.

Transport through a ligand-gated channel can be considered simple diffusion, although ATP is involved, because only a few ATP molecules are being used to open and close the channel through which many chloride ions diffuse. However, the distinction between ligand-gated channels and facilitative transporters is not always as clear. Many gated channels show saturation kinetics at very high concentrations of the compounds being transported, which is why Figure 10.7 characterizes ligand-gated channels as facilitative transport.

 All of the cells in the body have facilitative glucose transporters that transport glucose across the plasma membrane down an electrochemical (concentration) gradient as it is rapidly metabolized in the cell. In muscle and adipose tissue, insulin increases the content of facilitative glucose transporters in the cell membrane, thus increasing the ability of these tissues to take up glucose. Patients with type 1 diabetes mellitus, who do not produce insulin (e.g., **Di Abietes**, see Chapter 7), have a decreased ability to transport glucose into these tissues, thereby contributing to hyperglycemia (high blood glucose).

FIG. 10.9. CFTR, a ligand-gated channel controlled by phosphorylation. Two intracellular binding domains control opening of the channel, an adenine nucleotide-binding domain (*ABD*) and a regulatory domain (*R*). (*1*) Phosphorylation of the regulatory subunit by protein kinase A (*PKA*) causes a conformational change that allows *ATP* to bind to the *ABD*. (*2*) Hydrolysis of bound *ATP* opens the channel so that chloride ions can diffuse through.

The CFTR was named for its role in cystic fibrosis. A mutation in the gene encoding its transmembrane subunits results in dried mucus accumulation in the airways and pancreatic ducts. The CFTR is also involved in the dehydration experienced by cholera patients such as **Dennis Veere**. In intestinal mucosal cells, the cholera A-subunit indirectly promotes phosphorylation of the regulatory domain of CFTR by protein kinase A (PKA). Thus, the channel stays open and Cl^- and H_2O flow from the cell into the intestinal lumen, resulting in dehydration.

The dehydration of cholera is often treated with an oral rehydration solution containing sodium, potassium, and glucose or a diet of rice (which contains glucose and amino acids). Glucose is absorbed from the intestinal lumen via the Na^+-dependent glucose cotransporters, which cotransport Na^+ into the cells together with glucose. Many amino acids are also absorbed by Na^+-dependent cotransport. With the return of Na^+ to the cytoplasm, the release of water from the cell into the intestinal lumen decreases.

4. ACTIVE TRANSPORT REQUIRES ENERGY AND TRANSPORTER PROTEINS

Both active transport and facilitative transport are mediated by protein transporters (carriers) in the membrane. However, in facilitative transport, the compound is transported down an electrochemical gradient (the balance of concentration and charge across a membrane), usually from a high concentration to a low concentration, to equilibrate between the two sides of the membrane. In active transport, energy is used to concentrate the compound on one side of the membrane. If energy is applied directly to the transporter (e.g., ATP hydrolysis by Na^+,K^+-ATPase), the transport is called *primary active transport*; if energy is used to establish an ion gradient (e.g., the Na^+ gradient), and the gradient is used to concentrate another compound, the transport is called *secondary active transport*. Protein-mediated transport systems, whether facilitative or active, are classified as antiports if they specifically exchange compounds of similar charge across a membrane; they are called *symports* or *cotransporters* if they simultaneously transport two molecules across the membrane in the same direction. Band 3 in the red blood cell membrane, which exchanges chloride ion for bicarbonate, provides an example of an antiport.

The Na^+,K^+-ATPase spans the plasma membrane, much like a gated pore, with a binding site for three Na^+ ions open to the intracellular side (Fig. 10.10). Energy from ATP hydrolysis is used to phosphorylate an internal domain and change the transporters' conformation so that bound Na^+ ions are released to the outside, and two external K^+ ions bind. K^+ binding triggers hydrolysis of the bound phosphate group and a return to the original conformation, accompanied by release of K^+ ions inside the cell. As a consequence, cells are able to maintain a much lower intracellular Na^+ concentration and a much higher intracellular K^+ ion concentration than are present in the external fluid.

The Na^+ gradient, which is maintained by primary active transport, is used to power the transport of glucose, amino acids, and many other compounds into the cell through secondary active transport. An example is provided by the transport of glucose into cells of the intestinal epithelium in conjunction with Na^+ ions (Fig. 10.11). These cells create a gradient in Na^+ and then use this gradient to drive the transport of glucose from the intestinal lumen into the cell against its concentration gradient.

The Ca^{2+}-ATPase, a calcium pump, uses a mechanism similar to that of Na^+,K^+-ATPase to maintain intracellular Ca^{2+} concentration below 10^{-7} M in spite of the high extracellular concentration of 10^{-3} M. This transporter is inhibited by

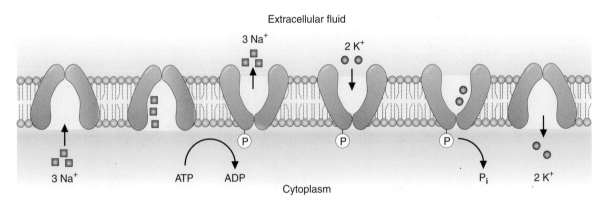

FIG. 10.10. Active transport by Na^+,K^+-ATPase. Three sodium ions bind to the transporter protein on the cytoplasmic side of the membrane. When ATP is hydrolyzed to adenosine diphosphate (ADP), the carrier protein is phosphorylated and undergoes a change in conformation that causes the sodium ions to be released into the extracellular fluid. Two potassium ions then bind on the extracellular side. Dephosphorylation of the carrier protein produces another conformational change, and the potassium ions are released on the inside of the cell membrane. The transporter protein then resumes its original conformation, ready to bind more sodium ions.

Transport protein

FIG. 10.11. Secondary active transport of glucose by the Na^+-glucose cotransporter. One sodium ion binds to the carrier protein in the luminal membrane, stimulating the binding of glucose. After a conformational change, the protein releases Na^+ and glucose into the cell and returns to its original conformation. Na^+,K^+-ATPase in the basolateral membrane pumps Na^+ against its concentration gradient into the extracellular fluid. Thus, the Na^+ concentration in the cell is low, and Na^+ moves from the lumen down its concentration gradient into the cell and is pumped against its gradient into the extracellular fluid. Glucose, consequently, moves against its concentration gradient from the lumen into the cell by traveling on the same carrier as Na^+. Glucose then passes down its concentration gradient into the extracellular fluid on a passive transporter protein.

binding of the regulatory protein calmodulin. When the intracellular Ca^{2+} concentration increases, Ca^{2+} binds to calmodulin, which dissociates from the transporter, thereby activating it to pump Ca^{2+} out of the cell (see Fig. 9.10 for the structure of calmodulin). High levels of intracellular Ca^{2+} are associated with irreversible progression from cell injury to cell death.

C. Vesicular Transport across the Plasma Membrane

Vesicular transport occurs when a membrane completely surrounds a compound, particle, or cell and encloses it into a vesicle, which buds from the membrane. When the released vesicle fuses with another membrane system, the entrapped compounds are released. *Endocytosis* refers to vesicular transport into the cell, and *exocytosis* refers to transport out of the cell. Endocytosis is further classified as phagocytosis if the vesicle forms around particulate matter (such as whole bacterial cells or metals and dyes from a tattoo) and pinocytosis if the vesicle forms around fluid containing dispersed molecules. *Receptor-mediated endocytosis* is the name given to the formation of clathrin-coated vesicles that mediate the internalization of membrane-bound receptors in vesicles coated on the intracellular side with subunits of the protein clathrin. Cholesterol uptake, as mediated by the low-density lipoprotein (LDL) receptor, occurs via this mechanism. *Potocytosis* is the name given to endocytosis that occurs via caveolae (small invaginations or "caves"), which are regions of the cell membrane with a unique lipid and protein composition (including the protein caveolin-1). The transport of the vitamin folate occurs via potocytosis.

III. LYSOSOMES

Lysosomes are the intracellular organelles of digestion and are enclosed by a single membrane to prevent the release of the lysosome's digestive enzymes into the cytosol. Lysosomes are central to a wide variety of body functions that involve eliminating unwanted material, including destruction of infectious bacteria and yeast, recovery from injury, tissue remodeling, involution of tissues during development, and normal turnover of cells and organelles. The destroyed components are typically recycled for additional use by the cell.

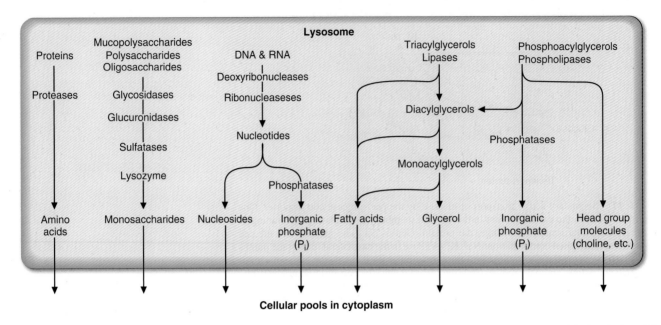

FIG. 10.12. Lysosomal reactions. Most lysosomal enzymes are hydrolases, which cleave peptide, ester, and glycosidic bonds by adding the components of water across the bond. These enzymes are active at the acidic pH of the lysosome and inactive if accidentally released into the cytosol.

 Genetic defects in lysosomal enzymes, or in proteins such as the mannose 6-phosphate receptors required for targeting the enzymes to the lysosome, lead to an abnormal accumulation of undigested material in lysosomes that may be converted to residual bodies. The accumulation may be so extensive that normal cellular function is compromised, particularly in neuronal cells. Genetic diseases such as the Tay-Sachs disease (an accumulation of partially digested gangliosides in lysosomes), and Pompe disease (an accumulation of glycogen particles in lysosomes) are caused by the absence or deficiency of specific lysosomal enzymes. Such diseases, in which a lysosomal function is compromised, are known as *lysosomal storage diseases*.

A. Lysosomal Hydrolases

The lysosomal digestive enzymes include nucleases, phosphatases, glycosidases, esterases, and proteases (Fig. 10.12). These enzymes are all hydrolases, enzymes that cleave amide, ester, and other bonds through the addition of water. Many of the products of lysosomal digestion, such as the amino acids, return to the cytosol. Lysosomes are therefore involved in recycling compounds. The proteases are classified as serine, cysteine, or aspartyl proteases, depending on the amino acid residue at the active site of the enzyme involved in the hydrolytic reaction. The cysteine proteases are also known as *cathepsins*.

Most of these lysosomal hydrolases have their highest activity near a pH of approximately 5.5 (the optimal pH for hydrolysis). The intralysosomal pH is maintained near 5.5 principally by v-ATPases (vesicular ATPases), which actively pump protons into the lysosome. The cytosol and other cellular compartments have a pH nearer 7.2 and are therefore protected from escaped lysosomal hydrolases.

B. Endocytosis, Phagocytosis, and Autophagy

Lysosomes are formed from digestive vesicles called *endosomes*, which are involved in receptor-mediated endocytosis. They also participate in digestion of foreign cells acquired through phagocytosis and the digestion of internal contents in the process of autophagocytosis.

1.   RECEPTOR-MEDIATED ENDOCYTOSIS

Lysosomes are involved in the digestion of compounds brought into the cells in endocytotic clathrin-coated vesicles formed by the plasma membrane. These vesicles fuse to form multivesicular bodies called *early endosomes*. The early endosomes can either recycle back to the cell surface or mature into late endosomes as they recycle clathrin, lipids, and other membrane components back to the plasma membrane in vesicles called *recycling endosomes*. The late endosomes mature into lysosomes as they progressively accumulate newly synthesized acid hydrolases and vesicular proton pumps brought to them in clathrin-coated vesicles from the Golgi. Thus, lysosomes do not acquire their full digestive power until after sorting of membrane lipids and proteins for recycling.

Within the Golgi, enzymes are targeted for endosomes (and eventually lysosomes) by addition of mannose 6-phosphate residues that bind to mannose 6-phosphate receptor proteins in the Golgi membrane. The mannose 6-phosphate receptors together with the associated bound acid hydrolases are incorporated into the clathrin-coated Golgi transport vesicles and the vesicles are released. The transport vesicles lose their clathrin coat and then fuse with the late endosomal membrane. The acidity of the endosome releases the acid hydrolases from the receptors into the vesicle lumen. The receptors are eventually recycled back to the Golgi.

2. PHAGOCYTOSIS AND AUTOPHAGY

One of the major roles of lysosomes is phagocytosis. Neutrophils and macrophages, the major phagocytic cells, devour pathogenic microorganisms and clean up wound debris and dead cells, thus aiding in repair. As bacteria or other particles are enclosed into clathrin-coated pits in the plasma membrane, these vesicles bud off to form intracellular phagosomes. The phagosomes fuse with lysosomes, where the acidity and digestive enzymes destroy the contents. Pinocytotic vesicles also may fuse with lysosomes.

In autophagy (self-eating), intracellular components such as organelles or glycogen particles are surrounded by a membrane derived from endoplasmic reticulum (ER) vesicles, forming an autophagosome. The autophagosome fuses with a lysosome, and lysosomal enzymes digest the contents of the phagolysosome. Organelles usually turn over much more rapidly than the cells in which they reside (e.g., approximately four mitochondria in each liver cell are degraded per hour). Cells that are damaged, but still viable, recover, in part, by using autophagy to eliminate damaged components.

If a significant amount of undigestible material remains within the lysosome after the digestion process is completed, the lysosome is called a *residual body*. Depending on the cell type, residual bodies may be expelled (exocytosis) or remain indefinitely in the cell as lipofuscin granules that accumulate with age.

IV. MITOCHONDRIA

Mitochondria contain most of the enzymes for the pathways of fuel oxidation and oxidative phosphorylation and thus generate most of the ATP required by mammalian cells. Each mitochondrion is surrounded by two membranes, an outer membrane and an inner membrane, separating the mitochondrial matrix from the cytosol (Fig. 10.13). The inner membrane forms invaginations known as *cristae* containing the electron-transport chain and ATP synthase. Most of the enzymes for the tricarboxylic acid (TCA) cycle and other pathways for oxidation are located in the mitochondrial matrix, the compartment enclosed by the inner mitochondrial membrane. (The TCA cycle and the electron-transport chain are described in more detail in Chapters 20 and 21.)

The inner mitochondrial membrane is highly impermeable, and the proton gradient that is built up across this membrane during oxidative phosphorylation is essential for ATP generation from adenosine diphosphate (ADP) and phosphate. The transport of ions occurs principally through facilitative transporters in a type of secondary active transport powered by the proton gradient established by the electron-transport chain. The outer membrane contains pores made from proteins called *porins* and is permeable to molecules with a molecular weight up to about 1,000 g/mol.

Mitochondria can replicate by division; however, most of their proteins must be imported from the cytosol. Mitochondria contain a small amount of DNA, which encodes for only 13 different subunits of proteins involved in oxidative phosphorylation. Most of the enzymes and proteins in mitochondria are encoded by nuclear DNA and synthesized on cytoplasmic ribosomes. They are imported through membrane pores by a receptor-mediated process involving members of the

The elevated level of uric acid in **Lotta Topaigne**'s blood led to the deposition of monosodium urate crystals in the joint space (synovial fluid) of her right great toe, resulting in podagra (painful great toe). Neutrophils, the mediators of the acute inflammation that followed, attempted to phagocytose the urate crystals. The engulfed urate crystals were deposited in the late endosomes and lysosomes of the neutrophil. Because urate crystals are particles that cannot be degraded by any of the lysosomal acid hydolases, their accumulation caused lysis of the lysosomal membranes, followed by cell lysis and release of lysosomal enzymes into the joint space. The urate crystals also resulted in release of chemical mediators of inflammation that recruited other cells into the area. This further amplified the acute inflammatory reaction in the tissues of the joint capsule (synovitis), leading to the extremely painful swelling of acute gouty arthritis.

Outer membrane

Matrix

Inner membrane folded into cristae

Outer membrane

Matrix

Inner membrane folded into cristae

FIG. 10.13. Mitochondrion. Electron micrograph (**top**); three-dimensional drawing (**bottom**).

Q: Pyruvate transfer across the inner mitochondrial membrane is dependent on the proton gradient, and the carrier for pyruvate transports both pyruvate and a proton into the matrix of the mitochondria. Such transport allows for the accumulation of pyruvate within the organelle at concentrations greater than in the cytosol. This is an example of which type of transport?

Several diseases are associated with peroxisomes. Peroxisomal diseases are caused by mutations that affect either the synthesis of functional peroxisomal enzymes or their incorporation into peroxisomes. For example, adrenoleukodystrophy involves a mutation that decreases the content of a fatty acid transporter in the peroxisomal membrane. Zellweger syndrome is caused by the failure to complete the synthesis of peroxisomes.

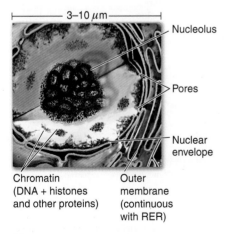

FIG. 10.14. Nucleus. Electron micrograph (**top**); three-dimensional drawing (**bottom**).

heat-shock family of proteins. Inherited mutations within mitochondrial DNA result in several genetic diseases that affect skeletal muscle, neuronal tissue, and renal tissue. Spontaneous mutations within mitochondrial DNA have been implicated with aging.

V. PEROXISOMES

Peroxisomes are cytoplasmic organelles, similar in size to lysosomes that are involved in oxidative reactions using molecular oxygen. These reactions produce the toxic chemical hydrogen peroxide (H_2O_2), which is subsequently used or degraded within the peroxisome by catalase and other enzymes. Peroxisomes function in the oxidation of very long-chain fatty acids (containing 20 or more carbons) to shorter chain fatty acids, the conversion of cholesterol to bile acids, and the synthesis of ether lipids called *plasmalogens*. They are bounded by a single membrane.

Like mitochondria, peroxisomes can replicate by division. However, they are dependent on the import of proteins to function. They contain no DNA.

VI. NUCLEUS

The largest of the subcellular organelles of animal cells is the nucleus (Fig. 10.14). Most of the genetic material of the cell is located in the nucleus in the form of chromosomes, which are composed of DNA, an equal weight of small, positively charged proteins called *histones*, and a variable amount of other proteins. This nucleoprotein complex is called *chromatin*. The *nucleolus*, a substructure of the nucleus, is the site of rRNA transcription and processing and of ribosome assembly. Replication, transcription, translation, and the regulation of these processes are the major focus of the molecular biology section of this text (see Section III).

The nucleus is separated from the rest of the cell (the cytoplasm) by the nuclear envelope, which consists of two membranes joined at nuclear pores. The outer nuclear membrane is continuous with the rough endoplasmic reticulum (RER). To convert the genetic code of the DNA into the primary sequence of a protein, DNA is transcribed into RNA, which is modified and edited into mRNA. The mRNA travels through the nuclear pores into the cytoplasm, where it is translated into the primary sequence of a protein on ribosomes. Ribosomes, which are generated in the nucleolus, also must travel through nuclear pores to the cytoplasm. Conversely, proteins required for replication, transcription, and other processes enter into the nucleus through these pores. These proteins contain a specific sequence of amino acids known as a *nuclear localization signal* (NLS). Thus, transport through the pore is specific for the molecule and the direction of transport.

VII. ENDOPLASMIC RETICULUM

The ER is a network of membranous tubules within the cell consisting of smooth endoplasmic reticulum (SER), which lacks ribosomes, and RER, which is studded with ribosomes (Fig. 10.15). The SER has several functions. It contains enzymes for the synthesis of many lipids, such as triacylglycerols and phospholipids. It also contains the cytochrome P450 oxidative enzymes involved in metabolism of drugs and toxic chemicals such as ethanol and the synthesis of hydrophobic molecules such as steroid hormones. Glycogen is stored in regions of liver cells that are rich in SER.

The RER is involved in the synthesis of certain proteins. Ribosomes attached to the membranes of the RER give them their "rough" appearance. Proteins produced on these ribosomes enter the lumen of the RER, travel to the Golgi complex in vesicles, and are subsequently either secreted from the cell, sequestered within membrane-enclosed organelles such as lysosomes, or embedded in the plasma membrane. Posttranslational modifications of these proteins, such as the initiation of *N*-linked glycosylation and the addition of GPI anchors, occur in the RER.

A: Cotransport of pyruvate and a proton, down the proton's electrochemical gradient, is an example of secondary active transport. Energy has been expended, during the transfer of electrons through the electron transfer chain, to generate the proton gradient across the inner mitochondrial membrane. The energy of the proton gradient is then used by the carrier to carry protons down their electrochemical gradient (favorable), bringing pyruvate along with the protons. This will allow pyruvate active transport, secondary to favorable proton entry into the mitochondrial matrix.

Chronic ingestion of ethanol has increased the content of MEOS, the microsomal ethanol oxidizing system, in **Al Martini's** liver. MEOS is a cytochrome P450 enzyme that catalyzes the conversion of ethanol, NADPH, and O_2 to acetaldehyde, $NADP^+$, and $2 H_2O$ (see Chapter 9). The adjective *microsomal* is a term derived from experimental cell biology that is sometimes used for processes that occur in the ER. When cells are lysed in the laboratory, the ER is fragmented into vesicles called *microsomes*, which can be isolated by centrifugation. Microsomes, as such, are not actually present in cells.

FIG. 10.15.   **A.** Smooth endoplasmic reticulum. **B.** Rough endoplasmic reticulum. **A** and **B** are electron micrographs. A three-dimensional drawing is in the **middle**.

In contrast, proteins encoded by the nucleus and found in the cytosol, peroxisomes, or mitochondria are synthesized on free ribosomes in the cytosol and are seldom modified by the attachment of oligosaccharides.

VIII. GOLGI COMPLEX

The Golgi complex is involved in modifying proteins produced in the RER and in sorting and distributing these proteins to the lysosomes, secretory vesicles, or the plasma membrane. It consists of a curved stack of flattened vesicles in the cytoplasm that is generally divided into three compartments: the *cis* Golgi network, which is often convex and faces the nucleus; the *medial* Golgi stacks; and the *trans* Golgi network, which often faces the plasma membrane. Vesicles transport material to and from the Golgi. The Golgi complex also participates in posttranslational modification of proteins, such as complex branched-chain oligosaccharide addition, sulfation, and phosphorylation.

IX. CYTOSKELETON

The structure of the cell, the shape of the cell surface, and the arrangement of subcellular organelles is organized by three major protein components: microtubules composed of tubulin, which move and position organelles and vesicles; thin filaments composed of actin, which form a cytoskeleton; and intermediate filaments (IFs) composed of different fibrous proteins. *Actin* and *tubulin*, which are also involved in cell movement, are dynamic structures composed of continuously associating and dissociating globular subunits. IFs, which play a structural role, are composed of stable fibrous proteins that turn over more slowly.

A. Microtubules

Microtubules, cylindrical tubes composed of tubulin subunits, are present in all nucleated cells and the platelets in blood (Fig. 10.16). They are responsible for

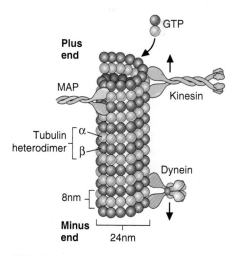

FIG. 10.16.   Microtubules composed of $\alpha\beta$-tubulin heterodimers. *MAP*, microtubule-associated protein. These proteins project outward to attach the microtubules to other cellular components. The microtubule grows by the addition of $\alpha\beta$-dimers containing bound guanosine triphosphate (GTP) to the plus end of the polymer. Kinesin and dyneins are motor proteins that transport cargo (e.g., vesicles) along the microtubule.

The monomeric G protein Arf (a member of the Ras superfamily of regulatory proteins, see Section III.C.2 in Chapter 9) was named for its contribution to the pathogenesis of cholera and not for its normal function in the assembly of intracellular vesicles. In the case of cholera, it is required for the transport of *Vibrio cholerae A* toxin subunit into the cell. The cholera toxin is endocytosed in caveolae vesicles that subsequently merge with lysosomes (or are transformed into lysosomes), where the acidic pH contributes to activation of the toxin. As the toxin is transported through the Golgi and ER, it is further processed and activated. Arf forms a complex with the A-subunit that promotes its travel between compartments. The A-subunit is actually an ADP-ribosylase (an enzyme that cleaves NAD and attaches the ADP portion to a protein) (see Chapter 6, Fig. 6.14), and hence, Arf became known as the *ADP-ribosylating factor*. The ADP-ribosylation of proteins regulating the CFTR chloride channel led to **Dennis Veere's** dehydration and diarrhea.

Lotta Topaigne was given colchicine, a drug that is frequently used to treat gout. One of its actions is to prevent phagocytic activity by binding to dimers of the α- and β-subunits of tubulin. When the tubulin dimer–colchicine complexes bind to microtubules, further polymerization of the microtubules is inhibited, depolymerization predominates, and the microtubules disassemble. Microtubules are necessary for vesicular movement of urate crystals during phagocytosis and release of mediators that activate the inflammatory response. Thus, colchicine diminishes the inflammatory response, swelling, and pain caused by formation of urate crystals.

the positioning of organelles in the cell cytoplasm and the movement of vesicles, including phagocytic vesicles, exocytotic vesicles, and the transport vesicles between the ER, Golgi, and endosomes. They also form the spindle apparatus for cell division. The microtubule network (the minus end) begins in the nucleus at the centriole and extends outward to the plasma membrane (usually the plus end). Microtubule-associated proteins (MAPs) attach microtubules to other cellular components and can determine cell shape and polarity.

Motor proteins called *kinesins* and *cytoplasmic dyneins* use ATP energy to move cargo along the microtubules. Kinesins move molecules, vesicles, and organelles toward the plus end of the microtubule, usually toward the plasma membrane. Cytoplasmic dyneins are huge proteins that move vesicles and organelles to the minus end, generally toward the nucleus. They are also involved in the positioning of the Golgi complex and the movement of chromosomes during mitosis.

Microtubules consist of polymerized arrays of α- and β-tubulin dimers that form 13 protofilaments organized around a hollow core (see Fig. 10.16). Three different tubulin polypeptides (α, β, and γ) of similar amino acid composition are encoded by related genes; α- and β-dimers polymerize to form most microtubules, and γ-tubulin is found only in the centrosomes and spindle pole bodies. Two other forms of tubulin, δ and ε, have been found in centrioles. Tubulin dimers composed of one α- and one β-subunit bind guanosine triphosphate (GTP), which creates a conformational change in the dimer that favors addition of dimers to the tubulin polymer. The dimers can add to and dissociate from both ends of the tubulin, but the end to which they add more rapidly (the plus end) has a net rate of growth, and the end to which they add more slowly (the minus end) has a net rate of loss. As GTP is hydrolyzed to GDP, the binding of tubulin subunits is weakened, resulting in their dissociation (dynamic instability). Thus, the net rate and direction of growth is dictated by the fastest growing end of the microtubule.

B. Actin Filaments

Actin filaments form a critical network that controls the shape of the cell and movement of the cell surface, thereby allowing cells to move, divide, engulf particles, and contract. Actin is present in all living cells. The actin polymer, called *F-actin*, is composed of a helical arrangement of globular G-actin subunits (Fig. 10.17). Within the polymer, each G-actin subunit contains a bound ATP or ADP that holds the actin fold into a closed conformation (see Chapter 7). The actin polymer is dynamic. New subunits of G-actin containing ATP continuously combine with the assembled F-actin polymer at the plus end. As F-actin elongates, bound ATP is hydrolyzed to ADP, so that most of the polymer contains G-actin–ADP subunits. The conformation of ADP-actin favors dissociation from the minus end of the polymer; thus, the polymer is capable of lengthening from the plus end. This directional growth can account for certain types of cell movement and shape changes: the formation of pseudopodia that surround other cells during phagocytosis, the migration of cells in the developing embryo, or the movement of white blood cells through tissues.

Actin polymers form the thin filaments (also called *microfilaments*) in the cells that are organized into compact-ordered bundles or loose network arrays by cross-linking proteins. Short actin filaments bind to the cross-linking protein spectrin to form the cortical actin skeleton network (see Fig. 10.5). In muscle cells, long actin filaments combine with thick filaments, composed of the protein myosin, to produce muscle contraction. The assembly of G-actin subunits into polymers, bundling of fibers, and attachments of actin to spectrin and to the plasma membrane proteins and organelles are mediated by several actin-binding proteins and G proteins from the Rho family.

C. Intermediate Filaments

IF are composed of fibrous protein polymers that provide structural support to membranes of the cells and scaffolding for attachment of other cellular components. Each IF subunit is composed of a long, rodlike α-helical core containing globular spacing domains and globular N- and C-terminal domains. The α-helical segments of two subunits coil around each other to form a coiled coil, and then combine with another dimer coil to form a tetramer. Depending on the type of filament, the dimers may be either heterodimers or homodimers. The tetramers join end to end to form protofilaments, and approximately eight protofilaments combine to form filaments (Fig. 10.18). Filament assembly is partially controlled through phosphorylation.

In contrast to actin thin filaments, the 50 or so different types of IFs are each composed of a different protein having the same general structure described previously. Some of the IFs, such as the nuclear lamins, are common to all cell types. These filaments provide a latticelike support network attached to the inner nuclear membrane. Other IFs are specific for types of cells (e.g., epithelial cells have cytokeratins, and neurons have neurofilaments). These provide an internal network that helps to support the shape and resilience of the cell.

 Colchicine, an initial drug used to treat **Lotta Topaigne**, has a narrow therapeutic index (i.e., the amount of drug that produces the desirable therapeutic effect is not much lower than the amount that produces an adverse effect). Its therapeutic effect depends on inhibiting tubulin synthesis in neutrophils, but it can also prevent tubulin synthesis (and thus, cell division and other cellular processes) in other cells. Fortunately, neutrophils concentrate colchicine, so they are affected at lower intakes than other cell types. Neutrophils lack the transport protein P-glycoprotein, a member of the *ABC* cassette family (which includes the CFTR channel). In most other cell types, P-glycoprotein exports chemicals such as colchicine, thus preventing their accumulation.

CLINICAL COMMENTS

 Al Martini. Al Martini has been drinking for 5 years and has begun to exhibit mental and systemic effects of chronic alcohol consumption. In his brain, ethanol has altered the fluidity of neuronal lipids, causing changes in their response to neurotransmitters released from exocytotic vesicles. In his liver, increased levels of the microsomal ethanol oxidizing system (MEOS, CYP2E1) located in the smooth endoplasmic reticulum (SER) have increased his rate of ethanol oxidation to *acetaldehyde*, a compound that is toxic to the cell. His liver also continues to oxidize ethanol to acetaldehyde through a cytosolic enzyme, liver alcohol dehydrogenase.

One of the toxic effects of acetaldehyde is inhibition of tubulin polymerization. Tubulin is used in the liver for secretion of very low-density lipoprotein (VLDL) particles containing newly synthesized triacylglycerols. As a result, these triacylglycerols accumulate in the liver, and he has begun to develop a fatty liver. Acetaldehyde may also damage protein components of the inner mitochondrial membrane and affect its ability to pump protons to the cytosol.

 Lotta Topaigne. Lotta Topaigne had a rapid and gratifying clinical response to the hourly administration of colchicine. This drug diminishes phagocytosis and the subsequent release of the lysosomal enzymes that initiate the inflammatory response in synovial tissue.

The inflammatory response that causes the symptoms of an acute gout attack begins when neutrophils and macrophages ingest urate crystals. In neutrophils, urate activates the conversion of the polyunsaturated fatty acid arachidonic acid (present in membrane phospholipids) to leukotriene B_4. The release of this messenger contributes to the pain. Colchicine, through its effect on tubulin, inhibits phagocytosis, leukotriene B_4 release, and recruitment and cell division of additional cells involved in inflammation. Colchicine also inhibits the tubulin-dependent release of histamine from mast cells. As a result, there was a rapid improvement in the pain and swelling in Lotta's great toe.

After the gout attack subsided, Ms. Topaigne was placed on daily *allopurinol,* a drug that inhibits urate production (see Chapter 8). During the next 6 months of allopurinol therapy, Ms. Topaigne's blood urate levels decreased. She did not have another gout attack during this time.

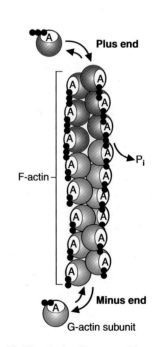

FIG. 10.17. Actin filaments. The polymer F-actin is assembled from G-actin subunits containing bound ATP. While bound, the ATP is slowly hydrolyzed to ADP. The conformational change shifts the equilibrium so that dissociation of the G-actin subunits is favorable at the minus end of the polymer. Once they are dissociated, the actin subunits exchange ADP for ATP, which may again associate with the actin polymer. At the plus end of the molecule, association is favored over dissociation.

FIG. 10.18.   Formation of a cytokeratin filament. The central rod of the keratin monomer is principally an α-helical structure. A specific acidic keratin monomer combines with a specific basic keratin monomer to form a heterodimer coil (a coiled-coil structure). Two dimers combine in antiparallel fashion to form a tetramer, and the tetramers combine head to tail to form protofilaments. Approximately eight protofilaments combine to form a filament. The filament is thicker than actin filaments (called *thin filaments* or *microfilaments*) and is thinner than microtubules (thick tubes) and is therefore called an *intermediate filament* (IF).

Dennis Veere. Dennis Veere was diagnosed with cholera. He was placed on intravenous rehydration therapy, followed by oral rehydration therapy with high glucose- and Na$^+$-containing fluids (to be continued in Chapter 11).

Vibrio cholerae secrete a toxin consisting of one A- and multiple B-subunits. The B-subunits allowing binding to the intestinal epithelia, and the A-subunit is processed and transported into the cell, where it associates with the monomeric G protein Arf (ADP-ribosylation factor). The cholera toxin A-subunit ADP-ribosylates the Gα-subunit of the heterotrimeric G protein Gα$_s$ (a process discussed in Chapter 11). The net result is activation of protein kinase A (PKA), which then phosphorylates the cystic fibrosis transmembrane conductance regulator (CFTR) chloride channel so that it remains permanently open. The subsequent efflux of chloride, sodium, and water into the bowel lumen is responsible for **Dennis Veere's** diarrhea and subsequent dehydration.

BIOCHEMICAL COMMENTS

Differences between Bacteria and Human Cells. Different species of bacteria have some common structural features that distinguish them from animal cells. They are single-cell organisms that are classified as prokaryotes ("before nucleus"). Their genetic material (DNA) is concentrated in the central region of the cell called a *nucleoid* rather than a nucleus because it is not separated from the rest of the cellular contents by a membrane. Likewise, bacteria contain no cytoplasmic organelles defined by membranes. They do have a plasma membrane that encloses the cytoplasm. External to the plasma membrane is a peptidoglycan cell wall composed of extensively cross-linked polysaccharides that form a protective shield on the surface of the cell.

Bacterial cells obtain nutrients from the medium on which they grow. Many of their metabolic pathways for fuel oxidation are similar to those in eukaryotes and generate reduced nicotinamide adenine dinucleotide (NADH) and adenosine triphosphate (ATP); however, individual steps in these pathways may use different coenzymes or very different enzymes for catalysis than do human cells. Like human cells, bacteria use intermediates of glycolysis and other basic degradative pathways to serve as precursors for biosynthetic pathways, and energy acquired from catabolic pathways is used in anabolic pathways. Aerobic bacteria, such as *Escherichia coli*, contain enzymes of the tricarboxylic acid (TCA) cycle and the components of the electron-transport chain, which are located in the cell membrane. However, many bacteria are anaerobes and can function in the absence of oxygen.

Many of the metabolic differences between human cells and bacteria are related to their interactions with their environment. Some bacteria, such as *E. coli*, can adapt to adverse or changing conditions (high vs. low O_2 tension, or a single supply of nutrients from which to synthesize all required components) by dramatic shifts in the genes that are transcribed. Other bacteria find a unique environmental niche where they do not have to compete with other bacteria for nutrients (e.g., *Lactobacilli* in yogurt are adapted to an acidic pH). In contrast, the human cells are adapted to interacting with blood and interstitial fluid, which provides a well-controlled pH, a constant nutrient supply, and a medium for communication between very distant cells. As a consequence of their constant environment, adult human cells seldom need to adapt (or can adapt) to widely fluctuating conditions through large variations in the genes transcribed. As a consequence of being organized into a multicellular organism, human cell types have been able to specialize in function, structure, and enzyme content.

Key Concepts

- The cell is the basic unit of living organisms.
- Unique features of each cell type define tissue specificity and function.
- Despite the variety of cell types, there are many common features that all cells share, such as the presence of a plasma membrane.
  - The plasma membrane is composed primarily of lipids and proteins (both integral and peripheral).
  - Specific transport proteins are required to allow compounds to cross membranes, either by facilitative diffusion, gated channels, or active transport.
  - Eukaryotes contain intracellular organelles, whereas prokaryotic cells do not.
- In eukaryotes, the intracellular organelles consist of lysosomes, the nucleus, ribosomes, the endoplasmic reticulum (ER), the Golgi apparatus, mitochondria, peroxisomes, and the cytoplasm. Each organelle contributes a different function to the cell. Some cells may lack one or more of these internal organelles.
  - Lysosomes are the intracellular organelles of digestion.
  - The nucleus contains the genetic material of the cell and is the site of RNA synthesis.
  - Ribosomes are intracellular organelles on which protein synthesis occurs.

Table 10.1   Diseases Discussed in Chapter 10

Disorder or Condition	Genetic or Environmental	Comments
Cholera	Environmental	Watery diarrhea leading to dehydration caused by cholera toxin ADP-ribosylating a class of G proteins, altering their function and affecting water and salt transport across the intestinal mucosa.
Gout	Both	Treat by inhibiting xanthine oxidase, thereby reducing the production of uric acid, using the analog allopurinol. Prior to allopurinol, the patient is treated with colchicine, which blocks microtubule formation and the migration of neutrophils to the affected area.
Gas gangrene	Environmental	Bacterial infection that secretes a toxin, which is a lipase, leading to cell membrane destruction. This leads to capillary destruction, and impaired blood flow to the affected area.
Alcoholism	Both	Ethanol poisoning caused by increased production of acetaldehyde, because of the combined actions of alcohol dehydrogenase and the induction of the microsomal ethanol oxidizing system (MEOS). MEOS is induced because of the high levels of ethanol in the patient's diet.

- The ER contains enzymes for the synthesis of many lipids, for drug and toxic chemical metabolism, and for posttranslational modification of proteins.
  - The Golgi complex modifies proteins produced in the ER and sorts and distributes them to other organelles.
  - The mitochondria are the cells' power plants, synthesizing adenosine triphosphate (ATP).
  - The peroxisomes sequester various oxidative reactions that have the potential to generate dangerous radical species.
  - The cytoskeleton aids in defining the structure of the cell, the shape of the cell surface, and the arrangement of subcellular organelles within the cytoplasm.
- The diseases discussed in this chapter are summarized in Table 10.1.

REVIEW QUESTIONS—CHAPTER 10

1. Which of the following is a characteristic of the plasma membrane?

    A. It is composed principally of triacylglycerols and cholesterol.
    B. It contains principally nonpolar lipids.
    C. It contains phospholipids with their acyl groups extending into the cytosol.
    D. It contains more phosphatidylserine in the inner than the outer leaflet.
    E. It contains oligosaccharides sandwiched between the inner and outer leaflets.

2. Transmembrane proteins can best be described by which one of the following?

    A. They can usually be dissociated from membranes without disrupting the lipid bilayer.
    B. They are classified as peripheral membrane proteins.
    C. They contain hydrophobic amino acid residues at their carboxy terminus.
    D. They contain hydrophilic amino acid residues extending into the lipid bilayer.
    E. They contain membrane-spanning regions that are α-helices.

3. A patient had a sudden heart attack caused by inadequate blood flow through the vessels of the heart. As a consequence, there was an inadequate supply of oxygen to generate ATP in his cardiomyocytes. The compartment of the cardiomyocyte most directly involved in ATP generation is which one of the following?

    A. Mitochondrion
    B. Peroxisome
    C. Lysosome
    D. Nucleus
    E. Golgi

4. The release of insulin from the β-cells of the pancreas requires Ca^{2+} influx through a channel that is activated by a change in the membrane potential across the plasma membrane. The movement of calcium across the membrane is an example of which one of the following?

    A. Voltage-gated channel
    B. Passive diffusion
    C. Active transport
    D. Ligand-gated channel
    E. Phosphorylation-gated channel

5. ATP is required for the appropriate functioning of the lysosome because of which one of the following?

    A. Maintaining an acidic environment in the lysosome
    B. Maintaining a basic environment in the lysosome
    C. Regulation of enzyme activity
    D. Activation of lysosomal zymogens
    E. As a cofactor for lysosomal hydrolases

11 Cell Signaling by Chemical Messengers

Within a complex organism such as the human, the different organs, tissues, and cell types have developed specialized functions. Yet each cell must contribute in an integrated way as the body grows, differentiates, and adapts to changing conditions. Such integration requires communication that is carried out by chemical messengers traveling from one cell to another by direct contact of cells with the extracellular matrix or by direct contact of one cell with another. The eventual goal of such signals is to change actions carried out in target cells by intracellular proteins (metabolic enzymes, gene regulatory proteins, ion channels, or cytoskeletal proteins). In this chapter, we present a basic overview of signaling by chemical messengers.

*Chemical Messengers. Chemical messengers (also called signaling molecules) transmit messages between cells. They are **secreted** from one cell in **response to a specific stimulus** and **travel to a target cell** where they **bind to a specific receptor** and **elicit a response** (Fig. 11.1). In the nervous system, these chemical messengers are called **neurotransmitters**; in the **endocrine system**, they are **hormones**; and in **the immune system**, they are called **cytokines**. Additional chemical messengers include **retinoids**, **eicosanoids**, and **growth factors**. Depending on the distance between the secreting and target cells, chemical messengers can be classified as **endocrine** (travel in the blood), **paracrine** (travel between nearby cells), or **autocrine** (act on the same cell that produces the message).*

*Receptors and Signal Transduction. Receptors are proteins that contain a binding site specific for a single chemical messenger and another binding site involved in transmitting the message (see Fig. 11.1). The second binding site may interact with another protein or with DNA. They may be either **plasma membrane receptors** (which span the plasma membrane and contain an extracellular binding domain for the messenger) or **intracellular binding proteins** (for messengers able to diffuse into the cell) (see Fig. 11.1). Most plasma membrane receptors fall into the categories of **ion channel receptors**, **tyrosine kinase receptors**, **tyrosine kinase-associated receptors**, **serine–threonine kinase receptors**, or **heptahelical receptors** (proteins with seven α-helices spanning the membrane). When a chemical messenger binds to a receptor, the signal it is carrying must be converted into an intracellular response. This conversion is called **signal transduction**.*

*Signal Transduction for Intracellular Receptors. Most intracellular receptors are **gene-specific transcription factors**, proteins that bind to DNA and regulate the transcription of certain genes. (Gene transcription is the process of copying the genetic code from DNA to RNA, and is discussed further in Chapter 14.)*

*Signal Transduction for Plasma Membrane Receptors. Mechanisms of signal transduction that follow the binding of signaling molecules to plasma membrane receptors include phosphorylation of receptors at tyrosine residues (**receptor tyrosine kinase** activity), conformational changes in **signal transducer proteins** (e.g., proteins with **SH2** domains, the **monomeric G proteins like Ras**, or **heterotrimeric G proteins**), or increases in the levels of **intracellular second***

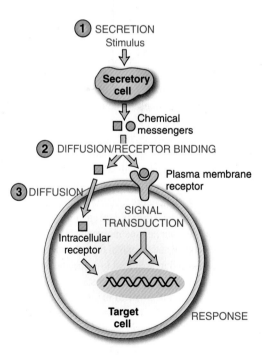

FIG. 11.1. General features of chemical messengers. (1) Secretion of chemical message. (2) Binding of message to cell surface receptor. (3) Diffusion of a hydrophobic message across plasma membrane and binding to an intracellular receptor.

*messengers. Second messengers are nonprotein molecules that are generated inside the cell in response to hormone binding and that continue transmission of the message. Examples include 3',5'-cyclic adenosine monophosphate (**cAMP**), inositol trisphosphate (**IP₃**), and diacylglycerol (**DAG**).*

Signaling often requires a rapid response and rapid termination of the message, which may be achieved by degradation of the receptor itself, by degradation of the messenger or second messenger, the conversion of guanosine triphosphate (GTP) to guanosine diphosphate (GDP) on GTP-dependent signaling molecules, deactivation of signal transduction kinases by phosphatases, or other means.

THE WAITING ROOM

Mya Sthenia is a 37-year-old woman who complains of increasing muscle fatigue in her lower extremities upon walking. If she rests for 5 to 10 minutes, her leg strength returns to normal. She also notes that if she talks on the phone, her ability to form words gradually decreases. By evening, her upper eyelids droop to the point that she has to pull her upper lids back to see normally. These symptoms are becoming increasingly severe. When Mya is asked to sustain an upward gaze, her upper eyelids eventually drift downward involuntarily. When she is asked to hold both arms straight out in front of her for as long as she is able, both arms begin to drift downward within minutes. Her physician suspects that Mya has myasthenia gravis and orders a test to determine whether she has antibodies in her blood directed against acetylcholine receptors.

Ann O'Rexia, who suffers from anorexia nervosa, has increased her weight to 102 lb from a low of 85 lb (see Chapter 9). On the advice of her physician, she has been eating more to prevent fatigue during her daily jogging regimen. She runs about 10 miles before breakfast every second day and forces herself to drink a high-energy supplement immediately afterward.

Dennis Veere was hospitalized for dehydration resulting from cholera toxin (see Chapter 10). In his intestinal mucosal cells, the cholera toxin A subunit indirectly activated the cystic fibrosis transmembrane conductance regulator (CFTR) channel, resulting in secretion of chloride and sodium ions into his intestinal lumen. Ion secretion was followed by loss of water, resulting in vomiting and watery diarrhea. Dennis is being treated for hypovolemic shock.

Acetylcholine (ACh) is released by neurons and acts on ACh receptors at neuromuscular junctions to stimulate muscular contraction. Myasthenia gravis is an acquired autoimmune disease in which the patient has developed pathogenic antibodies against these receptors. **Mya Sthenia's** decreasing ability to form words and her other symptoms of muscle weakness are being caused by the inability of ACh to stimulate repeated muscle contraction when the numbers of effective ACh receptors at neuromuscular junctions are greatly reduced.

Endocrine hormones enable **Ann O'Rexia** to mobilize fuels from her adipose tissue during her periods of fasting and during jogging. Although she fasts overnight, α-cells of her pancreas increase secretion of the polypeptide hormone glucagon. The stress of prolonged fasting and chronic exercise stimulates release of cortisol, a steroid hormone, from her adrenal cortex. The exercise of jogging also increases secretion of the hormones epinephrine and norepinephrine from the adrenal medulla. Each of these hormones is being released in response to a specific signal and causes a characteristic response in a target tissue, enabling her to exercise. However, each of these hormones binds to a different type of receptor and works in a different way.

I. GENERAL FEATURES OF CHEMICAL MESSENGERS

Certain universal characteristics of chemical messenger systems are illustrated in Figure 11.1. Signaling generally follows the sequence: (1) The chemical messenger is secreted from specific cells in response to a stimulus; (2) the messenger diffuses or is transported through blood or other extracellular fluid to the target cell; (3) a receptor in the target cell (a plasma membrane receptor or intracellular receptor) specifically binds the messenger; (4) binding of the messenger to the receptor elicits a response; and (5) the signal ceases and is terminated. Chemical messengers elicit their response in the target cell without being metabolized by the cell.

An additional feature of chemical messenger systems is that the specificity of the response is dictated by the type of receptor and its location. Generally, each receptor binds only one specific chemical messenger, and each receptor initiates a characteristic signal transduction pathway that will ultimately activate or inhibit certain processes in the cell. Only certain cells, the target cells, carry receptors for that messenger and are capable of responding to its message.

The means of signal termination is an exceedingly important aspect of cell signaling, and failure to terminate a signal contributes to several diseases such as cancer.

A. General Features of Chemical Messenger Systems Applied to the Nicotinic Acetylcholine Receptor

The individual steps involved in cell signaling by chemical messengers are illustrated with acetylcholine (ACh), a neurotransmitter that acts on nicotinic ACh receptors on the plasma membrane of certain muscle cells. This system exhibits the classic features of chemical messenger release and specificity of response.

Neurotransmitters are secreted from neurons in response to an electrical stimulus called the *action potential*—a voltage difference across the plasma membrane, caused by changes in Na^+ and K^+ gradients, that is propagated along a nerve. The neurotransmitters diffuse across a synapse to another excitable cell where they elicit a response (Fig. 11.2). ACh is the neurotransmitter at neuromuscular junctions where it transmits a signal from a motor nerve to a muscle fiber that elicits contraction of the fiber. Before ACh is released, it is sequestered in vesicles clustered near an active zone in the presynaptic membrane. This membrane also has voltage-gated Ca^{2+} channels that open when the action potential reaches them, resulting in an influx of Ca^{2+}. The Ca^{2+} triggers fusion of the vesicles with the plasma membrane, and ACh is released into the synaptic cleft. Thus, the chemical messenger is released from a specific cell in response to a specific stimulus. Most

 Ann O'Rexia's fasting is accompanied by high levels of the endocrine hormone glucagon, which is secreted in response to low blood glucose levels. It enters the blood and acts on the liver to stimulate several pathways, including the release of glucose from glycogen stores (glycogenolysis) (see Chapter 3). The specificity of its action is determined by the location of receptors. Although liver parenchymal cells have glucagon receptors, skeletal muscle and many other tissues do not. Therefore, glucagon cannot stimulate glycogenolysis in these tissues.

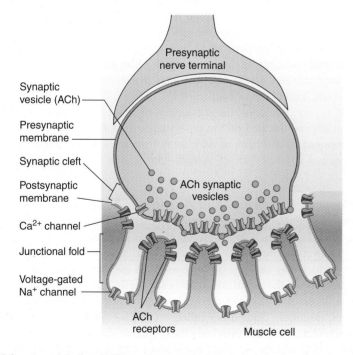

FIG. 11.2. Acetylcholine (ACh) receptors at the neuromuscular junction. A motor nerve terminates in several branches; each branch terminates in a bulb-shaped structure called the presynaptic bouton. Each bouton synapses with a region of the muscle fiber that contains junctional folds. At the crest of each fold there is a high concentration of ACh receptors, which are gated ion channels.

Myasthenia gravis is a disease of autoimmunity caused by the production of an antibody directed against the acetylcholine (ACh) receptor in skeletal muscle. In this disease, B and T lymphocytes cooperate in producing various antibodies against the nicotinic ACh receptor. The antibodies then bind to various locations in the receptor and cross-link the receptors, forming a multireceptor antibody complex. The complex is endocytosed and incorporated into lysosomes, where it is degraded. **Mya Sthenia**, therefore, has fewer functional receptors on the muscle cell membrane for ACh to activate.

 Acetylcholine (ACh) acts on two different types of receptors: nicotinic and muscarinic. Nicotinic receptors (for which nicotine is an activator) are found at the neuromuscular junction of skeletal muscle cells, as well as in the parasympathetic nervous system. Muscarinic receptors (for which muscarine, a mushroom toxin, is an activator) are found at the neuromuscular junction of cardiac and smooth muscle cells, as well as in the sympathetic nervous system. Curare (a paralyzing agent) is an inhibitor of nicotinic ACh receptors, whereas atropine is an inhibitor of muscarinic ACh receptors. Atropine may be used under conditions in which acetylcholinesterase has been inactivated by various nerve gases or chemicals such that atropine will block the effects of the excess ACh present at the synapse.

 Mya Sthenia was tested with an inhibitor of acetylcholinesterase, edrophonium chloride, administered intravenously. After this drug inactivates acetylcholinesterase, acetylcholine (ACh) that is released from the nerve terminal accumulates in the synaptic cleft. Although Mya expresses fewer ACh receptors on her muscle cells (due to the autoantibody-induced degradation of receptors), by increasing the local concentration of ACh, these receptors have a higher probability of being occupied and activated. Therefore, acute intravenous administration of this short-acting drug briefly improves muscular weakness in patients with myasthenia gravis.

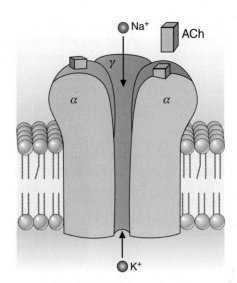

FIG. 11.3. The nicotinic acetylcholine (ACh) receptor. Each receptor is composed of five subunits, and each subunit has four membrane-spanning helical regions. For clarity, only three subunits are shown in this figure. The two α-subunits are identical and contain binding sites for ACh. When two ACh molecules are bound, the subunits change their conformation so that the channel in the center of the receptor is open, allowing K^+ ions to diffuse out and Na^+ ions to diffuse in.

chemical messengers use a similar vesicular system triggered by Ca^{2+} influx to release the messenger.

ACh diffuses across the synaptic cleft to bind to plasma membrane receptors on skeletal muscle cells called the *nicotinic acetylcholine receptor* (Fig. 11.3). The receptor subunits are assembled around a channel that has a funnel-shaped opening in the center. As ACh binds to the receptor, a conformational change opens the narrow portion of the channel (the gate), allowing Na^+ to diffuse in and K^+ to diffuse out. (A uniform property of all receptors is that signal transduction begins with conformational changes in the receptor.) The change in Na^+ and K^+ ion concentrations activates a sequence of events that eventually triggers the cellular response—contraction of the fiber.

Once ACh secretion stops, the message is rapidly terminated by acetylcholinesterase, an enzyme located on the postsynaptic membrane that cleaves ACh. It is also terminated by diffusion of ACh away from the synapse. Rapid termination of messages is a characteristic of systems that require a rapid response from the target cell.

B. Endocrine, Paracrine, and Autocrine Actions

The actions of chemical messengers are often classified as endocrine, paracrine, or autocrine (Fig. 11.4). Each endocrine hormone is secreted by a specific cell type (generally in an endocrine gland), enters the blood, and exerts its actions on specific target cells, which may be some distance away. In contrast to endocrine hormones, paracrine actions are those performed on nearby cells, and the location of the cells plays a role in the specificity of the response. Synaptic transmission by ACh and other neurotransmitters (sometimes called *neurocrine signaling*) is an example of paracrine signaling. ACh activates only those ACh receptors that are located across the synaptic cleft from the signaling nerve, not every muscle cell with ACh receptors. Paracrine actions are also very important in limiting the immune response to a specific location in the body, a feature that helps prevent the development of autoimmune disease. Autocrine actions involve a messenger that acts on the cell from which it is secreted.

C. Types of Chemical Messengers

The three major signaling systems in the body all employ chemical messengers: the nervous system, the endocrine system, and the immune system. Some messengers are difficult to place in just one such category.

1. THE NERVOUS SYSTEM

The nervous system secretes two types of messengers: small-molecule neurotransmitters, often called *biogenic amines*, and neuropeptides. Small-molecule neurotransmitters are nitrogen-containing molecules, several of which are amino acids or derivatives of amino acids (e.g., ACh, epinephrine, γ-aminobutyrate; Fig. 11.5). Neuropeptides are usually small peptides (between 4 and 35 amino acids) secreted by neurons that act as neurotransmitters at synaptic junctions or are secreted into the blood to act as neurohormones.

2. THE ENDOCRINE SYSTEM

Endocrine hormones are defined as compounds secreted from specific endocrine cells in endocrine glands, which reach their target cells following transport through the blood. Insulin, for example, is an endocrine hormone secreted from the β-cells of the pancreas. Classic hormones are generally divided into the structural categories of polypeptide hormones (e.g., insulin; see Fig. 6.12 for the structure of insulin), catecholamines such as epinephrine (which is also a neurotransmitter), steroid hormones (which are derived from cholesterol), and thyroid hormone (which is derived from tyrosine). Many of these endocrine hormones also exert paracrine or autocrine actions. The hormones that regulate metabolism are discussed throughout this chapter and in subsequent chapters.

Some compounds that are normally considered hormones are more difficult to categorize. For example, retinoids, which are derivatives of vitamin A (also called *retinol*) and vitamin D (which is derived from cholesterol), are usually classified as hormones although they are not synthesized in endocrine cells.

3. THE IMMUNE SYSTEM

The messengers of the immune system, called *cytokines*, are small proteins with a molecular weight of approximately 20,000 Da. Cytokines regulate a network of responses designed to kill invading microorganisms. The different classes of cytokines (interleukins, tumor necrosis factors, interferons, and colony-stimulating factors) are secreted by cells of the immune system and usually alter the behavior of other cells in the immune system by activating the transcription of genes for proteins involved in the immune response. *Chemokines* are chemotactic cytokines

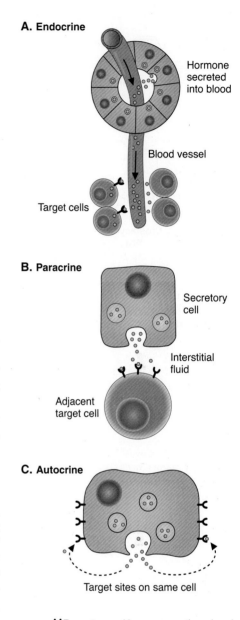

A. Endocrine

Hormone secreted into blood

Blood vessel

Target cells

B. Paracrine

Secretory cell

Interstitial fluid

Adjacent target cell

C. Autocrine

Target sites on same cell

Y Receptor   ○ Hormone or other chemical messenger

FIG. 11.4. Endocrine (**A**), paracrine (**B**), and autocrine (**C**) actions of hormones and other chemical messengers.

 The catecholamine hormone epinephrine (also called *adrenaline*) is the fright, fight, and flight hormone. Epinephrine and the structurally similar hormone norepinephrine are released from the adrenal medulla in response to various immediate stresses, including pain, hemorrhage, exercise, hypoglycemia, and hypoxia. Thus, as **Ann O'Rexia** begins to jog, there is a rapid release of epinephrine and norepinephrine into her blood.

$$H_3C-\overset{\overset{\displaystyle O}{\|}}{C}-O-CH_2-CH_2-\overset{+}{N}(CH_3)_3$$

Acetylcholine

$$^-OOC-CH_2-CH_2-CH_2-\overset{+}{N}H_3$$

γ-Aminobutyrate (GABA)

Epinephrine

FIG. 11.5. Small-molecule neurotransmitters.

Arachidonic acid
$(C_{20:4}, \Delta^{5,8,11,14})$

Prostacyclin
PGI$_2$

FIG. 11.6. Eicosanoids are derived from arachidonic acid and retain its original 20 carbons (thus the name "eicosanoids"). All prostaglandins, such as prostacyclin, also have an internal ring.

in that these molecules have the ability to induce movement in targeted cells toward the source of the chemokines.

4. THE EICOSANOIDS

The *eicosanoids* (including prostaglandins [PGs], thromboxanes, and leukotrienes) control cellular function in response to injury (Fig. 11.6). These compounds are all derived from arachidonic acid, a 20-carbon polyunsaturated fatty acid that is usually present in cells as part of the membrane lipid phosphatidylcholine (see Chapter 5, Fig. 5.19). Although almost every cell in the body produces an eicosanoid in response to tissue injury, different cells produce different eicosanoids. The eicosanoids act principally in paracrine and autocrine functions, affecting the cells that produce them or their neighboring cells. For example, vascular endothelial cells (cells that line the vessel wall) secrete the prostaglandin prostacyclin (PGI$_2$), which acts on nearby smooth muscle cells to cause vasodilation (expansion of the blood vessel). The synthesis and metabolism of the eicosanoids is discussed further in Chapter 35.

5. GROWTH FACTORS

Growth factors are polypeptides that function through stimulation of cellular proliferation (hyperplasia) or cell size (hypertrophy). For example, platelets aggregating at the site of injury to a blood vessel secrete platelet-derived growth factor (PDGF). PDGF stimulates the proliferation of nearby smooth muscle cells, which eventually form a plaque covering the injured site. Some growth factors are considered hormones, and some have been called cytokines.

II. INTRACELLULAR TRANSCRIPTION FACTOR RECEPTORS
A. Intracellular versus Plasma Membrane Receptors

The structural properties of a messenger determine, to some extent, the type of receptor it binds. Most receptors fall into two broad categories: intracellular receptors or plasma membrane receptors (Fig. 11.7). Messengers that use intracellular receptors must be hydrophobic molecules that are able to diffuse through the

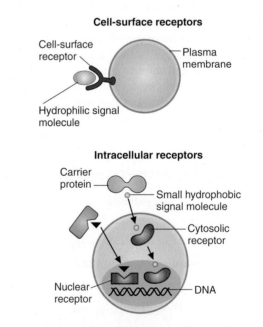

FIG. 11.7. Intracellular versus plasma membrane receptors. Plasma membrane receptors have extracellular binding domains. Intracellular receptors bind steroid hormones or other messengers that are able to diffuse through the plasma membrane. Their receptors may reside in the cytoplasm and translocate to the nucleus, reside in the nucleus bound to DNA, or reside in the nucleus bound to other proteins.

plasma membrane into cells. In contrast, polar molecules such as peptide hormones, cytokines, and catecholamines cannot rapidly cross the plasma membrane and must bind to a plasma membrane receptor.

Most of the intracellular receptors for lipophilic messengers are gene-specific transcription factors. A *transcription factor* is a protein that binds to a specific site on DNA and regulates the rate of transcription of a gene (i.e., synthesis of mRNA, see Chapter 16). External signaling molecules interact with transcription factors that bind to a specific sequence on DNA and regulate the expression of only certain genes; they are called *gene-specific* or *site-specific transcription factors*.

B. The Steroid Hormone/Thyroid Hormone Superfamily of Receptors

Lipophilic hormones that use intracellular gene-specific transcription factors include the steroid hormones, thyroid hormone, retinoic acid (the active form of vitamin A), and vitamin D (Fig. 11.8). Because these compounds are water-insoluble, they are transported in the blood bound to serum albumin, which has a hydrophobic binding pocket, or to more specific transport proteins such as steroid hormone-binding

 Lotta Topaigne suffered enormously painful gout attacks affecting her great toe (see Clinical Comments, Chapter 8). The extreme pain was caused by the release of a leukotriene that stimulated pain receptors. The precipitated urate crystals in her big toe stimulated recruited inflammatory cells to release the leukotriene.

FIG. 11.8. Steroid hormone–thyroid hormone superfamily. **A.** Cortisol (a glucocorticoid). **B.** Aldosterone (a mineralcorticoid). **C.** Thyroid hormone. **D.** Vitamin D₃. **E.** Retinoids.

The steroid hormone cortisol is synthesized and released from the adrenal cortex in response to the polypeptide hormone adrenocorticotropic hormone (ACTH). Chronic stress (e.g., pain, hypoglycemia, hemorrhage, exercise) signals are passed from the brain cortex to the hypothalamus to the anterior pituitary, which releases ACTH. Cortisol acts on tissues to change enzyme levels and redistribute nutrients in preparation for acute stress. For example, it increases transcription of the genes for regulatory enzymes in the pathway of gluconeogenesis (called *gene-specific activation of transcription*, or *induction of protein synthesis*). The net result of this activity is an increased cellular content of the enzymes. Induction of gluconeogenic enzymes prepares the liver to respond rapidly to hypoglycemia with increased synthesis of glucose. **Ann O'Rexia**, who has frequently been fasting and exercising, has an increased capacity for gluconeogenesis in her liver.

globulin (SHBG) or thyroid hormone-binding globulin (TBG). The intracellular receptors for these hormones are structurally similar and are referred to as the *steroid hormone/thyroid hormone superfamily of receptors.*

The members of the steroid hormone/thyroid hormone superfamily of receptors are primarily localized to the nucleus, although some members are also found in the cytoplasm. The glucocorticoid receptor, for example, exists as cytoplasmic multimeric complexes associated with heat-shock proteins. When the hormone cortisol (a glucocorticoid) binds, the receptor undergoes a conformational change and dissociates from the heat-shock proteins, exposing a nuclear localization signal. The receptors dimerize, and the complex (including bound hormone) translocates to the nucleus where it binds to a portion of the DNA called the *hormone response element* (e.g., the glucocorticoid receptor binds to the glucocorticoid response element [GRE]). Most of the members of this family of intracellular receptors reside principally in the nucleus, and some of these are constitutively bound, as dimers, to their response element in DNA (e.g., the thyroid hormone receptor). Binding of the hormone changes its activity and its ability to associate with or disassociate from DNA. Regulation of gene transcription by these receptors is described in more detail in Chapter 16.

As an example of the complexity that can occur with the steroid hormone superfamily of receptors, several nuclear receptors play important roles in intermediary metabolism, and they have become the targets of lipid-lowering drugs. These include the peroxisome proliferator-activated receptors (PPAR α, β, and γ), the liver X-activated receptor (LXR), the farnesoid X-activated receptor (FXR), and the pregnane X receptor (PXR). These receptors form heterodimers with the 9-*cis*-retinoic acid receptor (RXR) and bind to their appropriate response elements in DNA in an inactive state. When the activating ligand binds to the receptor (fatty acids and their derivatives for PPARs, oxysterols for LXR, bile salts for FXR, and secondary bile salts for PXR), the complex is activated, and gene expression is altered. Unlike the cortisol receptor, these receptors reside in the nucleus and are activated once their ligands enter the nucleus and bind to them.

III. PLASMA MEMBRANE RECEPTORS AND SIGNAL TRANSDUCTION

All plasma membrane receptors are proteins with certain features in common: an extracellular domain that participates in the binding of the chemical messenger, one or more membrane-spanning domains that are α-helices, and an intracellular domain that initiates signal transduction. As the ligand binds to the extracellular domain of its receptor, it causes a conformational change that is communicated to the intracellular domain through the rigid α-helix of the transmembrane domain. The activated intracellular domain initiates a characteristic signal transduction pathway that usually involves the binding of specific intracellular signal transduction proteins.

The pathways of signal transduction for plasma membrane receptors have two major types of effects on the cell: (1) rapid and immediate effects on cellular ion levels or activation/inhibition of enzymes and/or (2) slower changes in the rate of gene expression for a specific set of proteins. Often, a signal transduction pathway will ultimately produce both kinds of effects. Signal transduction pathways, like a river, run in one direction. From a given point in a signal transduction pathway, events closer to the receptor are referred to as *upstream*, and events closer to the response are referred to as *downstream*.

A. Major Classes of Plasma Membrane Receptors

Individual plasma membrane receptors are grouped into the categories of ion channel receptors, receptors that are kinases or bind to and activate kinases, and receptors that work through second messengers. This classification is based on the receptor's general structure and means of signal transduction.

FIG. 11.9. Receptors that are kinases or that bind kinases. The kinase domains are shown in *red*, and the phosphorylation sites are indicated with *red arrows*. **A.** Tyrosine kinase receptors. **B.** JAK-STAT receptors. **C.** Serine–threonine kinase receptors.

1. ION CHANNEL RECEPTORS

The ion channel receptors are similar in structure to the nicotinic ACh receptor (see Fig. 11.3). Signal transduction consists of the conformational change when ligand binds. Most small-molecule neurotransmitters and some neuropeptides use ion channel receptors.

2. RECEPTORS THAT ARE KINASES OR THAT BIND TO AND ACTIVATE KINASES

Several types of receptors that are kinases or that bind to and activate kinases are illustrated in Figure 11.9. Protein kinases transfer a phosphate group from adenosine triphosphate (ATP) to the hydroxyl group of a specific amino acid side chain in the target protein. Their common feature is that the intracellular kinase domain of the receptor (or the kinase domain of the associated protein) is activated when the messenger binds to the extracellular domain. The receptor kinase phosphorylates an amino acid residue (serine, threonine, tyrosine, or, rarely, histidine) on the receptor (autophosphorylation) or an associated protein. The message is propagated downstream through signal transducer proteins that bind to the activated messenger–receptor complex (e.g., STAT [*s*ignal *t*ransducer and *a*ctivator of *t*ranscription], Smad, or Src homology 2 [SH2] domain containing protein such as Grb2).

3. HEPTAHELICAL RECEPTORS

Heptahelical receptors (also called *G protein–coupled receptors* [GPCR]) contain seven membrane-spanning α-helices and are the most common type of plasma membrane receptor. They work through second messengers, which are small nonprotein compounds, such as 3′,5′-cyclic adenosine monophosphate (cAMP), generated inside the cell in response to messenger binding to the receptor (Fig. 11.10). They continue intracellular transmission of the message from the hormone/cytokine/neurotransmitter, which is the "first" messenger. Second messengers are present in low concentrations so that modulation of their level, and hence the message, can be rapidly initiated and terminated.

B. Signal Transduction through Tyrosine Kinase Receptors

The tyrosine kinase receptors are depicted in Figure 11.9A. They generally exist in the membrane as monomers with a single membrane-spanning helix. One molecule of the growth factor generally binds two molecules of the receptor and promotes their dimerization (Fig. 11.11). Once the receptor dimer has formed, the intracellular tyrosine kinase domains of the receptor phosphorylate each other on certain tyrosine residues (autophosphorylation). The phosphotyrosine residues form specific binding sites for signal transducer proteins.

FIG. 11.10. Serpentine receptors and second messengers. The secreted chemical messenger (hormone, cytokine, or neurotransmitter) is the first messenger, which binds to a plasma membrane receptor such as the heptahelical receptors. The activated hormone–receptor complex activates a heterotrimeric G protein and, via stimulation of membrane-bound enzymes, different G proteins lead to generation of one or more intracellular second messengers, such as cAMP, diacylglycerol (DAG), or inositol trisphosphate (IP_3).

FIG. 11.11.   Signal transduction by tyrosine kinase receptors. **1.** Binding and dimerization. **2.** Autophosphorylation. **3.** Binding of Grb2 and SOS. **4.** SOS is a GEF (guanine nucleotide exchange factor) that binds Ras, a monomeric G protein anchored to the plasma membrane. **5.** GEF activates the exchange of guanosine triphosphate (GTP) for bound guanosine diphosphate (GDP) on Ras. **6.** Activated Ras containing GTP binds the target enzyme Raf, thereby activating it and a series of downstream kinases known as the microtubule-associated protein (MAP) kinase pathway.

1.   RAS AND THE MAP KINASE PATHWAY

The Ras–MAP kinase pathway provides a nice example to demonstrate how receptor tyrosine kinases can activate signaling through the assembly of protein complexes, due to protein–protein interactions. In this pathway, one of the domains of the receptor containing a phosphotyrosine residue forms a binding site for intracellular proteins with a specific three-dimensional structure known as the *SH2 domain* (named for the first protein in which it was found, the src protein of the Rous sarcoma virus). The adaptor protein Grb2 is one of the proteins with an SH2 domain that binds to phosphotyrosine residues on growth factor receptors. Binding to the receptor causes a conformational change in Grb2 that activates another binding site called an *SH3 domain*. These activated SH3 domains bind the protein SOS (SOS is an acronym for "son of sevenless," a name that is not related to the function or structure of the compound). SOS is a guanine nucleotide exchange factor (GEF) for Ras, a monomeric G protein located in the plasma membrane (see Chapter 9, Section III.C.2). SOS catalyzes exchange of guanosine triphosphate (GTP) for guanosine diphosphate (GDP) on Ras, causing a conformational change in Ras that promotes binding of the protein Raf. Raf is a serine protein kinase that is also called *MAPKKK* (*m*itogen-*a*ctivated *p*rotein *k*inase *k*inase *k*inase). Raf begins a sequence of successive phosphorylation steps called a *phosphorylation cascade*. When one of the kinases in a cascade is phosphorylated, it binds and phosphorylates the next enzyme downstream in the cascade. The MAP kinase cascade ultimately leads to an alteration of gene transcription factor activity, thereby either upregulating or downregulating transcription of many genes involved in cell survival and proliferation.

Although many different signal transducer proteins have SH2 domains and many receptors have phosphotyrosine residues, a signal transducer protein may only be specific for one type of receptor. This specificity of binding results from the fact that each phosphotyrosine residue has a different amino acid sequence around it that forms the binding domain. Similarly, the SH2 domain of the transducer protein is only part of its binding domain. Conversely, however, several transducer proteins will bind to multiple receptors (such as Grb2).

Many tyrosine kinase receptors (as well as heptahelical receptors) also have additional signaling pathways involving intermediates such as phosphatidylinositol phosphates.

2. PHOSPHATIDYLINOSITOL PHOSPHATES IN SIGNAL TRANSDUCTION

Phosphatidylinositol signaling molecules can be generated through either tyrosine kinase receptors or heptahelical receptors. Phosphatidylinositol phosphates serve two different functions in signal transduction: (1) Phosphatidylinositol 4',5'-bisphosphate (PI-4,5-bisP) can be cleaved to generate the two intracellular second messengers, diacylglycerol (DAG) and inositol trisphosphate (IP$_3$); and (2) phosphatidylinositol 3',4',5'-trisphosphate (PI-3,4,5-trisP) can serve as a plasma-membrane docking site for signal transduction proteins.

Phosphatidylinositol, which is present in the inner leaflet of the plasma membrane, is converted to PI-4,5-bisP by kinases that phosphorylate the inositol ring at the 4' and 5' positions (Fig. 11.12). PI-4,5-bisP, which has three phosphate groups, is cleaved by a phospholipase C-isozyme to generate IP$_3$ and DAG. The phospholipase isozyme Cγ (PLCγ) is activated by tyrosine kinase growth factor receptors, and phospholipase C$_\beta$ is activated by a heptahelical receptor–G-protein signal transduction pathway.

PI-4,5-bisP can also be phosphorylated at the 3' position of inositol by the enzyme phosphatidylinositol 3'-kinase (PI 3-kinase) to form PI-3,4,5-trisP (see Fig. 11.12). PI-3,4,5-trisP (and PI-3,4-bisP) forms membrane docking sites for proteins that contain a certain sequence of amino acids called the *pleckstrin homology* (PH) domain. PI 3-kinase contains an SH2 domain and is activated by binding to a specific phosphotyrosine site on a tyrosine kinase receptor or receptor-associated protein. The protein phosphatase and tensin homolog (PTEN) catalyzes the dephosphorylation of PI-3,4,5-trisP to PI-4,5-bisP, thereby removing the primary signal from the pathway. Mutations within PTEN, or misexpression of PTEN, can lead to cancer (see Chapter 18).

3. THE INSULIN RECEPTOR

The insulin receptor, a member of the tyrosine kinase family of receptors, provides a good example of divergence in the pathway of signal transduction. Unlike other growth factor receptors, the insulin receptor exists in the membrane as a preformed dimer, with each half containing an α- and a β-subunit (Fig. 11.13). The β-subunits autophosphorylate each other when insulin binds, thereby activating the receptor. The activated phosphorylated receptor binds a protein called *insulin receptor substrate* (IRS). The activated receptor kinase phosphorylates IRS at multiple sites,

FIG. 11.12. Major route for generation of the phosphatidylinositide signal molecules, inositol 1,4,5-trisphosphate (IP$_3$), and phosphatidylinositol 3,4,5-trisphosphate (PI-3,4,5-trisP). PI 3-kinase phosphorylates PI-4,5-bisP and PI-4P (not shown) at the 3 position. Prime symbols are sometimes used in these names to denote the inositol ring. DAG is also a second messenger. PLC is phospholipase C.

FIG. 11.13. Insulin receptor signaling. The insulin receptor is a dimer of two membrane-spanning α–β pairs. The tyrosine kinase domains are shown in *red*, and *arrows* indicate autophosphorylation. The activated receptor binds IRS molecules (insulin receptor substrates) and phosphorylates IRS at multiple sites, thereby forming binding sites for proteins with SH2 domains, examples being Grb2, phospholipase Cγ (PLCγ), and PI 3-kinase. Both PLCγ and PI 3-kinase are associated with various phosphatidylinositol phosphates (all designated with *PIP*) in the plasma membrane. Grb2 associates with a protein known as *GAP1* (Grb2-associated protein), which has a pleckstrin homology domain that associates with phosphatidylinositol phosphates in the membrane.

FIG. 11.14. The insulin receptor–protein kinase B (Akt) signaling pathway. *Ins*, insulin; *IRS*, insulin receptor substrate; *PH* domains, pleckstrin homology domains; *PDK1*, phosphoinositide-dependent protein kinase 1; *PKB*, protein kinase B.

 Insulin is a growth factor that is essential for cell viability and growth. It increases general protein synthesis, which strongly affects muscle mass through hypertrophy. However, it also regulates immediate nutrient availability and storage, including glucose transport into skeletal muscle and glycogen synthesis. Thus, **Di Abietes** and other patients with type I diabetes mellitus who lack insulin rapidly develop hyperglycemia once insulin levels drop too low. They also exhibit muscle "wasting." To mediate the diverse regulatory roles of insulin, the signal transduction pathway diverges after activation of the receptor and phosphorylation of IRS, which has multiple binding sites for different signal-mediator proteins.

creating multiple binding sites for different proteins with SH2 domains. One of the sites binds Grb2, leading to activation of Ras and the MAP kinase pathway. At another phosphotyrosine site, PI 3-kinase binds and is activated. At the third site, PLCγ binds and is activated. The insulin receptor can also transmit signals through direct docking with other signal transduction intermediates.

The signal pathway initiated by the insulin receptor complex involving PI 3-kinase leads to activation of protein kinase B (also called Akt), a serine–threonine kinase that mediates many of the downstream effects of insulin (Fig. 11.14). PI 3-kinase binds to IRS and phosphorylates PI-4,5-bisP in the membrane to form PI-3,4,5-trisP. Protein kinase B and phosphoinositide-dependent kinase-1 (PDK1) are recruited to the membrane by their PH domains where PDK1 phosphorylates and activates protein kinase B. One of the signal transduction pathways for Akt leads to the effects of insulin on glucose metabolism. Other pathways result in the phosphorylation of a host of other proteins that affect cell growth and survival. In general, phosphorylation of these proteins by Akt promotes cell survival. The action of insulin is covered in more detail in Chapters 26, 36, and 43. It is important to note that other receptor tyrosine kinase receptors will also lead to the activation of the Akt pathway, through the direct binding of PI 3-kinase to activated receptors (see Section III.B.2 of this chapter).

C. Signal Transduction by Cytokine Receptors: Use of JAK-STAT Proteins

Tyrosine kinase–associated receptors in the cytokine receptor family transduce signals through janus kinase (JAK)-STAT proteins to regulate the proliferation of certain cells involved in the immune response (see Fig. 11.9B). The receptors themselves have no intrinsic kinase activity but bind (associates with) a tyrosine kinase of the JAK family. Their signal transducer proteins, called STATs, are themselves gene-specific transcription factors. Thus, cytokine receptors utilize a more direct route for propagation of the signal to the nucleus than tyrosine kinase receptors.

Each receptor monomer has an extracellular domain, a membrane-spanning region, and an intracellular domain. As the cytokine binds to these receptors, they form dimers (either homodimers or heterodimers, between two distinct receptor molecules) and may cluster (Fig. 11.15). The activated receptor-associated tyrosine kinases phosphorylate each other on tyrosine residues and also phosphorylate tyrosine residues on the receptor, forming phosphotyrosine-binding sites for the SH2 domain of a STAT. STATs are inactive in the cytoplasm until they bind

FIG. 11.15.   Steps in cytokine receptor signaling.

to the receptor complex where they are also phosphorylated by the bound JAK. Phosphorylation changes the conformation of the STAT, causing it to dissociate from the receptor and dimerize with another phosphorylated STAT, thereby forming an activated transcription factor. The STAT dimer translocates to the nucleus and binds to a response element on DNA, thereby regulating gene transcription.

There are many different STAT proteins, each with a slightly different amino acid sequence. Receptors for different cytokines bind different STATs, which then form heterodimers in various combinations. This microheterogeneity allows different cytokines to target different genes. STAT signaling is regulated in several ways. Two prominent types are a protein family known as *suppressors of cytokine signaling* (SOCS) and protein inhibitors of activated STAT (PIAS). The regulation of expression of SOCS and PIAS is very complex and is an active area of current research.

D. Receptor Serine–Threonine Kinases

Proteins in the transforming growth factor superfamily use receptors that have serine–threonine kinase activity and associate with proteins from the Smad family, which are gene-specific transcription factors (see Fig. 11.9C). This superfamily includes transforming growth factor β (TGF-β), a cytokine/hormone involved in tissue repair, immune regulation, and cell proliferation, and bone morphogenetic proteins (BMPs), which control proliferation, differentiation, and cell death during development.

A simplified version of TGF-β binding to its receptor complex and activating Smads is illustrated in Figure 11.16. The TGF-β receptor complex is composed of two different single membrane-spanning receptor subunits (type I and type II),

FIG. 11.16.   Serine–threonine receptors and Smad proteins. TGF-β (transforming growth factor β), which is composed of two identical subunits, communicates through a receptor dimer of type I and type II subunits that have serine kinase domains. The type I receptor phosphorylates an R Smad (receptor-specific Smad), which binds a Co-Smad (common Smad, also called Smad 4). The Smad dimer then translocates to the nucleus to activate or inhibit the expression of target genes.

which have different functions even though they both have serine kinase domains. TGF-β binds to a type II receptor. The activated type II receptor recruits a type I receptor, which it phosphorylates at a serine residue, forming an activated receptor complex. The type I receptor then binds a receptor-specific Smad protein called an *R-Smad*, which it phosphorylates on serine residues. The phosphorylated R-Smad undergoes a conformational change and dissociates from the receptor. It then forms a complex with another member of the Smad family, Smad 4 (Smad 4 is known as the common Smad, *Co-Smad*, and is not phosphorylated). The Smad complex, which may contain several Smads, translocates to the nucleus where it activates or inhibits the transcription of target genes. Receptors for distinct ligands bind different Smads, which bind to alternative sites on DNA and regulate the transcription of different sets of genes. There is also an inhibitory Smad that is activated, which acts to regulate the extent of Smad activation (another example of signal termination).

E. Signal Transduction through Heptahelical Receptors

The heptahelical receptors are named for their seven membrane-spanning domains, which are α-helices (see Fig. 11.10; see also Fig. 7.9). Although hundreds of hormones and neurotransmitters work through heptahelical receptors, the extracellular binding domain of each receptor is specific for just one polypeptide hormone, catecholamine, or neurotransmitter (or a close structural analog). Heptahelical receptors have no intrinsic kinase activity but initiate signal transduction through heterotrimeric G proteins composed of α-, β-, and γ-subunits. However, different types of heptahelical receptors bind different G proteins, and different G proteins exert different effects on their target proteins.

1. HETEROTRIMERIC G PROTEINS

The basic scheme for activation of heterotrimeric G proteins is illustrated in Figure 11.17 using a hormone that activates adenylyl cyclase (e.g., glucagon or epinephrine) as an example. When the α-subunit contains bound GDP, it remains associated with the β- and γ-subunits, either free in the membrane or bound to an unoccupied receptor (see Fig. 11.17, part 1). When the hormone binds, it causes a conformational change in the receptor that promotes GDP dissociation and GTP binding. The exchange of GTP for bound GDP causes dissociation of the α-subunit from the receptor and from the β- and γ-subunits (see Fig. 11.17, part 2). The α- and γ-subunits are tethered to the intracellular side of the plasma membrane through lipid anchors, but they can still move around on the membrane surface. The GTP-α subunit binds its target enzyme in the membrane, thereby changing its activity. In this example, the α-subunit binds and activates adenylyl cyclase, thereby increasing synthesis of cAMP (see Fig. 11.17, part 3).

With time, the Gα-subunit inactivates itself by hydrolyzing its own bound GTP to GDP and P_i (inorganic phosphate) (an intrinsic GTPase activity). This action is unrelated to the number of cAMP molecules formed. Like the monomeric G proteins, the α-subunit now containing GDP then dissociates from its target protein, adenylyl cyclase (see Fig. 11.17, part 4). It reforms the trimeric G protein complex, which may return to bind the empty hormone receptor. Because of this GTPase "internal clock," continued activation of the receptor is necessary for continued signal transduction and elevation of cAMP. G proteins in which the internal clock has become defective (either through mutation or modification by toxins) can become permanently activated, thereby continuously stimulating their signal transduction pathway.

A large number of different heterotrimeric G protein complexes are generally categorized according to the activity of the α-subunit (Table 11.1). The 20 or so different isoforms of Gα fall into five broad categories: Gα_s, G$\alpha_{i/o}$, Gα_T, G$\alpha_{q/11}$, and G$\alpha_{12/13}$. Gα_s refers to α-subunits, which, like the one in Figure 11.17, stimulate adenylyl cyclase (hence the "s"). Gα-subunits that inhibit adenylyl cyclase are called Gα_i. The β- and γ-subunits likewise exist as different isoforms, which also transmit messages.

Acetylcholine has two types of receptors: nicotinic ion channel receptors, the receptors inhibited by antibodies in myasthenia gravis, and muscarinic receptors, which exist as various subtypes. The M2 muscarinic receptors activate a G$\alpha_{i/o}$ heterotrimeric G protein in which release of the $\beta\gamma$-subunit controls K$^+$ channels and pacemaker activity in the heart. Epinephrine has several types and subtypes of heptahelical receptors: β-adrenergic receptors work through a Gα_s and stimulate adenylyl cyclase; α_2-adrenergic receptors in other cells work through a Gα_i protein and inhibit adenylyl cyclase; α_1-adrenergic receptors work through Gα_q-subunits and activate phospholipase C$_\beta$. This variety in receptor types allows a messenger to have different actions in different cells.

FIG. 11.17. Serpentine receptors and heterotrimeric G proteins. **1.** The intracellular domains of the receptor form a binding site for a G protein that contains GDP bound to the α-subunit. **2.** Hormone binding to the receptor promotes the exchange of GTP for GDP. As a result, the complex disassembles, releasing the G protein α-subunit from the β–γ complex. **3.** The G_s α-subunit binds to a target enzyme (in the example shown, the target is adenylyl cyclase), thereby changing its activity (for the "s" G proteins, the activity is stimulated). The β–γ complex may simultaneously target another protein and change its activity. **4.** Over time, bound GTP is hydrolyzed to GDP, causing dissociation of the α-subunit from the target protein, thereby reducing the activity of the target protein. The GDP α-subunit reassociates with the $\beta\gamma$-subunit and the receptor.

2. ADENYLYL CYCLASE AND cAMP PHOSPHODIESTERASE

cAMP is referred to as a second messenger because changes in its concentration reflect changes in the concentration of the hormone (the first messenger). When a hormone binds and adenylyl cyclase is activated, it synthesizes cAMP from ATP. cAMP is hydrolyzed to AMP by cAMP phosphodiesterase, which also resides in

Table 11.1   Subunits of Heterotrimeric G Proteins

$G\alpha$-Subunit	Action	Some Physiologic Uses
α_s; $G\alpha(s)$[a]	Stimulates adenylyl cyclase	Glucagon and epinephrine to regulate metabolic enzymes, regulatory polypeptide hormones to control steroid hormone and thyroid hormone synthesis, and by some neurotransmitters (e.g., dopamine) to control ion channels
$\alpha_{i/o}$; $G\alpha(i/o)$ (signal also flows through $\beta\gamma$-subunits)	Inhibits adenylyl cyclase	Epinephrine; many neurotransmitters, including acetylcholine, dopamine, serotonin
α_t; $G\alpha(t)$	Stimulates cGMP phosphodiesterase	Has a role in the transduction pathway, which mediates detection of light in the eye
$\alpha_{q/11}$; $G\alpha(q/11)$	Activates phospholipase C_β	Epinephrine, acetylcholine, histamine, thyroid-stimulating hormone (TSH), interleukin-8, somatostatin, angiotensin
$\alpha_{12/13}$; $G\alpha(12/13)$	Activate Rho-GEF (guanine nucleotide exchange factor)	Thromboxane A2, lysophosphatidic acid act as signals to alter cytoskeletal elements

[a]There is a growing tendency to designate the heterotrimeric G protein subunits without using subscripts so that they are actually visible to the naked eye.

FIG. 11.18. Formation and cleavage of the cyclic phosphodiester bond in cAMP. When activated by $G\alpha_s$, adenylyl cyclase converts ATP to 3′,5′-cyclic AMP (cAMP) + PPi (pyrophosphate). cAMP phosphodiesterase hydrolyzes cAMP to 5′-AMP.

Dennis Veere was hospitalized for dehydration resulting from cholera toxin (see Chapter 10). The cholera toxin A subunit was absorbed into the intestinal mucosal cells where it was processed and complexed with ADP-ribosylation factor (Arf), a small G protein that is normally involved in vesicular transport. Cholera A toxin is a NAD-glycohydrolase, which cleaves NAD and transfers the ADP ribose portion to other proteins. The A toxin ADP-ribosylates the $G\alpha_s$-subunit of heterotrimeric G proteins, thereby inhibiting the GTPase activity of the G protein. As a consequence, the G proteins remain actively bound to adenylyl cyclase, resulting in increased production of cAMP. The cystic fibrosis transmembrane conductance regulator (CFTR) channel is activated, resulting in secretion of chloride ion and Na^+ ion into the intestinal lumen. The ion secretion is followed by loss of water, resulting in vomiting and watery diarrhea.

the plasma membrane (Fig. 11.18). The concentration of cAMP and other second messengers is kept at very low levels in cells by balancing the activity of these two enzymes (the cyclase and the phosphodiesterase) so that cAMP levels can change rapidly when hormone levels change. Some hormones change the concentration of cAMP by targeting the phosphodiesterase enzyme rather than adenylyl cyclase. For example, insulin lowers cAMP levels by causing phosphodiesterase activation.

cAMP exerts diverse effects in cells. It is an allosteric activator of protein kinase A (see Chapter 9, Section III.B.3), which is a serine–threonine protein kinase that phosphorylates a large number of enzymes, thereby providing a rapid response to hormones such as glucagon and epinephrine. Protein kinase A substrates range from phosphorylase kinase (regulation of glycogen degradation) to phospholamban (regulation of cardiac contractility). The catalytic subunits of protein kinase A also enter the nucleus and phosphorylate a gene-specific transcription factor called *cyclic AMP response element-binding protein* (CREB). Thus, cAMP also activates a slower response pathway, gene transcription. In other cell types, cAMP activates ligand-gated channels directly.

Some signaling pathways cross from the receptor tyrosine kinase pathway of MAP kinase activation to CREB activation, and the heterotrimeric G protein pathways diverge to include a route to the MAP kinase pathway. These types of complex interconnections in signaling pathways are sometimes called *hormone cross-talk*.

3. PHOSPHATIDYLINOSITOL SIGNALING BY HEPTAHELICAL RECEPTORS

Certain heptahelical receptors bind the q isoform of the $G\alpha$-subunit ($G\alpha_q$), which activates the target enzyme phospholipase C_β (see Fig.11.12). When it is activated, phospholipase C_β hydrolyzes the membrane lipid phosphatidylinositol bisphosphate (PI-4,5-bisP) into two second messengers, DAG and 1,4,5-IP$_3$. IP$_3$ has a binding site in the sarcoplasmic reticulum and the endoplasmic reticulum that stimulates the release of Ca^{2+}. Ca^{2+} activates enzymes containing the calcium–calmodulin subunit, including a protein kinase. DAG, which remains in the membrane, activates protein kinase C, which then propagates the response by phosphorylating target proteins.

F. Changes in Response to Signals

Tissues vary in their ability to respond to a message through changes in receptor activity or number. Many receptors contain intracellular phosphorylation sites that alter their ability to transmit signals. Receptor number is also varied through down-regulation. After a hormone binds to the receptor, the hormone–receptor complex may be taken into the cell by the process of endocytosis in clathrin-coated pits (see Chapter 10, Section II.D). The receptors may be degraded or recycled back to the cell surface. This internalization of receptors decreases the number available on the surface under conditions of constant high hormone levels when more of the receptors are occupied by hormones. Hence, it is called *downregulation*.

IV. SIGNAL TERMINATION

Some signals, such as those that modify the metabolic responses of cells or that transmit neural impulses, need to turn off rapidly when the hormone is no longer being produced. Other signals, such as those that stimulate proliferation, turn off more slowly. In contrast, signals that regulate differentiation may persist throughout the lifetime. Many chronic diseases are caused by failure to terminate a response at the appropriate time.

Signal transduction pathways can be terminated by various means (Fig. 11.19). The first level of termination is the chemical messenger itself. When the stimulus is no longer applied to the secreting cell, the messenger is no longer secreted, and the existing messenger is catabolized. For example, many polypeptide hormones such as insulin are taken up into the liver and degraded. Termination of the ACh signal by acetylcholinesterase has already been mentioned.

Within each pathway of signal transduction, the signal may be turned off at specific steps. For example, serpentine receptors can be desensitized to the messenger by phosphorylation, internalization, and degradation. G proteins, both monomeric and heterotrimeric, automatically terminate messages as they hydrolyze GTP via their intrinsic GTPase activity. Although G proteins do have intrinsic GTPase activity, this activity is relatively weak and can be accelerated through interaction with a class of proteins known as GAPs (GTPase activating proteins). Termination also can be achieved through degradation of the second messenger (e.g., phosphodiesterase cleavage of cAMP). Each of these terminating processes is also highly regulated.

Another important pathway for reversing the message typically utilized by receptor kinase pathways is through protein phosphatases, enzymes that reverse the action of kinases by removing phosphate groups from proteins. Specific tyrosine or serine–threonine phosphatases (enzymes that remove the phosphate group from specific proteins) exist for all of the sites that are phosphorylated by signal transduction kinases. To complicate matters, some receptors exhibit protein phosphatase activity.

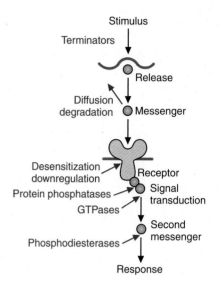

FIG. 11.19. Sites of signal termination. Processes that terminate signals are shown in *red*.

CLINICAL COMMENTS

  Mya Sthenia. Mya Sthenia has myasthenia gravis, an autoimmune disease caused by the production of antibodies directed against the nicotinic ACh receptor in skeletal muscles. The diagnosis is made by history (e.g., typical muscular symptoms), physical examination (i.e., inability to do specific repetitive muscular activity over time), and tests such as the inhibition of acetylcholinesterase activity. The diagnosis can be further confirmed with an electromyogram (EMG) showing a partial blockade of ion flux across muscular membranes and a diagnostic procedure involving repetitive electrical nerve stimulation.

M A laboratory test to confirm the diagnosis of myasthenia gravis uses the patient's sera as a source of antibodies directed against the acetylcholine (ACh) receptor. Human cell lines, grown in the laboratory and producing the ACh receptor, are used as a source of soluble receptor (the cells are lysed and a solubilized membrane fraction, which contains the receptor, is obtained). The soluble receptor is incubated with radioactively labeled α-bungarotoxin, which binds very specifically and tightly to the ACh receptor. A sample of the patient's sera is incubated with the bungarotoxin-receptor complex, and the extent to which antibodies bind to the receptor complex is determined. A positive result indicates anti-ACh receptor antibodies are in the sera.

Ann O'Rexia. Anorexia nervosa presents as a distorted visual self-image and is often associated with compulsive exercise. Although Ann has been gaining weight, she is still relatively low on stored fuels needed to sustain the metabolic requirements of exercise. Her prolonged starvation has resulted in release of the steroid hormone cortisol and the polypeptide hormone glucagon, whereas levels of the polypeptide hormone insulin have decreased. Cortisol activates transcription of genes for some of the enzymes of gluconeogenesis (the synthesis of glucose from amino acids and other precursors; see Chapter 3). Glucagon binds to heptahelical receptors in the liver and adipose tissue, working through cAMP and protein kinase A, and activates many enzymes involved in fasting fuel metabolism. Insulin, which is released when Ann drinks her high-energy supplement, works through a specialized tyrosine kinase receptor to promote fuel storage. *Epinephrine*, a catecholamine released when she exercises, promotes fuel mobilization.

 Dennis Veere. In the emergency room, Dennis received intravenous rehydration therapy (normal saline [0.9% NaCl]) and oral hydration therapy with a glucose-electrolyte solution to increase his glucose-dependent Na^+ uptake from the intestinal lumen (see Chapter 10). He was also given an antibiotic to decrease the duration of the diarrhea. Dennis quickly recovered from his bout of cholera. Cholera is self-limiting, possibly because the bacteria remain in the intestine, where they are washed out of the system by the diffuse watery diarrhea. Over the past 3 years, **Percy Veere** has persevered through the death of his wife and the subsequent calamities of his grandson, Dennis "the Menace" Veere, including salicylate poisoning, suspected malathion poisoning, and now cholera. Mr. Veere has decided to send his grandson home for the remainder of the summer.

BIOCHEMICAL COMMENTS

Guanylyl Cyclase Receptors. Membrane-bound guanylyl cyclase receptors convert GTP to the second messenger 3′,5′-cyclic GMP (cGMP), which is analogous to cAMP (Fig. 11.20). These receptors will directly synthesize cGMP in response to binding the appropriate ligand, unlike heptahelical receptors, which require G protein signaling to adenylyl cyclase to produce cAMP. Like cAMP, cGMP is degraded by a membrane-bound phosphodiesterase. Elevated cGMP activates protein kinase G, which then phosphorylates target proteins to propagate the response. To date, seven such receptors have been identified, although ligands for only four of the receptors have been positively confirmed.

A soluble form of guanylyl cyclase exists, located in the cytoplasm, and is a receptor for nitric oxide (NO), a neurotransmitter/neurohormone. NO is a lipophilic gas that is able to diffuse into the cell. Thus, this receptor is an exception to the rule that intracellular receptors are gene transcription factors. The membrane-bound receptors will bind atrial natriuretic peptides, brain natriuretic peptide, and C-type natriuretic peptide, as well as guanylin.

cGMP-elevating drugs have been used in humans to treat various disorders, such as angina pectoris (glycerol trinitrate decomposes to NO, which activates a guanylyl cyclase), heart failure (using nesiritide, which is synthetic β-natriuretic peptide, a ligand for activation of a guanylyl cyclase receptor), and erectile dysfunction (through drugs that inhibit a cGMP phosphodiesterase [designated PDE5], such as sildenafil).

Key Concepts

- To integrate cellular function with the needs of the organism, cells communicate with each other via chemical messengers. Chemical messengers include neurotransmitters (for the nervous system), hormones (for the endocrine system), cytokines (for the immune system), retinoids, eicosanoids, and growth factors.

FIG. 11.20. Structure of 3′,5′-cyclic GMP (cGMP).

Table 11.2   Diseases Discussed in Chapter 11

Disorder or Condition	Genetic or Environmental	Comments
Myasthenia gravis	Environmental	Autoantibodies to the acetylcholine receptor, leading to neuromuscular dysfunction.
Cholera	Environmental	Bacterial-derived toxin leads to disease, including hypovolemic shock. Treat with a glucose-electrolyte solution to increase coupled glucose-sodium uptake into the intestinal epithelial cells, reversing the loss of water from these cells.
Anorexia nervosa	Both	Effects of inadequate nutrition on hormone release and response. Cortisol, glucagon, and epinephrine levels are all increased under these conditions.

- Chemical messengers transmit their signals by binding to receptors on target cells. When a messenger binds to a receptor, a signal transduction pathway is activated, which generates second messengers within the cell.
- Receptors can be either plasma membrane proteins or intracellular binding proteins.
- Intracellular receptors act primarily as transcription factors, which regulate gene expression in response to a signal being released.
- Plasma membrane receptors fall into different classes, such as ion channel receptors, tyrosine kinase receptors, tyrosine kinase–associated receptors, serine–threonine kinase receptors, or G protein–coupled receptors (GPCRs), also known as serpentine receptors.
  - Ion channel receptors respond to a stimulus by allowing ion flux across the membrane.
  - Tyrosine kinase and tyrosine kinase–associated receptors respond to a stimulus through activation of a tyrosine kinase activity, which phosphorylates specific target proteins to elicit a cellular response.
  - Serine–threonine kinase receptors respond to a stimulus that activates a serine–threonine kinase, which then transmits signals through activation of Smad proteins, which are transcription factors.
  - GPCRs respond to a stimulus by activating a guanine nucleotide–binding protein (G protein), which, in its activated GTP-binding state, activates a target protein. G proteins contain intrinsic GTPase activity, thereby limiting the time for which they are active.
- Diseases discussed in this chapter are summarized in Table 11.2.

REVIEW QUESTIONS—CHAPTER 11

1. Which of the following is a general characteristic of all chemical messengers?

  A. They are secreted by one cell, enter the blood, and act on a distant target cell.

  B. To achieve a coordinated response, each messenger is secreted by several types of cells.

  C. Each messenger binds to a specific protein receptor in a target cell.

  D. Chemical messengers must enter cells to transmit their message.

  E. Chemical messengers are metabolized to intracellular second messengers to transmit their message.

2. Which of the following is a characteristic of chemical messengers that bind to intracellular transcription factor receptors?

  A. They are usually cytokines or polypeptide hormones.

  B. They are usually small-molecule neurotransmitters.

  C. They exert rapid actions in cells.

  D. They are transported through the blood bound to proteins.

  E. They are always present in high concentrations in the blood.

Use the following information to answer Questions 3 and 4. You do not need to know more about parathyroid hormone or pseudohypoparathyroidism than is in the information given.

   Pseudohypoparathyroidism is a heritable disorder caused by target-organ unresponsiveness to parathyroid hormone (a polypeptide hormone secreted by the parathyroid gland). One of the mutations that cause this disease occurs in the gene encoding $G_s\alpha$ in certain cells.

3. The receptor for parathyroid hormone is most likely which one of the following?

  A. An intracellular transcription factor

  B. A cytoplasmic guanylyl cyclase

C. A receptor that must be endocytosed in clathrin-coated pits to transmit its signal

D. A heptahelical receptor

E. A tyrosine kinase receptor

4. This mutation most likely has which one of the following characteristics?

A. It is a gain-of-function mutation.

B. It decreases the GTPase activity of the $G\alpha_s$-subunit.

C. It decreases synthesis of cAMP in response to parathyroid hormone.

D. It decreases generation of IP_3 in response to parathyroid hormone.

E. It decreases synthesis of phosphatidylinositol 3,4,5-trisphosphate in response to parathyroid hormone.

5. Techniques are available to allow one to introduce mutations in proteins at a selected amino acid residue (site-directed mutagenesis). Which step of the signal transduction pathway would be blocked if you created a tyrosine kinase receptor in which all of the tyrosine residues normally phosphorylated on the receptor were converted to phenylalanine residues?

A. GRB2 binding to the receptor to propagate the response.

B. Binding of the growth factor to the receptor.

C. Induction of a conformational change in the receptor upon growth factor binding.

D. Activation of the receptor's intrinsic tyrosine kinase activity.

E. Dimerization of the receptors.

Gene Expression and the Synthesis of Proteins

I n the middle of the 20th century, DNA was identified as the genetic material and its structure was determined. Using this knowledge, researchers then discovered the mechanisms by which genetic information is inherited and expressed. During the last quarter of the 20th century, our understanding of this critical area of science, known as *molecular biology*, grew at an increasingly rapid pace. We now have techniques to probe the human genome that will completely revolutionize the way medicine is practiced in the 21st century.

The genome of a cell consists of all its genetic information encoded in DNA (*d*eoxyribo*nucleic acid*). In eukaryotes, DNA is located mainly in nuclei, but small amounts are also found in mitochondria. Nuclear genes are packaged in chromosomes that contain DNA and protein in tightly coiled structures (Chapter 12).

The molecular mechanism of inheritance involves a process known as *replication*, in which the strands of parental DNA serve as templates for the synthesis of DNA copies (Fig. III.1) (Chapter 13). After DNA replication, cells divide, and these DNA copies are passed to daughter cells. Alterations in genetic material occur by *recombination* (the exchange of genetic material between chromosomes) and by *mutation* (the result of chemical changes that alter DNA). DNA repair mechanisms correct much of this damage, but, nevertheless, many gene alterations are passed to daughter cells.

The expression of genes within cells requires two processes: transcription and translation (see Fig. III.1) (Chapters 14 and 15). DNA is transcribed to produce ribonucleic acid (RNA). Three major types of RNA are transcribed from DNA and subsequently participate in the process of translation (the synthesis of proteins). Messenger RNA (mRNA) carries the genetic information from the nucleus to the cytoplasm, where translation occurs on ribosomes—structures that contain proteins complexed with ribosomal RNA (rRNA). Transfer RNA (tRNA) carries individual amino acids to the ribosomes, where they are joined in peptide linkage to form proteins. During translation, the sequence of nucleic acid bases in mRNA is read in sets of three (each set of three bases constitutes a codon). The sequence of codons in the mRNA dictates the sequence of amino acids in the protein. Proteins function in cell structure, signaling, and catalysis and, therefore, determine the appearance and behavior of cells and the organism as a whole. The regulation of gene expression (Chapter 16) determines which proteins are synthesized and the amount synthesized at any time, thus allowing cells to undergo development and differentiation and to respond to changing environmental conditions.

Research in molecular biology has produced a host of techniques, known collectively as *recombinant DNA technology*, *biotechnology*, or *genetic engineering* that can be used for the diagnosis and treatment of disease (Chapter 17). These techniques can detect several genetic diseases that previously could only be diagnosed after symptoms appeared. Diagnosis of these diseases can now be made with considerable accuracy even before birth, and carriers of these diseases also can be identified.

With recent developments in the field of gene therapy, diseases that for centuries have been considered hopeless are now potentially curable. Much of the therapy for

 Many drugs used in medicine to treat bacterial infections are targeted to interfere with the bacteria's ability to synthesize RNA and proteins. Thus, medical students need to know the basics of bacterial DNA replication, RNA synthesis, and protein synthesis to understand the mechanism of action of these drugs.

FIG. III.1. Replication, transcription, and translation. Replication: DNA serves as a template for producing DNA copies. Transcription: DNA serves as a template for the synthesis of RNA. Translation: RNA provides the information for the synthesis of proteins.

Ethical dilemmas have come together with technological advances in molecular biology. Consider the case of a patient with a mild case of ornithine transcarbamoylase deficiency, a urea-cycle defect that, if untreated, leads to elevated ammonia levels and nervous system dysfunction. The patient was being treated effectively by dietary restriction of protein. However, in 1999, he was treated with a common virus carrying the normal gene for ornithine transcarbamoylase. The patient developed a severe immune response to the virus and died as a result of the treatment. This case history raises the issues of appropriate patient consent, appropriate criteria to be included in this type of study, and the types of diseases for which gene therapy is appropriate. These are issues that are still applicable over 10 years after this unfortunate incident, and that you, the student, will be facing as you enter your practice of medicine.

 Tumors may be benign or malignant. A tumor is malignant if it invades locally or if cells break away from the tumor, enter the bloodstream, and travel to other parts of the body where they establish new growths (a process called *metastasis*), resulting in destruction of the tissues they invade. Many of the drugs used to treat malignant tumors are directed toward inhibition of DNA replication. These chemotherapeutic drugs are more toxic to cancer cells than normal cells, because the cancer cells divide more rapidly. However, such drugs also may inhibit normal rapidly dividing cells such as the cells of the bone marrow (causing a decrease in white blood cell count) or cells in the hair follicles (resulting in hair loss during chemotherapy).

these diseases is currently experimental. However, during the 21st century, physicians may be using genetic engineering techniques routinely for both the diagnosis and treatment of their patients.

Replication and cell division are highly regulated processes in the human. *Cancer* is a group of diseases in which a cell in the body has been transformed and begins to grow and divide out of control (Chapter 18). It results from multiple mutations or changes in DNA structure in the genes that activate cell growth, called *proto-oncogenes*, and those that ensure that DNA replication and repair are normal, called *growth-suppressor* or *tumor-suppressor genes*. Mutations that activate proto-oncogenes to oncogenes disturb the regulation of the cell cycle and the rate of cell proliferation. Mutations that disrupt tumor-suppressor genes lead to an increased incidence of these proto-oncogene–activating mutations. Such mutations may be inherited, causing a predisposition to a type of cancer. They also may arise from DNA replication or copying errors that remain uncorrected, from chemicals or radiation that damages DNA, from translocation of pieces of chromosomes from one chromosome to another during replication, or from incorporation of viral-encoded DNA into the genome.

12 Structure of the Nucleic Acids

Nucleotides in DNA and RNA. Nucleotides *are the monomeric units of the nucleic acids, DNA (**d**eoxyribo**n**ucleic **a**cid) and RNA (**r**ibo**n**ucleic **a**cid). Each nucleotide consists of a heterocyclic **nitrogenous base**, a **sugar**, and **phosphate**. DNA contains the purine bases, **adenine** (A) and **guanine** (G), and the pyrimidine bases, **cytosine** (C) and **thymine** (T). RNA contains A, G, and C, but it has **uracil** (U) instead of thymine. In DNA, the sugar is **deoxyribose**, whereas in RNA, it is **ribose**.*

*Polynucleotides such as DNA and RNA are linear sequences of nucleotides linked by **3'- to 5'-phosphodiester bonds** between the sugars (Fig. 12.1). The bases of the nucleotides can interact with other bases or with proteins.*

DNA Structure. *Genetic information is encoded by the sequence of different nucleotide bases in DNA. **DNA** is **double stranded**; it contains **two antiparallel polynucleotide strands**. The two strands are joined by hydrogen bonding between their bases to form **base pairs**. **Adenine** pairs with **thymine**, and **guanine** pairs with **cytosine**. The two DNA strands run in **opposite directions**. One strand runs 5' to 3', and the other strand runs 3' to 5'. The two DNA strands wind around each other forming a **double helix**.*

*Transcription of a gene generates a **single-stranded RNA** that is identical in nucleotide sequence to one of the strands of the duplex DNA. The three major types of RNA are **messenger RNA** (mRNA), **ribosomal RNA** (rRNA), and **transfer RNA** (tRNA).*

RNA Structures. mRNAs *contain the nucleotide sequence that is converted into the amino acid sequence of a protein in the process of translation. Eukaryotic mRNA has a structure known as a **cap** at the 5'-end, a sequence of adenine nucleotides (a **poly[A] tail**) at the 3'-end, and a **coding region** in between containing **codons** that dictate the sequence of amino acids in a protein or relay a signal. Each codon in the genetic code is a different sequence of three nucleotides.*

*rRNAs and tRNAs are part of the apparatus for protein synthesis, but they do not encode proteins. **rRNA** has **extensive internal base pairing** and complexes with proteins to form **ribonucleoprotein particles** called **ribosomes**. The ribosomes bind mRNA and tRNAs during translation. Each **tRNA** binds and **activates a specific amino acid** for insertion into the polypeptide chain and therefore has a somewhat different nucleotide sequence than other tRNAs. A unique trinucleotide sequence on each tRNA called an **anticodon** binds to a complementary codon on the mRNA, thereby ensuring insertion of the correct amino acid. In spite of their differences, all tRNAs contain several unusual nucleotides and assume a similar **cloverleaf** structure.*

FIG. 12.1. Structure of a polynucleotide. The 5'-carbon of the top sugar and the 3'-carbon of the bottom sugar are indicated. Because the sugar is ribose, this is an example of RNA.

An *adenoma* is a mass of rapidly proliferating cells, called a *neoplasm* (neo = new; plasm = growth), that is formed from epithelial cells growing into a glandlike structure. The cells lining all the external and internal organs are epithelial cells, and most human tumors are adenocarcinomas. *Adenomatous polyps* are adenomas that grow into the lumen of the colon or rectum. The term *malignant* applied to a neoplasm refers to invasive unregulated growth. **Colin Tuma** has an adenocarcinoma, which is a malignant adenoma that has started to grow through the wall of the colon into surrounding tissues. Cells from adenocarcinomas can break away and spread through the blood or lymph to other parts of the body, where they form "colony" tumors. This process is called *metastasis*.

 The *Gram stain* is a standard laboratory test that can be used to determine what type of bacteria is present in an infection. The test is based on the cell wall of the bacteria trapping a specific dye (crystal violet). Gram-positive bacteria, which trap the dye, have a thicker cell wall than gram-negative bacteria, which exclude the dye. Gram-positive and gram-negative bacteria have differences in the sugar and protein composition of their outer cell walls, as well as the lipid components associated with the cell walls. Because of these differences in cell wall structure, antibiotics will affect each class of bacteria differently. Typing the bacteria using the Gram stain should allow the appropriate treatment options for the patient to be better determined.

THE WAITING ROOM

 Ivy Sharer is a 26-year-old intravenous (IV) drug user who has shared needles with another addict for several years. Five months before presenting to the emergency department with soaking night sweats, she experienced a 3-week course of a flulike syndrome with fever, malaise, and muscle aches. Four months ago, she noted generalized lymph node enlargement associated with chills, anorexia, and diarrhea, which led to a 22-lb weight loss. Tests were positive for human immunodeficiency virus (HIV). Because of her symptoms and a low CD4 count (indicating a decreased number of one class of circulating T lymphocytes), a multidrug regimen including zidovudine (ZDV), formerly called azidothymidine (AZT), was initiated.

Colin Tuma had two intestinal polyps at age 50, which were removed via a colonoscope. However, he did not return for a 5-year colonoscopic examination as instructed. At age 59, he reappeared, complaining of maroon-colored stools, an indication of intestinal bleeding. The source of the blood loss was an adenocarcinoma growing from a colonic polyp of the large intestine. At surgery, it was found that the tumor had invaded the gut wall and perforated the visceral peritoneum. Several pericolic lymph nodes contained cancer cells, and several small nodules of metastatic cancer were found in the liver. After resection of the tumor, the oncologist began treatment with 5-fluorouracil (5-FU) combined with other chemotherapeutic agents.

Newman Itis complains to his physician of a fever and cough. His cough produces thick yellow-brown sputum. He is empirically started on azithromycin for community-acquired pneumonia. A stain of his sputum shows many gram-positive diplococci. A sputum culture confirms that he has a respiratory infection in this case caused by *Streptococcus pneumoniae*.

I. DNA STRUCTURE
A. Location of DNA

DNA and RNA serve as the genetic material for prokaryotic and eukaryotic cells, for viruses, and for plasmids, each of which stores it in a different arrangement or location. In prokaryotes, DNA is not separated from the rest of the cellular contents. In eukaryotes, however, DNA is located in the nucleus, where it is separated from the rest of the cell by the nuclear envelope (see Fig. 10.14). Eukaryotic DNA is bound to proteins, forming a complex called *chromatin*. During interphase (when cells are not dividing), some of the chromatin is diffuse (euchromatin) and some is dense (heterochromatin), but no distinct structures can be observed. However, before mitosis (when cells divide), the DNA is replicated, resulting in two identical chromosomes called *sister chromatids*. During metaphase (a period in mitosis), these condense into discrete, visible chromosomes.

DNA is a double-stranded molecule that forms base pairs, via hydrogen bonding, between strands (see the following). The base pairs designation is often used to indicate the size of a DNA molecule. For example, in a stretch of DNA 200 base pairs long, both strands are included, with 200 bases in each strand, for a total of 400 bases.

Less than 0.1% of the total DNA in a cell is present in mitochondria. The genetic information in a mitochondrion is encoded in <20,000 base pairs of DNA; the information in a human haploid nucleus (i.e., an egg or a sperm cell) is encoded in approximately 3×10^9 (3 billion) base pairs. The DNA and protein-synthesizing systems in mitochondria more closely resemble the systems in bacteria, which do not have membrane-enclosed organelles, than they do to those in the eukaryotic nucleus and cytoplasm. It has been suggested that mitochondria were derived from ancient bacterial invaders of primordial eukaryotic cells.

Viruses are small infectious particles consisting of a DNA or RNA genome (but not both), proteins (required for pathogenesis and/or replication), and a protein coat. They lack, however, complete systems for replication, transcription, and translation, and consequently, viruses must invade other cells and commandeer their DNA, RNA, and protein-synthesizing machinery to reproduce. Both eukaryotes and prokaryotes can be infected by viruses. Viruses that infect bacteria are known as *bacteriophage* (or more simply as *phage*).

Plasmids are small, circular DNA molecules that can enter bacteria and replicate autonomously, that is, outside the host genome. In contrast to viruses, plasmids are not infectious; they do not convert their host cells into factories devoted to plasmid production. Plasmids do, however, often carry genes, some of which confer resistance to antibiotics. Genetic engineers use plasmids as tools for transfer of foreign genes into bacteria because segments of DNA can readily be incorporated into plasmids.

B. Determination of the Structure of DNA

In 1865, Frederick Miescher first isolated DNA, obtaining it from pus scraped from surgical bandages. Initially, scientists speculated that DNA was a cellular storage form for inorganic phosphate, an important but unexciting function that did not spark widespread interest in determining its structure. In fact, the details of DNA structure were not fully determined until 1953, almost 90 years after it had first been isolated, but only 9 years after it had been identified as the genetic material.

Early in the 20th century, the bases of DNA were identified as the purines adenine (A) and guanine (G), and the pyrimidines cytosine (C) and thymine (T) (Fig. 12.2). The sugar was found to be deoxyribose, a derivative of ribose, lacking a hydroxyl group on carbon 2 (see Fig. 12.2).

Nucleotides, composed of a base, a sugar, and phosphate, were found to be the monomeric units of the nucleic acids (Table 12.1). In nucleosides, the nitrogenous base is linked by an *N*-glycosidic bond to the anomeric carbon of the sugar, either ribose or deoxyribose. A nucleotide is a nucleoside with an inorganic phosphate attached to a 5′-hydroxyl group of the sugar in ester linkage (Fig. 12.3). The names and abbreviations of nucleotides specify the base, the sugar, and the number of phosphates attached (MP, *mono*phosphate; DP, *di*phosphate; TP, *tri*phosphate). In deoxynucleotides, the prefix "d" precedes the abbreviation. For example, GDP is guanosine diphosphate (the base guanine attached to a ribose that has two phosphate

A. Purines

Adenine (A)

Guanine (G)

Pyrimidines

Cytosine (C)

Thymine (T)

B.

Deoxyribose

Table 12.1 Names of Bases and Their Corresponding Nucleosides[a]

Base	Nucleoside
Adenine (A)	Adenosine
Guanine (G)	Guanosine
Cytosine (C)	Cytidine
Thymine (T)	Thymidine
Uracil (U)	Uridine
Hypoxanthine (I)	Inosine[b]

[a]If the sugar is deoxyribose rather than ribose, the nucleoside has "deoxy" as a prefix (e.g., deoxyadenosine). Nucleotides are given the name of the nucleoside plus monophosphate, diphosphate, or triphosphate (e.g., adenosine triphosphate or deoxyadenosine triphosphate).

[b]The base hypoxanthine is not found in DNA but is produced during degradation of the purine bases. It is found in certain tRNA molecules. Its nucleoside, inosine, is produced during synthesis of the purine nucleotides (see Chapter 41).

FIG. 12.2. A. Purine and pyrimidine bases in DNA. **B.** Deoxyribose and ribose, the sugars of DNA and RNA. The carbon atoms are numbered from 1 to 5. When the sugar is attached to a base, the carbon atoms are numbered from 1′ to 5′ to distinguish it from the base. In deoxyribose, the X = H; in ribose, the X = OH.

FIG. 12.3. Nucleoside and nucleotide structures. Shown with ribose as the sugar. The corresponding deoxyribonucleotides are abbreviated dNMP, dNDP, and dNTP. N, = any base (A, G, C, U, or T).

After **Ivy Sharer** was diagnosed with AIDS, she was treated with a mixture of drugs, including zidovudine (ZDV), formerly called azidothymidine (AZT). This drug is an analog of the thymine nucleotide found in DNA (the modified group is shown in the dashed box). ZDV is phosphorylated in the body by the kinases that normally phosphorylate nucleosides and nucleotides. As the viral DNA chain is being synthesized in a human cell, ZDV is then added to the growing 3'-end by viral reverse transcriptase. However, ZDV lacks a 3'-OH group, and therefore no additional nucleotides can be attached through a $5' \rightarrow 3'$-bond. Thus, chain elongation of the DNA is terminated. Reverse transcriptase has a higher affinity for ZDV than does normal human cellular DNA polymerases, enabling the drug to target viral replication more specifically than cellular replication.

ZDV,
an analog of deoxythymidine

groups), and dATP is deoxyadenosine triphosphate (the base adenine attached to a deoxyribose with three phosphate groups).

In 1944, after Oswald Avery's experiments establishing DNA as the genetic material were published, interest in determining the structure of DNA intensified. Digestion with enzymes of known specificity proved that inorganic phosphate joined the nucleotide monomers, forming a phosphodiester bond between the 3'-carbon of one sugar and the 5'-carbon of the next sugar along the polynucleotide chain (Fig. 12.4). Another key to DNA structure was provided by Erwin Chargaff. He analyzed the base composition of DNA from various sources and concluded that, on a molar basis, the amount of adenine was always equal to the amount of thymine, and the amount of guanine was equal to the amount of cytosine.

During this era, James Watson and Francis Crick joined forces and, using the X-ray diffraction data of Maurice Wilkins and Rosalind Franklin, incorporated the available information into a model for DNA structure. In 1953, they published a brief article (approximately 900 words) describing DNA as a double helix consisting of two polynucleotide strands joined by pairing between the bases (adenine with thymine and guanine with cytosine). The model of base pairing they proposed and the implications of the model for understanding DNA replication formed the basis of modern molecular biology.

C. Concept of Base Pairing

As proposed by Watson and Crick, each DNA molecule consists of two polynucleotide chains joined by hydrogen bonds between the bases. In each base pair, a purine on one strand forms hydrogen bonds with a pyrimidine on the other strand. In one type of base pair, adenine on one strand pairs with thymine on the other strand (Fig. 12.5). This base pair is stabilized by two hydrogen bonds. The other base pair, formed between guanine and cytosine, is stabilized by three hydrogen bonds. As a consequence of base pairing, the two strands of DNA are complementary; that is, adenine on one strand corresponds to thymine on the other strand, and guanine corresponds to cytosine.

The concept of base pairing proved to be essential for determining the mechanism of DNA replication (in which the copies of DNA are produced that are distributed to daughter cells) and the mechanisms of transcription and translation (in which mRNA is produced from genes and used to direct the process of protein

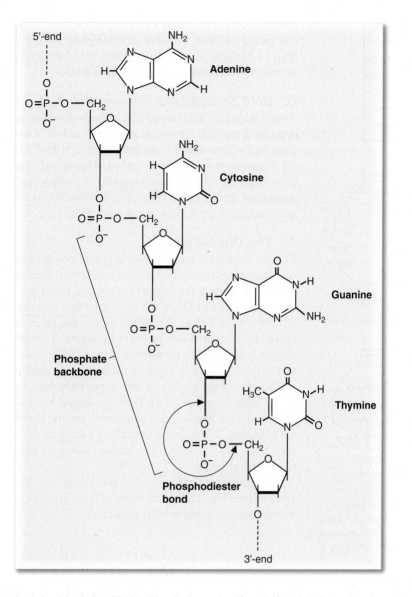

FIG. 12.4. A segment of a polynucleotide chain of DNA. The *dashes* at the 5′- and 3′-ends indicate that the molecule contains more nucleotides than are shown.

FIG. 12.5. Base pairs of DNA. Note that the purine bases are "flipped over" from the positions in which they are usually shown (see Fig. 12.4). The bases must be in this orientation to form base pairs. The *dotted lines* indicate hydrogen bonds between the bases. Although the hydrogen bonds hold the bases and thus the two DNA strands together, they are weaker than covalent bonds and allow the DNA strands to separate during replication and transcription.

FIG. 12.6. DNA strands serve as templates. During replication, the strands of the helix separate in a localized region. Each parental strand serves as a template for the synthesis of a new DNA strand.

synthesis). As Watson and Crick implied in their classic article, base pairing allows one strand of DNA to serve as a template for the synthesis of the other strand (Fig. 12.6). Base pairing also allows a strand of DNA to serve as a template for the synthesis of a complementary strand of RNA.

D. DNA Strands Are Antiparallel

As concluded by Watson and Crick, the two complementary strands of DNA run in opposite directions. On one strand, the 5′-carbon of the sugar is above the 3′-carbon (Fig. 12.7). This strand is said to run in a 5′-to-3′ direction. On the other strand, the 3′-carbon is above the 5′-carbon. This strand is said to run in a 3′-to-5′ direction. Thus, the strands are antiparallel (i.e., they run in opposite directions). This concept of directionality of nucleic acid strands is essential for understanding the mechanisms of replication and transcription.

E. The Double Helix

Because each base pair contains a purine bonded to a pyrimidine, the strands are equidistant from each other throughout. If two strands that are equidistant from each other are twisted at the top and the bottom, they form a double helix (Fig. 12.8). In the double helix of DNA, the base pairs that join the two strands are stacked like a spiral staircase along the central axis of the molecule. The stacked bases are stabilized by van der Waals interactions and the hydrophobic effect (the hydrophobic portion of the bases in the interior of the helix exclude water). These forces, in addition to the hydrogen bonding of the base pairs, stabilize the helix.

The phosphate groups of the sugar–phosphate backbones are on the outside of the helix (see Fig. 12.8). Each phosphate has two oxygen atoms forming the phosphodiester bonds that link adjacent sugars. However, the third –OH group on the phosphate is free and dissociates a hydrogen ion at physiologic pH. Therefore, each DNA helix has negative charges coating its surface that facilitate the binding of specific proteins.

The helix contains grooves of alternating size, known as the *major and minor grooves* (see Fig. 12.8). The bases in these grooves are exposed and therefore can interact with proteins or other molecules.

Multidrug regimens used to treat cancers (e.g., lymphomas) sometimes include the drug doxorubicin (Adriamycin). It is a natural product with a complex multiring structure that intercalates or slips in between the stacked base pairs of DNA and inhibits replication and transcription.

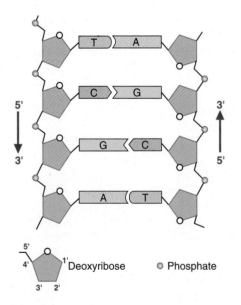

FIG. 12.7. Antiparallel strands of DNA. For the strand on the left, the 5′-carbon of each sugar is above the 3′-carbon, so it runs 5′ to 3′. For the strand on the right, the 3′-carbon of each sugar is above the 5′-carbon, so it runs 3′ to 5′.

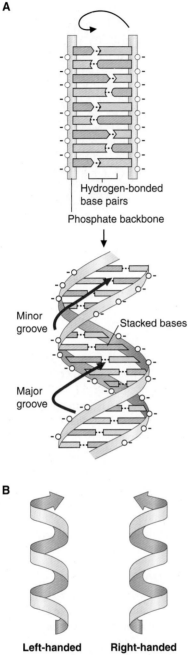

A

Hydrogen-bonded base pairs

Phosphate backbone

Minor groove

Stacked bases

Major groove

B

Left-handed   **Right-handed**

FIG. 12.8.   **A.** Two DNA strands twist to form a double helix. The distance between the two phosphodiester backbones is about 11 Å. The hydrogen-bonded base pairs, shown bonded by *dotted lines*, create stacking forces with adjacent base pairs. Each phosphate group contains one negatively charged oxygen atom that provides the phosphodiester backbone with a negative charge. Because of the twisting of the helix, grooves are formed along the surface, the larger one being the major groove and the smaller one being the minor groove. **B.** If you look up through the bottom of a helix along the central axis and the helix spirals away from you in a clockwise direction (toward the arrowhead in the drawing), it is a right-handed helix. If it spirals away from you in a counterclockwise direction, it is a left-handed helix.

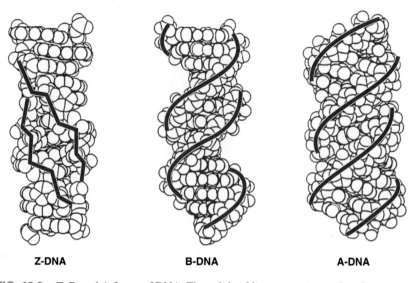

Z-DNA   **B-DNA**   **A-DNA**

FIG. 12.9.   Z, B, and A forms of DNA. The *solid red lines* connect one phosphate group to the next. (Modified from Saenger W. *Principles of Nucleic Acid Structure.* New York, NY: Springer-Verlag; 1984:257–286.)

Watson and Crick described the B form of DNA, a right-handed helix, with 3.4 Å between base pairs and 10.4 base pairs per turn. Although this form predominates in vivo, other forms also occur (Fig. 12.9). The A form, which predominates in DNA–RNA hybrids, is similar to the B form but is more compact (2.3 Å between base pairs and 11 base pairs per turn). In the Z form, the bases of the two DNA strands are positioned toward the periphery of a left-handed helix. There are 3.8 Å between base pairs and 12 base pairs per turn in Z-DNA. This form of the helix was designated "Z" because, in each strand, a line connecting the phosphates "zigs" and "zags" (see Fig. 12.9). Z-DNA is formed transiently in cells and can be stabilized by specific Z-DNA–binding proteins. Z-DNA formation has been linked to transcriptional initiation (the initiation of RNA synthesis from the DNA template); however, its physiologic significance is still elusive. For the rest of this text, we will focus only on B-DNA.

F. Characteristics of DNA

Both alkali and heat cause the two strands of the DNA helix to separate (denature). Many techniques employed to study and analyze DNA or to produce recombinant DNA molecules make use of this property. Although alkali causes the two strands of DNA to separate, it does not break the phosphodiester bonds (Fig. 12.10). In contrast, the phosphodiester bonds of RNA are cleaved by alkali, because of the hydroxyl group on the 2′-carbon losing its proton, allowing the negatively charged oxygen to attack and break the phosphodiester linkage. Therefore, alkali is used to remove RNA from DNA and to separate DNA strands before or after electrophoresis (separation by size in an electric field) on polyacrylamide or agarose gels.

Heat alone converts double-stranded DNA to single-stranded DNA. The separation of strands is called *melting*, and the temperature at which 50% of the DNA is separated is called the T_m. If the temperature is slowly decreased, complementary single strands can realign and base-pair, reforming a double helix that is essentially identical to the original DNA. This process is known as *renaturation*, *reannealing*, or *hybridization*. The process by which a single-stranded DNA anneals with complementary strands of RNA is also called *hybridization* (Fig. 12.11). Hybridization is used extensively in research and clinical testing (see Chapter 17).

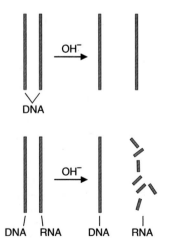

FIG. 12.10.   Effect of alkali on DNA and RNA. DNA strands stay intact but they separate. RNA strands are degraded to nucleotides.

II. STRUCTURE OF CHROMOSOMES

A. Size of DNA Molecules

A prokaryotic cell generally contains a single chromosome composed of double-stranded DNA that forms a circle. These circular DNA molecules are extremely large. The entire chromosome of the bacterium *Escherichia coli,* composed of a single, circular double-stranded DNA molecule, contains $>4 \times 10^6$ base pairs. Its molecular weight is $>2,500 \times 10^6$ g/mol (compared to the molecular weight for a glucose molecule of 180 g/mol). If this molecule were linear, its length would measure almost 2 mm.

DNA from eukaryotic cells is approximately 1,000 times larger than that from bacterial cells. In eukaryotes, each chromosome contains one continuous, linear DNA helix. The DNA of the longest human chromosome is >7 cm in length. In fact, if the DNA from all 46 chromosomes in a diploid human cell were placed end to end, our total DNA would span a distance of about 2 m (>6 ft). Our total DNA contains about 6×10^9 base pairs.

B. Packaging of DNA

DNA molecules require special packaging to enable them to reside within cells because the molecules are so large. In *E. coli*, the circular DNA is supercoiled and attached to an RNA-protein core. Recall that DNA consists of a double helix, with the two strands of DNA wrapping around each other to form a helical structure. To compact, the DNA molecule coils about itself to form a structure called a *supercoil.* A telephone cord, which connects the handpiece to the phone, displays supercoiling when the coiled cord wraps about itself. When the strands of a DNA molecule separate and unwind over a small local region (which occurs during DNA replication), supercoils are introduced into the remaining portion of the molecule, thereby increasing stress on this portion of the DNA. Enzymes known as *topoisomerases* relieve this stress so that unwinding of the DNA strands can occur. This will be discussed in greater detail in Chapter 13.

Packaging of eukaryotic DNA is much more complex than that of prokaryotic DNA because eukaryotic DNA is larger and must be contained within the nucleus of the cell. Eukaryotic DNA binds to an equal weight of histones, which are small basic proteins containing large amounts of arginine and lysine. The complex of DNA and proteins is called *chromatin.* The organization of eukaryotic DNA into chromatin is essential for controlling transcription as well as for packaging. When chromatin is extracted from cells, it has the appearance of beads on a string (Fig. 12.12). The beads with DNA protruding from each end are known as *nucleosomes*, and the beads themselves are known as *nucleosome cores* (Fig. 12.13). Two molecules of each of four core histone classes (histones H2A, H2B, H3, and H4) form the center of the core around which approximately 140 base pairs of double-stranded DNA are wound. The DNA wrapped around the nucleosome core is continuous and joins one nucleosome core to the next. The DNA joining the cores is complexed with the fifth type of histone, H1. Further compaction of chromatin occurs as the strings of nucleosomes wind into helical, tubular coils called *solenoid structures.*

Although complexes of DNA and histones form the nucleosomal substructures of chromatin, other types of proteins are also associated with DNA in the nucleus. These proteins were given the unimaginative name of "nonhistone chromosomal proteins." The cells of different tissues contain different amounts and types of these proteins, which include enzymes that act on DNA and factors that regulate transcription.

C. The Human Genome

The *genome*, or total genetic content, of a human haploid cell (a sperm or an egg) is distributed in 23 chromosomes. Haploid cells contain one copy of each chromosome. The haploid egg and haploid sperm cells combine to form the diploid zygote, which

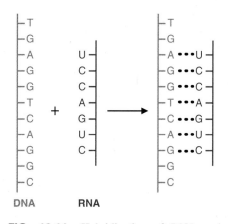

FIG. 12.11. Hybridization of DNA and complementary RNA.

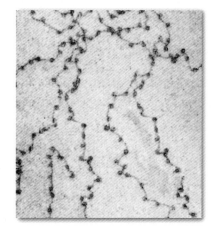

FIG. 12.12. Chromatin showing "beads on a string" structure.

 If histones contain large amounts of arginine and lysine, will their net charge be positive or negative?

At physiologic pH, arginine and lysine carry positive charges on their side chains; therefore, histones have a net positive charge. The arginine and lysine residues are clustered in regions of the histone molecules. These positively charged regions of the histones interact with the negatively charged DNA phosphate groups.

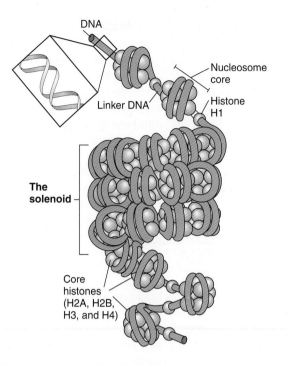

FIG. 12.13. A polynucleosome, indicating the histone cores and linker DNA. The DNA is depicted in *blue*, whereas the histones are depicted as *light brown* spheres.

continues to divide to form our other cells (mitosis), which are diploid. Diploid cells thus contain 22 pairs of autosomal chromosomes, with each pair composed of two homologous chromosomes containing a similar series of genes (Fig. 12.14). In addition to the autosomal chromosomes, each diploid cell has two sex chromosomes, designated X and Y. A female has two X chromosomes, and a male has one X and one Y chromosome. The total number of chromosomes per diploid cell is 46.

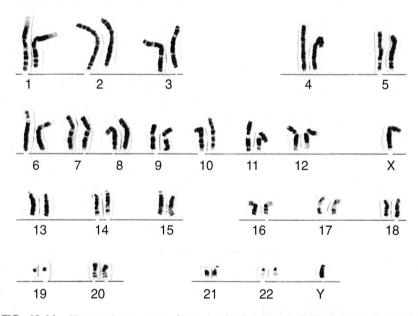

FIG. 12.14. Human chromosomes from a male diploid cell. Each diploid cell contains 22 pairs of autosomes (the numbered chromosomes 1 through 22) plus one X and one Y. Each female diploid cell contains two X chromosomes. Each haploid cell contains chromosomes 1 through 22 plus either an X or a Y. (From Gelehrter TD, Collins FS, Ginsburg D. *Principles of Human Genetics*. 2nd ed. Baltimore, MD: Williams & Wilkins; 1998:18.)

Genes are arranged linearly along each chromosome. A *gene*, in genetic terms, is the fundamental unit of heredity. In structural terms, a gene encompasses the DNA sequence that encodes the structural components of the gene product (whether it be a polypeptide chain or RNA molecule) along with the DNA sequences adjacent to the 5′-end of the gene that regulates its expression. A genetic locus is a specific position or location on a chromosome. Each gene on a chromosome in a diploid cell is matched by an alternate version of the gene at the same genetic locus on the homologous chromosome (Fig. 12.15). These alternate versions of a gene are called *alleles*. We thus have two alleles of each gene, one from our mother and one from our father. If the alleles are identical in base sequence, we are homozygous for this gene. If the alleles differ, we are heterozygous for this gene and may produce two versions of the encoded protein that differ somewhat in primary structure.

The genomes of prokaryotic and eukaryotic cells differ in size. The genome of the bacterium *E. coli* contains approximately 3,000 genes. All of this bacterial DNA has a function; it either codes for proteins, rRNA, and tRNA, or it serves to regulate the synthesis of these gene products. In contrast, the genome of the human haploid cell contains between 20,000 and 25,000 genes, seven to eight times the number in *E. coli*. The function of most of this extra DNA has not been determined (an issue considered in more detail in Chapter 16).

III. STRUCTURE OF RNA
A. General Features of RNA

RNA is similar to DNA. Like DNA, it is composed of nucleotides joined by 3′- to 5′-phosphodiester bonds, the purine bases adenine and guanine, and the pyrimidine base cytosine. However, its other pyrimidine base is uracil rather than thymine. Uracil and thymine are identical bases except that thymine has a methyl group at position 5 of the ring (Fig. 12.16). In RNA, the sugar is ribose, which contains a hydroxyl group on the 2′-carbon (see Fig. 12.3; the *prime* refers to the position on the ribose ring). As indicated previously, the presence of the 2′-hydroxyl is what renders RNA susceptible to alkaline hydrolysis.

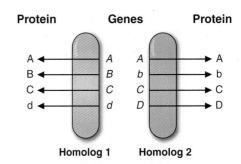

FIG. 12.15. Homologous chromosomes and their protein products. A set of homologous chromosomes is shown diagrammatically. (Of course, during interphase, when they are producing their protein products, they cannot be visualized as discrete entities.) Four genes are shown as examples on each homolog. The genes of the homologs are alleles (e.g., *AA*, *Bb*, *CC*, *dD*). They may be identical (e.g., *AA*, *CC*) or they may differ (e.g., *Bb*, *dD*) in DNA sequence. Thus, the corresponding protein products may be identical or they may differ in amino acid sequence.

Will Sichel has sickle cell anemia (see Chapters 6 and 7). He has two alleles for the β-globin gene that both generate the mutated form of hemoglobin, sickle hemoglobin (HbS). His younger sister Amanda, a carrier for sickle cell trait, has one normal allele (which produces adult hemoglobin [HbA]) and one that produces HbS. A carrier would theoretically be expected to produce HbA:HbS in a 50:50 ratio. However, what is generally seen in electrophoresis is 60:40 ratio of HbA:HbS. Dramatic deviations from this ratio imply the occurrence of an additional hemoglobin mutation (e.g., thalassemia).

FIG. 12.16. **A.** Comparison of the structures of uracil and thymine. They differ in structure only by a methyl group, outlined in the *yellow* box. **B.** A uracil–adenine base pair in RNA.

Colin Tuma's original benign adenomatous polyp was located in the ascending colon, where 10% of large bowel cancers eventually arise. Because Mr. Tuma's father died of a cancer of the colon, his physician had warned him that his risk of developing colon cancer was three times higher than for the general population. Unfortunately, Mr. Tuma neglected to have annual colonoscopic examinations as recommended, and he developed an adenocarcinoma that metastasized.

Mr. Tuma is being treated with 5-fluorouracil (5-FU), a pyrimidine base similar to uracil and thymine. 5-FU inhibits the synthesis of thymine nucleotides required for DNA replication. Thymine is normally produced by a reaction catalyzed by thymidylate synthase, an enzyme that converts deoxyuridine monophosphate (dUMP) to deoxythymidine monophosphate (dTMP). 5-FU is converted in the body to 5-FdUMP, which binds tightly to thymidylate synthase in a transition-state complex and inhibits the reaction (recall that thymine is 5-methyluracil). Thus, thymine nucleotides cannot be generated for DNA synthesis, and the rate of tumor cell proliferation is greatly reduced.

**5-Fluorouracil (5-FU),
an analogue of uracil or thymine**

5-FU $\longrightarrow$ F-dUMP

dUMP $\longrightarrow$ ■ $\longrightarrow$ dTMP $\longrightarrow$ dTTP $\longrightarrow$ DNA

RNA chains are usually single stranded and lack the continuous helical structure of double-stranded DNA. However, RNA still has considerable secondary and tertiary structure because base pairs can form in regions where the strand loops back on itself. As in DNA, pairing between the bases is complementary and antiparallel. But in RNA, adenine pairs with uracil rather than thymine (see Fig. 12.16B). Base pairing in RNA can be extensive, and the irregular looped structures that are generated are important for the binding of molecules, such as enzymes, that interact with specific regions of the RNA.

The three major types of RNA (mRNA, rRNA, and tRNA) participate directly in the process of protein synthesis. Other less abundant RNAs are involved in replication or in the processing of RNA, that is, in the conversion of RNA precursors to their mature forms or destruction of existing RNA molecules (see Chapter 17). Other forms of RNA are involved in gene regulation (such as micro RNAs, see Chapter 16).

Some RNA molecules are capable of catalyzing reactions. Thus, RNA as well as protein can have enzymatic activity. Certain rRNA precursors can remove internal segments of themselves, splicing the remaining fragments together. Because this RNA is changed by the reaction it catalyzes, it is not truly an enzyme and therefore has been termed a *ribozyme*. Other RNAs act as true catalysts, serving as ribonucleases that cleave other RNA molecules or as a *peptidyl transferase*, the enzyme in protein synthesis that catalyzes the formation of peptide bonds.

B. Structure of mRNA

Each mRNA molecule contains a nucleotide sequence that is converted into the amino acid sequence of a polypeptide chain in the process of translation. In eukaryotes, mRNA is transcribed from protein-coding genes as a long primary transcript that is processed in the nucleus to form mRNA. The various processing intermediates, which are mRNA precursors, are called pre-mRNA or hnRNA (*h*eterogenous *n*uclear RNA). mRNA travels through nuclear pores to the cytoplasm where it binds to ribosomes and tRNAs and directs the sequential insertion of the appropriate amino acids into a polypeptide chain.

Eukaryotic mRNA consists of a leader sequence at the 5′-end, a coding region, and a trailer sequence at the 3′-end (Fig. 12.17). The leader sequence begins with a guanosine cap structure at its 5′-end. The coding region begins with a trinucleotide start codon that signals the beginning of translation, followed by the trinucleotide codons for amino acids, and ends at a termination signal. The trailer sequence terminates at its 3′-end with a poly(A) tail that may be up to 200 nucleotides long. Most of the leader sequence, all of the coding region, and most of the trailer are formed by transcription of the complementary nucleotide sequence in DNA. However, the terminal guanosine in the cap structure and the poly(A) tail do not have complementary sequences; they are added after transcription has been completed (posttranscriptionally).

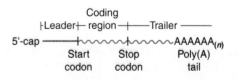

FIG. 12.17. The regions of eukaryotic mRNA. The *wavy line* indicates the polynucleotide chain of the mRNA and the A's constituting the poly(A) tail. The 5′-cap consists of a guanosine residue linked at its 5′-hydroxyl group to three phosphates, which are linked to the 5′-hydroxyl group of the next nucleotide in the RNA chain (a 5′–5′ triphosphate linkage). The start and stop codons represent where protein synthesis is initiated and terminated from this mRNA.

C. Structure of rRNA

Ribosomes are subcellular ribonucleoprotein complexes on which protein synthesis occurs. Different types of ribosomes are found in prokaryotes and in the cytoplasm and mitochondria of eukaryotic cells (Fig. 12.18). Prokaryotic ribosomes contain three types of rRNA molecules with sedimentation coefficients of 16, 23, and 5S. A *sedimentation coefficient* is a measure of the rate of sedimentation of a macromolecule in a high-speed centrifuge (ultracentrifuge). The units of sedimentation are expressed in Svedberg units (S). The 30S ribosomal subunit contains the 16S rRNA complexed with proteins, and the 50S ribosomal subunit contains the 23S and 5S rRNAs complexed with proteins. The 30S and 50S ribosomal subunits join to form the 70S ribosome, which participates in protein synthesis. Although larger macromolecules generally have higher sedimentation coefficients than do smaller macromolecules, sedimentation coefficients are not additive. Because frictional forces acting on the surface of a macromolecule slow its migration through the solvent, the rate of sedimentation depends not only on the density of the macromolecule, but also on its shape.

Cytoplasmic ribosomes in eukaryotes contain four types of rRNA molecules of 18, 28, 5, and 5.8S. The 40S ribosomal subunit contains the 18S rRNA complexed with proteins, and the 60S ribosomal subunit contains the 28, 5, and 5.8S rRNAs complexed with proteins. In the cytoplasm, the 40S and 60S ribosomal subunits combine to form the 80S ribosomes that participate in protein synthesis.

Mitochondrial ribosomes, with a sedimentation coefficient of 55S, are smaller than cytoplasmic ribosomes. Their properties are similar to those of the 70S ribosomes of bacteria.

rRNAs contain many loops and exhibit extensive base pairing in the regions between the loops. The sequences of the rRNAs of the smaller ribosomal subunits exhibit secondary structures that are common to many different species.

D. Structure of tRNA

During protein synthesis, tRNA molecules carry amino acids to ribosomes and ensure that they are incorporated into the appropriate positions in the growing polypeptide chain (Fig. 12.19). This is done through base pairing of three bases of the tRNA (the anticodon) with the three base codons within the coding region of the mRNA. Therefore, cells contain at least 20 different tRNA molecules that differ somewhat in nucleotide sequence, one for each of the amino acids found in proteins. Many amino acids have more than one tRNA.

tRNA molecules contain not only the usual nucleotides, but also derivatives of these nucleotides that are produced by posttranscriptional modifications. In eukaryotic cells, 10% to 20% of the nucleotides of tRNA are modified. Most tRNA molecules contain ribothymidine (T), in which a methyl group is added to uridine to form ribothymidine. They also contain dihydrouridine (D), in which one of the double bonds of the base is reduced, and pseudouridine (ψ), in which uracil is attached to ribose by a carbon–carbon bond rather than a nitrogen–carbon bond (see Chapter 14).The base at the 5′-end of the anticodon of tRNA is also frequently modified.

tRNA molecules are rather small compared with both mRNA and the large rRNA molecules. On average, tRNA molecules contain approximately 80 nucleotides and have a sedimentation coefficient of 4S. Because of their small size and high content of modified nucleotides, tRNAs were the first nucleic acids to be sequenced. Since 1965, when Robert Holley deduced the structure of the first tRNA, the nucleotide sequences of many different tRNAs have been determined. Although their primary sequences differ, all tRNA molecules can form a structure resembling a cloverleaf (discussed in more detail in Chapter 15).

E. Other Types of RNA

In addition to the three major types of RNA described previously, other RNAs are present in cells. These RNAs include the oligonucleotides that serve as primers for DNA replication and the RNAs in the small nuclear ribonucleoproteins

Prokaryotes

FIG. 12.18. Comparison of prokaryotic and eukaryotic ribosomes. The cytoplasmic ribosomes of eukaryotes are shown. Mitochondrial ribosomes are similar to prokaryotic ribosomes, but they are smaller (55S rather than 70S).

Azithromycin, the antibiotic used to treat **Newman Itis**, inhibits protein synthesis on prokaryotic ribosomes but not on eukaryotic ribosomes. It binds to the 50S ribosomal subunit, which is absent in eukaryotes. Therefore, it will selectively inhibit bacterial growth. However, because mitochondrial ribosomes are similar to those of bacteria, mitochondrial protein synthesis can also be inhibited. This fact is important in understanding some of the side effects of antibiotics that work by inhibiting bacterial protein synthesis.

FIG. 12.19. The typical cloverleaf structure of tRNA.

Colin Tuma completed his first course of intravenous (IV) 5-fluo-uracil (5-FU) in the hospital. He tolerated the therapy with only mild anorexia and diarrhea and with only a mild *leukopenia* (a decreased white blood cell count; leuko = white). Thirty days after the completion of the initial course, these symptoms abated and he started his second course of chemotherapy with 5-FU as an outpatient.

Because 5-FU inhibits synthesis of thymine, DNA synthesis is affected in all cells in the human body that are rapidly dividing, such as the cells in the bone marrow that produce leukocytes and the mucosal cells lining the intestines. Inhibition of DNA synthesis in rapidly dividing cells contributes to the side effects of 5-FU and many other chemotherapeutic drugs.

(snRNPs or snurps) that are involved in the splicing and modification reactions that occur during the maturation of RNA precursors (see Chapter 14). Also included are micro RNAs, which participate in the regulation of gene expression (see Chapters 16 and 18).

CLINICAL COMMENTS

Ivy Sharer. **Ivy Sharer's** clinical course was typical for the development of AIDS, in this case caused by the use of needles contaminated with HIV. The progressive immunologic deterioration that accompanies this disease ultimately can result in life-threatening opportunistic infections with fungi (e.g., *Candida*, *Pneumocystis carinii*, cryptococcus), other viruses (e.g., cytomegalovirus, herpes simplex), and bacteria (e.g., *Mycobacterium*, *Pneumocystis jirovecii* [previously known as *carinii*], *Salmonella*). The immunologic incompetence also frequently results in the development of certain neoplasms (e.g., Kaposi sarcoma, non-Hodgkin lymphoma) as well as meningitis, neuropathies, and neuropsychiatric disorders causing cognitive dysfunction. Although recent advances in drug therapy can slow or stop the course of the disease, no cure is yet available.

Colin Tuma. **Colin Tuma's** original benign adenomatous polyp was located in the ascending colon, where 10% of large bowel cancers eventually arise. Because Mr. Tuma's father died of a cancer of the colon, his physician had warned him that his risk of developing colon cancer was three times higher than for the general population. Unfortunately, Mr. Tuma neglected to have his annual colonoscopic examinations as recommended, and he developed an adenocarcinoma that metastasized.

The most malignant characteristic of neoplasms is their ability to metastasize, that is, form a new neoplasm at a noncontiguous site. The initial site of metastasis for a tumor is usually at the first capillary bed encountered by the malignant cells once they are released. Thus, cells from tumors of the gastrointestinal tract often pass through the portal vein to the liver, which is **Colin Tuma's** site of metastasis. Because his adenocarcinoma has metastasized, there is little hope of eradicating it, and his therapy with 5-fluororacil (5-FU) is palliative (directed toward reducing the severity of the disease and alleviating the symptoms without actually curing the disease), although if the metastatic disease in the liver responds to the chemotherapy, those lesions may then be able to be resected for a cure.

Newman Itis. **Newman Itis's** infection was treated with azithromycin, a macrolide antibiotic. Because this agent can inhibit mitochondrial protein synthesis in eukaryotic cells, it has the potential to alter host cell function, leading to such side effects as epigastric distress, diarrhea, and, infrequently, cholestatic jaundice.

BIOCHEMICAL COMMENTS

Retroviruses. RNA also serves as the genome for certain types of viruses including retroviruses. HIV, the human immunodeficiency virus, is the retrovirus that causes AIDS (Fig. 12.20). Viruses must invade host cells to reproduce. They are not capable of reproducing independently. Some viruses that are pathogenic to humans contain DNA as their genetic material. Others contain RNA as their genetic material. HIV invades cells of the immune system and prevents the affected individual from mounting an adequate immune response to combat infections.

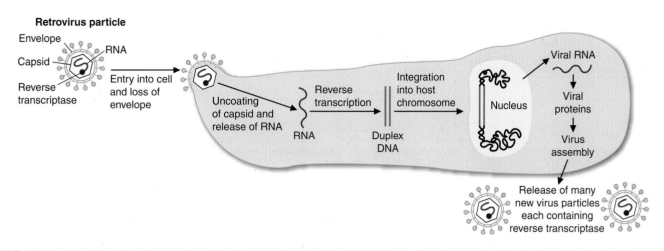

FIG. 12.20.   The life cycle of a retrovirus. The virus contains two identical RNA strands, only one of which is shown for clarity. After penetrating the plasma membrane, the single-stranded viral RNA genome is reverse-transcribed to a double-stranded DNA form. The viral DNA migrates to the nucleus and integrates into the chromosomal DNA, where it is transcribed to form a viral RNA transcript. The viral transcript can form the viral RNA genome for progeny viruses, or it can be translated to generate viral structural proteins.

According to the "central dogma" proposed by Francis Crick, information flows from DNA to RNA to proteins. For the most part, this concept holds true. However, retroviruses provide one violation of this rule. When retroviruses invade cells, their RNA genome is transcribed to produce a DNA copy. The enzyme that catalyzes this process is encoded in the viral RNA and is known as *reverse transcriptase*. This DNA copy integrates into the genome of the infected cell, and enzymes of the host cell are used to produce many copies of the viral RNA as well as viral proteins, which can be packaged into new viral particles.

Key Concepts

- The central dogma of molecular biology is that DNA is transcribed to RNA, which is translated to protein.
- Nucleotides, consisting of a nitrogenous base, a five-carbon sugar, and phosphate, are the monomeric units of the nucleic acids, DNA and RNA (see Chapter 5).
- DNA contains the sugar 2′-deoxyribose; RNA contains ribose.
- DNA and RNA contain the purine bases adenine (A) and guanine (G).
- DNA contains the pyrimidine bases cytosine (C) and thymine (T), whereas RNA contains C and uracil (U).
- DNA and RNA are linear sequences of nucleotides linked by phosphodiester bonds between the 3′-sugar of one nucleotide and the 5′-sugar of the next nucleotide.
- Genetic information is encoded by the sequence of the nucleotide bases in DNA.
- DNA is double stranded; one strand runs in the 5′-to-3′ direction, whereas the other is antiparallel and runs in the 3′-to-5′ direction.
- The two strands of DNA wrap about each other to form a double helix and are held together by hydrogen bonding between bases in each strand.
- A hydrogen-bonds to T, whereas C hydrogen-bonds to G.
- Transcription of a gene generates a single-stranded RNA; the three major types of RNA are messenger RNA (mRNA), ribosomal RNA (rRNA), and transfer RNA (tRNA).
- Eukaryotic mRNA is modified at both the 5′- and 3′-ends. In between, it contains a coding region for the synthesis of a protein.
- Codons within the coding region dictate the sequence of amino acids in a protein. Each codon is three nucleotides long.
- rRNA and tRNA are required for protein synthesis.
  - rRNA is complexed with proteins to form ribonucleoprotein particles called *ribosomes*, which bind mRNA and tRNAs during translation.
  - The tRNA contains an anticodon that binds to a complementary codon on mRNA, ensuring insertion of the correct amino acid into the protein being synthesized.
- The diseases discussed in this chapter are summarized in Table 12.2.

Table 12.2   Diseases Discussed in Chapter 12

Disorder or Condition	Genetic or Environmental	Comments
AIDS	Environmental	AIDS is due to infection by HIV, a retrovirus containing an RNA genome.
Adenocarcinoma	Both	Use of nucleotide analogs as chemotherapeutic agents. Specifically, 5-fluorouracil is used to inhibit deoxythymidine monophosphate (dTMP) synthesis by the enzyme thymidylate synthase, which will lead to the death of rapidly proliferating cells.
Pneumonitis	Environmental	A bacterial-induced illness, primarily in lungs, leading to fever and coughs. Treated with antibiotics. Certain antibiotics target bacterial protein synthesis but may also inhibit mitochondrial protein synthesis.

REVIEW QUESTIONS—CHAPTER 12

Directions: For each question that follows, select the single best answer.

1. For the DNA sequence, 5′-ATCGATCGATCGATCG-3′, which of the following represents the sequence and polarity of the complementary strand?

    A. 5′-ATCTATCGATCGATCG-3′
    B. 3′-ATCGATCGATCGATCG-5′
    C. 5′-CGAUCGAUCAUCGAU-3′
    D. 5′-CGATCGATCGATCGAT-3′
    E. 3′-CGATCGATCGATCGAT-5′

2. If the DNA strand, 5′-GCTATGCATCGTGATC GAATTGCGT-3′, serves as a template for the synthesis of RNA, which of the following choices gives the sequence and polarity of the newly synthesized RNA?

    A. 5′-ACGCAATTCGATCACGATGCATAGC-3′
    B. 5′-UGCGUUAAGCUAGUGCUACGUAUCG-3′
    C. 5′-ACGCAAUUCGAUCACGAUGCAUAGC-3′
    D. 5′-CGAUACGUAGCACUAGCUUAACGCA-3′
    E. 5′-GCTATGCATCGTGATCGAATTGCGT-3′

3. In DNA, the bond between the deoxyribose sugar and the phosphate is best described by which of the following?

    A. A polar bond
    B. An ionic bond
    C. A hydrogen bond
    D. A covalent bond
    E. A van der Waals bond

4. How many double-stranded DNA molecules 8 base pairs long are theoretically possible?

    A. 12
    B. 32
    C. 64
    D. 256
    E. 65,536

5. The backbone of a DNA strand is composed of which of the following?

    A. Sugars and bases
    B. Phosphates and sugars
    C. Bases and phosphates
    D. Nucleotides and sugars
    E. Phosphates and nucleosides

13 Synthesis of DNA

DNA synthesis occurs by the process of **replication**. During replication, each of the two parental strands of DNA serves as a **template** for the synthesis of a complementary strand. Thus, each DNA molecule generated by the replication process contains one intact parental strand and one newly synthesized strand (Fig. 13.1). In eukaryotes, **DNA replication** occurs during the **S phase** of the **cell cycle**, which is followed by the G_2 phase. The cell **divides** during the next phase (**M**), and each daughter cell receives an exact copy of the DNA of the parent cell.

The Replication Fork. In both prokaryotes and eukaryotes, the site at which replication is occurring at any given moment is called the **replication fork**. As replication proceeds, the two parental strands separate in front of the fork. Behind the fork, each newly synthesized strand of DNA base-pairs with its complementary parental template strand. A complex of proteins is involved in replication. **Helicases** and **topoisomerases** unwind the parental strands, and **single-strand binding proteins** prevent them from reannealing.

The major enzyme involved in replication is a **DNA polymerase** that copies each parental template strand in the 3'-to-5' direction, producing new strands in a 5'-to-3' direction. **Deoxyribonucleoside triphosphates** serve as the precursors. One strand of newly synthesized DNA grows continuously, whereas the other strand is synthesized discontinuously in short segments known as **Okazaki fragments**. These fragments are subsequently joined by **DNA ligase**.

Initiation. DNA polymerase **cannot initiate** the synthesis of new strands. Therefore, a short **primer** is produced, which contains ribonucleotides (RNA). DNA polymerase can add deoxyribonucleotides to the 3'-end of this primer. This RNA primer is subsequently removed and replaced by deoxyribonucleotides.

Telomeres. The ends of linear chromosomes are called **telomeres**. The enzyme **telomerase**, an RNA-dependent DNA polymerase that carries its own RNA template, is required for the replication of telomeres.

Errors and Repair. Errors that occur **during replication** can lead to deleterious **mutations**. However, many errors are corrected by enzyme activities associated with the complex at the replication fork. The **error rate** is thus kept at a very low level.

Damage to DNA molecules also causes mutations. **Repair mechanisms** correct DNA damage, usually by removing and replacing the damaged region. The intact, undamaged strand serves as a template for the DNA polymerase involved in the repair process.

Recombination. Although cells have mechanisms to correct replication errors and to repair DNA damage, some genetic change is desirable. It produces new proteins or variations of proteins that may increase the survival rate of the species. Genetic change is produced by unrepaired mutations and by a mechanism known as **recombination**, in which portions of chromosomes are exchanged.

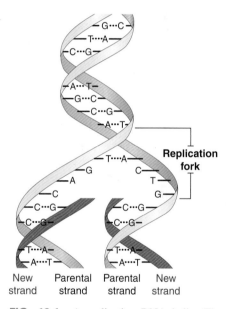

FIG. 13.1. A replicating DNA helix. The parental strands separate at the replication fork. Each parental strand serves as a template for the synthesis of a new strand.

THE WAITING ROOM

 Ivy Sharer is having difficulty complying with her multidrug regimen. She often forgets to take her pills. When she returns for a checkup, she asks whether such a large number of pills are really necessary for treatment of AIDS.

 Di Abietes responded to treatment for her diabetes mellitus but subsequently developed a low-grade fever, an increase in urinary urgency and frequency, and burning at the urethral opening with urination (dysuria). A urinalysis showed a large number of white blood cells and many gram-negative bacilli. A urine culture indicated many colonies of *Escherichia coli,* which is sensitive to several antibiotics, including the quinolone ciprofloxacin.

Melvin (Mel) Anoma is a 46-year-old man who noted a superficial, brownish black, 5-mm nodule with irregular borders in the skin on his chest. He was scheduled for outpatient surgery, at which time a wide excision biopsy was performed. (In an excision biopsy, the entire mole is surgically removed). Microscopic examination of the nodule indicated histologic changes characteristic of a malignant melanoma reaching a thickness of only 0.7 mm (stage I).

Nick O'Tyne is a 62-year-old electrician who has smoked two packs of cigarettes a day for 40 years. He recently noted that his chronic cough had gotten worse. His physician ordered a chest radiograph, which showed a 2-cm nodule in the upper lobe of the right lung. A computed tomography (CT) scan was performed and confirmed a 2-cm nodule very concerning for malignancy. The patient was taken for surgery and the nodule was excised. The pathology of the excised nodule indicated a poorly differentiated adenocarcinoma of the lung. Malignant neoplasms (new growth, a tumor) of epithelial cell origin (including the intestinal lining, cells of the skin, and cells lining the airways of the lungs) are called *carcinomas.* If the cancer grows in a glandlike pattern, it is an *adenocarcinoma.*

 Collection of a patient's urine allows many variables to be examined, including sugar (glucose) levels, creatinine (kidney function) levels, ketone bodies (significant fatty acid oxidation), and crystal or bacterial infiltration. In the case of bacteria, the finding of any bacteria in the urine is unusual, because normal urine is sterile. If large numbers of organisms are seen microscopically or there are small numbers accompanied by white blood cells, a urinary tract infection is the most likely diagnosis. In **Di Abietes's** case, the bacteria were demonstrated to be gram-negative (see Chapter 12), specifically *E. coli.* Typing the bacteria will allow the appropriate antibiotic to be given to cure the infection.

I.   *DNA SYNTHESIS IN PROKARYOTES*

The basic features of the mechanism of DNA replication are illustrated by the processes that occur in the bacterium *Escherichia coli.* This bacillus grows symbiotically in the human colon. It has been studied extensively and serves as a model for the more complex, and consequently less understood, processes that occur in eukaryotic cells.

A.   *Replication Is Bidirectional*

Replication of the circular, double-stranded DNA of the chromosome of *E. coli* begins with the binding of approximately 30 molecules of the protein DnaA at a single point of origin, designated *oriC,* where the DNA coils around the DnaA core (Fig. 13.2). With the assistance of other proteins (e.g., a helicase, gyrase, and single-stranded binding protein), the two parental strands separate within this region, and both strands are copied simultaneously. Synthesis begins at the origin and occurs at two replication forks that move away from the origin bidirectionally (in both directions at the same time). Replication ends on the other side of the chromosome at a termination point. One round of synthesis, involving the

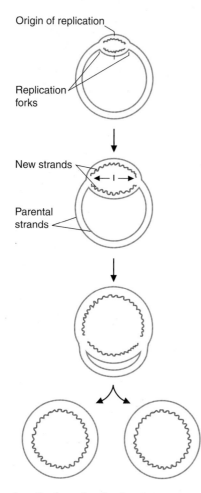

Origin of replication

Replication
forks

New strands

Parental
strands

FIG. 13.2. Bidirectional replication of a circular chromosome. Replication begins at the point of origin (*oriC*) and proceeds in both directions at the same time. Parental strands are shown in *blue*; newly synthesized strands are shown in *red*.

incorporation of >4 million nucleotides in each new strand of DNA, is completed in approximately 40 minutes. However, a second round of synthesis can begin at the origin before the first round is finished. These multiple initiations of replication allow bacterial multiplication to occur much more quickly than the time it takes to complete a single round of replication.

B. Replication Is Semiconservative
Each daughter chromosome contains one of the parental DNA strands and one newly synthesized complementary strand. Therefore, replication is said to be semiconservative (i.e., the parental strands are conserved but are no longer together). Each one is paired with a newly synthesized strand (see Figs. 13.1 and 13.2).

C. Unwinding of Parental Strands
Replication requires separation of the parental DNA strands and unwinding of the helix ahead of the replication fork. Helicases (an example of which is the protein DnaB) separate the DNA strands and unwind the parental duplex. Single-strand binding proteins prevent the strands from reassociating and protect them from enzymes that cleave single-stranded DNA (Fig. 13.3). *Topoisomerases*, enzymes that can break phosphodiester bonds and rejoin them, relieve the supercoiling of the parental duplex caused by unwinding. DNA gyrase is a major topoisomerase in bacterial cells.

FIG. 13.3. Proteins involved in separating and unwinding parental DNA strands at the replication fork in prokaryotes.

Table 13.1 Functions of Bacterial DNA Polymerases

Polymerases	Functions[a]	Exonuclease Activity[b]
Pol I	Filling of gap after removal of RNA primer DNA repair Removal of RNA primer in conjunction with RNAse H	5'-to-3' and 3'-to-5'
Pol II	DNA repair	3'-to-5'
Pol III	Replication—synthesis of DNA	3'-to-5'

[a]Synthesis of new DNA strands always occurs 5'-to-3'.
[b]Exonucleases remove nucleotides from DNA strands and act at the 5'-end (cleaving 5'-to-3') or at the 3'-end (cleaving 3'-to-5'). Endonucleases cleave bonds within polynucleotide chains.

D. Action of DNA Polymerase

Enzymes that catalyze the synthesis of DNA are known as *DNA polymerases.* *E. coli* has three DNA polymerases: pol I, pol II, and pol III. *Pol III* is the major replicative enzyme (Table 13.1). All DNA polymerases that have been studied copy a DNA template strand in its 3'-to-5' direction, producing a new strand in the 5'-to-3' direction (Fig. 13.4). Deoxyribonucleoside triphosphates (dATP, dGTP, dCTP, and dTTP) serve as substrates for the addition of nucleotides to the growing chain.

The incoming nucleotide forms a base pair with its complementary nucleotide on the template strand. Then an ester bond is formed between the first (or α) 5'-phosphate of the incoming nucleotide and the free 3'-hydroxyl group at the end of the growing chain. Pyrophosphate is released. The release of pyrophosphate (formed from the β- and γ-phosphates of the nucleotide) and its subsequent cleavage by a pyrophosphatase provide the energy that drives the polymerization process.

DNA polymerases that catalyze the synthesis of new strands during replication exhibit a feature called *processivity*. They remain bound to the parental template strand while continuing to "process" down the chain, rather than dissociating and

 Di Abietes's urinary tract infection was treated with ciprofloxacin, a fluorinated member of the quinolone family. This group of drugs inhibits bacterial DNA gyrase, a topoisomerase that unwinds the closed circular bacterial DNA helix ahead of the replication fork and thus inhibits bacterial DNA synthesis. Because eukaryotic cells have linear DNA and do not contain DNA gyrase, they are not affected by quinolones.

FIG. 13.4. Action of DNA polymerase. Deoxyribonucleoside triphosphates serve as precursors (substrates) used by DNA polymerase to lengthen the DNA chain. DNA polymerase copies the DNA template strand in the 3'-to-5' direction. The new strand grows 5'-to-3'.

reassociating as each nucleotide is added. Consequently, synthesis is much more rapid than it would be with an enzyme that was not processive.

E. Elimination of Base-Pairing Errors

In *E. coli,* the replicative enzyme pol III also performs a proofreading or editing function. This enzyme has 3′-to-5′ exonuclease activity (a nuclease activity is one that cleaves phosphodiester bonds) in addition to its polymerase activity (see Table 13.1). If the nucleotide at the end of the growing chain is incorrectly base-paired with the template strand, pol III removes this nucleotide before continuing to lengthen the growing chain. This proofreading activity eliminates most base-pairing errors as they occur. Only about one base pair in a million is mismatched in the final DNA product; the error rate is about 10^{-6}. If this proofreading activity is experimentally removed from the enzyme, the error rate increases to about 10^{-3}.

After replication, other mechanisms replace mismatched bases that escaped proofreading so that the fidelity of DNA replication is very high. The two processes of proofreading and postreplication mismatch repair result in an overall error rate of about 10^{-10}, that is, less than one mismatched base pair in 10 billion.

F. Function of RNA Primers

DNA polymerase cannot initiate the synthesis of new strands; it requires the presence of a free 3′-OH group to function. Therefore, a primer is required to supply the free 3′-OH group. This primer is an RNA oligonucleotide. It is synthesized in a 5′-to-3′ direction by an RNA polymerase (primase) that copies the DNA template strand. DNA polymerase initially adds a deoxyribonucleotide to the 3′-hydroxyl group of the primer and then continues adding deoxyribonucleotides to the 3′-end of the growing strand (Fig. 13.5).

G. DNA Synthesis at the Replication Fork

Both parental strands are copied at the same time in the direction of the replication fork, an observation that is difficult to reconcile with the known activity of DNA polymerase, which can produce chains only in a 5′-to-3′ direction. Because the parental strands run in opposite directions relative to each other, synthesis should occur in a 5′-to-3′ direction *toward* the fork on one template strand and in a 5′-to-3′ direction *away* from the fork on the other template strand.

Okazaki resolved this dilemma by showing that synthesis on one strand, called the *leading strand,* is continuous in the 5′-to-3′ direction toward the fork. The other strand, called the *lagging strand,* is synthesized discontinuously in short fragments (see Fig. 13.5). These fragments, named for Okazaki, are produced in a 5′-to-3′ direction (away from the fork), but then are joined together so that, overall, synthesis proceeds toward the replication fork.

H. Function of DNA Ligase

As replication progresses, the RNA primers are removed from Okazaki fragments, probably by the combined action of DNA polymerase I (pol I, using its 5′-to-3′ exonuclease activity) and *RNase H,* an enzyme that removes RNA from DNA:RNA hybrids. Pol I fills in the gaps produced by removal of the primers. Because DNA polymerases cannot join two polynucleotide chains together, an additional enzyme, DNA ligase, is required to perform this function. The 3′-hydroxyl group at the end of one fragment is ligated to the phosphate group at the 5′-end of the next fragment (Fig. 13.6).

II. DNA SYNTHESIS IN EUKARYOTES

The process of replication in eukaryotes is similar to that in prokaryotes. Differences in the processes are related mainly to the vastly larger amount of DNA in eukaryotic cells (>1,000 times the amount in *E. coli*) and the association of eukaryotic DNA with histones in nucleosomes. Enzymes with DNA polymerase, primase, ligase,

One of the drugs used to treat **Ivy Sharer** was didanosine (ddI), a nucleotide reverse transcriptase inhibitor (NRTI). It is a dideoxynucleoside, an example of which is shown in the following.

A dideoxynucleoside

The dideoxynucleosides do not have a hydroxyl group on either the 2′- or 3′-carbon. They can be converted to dideoxynucleoside triphosphates in cells and, like zidovudine (ZDV), terminate chain growth when incorporated into DNA. In the case of the dideoxynucleosides, chain termination results from the absence of a hydroxyl group on the 3′-carbon. The HIV virus mutates very rapidly (mostly because reverse transcriptase lacks 3′-to-5′ exonuclease activity, the proofreading activity) and frequently develops resistance to one or more of these drugs. Therefore, it is recommended that AIDS patients take several drugs, including two NRTIs.

RNase H is a ribonuclease that specifically degrades RNA from an RNA–DNA hybrid. The HIV virus (see Chapter 12) converts an RNA genome to a double-stranded DNA copy using the enzyme reverse transcriptase. An intermediate in the conversion of the single-stranded RNA genome to double-stranded DNA is an RNA–DNA hybrid. To remove the RNA so a double-stranded DNA molecule can be made, reverse transcriptase also contains RNase H activity. Because reverse transcriptase lacks error-checking capabilities, the HIV genome can mutate at a rapid rate. **Ivy Sharer** takes many drugs because of the need to block HIV replication at multiple steps in order to "keep ahead" of the high mutation rate of the virus. The RNAse H activity of reverse transcriptase has proven to be a difficult target for drug development to block HIV genome replication, although research in this area is still quite active.

FIG. 13.5. Synthesis of DNA at the replication fork. (See Fig. 13.6 for the ligation reaction.)

helicase, and topoisomerase activity are all present in eukaryotes, although these enzymes differ in some respects from those of prokaryotes.

A. Eukaryotic Cell Cycle

The cell cycle of eukaryotes consists of four phases (Fig. 13.7). The first three phases (G_1, S, and G_2) constitute interphase. Cells spend most of their time in these three phases, carrying out their normal metabolic activities. The fourth phase is *mitosis*, the process of cell division. This phase is very brief.

The first phase of the cell cycle, G_1 (the first "gap" phase), is the most variable in length. Late in G_1, the cells prepare to duplicate their chromosomes (e.g., by producing nucleotide precursors). In the second or *S phase*, DNA replicates.

FIG. 13.6. Action of DNA ligase. Two polynucleotide chains, one with a free 3'-OH group and one with a free 5'-phosphate group, are joined by DNA ligase, which forms a phosphodiester bond.

DNA = $2n \rightarrow 4n$
(6–8 h)

DNA = $2n$
(6–12 h)

DNA = $4n$
(3–4 h)

DNA = $4n \rightarrow 2n$
(1 h)

FIG. 13.7. Eukaryotic cell cycle. The times given for the length of each phase are for cells growing in culture.

Nucleosomes disassemble as the replication forks advance. Throughout S phase, the synthesis of histones and other proteins associated with DNA is markedly increased. The amounts of DNA and histones both double, and chromosomes are duplicated. Histones complex with DNA, and nucleosomes are formed very rapidly behind the advancing replication forks.

During the third phase of the cell cycle, G_2 (the second "gap" phase), the cells prepare to divide and synthesize tubulin for construction of the microtubules of the spindle apparatus. Finally, division occurs in the brief mitotic or M phase.

After mitosis, some cells reenter G_1, repeatedly going through the phases of the cell cycle and dividing. Other cells leave the cycle after mitosis, never to divide again, or they enter an extended G_1 phase (sometimes called G_0), in which they remain for long periods. On the appropriate signal, cells in G_0 are stimulated to reenter the cycle and divide.

B. Points of Origin for Replication

In contrast to bacterial chromosomes (see Section I.A of this chapter), eukaryotic chromosomes have multiple points of origin at which replication begins. "Bubbles" appear at these points on the chromosomes. At each end of a bubble, a replication fork forms; thus, each bubble has two forks. DNA synthesis occurs at each of these forks, as illustrated in Figure 13.8. As the bubbles enlarge, they eventually merge, and replication is completed. Because eukaryotic chromosomes contain multiple points of origin of replication (and, thus, multiple replicons—units of replication), duplication of such large chromosomes can occur within a few hours.

C. Eukaryotic DNA Polymerases

Fifteen different DNA polymerases have been identified in eukaryotic cells. Examples of some of these polymerases, and their properties, are shown in Table 13.2. Polymerases δ (pol δ) and ε (pol ε) are the major replicative enzymes. Pol α is also involved in replication. Pols δ and ε, as well as pol α, appear to be involved in DNA repair. Pol γ is located in mitochondria and replicates the DNA of this organelle. Pols ζ, κ, η, and ι, which lack 5'-exonuclease activity, are used when DNA is damaged and are known as *bypass polymerases*, because they can "bypass" the damaged area.

D. Eukaryotic Replication Complex

Many proteins bind at or near the replication fork and participate in the process of duplicating DNA (Fig. 13.9 and Table 13.3). Pols δ and ε are the major replicative

 Although Prometheus was chained to a rock as punishment for his theft of fire from the gods and a vulture pecked at his liver each day, he survived. Can you guess why?

In the human body, many cells cycle frequently—for example, hair follicles, skin cells, and cells of the duodenal crypts. Other cells, such as the precursors of red blood cells, divide several times, then lose their nuclei and leave the cell cycle to form mature red blood cells. These cells transport oxygen and carbon dioxide between the lungs and other tissues for about 120 days, and then die. Other cells are normally quiescent (in G_0). However, they can be stimulated to divide. In many instances, the stimuli are growth factors or hormones (e.g., mammary alveolar cells and uterine cells). In the case of liver cells, the stimulus is produced by death of some of the cells.

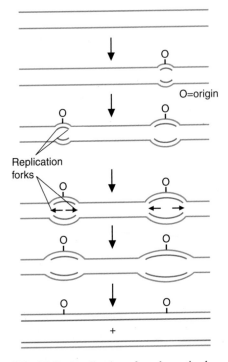

FIG. 13.8. Replication of a eukaryotic chromosome. Synthesis is bidirectional from each point of origin (*O*) and semiconservative; each daughter DNA helix contains one intact parental strand (*blue line*) and one newly synthesized strand (*red line*).

Table 13.2   Functions of Some Eukaryotic DNA Polymerases

Polymerase	Functions[a]	Exonuclease Activity
Pol α	Replication (in a complex with primase and aids in starting the primer) DNA repair	None
Pol β	DNA repair exclusively	None
Pol γ	DNA replication in mitochondria	3'-to-5'
Pol δ	Replication (processive DNA synthesis on lagging strand) DNA repair	3'-to-5'
Pol ε	Replication (processive DNA synthesis on leading strand) DNA repair	3'-to-5'
Pol κ	DNA repair (bypass polymerase)[b]	None
Pol η	DNA repair (bypass polymerase)	None
Pol ξ	DNA repair (bypass polymerase)	None
Pol ι	DNA repair (bypass polymerase)	None

[a]Synthesis of new DNA strands always occurs 5'-to-3'.
[b]Bypass polymerase is able to "bypass" areas of DNA damage and continue DNA replication. Some enzymes are error-free and insert the correct bases; other enzymes are error-prone and insert random bases.

enzyme. However, before it acts, a primase associated with pol α produces an RNA primer (approximately 10 nucleotides in length). Then pol α adds about 20 deoxyribonucleotides to this RNA and dissociates from the template because of the low processivity of pol α. Pol α also lacks proofreading activity (3'-to-5' exonuclease activity). On the leading strand, pol ε adds deoxyribonucleotides to this RNA–DNA primer, continuously producing this strand. Pol ε is a highly processive enzyme.

The lagging strand is produced from a series of Okazaki fragments (see Fig. 13.5). Synthesis of each Okazaki fragment is initiated by pol α and its associated primase, as described previously. After pol α dissociates, pol δ adds deoxyribonucleotides

 Liver cells are in G_0. Up to 90% of the human liver can be removed. The remaining liver cells are stimulated to reenter the cell cycle and divide, regenerating a mass equivalent to the original mass of the liver within a few weeks. The myth of Prometheus indicates that the capacity of the liver to regenerate was recognized even in ancient times.

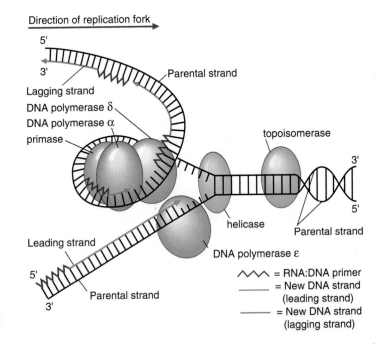

FIG. 13.9. Replication complex in eukaryotes. The lagging strand is shown looped around the replication complex to demonstrate that all DNA synthesis is in the 5'-to-3' direction. Single-strand binding proteins (not shown) are bound to the unpaired, single-stranded DNA. Other proteins also participate in this complex (see text).

Table 13.3 Major Proteins Involved in Replication

DNA polymerases	Add nucleotides to a strand growing 5'-to-3', copying a DNA template 3'-to-5'
Primase	Synthesizes RNA primers
Helicases	Separate parental DNA strands (i.e., unwind the double helix)
Single-strand binding proteins	Prevent single strands of DNA from reassociating
Topoisomerases	Relieve torsional strain on parental duplex caused by unwinding
Enzymes that remove primers	RNase H hydrolyzes RNA of DNA–RNA hybrids
	Flap endonuclease 1 (FEN1) recognizes "flap" (unannealed portion of RNA) near 5'-end of primer and cleaves downstream in DNA region of primer; the flap is created by polymerase δ, displacing the primer as the Okazaki fragment is synthesized
DNA ligase	Joins, by forming a phosphodiester bond, two adjacent DNA strands that are bound to the same template
Proliferating cell nuclear antigen (PCNA)	Enhances processivity of the DNA polymerases; binds to many proteins present at the replication fork

to the primer, producing an Okazaki fragment. Pol δ stops synthesizing one fragment when it reaches the start of the previously synthesized Okazaki fragment (see Fig. 13.5). The primer of the previously synthesized Okazaki fragment is removed by flap endonuclease 1 (FEN1) and RNase H. The gap left by the primer is filled by pol δ using the parental DNA strand as its template and the newly synthesized Okazaki fragment as its primer. DNA ligase subsequently joins the Okazaki fragments together (see Fig. 13.6). Okazaki fragments are much smaller in eukaryotes than in prokaryotes (about 200 nucleotides vs. 1,000 to 2,000 nucleotides). Because the size of eukaryotic Okazaki fragments is equivalent to the size of the DNA found in nucleosomes, it seems likely that one nucleosome at a time may release its DNA for replication.

Obviously, eukaryotic replication requires many proteins. The complexity of the fork and the fact that it is not completely understood limits the detail shown in Figure 13.9. One protein that is not shown is proliferating cell nuclear antigen (PCNA), which is involved in organizing and orchestrating the replication process on both the leading and lagging strands. PCNA is often used clinically as a diagnostic marker for proliferating cells.

Additional activities that occur during replication include proofreading and DNA repair. Pols δ and ε, which are part of the replication complex, have the 3'-to-5' exonuclease activity required for proofreading. Enzymes that catalyze repair of mismatched bases are also present (see Section III.B.3). Consequently, eukaryotic replication occurs with high fidelity; approximately one mispairing occurs for every 10^9 to 10^{12} nucleotides incorporated into growing DNA chains.

E. Replication of the Ends of Chromosomes

Eukaryotic chromosomes are linear, and the ends of the chromosomes are called *telomeres*. As DNA replication approaches the end of the chromosome, a problem develops in the lagging strand (Fig. 13.10). Either primase cannot lay down a primer at the very end of the chromosome or, after DNA replication is complete, the RNA at the end of the chromosome is degraded. Consequently, the newly synthesized strand is shorter at the 5'-end, and there is a 3'-overhang in the DNA strand being replicated. If the chromosome became shorter with each successive replication, genes would be lost. How is this problem solved?

The 3'-overhang is lengthened by the addition of nucleotides so that primase can bind and synthesize the complementary strand. Telomeres consist of a repeating sequence of bases (TTAGGG for humans), which may be repeated thousands of times. The enzyme telomerase contains both proteins and RNA and acts as an RNA-dependent DNA polymerase (just like reverse transcriptase). The RNA within telomerase contains the complementary copy of the repeating sequence in the telomeres

FIG. 13.10. The "end-replication" problem in linear chromosomes. After replication and removal of the RNA primers, the telomeres have 3'-overhangs. When these molecules are replicated, chromosome shortening will result. The figure depicts a linear chromosome with one origin of replication. At the origin, two replication forks are generated, moving in opposite directions, labeled as *Fork 1* and *Fork 2*. As *Fork 1* moves to the right, the bottom strand is read in the 3'-to-5' direction, which means that it is the template for the leading strand. The newly synthesized DNA complementary to the upper strand at *Fork 1* will be the lagging strand. Now consider *Fork 2*. As this replication fork moves to the left, the upper strand is read in the 3'-to-5' direction, so the newly synthesized DNA complementary to this strand will be the leading strand. For this fork, the newly synthesized DNA complementary to the bottom strand will be the lagging strand.

FIG. 13.11. Telomerase action. The RNA present in telomerase base-pairs with the overhanging 3′-end of telomeres and extends it by acting as both a template and a reverse transcriptase. After copying a small number of repeats, the complex moves down to the 3′-end of the overhang and repeats the process.

 An inability to replicate telomeres has been linked to cell aging and death. Many somatic cells do not express telomerase; when they are placed in culture, they survive a fixed number of population doublings, enter senescence, and then die. Analysis has shown significant telomere shortening in those cells. In contrast, stem cells do express telomerase and appear to have an infinite lifetime in culture. Research is under way to understand the role of telomeres in cell aging, growth, and cancer.

and can base-pair with the existing 3′-overhang (Fig. 13.11). The polymerase activity of telomerase then uses the existing 3′-hydroxyl group of the overhang as a primer, and its own RNA as a template, and synthesizes new DNA that lengthens the 3′-end of the DNA strand. The telomerase moves down the DNA toward the new 3′-end and repeats the process several times. When the 3′-overhang is sufficiently long, primase binds and synthesis of the complementary strand is completed. Even after this lengthening process, there is still a 3′-overhang, which forms a complicated structure with telomere-binding proteins to protect the ends of the chromosomes from damage and nuclease attack once they have been lengthened.

III. DNA REPAIR

A. Actions of Mutagens

Despite proofreading and mismatch repair during replication, some mismatched bases do persist. Additional problems may arise from DNA damaged by mutagens—chemicals produced in cells, inhaled, or absorbed from the environment that cause mutations. Mutagens that cause normal cells to become cancer cells are known as *carcinogens*. Unfortunately, mismatching of bases and DNA damage produce thousands of potentially mutagenic lesions in each cell every day. Without repair mechanisms, we could not survive these assaults on our genes.

DNA damage can be caused by radiation and by chemicals (Fig. 13.12). These agents can directly affect the DNA or they can act indirectly. For example, X-rays,

FIG. 13.12. Oxidation of benzo[*a*]pyrene and covalent binding to DNA. Benzo[*a*]pyrene is not carcinogenic until it is oxidized within cells. Then it can bind covalently to guanine residues in DNA, interrupting hydrogen bonding in G–C base pairs and producing distortions of the helix.

FIG. 13.13. A thymine dimer in a DNA strand. Ultraviolet light can cause two adjacent pyrimidines to form a covalent dimer.

Nick O'Tyne has been smoking for 40 years in spite of the warnings on cigarette packs that this habit can be dangerous and even deadly. The burning of tobacco, and, for that matter, the burning of any organic material, produces many different carcinogens, such as benzo[*a*]pyrene. These carcinogens coat the airways and lungs. They can cross cell membranes and interact with DNA, causing damage to bases that interferes with normal base pairing. If these DNA lesions cannot be repaired or if they are not repaired rapidly enough, a permanent mutation can be produced when the cells replicate. Some mutations are silent, whereas other mutations can lead to abnormal cell growth, and cancer results.

a type of ionizing radiation, act indirectly to damage DNA by exciting water in the cell and generating the hydroxyl radical, which reacts with DNA, thereby altering the structure of the bases or cleaving the DNA strands.

Although exposure to X-rays is infrequent, it is more difficult to avoid exposure to cigarette smoke and virtually impossible to avoid exposure to sunlight. Cigarette smoke contains carcinogens such as the aromatic polycyclic hydrocarbon benzo[*a*] pyrene (see Fig. 13.12). When this compound is oxidized by cellular enzymes, which normally act to make foreign compounds more water-soluble and easy to excrete, it becomes capable of forming bulky adducts with guanine residues in DNA. Ultraviolet (UV) rays from the sun, which also produce distortions in the DNA helix, excite adjacent pyrimidine bases on DNA strands, causing them to form covalent dimers (Fig. 13.13).

Melanomas develop from exposure of the skin to the UV rays of the sun. The UV radiation causes pyrimidine dimers to form in DNA. Mutations may result from nonrepair of the dimers that produce melanomas, appearing as dark brown growths on the skin.

Fortunately, **Mel Anoma's** malignant skin lesion was discovered at an early stage. Because there was no evidence of cancer in the margins of the resected mass, full recovery was expected. However, lifelong surveillance for return of the melanoma was planned.

B. Repair Mechanisms

The mechanisms used for the repair of DNA in mammalian cells have many similarities (Fig. 13.14). First, a distortion in the DNA helix is recognized and the region containing the distortion is removed. The gap in the damaged strand is replaced by the action of a DNA polymerase that uses the intact, undamaged strand as a template, and synthesizes DNA in the 5′-to-3′ direction. Finally, a ligase seals the nick in the strand that has undergone repair.

1. NUCLEOTIDE EXCISION REPAIR

Nucleotide excision repair (NER) involves local distortions of the DNA helix, such as mismatched bases or bulky adducts (e.g., oxidized benzo[*a*]pyrene) (Fig. 13.15; see also Fig. 13.14). Specific repair endonucleases cleave the abnormal chain and remove the distorted region. The gap is then filled by a DNA polymerase that adds deoxyribonucleotides, one at a time, to the 3′-end of the cleaved DNA, using the intact complementary DNA strand as a template. The newly synthesized segment is joined to the 5′-end of the remainder of the original DNA strand by a DNA ligase.

2. BASE EXCISION REPAIR

DNA glycosylases recognize small distortions in DNA involving lesions caused by damage to a single base. A glycosylase cleaves the *N*-glycosidic bond that joins the

Pyrimidine dimers occur frequently in the skin. Usually, repair mechanisms correct this damage, and cancer rarely occurs. However, in individuals with xeroderma pigmentosum, cancers are extremely common. These individuals have defects in their DNA repair systems. The first defect to be identified was a deficiency of the endonuclease involved in the removal of pyrimidine dimers from DNA. Because of the inability to repair DNA, the frequency of mutation increases. A cancer develops once proto-oncogenes or tumor-suppressor genes mutate. By scrupulously avoiding sunlight, these individuals can reduce the number of skin cancers that develop.

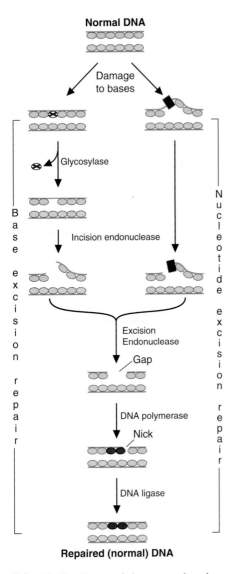

FIG. 13.15. Types of damage and various repair mechanisms. In base excision repair, the glycosylase cleaves the glycosidic bond between the altered base (shown with an *X*) and ribose. In nucleotide excision repair, the entire nucleotide is removed at once. The gap formed by the incision (cut) and excision (removal) endonucleases is usually several nucleotides wider than that shown.

 Spontaneous deamination occurs frequently in human DNA, and cytosine is a base which is often deaminated. How will cytosine deamination, if not repaired, lead to a mutation in the DNA?

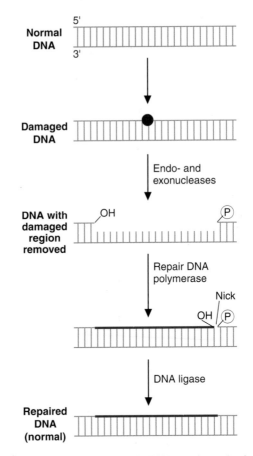

FIG. 13.14. Common steps in DNA repair mechanisms.

damaged base to deoxyribose (see Fig. 13.15). The sugar–phosphate backbone of the DNA now lacks a base at this site (known as an apurinic or apyrimidinic site, or an AP site). Then an AP endonuclease cleaves the sugar–phosphate strand at this site. Subsequently, the same types of enzymes involved in other types of repair mechanisms restore this region to normal.

3. MISMATCH REPAIR

Mismatched bases (bases that do not form normal Watson–Crick base pairs) are recognized by enzymes of the mismatch repair system. Because neither of the bases in a mismatch is damaged, these repair enzymes must be able to determine which base of the mismatched pair to correct.

The mismatch repair enzyme complex acts during replication when an incorrect but normal base (i.e., A, G, C, or T) is incorporated into the growing chain (Fig. 13.16). In bacteria, parental DNA strands contain methyl groups on adenine bases in specific sequences. During replication, the newly synthesized strands are not immediately methylated. Before methylation occurs, the proteins involved in mismatch repair can distinguish parental from newly synthesized strands. A region of the new, unmethylated strand, containing the mismatched base, is removed and replaced.

Human enzymes also can distinguish parental from newly synthesized strands and repair mismatches. However, the mechanism for strand recognition has not yet been as clearly defined as those in bacteria. Otherwise, the process in bacteria and eukaryotes is very similar.

Hereditary nonpolyposis colorectal cancer (a human cancer that does not arise from intestinal polyps) is caused by mutations in genes for proteins involved in mismatch repair (*MLH1*, *MSH2*, *MSH6*, and *PMS2*, with *MLH1* and *MSH2* being the genes most often mutated). The inability to repair mismatches increases the mutation frequency, resulting in cancers from mutations in growth regulatory genes.

When cytosine is deaminated, uracil is produced. Uracil is not normally found in DNA and is potentially harmful because U pairs with A, forming U–A base pairs instead of the normal C–G pairs. Therefore, if not repaired, after one round of DNA replication, one of the daughter cells will have a U–A base pair in this position instead of the normal C–G base pair. To prevent this change from occurring, a uracil *N*-glycosylase removes uracil, and it is replaced by a cytosine via base excision repair.

FIG. 13.16. Mismatch repair. Normal, undamaged, but mismatched bases bind proteins of the mismatch repair system. In bacteria, these proteins recognize the older, parental strand because it is methylated and replace a segment of newly synthesized (and unmethylated) DNA containing the mismatched base. The mechanism for distinguishing between parental and newly synthesized strands in humans is not as well understood.

4. TRANSCRIPTION-COUPLED REPAIR

Genes that are actively transcribed to produce mRNA are preferentially repaired. The RNA polymerase that is transcribing a gene (see Chapter 14 for a description of the process) stalls when it encounters a damaged region of the DNA template. Excision repair proteins are attracted to this site and repair the damaged region, similar to the process of NER. Subsequently, RNA polymerase can resume transcription.

IV. GENETIC REARRANGEMENTS

The exchange of segments between DNA molecules occurs quite frequently and is responsible for genetic alterations that can have beneficial or devastating consequences for affected individuals and, in some instances, for their offspring. The DNA segments that are exchanged may be homologous (i.e., of very similar sequence) or they may be totally unrelated. The size of these segments can range from a few nucleotides to tens of thousands of nucleotides and can include many different genes or portions of genes. Many of the enzymes involved in these exchanges are the same as or similar to those used for replication and repair and include endonucleases, exonucleases, unwinding enzymes, topoisomerases, DNA polymerases, and ligases.

One type of genetic rearrangement that has been observed for many years is "crossing over" between homologous chromosomes during meiosis. Another type occurs in stem cells as they differentiate into lymphocytes. Segments of the genes of stem cells are rearranged so that the mature cell is capable of producing only a single type of antibody (see Figs. 16.10 and 7.15). Other types of genetic exchanges involve transposable elements (transposons) that can move from one site in the genome to another or produce copies that can be inserted into new sites. Translocations occur when chromosomes break and portions randomly become joined to other chromosomes, producing gross changes that can be observed under the light microscope. Genetic exchanges can even occur between species, for example, when foreign DNA is inserted into the human genome as a result of viral infection.

A. General or Homologous Recombination

Various models, supported by experimental evidence, have been proposed for the mechanism of recombination between homologous DNA sequences. Although these mechanisms are complex, a simplified scheme for one type of recombination is presented in Figure 13.17.

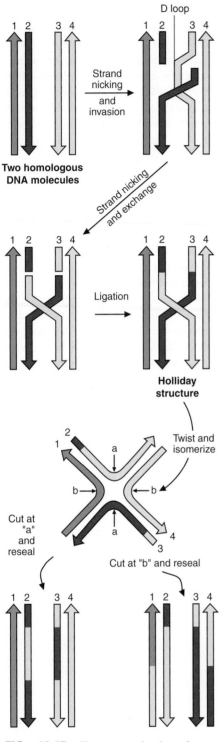

FIG. 13.17. Key steps in homologous recombination.

Initially, two homologous chromosomes or segments of double-helical (duplex) DNA that have very similar, but not necessarily identical, sequences become aligned (see Fig. 13.17). One strand of one duplex is nicked by an enzyme and invades the other DNA duplex, base-pairing with a region of complementary sequence. The match between the sequences does not have to be perfect, but a significant number of bases must pair so that the strand displaced from its partner can form a displacement (D) loop. This D loop is nicked, and the displaced strand now base-pairs with the former partner of the invading strand. Ligation occurs, and a Holliday structure is generated (see Fig. 13.17). The branch point of the Holliday structure can migrate and may move many thousands of nucleotides from its original position. The Holliday structure, named for the scientist who discovered it, is finally cleaved and then religated, forming two chromosomes that have exchanged segments. In addition to enzymes similar to those used in DNA replication, enzymes for strand invasion, branch migration, and cleavage of the Holliday structure are required. Homologous recombination is also an important component of repairing double-strand breaks in DNA.

B. Translocations

Breaks in chromosomes, caused by agents such as X-rays or chemical carcinogens, can result in gross chromosomal rearrangements (Fig. 13.18). If the free ends of the DNA at the break point reseal with the free ends of a different broken chromosome, a translocation is produced. These exchanges of large portions of chromosomes can have deleterious effects and are frequently observed in cancer cells.

C. Transposable Elements

Movable (or transposable) genetic elements, "jumping genes," were first observed by Barbara McClintock in the 1940s. Her work, initially greeted with skepticism, was ultimately accepted, and she was awarded the Nobel Prize in 1983.

FIG. 13.18. A chromosomal translocation. A portion of the long arm of chromosome 8 is exchanged for a portion of the long arm of chromosome 14. This chromosomal translocation occurs in Burkitt lymphoma.

Transposons are segments of DNA that can move from their original position in the genome to a new location (Fig. 13.19). They are found in all organisms. Transposons contain the gene for an enzyme called a *transposase*, which is involved in cleaving the transposon from the genome and moving it from one location to another.

Retroposons are similar to transposons except that they involve an RNA intermediate. Reverse transcriptase (see the following discussion) makes a single-stranded DNA copy of the RNA. A double-stranded DNA is then produced that is inserted into the genome at a new location.

V. REVERSE TRANSCRIPTASE

Reverse transcriptase is an enzyme that uses a single-stranded RNA template and makes a DNA copy (Fig. 13.20). The RNA template can be transcribed from DNA by RNA polymerase or obtained from another source, such as an RNA virus. The DNA copy of the RNA produced by reverse transcriptase is known as *complementary DNA* (because it is complementary to the RNA template), or cDNA. Retroviruses (RNA viruses) contain a reverse transcriptase, which copies the viral RNA genome. A double-stranded cDNA is produced, which can become integrated into the human genome (see Fig. 12.21). After integration, the viral genes may be inactive or they may be transcribed, sometimes causing diseases such as AIDS or cancer (see Chapter 18). The integration event may also disrupt an adjacent cellular gene, which may also lead to disease (see Chapter 18).

CLINICAL COMMENTS

 Ivy Sharer. Ivy Sharer contracted AIDS when she used needles contaminated with HIV to inject drugs intravenously. Intravenous drug users account for 10% of newly diagnosed HIV cases and about 15% of newly diagnosed AIDS cases in the United States. HIV mutates rapidly, and therefore, current treatment involves a combination of drugs that affect different aspects of its life cycle. This multidrug therapy lowers the viral titer (the number of viral particles found in a given volume of blood), sometimes to undetectable levels. However, if treatment is not followed carefully (i.e., if the patient is not "compliant"), the titer increases rapidly. Therefore, Ivy's physician emphasized that she must follow her drug regimen carefully.

 Di Abietes. Di Abietes's poorly controlled diabetes mellitus predisposed her to a urinary tract infection because glucose in the urine serves as a "culture medium" for bacterial growth. The kidney glomerulotubular unit reabsorbs filtered glucose so that, normally, the urine is glucose-free. However, when serum blood glucose levels exceed 175 to 185 mg/dL (the tubular threshold for glucose), the capacity for reabsorption is exceeded. In Ms. Abietes's case, blood glucose levels frequently exceed this threshold.

 Mel Anoma. The average person has 20 moles on the body surface; however, only 7 people of every 100,000 develop a malignant melanoma. The incidence of malignant melanoma, however, is rising rapidly. Because 12% to 15% of patients with malignant melanoma die as a result of this cancer, the physician's decision to perform a biopsy on a pigmented mole with an irregular border and variation of color probably saved Mel's life.

 Nick O'Tyne. Lung cancer accounts for about 30% of all cancers in men and women. The overall 5-year survival rate is approximately 15%. Thankfully, cigarette smoking has declined in the United States. Whereas 50% of men and 32% of women smoked in 1965, these figures have, in 2008, fallen to 23% and 18%, respectively.

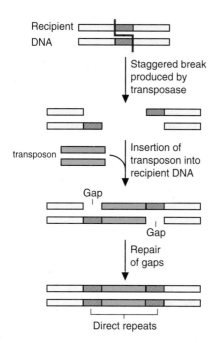

FIG. 13.19. Transposons. The steps involved in transposon action are shown. Direct repeats (the areas in *blue*) are regions of DNA that have the same base sequence in the 5′-to-3′ direction. They are created after the transposon integrates into the chromosome.

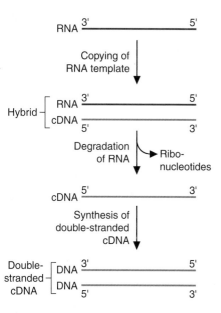

FIG. 13.20. Action of reverse transcriptase. This enzyme catalyzes the production of a DNA copy from an RNA template. The RNA of a DNA–RNA hybrid is degraded by an associated RNase activity of reverse transcriptase (designated as RNase H), and the single DNA strand is used as a template to make double-stranded DNA. This figure is a simplified version of a more complex process.

DNA Repair and Disease. DNA serves a unique role within a cell in that it produces the blueprint for gene expression throughout the lifetime of the cell. However, DNA is present in limited copies within cells (unlike RNA and proteins), and various agents often compromise its structural integrity. The DNA, then, must be continually monitored for damage, and when damage is found, repair mechanisms are required to restore the DNA to its original structure. If the integrity of the DNA cannot be maintained, deleterious mutations may accumulate in the genome, ultimately negatively impacting the person as a whole. Failures in DNA repair mechanisms will lead to disease, as indicated by the examples discussed subsequently.

DNA can undergo various types of damage within the cells' aqueous environment. DNA undergoes spontaneous hydrolysis of the *N*-glycosidic bonds, generating apurinic or apyrimidinic sites within the DNA. Failure to repair these sites (via base excision repair) will lead to changes in nucleotide sequence of the DNA. DNA, when exposed to ultraviolet (UV) light, rapidly forms thymine dimers, which will interfere with DNA replication unless repaired. DNA exposure to X-rays or ionizing radiation will lead to single-strand or double-strand breaks within the DNA. Failure to repair these breaks will lead to replicative errors. The DNA is also exposed to environmental toxins, leading to chemically modified bases, which need to be repaired before DNA replication occurs, otherwise the risk of inappropriate base pairing during replication is greatly increased.

DNA repair disorders, due to mutations in single genes, often give rise to a cell that actively accumulates mutations and can eventually turn into a cancer cell (see Chapter 18). A common theme in DNA repair enzyme mutations is the clinical display of cancer. It is important to note that the mutations themselves do not directly lead to cancer, rather successive cell generations, each with accumulated mutations due to DNA repair defects, will eventually acquire a mutation that leads to growth advantages and cancer. Distinct examples of such diseases are described as follows.

The first example is the mutations that give rise to xeroderma pigmentosum (XP). XP is primarily a defect in nucleotide excision repair (NER) (see Fig. 13.15). There are at least 13 genes responsible for XP and its variants, all of which are involved in NER and/or transcription-coupled repair. The disorder is seen clinically as sun-induced skin abnormalities and a 2,000-fold greater risk of developing skin cancer in the general population. This results from an inability to remove UV-induced thymine dimers in the DNA, leading to mismatches being created during DNA replication through the thymine dimer.

Mutations in proteins specifically responsible for transcription-coupled repair lead to Cockayne syndrome, which presents clinically as premature aging. Cells with these mutations cannot transcribe damaged genes. If the DNA cannot be repaired due to the defect in transcription-coupled repair, premature cell death can result from the reduction of gene expression. There are also specific mutations within the XP constellation of genes that give rise to a phenotype that reflects traits of both XP and Cockayne syndrome, indicating that there are commonalities in symptoms when either NER or transcription-coupled repair is defective.

Hereditary nonpolyposis colon cancer (HNPCC) is due to mutations in enzymes present in intestinal epithelial cells that are responsible for mismatch repair. The inability to repair mismatches will eventually lead to a series of mutations within the cells leading to right-sided colon cancer. This disorder is inherited, and the affected individuals have an early age of onset of the disease (fourth decade of life) as compared to the general population.

Hereditary breast cancer (*BRCA1* and *BRCA2*) results from the inheritance of mutations in proteins responsible for the DNA repair of single-strand and double-strand breaks. Inheritance of mutations in these genes will predispose the patients to an earlier age of onset of the disorder. The roles of *BRCA1* and *BRCA2* will be discussed further in Chapter 18.

Table 13.4   Diseases Discussed in Chapter 13

Disorder or Condition	Genetic or Environmental	Comments
AIDS	Environmental	The rationale for multidrug regime for AIDS patients is explained
Urinary tract infection	Environmental	Antibiotics to treat such infections can target prokaryotic-specific enzymes involved in DNA synthesis
Melanoma	Both	Drugs used to treat cancer can inhibit DNA replication by a variety of mechanisms
Lung cancer	Both	Drugs used to treat cancer can inhibit DNA replication
Hereditary nonpolyposis colon cancer	Genetic	Mutations in enzymes required for DNA mismatch repair, which can lead to mutations in genes regulating cell proliferation
Cockayne syndrome	Genetic	Mutations in enzymes required for transcription-coupled DNA repair; leads to premature cell death
Xeroderma pigmentosum	Genetic	Mutations involved in nucleotide excision repair, leading to a greatly elevated risk for the development of skin cancer
Hereditary breast cancer	Genetic	Mutations in the genes *BRCA1* and *BRCA2*, which lead to defects in the repair of single-strand and double-strand breaks in DNA

Key Concepts

- Replication of the genome requires DNA synthesis.
- During replication, each of the two parental strands of DNA serves as a template for the synthesis of a complementary strand.
- The site at which replication is occurring is called the replication fork.
- Helicases and topoisomerases are required to unwind the DNA helix of the parental strands.
- DNA polymerase is the major enzyme involved in replication.
- DNA polymerase copies each parental template strand in the 3′-to-5′ direction, producing new strands in a 5′-to-3′ direction.
- The precursors for replication are deoxyribonucleotide triphosphates.
- As DNA synthesis proceeds in the 5′-to-3′ direction, one parental strand is synthesized continuously, whereas the other exhibits discontinuous synthesis, creating small fragments that are subsequently joined, because of the requirement that DNA polymerase must synthesize DNA in the 5′-to-3′ direction.
- DNA polymerase requires a free 3′-hydroxyl group of a nucleotide primer in order to replicate DNA. The primer is synthesized by the enzyme primase, which provides an RNA primer.
- The enzyme telomerase synthesizes the replication of the ends of linear chromosomes (telomeres).
- Errors during replication can lead to mutations, so error checking and repair systems function to maintain the integrity of the genome.
- Table 13.4 summarizes the diseases discussed in this chapter.

REVIEW QUESTIONS—CHAPTER 13

1. Reverse transcriptase, an RNA-dependent DNA polymerase, differs from DNA polymerase δ by which of the following?

    A. Synthesizes DNA in the 5′-to-3′ direction
    B. Contains 3′-to-5′ exonuclease activity
    C. Follows Watson–Crick base pair rules
    D. Synthesizes DNA in the 3′-to-5′ direction
    E. Can insert inosine into a growing DNA chain

2. If a 1,000-kilobase (kb) fragment of DNA has 10 evenly spaced and symmetric replication origins and DNA polymerase moves at 1 kb per second, how many seconds will it take to produce two daughter molecules (ignore potential problems at the ends of this linear piece of DNA)? Assume that the 10 origins are evenly spaced from each other but not from the ends of the chromosome.

    A. 20
    B. 30

C. 40
D. 50
E. 100

3. Primase is not required during DNA repair processes because of which of the following?

   A. All of the primase is associated with replication origins.
   B. RNA would be highly mutagenic at a repair site.
   C. DNA polymerase I does not require a primer.
   D. DNA polymerase III does not require a primer.
   E. DNA polymerase I or III can use any 3′-OH for elongation.

4. Which of the following enzymes is required to actively enhance the separation of DNA strands during replication?

A. Helicase
B. 3′-to-5′ exonuclease
C. DNA ligase
D. Primase
E. AP endonuclease

5. The key mechanistic failure in patients with xeroderma pigmentosum involves which of the following?

   A. Mutation in the primase gene
   B. Inability to excise a section of the UV-damaged DNA
   C. Mutation of one of the mismatch repair components
   D. Inability to synthesize DNA across the damaged region
   E. Loss of proofreading capacity

14 Transcription: Synthesis of RNA

Synthesis of RNA from a **DNA template** is called **transcription**. Genes are transcribed by enzymes called **RNA polymerases** that generate a **single-stranded RNA** identical in sequence (with the exception of U in place of T) to one of the strands of the double-stranded DNA. The DNA strand that directs the sequence of nucleotides in the RNA by **complementary base pairing** is the template strand. The RNA strand that is initially generated is the **primary transcript**. The DNA **template is copied** in the **3′-to-5′ direction**, and the **RNA transcript** is **synthesized** in the **5′-to-3′ direction**. RNA polymerases differ from DNA polymerases in that they can **initiate** the **synthesis** of new strands in the absence of a primer.

In addition to catalyzing the polymerization of **ribonucleotides**, RNA polymerases must be able to recognize the appropriate gene to transcribe—the appropriate strand of the double-stranded DNA to copy—and the **start point** of transcription (Fig. 14.1). Specific sequences on DNA, called **promoters**, determine where the RNA polymerase binds and how frequently it initiates transcription. Other regulatory sequences such as **promoter-proximal elements** and **enhancers** also affect the frequency of transcription.

In **bacteria**, a **single RNA polymerase** produces the primary transcript precursors for all three major classes of RNA: messenger RNA (mRNA), ribosomal RNA (rRNA), and transfer RNA (tRNA). Because bacteria do not contain nuclei, ribosomes bind to mRNA while it is being transcribed, and protein synthesis occurs simultaneously with transcription.

Eukaryotic genes are transcribed in the nucleus by **three different RNA polymerases**, each principally responsible for one of the major classes of RNA. The primary transcripts are **modified** and **trimmed** to produce the mature RNAs. The precursors of **mRNA** (called **pre-mRNA**) have a **guanosine** "cap" added at the 5′-end and a **poly(A) "tail"** at the 3′-end. **Exons**, which contain the coding sequences for the proteins, are separated in **pre-mRNA** by **introns**, regions that have no coding function. During **splicing reactions**, introns are removed and the exons connect to form the mature mRNA. In eukaryotes, tRNA and rRNA precursors are also modified and trimmed, although not as extensively as pre-mRNA.

FIG. 14.1. Regions of a gene. A gene is a segment of DNA that functions as a unit to generate an RNA product or, through the processes of transcription and translation, a polypeptide chain. The transcribed region of a gene contains the template for synthesis of an RNA, which begins at the start point. A gene also includes regions of DNA that regulate production of the encoded product, such as a promoter region. In a structural gene, the transcribed region contains the coding sequences that dictate the amino acid sequence of a polypeptide chain.

The thalassemias are a heterogeneous group of hereditary anemias that constitute the most common gene disorder in the world, with a carrier rate of almost 7%. The disease was first discovered in countries around the Mediterranean Sea and was named for the Greek word "thalassa," meaning "sea." However, it is also present in areas extending into India and China that are near the equator.

The thalassemia syndromes are caused by mutations that decrease or abolish the synthesis of the α- or β-chains in the adult hemoglobin A tetramer. Individual syndromes are named according to the chain whose synthesis is affected and the severity of the deficiency. Thus, in β^0-thalassemia, the superscript 0 denotes none of the β-chain is present; in β^+-thalassemia, the + denotes a partial reduction in the synthesis of the β-chain. More than 170 different mutations have been identified that cause β-thalassemia; most of these interfere with the transcription of β-globin mRNA or its processing or translation.

The measurement of hemoglobin levels in blood is important for the appropriate diagnosis of many diseases, such as anemia. Laboratories measure hemoglobin content by first exposing the sample (usually lysed blood cells, to release the hemoglobin from the red blood cells) to an oxidizing agent, which converts the ferrous iron (Fe^{2+}) in hemoglobin to its ferric state (Fe^{3+}). The level of ferric iron is then determined with a second reagent (either a cyanide or azide derivative), which reacts with the ferric iron and generates a colored product, whose concentration can be determined spectrophotometrically.

THE WAITING ROOM

Anne Niemick is a 4-year-old girl of Mediterranean ancestry whose height and body weight are less than the 20th percentile for girls of her age. She is listless, tires easily, and complains of loss of appetite and shortness of breath on exertion. A dull pain has been present in her right upper quadrant for the last 3 months. Her complexion is slate gray and she appears pale. Initial laboratory studies indicate a severe anemia (decreased red blood cell count) with a hemoglobin of 6.2 g/dL (reference range, 12 to 16 g/dL). A battery of additional hematologic tests shows that Anne has β^+-thalassemia, intermediate type.

Ivy Sharer, a patient with AIDS (see Chapters 12 and 13), has developed a cough that produces a grayish, slightly blood-tinged sputum. A chest radiograph indicates infiltrates in the cavities of both upper lung fields (cavitary infiltrates). A stain of sputum shows acid-fast bacilli, suggesting a diagnosis of pulmonary tuberculosis caused by *Mycobacterium tuberculosis*.

Amanda Tin picked mushrooms in a wooded area near her home. A few hours after eating one small mushroom, she experienced mild nausea and diarrhea. She brought a mushroom with her to the hospital emergency room. A poison expert identified it as *Amanita phalloides* (the "death cap"). These mushrooms contain the toxin α-amanitin.

Sis Lupus, a 28-year-old computer programmer, notes increasing fatigue, pleuritic chest pain, and a nonproductive cough. In addition, she complains of joint pains, especially in her hands. A rash on both cheeks and the bridge of her nose ("butterfly rash") has been present for the last 6 months. Initial laboratory studies indicate a subnormal white blood cell count and a mild reduction in hemoglobin. Tests resulted in a diagnosis of systemic lupus erythematosus (SLE) (frequently called lupus).

I. ACTION OF RNA POLYMERASE

Transcription, the synthesis of RNA from a DNA template, is carried out by RNA polymerases (Fig. 14.2). Like DNA polymerases, *RNA polymerases* catalyze the formation of ester bonds between nucleotides that base-pair with the complementary nucleotides on the DNA template. Unlike DNA polymerases, RNA polymerases can initiate the synthesis of new chains in the absence of primers. They also lack the 3'-to-5' exonuclease activity found in DNA polymerases, although they do perform rudimentary error checking through a different mechanism. A strand of DNA serves as the template for RNA synthesis and is copied in the 3'-to-5' direction. Synthesis of the new RNA molecule occurs in the 5'-to-3' direction. The ribonucleoside triphosphates' adenosine triphosphate (ATP), GTP, CTP, and UTP serve as the precursors. Each nucleotide base-pairs sequentially with the complementary deoxyribonucleotide base on the DNA template (A, G, C, and U pair with T, C, G, and A, respectively). The polymerase forms an ester bond between the α-phosphate on the ribose 5'-hydroxyl of the nucleotide precursor and the ribose 3'-hydroxyl at the end of the growing RNA chain. The cleavage of a high-energy phosphate bond in the nucleotide triphosphate and release of pyrophosphate (from the β- and γ-phosphates) provides the energy for this polymerization reaction. Subsequent cleavage of the pyrophosphate by a pyrophosphatase also helps to drive the polymerization reaction forward by removing a product. The overall error rate of RNA polymerase is 1 in 100,000 bases.

FIG. 14.2. RNA synthesis. The α-phosphate from the added nucleotide (shown in *black*) connects the ribosyl groups.

RNA polymerases must be able to recognize the start point for transcription of each gene and the appropriate strand of DNA to use as a template. They also must be sensitive to signals that reflect the need for the gene product and control the frequency of transcription. A region of regulatory sequences called the *promoter*, usually contiguous with the transcribed region, controls the binding of RNA polymerase to DNA and identifies the start point (see Fig. 14.1). The frequency of transcription is controlled by regulatory sequences within the promoter, nearby the promoter (promoter-proximal elements), and by other regulatory sequences, such as enhancers (also called distal-promoter elements), that may be located at considerable distances, sometimes thousands of nucleotides, from the start point. Both the promoter-proximal elements and the enhancers interact with proteins that stabilize RNA polymerase binding to the promoter.

II. TYPES OF RNA POLYMERASES

Bacterial cells have a single RNA polymerase that transcribes DNA to generate all of the different types of RNA (messenger RNA [mRNA], ribosomal RNA [rRNA], and transfer RNA [tRNA]). The RNA polymerase of *Escherichia coli* contains four subunits ($\alpha_2\beta\beta'$), which form the core enzyme. Another protein called σ (*sigma*) *factor* binds the core enzyme and directs binding of RNA polymerase to specific promoter regions of the DNA template. The σ-factor dissociates shortly after transcription begins. *E. coli* has several different σ-factors that recognize the promoter regions of different groups of genes. The major σ-factor is σ^{70}, a designation related to its molecular weight of 70,000 Da.

In contrast to prokaryotes, eukaryotic cells have three RNA polymerases (Table 14.1). Polymerase I produces most of the rRNAs, polymerase II produces mRNA and micro RNAs (micro RNAs regulate gene expression and are discussed

 Patients with AIDS frequently develop tuberculosis. After **Ivy Sharer's** sputum stain suggested that she had tuberculosis, a multidrug antituberculous regimen, which includes an antibiotic of the rifamycin family (rifampin), was begun. A culture of her sputum was taken to confirm the diagnosis.

Rifampin inhibits bacterial RNA polymerase, selectively killing the bacteria that cause the infection. The nuclear RNA polymerase from eukaryotic cells is not affected. Although rifampin can inhibit the synthesis of mitochondrial RNA, the concentration required is considerably higher than that used for treatment of tuberculosis.

Table 14.1 Products of Eukaryotic RNA Polymerases

Polymerase	Product
RNA polymerase I	rRNA
RNA polymerase II	mRNA + micro RNA (miRNA)
RNA polymerase III	tRNA + other small RNAs

DNA coding strand (sense strand, non-template strand)	5'-ATGCCAGTAGGCCACTTGTCA-3'
DNA template strand (antisense strand)	3'-TACGGTCATCCGGTGAACAGT-5'
mRNA	5'-AUG CCA GUA GGC CAC UUG UCA-3'
Protein	N-Met-Pro-Val-Gly-His-Leu-Ser-C

FIG. 14.3. Relationship between the coding strand of DNA (also known as the sense strand or the nontemplate strand), the DNA template strand (also known as the antisense strand), the mRNA transcript, and the protein produced from the gene. The bases in mRNA are used in sets of three (called *codons*) to specify the order of the amino acids inserted into the growing polypeptide chain during the process of translation (see Chapter 15).

The mushrooms picked by **Amanda Tin** contained α-amanitin, an inhibitor of eukaryotic RNA polymerases:

α-Amanitin

It is particularly effective at blocking the action of RNA polymerase II. This toxin initially causes gastrointestinal disturbances, then electrolyte imbalance and fever, followed by liver and kidney dysfunction. Between 40% and 90% of individuals who ingest α-amanitin die within a few days.

in more detail in Chapter 16), and polymerase III produces small RNAs, such as tRNA and 5S rRNA. All of these RNA polymerases have the same mechanism of action. However, they recognize different types of promoters.

A. Sequences of Genes

Double-stranded DNA consists of a coding strand and a template strand (Fig. 14.3). The DNA template strand is the strand that is actually used by RNA polymerase during the process of transcription. It is complementary and antiparallel both to the coding (nontemplate) strand of the DNA and to the RNA transcript produced from the template. Thus, the coding strand of the DNA is identical in base sequence and direction to the RNA transcript, except, of course, that wherever this DNA strand contains a T, the RNA transcript contains a U. By convention, the nucleotide sequence of a gene is represented by the letters of the nitrogenous bases of the coding strand of the DNA duplex. It is written from left to right in the 5'-to-3' direction.

During translation, mRNA is read 5' to 3' in sets of three bases, called *codons*, that determine the amino acid sequence of the protein (see Fig. 14.3). Thus, the base sequence of the coding strand of the DNA can be used to determine the amino acid sequence of the protein. For this reason, when gene sequences are given, they refer to the coding strand.

A gene consists of the transcribed region and the regions that regulate transcription of the gene (e.g., promoter and enhancer regions) (Fig. 14.4). The base in the coding strand of the gene serving as the start point for transcription is numbered +1. This nucleotide corresponds to the first nucleotide incorporated into the RNA at the 5'-end of the transcript. Subsequent nucleotides within the transcribed region of the gene are numbered +2, +3, and so on toward the 3'-end of the gene. Untranscribed sequences to the left of the start point, known as the 5'-flanking region of the gene, are numbered −1, −2, −3, and so on, starting with the nucleotide (−1) immediately to the left of the start point (+1) and moving from right to left. By analogy to a river, the sequences to the left of the start point are said to be upstream from the start point, and those to the right are said to be downstream.

B. Recognition of Genes by RNA Polymerase

For genes to be expressed, RNA polymerase must recognize the appropriate point on which to start transcription and the strand of the DNA to transcribe (the template strand). RNA polymerase also must recognize which genes to transcribe, because transcribed genes are only a small fraction of the total DNA. The genes that are transcribed differ from one type of cell to another and change with changes in physiologic conditions. The signals in DNA that RNA polymerase recognizes are called promoters. *Promoters* are sequences in DNA (often composed of smaller sequences called *boxes* or *elements*) that determine the start point and the frequency of transcription. Because promoters are located on the same molecule of DNA and near the gene they regulate, they are said to be *cis*-acting (i.e., "*cis*" refers to acting on the same side). Proteins that bind to these DNA sequences and facilitate or prevent the binding of RNA polymerase are said to be *trans*-acting.

Q: Why is it important for RNA polymerase to distinguish between the two DNA strands at the promoter?

FIG. 14.4. A schematic view of a eukaryotic gene and steps required to produce a protein product. The gene consists of promoter and transcribed regions. The transcribed region contains introns, which do not contain coding sequences for proteins, and exons, which do carry coding sequences for proteins. The first RNA form produced is heterogeneous nuclear RNA (hnRNA), which contains both intronic and exonic sequences. The hnRNA is modified such that a cap is added at the 5′-end (cap site), and a poly(A) tail is added to the 3′-end. The introns are removed (a process called *splicing*) to produce the mature mRNA, which leaves the nucleus to direct protein synthesis in the cytoplasm. Py is pyrimidine (C or T). Although the *TATA box* is still included in this figure for historical reasons, only 12.5% of eukaryotic promoters contain this sequence.

C. Promoter Regions of Genes for mRNA

The binding of RNA polymerase and the subsequent initiation of gene transcription involves several consensus sequences in the promoter regions of the gene (Fig. 14.5). A *consensus sequence* is the sequence that is most commonly found in a given region when many genes are examined. In prokaryotes, an adenine- and thymine-rich consensus sequence in the promoter determines the start point of transcription by binding proteins that facilitate the binding of RNA polymerase. In the prokaryote *E. coli*, this consensus sequence is TATAAT, which is known as the TATA or Pribnow box. It is centered

 The two strands of DNA are antiparallel, with complementary nucleotides at each position. Because RNA synthesis always occurs in the 5′-to-3′ direction, each strand would produce a different mRNA, resulting in different codons for amino acids and a different protein product. Therefore, it is critical that RNA polymerase transcribe the correct strand.

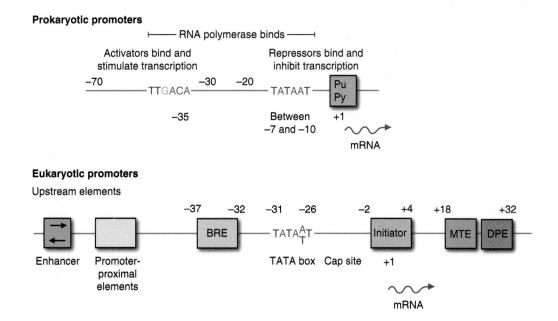

FIG. 14.5. Prokaryotic and eukaryotic promoters. The promoter-proximal region contains binding sites for transcription factors that can accelerate the rate at which RNA polymerase binds to the promoter. *BRE*, TF_{II}B recognition element; *Inr*, initiator element; *MTE*, motif ten element; *DPE*, downstream promoter element.

Anne Niemick has a β^+-thalassemia classified clinically as β-thalassemia intermedia. She produces an intermediate amount of functional β-globin chains (her hemoglobin is 6.2 g/dL; normal is 12 to 16 g/dL). β-Thalassemia intermedia is usually the result of two different mutations (one that mildly affects the rate of synthesis of β-globin and one that severely affects its rate of synthesis) or, less frequently, homozygosity for a mild mutation in the rate of synthesis, or a complex combination of mutations. For example, mutations within the promoter region of the β-globin gene could result in a significantly decreased rate of β-globin synthesis in an individual who is homozygous for the allele, without completely abolishing synthesis of the protein.

Two of the point mutations that result in a β^+-phenotype are within the TATA box (A → G or A → C in the −28 to −31 region) for the β-globin gene. These mutations reduce the accuracy of the start point of transcription so that only 20% to 25% of the normal amount of β-globin is synthesized. Other mutations that also reduce the frequency of β-globin transcription have been observed farther upstream in the promoter region (−87 C → G and −88 C → T).

What property of an AT-rich region of a DNA double helix makes it suitable to serve as a recognition site for the start point of transcription?

about −10 and is recognized by the sigma factor σ^{70}. A similar sequence in the −25 region of about 12.5% of eukaryotic genes has a consensus sequence of TATA(A/T)A (the [A/T] in the fifth position indicates that either A or T occurs with equal frequency). This eukaryotic sequence is also known as a TATA box, but it is sometimes named the Hogness or Hogness–Goldberg box after its discoverers. Other consensus sequences involved in binding of RNA polymerase are found farther upstream in the promoter region (see Fig. 14.5), or downstream after the transcriptional start signal. Bacterial promoters contain a sequence TTGACA in the −35 region. Eukaryotes frequently have disparate sequences, such as the TF$_{II}$B-recognition element (a GC-rich sequence, abbreviated as BRE), the initiator element, the downstream promoter element (DPE), and the motif ten element (MTE). The DPE and MTE are found downstream from the transcription start site. Eukaryotic genes also contain promoter-proximal elements (in the region of −100 to −200), which are sites that bind other gene regulatory proteins. Genes vary in the number of such sequences present. An analysis of close to 10,000 promoter sequences indicated that the initiator element was the most common element in these promoters (about 50%), whereas BRE and DPE were present in about 15% of the promoters, and TATA the least abundant, at 12.5% of the promoters.

In bacteria, several protein-producing genes may be linked together and controlled by a single promoter. This genetic unit is called an *operon* (Fig. 14.6). Proteins bind to the promoter and either inhibit or facilitate transcription of the operon. *Repressors* are proteins that bind to a region in the promoter known as the operator and inhibit transcription by preventing the binding of RNA polymerase to DNA. Activators are proteins that stimulate transcription by binding within the −35 region or upstream from it, facilitating the binding of RNA polymerase. (Operons are described in more detail in Chapter 16.)

In eukaryotes, proteins known as general transcription factors (or basal factors) bind to the TATA box (or other promoter elements, in the case of TATA-less promoters) and facilitate the binding of RNA polymerase II, the polymerase that transcribes mRNA (Fig. 14.7). This binding process involves at least six basal transcription factors (labeled as TF$_{II}$s, transcription factors for RNA polymerase II). The TATA-binding protein (TBP), which is a component of TF$_{II}$D, initially binds to the TATA box. TF$_{II}$D consists of both the TBP and several transcriptional coactivators. Components of TF$_{II}$D will also recognize initiator and DPE boxes in the absence of a TATA box. TF$_{II}$A and TF$_{II}$B interact with TBP. RNA polymerase II binds to the complex of transcription factors and to DNA and is aligned at the start point for transcription. TF$_{II}$E, TF$_{II}$F, and TF$_{II}$H subsequently bind, cleaving ATP, and transcription of the gene is initiated.

FIG. 14.6. Bacterial operon. A cistron encodes a single polypeptide chain. In bacteria, a single promoter may control transcription of an operon containing many cistrons. A single polycistronic mRNA is transcribed. Its translation produces several polypeptide chains.

FIG. 14.7. Transcription apparatus. The TATA-binding protein (TBP), a component of TF$_{II}$D, binds to the TATA box. Transcription factors TF$_{II}$ A and B bind to TBP. RNA polymerase binds, then TF$_{II}$ E, F, and H bind. This complex can transcribe at a basal level. Some coactivator proteins are present as a component of TF$_{II}$D, and these can bind to other regulatory DNA-binding proteins (called *specific transcription factors* or *transcriptional activators*). TF$_{II}$D also recognizes the initiator element and the DPE in the case of TATA-less promoters.

With only these transcription (or basal) factors and RNA polymerase II attached (the basal transcription complex), the gene is transcribed at a low or basal rate. TF$_{II}$H plays several roles in both transcription and DNA repair. In both processes, it acts as an ATP-dependent DNA helicase, unwinding DNA for either transcription or repair to occur. Two of the forms of xeroderma pigmentosum (XPB and XPD; see Chapter 13)—arise from mutations within two different helicase subunits of TF$_{II}$H. TF$_{II}$H also contains a kinase activity, and RNA polymerase II is phosphorylated by this factor during certain phases of transcription.

The rate of transcription can be further increased by binding of other regulatory DNA-binding proteins to additional gene regulatory sequences (such as the promoter-proximal or enhancer regions). These regulatory DNA-binding proteins are called *gene-specific transcription factors* (or transactivators) because they are specific to the gene involved (see Chapter 16). They interact with coactivators in the basal transcription complex. These are depicted in Figure 14.7 under the general term *coactivators*. Coactivators consist of transcription-associated factors (TAF) that interact with transcription factors through an activation domain on the transcription factor (which is bound to DNA). The TAFs interact with other factors (described as the mediator proteins), which in turn interact with the RNA polymerase complex. These interactions are further discussed in Chapter 16.

 In regions in which DNA is being transcribed, the two strands of the DNA must be separated. AT base pairs in DNA are joined by only two hydrogen bonds, whereas GC pairs have three hydrogen bonds. Therefore, in AT-rich regions of DNA, the two strands can be separated more readily than in regions that contain GC base pairs.

III. TRANSCRIPTION OF BACTERIAL GENES

In bacteria, binding of RNA polymerase with a σ-factor to the promoter region of DNA causes the two DNA strands to unwind and separate within a region approximately 10 to 20 nucleotides in length. As the polymerase transcribes the DNA, the untranscribed region of the helix continues to separate, whereas the transcribed region of the DNA template rejoins its DNA partner (Fig. 14.8). The σ-factor is released when the growing RNA chain is approximately 10 nucleotides long. The elongation reactions continue until the RNA polymerase encounters a transcription termination signal. One type of termination signal involves the formation of a hairpin loop in the transcript, preceding several U residues. The second type of mechanism for termination involves the binding of a protein, the rho factor, which causes release of the RNA transcript from the template in an energy-requiring mechanism. The signal for both termination processes is the sequence of bases in the newly synthesized RNA.

A cistron is a region of DNA that encodes a single polypeptide chain. In bacteria, mRNA is usually generated from an operon as a polycistronic transcript (one that

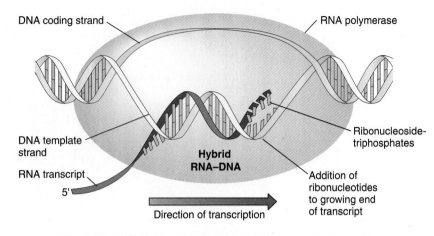

FIG. 14.8.   An overview of transcription at the site of RNA synthesis.

contains the information to produce several different proteins). The polycistronic transcript is translated as it is being transcribed. This transcript is not modified and trimmed, and it does not contain introns (regions within the coding sequence of a transcript that are removed before translation occurs). Several different proteins are produced during translation of the polycistronic transcript, one from each cistron (see Fig. 14.6).

In prokaryotes, rRNA is produced as a single, long transcript that is cleaved to produce the 16S, 23S, and 5S rRNAs. tRNA is also cleaved from larger transcripts (Fig. 14.9). One of the cleavage enzymes, *RNase P,* is a protein containing an RNA molecule. This RNA actually catalyzes the cleavage reaction.

IV. TRANSCRIPTION OF EUKARYOTIC GENES

The process of transcription in eukaryotes is similar to that in prokaryotes. RNA polymerase binds to the transcription factor complex in the promoter region and to the DNA, the helix unwinds within a region near the start point of transcription, DNA strand separation occurs, synthesis of the RNA transcript is initiated, and the RNA transcript is elongated, copying the DNA template. The DNA strands separate as the polymerase approaches and rejoin as the polymerase passes.

One of the major differences between eukaryotes and prokaryotes is that eukaryotes have more elaborate mechanisms for processing the transcripts, particularly the precursors of mRNA (pre-mRNA). Eukaryotes also have three polymerases, rather than just the one present in prokaryotes. Other differences include the facts that eukaryotic mRNA usually contains the coding information for only one polypeptide chain and that eukaryotic RNA is transcribed in the nucleus and migrates to the cytoplasm where translation occurs.

FIG. 14.9.   Bacterial rRNA and tRNA transcripts. One large precursor is cleaved (at *arrows*) to produce 16S, 23S, and 5S rRNA and some tRNAs.

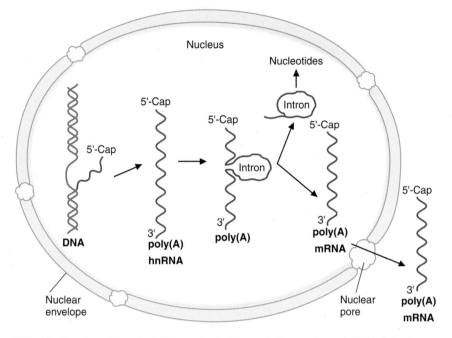

FIG. 14.10. Overview of mRNA synthesis. Transcription produces hnRNA (also known as pre-mRNA) from the DNA template. hnRNA processing involves addition of a 5′-cap and a poly(A) tail and splicing to join exons and remove introns. The product, mRNA, migrates to the cytoplasm, in which it will direct protein synthesis.

A. Synthesis of Eukaryotic mRNA

In eukaryotes, extensive processing of the primary transcript occurs before the mature mRNA is formed and can migrate to the cytosol, where it is translated into a protein product. RNA polymerase II synthesizes a large primary transcript from the template strand that is capped at the 5′-end as it is transcribed (Fig. 14.10). The transcript also rapidly acquires a poly(A) tail at the 3′-end. Pre-mRNAs thus contain untranslated regions at both the 5′- and 3′-ends (the leader and trailing sequences, respectively). These untranslated regions are retained in the mature mRNA. The coding region of the pre-mRNA, which begins with the start codon for protein synthesis and ends with the stop codon, contains both exons and introns. *Exons* consist of the nucleotide codons that dictate the amino acid sequence of the eventual protein product. Between the exons, interspersing regions called *introns* contain nucleotide sequences that are removed by splicing reactions to form the mature RNA. The mature RNA thus contains a leader sequence (which includes the cap), a coding region comprising exons, and a tailing sequence that includes the poly(A) tail.

This mature mRNA complexes with the poly(A)-binding protein and other proteins. It travels through pores in the nuclear envelope into the cytoplasm. There it combines with ribosomes and directs the incorporation of amino acids into proteins.

1.   TRANSCRIPTION AND CAPPING OF mRNA

"Capping" of the primary transcript synthesized by RNA polymerase II occurs at its 5′-end as it is being transcribed (Fig. 14.11). The *5′-terminal*, the initial nucleotide of the transcript, is a pyrimidine with three phosphate groups attached to the 5′-hydroxyl of the ribose. To form the cap, the terminal triphosphate loses one phosphate, forming a 5′-diphosphate. The β-phosphate of the diphosphate then attacks the α-phosphate of GTP, liberating pyrophosphate, and forming an unusual 5′-to-5′ triphosphate linkage. A methyl group is transferred from *S*-adenosylmethionine (SAM), a universal methyl donor, to position 7 of the added guanine ring.

There are three different types of methyl caps, shown in *red*:

CAP 0 refers to the methylated guanosine (on the nitrogen at the seven position, N^7) added in the 5′-to-5′ linkage to the mRNA; *CAP 1* refers to CAP 0 with the addition of a methyl group to the 2′-carbon of ribose on the nucleotide (N_1) at the 5′-end of the chain; and *CAP 2* refers to CAP 1 with the addition of another 2′-methyl group to the next nucleotide (N_2). The methyl groups are donated by *S*-adenosylmethionine (SAM).

Once SAM donates its methyl group, it must be regenerated by reactions that require the vitamins folate and B_{12}. Thus, formation of mRNA is also one of the processes affected by a deficiency of these vitamins.

FIG. 14.11.   The cap structure in eukaryotic mRNA. The phosphates in *red* originated from the original RNA transcript; the phosphate in *black* comes from GTP. SAM donates the methyl groups (shown in *red*) required for cap synthesis. A CAP 1 structure is shown.

 Within a few months of initiation of treatment for tuberculosis, laboratory staining results of **Ivy Sharer's** sputum confirmed the diagnosis of pulmonary tuberculosis caused by *M. tuberculosis*. Therefore, the multidrug therapy, which included the antibiotic rifampin, was continued. Rifampin binds to the RNA polymerases of several bacteria. *M. tuberculosis* rapidly develops resistance to rifampin through mutations that result in an RNA polymerase that cannot bind the complex structure. Simultaneous treatment with drugs that work through different mechanisms decreases the selective advantage of the mutation and the rate at which resistance develops.

Methylation also occurs on the ribose 2′-hydroxyl group in the terminal nucleotide to which the cap is attached, and sometimes the 2′-hydroxyl group of the adjacent nucleotide ribose. This cap "seals" the 5′-end of the primary transcript and decreases the rate of degradation. It also serves as a recognition site for the binding of the mature mRNA to a ribosome at the initiation of protein synthesis.

2.   ADDITION OF A POLY(A) TAIL

After the RNA polymerase transcribes the stop codon for protein translation, it passes a sequence called the *polyadenylation signal* (AAUAAA) (Fig. 14.12). It continues past the polyadenylation signal until it reaches an unknown, and

FIG. 14.12.   Synthesis of the poly(A) tail. As RNA polymerase continues to transcribe the DNA, enzymes cleave the transcript (hnRNA) at a point 10 to 20 nucleotides beyond an AAUAAA sequence, just before a run of Us (or Gs). Approximately 250 adenine nucleotides are then added to the 3′-end of the hnRNA, one at a time, by poly(A) polymerase.

possibly nonspecific, termination signal many nucleotides later. However, as the primary transcript is released from the RNA polymerase elongation complex, an enzyme complex binds to the polyadenylation signal and cleaves the primary transcript approximately 10 to 20 nucleotides downstream, thereby forming the 3′-end. After this cleavage, a poly(A) tail that can be >200 nucleotides in length is added to the 3′-end. Thus, there is no poly(dT) sequence in the DNA template that corresponds to this tail; it is added posttranscriptionally. ATP serves as the precursor for the sequential addition of the adenine nucleotides. They are added one at a time, with poly(A) polymerase catalyzing each addition. The poly(A) tail is a protein-binding site that protects the mRNA from degradation.

3. REMOVAL OF INTRONS

Eukaryotic pre-mRNA transcripts contain regions known as *exons* and *introns*. Exons appear in the mature mRNA; introns are removed from the transcript and are not found in the mature mRNA (see Fig. 14.10). Therefore, introns do not contribute to the amino acid sequence of the protein. Some genes contain 50 or more introns. These introns are carefully removed from the pre-mRNA transcript and the exons are spliced together, so that the appropriate protein is produced from the gene.

The consensus sequences at the intron/exon boundaries of the pre-mRNA are AGGU (AGGT in the DNA). The sequences vary to some extent on the exon side of the boundaries, but almost all introns begin with a 5′-GU and end with a 3′-AG (Fig. 14.13). These intron sequences at the left splice site and the right splice site are therefore invariant. Because every 5′-GU and 3′-AG combination does not result in a functional splice site, other features (still to be determined) within the exon or intron help to define the appropriate splice sites.

A complex structure known as a *spliceosome* ensures that exons are spliced together with great accuracy (Fig. 14.14). Small nuclear ribonucleoproteins (snRNPs), called "snurps," are involved in formation of the spliceosome. Because snurps are rich in uracil, they are identified by numbers preceded by a U.

Exons frequently code for separate functional or structural domains of proteins. Proteins with similar functional regions (e.g., ATP- or NAD-binding regions) frequently have similar domains, although their overall structure and amino acid sequence are quite different. A process known as *exon shuffling* has probably occurred throughout evolution, allowing new proteins to develop with functions similar to those of other proteins.

B. Synthesis of Eukaryotic rRNA

rRNAs form the ribonucleoprotein complexes on which protein synthesis occurs. In eukaryotes, the rRNA gene exists as many copies in the nucleolar organizer region of the nucleus (Fig. 14.15, circle 1). Each gene produces a large 45S transcript (synthesized by RNA polymerase I) that is cleaved to produce the 18S, 28S, and 5.8S rRNAs. Approximately 1,000 copies of this gene are present in the human genome. The genes are linked in tandem, separated by spacer regions that contain the termination signal for one gene and the promoter for the next. Promoters for rRNA genes are located in the 5′-flanking region of the genes and extend into the region surrounding the start point. rRNA genes caught in the act of transcription by electron micrographs show that many RNA polymerase I molecules can be attached to a gene at any given time, all moving toward the 3′-end as the 45S rRNA precursors are synthesized.

As the 45S rRNA precursors are released from the DNA, they complex with proteins, forming ribonucleoprotein particles that generate the granular regions of the nucleolus (see Fig. 14.15, circle 2). Processing of the transcript occurs in the granular regions. 5S rRNA, produced by RNA polymerase III from genes located outside the nucleolus in the nucleoplasm, migrates into the nucleolus and joins the ribonucleoprotein particles.

 Anne Niemick has β^+-thalassemia (enough of the β-chain is produced to maintain blood hemoglobin levels >6.0 g/dL). One mutation resulting in β^+-thalassemia is a point mutation (AATAAA → AACAAA) that changes the sequence in heterogeneous nuclear RNA (hnRNA) at the polyadenylation signal site from AAUAAA to AACAAA. Homozygous individuals with this mutation produce only one-tenth the amount of normal β-globin mRNA.

 Some types of β^0-thalassemia (little or none of the hemoglobin β-chain produced) are caused by homozygous mutations in the splice-junction sequences at intron/exon boundaries. In some individuals, an AT replaces a GT in the gene at the 5′-end of the first or second intron. Mutations also occur within the splice-junction sequences at the 3′-ends of introns (which are normally GT at the donor-site 5′-end and AG at the acceptor-site 3′-end). Mutations at either site totally abolish normal splicing and result in β^0-thalassemia.

FIG. 14.13. Splice junctions in hnRNA. The intron sequences shown in the boxes are invariant. They always appear at this position in introns. The sequences on the exon side of the splice sites are more variable.

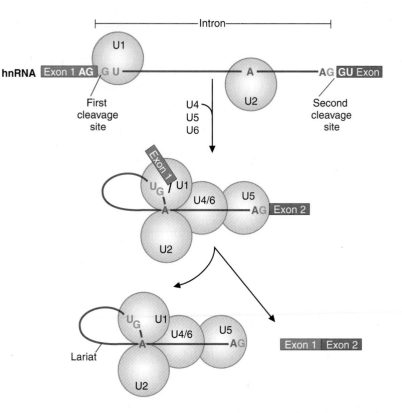

FIG. 14.14. Splicing process. Nuclear ribonucleoproteins (snurps U1 to U6) bind to the intron, causing it to form a loop. The complex is called a *spliceosome*. The U1 snurp binds near the first exon/intron junction, and U2 binds within the intron in a region containing an adenine nucleotide residue. Another group of snurp—U4, U5, and U6—binds to the complex, and the loop is formed. The phosphate attached to the G residue at the 5'-end of the intron forms a 2'-to-5' linkage with the 2'-hydroxyl group of the adenine nucleotide residue. Cleavage occurs at the end of the first exon, between the AG residues at the 3'-end of the exon and the GU residues at the 5'-end of the intron. The complex continues to be held in place by the spliceosome. A second cleavage occurs at the 3'-end of the intron after the AG sequence. The exons are joined together. The intron, shaped like a lariat, is released and degraded to nucleotides.

Systemic lupus erythematosus (SLE) is an autoimmune disease characterized by a particular spectrum of auto-antibodies against many cellular components, including chromatin, ribonucleoprotein, and cell membrane phospholipids. In this disorder, the body makes these antibodies against its own components. snRNPs are one of the targets of these antibodies. In fact, snRNPs were discovered because of studies using antibodies obtained from patients with SLE.

Tests were performed on **Sis Lupus's** blood to detect levels of antibodies, including antibodies to nuclear antigens (ANA), antibodies to double-stranded DNA (anti-dsDNA), and antibodies to ribonucleoproteins (these were historically known as Smith proteins, for the first patient in which they were discovered. It has since been shown that the snRNPs correspond to the Smith antigens). The tests were strongly positive and, in conjunction with her symptoms, led to a diagnosis of SLE.

One to two percent of the nucleotides of the 45S precursor become methylated, primarily on the 2'-hydroxyl groups of ribose moieties (see Fig. 14.15, circle 3). These methyl groups may serve as markers for cleavage of the 45S precursors and are conserved in the mature rRNA. A series of cleavages in the 45S transcripts occur to produce the mature rRNAs (see Fig. 14.16).

In the production of cytoplasmic ribosomes in human cells, one portion of the 45S rRNA precursor becomes the 18S rRNA that, complexed with proteins, forms the small 40S ribosomal subunit (see Fig. 14.15, circle 4). Another segment of the precursor folds back on itself and is cleaved, forming 28S rRNA, hydrogen-bonded to the 5.8S rRNA. The 5S rRNA, transcribed from nonnucleolar genes, and several proteins complex with the 28S and 5.8S rRNAs to form the 60S ribosomal subunit (see Fig. 14.15, circle 5). The ribosomal subunits migrate through the nuclear pores. In the cytoplasm, the 40S and 60S ribosomal subunits interact with mRNA, forming the 80S ribosomes on which protein synthesis occurs.

C. *Synthesis of Eukaryotic tRNA*

A tRNA has one binding site for a specific sequence of three nucleotides in mRNA (the anticodon site) and another binding site for the encoded amino acid. tRNAs thus ensure that the genetic code is translated into the correct sequence of amino acids. At least 20 types of tRNAs occur in cells, one for every amino acid that is incorporated

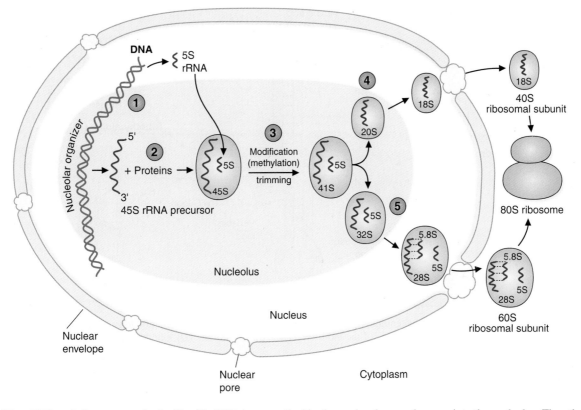

FIG. 14.15. rRNA and ribosome synthesis. The 5S rRNA is transcribed in the nucleoplasm and moves into the nucleolus. The other rRNAs are transcribed from DNA and mature in the nucleolus, forming the 40S and 60S ribosomal subunits, which migrate to the cytoplasm. See the text for a detailed explanation.

into growing polypeptide chains during the synthesis of proteins. tRNAs have a cloverleaf structure that folds into a three-dimensional L shape and contain several bases that are modified posttranscriptionally (Fig. 14.17). The loop closest to the 5′-end is known as the D-loop because it contains dihydrouridine (D). The second or anticodon, loop contains the trinucleotide anticodon that base-pairs with the codon on mRNA. The third loop (the TΨC loop) contains both ribothymidine (T) and pseudouridine (Ψ). A fourth loop, known as the variable loop because it varies in size, is frequently found between the anticodon and TΨC loops. Base pairing occurs in the stem regions of tRNA, and a three-nucleotide sequence (e.g., CCA) at the 3′-end is the attachment site for the specific amino acid carried by each tRNA. Different tRNAs bind different amino acids. The three-dimensional structure of tRNA has been determined and is shown in Figure 14.18. tRNA is produced by RNA polymerase III, which recognizes, along with promoter-proximal elements, a split promoter within the transcribed region of the gene (Fig. 14.19). One segment of the promoter is located between +8 and +19. A second segment is 30 to 60 base pairs downstream from the first.

tRNA precursors of approximately 100 nucleotides in length are generated (Fig. 14.20, circle 1). The pre-tRNA assumes a cloverleaf shape and is subsequently cleaved at the 5′- and 3′-ends (see Fig. 14.20, circle 2). The enzyme that acts at the 5′-end is RNase P, similar to the RNase P of bacteria. Both enzymes contain a small RNA (M1) that has catalytic activity and serves as an endonuclease. Some tRNA precursors contain introns that are removed by endonucleases. To close the opening, a 2′- or 3′-phosphate group from one end is ligated to a 5′-hydroxyl on the other end by an RNA ligase.

The bases are modified at the same time the endonucleolytic cleavage reactions are occurring (see Fig. 14.20, circle 3). Three modifications occur in most tRNAs: (1) Uracil is methylated by SAM to form thymine; (2) one of the double bonds of

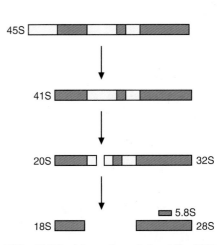

FIG. 14.16. Maturation of the 45S rRNA precursor. The *clear regions* are removed, and the *red regions* become the mature rRNAs. (The 5S rRNA is not produced from this precursor.)

FIG. 14.17. The tRNA cloverleaf. Bases that commonly occur in a particular position are indicated by letters. Base pairing in stem regions is indicated by *lines* between the strands. The locations of the modified bases: dihydrouridine (*D*), ribothymidine (*T*), and pseudouridine (*Ψ*) are indicated.

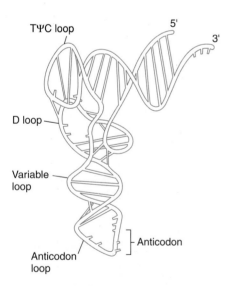

FIG. 14.18. The three-dimensional folding of tRNA. (Reprinted with permission from Kim SH, Suddath FL, Quigley GJ, et al. Three-dimensional tertiary structure of yeast phenylalanine transfer RNA. *Science*. 1974;185:436. Copyright © 1974 American Association for the Advancement of Science.)

uracil is reduced to form dihydrouracil; and (3) a uracil residue (attached to ribose by an *N*-glycosidic bond) is rotated to form pseudouridine, which contains uracil linked to ribose by a carbon–carbon bond (see Fig. 14.17). Other, less common but more complex, modifications also occur and involve bases other than uracil. Of particular note is the deamination of adenine to form the base hypoxanthine.

The final step in forming the mature tRNA is the addition of a CCA sequence at its 3′-end (see Fig. 14.20, circle 4). These nucleotides are added one at a time by nucleotidyltransferase. The tRNA then migrates to the cytoplasm. The terminal adenosine at the 3′-end is the site at which the specific amino acid for each tRNA is bound and activated for incorporation into a protein.

V. DIFFERENCES IN SIZE BETWEEN EUKARYOTIC AND PROKARYOTIC DNA

A. Human Cells Are Diploid

Except for the germ cells, most normal human cells are diploid. Therefore, they contain two copies of each chromosome, and each chromosome contains genes that are alleles of the genes on the homologous chromosome. Because one chromosome in each set of homologous chromosomes is obtained from each parent, the alleles can be identical, containing the same DNA sequence, or they can differ. A diploid human cell contains 2,000 times more DNA than the genome of the bacterium in the haploid *E. coli* cell (approximately 4×10^6 base pairs).

FIG. 14.19. Promoter for tRNA transcription. The segments of the genes from which the mature tRNA is produced are indicated by the *purple color*. The two regions of the promoter lie within these segments and are indicated by the *green color*.

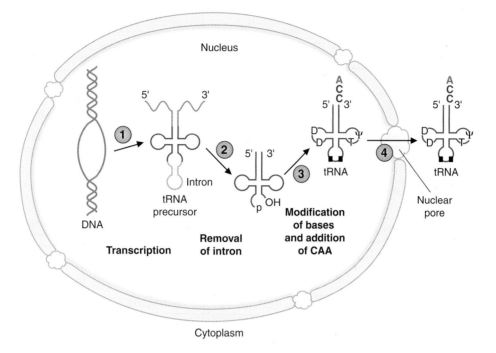

Nucleus

Cytoplasm

FIG. 14.20. Overview of tRNA synthesis. *D*, *T*, *Ψ*, and ■ indicate modified bases. *D*, dihydrouracil; *T*, ribothymidine; *Ψ*, pseudouridine; ■, other modified bases.

B. Human Genes Contain Introns

Eukaryotic introns contribute to the DNA size difference between bacteria and human cells. In eukaryotic genes, introns (noncoding regions) occur within sequences that code for proteins. Consequently, the primary transcript (heterogeneous nuclear RNA or hnRNA) averages roughly 10 times longer than the mature mRNA produced by removal of the introns. In contrast, bacterial genes do not contain introns.

C. Repetitive Sequences in Eukaryotic DNA

Although diploid and introns account for some of the difference between the DNA content of humans and bacteria, a large difference remains that is related to the greater complexity of the human organism. Bacterial cells have a single copy of each gene, called *unique DNA*, and they contain very little DNA that does not produce functional products. Eukaryotic cells contain substantial amounts of DNA that does not code for functional products (i.e., proteins or rRNA and tRNA). In addition, some genes that encode functional products are present in multiple copies, called *highly repetitive or moderately repetitive DNA*. Approximately 64% of the DNA in the human genome is unique, consisting of DNA sequences present in one or a very few copies in the genome (Fig. 14.21). Unique DNA sequences are transcribed to generate mRNA, which is translated to produce proteins.

Highly repetitive DNA consists of sequences approximately 6 to 100 base pairs in length that are present in hundreds of thousands to millions of copies, clustered within a few locations in the genome (see Fig. 14.21). It occurs in centromeres (which join sister chromatids during mitosis) and in telomeres (the ends of chromosomes). This DNA represents approximately 10% of the human genome. It is not transcribed.

Moderately repetitive DNA is present in a few to tens of thousands of copies in the genome (see Fig. 14.21). This fraction constitutes approximately 25% of the human genome. It contains DNA that is functional and transcribed to produce rRNA, tRNA, and also some mRNA. The histone genes, present in a few hundred copies in the genome, belong to this class. Moderately repetitive DNA also includes

Q: Calculate the number of different proteins, 300 amino acids in length, that could be produced from the *E. coli* genome (4×10^6 base pairs of DNA).

FIG. 14.21. Distribution of unique, moderately repetitive, and highly repetitive sequences in a hypothetical human chromosome. Unique genes encode mRNA. These genes occur in single copies. The genes for the large rRNA and the tRNA precursors occur in multiple copies that are clustered in the genome. The large rRNA genes form the nucleolar organizer. Moderately repetitive sequences are dispersed throughout the genome, and highly repetitive sequences are clustered around the centromere and at the ends of the chromosome (the telomeres). snRNA, small nuclear RNA and scRNA, small cytoplasmic RNA, usually found in ribonucleoprotein particles. (From Wolfe SL. *Mol and Cell Biol*. 1993:761.)

 Four million base pairs contain (4×10^6) / 3 or 1.33 million codons. If each protein contained approximately 300 amino acids, *E. coli* could produce about 4,000 different proteins [(1.33×10^6) / 300].

 Alu sequences in DNA were named for the enzyme Alu (obtained from *Arthrobacter luteus*), which is able to cleave them. Alu sequences make up 6% to 8% of the human genome. In some cases of familial hypercholesterolemia, homologous recombination is believed to have occurred between two Alu repeats, resulting in a large deletion in the low-density lipoprotein (LDL) receptor gene. The LDL receptor mediates uptake of the cholesterol-containing LDL particle into many cell types and, in the absence of functional LDL receptors, blood cholesterol levels are elevated. Patients who are homozygous for this mutation may die from cardiac disease as early as in their second or third decade of life.

some gene sequences that are functional but not transcribed. Promoters and enhancers (which are involved in regulating gene expression) are examples of gene sequences in this category. Other groups of moderately repetitive gene sequences that have been found in humans are called the *Alu sequences* (approximately 300 base pairs in length). Alu sequences are also examples of SINEs (*short interspersed elements*). The LINE (*long interspersed elements*) sequences are 6,000 to 7,000 base pairs in length. The functions of the Alu and LINE sequences have not been determined.

D. Summary of the Differences between Eukaryotic and Prokaryotic DNA and RNA

Several differences between eukaryotes and prokaryotes affect the processes of replication, transcription, and translation, in addition to the content of their DNA. Eukaryotic DNA is complexed with histones, and prokaryotic DNA is not. In eukaryotic cells, the process of transcription, which occurs in the nucleus, is separated by the nuclear envelope from the process of translation (protein synthesis from the mRNA template), which occurs in the cytoplasm. Because prokaryotes lack nuclei, the processes of transcription and translation occur simultaneously. Transcription of bacterial DNA requires only one promoter per operon. In contrast, human DNA requires one promoter for each gene.

Complexity may explain some of the differences between the DNA content of bacteria and humans. However, an extension of this line of reasoning would lead to the conclusion that frogs are more complex than humans, because frogs have 8 ft of DNA per diploid nucleus, compared to the 6 ft in a human cell. Logic, or perhaps vanity, suggests that the amount of DNA per cell does not necessarily reflect the complexity of the organism. One of the features of frog DNA that may explain its

Table 14.2   Certain Differences between Eukaryotes and Prokaryotes

	Eukaryotes (Human)	*Prokaryotes (Escherichia coli)*
Nucleus	Yes	No
Chromosomes		
Number	23 per haploid cell	1 per haploid cell
DNA	Linear	Circular
Histones	Yes	No
Genome		
Diploid	Somatic cells	No
Haploid	Germ cells	All cells
Size	3×10^9 base pairs per haploid cell	4×10^6 base pairs
Genes		
Unique	64%	100%
Repetitive		
Moderately	25%	None
Highly	10%	None
Operons	No	Yes
mRNA		
Polycistronic	No	Yes
Introns (hnRNA)	Yes	No
Translation	Separate from transcription	Coupled with transcription

length is that frogs have more repetitive DNA than humans. More than 75% of the frog genome is in the moderately and highly repetitive category, whereas only about 35% of the human genome is repetitive.

Major differences between prokaryotic and eukaryotic DNA and RNA are summarized in Table 14.2. LINEs make up about 5% of the human genome. In some patients with hemophilia (a disease in which blood does not clot normally), a LINE sequence has been inserted into exon 14 of the gene for Factor VIII, a protein of the blood-clotting system. The insertion of the LINE sequence leads to the production of a nonfunctional protein.

CLINICAL COMMENTS

Anne Niemick. Patients with β^+-thalassemia who maintain their hemoglobin levels >6.0 to 7.0 g/dL are usually classified as having thalassemia intermedia. In the β-thalassemias, the α-chains of adult hemoglobin A ($\alpha_2\beta_2$) continue to be synthesized at a normal rate. These chains accumulate in the bone marrow, in which the red blood cells are synthesized during the process of erythropoiesis (generation of red blood cells). The accumulation of α-chains diminishes erythropoiesis, resulting in an anemia. Individuals who are homozygous for a severe mutation require constant transfusions.

Individuals with thalassemia intermedia, such as **Anne Niemick**, could have inherited two different defective alleles, one from each parent. One parent may be a "silent" carrier, with one normal allele and one mildly affected allele. This parent produces enough functional β-globin, so no clinical symptoms of thalassemia appear. (However, they generally have a somewhat decreased amount of hemoglobin, resulting in microcytic hypochromic red blood cells.) When this parent contributes the mildly defective allele, and the other heterozygous parent contributes a more severely defective allele, thalassemia intermedia occurs in the child. The child is thus heterozygous for two different defective alleles.

Ivy Sharer. Ivy Sharer was treated with a multidrug regimen for tuberculosis because the microbes that cause the disease frequently become resistant to the individual drugs. The current approach in patients with AIDS who develop opportunistic infection with *Mycobacterium tuberculosis* is to initiate antimycobacterial therapy with four agents because the mycobacteria frequently become resistant to one or more of the individual antitubercular drugs.

The mutations that cause the thalassemias affect the synthesis of either the α- or the β-chain of adult hemoglobin, causing an anemia. They are classified by the chain affected (α- or β-chain) and by the amount of chain synthesized (0 for no synthesis and + for synthesis of some functional chains). They are also classified as major, intermediate, or minor, according to the severity of the clinical disorder. β-Thalassemia major (also called homozygous β-thalassemia) is a clinically severe disorder requiring frequent blood transfusions. It is caused by the inheritance of two alleles for a severe mutation. In β-thalassemia intermedia, the patient exhibits a less severe clinical phenotype and is able to maintain hemoglobin levels >6 g/dL. It is usually the result of two different mild mutations or homozygosity for a mild mutation. β-Thalassemia minor (also known as β-thalassemia trait) is a heterozygous disorder involving a single mutation that is often clinically asymptomatic.

During embryonic and fetal life, the β-chain is replaced by the ε- and γ-chains, respectively. As a result, patients with severe mutations in the α-chain tend to die in utero, whereas those with mutations in the β-chains exhibit symptoms postnatally, as hemoglobin F is normally replaced with adult hemoglobin A.

Ivy was started on isoniazid (INH), rifampin, pyrazinamide, and ethambutol. Isoniazid inhibits the biosynthesis of mycolic acids, which are important constituents of the mycobacterial cell wall. Rifampin binds to and inhibits bacterial RNA polymerase, which selectively kills the bacteria that cause the infection. Pyrazinamide, a synthetic analog of nicotinamide, targets the mycobacterial fatty acid synthase I gene involved in mycolic acid biosynthesis in *M. tuberculosis*. Ethambutol blocks arabinosyl transferases that are involved in cell wall biosynthesis.

Just as bacteria can become resistant to drugs, so can HIV. A great concern to physicians treating patients with AIDS is the appearance of resistant strains of HIV-1 in patients taking a single drug, such as zidovudine (ZDV) for 6 months or more. Therefore, multidrug regimens are used that include other nucleoside reverse transcriptase inhibitors, such as dideoxyinosine (didanosine, formerly called ddI) and dideoxycytidine (zalcitabine, formerly called ddC). The multidrug therapy often includes nonnucleoside inhibitors (e.g., efavirenz), which act allosterically on reverse transcriptase, and/or protease inhibitors (e.g., indinavir), which prevent the HIV polyprotein from being cleaved into its mature products (see Biochemical Comments). **Ivy Sharer** was started on efavirenz and was counseled on not getting pregnant, because this drug is teratogenic.

Amanda Tin. The toxin α-amanitin is capable of causing irreversible hepatocellular and renal dysfunction through inhibition of mammalian RNA polymerases. α-Amanitin is particularly effective at blocking the action of RNA polymerase II. Fortunately, **Amanda Tin's** toxicity proved mild. She developed only gastrointestinal symptoms and slight changes in her hepatic and renal function, which returned to normal within a few weeks. Treatment was primarily supportive, with fluid and electrolyte replacement for that lost through the gastrointestinal tract. No effective antidote is available for the *Amanita phalloides'* toxin.

Sis Lupus. *Systemic lupus erythematosus* (SLE) is a multisystem disease of unknown origin characterized by inflammation related to autoantibodies in the blood. These autoantibodies react with antigens normally found in the nucleus, cytoplasm, and plasma membrane of the cell. Such "self" antigen–antibody (autoimmune) interactions initiate an inflammatory cascade that produces the broad symptom profile of multiorgan dysfunction found in **Sis Lupus**.

Pharmacologic therapy for SLE is directed at immunosuppression. It can include corticosteroids, or several newer agents that cause immunosuppression. The use of the antimalarial drug Plaquenil has been shown to be beneficial in patients with SLE, although its mechanism of action in these patients has yet to be determined. Sis was placed on such a drug regimen.

Studies have indicated that a failure to dispose properly of cellular debris, a normal by-product of cell death, may lead to the induction of autoantibodies directed against chromatin in patients with SLE. Normal cells have a finite lifetime and are programmed to die (apoptosis) through a distinct biochemical mechanism. One of the steps in this mechanism is the stepwise degradation of cellular DNA (and other cellular components). If the normal intracellular components are exposed to the immune system, autoantibodies against them may be generated. The enzyme in cells that degrades DNA is deoxyribonuclease I (DNase I), and individuals with SLE have reduced serum activity levels of DNase I compared to individuals who do not have the disease. Through an understanding of the molecular mechanism whereby autoantibodies are generated, it may be possible to develop therapies to combat this disorder.

BIOCHEMICAL COMMENTS

Production of the Virus that Causes AIDS. AIDS is caused by the human immunodeficiency virus (HIV). Two forms of the virus have been discovered, HIV-1, which is prevalent in industrialized countries, and HIV-2, which is prevalent in certain regions of Africa. About 8 to 10 years or more can elapse between the initial infection and development of the full-blown syndrome.

Proteins in the viral coat bind to membrane protein receptors (named CD4) of helper T lymphocytes, a class of cells involved in the immune response. Subsequently, conformational changes occur that allow the viral coat proteins to bind to a chemokine coreceptor in the cell membrane. The lipid in the viral coat then fuses with the cell membrane, and the viral core enters the cell, releasing its RNA and enzymes (including the reverse transcriptase) by a process called "uncoating."

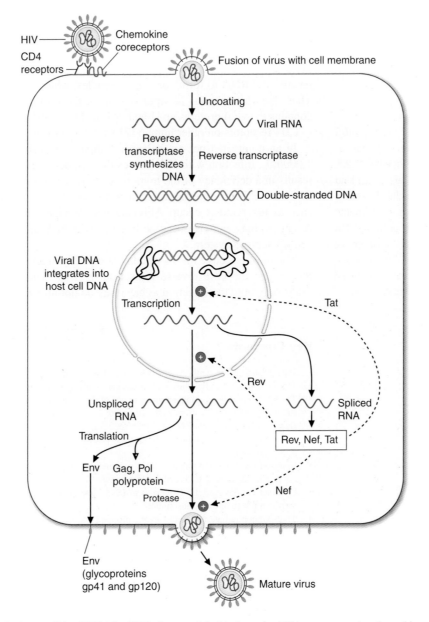

FIG. 14.22. Infection of a host cell by HIV. The HIV virus particle binds to the CD4 receptor and a chemokine coreceptor in the host cell membrane. The virus enters the cell and uncoats, releasing its RNA and proteins. The viral enzyme reverse transcriptase produces a double-stranded DNA copy that is integrated into the host cell genome. HIV is now a provirus. Transcripts of the viral DNA are spliced and translated to produce the proteins Tat, Rev, and Nef. Tat stimulates transcription of the viral DNA, and Rev causes the viral RNA transcripts to leave the nucleus unspliced. The unspliced RNA serves as the viral genome and codes for the proteins of the viral core and envelope. The envelope proteins (gp41 and gp120, which are derived from the env protein) enter the cell membrane. The viral core proteins are synthesized as a polyprotein, which is cleaved by a protease as the viral particles form and bud from the cell membrane. The particles carry membrane lipid as a coat that contains gp41 and gp120. Nef indirectly aids in the assembly of viral particles. *Pol* is the reverse transcriptase produced from the viral RNA. ⊕, stimulates.

Reverse transcriptase uses the viral RNA as a template to produce a single-stranded DNA copy, which then serves as a template for synthesis of a double-stranded DNA. An integrase enzyme, also carried by the virus, enables this DNA to integrate into the host cell genome as a provirus (Fig. 14.22).

In the initial stage of transcription of the provirus, the transcript is spliced, and three proteins—Nef, Tat, and Rev—are produced. Tat stimulates transcription of the viral genes. As Rev accumulates, it allows unspliced viral RNA to leave the nucleus and to produce proteins of the viral envelope and viral core, including reverse transcriptase. Two of the envelope glycoproteins (gp41 and gp120, which are derived from the env gene product) form a complex that embeds in the cell membrane. The other proteins, which are translated as a polyprotein and cleaved by the viral protease (one of the targets of anti-HIV drugs), combine with the full-length viral RNA to form core viral particles, which bud from the cell membrane. Thus, the virus obtains its lipid coat from the host cell membrane, and the coat contains the viral proteins gp41 and gp120. These surface proteins of the virus bind to CD4 receptors on other human helper T lymphocytes, and the infection spreads.

In an uninfected person, helper T lymphocytes usually number approximately 1,000/mL. Infection with HIV causes the number of these cells to decrease, which results in a deficiency of the immune system. When the number of T lymphocytes drops to <200/mL, the disease is in an advanced stage, and opportunistic infections such as tuberculosis occur. Although macrophages and dendritic cells lack CD4 receptors, they can also become infected with HIV and can carry the virus to the central nervous system.

The most effective means of combating HIV infection involves the use of drugs that inhibit the viral reverse transcriptase or the viral protease. However, these drugs only hold the infection at bay; they do not affect a cure.

 Drugs currently used to treat AIDS act on the viral reverse transcriptase or the protease (see Fig. 14.22). The nonnucleoside drugs (e.g., efavirenz) bind to reverse transcriptase and inhibit its action. The nucleoside analogs (e.g., zidovudine [ZDV]) add to the 3'-end of the growing DNA transcript produced by reverse transcriptase and prevent further elongation. The protease inhibitors (e.g., indinavir) bind to the protease and prevent it from cleaving the polyprotein.

Key Concepts

- Transcription is the synthesis of RNA from a DNA template.
- The enzyme RNA polymerase transcribes genes into a single-stranded RNA.
- The RNA produced is complementary to one of the strands of DNA, which is known as the template strand. The other DNA strand is the coding or sense strand.
- Bacteria contain a single RNA polymerase; eukaryotic cells use three different RNA polymerases.
- The DNA template is copied in the 3'-to-5' direction and the RNA transcript is synthesized in the 5'-to-3' direction.
- In contrast to DNA polymerases, RNA polymerases do not require a primer to initiate transcription, nor do they contain 3'-to-5' exonuclease activity.
- Promoter regions, specific sequences in DNA, determine where on the DNA template RNA polymerase binds to initiate transcription.
- Transcription initiation requires several protein factors to allow for efficient RNA polymerase binding to the promoter.
- Other DNA sequences, such as promoter-proximal elements and enhancers, affect the rate of transcription initiation through the interactions of DNA-binding proteins with RNA polymerase and other initiation factors.
- Eukaryotic genes contain exons and introns. Exons specify the coding region of proteins, whereas introns have no coding function.
- The primary transcript of eukaryotic genes is modified to remove the introns (splicing) before a final, mature mRNA is produced.
- Table 14.3 summarizes the diseases discussed in this chapter.

Table 14.3   Diseases Discussed in Chapter 14

Disorder or Condition	Genetic or Environmental	Comments
β-Thalassemia	Genetic	An anemia caused by an imbalance in β- and α-globin chain synthesis. For a β-thalassemia, more α-chain is synthesized than functional β-chain.
Tuberculosis, a complication of AIDS	Environmental	The drug rifampin, among others, is used to treat tuberculosis via inhibition of bacterial RNA polymerase.
Mushroom poisoning (α-amanitin poisoning)	Environmental	Inhibition of RNA polymerase II by α-amanitin. There is no effective antidote for this poison.
Systemic lupus erythematosus (SLE)	Both	The development of autoantibodies directed against various cellular proteins, including those involved in RNA processing (such as complexes involved in RNA splicing, the snurps).

1. The short transcript AUCCGUACG would be derived from which of the following template DNA sequences? (Note that all sequences are written from 5′ to 3′.)

    A. ATCCGTACG
    B. CGTACGGAT
    C. AUCCGUACG
    D. TAGGCATGC
    E. GCATGCCTA

2. Given that the LD_{50} (the dose at which 50% of the recipients die) of amanitin is 0.1 mg/kg body weight, and that the average mushroom contains 7 mg amanitin, how many mushrooms must be consumed by **Amanda Tin** (50-kg body weight) to be more than the LD_{50}?

    A. 1
    B. 2
    C. 3
    D. 4
    E. 5

3. Which of the following eukaryotic DNA control sequences does not need to be in a fixed location, and is most responsible for high rates of transcription of particular genes?

    A. Promoter
    B. Promoter-proximal element
    C. Enhancer
    D. Operator
    E. Splice donor site

4. Which of the following is true of both eukaryotic and prokaryotic gene expression?

    A. After transcription, a 3′-poly(A) tail and a 5′-cap are added to mRNA.
    B. Translation of mRNA can begin before transcription is complete.
    C. mRNA is synthesized in the 3′-to-5′ direction.
    D. RNA polymerase binds at a promoter region upstream of the gene.
    E. Mature mRNA is always precisely collinear to the gene from which it was transcribed.

5. A family has two children, both of whom have a form of β-thalassemia. One child is almost nonsymptomatic, whereas the other requires frequent blood transfusion for his disease. The α-globin to β-globin ratio in the more severely affected child is most likely to be which one of the following:

    A. 5:1.
    B. 2:1.
    C. 1:1.
    D. 1:2.
    E. 1:5.

FIG. 15.1. Binding of tRNA to a codon on mRNA. The tRNA contains an amino acid at its 3'-end that corresponds to the codon on mRNA with which the anticodon of the tRNA can base-pair. Note that the codon–anticodon pairing is complementary and antiparallel.

Proteins are produced by the process of **translation**, which occurs on **ribosomes** and is directed by **mRNA**. The genetic message encoded in DNA is first transcribed into mRNA, and the **nucleotide sequence** in the coding region of the mRNA is then translated into the **amino acid sequence** of the protein.

Translation of the Code. The portion of mRNA that specifies the amino acid sequence of the protein is read in **codons**, which are **sets of three nucleotides** that specify individual amino acids (Fig. 15.1). The codons on mRNA are read sequentially in the 5'-to-3' direction, starting with the **5'-AUG** (or "start" codon) that specifies **methionine** and sets the **reading frame** and ending with a **3'-termination** (or "stop") codon (UAG, UGA, or UAA). The protein is synthesized from its **N-terminus** to its **C-terminus**.

Each amino acid is carried to the ribosome by an **aminoacyl-tRNA** (i.e., a tRNA with an amino acid covalently attached). **Base pairing** between the **anticodon** of the tRNA and the **codon** on the mRNA ensures that each amino acid is inserted into the growing polypeptide at the appropriate position.

Synthesis of the Protein. **Initiation** involves formation of a complex containing the initial **methionyl-tRNA** bound to the AUG "start" codon of the **mRNA** and to the "P" site of the **ribosome**. It requires guanosine triphosphate (**GTP**) and proteins known as **eukaryotic initiation factors** (*eIFs*).

Elongation of the polypeptide involves **three steps:** (1) **binding** of an **aminoacyl-tRNA** to the "A" site on the ribosome where it base-pairs with the second codon on the mRNA; (2) **formation** of a **peptide bond** between the first and second amino acids; and (3) **translocation**, movement of the mRNA relative to the ribosome, so that the third mRNA codon moves into the "A" site. These three **elongation steps** are **repeated** until a **termination** codon aligns with the site on the ribosome where the next aminoacyl-tRNA would normally bind. **Release factors** bind instead, causing the completed protein to be released from the ribosome.

After one ribosome binds and moves along the mRNA, translating the polypeptide, another ribosome can bind and begin translation. The complex of a single mRNA with multiple ribosomes is known as a **polysome**.

Folding and Modification and Targeting of the Protein. **Folding** of the polypeptide into its three-dimensional configuration occurs as the polypeptide is being translated. This process involves proteins called **chaperones**. **Modification** of amino acid residues in a protein occurs during or after translation. Proteins synthesized on **cytosolic ribosomes** are released into the cytosol or transported into the mitochondria, peroxisomes, and nucleus. Proteins synthesized on ribosomes attached to the **rough endoplasmic reticulum** (RER) are destined for lysosomes, cell membranes, or secretion from the cell. These proteins are transferred to the **Golgi complex**, where they are modified and **targeted** to their ultimate locations.

THE WAITING ROOM

Anne Niemick, a 4-year-old patient with β^+-thalassemia intermedia (see Chapter 14), showed no improvement in her symptoms at her second visit. Her hemoglobin level was 7.0 g/dL (reference range for females, 12 to 16 g/dL).

Jay Sakz is a 9-month-old male infant of Ashkenazi Jewish parentage. His growth and development were normal until age 5 months, when he began to exhibit mild, generalized muscle weakness. By 7 months, he had poor head control, slowed development of motor skills, and was increasingly inattentive to his surroundings. His parents also noted unusual eye movements and staring episodes. On careful examination of his retinae, his pediatrician observed a "cherry red" spot within a pale macula. The physician suspected Tay-Sachs disease and sent samples of his whole blood to the molecular biology–genetics laboratory.

Newman Itis returned to his physician's office after 5 days of azithromycin therapy (see Chapter 12), feeling significantly better. The sputum sample from his previous visit had been cultured. The results confirmed that his respiratory infection was caused by *Streptococcus pneumoniae* and that the organism was sensitive to penicillin, macrolides (e.g., erythromycin, clarithromycin), tetracycline, and other antibiotics.

Erna Nemdy, a 25-year-old junior medical student, brings her healthy 4-month-old daughter, **Beverly**, to the pediatrician for her second diphtheria, tetanus, pertussis (DTaP, acellular pertussis) immunization, along with immunizations for pneumococcal, inactivated polio, haemophilus influenza, and rotovirus. Erna tells the doctor that her great-great-aunt had died of diphtheria during an epidemic many years ago.

The results of tests performed in the molecular biology laboratory show that **Jay Sakz** has an insertion in exon 11 of the α-chain of the hexosaminidase A gene, the most common mutation found in patients of Ashkenazi Jewish background who have Tay-Sachs disease. Hexosaminidase A, the enzyme activity that is lacking in **Jay Sakz**, can be assayed using a serum sample and a substrate that releases a fluorescent dye upon being hydrolyzed. When measuring enzyme activity, one needs to be careful to distinguish between hexosaminidase A activity and a closely related activity due to hexosaminidase B. This is accomplished by differential heat inactivation of the sample (exposure of the sample to 50°C will inactivate hexosaminidase A activity but not hexosaminidase B activity). For prenatal screening, molecular techniques are the preferred method because of their sensitivity and the amount of sample available (see Chapter 17).

I. THE GENETIC CODE

Transcription, the transfer of the genetic message from DNA to RNA, and *translation*, the transfer of the genetic message from the nucleotide language of nucleic acids to the amino acid language of proteins, both depend on base pairing. In the late 1950s and early 1960s, molecular biologists attempting to decipher the process of translation recognized two problems. The first involved decoding the relationship between the "language" of the nucleic acids and the "language" of the proteins, and the second involved determining the molecular mechanism by which translation between these two languages occurs.

Twenty different amino acids are commonly incorporated into proteins, and therefore the protein "alphabet" has 20 characters. The nucleic acid alphabet, however, has only four characters, corresponding to the four nucleotides of mRNA (A, G, C, and U). If two nucleotides constituted the code for an amino acid, then only 4^2 or 16 amino acids could be specified. Therefore, the number of nucleotides that code for an amino acid has to be at least three, providing 4^3 or 64 possible combinations or "codons," more than required but not overly excessive.

Scientists set out to determine the specific codons for each amino acid. In 1961, Marshall Nirenberg produced the first crack in the genetic code (the collection of codons that specifies all the amino acids found in proteins). He showed that *poly(U)*, a polynucleotide in which all the bases are uracil, produced polyphenylalanine in a cell-free protein-synthesizing system. Thus, UUU must be the codon for phenylalanine. As a result of experiments using synthetic polynucleotides in place of mRNA, other codons were identified.

A. Codons for alanine

```
5' — G  C  U — 3'
      G  C  C
      G  C  A
      G  C  G
```

B. Base pairing of three alanine codons with anticodon IGC

```
              U
5' — G  C  C — 3'      Codon
              A        on mRNA
         ┊  ┊  ┊
3' — C  G  I — 5'      Anticodon
                       on tRNA
```

FIG. 15.2. Base pairing of codons for alanine with 5'-IGC-3'. **A.** The variation is in the third base. **B.** The first three of these codons can pair with a tRNA that contains the anticodon 5'-IGC-3'. Hypoxanthine (I) is an unusual base found in tRNA that can form base pairs with U, C, or A. It is formed by the deamination of adenine. Hypoxanthine is the base attached to ribose in the nucleoside inosine. The single-letter abbreviation for hypoxanthine is I, referring to the nucleoside inosine.

The pioneering molecular biologists recognized that because amino acids cannot bind directly to the sets of three nucleotides that form their codons, "adapters" are required. The "adapters" were found to be tRNA molecules. Each tRNA molecule contains an anticodon and binds covalently a specific amino acid at its 3'-end (see Chapters 12 and 14). The anticodon of a tRNA molecule is a set of three nucleotides that can interact with a codon on mRNA (Fig. 15.2). To interact, the codon and anticodon must be complementary (i.e., they must be able to form base pairs in an antiparallel orientation). Thus, the anticodon of a tRNA serves as the link between an mRNA codon and the amino acid that the codon specifies.

Obviously, each codon present within mRNA must correspond to a specific amino acid. Nirenberg found that trinucleotides of known base sequence could bind to ribosomes and induce the binding of specific aminoacyl-tRNAs (i.e., tRNAs with amino acids attached covalently). As a result of these and the earlier experiments, the relationship between all 64 codons and the amino acids they specify (the entire genetic code) was determined by the mid-1960s (Table 15.1).

Three of the 64 possible codons (UGA, UAG, and UAA) terminate protein synthesis and are known as "stop" or nonsense codons. The remaining 61 codons specify amino acids. Two amino acids each have only 1 codon (AUG = methionine; UGG = tryptophan). The remaining amino acids have multiple codons.

A. *The Code Is Degenerate but Unambiguous*

Because many amino acids are specified by more than one codon, the genetic code is described as "degenerate," which means that an amino acid may have more than one codon. However, each codon specifies only one amino acid, and the genetic code is thus unambiguous.

Inspection of a codon table shows that in most instances of multiple codons for a single amino acid, the variation occurs in the third base of the codon (see Table 15.1). Crick noted that the pairing between the 3'-base of the codon and the 5'-base of the anticodon does not always follow the strict base-pairing rules that he and Watson had previously discovered (i.e., A pairs with U, and G pairs with C). This observation resulted in the "wobble" hypothesis.

At the third base of the codon (the 3'-position of the codon and the 5'-position of the anticodon), the base pairs can wobble; for example, G can pair with U, and A, C, or U can pair with the unusual base hypoxanthine (I) found in tRNA. Thus, three of the four codons for alanine (GCU, GCC, and GCA) can pair with a single tRNA that contains the anticodon 5'-IGC-3' (see Fig. 15.2). If each of the 61 codons for amino acids required a distinct tRNA, cells would contain 61 tRNAs. However, because of wobble between the codon and anticodon, fewer than 61 tRNAs are required to translate the genetic code.

Table 15.1 The Genetic Code

First Base	Second Base			Third Base
(5')	U	C	A	G	(3')
U	Phe	Ser	Tyr	Cys	U
	Phe	Ser	Tyr	Cys	C
	Leu	Ser	Stop	Stop	A
	Leu	Ser	Stop	Trp	G
C	Leu	Pro	His	Arg	U
	Leu	Pro	His	Arg	C
	Leu	Pro	Gln	Arg	A
	Leu	Pro	Gln	Arg	G
A	Ile	Thr	Asn	Ser	U
	Ile	Thr	Asn	Ser	C
	Ile	Thr	Lys	Arg	A
	Met	Thr	Lys	Arg	G
G	Val	Ala	Asp	Gly	U
	Val	Ala	Asp	Gly	C
	Val	Ala	Glu	Gly	A
	Val	Ala	Glu	Gly	G

A

1 -- A U G C A C A G U G G A G U ---

2 -- A U G C A C A G U G G A G U ---

3 -- A U G C A C A G U G G A G U ---

B

Start

mRNA 5'-- A U G C A C A G U G G A G U C ---- **UGA–** 3'

Stop

Protein N-terminal -- Met – His – Ser – Gly – Val ----- C-terminal

FIG. 15.3.   Reading frame of mRNA. **A.** For any given mRNA sequence, there are three possible reading frames (1, 2, and 3). **B.** An AUG near the 5'-end of the mRNA (the start codon) sets the reading frame for translation of a protein from the mRNA. The codons are read in linear order, starting with this AUG. (The other potential reading frames are not used. They would give proteins with different amino acid sequences.)

B. The Code Is Almost Universal

All organisms studied so far use the same genetic code, with some rare exceptions. One exception occurs in human mitochondrial mRNA, in which UGA codes for tryptophan instead of serving as a stop codon, AUA codes for methionine instead of isoleucine, and CUA codes for threonine instead of leucine.

C. The Code Is Nonoverlapping

mRNA does not contain "extra nucleotides," or punctuation, to separate one codon from the next, and the codons do not overlap. Each nucleotide is read only once. Beginning with a start codon (AUG) near the 5'-end of the mRNA, the codons are read sequentially, ending with a stop codon (UGA, UAG, or UAA) near the 3'-end of the mRNA.

II. RELATIONSHIP BETWEEN mRNA AND THE PROTEIN PRODUCT

The start codon (AUG) sets the reading frame, the order in which the sequence of bases in the mRNA is sorted into codons (Fig. 15.3). The order of the codons in the mRNA determines the sequence in which amino acids are added to the growing polypeptide chain. Thus, the order of the codons in the mRNA determines the linear sequence of amino acids in the protein.

III. EFFECTS OF MUTATIONS

Mutations that result from damage to the nucleotides of DNA molecules or from unrepaired errors during replication (see Chapter 13) can be transcribed into mRNA and therefore can result in the translation of a protein with an abnormal amino acid sequence. Various types of mutations can occur, which have different effects on the encoded protein (Table 15.2).

Table 15.2   Types of Mutations

Type	Description	Example
Point	A single base change	
Silent	A change that specifies the same amino acid	CGA → CGG
		Arg → Arg
Missense	A change that specifies a different amino acid	CGA → CCA
		Arg → Pro
Nonsense	A change that produces a stop codon	CGA → UGA
		Arg → Stop
Insertion	An addition of one or more bases	
Deletion	A loss of one or more bases	

Sickle cell anemia is caused by a missense mutation. In each of the alleles for β-globin, **Will Sichel's** DNA has a single base change (see Chapter 6). In the sickle cell gene, GTG replaces the normal GAG. Thus, in the mRNA, the codon GUG replaces GAG and a valine residue replaces a glutamate residue in the protein. The amino acid change is indicated as E6V; the normal glutamate (E) at position 6 of the β-chain has been replaced by a valine (V).

One type of thalassemia is caused by a nonsense mutation. Codon 17 of the β-globin chain is changed from UGG to UGA. This change results in the conversion of a codon for a tryptophan residue to a stop codon. Other types of thalassemia are caused by deletions in the globin genes. Patients have been studied who have large deletions in either the 5′ or the 3′ coding region of the β-globin gene, removing almost one-third of the DNA sequence.

Is it possible that **Anne Niemick** has either a nonsense mutation in codon 17 or a large deletion of the β-globin gene?

A. Point Mutations

Point mutations occur when only one base in DNA is altered, producing a change in a single base of an mRNA codon. There are three basic types of point mutations: silent mutations, missense mutations, and nonsense mutations. Point mutations are said to be "silent" when they do not affect the amino acid sequence of the protein. For example, a codon change from CGA to CGG does not affect the protein because both of these codons specify arginine (see Table 15.1). In missense mutations, one amino acid in the protein is replaced by a different amino acid. For example, a change from CGA to CCA causes arginine to be replaced by proline. A "nonsense" mutation causes the premature termination of a polypeptide chain. For example, a codon change from CGA to UGA causes a codon for arginine to be replaced by a stop codon, so synthesis of the mutant protein terminates at this point.

B. Insertions, Deletions, and Frameshift Mutations

An *insertion* occurs when one or more nucleotides are added to DNA. If the insertion does not generate a stop codon, a protein with more amino acids than normal could be produced. When one or more nucleotides are removed from DNA, the mutation is known as a *deletion*. If the deletion does not affect the normal start and stop codons, a protein with fewer than the normal number of amino acids could be produced.

A *frameshift mutation* occurs when the number of inserted or deleted nucleotides is not a multiple of three (Fig. 15.4). The reading frame shifts at the point where the insertion or deletion begins. Beyond that point, the amino acid sequence of the protein translated from the mRNA differs from the normal protein.

IV. FORMATION OF AMINOACYL-TRNA

A tRNA that contains an amino acid attached covalently to its 3′-end is called an *aminoacyl-tRNA* and is said to be "charged." Aminoacyl-tRNAs are named for both the amino acid and the tRNA that carries the amino acid. For example, the tRNA for alanine (tRNA^{Ala}) acquires alanine to become alanyl-tRNA^{Ala}. A particular tRNA recognizes only the AUG start codon that initiates protein synthesis and not other AUG codons that specify insertion of methionine within the polypeptide chain. This initiator methionyl-tRNA^{Met} is denoted by the subscript "i" in methionyl-tRNA$_i^{Met}$.

Amino acids are attached to their tRNAs by highly specific enzymes known as *aminoacyl-tRNA synthetases*. Twenty different synthetases exist, one for each amino acid. Each synthetase recognizes a particular amino acid and all of the tRNAs that carry that amino acid.

FIG. 15.4. A frameshift mutation. The insertion of a single nucleotide (the A in the *dotted box*) causes the reading frame to shift so that the amino acid sequence of the protein translated from the mRNA is different after the point of insertion. A similar effect can result from the insertion or deletion of nucleotides if the number inserted or deleted is not a multiple of 3.

The formation of the ester bond that links the amino acid to the tRNA by an aminoacyl-tRNA synthetase is an energy-requiring process that occurs in two steps. The amino acid is activated in the first step when its carboxyl group reacts with adenosine triphosphate (ATP) to form an enzyme/aminoacyl–adenosine monophosphate (AMP) complex and pyrophosphate (Fig. 15.5). The cleavage of a high-energy bond of ATP in this reaction provides energy, and the subsequent cleavage of pyrophosphate by a pyrophosphatase helps to drive the reaction by removing one of the products. In the second step, the activated amino acid is transferred to the 2'- or 3'-hydroxyl group (depending on the type of aminoacyl-tRNA synthetase that catalyzes the reaction) of the ribose connected to the 3'-terminal A residue of the tRNA, and AMP is released (recall that all tRNAs have a CCA added to their 3'-end posttranscriptionally). The energy in the aminoacyl-tRNA ester bond is subsequently used in the formation of a peptide bond during the process of protein synthesis. The aminoacyl tRNA synthetase provides the first error-checking step in preserving the fidelity of translation. The enzymes check their work, and if the incorrect amino acid has been linked to a particular tRNA, the enzyme will remove the amino acid from the tRNA, and try again using the correct amino acid.

Some aminoacyl-tRNA synthetases use the anticodon of the tRNA as a recognition site as they attach the amino acid to the hydroxyl group at the 3'-end of the tRNA (Fig. 15.6). However, other synthetases do not use the anticodon but recognize only bases located at other positions in the tRNA. Nevertheless, insertion of the amino acid into a growing polypeptide chain depends solely on the bases of the anticodon, through complementary base pairing with the mRNA codon.

V. PROCESS OF TRANSLATION

Translation of a protein involves three steps: initiation, elongation, and termination. It begins with the formation of the initiation complex. Subsequently, synthesis of the polypeptide occurs by a series of elongation steps that are repeated as each amino acid is added to the growing chain (Fig. 15.7). Termination occurs where the mRNA contains an in-frame stop codon, and the completed polypeptide chain is released.

A. Initiation of Translation

In eukaryotes, initiation of translation involves formation of a complex composed of methionyl-tRNA$_i^{Met}$, mRNA, and a ribosome (Fig. 15.8). Methionyl-tRNA$_i^{Met}$ (also known as Met-tRNA$_i^{Met}$) initially forms a complex

A nonsense mutation at codon 17 would cause premature termination of translation. A nonfunctional peptide containing only 16 amino acids would result, producing a β^0-thalassemia if the mutation occurred in both alleles. A large deletion in the coding region of the gene could also produce a truncated protein. If **Anne Niemick** has a nonsense mutation or a large deletion, it could only be in one allele. The mutation in the other allele must be milder because she produces some normal β-globin. Her hemoglobin is 7 g/dL, typical of thalassemia intermedia (a β^+-thalassemia).

FIG. 15.5. Formation of aminoacyl-tRNA. The amino acid is first activated by reacting with ATP. The amino acid is then transferred from the aminoacyl-AMP to tRNA.

FIG. 15.6. Some aminoacyl-tRNA synthetase recognition sites on tRNA. Each aminoacyl-tRNA synthetase is specific for certain tRNA, which it "recognizes" by binding the sequences of nucleotides called *recognition sites*, shown in *green*. In some cases, the anticodon is a recognition site, in others it is not. This is true for human tRNAs as well as for those shown here.

FIG. 15.7.   Overview of the process of translation. *(1)* Once a tRNA has donated its amino acid to the growing polypeptide chain (which itself is still linked to a tRNA), it is released from the mRNA. *(2)* A new aminoacyl-tRNA binds to the correct codon in the mRNA to donate its amino acid to the growing polypeptide chain.

with the protein eukaryotic initiation factor 2 (eIF2), which binds guanosine triphosphate (GTP). This complex then binds to the small (40S) ribosomal subunit with the participation of eukaryotic initiation factor 3 (eIF3). eIF3 also participates in preventing premature association of the 60S ribosomal subunit with the preinitiation complex. The cap at the 5′-end of the mRNA binds to components of the eIF4 complex, eIF4F, known as the *cap-binding complex.* eIF4F is a complex comprising eIF4E, eIF4A, and eIF4G. The mRNA, in association with the cap-binding complex, then binds to the eIFs-Met-tRNA$_i^{Met}$–40S ribosome complex. In a reaction that requires hydrolysis of ATP (because of the helicase activity of an eIF subunit), this complex unwinds a hairpin loop in the mRNA and scans the mRNA until it locates the AUG start codon (usually the first AUG in the mRNA). GTP is hydrolyzed, the initiation factors are released, and the large ribosomal (60S) subunit binds. The ribosome is now complete. It contains one small and one large subunit, and it has three binding sites for tRNA, known as the P (peptidyl), A (aminoacyl), and E (ejection) sites. During

FIG. 15.8.   Initiation of protein synthesis. *P site*, peptidyl site on the ribosome; *A site*, aminoacyl site on the ribosome; *E site*, free tRNA ejection site (the A, P, and E sites or portions of them are indicated by *dashed lines*); *eIF*, eukaryotic initiation factor. This is a simplified version of translational initiation because many more initiation factors and steps are required.

Table 15.3   Differences between Eukaryotes and Prokaryotes in the Initiation of Protein Synthesis

	Eukaryotes	*Prokaryotes*
Binding of mRNA to small ribosomal subunit	Cap at 5′-end of mRNA binds eIFs and 40S ribosomal subunit containing tRNA$_i^{Met}$; mRNA is scanned for AUG start codon within the Kozak consensus sequence	Shine–Dalgarno sequence upstream of initiating AUG binds to complementary sequence in 16S rRNA
First amino acid	Methionine	Formyl-methionine
Initiation factors	eIFs (12 or more)	IFs (3)
Ribosomes	80S	70S
	(40S and 60S subunits)	(30S and 50S subunits)

initiation, Met-tRNA$_i^{Met}$ binds to the ribosome at the P site, which is located initially at the start codon for translation. Eukaryotes also contain a Kozak consensus sequence, which is recognized by the ribosome as the translational start site (the sequence is A or G – CC*AUG*G, where the purine base is three bases upstream of the AUG start codon). The Kozak sequence aids in defining the initial AUG codon for translation. Loss of this sequence reduces the efficiency of translational initiation.

The initiation process differs for prokaryotes and eukaryotes (Table 15.3). In bacteria, the initiating methionyl-tRNA is formylated, producing a formyl-methionyl-tRNA$_f^{Met}$ that participates in formation of the initiation complex (Fig. 15.9). Only three initiation factors (IFs) are required to generate this complex in prokaryotes, compared with the dozen or more required by eukaryotes. The ribosomes also differ in size. Prokaryotes have 70S ribosomes, composed of 30S and 50S subunits, and eukaryotes have 80S ribosomes, composed of 40S and 60S subunits. Unlike eukaryotic mRNA, bacterial mRNA is not capped. Identification of the initiating AUG triplet in prokaryotes occurs when a sequence in the mRNA (known as the *Shine–Dalgarno sequence*) binds to a complementary sequence near the 3′-end of the 16S rRNA of the small ribosomal subunit.

Initiation of translation is also regulated at the level of the initiation factors. For example, insulin, an anabolic hormone, stimulates general protein synthesis by activating the initiation factor eIF4E. Normally, eIF4E is bound to an inhibitor protein, designated 4E-binding protein (4E-BP). When insulin binds to its cell surface receptor, it initiates an intracellular sequence of events resulting in phosphorylation of 4E-BP. Phosphorylated 4E-BP no longer binds to eIF4E, and eIF4E is now free to participate in the initiation of protein synthesis.

Similarly, eIF2 is a regulator of the initiation step in protein synthesis. When it is phosphorylated, it is inactive, and protein synthesis cannot begin. Conditions such as starvation, heat shock, and viral infection result in phosphorylation of eIF2 by a specific kinase.

The regulation of globin synthesis by heme in reticulocytes illustrates the role of eIF2 in the regulation of translation. Reticulocytes, which are the precursors of red blood cells, synthesize the oxygen-carrying hemoglobin molecules from the globin polypeptide chains and the Fe-binding pigment, heme. In the absence of heme, the rate of initiation of globin synthesis decreases. Heme acts by inhibiting the phosphorylation of the initiation factor eIF2. Thus, eIF2 is active in the presence of heme and globin synthesis is initiated.

And finally, both eIF2 and elongation factor 1 (EF1) are types of heterotrimeric G proteins (see Chapter 11). They dramatically change their conformation and actively form complexes when they bind GTP but become inactive and dissociate when they hydrolyze this GTP to guanosine diphosphate (GDP). GTP can then displace the bound GDP to reactivate the initiation factor eIF2 or the EF1.

FIG. 15.9. Bacterial tRNA containing formyl-methionine. The initial methionine is not formylated in eukaryotic protein synthesis.

Many antibiotics that are used to combat bacterial infections in humans take advantage of the differences between the mechanisms for protein synthesis in prokaryotes and eukaryotes. For example, streptomycin binds to the 30S ribosomal subunit of prokaryotes. It interferes with initiation of protein synthesis and causes misreading of mRNA. Streptomycin, however, was not used to treat **Newman Itis** because it can cause permanent hearing loss. Its use is therefore confined mainly to the treatment of tuberculosis or other infections that do not respond adequately to other antibiotics.

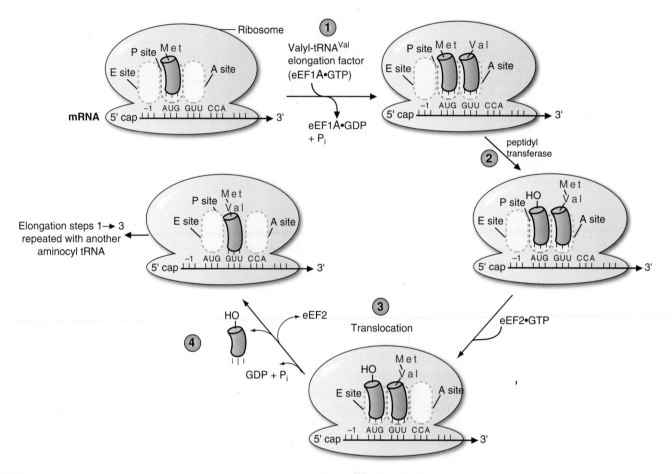

FIG. 15.10.   Elongation of a polypeptide chain. *(1)* Binding of valyl-tRNA^Val to the A site. *(2)* Formation of a peptide bond. *(3)* Translocation. *(4)* Ejection of the free tRNA. After step 4, step 1 is repeated using the aminoacyl-tRNA for the new codon in the A site. Steps 2, 3, and 4 follow. These four steps keep repeating until termination occurs. *EF,* elongation factor.

B. Elongation of Polypeptide Chains

After the initiation complex is formed, addition of each amino acid to the growing polypeptide chain involves binding of an aminoacyl-tRNA to the A site on the ribosome, formation of a peptide bond, and translocation of the peptidyl-tRNA to the P site (Fig. 15.10). The peptidyl-tRNA contains the growing polypeptide chain.

1.   BINDING OF AMINOACYL-tRNA TO THE A SITE

When Met-tRNA$_i$ (or a peptidyl-tRNA) is bound to the P site, the mRNA codon in the A site determines which aminoacyl-tRNA will bind to that site. An aminoacyl-tRNA binds when its anticodon is antiparallel and complementary to the mRNA codon. In eukaryotes, the incoming aminoacyl-tRNA first combines with elongation factor eEF1A containing bound GTP before binding to the mRNA–ribosome complex (eEF1A is similar to the α-subunit of a heterotrimeric G protein, in that it contains GTPase activity; see Chapter 11). When the aminoacyl-tRNA-eEF1A-GTP complex binds to the A site, GTP is hydrolyzed to GDP as the ribosome activates the GTPase activity of eEF1A. This prompts dissociation of eEF1A-GDP from the aminoacyl-tRNA ribosomal complex, thereby allowing protein synthesis to continue. The binding of the appropriate aminoacyl-tRNA to the A site comprises the second error-checking step in protein synthesis. If an improper aminoacyl-tRNA is brought to the A site, the ribosomal activation of the GTPase of eEF1A does not occur, and the complex will leave the binding site, along with the aminoacyl-tRNA. Only when the GTP is hydrolyzed can eEF1A release the aminoacyl-tRNA, and dissociate from the complex.

 The antibiotic levofloxacin (a quinolone) inhibits two bacterial enzymes: DNA gyrase and topoisomerase IV. The bacterium causing **Newman Itis's** infection was found to be sensitive to levofloxacin, and this could have been used in place of azithromycin.

FIG. 15.11. Recycling of eEF1A in eukaryotes. eEF1A contains a GTPase activity, which is activated upon binding to the ribosome. GTP is hydrolyzed, and eEF1A is released from the ribosome, binding to eEF1Bα. eEF1Bα is a guanine nucleotide exchange factor and accelerates the substitution of GTP for the GDP on eEF1A. Once this occurs, eEF1A is ready for another round of translation. In prokaryotes, eEF1A corresponds to EF-Tu, and the protein corresponding to eEF1Bα is EF-Ts.

Once released, the free eEF1A-GDP binds with the eEFB1α, which accelerates the replacement of bound GDP with GTP (Fig. 15.11). Thus, eEF1A-GTP is ready to bind another aminoacyl-tRNA molecule, and to continue protein synthesis.

The process of elongation is very similar in prokaryotes, except that the corresponding factor for eEF1A is named EF-Tu and the associating elongation factors are called EF-Ts instead of eEFB1α.

2. FORMATION OF A PEPTIDE BOND

In the first round of elongation, the amino acid on the tRNA in the A site forms a peptide bond with the methionine on the tRNA in the P site. In subsequent rounds of elongation, the amino acid on the tRNA in the A site forms a peptide bond with the peptide on the tRNA in the P site (see Fig. 15.10). *Peptidyltransferase*, which is not a protein but the rRNA of the large ribosomal subunit, catalyzes the formation of the peptide bond. The tRNA in the A site now contains the growing polypeptide chain, and the tRNA in the P site is uncharged (i.e., it no longer contains an amino acid or peptide).

3. TRANSLOCATION

Translocation in eukaryotes involves another G protein, elongation factor eEF2 (EF-G in prokaryotes) that complexes with GTP and binds to the ribosome, causing a conformational change that moves the mRNA and its base-paired tRNAs with respect to the ribosome. The uncharged tRNA moves from the P site to the E site. It is released from the ribosome when the next charged tRNA enters the A site. The peptidyl-tRNA moves into the P site, and the next codon of the mRNA occupies the A site. During translocation, GTP is hydrolyzed to GDP, which is released from the ribosome along with the elongation factor (see Fig. 15.10).

C. Termination of Translation

The three elongation steps are repeated until a termination (stop) codon moves into the A site on the ribosome. Because no tRNAs with anticodons that can pair with stop codons normally exist in cells, release factors bind to the ribosome instead, causing peptidyltransferase to hydrolyze the bond between the peptide chain and

 The macrolide antibiotics (e.g., erythromycin, clarithromycin, azithromycin) bind to the 50S ribosomal subunit of bacteria and inhibit translocation. Azithromycin was used to treat **Newman Itis** because he had taken it previously without difficulty. It has less serious side effects than many other antibiotics and is used as an alternative drug in patients, such as Mr. Itis, who are allergic to penicillin. After 2 weeks of therapy, Mr. Itis recovered from his infection.

 Chloramphenicol is an antibiotic that interferes with the peptidyltransferase activity of the 50S ribosomal subunit of bacteria. It was not used to treat **Newman Itis** because it is very toxic to humans, partly because of its effect on mitochondrial protein synthesis.

Diphtheria is a highly contagious disease caused by a toxin secreted by the bacterium *Corynebacterium diphtheriae.* Although the toxin is a protein, it is not produced by a bacterial gene but by a gene brought into the bacterial cell by an infecting bacteriophage.

Diphtheria toxin is composed of two protein subunits. The B-subunit binds to a cell surface receptor, facilitating the entry of the A-subunit into the cell. In the cell, the A-subunit catalyzes a reaction in which the adenosine diphosphate (ADP)-ribose (ADPR) portion of NAD is transferred to eEF2 (ADP-ribosylation). In this reaction, the ADPR is attached covalently to a posttranslationally modified histidine residue, known as *diphthamide.* ADP-ribosylation of eEF2 inhibits protein synthesis, leading to cell death. Children, including **Erna Nemdy's** daughter, are usually immunized against this often fatal disease at an early age.

 Currently, some parents are not having their children immunized. The decrease in the incidence of infectious disease in the United States has led to complacency. Other parents who lack health insurance cannot afford to have their children vaccinated. Anyone who remembers the summertime fear of poliomyelitis in the 1940s and 1950s realizes that immunizations are a blessing that should be available to all children.

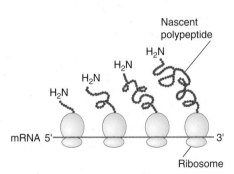

FIG. 15.12. A polysome. The complex of mRNA and multiple ribosomes, each of which is producing a polypeptide chain, is called a *polysome.*

tRNA. The newly synthesized polypeptide is released from the ribosome, which dissociates into its individual subunits, releasing the mRNA.

Protein synthesis requires a considerable amount of energy. Formation of each aminoacyl-tRNA requires the equivalent of two high-energy phosphate bonds because ATP is converted to AMP and pyrophosphate, which is cleaved to form two inorganic phosphates. As each amino acid is added to the growing peptide chain, two GTPs are hydrolyzed, one at the step involving eEF1A and the second at the translocation step. Thus, four high-energy bonds are cleaved for each amino acid of the polypeptide. In addition, energy is required for initiation of synthesis of a polypeptide chain and for synthesis from nucleoside triphosphate precursors of the mRNA, tRNA, and rRNA involved in translation.

VI. POLYSOMES

As one ribosome moves along the mRNA, producing a polypeptide chain, a second ribosome can bind to the vacant 5'-end of the mRNA. Many ribosomes can simultaneously translate a single mRNA, forming a complex known as a *polysome* (Fig. 15.12). A single ribosome covers approximately 80 nucleotides of mRNA. Therefore, ribosomes are positioned on mRNA at intervals of approximately 100 nucleotides. The growing polypeptide chains attached to the ribosomes become longer as each ribosome moves from the 5'-end toward the 3'-end of the mRNA.

VII. PROCESSING OF PROTEINS

Nascent polypeptide chains (i.e., polypeptides that are in the process of being synthesized) are processed. As they are being produced, they travel through a tunnel in the ribosome, which can hold roughly 30 amino acid residues. As polymerization of the chain progresses, the amino acid residues at the N-terminal end begin to emerge from this protected region within the ribosome and to fold and refold into the three-dimensional conformation of the polypeptide. Proteins bind to the nascent polypeptide and mediate the folding process. These mediators are called *chaperones* (they are members of the heat-shock family of proteins; see Chapter 7) because they prevent improper interactions from occurring. Disulfide bond formation between cysteine residues is catalyzed by disulfide isomerases and may also be involved in producing the three-dimensional structure of the polypeptide.

VIII. POSTTRANSLATIONAL MODIFICATIONS

After proteins emerge from the ribosome, they may undergo posttranslational modifications. The initial methionine is removed by specific proteases; methionine is not the N-terminal amino acid of all mature proteins. Subsequently, other specific cleavages also may occur that convert proteins to more active forms (e.g., the conversion of proinsulin to insulin). In addition, amino acid residues within the peptide chain can be modified enzymatically to alter the activity or stability of the proteins, direct it to a subcellular compartment, or prepare it for secretion from the cell.

Amino acid residues are modified enzymatically by the addition of various types of functional groups (Table 15.4). For example, the N-terminal amino acid is sometimes acetylated, and methyl groups can be added to lysine residues. These changes alter the charge on the protein. Proline and lysine residues can be modified by hydroxylation. In collagen, hydroxylations lead to stabilization of the protein. Carboxylations are important, especially for the function of proteins involved in blood coagulation. Formation of γ-carboxylglutamate allows these proteins to chelate Ca^{2+}, a step in clot formation. Fatty acids or other hydrophobic groups (e.g., prenyl groups) anchor the protein in membranes. An adenosine diphosphate (ADP)-ribose group can be transferred from NAD^+ to certain proteins. The addition and removal of phosphate groups (which bind covalently to serine, threonine, or tyrosine residues) serve to regulate the activity of many proteins (e.g., the enzymes of glycogen degradation and regulators of gene transcription). *Glycosylation*, the addition of carbohydrate groups, is a common modification that occurs mainly on proteins that are destined to be secreted or incorporated into lysosomes or cellular membranes.

IX. TARGETING OF PROTEINS TO SUBCELLULAR AND EXTRACELLULAR LOCATIONS

Many proteins are synthesized on polysomes in the cytosol. After they are released from ribosomes, they remain in the cytosol where they carry out their functions. Other proteins synthesized on cytosolic ribosomes enter organelles, such as mitochondria or nuclei. These proteins contain amino acid sequences called *targeting sequences* or *signal sequences* that facilitate their transport into a certain organelle. Another group of proteins is synthesized on ribosomes bound to the rough endoplasmic reticulum (RER). These proteins are destined for secretion or for incorporation into various subcellular organelles (e.g., lysosomes, endoplasmic reticulum [ER], Golgi complex) or cellular membranes, including the plasma membrane. Proteins that enter the RER as they are being synthesized have signal peptides near their N-termini that do not have a common amino acid sequence. However, they do contain several hydrophobic residues and are 15 to 30 amino acids in length (Fig. 15.13). A signal recognition particle (SRP) binds to the ribosome and to the signal peptide as the nascent polypeptide emerges from the tunnel in the ribosome, and translation ceases. When the SRP subsequently binds to an SRP receptor (docking protein) on the RER, translation resumes, and the polypeptide begins to enter the lumen of the RER. The signal peptide is removed by the signal peptidase, and the remainder of the newly synthesized protein enters the lumen of the RER. These proteins are transferred in small vesicles to the Golgi complex.

The Golgi complex serves to process the proteins it receives from the RER and to sort them so that they are delivered to their appropriate destinations (Fig. 15.14). Processing, which can be initiated in the ER, involves glycosylation (the addition of carbohydrate groups) and modification of existing carbohydrate chains. Sorting signals permit delivery of proteins to their target locations. For example, glycosylation of enzymes destined to become lysosomal enzymes results in the presence of a mannose 6-phosphate residue on an oligosaccharide attached to the

Table 15.4   Posttranslational Modifications of Proteins

Acetylation
ADP-ribosylation
Carboxylation
Fatty acylation
Glycosylation
Hydroxylation
Methylation
Phosphorylation
Prenylation

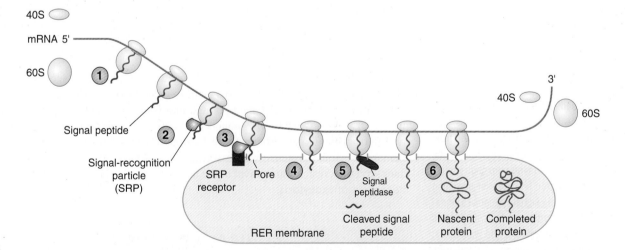

FIG. 15.13. Synthesis of proteins on the RER. *(1)* Translation of the protein begins in the cytosol. *(2)* As the signal peptide emerges from the ribosome, an SRP binds to it and to the ribosome and inhibits further synthesis of the protein. *(3)* The SRP binds to the SRP receptor in the RER membrane, docking the ribosome on the RER. *(4)* The SRP is released and protein synthesis resumes. *(5)* As the signal peptide moves through a pore into the RER, a signal peptidase removes the signal peptide. *(6)* Synthesis of the nascent protein continues, and the completed protein is released into the lumen of the RER.

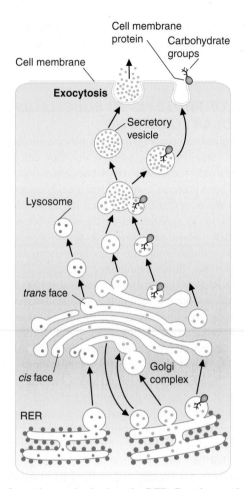

FIG. 15.14. Fate of proteins synthesized on the RER. Proteins synthesized on ribosomes attached to the ER travel in vesicles to the *cis* face of the Golgi complex. After the membranes fuse, the proteins enter the Golgi complex. Structural features of the proteins determine their fate. Some remain in the Golgi complex and some return to the RER. Others bud from the *trans* face of the Golgi complex in vesicles. These vesicles can become lysosomes or secretory vesicles, depending on their contents. Secretory proteins are released from the cell when secretory vesicles fuse with the cell membrane (exocytosis). Proteins with hydrophobic regions embedded in the membrane of secretory vesicles become cell membrane proteins. See Chapter 10 for descriptions of the endoplasmic reticulum, Golgi complex, lysosomes, and the cell membrane, and also for an explanation of the process of exocytosis.

 I-cell disease (mucolipidosis II) is a disorder of protein targeting. Lysosomal proteins are not sorted properly from the Golgi to the lysosomes, and lysosomal enzymes end up being secreted from the cell. This is because of a mutation in the enzyme *N*-acetylglucosamine phosphotransferase, which is a required first step for attaching the lysosomal targeting signal, mannose 6-phosphate, to lysosomal proteins. Thus, lysosomal proteins cannot be targeted to the lysosomes, and these organelles become clogged with materials that cannot be digested, destroying overall lysosomal function. This leads to a lysosomal storage disease of severe consequence, with death before the age of 8 years.

enzyme. This residue is recognized by the mannose 6-phosphate receptor protein, which incorporates the enzyme into a clathrin-coated vesicle. The vesicle travels to endosomes and is eventually incorporated into lysosomes. Other proteins containing a KDEL (lys–asp–glu–leu) sequence at their carboxyl terminal are returned to the ER from the Golgi. Proteins with hydrophobic regions can embed in various membranes. Some proteins, whose sorting signals have not yet been determined, enter secretory vesicles and travel to the cell membrane where they are secreted by the process of exocytosis.

CLINICAL COMMENTS

 Ann Niemick. Ann Niemick has a β^+-thalassemia classified clinically as β-thalassemia intermedia. She produces an intermediate amount of functional β-globin chains (her hemoglobin is 7 g/dL; normal is 12 to 16 g/dL). In β^0-thalassemia, little or none of the hemoglobin β-chain is produced.

Table 15.5 Some Examples of Mutations in β-Thalassemia

	Phenotype	Origin
Nonsense		
Codon 17 (A → T)	β^0	Chinese
Codon 39 (C → T)	β^0	Mediterranean
Codon 121 (A → T)	β^0	Polish
Frameshift		
Codon 6 (−1 bp)	β^0	Mediterranean
Codon 16 (−1 bp)	β^0	Asian Indian
Codon 41/42 (−4 bp)	β^0	Asian Indian, Chinese
Codon 71/72 (+1 bp)	β^0	Chinese
Promoter		
Position −88 (C → T)	β^+	African American
Position −31 (A → G)	β^+	Japanese
Position −28 (A → C)	β^+	Kurdish
Cap site		
Position +1 (A → C)	β^+	Asian Indian
Splice junction		
Intron 1, position 1 (G → A)	β^0	Mediterranean
Intron 1, 3′-end (−25 bp)	β^0	Asian Indian
Intron 2, position 1 (G → A)	β^0	Mediterranean
Intron 2, 3′-end (A → G)	β^0	African American
Intron, internal		
Intron 1, position 5 (G → T)	β^+	Mediterranean
Intron 1, position 6 (T → C)	β^+	Mediterranean
Intron 2, position 110 (G → A)	β^+	Mediterranean
Intron 2, position 654 (C → T)	β^0	Chinese
Intron 2, position 745 (C → G)	β^+	Mediterranean
Exon, internal		
Codon 24 (T → A)	β^+	African American
Codon 26 (G → A)	β^E	Southeast Asian
Codon 27 (G → T)	$\beta^{Knossos}$	Mediterranean
RNA		
cleavage/polyadenylation		
AATAAA to AACAAA	β^+	African American

Data from Scriver CR, Beaudet AL, Sly WS, et al. *The Metabolic and Molecular Basis of Inherited Diseases.* Vol. 3. New York, NY: McGraw-Hill; 1995:3456–3457.

β-Thalassemia intermedia is usually the result of two different mutations (one that mildly affects the rate of synthesis of β-globin and one that severely affects its rate of synthesis), or, less frequently, homozygosity for a mild mutation in the rate of synthesis or a complex combination of mutations. The mutations that cause the thalassemias have been studied extensively, and some are summarized in Table 15.5. For each of these mutations, the student should now be able to explain why the mutation results in a β^+- or β^0-thalassemia.

 Jay Sakz. The molecular biology–genetics laboratory's report on **Jay Sakz's** white blood cells indicated that he had a deficiency of hexosaminidase A caused by a defect in the gene encoding the α-subunit of this enzyme (variant B, Tay-Sachs disease). *Hexosaminidases* are lysosomal enzymes that are necessary for the normal degradation of glycosphingolipids, such as the gangliosides. Gangliosides are found in high concentrations in neural ganglia, although they are produced in many areas of the nervous system. When the activity of these degradative enzymes is absent or subnormal, partially degraded gangliosides accumulate in lysosomes in various cells of the central nervous system, causing a wide array of neurologic disorders known collectively as *gangliosidoses*. When the enzyme deficiency is severe, symptoms appear within the first 3 to 5 months of life. Eventually, symptoms include upper and lower motor neuron deficits, visual difficulties that can progress to blindness, seizures, and increasing cognitive dysfunction. By the second year of life, the patient may regress to a completely vegetative state, often succumbing to bronchopneumonia caused by aspiration or an inability to cough.

Erna Nemdy. With the availability of diphtheria toxoid as part of the almost universal diphteria, tetanus, pertussis (DTaP) immunization practiced in the United States, fatalities due to infection by the gram-positive bacillus *Corynebacterium diphtheriae* are rare. Most children, as is the case with **Erna Nemdy's** daughter Beverly, are immunized. In unimmunized individuals, however, symptoms are caused by a bacterial exotoxin encoded by a phage that infects the bacterial cells. The toxin enters human cells, inhibiting protein synthesis and, ultimately, causing cell death. Complications related to cardiac and nervous system involvement are the major causes of morbidity and mortality. Patients for whom a definitive diagnosis of diphtheria is established are treated with equine diphtheria antitoxin and antibiotics.

BIOCHEMICAL COMMENTS

 Antibiotics that Inhibit Protein Synthesis. The processes of translation on bacterial ribosomes and on the cytoplasmic ribosomes of eukaryotic cells have many similarities, but there are several subtle differences. Antibiotics act at steps at which these differences occur, and different antibiotics target each of the major steps of protein synthesis (Table 15.6). Therefore, these compounds can be used selectively to prevent bacterial protein synthesis and inhibit bacterial proliferation while having little or no effect on human cells. Caution must be exercised in their use, however, because some of the antibiotics affect human mitochondria, which have a protein-synthesizing system similar to that of bacteria. Another problem with these drugs is that bacteria can become resistant to their action. Mutations in genes that encode the proteins or RNA of bacterial ribosomes can cause resistance. Resistance also results when bacteria take up plasmids that carry genes for inactivation of the antibiotic. Because of the widespread and often indiscriminate use of antibiotics, strains of bacteria are rapidly developing that are resistant to all known antibiotics.

 Streptomycin. Streptomycin inhibits initiation by binding to three proteins and probably the 16S rRNA of the 30S ribosomal subunit of bacteria. Abnormal initiation complexes, known as *streptomycin monosomes*, accumulate. Streptomycin can also cause misreading of mRNA, resulting in premature termination of translation or in the incorporation of incorrect amino acids into polypeptide chains that have already been initiated. The use of this antibiotic is limited because it causes ototoxicity that can result in loss of hearing.

Tetracycline. Tetracycline binds to the 30S ribosomal subunit of bacteria and prevents an aminoacyl-tRNA from binding to the A site on the ribosome. This effect of the drug is reversible; thus, when the drug is removed, bacteria resume protein synthesis and growth, resulting in a rekindling of the infection. Furthermore, tetracycline is not absorbed well from the intestine, and its concentration can become elevated in the contents of the gut, leading to changes in the intestinal flora. Because it has been used to treat human infections and has been added to animal feed to prevent animal infections, humans have had extensive exposure to tetracycline. As a result, resistant strains of bacteria have developed.

Table 15.6   Inhibitors of Protein Synthesis in Prokaryotes

Antibiotic	Mode of Action
Streptomycin	Binds to the 30S ribosomal subunit of prokaryotes, thereby preventing formation of the initiation complex. It also causes misreading of mRNA.
Tetracycline	Binds to the 30S ribosomal subunit and inhibits binding of aminoacyl-tRNA to the A site.
Chloramphenicol	Binds to the 50S ribosomal subunit and inhibits peptidyltransferase.
Erythromycin	Binds to the 50S ribosomal subunit and prevents translocation.

Chloramphenicol. Chloramphenicol binds to the 50S ribosomal subunit of bacteria and prevents binding of the amino acid portion of the aminoacyl-tRNA, effectively inhibiting peptidyltransferase action. This antibiotic is used only for certain extremely serious infections, such as meningitis and typhoid fever. Chloramphenicol readily enters human mitochondria where it inhibits protein synthesis. Cells of the bone marrow often fail to develop in patients treated with chloramphenicol, and use of this antibiotic has been linked to fatal blood dyscrasias, including an aplastic anemia.

Erythromycin. Erythromycin and the other macrolide antibiotics bind to the 50S ribosomal subunit of bacteria near the binding site for chloramphenicol. They prevent the translocation step, the movement of the peptidyl-tRNA from the A to the P site on the ribosome. Because the side effects are less severe and more readily reversible than those of many other antibiotics, the macrolides are often used to treat infections in persons who are allergic to *penicillin*, an antibiotic that inhibits bacterial cell wall synthesis. However, bacterial resistance to erythromycin is increasing. Therefore, its close relative, clarithromycin, is often used.

Key Concepts

- Translation is the process of translating the sequence of nucleotides in mRNA to an amino acid sequence of a protein.
- Translation proceeds from the amino terminus to the carboxy terminus, reading the mRNA in the 5′-to-3′ direction.
- Protein synthesis occurs on ribosomes.
- The mRNA is read in codons, sets of three nucleotides that specify individual amino acids.
- AUG, which specifies methionine, is the start codon for all protein synthesis.
- Specific stop codons (UAG, UGA, and UAA) signal when the translation of the mRNA is to end.
- Amino acids are linked covalently to tRNA by the enzyme aminoacyl-tRNA synthetase, creating a charged tRNA.
- Charged tRNAs base-pair with the codon via the anticodon region of the tRNA.
- Protein synthesis is divided into three stages: initiation, elongation, and termination.
- Multiprotein factors are required for each stage of protein synthesis.
- Proteins fold as they are synthesized.
- Specific amino acid side chains may be modified after translation by a process known as posttranslational modification.
- Mechanisms are present within cells to specifically target newly synthesized proteins to different compartments in the cell.
- Table 15.7 summarizes the diseases discussed in this chapter.

Table 15.7   Diseases Discussed in Chapter 15

Disorder or Condition	Genetic or Environmental	Comments
β-Thalassemia	Genetic	Anne Niemick has β-thalassemia intermedia, indicating that the β-globin gene product is produced at reduced levels as compared to the α-globin gene product. This can happen by various mutations.
Tay-Sachs disease	Genetic	Mutation in a gene encoding a lysosomal enzyme, leading to loss of lysosomal function and death at an early age for the patient.
Pneuomocystis	Environmental	While rifampin was used to treat the bacterial infection previously, the mechanism of other antibiotics, which target prokaryotic protein synthesis, are also discussed.
Diphtheria, pertussis	Environmental	Diphtheria toxin catalyzes the ADP-ribosylation of eEF2, a necessary factor for eukaryotic protein synthesis. This results in cell death. Vaccination against pertussis toxin will prevent the enzymatic actions of the toxin.
I-cell disease	Genetic	Mutation in posttranslational processing that leads to mistargeting of enzymes destined for the lysosomes. Disease leads to lysosomal dysfunction and early death.

1. In the readout of the genetic code in prokaryotes, which one of the following processes acts before any of the others?

    A. tRNAi alignment with mRNA
    B. Termination of transcription
    C. Movement of the ribosome from one codon to the next
    D. Recruitment of termination factors to the A site
    E. Export of mRNA from the nucleus

2. tRNA charged with cysteine can be chemically treated so that the amino acid changes its identity to alanine. If some of this charged tRNA is added to a protein-synthesizing extract that contains *all* the normal components required for translation, which of the following statements represents the most likely outcome after adding an mRNA that has both Cys and Ala codons in the normal reading frame?

    A. Cysteine would be added each time the alanine codon was translated.
    B. Alanine would be added each time the cysteine codon was translated.
    C. The protein would have a deficiency of cysteine residues.
    D. The protein would have a deficiency of alanine residues.
    E. The protein would be entirely normal.

3. The genetic code is said to be degenerate because of which of the following?

    A. Many codons have pairs of identical bases next to each other.

    B. Some triplets are made up of repeating purines or pyrimidines.
    C. Many of the amino acids have more than one triplet code.
    D. There is wobble in the bond between the first base of the anticodon and the third base of the codon.
    E. All triplets seem to have at least one uracil.

4. A series of eukaryotic gene sequences (coding sequences) is given below. Based on this portion of the sequence, which gene could produce a protein that contains 300 amino acids and has a phenylalanine residue near its N-terminus? The phenylalanine codons (5′-to-3′) are UUU and UUC.

    A. 5′-CCATGCCATTTGCATCA-3′
    B. 5′-CCATGCCATTTGCATGA-3′
    C. 5′-CCATGCCAATTTGCATC-3′
    D. 5′-CCATCCCATTTGCATGA-3′
    E. 5′-CCATCCCATTTGCATCA-3′

5. The reason there are 64 possible codons is which of the following?

    A. There are 64 aminoacyl tRNA synthetases.
    B. Each base is able to participate in wobbling.
    C. All possible reading frames can be used this way.
    D. There are four possible bases at each of three codon positions.
    E. The more codons, the faster protein synthesis can be accomplished.

16 Regulation of Gene Expression

Gene expression, the generation of a protein or RNA product from a particular gene, is controlled by complex mechanisms. Normally, only a fraction of the genes in a cell are expressed at any time. Gene expression is regulated differently in prokaryotes and eukaryotes.

Regulation of Gene Expression in Prokaryotes. In **prokaryotes**, gene expression is regulated mainly by controlling the **initiation of gene transcription**. Sets of genes that encode proteins with related functions are organized into **operons**, and each operon is under the control of **a single promoter** (or regulatory region). Regulatory proteins called **repressors** bind to the promoter and inhibit the binding of RNA polymerase (**negative control**), whereas **activator proteins** facilitate RNA polymerase binding (**positive control**). Repressors are controlled by nutrients or their metabolites, classified as **inducers** or corepressors. Regulation also may occur through **attenuation of transcription**.

Eukaryotes: Regulation of Gene Expression at the Level of DNA. In eukaryotes, activation of a gene requires changes in the state of chromatin (**chromatin remodeling**) that are facilitated by **acetylation of histones and methylation of bases**. These changes in DNA determine which genes are available for transcription.

Regulation of Eukaryotic Gene Transcription. Transcription of specific genes is regulated by proteins (called **specific transcription factors** or **transactivators**) that bind to **gene regulatory sequences** (called **promoter-proximal elements**, **response elements**, or **enhancers**) that activate or inhibit assembly of the basal transcription complex and RNA polymerase at a TATA box. These specific transcription factors, which may bind to DNA sequences some distance from the promoter, interact with coactivators or corepressors that bind to components of the basal transcription complex. These protein factors are said to work in "**trans**"; the DNA sequences to which they bind are said to work in "**cis**."

Other Sites for Regulation of Eukaryotic Gene Expression. Regulation also occurs during the **processing** of RNA, during RNA **transport** from the nucleus to the cytoplasm, and at the level of **translation** in the cytoplasm. Regulation can occur simultaneously at multiple levels for a specific gene, and many factors act in concert to stimulate or inhibit expression of a gene.

Many of the drugs used by **Arlyn Foma** inhibit the proliferation of cancer cells in a different way. Doxorubicin (Adriamycin) is a large, nonpolar molecule synthesized by fungi that intercalates between DNA bases, inhibiting replication and transcription and forming DNA with single- and double-stranded breaks. Vincristine binds to tubulin and inhibits formation of the mitotic spindle, thereby preventing cell division. Cyclophosphamide is an alkylating agent that damages DNA by covalently attaching alkyl groups to DNA bases. Rituximab is an anti-CD20 antibody that specifically targets B cells (including the tumor cells) for destruction (a form of immunotherapy). Prednisone is a steroid hormone given to help manage the side effects of the other agents.

 The measurement of iron in the blood needs to account for iron associated with hemoglobin, free iron, and iron bound to its carrier protein, transferrin. When a physician orders a determination of serum iron, the order refers to ferric iron (Fe^{3+}) bound to transferrin, and not the ferrous iron (Fe^{2+}) bound to circulating hemoglobin (which may be present in the plasma as a result of occasional red-cell lysis). Measurement of ferric iron has been adapted to automated spectrophotometric analysis. In most cases, the samples are acidified to remove the ferric ion from transferrin. The iron is then reduced to the ferrous state by a reducing agent (such as ascorbic acid), and the level of iron is determined by its binding to a dye that changes color when ferrous ion binds to it.

The total iron-binding capacity (TIBC) is determined by adding ferric ion to the sample to saturate all transferrin-binding sites in the sample. Excess iron (free iron, not bound to transferrin) is precipitated by treatment with $MgCO_3$ and the precipitate is removed by centrifugation. The resulting soluble sample is then analyzed for Fe^{3+} as described earlier. By comparing the levels of Fe^{3+} bound both before and after saturation, one can determine what percentage of transferrin contained bound iron. For a woman between the ages of 16 and 40 years, the percentage saturation should be in the range of 15% to 50%. **Ann O'Rexia's** iron saturation is below this normal range, indicating an iron deficiency.

THE WAITING ROOM

 Arlyn Foma, a 68-year-old man, complained of fatigue, loss of appetite, and a low-grade fever. An open biopsy of a lymph node indicated the presence of non-Hodgkin lymphoma, follicular type. Computed tomography and other noninvasive procedures showed a diffuse process with bone marrow involvement. He is receiving multidrug chemotherapy with R-CHOP (rituximab, cyclophosphamide, doxorubicin, vincristine, and prednisone).

Mannie Weitzels is a 56-year-old man who complains of headaches, weight loss related to a declining appetite for food, and a decreasing tolerance for exercise. He notes discomfort and fullness in the left upper quadrant of his abdomen. On physical examination, he is noted to be pale and to have ecchymoses (bruises) on his arms and legs. His spleen is markedly enlarged.

Initial laboratory studies show a hemoglobin of 10.4 g/dL (normal, 13.5 to 17.5 g/dL) and a leukocyte (white blood cell) count of 86,000 cells/mm³ (normal, 4,500 to 11,000 cells/mm³). Most of the leukocytes are granulocytes (white blood cells arising from the myeloid lineage), some of which have an "immature" appearance. The percentage of lymphocytes in the peripheral blood is decreased. A bone marrow aspiration and biopsy show the presence of an abnormal chromosome (the Philadelphia chromosome) in dividing marrow cells.

Ann O'Rexia, who has anorexia nervosa, has continued on an almost meat-free diet (see Chapters 1, 3, 9, and 11). She now appears emaciated and pale. Her hemoglobin is 9.7 g/dL (normal, 12 to 16 g/dL), her hematocrit (volume of packed red cells) is 31% (reference range for women, 36% to 46%), and her mean corpuscular volume (the average volume of a red cell) is 70 femtoliters (fL; 1 fL is 10^{-15} L) (reference range, 80 to 100 fL). These values indicate an anemia that is microcytic (small red cells) and hypochromic (light in color, indicating a reduced amount of hemoglobin per red cell). Her serum ferritin (the cellular storage form of iron) is also subnormal. Her plasma level of transferrin (the iron transport protein in plasma) is higher than normal, but its percentage saturation with iron is below normal. This laboratory profile is consistent with changes that occur in an iron deficiency state.

I. GENE EXPRESSION IS REGULATED FOR ADAPTATION AND DIFFERENTIATION

Although most cells of an organism contain identical sets of genes, at any given time, only a small number of the total genes in each cell are expressed (i.e., generate a protein or RNA product). The remaining genes are inactive. Organisms gain several advantages by regulating the activity of their genes. For example, both prokaryotic and eukaryotic cells adapt to changes in their environment by turning the expression of genes on and off. Because the processes of RNA transcription and protein synthesis consume a considerable amount of energy, cells conserve fuel by making proteins only when they are needed.

In addition to regulating gene expression to adapt to environmental changes, eukaryotic organisms alter expression of their genes during development. As a fertilized egg becomes a multicellular organism, different kinds of proteins are synthesized in varying quantities. In the human, as the child progresses through adolescence and then into adulthood, physical and physiologic changes result from variations in gene expression and, therefore, of protein synthesis. Even after an organism has reached the adult stage, regulation of gene expression enables certain cells to undergo differentiation to assume new functions.

II. REGULATION OF GENE EXPRESSION IN PROKARYOTES

Prokaryotes are single-celled organisms and therefore require less complex regulatory mechanisms than the multicellular eukaryotes (Fig. 16.1). The most extensively studied prokaryote is the bacterium *Escherichia coli*, an organism that thrives in the human colon, usually enjoying a symbiotic relationship with its host. Based on the size of its genome (4×10^6 base pairs), *E. coli* should be capable of making several thousand proteins. However, under normal growth conditions, *E. coli* synthesizes only about 600 to 800 different proteins. Obviously, many genes are inactive, and *E. coli* will only synthesize those genes that generate the proteins required for growth in that particular environment.

All *E. coli* cells of the same strain are morphologically similar and contain an identical circular chromosome (see Fig. 16.1). As in other prokaryotes, DNA is not complexed with histones, no nuclear envelope separates the genes from the contents of the cytoplasm, and gene transcripts do not contain introns. In fact, as messenger RNA (mRNA) is being synthesized, ribosomes bind and begin to produce proteins, so that transcription and translation occur simultaneously. The mRNAs in *E. coli* have very short half-lives and are degraded within a few minutes, so an mRNA must be constantly generated from transcription to maintain synthesis of its proteins. Thus, regulation of transcription, principally at the level of initiation, is sufficient to regulate the level of proteins within the cell.

A. Operons

The genes that encode proteins are called *structural genes*. In the bacterial genome, the structural genes for proteins involved in performing a related function (such as the enzymes of a biosynthetic pathway) are often grouped sequentially into units called *operons* (Fig. 16.2, and see Fig. 14.6). The genes in an operon are expressed coordinately; that is, they are either all "turned on" or all "turned off." When an operon is expressed, all of its genes are transcribed (refer to Chapter 14, Section III). A single polycistronic mRNA is produced that codes for all the proteins of the operon. This polycistronic mRNA contains multiple sets of start and stop codons that allow several different proteins to be produced from this single transcript at the translational level. Its promoter, a specific DNA sequence to which RNA polymerase binds, regulates transcription of the genes in an operon. The promoter is located in the operon at the 5'-end, upstream from the structural genes.

B. Regulation of RNA Polymerase Binding by Repressors

In bacteria, the principal means of regulating gene transcription is through repressors, which are regulatory proteins that prevent the binding of RNA polymerase to the promoter and thus act on initiation of transcription (Fig. 16.3). In general, regulatory mechanisms such as repressors that work through inhibition of gene

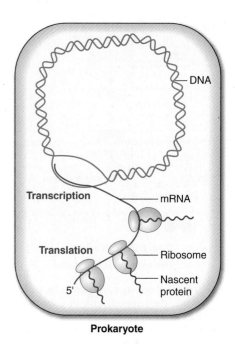

Prokaryote

FIG. 16.1.   *E. coli* cell. In prokaryotes, DNA is not separated from the rest of the cellular contents by a nuclear envelope; therefore, simultaneous transcription and translation occur in bacteria. Once a small piece of mRNA is synthesized, ribosomes bind to the mRNA, and translation begins.

FIG. 16.2.   An operon. The structural genes of an operon are transcribed as one long polycistronic mRNA. During translation, different start (AUG) and stop (UAA, UGA, or UAG) codons lead to several distinct proteins being produced from this single mRNA.

Repressors

FIG. 16.3. Regulation of operons by repressors. When the repressor protein is bound to the operator (a DNA sequence adjacent to or within the promoter), RNA polymerase cannot bind, and transcription therefore does not occur.

Inducers

FIG. 16.4. An inducible operon. In the absence of an inducer, the repressor binds to the operator, preventing the binding of RNA polymerase. When the inducer is present, the inducer binds to the repressor, inactivating it. The inactive repressor no longer binds to the operator. Therefore, RNA polymerase can bind to the promoter region and transcribe the structural genes.

transcription are referred to as *negative control*, and mechanisms that work through stimulation of gene transcription are called *positive control*.

The repressor is encoded by a regulatory gene (see Fig. 16.3). Although this gene is considered part of the operon, it is not always located near the remainder of the operon. Its product, the repressor protein, diffuses to the promoter and binds to a region of the operon called the *operator*. The operator is located within the promoter or near its 3'-end, just upstream from the transcription start point. When a repressor is bound to the operator, the operon is not transcribed because the repressor either blocks the binding of RNA polymerase to the promoter, or the ability of RNA polymerase to initiate transcription. Two regulatory mechanisms work through controlling repressors: induction (an inducer inactivates the repressor) and repression (a corepressor is required to activate the repressor).

1. INDUCERS

Induction involves a small molecule, known as an *inducer*, which stimulates expression of the operon by binding to the repressor and changing its conformation so that it can no longer bind to the operator (Fig. 16.4). The inducer is either a nutrient or a metabolite of the nutrient. In the presence of the inducer, RNA polymerase can therefore bind to the promoter and transcribe the operon. The key to this mechanism is that in the absence of the inducer, the repressor is active, the transcription is repressed, and the genes of the operon are not expressed.

Consider, for example, induction of the *lac* operon of *E. coli* by lactose (Fig. 16.5). The enzymes for metabolizing glucose by glycolysis are produced constitutively; that is, they are constantly being made. If the milk sugar lactose is available, the cells adapt and begin to produce the three additional enzymes required for lactose metabolism, which are encoded by the *lac* operon. A metabolite of lactose (allolactose) serves as an inducer, binding to the repressor and inactivating it. Because the inactive repressor no longer binds to the operator, RNA polymerase can bind to the promoter and transcribe the structural genes of the *lac* operon, producing a polycistronic mRNA

The *lac* operon

FIG. 16.5. The protein products of the *lac* operon. Lactose is a disaccharide that is hydrolyzed to glucose and galactose by β-galactosidase (the Z gene). Both glucose and galactose can be oxidized by the cell for energy. The permease (*Y* gene) enables the cell to take up lactose more readily. The A gene produces a transacetylase that acetylates β-galactosides. The function of this acetylation is not clear. The promoter binds RNA polymerase and the operator binds a repressor protein. Lactose is converted to allolactose, an inducer that binds the repressor protein and prevents it from binding to the operator. Transcription of the *lac* operon also requires activator proteins that are inactive when glucose levels are high.

Co-repressors

FIG. 16.6.   A repressible operon. The repressor is inactive until a small molecule, the core-pressor, binds to it. The repressor–corepressor complex binds to the operator and prevents transcription.

that encodes for the three additional proteins. However, the presence of glucose can prevent activation of the *lac* operon (see "Stimulation of RNA Polymerase Binding"). It is important to realize that the *lac* operon is expressed at very low levels (basal levels), even in the absence of repressor. Thus, even in the absence of lactose, a small amount of permease is present in the cellular membrane. Therefore, when lactose does become available in the environment, a few molecules of lactose are able to enter the cell and can be metabolized to allolactose. The few molecules of allolactose produced are sufficient to induce the operon. As the amount of permease increases, more lactose can be transported into the cell to be used as an energy source.

2.   COREPRESSORS

In a regulatory model called *repression*, the repressor is inactive until a small molecule called a *corepressor* (a nutrient or its metabolite) binds to the repres-sor, activating it (Fig. 16.6). The repressor–corepressor complex then binds to the operator, preventing binding of RNA polymerase and gene transcription. Consider, for example, the *trp* operon, which encodes the five enzymes required for the syn-thesis of the amino acid tryptophan. When tryptophan is available, *E. coli* cells save energy by no longer making these enzymes. Tryptophan is a corepressor that binds to the inactive repressor, causing it to change conformation and bind to the operator, thereby inhibiting transcription of the operon. Thus, in the repression model, the repressor is inactive without a corepressor; in the induction model, the repressor is active unless an inducer is present.

C. *Stimulation of RNA Polymerase Binding*

In addition to regulating transcription by means of repressors that inhibit RNA polymerase binding to promoters (negative control), bacteria regulate transcrip-tion by means of activating proteins that bind to the promoter and stimulate the binding of RNA polymerase (positive control). Transcription of the *lac* operon, for example, can be induced by allolactose only if glucose is absent. The presence or absence of glucose is communicated to the promoter by a regulatory protein named the *cyclic adenosine monophosphate* (cAMP) *receptor protein* (CRP) (Fig. 16.7). This regulatory protein is also called a *catabolite activator protein* (CAP). A decrease in glucose levels increases levels of the intracellular second-messenger cAMP by a mechanism that is not well understood. cAMP binds to CRP, and the cAMP–CRP complex binds to a regulatory region of the operon, stimulating bind-ing of RNA polymerase to the promoter and transcription. When glucose is present, cAMP levels decrease, CRP assumes an inactive conformation that does not bind to the operon, and the recruitment of RNA polymerase to the promoter is reduced,

A. In the presence of lactose and glucose

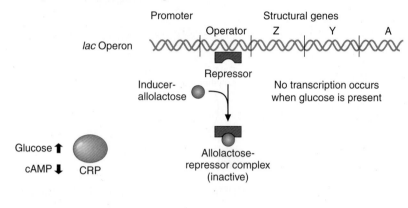

B. In the presence of lactose and absence of glucose

FIG. 16.7. Catabolite repression of stimulatory proteins. The *lac* operon is used as an example. **A.** The inducer allolactose (a metabolite of lactose) inactivates the repressor. However, because of the absence of the required coactivator, cAMP–CRP, no transcription occurs unless glucose is absent. **B.** In the absence of glucose, cAMP levels rise. cAMP forms a complex with the cAMP receptor protein (CRP). The binding of the cAMP–CRP complex to a regulatory region of the operon permits the binding of RNA polymerase to the promoter. Now, the operon is transcribed and the proteins are produced.

resulting in inhibition of transcription. Thus, the enzymes encoded by the *lac* operon are not produced if cells have an adequate supply of glucose, even if lactose is present at very high levels.

D. Regulation of RNA Polymerase Binding by Sigma Factors

E. coli has only one RNA polymerase. Sigma factors bind to this RNA polymerase, stimulating its binding to certain sets of promoters, thus simultaneously activating transcription of several operons. The standard sigma factor in *E. coli* is σ^{70}, a protein with a molecular weight of 70,000 Da (see Chapter 14). Other sigma factors also exist. For example, σ^{32} helps RNA polymerase recognize promoters for the different operons that encode the heat-shock proteins. Thus, increased transcription of the genes for heat-shock proteins, which prevent protein denaturation at high temperatures, occurs in response to elevated temperatures.

E. Attenuation of Transcription

Some operons are regulated by a process that interrupts (attenuates) transcription after it has been initiated (Fig. 16.8). For example, high levels of tryptophan attenuate transcription of the *E. coli trp* operon as well as repress its transcription. Because

FIG. 16.8.   Attenuation of the *trp* operon. Sequences 2, 3, and 4 in the mRNA transcript can form base pairs (2 with 3 or 3 with 4) that generate hairpin loops. When tryptophan levels are low, the ribosome stalls at the adjacent *trp* codons in sequence 1, the 2–3 loop forms, and transcription continues. When tryptophan levels are high, translation is rapid and the ribosome blocks formation of the 2–3 loop. Under these conditions, the 3–4 loop forms and terminates transcription.

mRNA is being transcribed from the *trp* operon, ribosomes bind and rapidly begin to translate the transcript. Near the 5′-end of the transcript are a number of codons for tryptophan. Initially, high levels of tryptophan in the cell result in high levels of Trp-tRNA^{Trp} and rapid translation of the transcript. However, rapid translation generates a hairpin loop in the mRNA that serves as a termination signal for RNA polymerase, and transcription terminates. Conversely, when tryptophan levels are low, levels of Trp-tRNA^{Trp} are low and ribosomes stall at codons for tryptophan. A different hairpin loop forms in the mRNA that does not terminate transcription, and the complete mRNA is transcribed. Attenuation requires coupled transcription and translation, so this mechanism is not applicable to eukaryotic systems.

The tryptophan, histidine, leucine, phenylalanine, and threonine operons are regulated by attenuation. Repressors and activators also act on the promoters of some of these operons, allowing the levels of these amino acids to be very carefully and rapidly regulated.

III. REGULATION OF PROTEIN SYNTHESIS IN EUKARYOTES

Multicellular eukaryotes are much more complex than single-celled prokaryotes. Because the human embryo develops into a multicellular organism, different sets of genes are turned on and different groups of proteins are produced, resulting in differentiation into morphologically distinct cell types that are able to perform different functions. Even beyond the reproductive age, certain cells within the organism continue to differentiate, such as those that produce antibodies in response to an infection, renew the population of red blood cells, and replace digestive cells that have been sloughed into the intestinal lumen. All of these physiologic changes are dictated by complex alterations in gene expression.

A. Regulation of Eukaryotic Gene Expression at Multiple Levels

Differences between eukaryotic and prokaryotic cells result in different mechanisms for regulating gene expression. DNA in eukaryotes is organized into the nucleosomes of chromatin, and genes must be in an active structure to be expressed in a cell. Furthermore, operons are not present in eukaryotes, and the genes that encode proteins that function together are usually located on different chromosomes. For example, the gene for α-globin is on chromosome 16, whereas the gene for β-globin is on chromosome 11. Thus, each gene needs its own promoter. In addition, the processes of transcription and translation are separated in eukaryotes by intracellular compartmentation (nucleus and cytosol, or endoplasmic reticulum [ER]) and by time (eukaryotic heteronuclear [hnRNA] must be processed and translocated out of the nucleus before it is translated). Thus, regulation of eukaryotic gene expression occurs at multiple levels:

- DNA and the chromosome, including chromosome remodeling and gene rearrangement
- Transcription, primarily through transcription factors that affect binding of RNA polymerase to the promoter
- Processing of transcripts
- Initiation of translation and stability of mRNA

Once a gene is activated through chromatin remodeling, the major mechanism of regulating expression affects initiation of transcription at the promoter.

B. Regulation of Availability of Genes for Transcription

Once a haploid sperm and egg combine to form a diploid cell, the number of genes in human cells remains approximately the same. Because cells differentiate, different genes are available for transcription. A typical nucleus contains chromatin that is condensed (heterochromatin) and chromatin that is diffuse (euchromatin) (see Chapter 12). The genes in heterochromatin are inactive, whereas those in euchromatin produce mRNA. Long-term changes in the activity of genes occur during development because chromatin goes from a diffuse to a condensed state or vice versa.

The cellular genome is packaged together with histones into nucleosomes, and initiation of transcription is prevented if the promoter region is part of a nucleosome. Thus, activation of a gene for transcription requires changes in the state of the chromatin, called *chromatin remodeling*. The availability of genes for transcription also can be affected in certain cells, or under certain circumstances, by gene rearrangements, amplification, or deletion. For example, during lymphocyte maturation, genes are rearranged to produce a variety of different antibodies. The term *epigenetics* is used to refer to changes in gene expression without altering the sequence of the DNA. Chromatin remodeling and DNA methylation are such changes that can be inherited, and which contribute to the regulation of gene expression.

1. CHROMATIN REMODELING

The remodeling of chromatin generally refers to displacement of the nucleosome from specific DNA sequences so that transcription of the genes in that sequence can be initiated. This occurs through two different mechanisms. The first mechanism is by an adenosine triphosphate (ATP)-driven chromatin remodeling complex, which uses energy from ATP hydrolysis to unwind certain sections of DNA from

FIG. 16.9.   Histone acetylation. *HAC*, histone acetylase; *HDAC*, histone deacetylase.

 Alteration of gene expression is a common finding in cancer cells. Alterations in HAT or HDAC activity may contribute to dysregulation of cellular proliferation in certain tumors. These alterations in HAT or HDAC activity are usually caused by mutations in transcription factors or coactivators, which have either enhanced or reduced their ability to recruit HATs or HDACs to a preinitiation complex at the promoter. HDACs have been shown to be excellent therapeutic targets for drugs that inhibit their activity. Some of these inhibitors display antiproliferative activity on a variety of human cancer cell lines and are currently in clinical trials.

the nucleosome core. The second mechanism is by covalent modification of the histone tails through acetylation (Fig. 16.9). Histone acetyltransferases (HATs) transfer an acetyl group from acetyl coenzyme A (acetyl-CoA) to lysine residues in the tail (the amino-terminal ends of histones H2A, H2B, H3, and H4) of the histone octamer. This reaction removes a positive charge from the ε-amino group of the lysine, thereby reducing the electrostatic interactions between the histones and the negatively charged DNA, making it easier for DNA to unwind from the histones. The acetyl groups can be removed by histone deacetylases (HDACs). Each histone has several lysine residues that may be acetylated and, through a complex mixing of acetylated and nonacetylated sites, different segments of DNA can be freed from the nucleosome. Several transcription factors and coactivators contain histone acetylase activity, which facilitates the binding of these factors to the DNA and simultaneous activation of the gene and initiation of its transcription.

2. METHYLATION OF DNA

Cytosine residues in DNA can be methylated to produce 5-methylcytosine. The methylated cytosines are located in CG-rich sequences (called CpG islands), which are often near or in the promoter region of a gene. In certain instances, genes that are methylated are less readily transcribed than those that are not methylated. For example, globin genes are more extensively methylated in nonerythroid cells (cells that are not a part of the erythroid, or red blood cell, lineage) than in cells in which these genes are expressed (such as erythroblasts and reticulocytes). Methylation is a mechanism for regulating gene expression during differentiation, particularly in fetal development.

3. GENE REARRANGEMENT

Segments of DNA can move from one location to another in the genome, associating with each other in various ways so that different proteins are produced (Fig. 16.10). The most thoroughly studied example of gene rearrangement occurs in cells that produce antibodies. Antibodies contain two light chains and two heavy chains, each of which contains both a variable region and a constant region (see Chapter 7, Section VIII, Fig. 7.15). Cells called B cells make antibodies. In the precursors of B cells, hundreds of V_H sequences, approximately 20 D_H sequences, and approximately 6 J_H sequences are located in clusters within a long region of the chromosome (see Fig. 16.10). During the production of the immature B cells, a series of recombinational events occur that joins one V_H, one D_H, and one J_H sequence into a single exon. This now encodes the variable region of the heavy chain of the antibody. Given the large number of immature B cells that are produced, virtually every recombinational possibility occurs, so all VDJ combinations

Methylation has been implicated in genomic imprinting, a process that occurs during the formation of eggs or sperm that blocks the expression of the gene in the fertilized egg. Males methylate a different set of genes than females. This sex-dependent differential methylation has been studied most extensively in two human disorders, Prader-Willi syndrome and Angelman syndrome. Both syndromes, which have very different symptoms, result from deletions of the same region of chromosome 15 (a microdeletion of <5 megabases in size). If the deletion is inherited from the father, Prader-Willi syndrome is seen in the child; if the deletion is inherited from the mother, Angelman syndrome is observed. A disease occurs when a gene that is in the deleted region of one chromosome is methylated on the other chromosome. The mother methylates different genes than the father, so different genes are expressed depending on which parent transmitted the intact chromosome. For example, for Prader-Willi syndrome, if genes 1, 2, and 3 are deleted in the paternal chromosome and gene 2 is methylated in the maternal chromosome, only genes 1 and 3 will be expressed. For Angelman syndrome, genes 1, 2, and 3 are deleted on the maternal chromosome and gene 1 is methylated on the paternal chromosome, so only genes 2 and 3 are expressed.

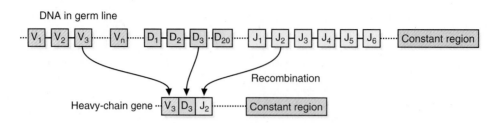

FIG. 16.10. Rearrangement of DNA. The heavy-chain gene from which lymphocytes produce immunoglobulins is generated by combining specific segments from among a large number of potential sequences in the DNA of precursor cells. The variable and constant regions of immunoglobulins (antibodies) are described in Chapter 7.

 Although rearrangements of short DNA sequences are difficult to detect, microscopists have observed major rearrangements for many years. Such major rearrangements known as *translocations* can be observed in metaphase chromosomes under the microscope. **Mannie Weitzels** has such a translocation known as the *Philadelphia chromosome* because it was first observed in that city. The Philadelphia chromosome is produced by a balanced exchange between chromosomes 9 and 22.

 Historically, non-Hodgkin lymphoma was treated with methotrexate, a drug that inhibits cell proliferation by inhibiting dihydrofolate reductase. Dihydrofolate reductase reduces dihydrofolate to tetrahydrofolate, a cofactor required for synthesis of thymine and purine nucleotides. Methotrexate resistance, however, was frequently observed in patients. Sometimes, rapidly dividing cancer cells treated with methotrexate amplify the gene for dihydrofolate reductase, producing hundreds of copies in the genome. These cells generate large amounts of dihydrofolate reductase, and normal doses of methotrexate are no longer adequate. Gene amplification is one of the mechanisms by which patients become resistant to a drug. Methotrexate is no longer used for the treatment of non-Hodgkin lymphoma, having been supplanted by specific immunotherapy.

are represented within this cell population. Later in development, during differentiation of mature B cells, recombinational events join a VDJ sequence to one of the nine heavy-chain elements. When the immune system encounters an antigen, the one immature B cell that can bind to that antigen (because of its unique manner of forming the VDJ exon) is stimulated to proliferate (clonal expansion) and to produce antibodies against the antigen.

4. GENE AMPLIFICATION

Gene amplification is not the usual physiologic means of regulating gene expression in normal cells, but it does occur in response to certain stimuli if the cell can obtain a growth advantage by producing large amounts of a protein. In gene amplification, certain regions of a chromosome undergo repeated cycles of DNA replication. The newly synthesized DNA is excised and forms small, unstable chromosomes called *double minutes*. The double minutes integrate into other chromosomes throughout the genome, thereby amplifying the gene in the process. Normally, gene amplification occurs through errors during DNA replication and cell division and, if the environmental conditions are appropriate, cells containing amplified genes may have a growth advantage over those without the amplification.

5. GENE DELETIONS

With a few exceptions, the deletion of genetic material is likewise not a normal means of controlling transcription, although such deletions do result in disease. Gene deletions can occur through errors in DNA replication and cell division and are usually noticed only if a disease results. For example, various types of cancers result from the loss of a good copy of a tumor suppressor gene, leaving the cell with a mutated copy of the gene (see Chapter 18).

C. Regulation at the Level of Transcription

The transcription of active genes is regulated by controlling assembly of the basal transcription complex containing RNA polymerase and its binding to distinct elements of the promoter, such as the TATA box (see Chapter 14). The basal transcription complex contains $TF_{II}D$ (which binds to elements within the promoter, such as the TATA box, using the TATA-binding protein [TBP]) and other proteins called general (basal) transcription factors (such as $TF_{II}A$) that form a complex with RNA polymerase II. Additional transcription factors that are ubiquitous to all promoters bind upstream at various sites in the promoter region. They increase the frequency of transcription and are required for a promoter to function at an adequate level. Genes that are regulated solely by these consensus elements in the promoter region are said to be constitutively expressed.

The control region of a gene also contains DNA regulatory sequences that are specific for that gene and may increase its transcription 1,000-fold or more (Fig. 16.11). Gene-specific transcription factors (also called *transactivators* or *activators*) bind to these regulatory sequences and interact with mediator proteins such as coactivators. By forming a loop in the DNA, coactivators interact with the

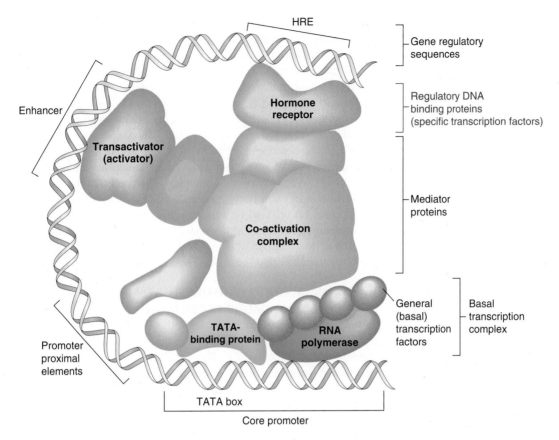

FIG. 16.11.   The gene regulatory control region consists of the promoter region and additional gene regulatory sequences, including enhancers and hormone response elements. In this case, a promoter containing a TATA box is shown. Gene regulatory proteins that bind directly to DNA (regulatory DNA-binding proteins) are usually called *specific transcription factors* or *transactivators*; they may be either activators or repressors of the transcription of specific genes. The specific transcription factors bind mediator proteins (coactivators or corepressors) that interact with the general transcription factors of the basal transcription complex. The basal transcription complex contains RNA polymerase and associated general transcription factors (TFII factors) and binds, in this case, to the TATA box of the promoter, initiating gene transcription.

basal transcription complex and can activate its assembly at the initiation site on the promoter. These DNA regulatory sequences may be some distance from the promoter and may be either upstream or downstream of the initiation site.

Depending on the system, the terminology used to describe components of gene-specific regulation varies somewhat. For example, in the original terminology, DNA regulatory sequences called *enhancers* bound transactivators, which bound coactivators. Similarly, silencers bound corepressors. Hormones bound to hormone receptors, which bound to hormone response elements in DNA. Although these terms are still used, they are often replaced by more general terms such as *DNA regulatory sequences* and *specific transcription factors*, in recognition of the fact that many transcription factors activate one gene while inhibiting another or that a specific transcription factor may be changed from a repressor to an activator by phosphorylation.

1. GENE-SPECIFIC REGULATORY PROTEINS

The regulatory proteins that bind directly to DNA sequences are most often called *transcription factors* or *gene-specific transcription factors* (if it is necessary to distinguish them from the general transcription factors of the basal transcription complex). They also can be called *activators* (or *transactivators*), *inducers*, *repressors*, or *nuclear receptors*. In addition to their DNA-binding domain, these proteins usually have a domain that binds to mediator proteins (coactivators, corepressors, or TATA-binding protein–associated factors [TAFs]). Coactivators, corepressors, and other mediator proteins do not bind directly to DNA but generally bind to components of the basal

 In fragile X syndrome, a GCC triplet is amplified on the 5′-side of a gene (*FMR-1*) associated with the disease. This gene is located on the X chromosome. The disease is named for the finding that in the absence of folic acid (which impairs nucleotide production and hence the replication of DNA), the X chromosome develops single- and double-stranded breaks in its DNA. These were termed *fragile sites*. It was subsequently determined that the *FMR-1* gene was located in one of these fragile sites. A normal person has about 30 copies of the GCC triplet, but in affected individuals, thousands of copies can be present. This syndrome, which is a common form of inherited mental retardation, affects about 1 in 3,500 males and 1 in 6,000 females.

transcription complex and mediate its assembly at the promoter. They may be specific for a given gene transcription factor or may be general and bind many different gene-specific transcription factors. Certain coactivators have histone acetylase activity, and certain corepressors have HDAC activity. When the appropriate interactions among the transactivators, the coactivators, and the basal transcription complex occur, the rate of transcription of the gene is increased (induction).

Some regulatory DNA-binding proteins inhibit (repress) transcription and may be called *repressors*. Repression can occur in several ways. A repressor bound to its specific DNA sequence may inhibit binding of an activator to its regulatory sequence. Alternatively, the repressor may bind a corepressor that inhibits binding of a coactivator to the basal transcription complex. The repressor may bind a component of the basal transcription complex directly. Some steroid hormone receptors that are transcription factors bind either coactivators or corepressors, depending on whether the receptor contains bound hormone. Furthermore, a particular transcription factor may induce transcription when it is bound to the regulatory sequence of one gene and may repress transcription when it is bound to the regulatory sequence of another gene.

2. TRANSCRIPTION FACTORS THAT ARE STEROID HORMONE/ THYROID HORMONE RECEPTORS

In the human, steroid hormones and other lipophilic hormones activate or inhibit transcription of specific genes through binding to nuclear receptors that are gene-specific transcription factors (Fig. 16.12A). The nuclear receptors bind to DNA regulatory sequences called *hormone response elements* and induce or repress

A. Domains of the steroid hormone receptor

B. Transcriptional regulation by steroid hormone receptors

GR dimer

FIG. 16.12.   Steroid hormone receptors. **A.** Domains of the steroid hormone receptor. The transactivation domain (TAD) binds coactivators; DNA-binding domain (DBD) binds to the hormone response element in DNA; ligand-binding domain (LBD) binds hormone; NLS is the nuclear localization signal; the dimerization sites are the portions of the protein involved in forming a dimer. The inhibitor-binding site binds heat-shock proteins and masks the nuclear localization signal. **B.** Transcriptional regulation by steroid hormone receptors. *HSP*, heat-shock proteins; *GRE*, glucocorticoid response element; *GR*, glucocorticoid receptor.

transcription of target genes. The receptors contain a hormone (ligand)-binding domain, a DNA-binding domain, and a dimerization domain that permits two receptor molecules to bind to each other, forming characteristic homodimers or heterodimers. A transactivation domain binds the coactivator proteins that interact with the basal transcription complex. The receptors also contain a nuclear localization signal domain that directs them to the nucleus at various times after they are synthesized.

Various members of the steroid hormone/thyroid hormone receptor family work in different ways. The glucocorticoid receptor, which binds the steroid hormone cortisol, resides principally in the cytosol bound to heat-shock proteins. As cortisol binds, the receptor dissociates from the heat-shock proteins, exposing the nuclear localization signal (see Fig. 16.12B). The receptors form homodimers that are translocated to the nucleus, where they bind to the hormone response elements (glucocorticoid response elements [GREs]) in the DNA control region of certain genes. The transactivation domains of the receptor dimers bind mediator proteins, thereby activating transcription of specific genes and inhibiting transcription of others.

Other members of the steroid hormone/thyroid hormone family of receptors are also gene-specific transactivation factors but generally form heterodimers that bind constitutively to a DNA regulatory sequence in the absence of their hormone ligand and repress gene transcription (Fig. 16.13). For example, the thyroid hormone receptor forms a heterodimer with the retinoid X receptor (RXR) that binds to thyroid hormone response elements and to corepressors (including one with deacetylase activity), thereby inhibiting expression of certain genes. When thyroid hormone binds, the receptor dimer changes conformation and the transactivation domain binds coactivators, thereby initiating transcription of the genes.

The RXR receptor, which binds the retinoid 9-*cis*-retinoic acid, can form heterodimers with at least eight other nuclear receptors. Each heterodimer has a different DNA-binding specificity. This allows the RXR to participate in the regulation of a wide variety of genes and to regulate gene expression differently, depending on the availability of other active receptors.

3. STRUCTURE OF DNA-BINDING PROTEINS

Several unique structural motifs have been characterized for specific transcription factors. Each of these proteins has a distinct recognition site (DNA-binding domain) that binds to the bases of a specific sequence of nucleotides in DNA. Four of the best characterized structural motifs are zinc fingers, b-zip proteins (including leucine zippers), helix-turn-helix, and helix-loop-helix.

Zinc-finger motifs (commonly found in the DNA-binding domain of steroid hormone receptors) contain a bound zinc chelated at four positions with either histidine or cysteine in a sequence of approximately 20 amino acids (Fig. 16.14). The result is

In a condition known as testicular feminization, patients produce androgens (the male sex steroids), but target cells fail to respond to these steroid hormones because they lack the appropriate intracellular transcription factor receptors. Therefore, the transcription of the genes responsible for masculinization is not activated. A patient with this condition has an XY (male) karyotype (set of chromosomes) but looks like a female. External male genitalia do not develop, but testes are present, usually in the inguinal region.

FIG. 16.13. Activity of the thyroid hormone receptor–retinoid receptor dimer (TR-RXR) in the presence and absence of thyroid hormone (T$_3$). *HAC*, histone acetylase; *HDAC*, histone deacetylase.

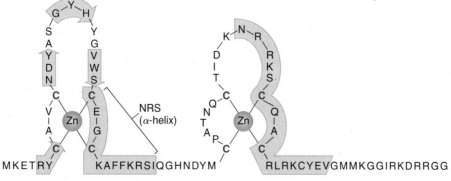

FIG. 16.14. Zinc fingers of the estrogen receptor. In each of the two zinc fingers, one zinc ion is coordinated with four cysteine residues, shown in *red*. The region labeled α-helix with nucleotide recognition signal (NRS) forms an α-helix that contains an NRS. This signal consists of a sequence of amino acid residues that bind to a specific base sequence in the major groove of DNA. Regions enclosed in *boxed arrows* participate in rigid helices.

FIG. 16.15. Interaction of DNA-binding proteins with DNA. **A.** Zinc-finger motifs consist of an α-helix and a β-sheet in which four cysteine and/or histidine residues coordinately bind a zinc ion. The nucleotide recognition signal (contained within the α-helix) of at least one zinc finger binds to a specific sequence of bases in the major groove of DNA. **B.** Leucine-zipper motifs form from two distinct polypeptide chains. Each polypeptide contains a helical region in which leucine residues are exposed on one side. These leucines form hydrophobic interactions with each other, causing dimerization. The remaining helices interact with DNA. **C.** Helix-turn-helix motifs contain three (or sometimes four) helical regions, one of which binds to DNA, whereas the others lie on top and stabilize the interaction. **D.** Helix-loop-helix motifs contain helical regions that bind to DNA like leucine zippers. However, their dimerization domains consist of two helices, each of which is connected to its DNA-binding helix by a loop.

a relatively small, tight, autonomously folded domain. The zinc is required to maintain the tertiary structure of this domain. Eukaryotic transcription factors generally have two to six zinc-finger motifs that function independently. At least one of the zinc fingers forms an α-helix containing a nucleotide recognition signal, a sequence of amino acids that fits specifically into the major groove of DNA (Fig. 16.15A).

As an example of zinc-finger transcription factors, two estrogen receptors combine to form a dimer that binds to a palindrome in the promoter region of certain genes (see Figs. 16.11 and 16.12). A palindrome is a sequence of bases that is identical on the antiparallel strand when it is read in the opposite direction. For example, the sequence ATCGCGAT base-pairs to the sequence TAGCGCTA, which, when read in the opposite direction, is ATCGCGAT. Each estrogen receptor is approximately 73 amino acids long and contains two zinc fingers. Each zinc is chelated to two cysteines in an α-helix and two cysteines in a β-sheet region. The position of the nucleotide recognition sequence in an α-helix keeps the sequence in a relatively rigid conformation as it fits into the major groove of DNA. The zinc finger that lies closest to the carboxyl terminal is involved in dimerization with the second estrogen receptor, thus inverting the nucleotide recognition sequence to match the other half of the palindrome. The dimer-palindrome requirement enormously enhances the specificity of binding, and, consequently, only those genes with the appropriate DNA sequences are affected. A wide variety of transcription factors contain the zinc-finger motif, including the steroid hormone receptors, such as the estrogen and the glucocorticoid receptors. Other transcription factors that contain zinc-finger motifs include Sp1 and polymerase III transcription factor $TF_{III}A$ (part of the basal transcription complex), which has nine zinc-finger motifs.

Leucine zippers also function as dimers to regulate gene transcription (see Fig. 16.15B). The leucine-zipper motif is an α-helix of 30 to 40 amino acid residues that contains a leucine every seven amino acids, positioned so that they align on the same side of the helix. Two helices dimerize so that the leucines of one helix align with the other helix through hydrophobic interactions to form a coiled coil. The dimers can be either homodimers or heterodimers (e.g., the transcription factor AP1 is a heterodimer whose subunits are coded by the *fos* and *jun* genes). The portions of the dimer adjacent to the zipper "grip" the DNA through basic amino acid residues (arginine and lysine) that bind to the negatively charged phosphate groups. This DNA-binding portion of the molecule also contains a nucleotide recognition signal.

In the helix-turn-helix motif, one helix fits into the major groove of DNA, making most of the DNA-binding contacts (see Fig. 16.15C). It is joined to a segment containing two additional helices that lie across the DNA-binding helix at right angles. Thus, a very stable structure is obtained without dimerization. An example of helix-turn-helix transcription factors is the homeodomain proteins (proteins that play critical roles in the regulation of gene expression during development).

Helix-loop-helix transcription factors are a fourth structural type of DNA-binding protein (see Fig. 16.15D). They also function as dimers that fit around and grip DNA in a manner geometrically similar to leucine-zipper proteins. The dimerization region consists of a portion of the DNA-gripping helix and a loop to another helix. Like leucine zippers, helix-loop-helix factors can function as either heterodimers or homodimers. These factors also contain regions of basic amino acids near the amino terminus and are also called *basic helix-loop-helix* (bHLH) proteins. Many of the transcription factors containing the helix-loop-helix motif are involved in cellular differentiation (such as myogenin in skeletal muscle, neurogenin in neurogenesis, and SCL/tal-1 in hematopoiesis and blood cell development).

4. REGULATION OF TRANSCRIPTION FACTORS

The activity of gene-specific transcription factors is regulated in several different ways. Because transcription factors need to interact with a variety of coactivators to stimulate transcription, the availability of coactivators or other mediator proteins is critical for transcription factor function. If a cell upregulates or downregulates its synthesis of coactivators, the rate of transcription can also be increased or decreased. Transcription factor activity can be modulated by changes in the amount of transcription factor synthesized (see Section III.C.5), by binding a stimulatory or inhibitory ligand (such as steroid hormone binding to the steroid hormone receptors), and by stimulation of nuclear entry (illustrated by the glucocorticoid receptor). The ability of a transcription factor to influence the transcription of a gene is also augmented or antagonized by the presence of other transcription factors. For example, the thyroid hormone receptor is critically dependent on the concentration of the retinoid receptor to provide a dimer partner. Another example is provided by the phosphoenolpyruvate carboxykinase (PEPCK) gene, which is induced or repressed by a variety of hormone-activated transcription factors (see Section III.C.5). Frequently, transcription factor activity is regulated through phosphorylation.

Growth factors, cytokines, polypeptide hormones, and several other signal molecules regulate gene transcription through phosphorylation of specific transcription factors by receptor kinases. Examples include signal transducer and activator of transcription (STAT) proteins, which are transcription factors phosphorylated by cytokine receptors, and SMAD proteins, which are transcription factors phosphorylated by serine/threonine kinase receptors such as the transforming growth factor-β (TGF-β) receptor (see Chapter 11).

Nonreceptor kinases, such as protein kinase A, also regulate transcription factors through phosphorylation. Many hormones generate the second messenger cAMP, which activates protein kinase A. Activated protein kinase A enters the nucleus and phosphorylates the transcription factor CREB (*cAMP response element binding* protein). CREB is constitutively bound to the DNA response element CRE (*cAMP response element*) and is activated by phosphorylation. Other hormone-signaling pathways, such as the mitogen-activated protein (MAP) kinase pathway, also phosphorylate CREB (as well as many other transcription factors).

5. MULTIPLE REGULATORS OF PROMOTERS

The same transcription factor inducer can activate transcription of many different genes if the genes each contain a common response element. Furthermore, a single inducer can activate sets of genes in an orderly, programmed manner (Fig. 16.16). The inducer initially activates one set of genes. One of the protein products of this

Before the advent of specifically targeted monoclonal antibody therapy, the cytokine interferon was used to treat tumors of blood cell origin. Interferons, cytokines produced by cells that have been infected with a virus, bind to the cytokine family of cell surface receptors. When an interferon binds, JAK (a receptor-associated tyrosine kinase) phosphorylates STAT transcription factors bound to the receptors (see Chapter 11). The phosphorylated STAT proteins are released, dimerize, enter the nucleus, and bind to specific gene regulatory sequences. Different combinations of phosphorylated STAT proteins bind to different sequences and activate transcription of a different set of genes. One of the genes activated by interferon produces the oligonucleotide 2'-5'-oligo(A), which is an activator of a ribonuclease. This RNase degrades messenger RNA (mRNA), thus inhibiting synthesis of the viral proteins required for its replication. In addition to stimulating degradation of mRNA, interferon also leads to the phosphorylation of eIF2 (a necessary factor for protein synthesis), which inactivates the eIF2 complex. This enables interferon to prevent the synthesis of viral proteins. In addition to antiviral effects, interferons were shown to have antitumor effects. The mechanisms of the antitumor effects are not well understood but are probably likewise related to stimulation of specific gene expression by STAT proteins. Interferon-α, produced by recombinant DNA technology, had been used in the past to treat patients such as **Arlyn Foma** who have certain types of nodular lymphomas, and patients such as **Mannie Weitzels** who have chronic myelogenous leukemia. As targeted therapy became available to reduce the side effects of treatment, interferon therapy was reduced in scope.

The enzyme PEPCK is required for the liver to produce glucose from amino acids and lactate. **Ann O'Rexia**, who has an eating disorder, needs to maintain a certain blood glucose level to keep her brain functioning normally. When her blood glucose levels drop, cortisol (a glucocorticoid) and glucagon (a polypeptide hormone) are released. In the liver, glucagon increases intracellular cAMP levels, resulting in activation of protein kinase A and subsequent phosphorylation of CREB. Phosphorylated CREB binds to its response element in DNA, as does the cortisol receptor. Both transcription factors enhance transcription of the PEPCK gene (see Fig. 16.17). Insulin, which is released when blood glucose levels rise after a meal, can inhibit expression of this gene.

FIG. 16.16. Activation of sets of genes by a single inducer. Each gene in a set has a common DNA regulatory element, so one regulatory protein can activate all the genes in the set. In the example shown, the first regulatory protein stimulates the transcription of genes *A* and *B*, which have a common DNA regulatory sequence in their control regions. The protein product of gene *B* is itself a transcriptional activator, which in turn stimulates the transcription of genes *E*, *F*, and *G*, which likewise contain common response elements.

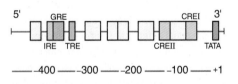

FIG. 16.17. A simplified view of the regulatory region of the PEPCK gene. *Boxes* represent various response elements in the 5'-flanking region of the gene. Not all elements are labeled. Regulatory proteins bind to these DNA elements and stimulate or inhibit the transcription of the gene. This gene encodes the enzyme PEPCK, which catalyzes a reaction of gluconeogenesis (the pathway for production of glucose) in the liver. Synthesis of the enzyme is stimulated by glucagon (by a cAMP-mediated process), by glucocorticoids, and by thyroid hormone. Synthesis of PEPCK is inhibited by insulin. *CRE*, cAMP response element; *TRE*, thyroid hormone response element; *GRE*, glucocorticoid response element; *IRE*, insulin response element.

set of genes can then act as a specific transcription factor for another set of genes. If this process is repeated, the net result is that one inducer can set off a series of events that results in the activation of many different sets of genes.

An example of a transcriptional cascade of gene activation is observed during adipocyte (fat cell) differentiation. Fibroblastlike cells can be induced to form adipocytes by the addition of dexamethasone (a steroid hormone), cAMP-elevating agents, and insulin to the cells. These factors induce the transient expression of two similar transcription factors named C/EPBβ and C/EPBδ. The names stand for CCAAT enhancer-binding protein, and β and δ are two forms of these factors that recognize CCAAT sequences in DNA. The C/EPB transcription factors then induce the synthesis of yet another transcription factor, named the peroxisome proliferator-activated receptor γ (PPARγ), which forms heterodimers with RXR to regulate the expression of yet another transcription factor, C/EPBα. The combination of PPARγ and C/EPBα then leads to the expression of adipocyte-specific genes.

An individual gene contains many different response elements and enhancers, and genes that encode different protein products contain different combinations of response elements and enhancers. Thus, each gene does not have a single, unique protein that regulates its transcription. Rather, as different proteins are stimulated to bind to their specific response elements and enhancers in a given gene, they act cooperatively to regulate expression of that gene (Fig. 16.17). Overall, a relatively small number of response elements and enhancers and a relatively small number of regulatory proteins generate a wide variety of responses from different genes.

D. Posttranscriptional Processing of RNA

After the gene is transcribed (i.e., posttranscription), regulation can occur during processing of the RNA transcript (hnRNA) into the mature mRNA. The use of alternative splice sites or sites for addition of the poly(A) tail (polyadenylation sites) can result in the production of different mRNAs from a single hnRNA and, consequently, in the production of different proteins from a single gene.

1. ALTERNATIVE SPLICING AND POLYADENYLATION SITES

Processing of the primary transcript involves the addition of a cap to the 5′-end, removal of introns, and polyadenylation (the addition of a poly[A] tail to the 3′-end) to produce the mature mRNA (see Chapter 14). In certain instances, the use of alternative splicing and polyadenylation sites causes different proteins to be produced from the same gene. For example, genes that code for antibodies are regulated by alterations in the splicing and polyadenylation sites, in addition to undergoing gene rearrangement (Fig. 16.18). At an early stage of maturation, pre–B-lymphocytes produce immunoglobulin M (IgM) antibodies that are bound to the cell membrane. Later, a shorter protein (immunoglobulin D [IgD]) is produced that no longer binds to the cell membrane but rather is secreted from the cell.

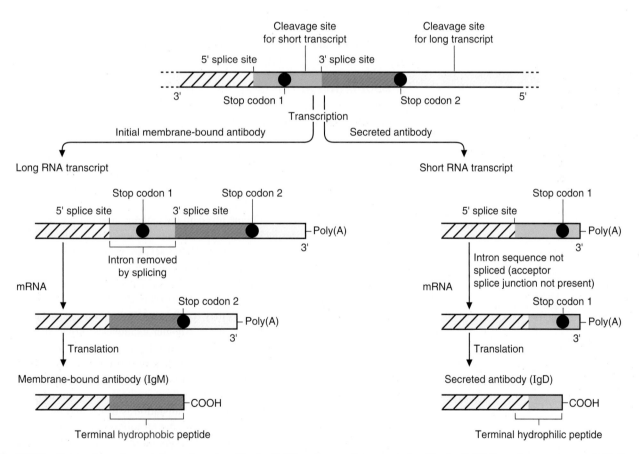

FIG. 16.18. Production of a membrane-bound antibody (IgM) and a smaller secreted antibody (IgD) from the same gene. Initially, the lymphocytes produce a long transcript that is cleaved and polyadenylated after the second stop codon. The intron that contains the first stop codon is removed by splicing between the 5′- and 3′-splice sites. Therefore, translation ends at the second stop codon, and the protein contains a hydrophobic exon at its C-terminal end that becomes embedded in the cell membrane. After antigen stimulation, the cells produce a shorter transcript by using a different cleavage and polyadenylation site. This transcript lacks the 3′-splice site for the intron, so the intron is not removed. In this case, translation ends at the first stop codon. The IgD antibody does not contain the hydrophobic region at its C-terminus, so it is secreted from the cell.

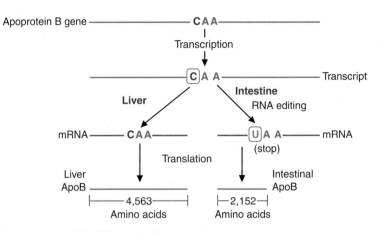

FIG. 16.19. RNA editing. In liver, the apoprotein B (*ApoB*) gene produces a protein that contains 4,563 amino acids. In intestinal cells, the same gene produces a protein that contains only 2,152 amino acids. Conversion of a C to a U (through deamination) in the RNA transcript generates a stop codon in the intestinal mRNA. Thus, the protein produced in the intestine (named apo B-48) is only 48% of the length of the protein produced in the liver (named apo B-100).

2. RNA EDITING

In some instances, RNA is "edited" after transcription. Although the sequence of the gene and the primary transcript (hnRNA) are the same, bases are altered or nucleotides are added or deleted after the transcript is synthesized, so the mature mRNA differs in different tissues (Fig. 16.19).

E. Regulation at the Level of Translation and the Stability of mRNA

1. INITIATION OF TRANSLATION

In eukaryotes, regulation of gene expression at the level of translation usually involves the initiation of protein synthesis by eukaryotic initiation factors (eIFs), which are regulated through mechanisms that involve phosphorylation (see Chapter 15, Section V). For example, heme regulates translation of globin mRNA in reticulocytes by controlling the phosphorylation of eIF2α (Fig. 16.20). In reticulocytes (red blood cell precursors), globin is produced when heme levels in the cell are high but not when they are low. Because reticulocytes lack nuclei, globin synthesis must be regulated at the level of translation rather than at transcription. Heme acts by preventing phosphorylation of eIF2α by a specific kinase (heme-regulated inhibitor kinase) that is inactive when heme is bound. Thus, when heme levels are high, eIF2α is not phosphorylated and is active, resulting in globin synthesis. Similarly, in other cells, conditions such as starvation, heat shock, or viral infections may result in activation of a specific kinase that phosphorylates eIF2α to an inactive form. Another example is provided by insulin, which stimulates general protein synthesis by inducing the phosphorylation of 4E-BP (a binding protein for eIF4E). 4E-BP, in its nonphosphorylated state, binds eIF4E and sequesters eIF4E from participating in protein synthesis. When 4E-BP is phosphorylated, it dissociates, leaving eIF4E in the active form, and protein synthesis is initiated.

A different mechanism for regulation of translation is illustrated by iron regulation of ferritin synthesis (Fig. 16.21). Ferritin, the protein involved in the storage of iron within cells, is synthesized when iron levels increase. The mRNA for ferritin has an iron response element (IRE), consisting of a hairpin loop near its 5′-end, which can bind a regulatory protein called the *iron response element–binding protein* (IRE-BP). When IRE-BP does not contain bound iron, it binds to the IRE and prevents initiation of translation. When iron levels increase and IRE-BP binds iron, it changes to a conformation that can no longer bind to the IRE on the ferritin mRNA. Therefore, the mRNA is translated and ferritin is produced.

FIG. 16.20. Heme prevents inactivation of eIF2α. When eIF2α is phosphorylated by the heme-regulated inhibitor kinase, it is inactive and protein synthesis cannot be initiated. Heme inactivates the heme-regulated inhibitor kinase, thereby preventing phosphorylation of eIF2α and activating translation of the globin mRNA.

2. microRNAs

microRNAs (miRNAs) are small RNA molecules that regulate protein expression at a posttranscriptional level. A miRNA can either induce the degradation of a target mRNA, or block translation of the target mRNA. In either event, the end result is reduced expression of the target mRNA.

miRNAs were first discovered in nematodes and have since been shown to be present in plant and animal cells. There are believed to be approximately 1,000 miRNA genes in the human genome, some of which are located within the introns of the genes they regulate. Other miRNA genes are organized into operons, such that certain miRNA families are produced at the same time. It is also evident that one miRNA can regulate multiple mRNA targets, and that a particular mRNA may be regulated by more than one miRNA.

The biogenesis of miRNA is shown in Figure 16.22. miRNA is transcribed by RNA polymerase II and is capped and polyadenylated in the same manner as mRNA. The initial RNA product is designated the primary miRNA (pri-miRNA). The pri-miRNA is modified in the nucleus by an RNA-specific endonuclease named *Drosha*, in concert with a double-stranded RNA-binding protein named *DGCR8/ Pasha*. The action of Drosha is to create a stem-loop RNA structure of about 70 to 80 nucleotides in length, which is the precursor-miRNA (pre-miRNA). The pre-miRNA is exported from the nucleus to the cytoplasm (via the protein exportin 5), where it interacts with another RNA endonuclease named *Dicer*, and Dicer's binding partner TRBP. Dicer cleaves the pre-miRNA to mature miRNA (a double-stranded RNA with a two-nucleotide overhang at the ends). One of the strands of the miRNA (known as the *guide strand*) is incorporated into the RNA-induced silencing complex (RISC), whereas the other RNA strand (the passenger strand) is degraded. The major protein in RISC is known as *argonaute*. It is the RISC that will block translation of the target mRNA.

The guide strand leads the RISC to the target mRNA because the guide strand forms base pairs within a section of the 3′-untranslated region of the mRNA. If there is a high homology in base pairing, then argonaute, a ribonuclease, will degrade the mRNA. However, if the homology between the guide strand and the target mRNA is poor (due to mismatches), then translation of the mRNA will be blocked.

The net result of miRNA expression is the loss of target mRNA translation. Because miRNAs have multiple targets, and these targets will vary from tissue

Ferritin synthesis

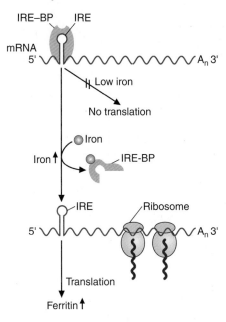

FIG. 16.21. Translational regulation of ferritin synthesis. The mRNA for ferritin has an IRE. When the IRE-BP does not contain bound iron, it binds to IRE, preventing translation. When IRE-BP binds iron, it dissociates, and the mRNA is translated.

 Follicular lymphoma is one type of non-Hodgkin lymphoma. The most frequent form of non-Hodgkin lymphoma is diffuse large B-cell lymphoma. A study has recently shown that microRNA (miRNA) expression is different between these two different types of tumors and from normal B cells. miRNA "signatures" are being developed for different tumor types, with the ultimate goal being individualized therapy based on the miRNA expression profile in a particular tumor. For example, in follicular lymphoma (which is the disorder displayed by **Arlyn Foma**), most misexpressed miRNAs are overexpressed, whereas in diffuse large B-cell lymphoma, these genes exhibit reduced expression. Therapeutic treatments are being developed to downregulate expression of the altered miRNAs in follicular lymphoma, which should alter overall gene expression in the tumor cells, and perhaps halt their runaway proliferation. Such approaches show promise as molecular medicine becomes an important tool in the physician's arsenal for treating disease.

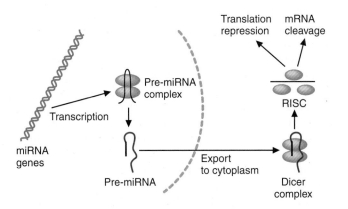

FIG. 16.22. miRNA synthesis and action. miRNA genes are transcribed in the nucleus by RNA polymerase II, generating the primary miRNA, processed to a pre-miRNA, and then exported to the cytoplasm. In the cytoplasm, the pre-miRNA is further processed by a ribonuclease (Dicer), and resulting double-stranded miRNA is strand selected, with the guide strand (designated in *black*) entering the RISC. The guide strand of RISC targets the complex to the 3′-untranslated region of the target mRNA, leading to either degradation of the mRNA or an inhibition of translation.

Transferrin receptor synthesis

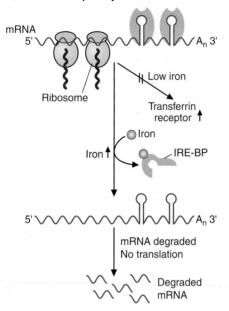

FIG. 16.23. Regulation of degradation of the mRNA for the transferrin receptor. Degradation of the mRNA is prevented by binding of the IRE-BP to IREs, which are hairpin loops located at the 3'-end of the transferrin receptor mRNA. When iron levels are high, IRE-BP binds iron and is not bound to the mRNA. The mRNA is rapidly degraded, preventing synthesis of the transferrin receptor.

to tissue, an alteration in miRNA expression will have profound effects on gene expression within cells. As will be discussed in Chapter 18, tumors can result from the loss, or overexpression, of miRNA genes.

F. Transport and Stability of mRNA

Stability of an mRNA also plays a role in regulating gene expression because mRNAs with long half-lives can generate more protein than can those with shorter half-lives. The mRNA of eukaryotes is relatively stable (with half-lives measured in hours to days), although it can be degraded by nucleases in the nucleus or cytoplasm before it is translated. To prevent degradation during transport from the nucleus to the cytoplasm, mRNA is bound to proteins that help to prevent its degradation. Sequences at the 3'-end of the mRNA appear to be involved in determining its half-life and binding proteins that prevent degradation. One of these is the poly(A) tail, which protects the mRNA from attack by nucleases. As mRNA ages, its poly(A) tail becomes shorter.

An example of the role of mRNA degradation in control of translation is provided by the transferrin receptor mRNA (Fig. 16.23). The transferrin receptor is a protein located in cell membranes that permits cells to take up transferrin, the protein that transports iron in the blood. The rate of synthesis of the transferrin receptor increases when intracellular iron levels are low, enabling cells to take up more iron. Synthesis of the transferrin receptor, like that of the ferritin receptor, is regulated by the binding of the IRE-BP to the IRE. However, in the case of the transferrin receptor mRNA, the IREs are hairpin loops located at the 3'-end of the mRNA, and not at the 5'-end where translation is initiated. When the IRE-BP does not contain bound iron, it has a high affinity for the IRE hairpin loops. Consequently, IRE-BP prevents degradation of the mRNA when iron levels are low, thus permitting synthesis of more transferrin receptor so that the cell can take up more iron. Conversely, when iron levels are elevated, IRE-BP binds iron and has a low affinity for the IRE hairpin loops of the mRNA. Without bound IRE-BP at its 3'-end, the mRNA is rapidly degraded and the transferrin receptor is not synthesized.

CLINICAL COMMENTS

Arlyn Foma. Follicular lymphomas are one of the most common subset of non-Hodgkin lymphomas (25% to 40% of cases). Patients with a more aggressive course, as seen in **Arlyn Foma**, die within 3 to 5 years after diagnosis if left untreated. In patients pretreated with multidrug chemotherapy (in this case, R-CHOP), a positive response rate of 96% has been reported, with a 4-year overall survival of approximately 83%.

Mannie Weitzels. Mannie Weitzels has chronic myelogenous leukemia (CML), a hematologic disorder in which the proliferating leukemic cells are believed to originate from a single line of primitive myeloid cells. Although it is classified as one of the myeloproliferative disorders, CML is distinguished by the presence of a specific cytogenetic abnormality of the dividing marrow cells known as the *Philadelphia chromosome*, found in more than 90% of cases. In most instances, the cause of CML is unknown, but the disease occurs with an incidence of around 1.5 per 100,000 population in Western societies.

Ann O'Rexia. Ann O'Rexia's iron stores are depleted. Normally, about 16% to 18% of total body iron is contained in ferritin, which contains a spherical protein (apoferritin) that is capable of storing as many as 4,000 atoms of iron in its center. When an iron deficiency exists, serum and tissue ferritin levels fall. Conversely, the levels of transferrin (the blood protein that transports iron) and the levels of the transferrin receptor (the cell surface receptor for transferrin) increase.

BIOCHEMICAL COMMENTS

Regulation of Transcription by Iron. A cell's ability to acquire and store iron is a carefully controlled process. Iron obtained from the diet is absorbed in the intestine and released into the circulation, where it is bound by transferrin, the iron transport protein in plasma. When a cell requires iron, the plasma iron–transferrin complex binds to the transferrin receptor in the cell membrane and is internalized into the cell. Once the iron is freed from transferrin, it then binds to ferritin, which is the cellular storage protein for iron. Ferritin has the capacity to store up to 4,000 molecules of iron per ferritin molecule. Both transcriptional and translational controls work to maintain intracellular levels of iron (see Figs. 16.21 and 16.23). When iron levels are low, the iron response element–binding protein (IRE-BP) binds to specific looped structures on both the ferritin and transferrin receptor messenger RNAs (mRNAs). This binding event stabilizes the transferrin receptor mRNA so that it can be translated and the number of transferrin receptors in the cell membrane increased. Consequently, cells will take up more iron, even when plasma transferrin/iron levels are low. The binding of IRE-BP to the ferritin mRNA, however, blocks translation of the mRNA. With low levels of intracellular iron, there is little iron to store and less need for intracellular ferritin. Thus, the IRE-BP can stabilize one mRNA and block translation from a different mRNA.

What happens when iron levels rise? Iron will bind to the IRE-BP, thereby decreasing its affinity for mRNA. When the IRE-BP dissociates from the transferrin receptor mRNA, the mRNA becomes destabilized and is degraded, leading to less receptor being synthesized. Conversely, dissociation of the IRE-BP from the ferritin mRNA allows the mRNA to be translated, thereby increasing intracellular levels of ferritin and increasing the capacity of the cell for iron storage.

Why does an anemia result from iron deficiency? When an individual is deficient in iron, the reticulocytes do not have sufficient iron to produce heme, the required prosthetic group of hemoglobin. When heme levels are low, the eukaryotic initiation factor eIF2α (see Fig. 16.20) is phosphorylated and inactive. Thus, globin mRNA cannot be translated because of the lack of heme. This results in red blood cells with inadequate levels of hemoglobin for oxygen delivery and an anemia.

Omnipotent stem cells in the bone marrow normally differentiate and mature in a highly selective and regulated manner, becoming red blood cells, white blood cells, or platelets. Cytokines stimulate differentiation of the stem cells into the lymphoid and myeloid lineages. The lymphoid lineage gives rise to B and T lymphocytes, which are white blood cells that generate antibodies for the immune response. The myeloid lineage gives rise to three types of progenitor cells: erythroid, granulocytic–monocytic, and megakaryocytic. The erythroid progenitor cells differentiate into red blood cells (erythrocytes), and the other myeloid progenitors give rise to nonlymphoid white blood cells and platelets. Various medical problems can affect this process. In **Mannie Weitzels**, who has chronic myelogenous leukemia (CML), a single line of primitive myeloid cells produces leukemic cells that proliferate abnormally, causing a large increase in the number of white blood cells in the circulation. In **Anne Niemick**, who has a deficiency of red blood cells caused by her β^+-thalassemia (see Chapter 15), differentiation of precursor cells into mature red blood cells is stimulated to compensate for the anemia.

Ann O'Rexia has a hypochromic anemia, which means that her red blood cells are pale because they contain low levels of hemoglobin. Because of her iron deficiency, she is not producing adequate amounts of heme. Consequently, eIF2α is phosphorylated in her reticulocytes and cannot activate initiation of globin translation.

Key Concepts

- Prokaryotic gene expression is regulated primarily at the level of initiation of gene transcription. In general, there is one protein per gene.
  - Sets of genes that encode proteins with related functions are organized into operons.
  - Each operon is under the control of a single promoter.
  - Repressors bind to the promoter to inhibit RNA polymerase binding.
  - Activators facilitate RNA polymerase binding to the repressor.
- Eukaryotic gene regulation occurs at several levels.
  - The DNA structural level—chromatin must be remodeled to allow access for RNA polymerase.
  - Transcription is regulated by proteins (specific transcription factors or transactivators) that bind to gene regulatory sequences (promoter-proximal elements, response elements, or enhancers).
  - Transcription factors either enhance or inhibit assembly of the basal transcription complex and RNA polymerase at a promoter.
  - RNA processing (including alternative splicing), transport from the nucleus to the cytoplasm, and translation are also regulated in eukaryotes.
  - Micro RNA expression alters translation of expressed mRNAs.
- Diseases discussed in this chapter are found in Table 16.1.

Table 16.1   Diseases Discussed in Chapter 16

Disorder or Condition	Genetic or Environmental	Comments
Non-Hodgkin lymphoma, follicular type	Both	Treatment with multiple drugs, all targeted to inhibiting cell proliferation but through different mechanisms. DNA synthesis is targeted, as is tubulin action (to block cell division). DNA damage is induced, and thymidine synthesis is also blocked to inhibit further DNA replication.
Chronic myelogenous leukemia (CML)	Both	Ninety percent of CML arises because of the generation of the Philadelphia chromosome, which is created by an exchange of genetic material between chromosomes 9 and 22. This translocation creates a unique fusion protein (*bcr-abl*), which facilitates uncontrolled proliferation of cells that express this fusion protein.
Anorexia nervosa	Both	The patient's poor diet has led to a hypochromic anemia caused by low iron levels. This leads to a reduction of expression of serum and tissue ferritin, but an increase of expression of the transferrin protein and the transferrin receptor.
Angelman and Prader-Willi syndromes	Genetic	The use of base methylation, within promoter regions, to regulate gene expression. The methylation of key bases within the promoter leads to nonexpression of the gene and forms the basis for imprinting. This is an example of epigenetic modification of gene expression.
Fragile X disease	Genetic	A significant number of triplet repeat expansions within a gene may lead to dysfunction of the protein product, leading to disease. In fragile X, mental retardation is the primary symptom caused by expansions in the FMR-1 gene on the X chromosome.
Testicular feminization	Genetic	Lack of androgen receptors, leading to default female sexual characteristics. The patient produces androgens but cannot respond to them. These patients have an XY genotype but female sexual characteristics.

REVIEW QUESTIONS—CHAPTER 16

1. Which of the following explains why several different proteins can be synthesized from a typical prokaryotic mRNA?

   A. Any of the three reading frames can be used.
   B. There is redundancy in the choice of codon/tRNA interactions.
   C. The gene contains several operator sequences from which to initiate translation.
   D. Alternative splicing events are commonly found.
   E. Many RNAs are organized in a series of consecutive translational cistrons.

2. In *E. coli*, under high-lactose, high-glucose conditions, which of the following could lead to maximal transcription activation of the *lac* operon?

   A. A mutation in the *lac I* gene (which encodes the repressor)
   B. A mutation in the CRP-binding site leading to enhanced binding
   C. A mutation in the operator sequence
   D. A mutation leading to enhanced cAMP levels
   E. A mutation leading to lower binding of repressor

3. A mutation in the *I* (repressor) gene of a "noninducible" strain of *E. coli* resulted in an inability to synthesize any of the proteins of the *lac* operon. Which of the following provides a rational explanation?

   A. The repressor has lost its affinity for inducer.
   B. The repressor has lost its affinity for operator.
   C. A *trans*-acting factor can no longer bind to the promoter.
   D. The CAP protein is no longer being made.
   E. Lactose feedback inhibition becomes constitutive.

4. Which of the following double-stranded DNA sequences shows perfect dyad symmetry (the same sequence of bases on both strands)?

    A. GAACTGCTAGTCGC
    B. GGCATCGCGATGCC
    C. TAATCGGAACCAAT
    D. GCAGATTTTAGACG
    E. TGACCGGTGACCGG

5. Which of the following describes a common theme in the structure of DNA-binding proteins?

    A. The presence of a specific helix that lies across the major or minor groove of DNA
    B. The ability to recognize RNA molecules with the same sequence
    C. The ability to form multiple hydrogen bonds between the protein peptide backbone and the DNA phospho-diester backbone
    D. The presence of zinc
    E. The ability to form dimers with disulfide linkages

The rapid development of techniques in molecular biology is revolutionizing the practice of medicine. The potential uses of these techniques for the diagnosis and treatment of disease are vast.

__Clinical Applications.__ __Polymorphisms__, inherited differences in DNA base sequences, are abundant in the human population, and many alterations in DNA sequences are associated with diseases. Tests for DNA sequence variations are more sensitive than many other techniques (such as enzyme assays) and permit recognition of diseases at earlier and, therefore, potentially more treatable stages. These tests can also identify carriers of inherited diseases so they can receive appropriate counseling. Because genetic variations are so distinctive, __DNA fingerprinting__ (analysis of DNA sequence differences) can be used to determine family relationships or to help identify the perpetrators of a crime.

Techniques of molecular biology are used in the __prevention__ and __treatment__ of disease. For example, recombinant DNA techniques provide human insulin for the treatment of diabetes, Factor VIII for the treatment of hemophilia, and vaccines for the prevention of hepatitis. Although treatment of disease by gene therapy is in the experimental phase of development, the possibilities are limited only by the human imagination and, of course, by ethical considerations. The ability to rapidly analyze the genome and __proteome__ (all expressed proteins) of a cell enables different variants of a particular disease to be identified and treated appropriately.

__Techniques.__ To recognize normal or pathologic genetic variations, DNA must be isolated from the appropriate source, and adequate amounts must be available for study. Techniques for __isolating__ and __amplifying__ genes and studying and __manipulating__ DNA sequences involve the use of __restriction enzymes__, __cloning vectors__, __polymerase chain reaction (PCR)__, __gel electrophoresis__, __blotting onto nitrocellulose paper__, and the preparation of __labeled probes that hybridize__ to the appropriate target DNA sequences. Techniques to analyze all expressed genes within a cell require __gene chip__ assays, which can lead to a genetic profile of normal versus diseased cells. __Gene therapy__ involves isolating normal genes and inserting them into diseased cells so that the normal genes are expressed, permitting the diseased cells to return to a normal state. Ablation of gene expression is possible using techniques based on __silencing RNA__ (siRNA). Students should have a general understanding of recombinant DNA techniques to appreciate their current use and the promise they hold for the future.

THE WAITING ROOM

Erna Nemdy, a third-year medical student, has started working in the hospital blood bank two nights a week (see Chapter 15 for an introduction to Erna Nemdy and her daughter, Beverly). Because she will be handling human blood products, she must have a series of hepatitis B vaccinations. She has reservations about having these vaccinations and inquires about the efficacy and safety of the vaccines currently in use.

Sissy Fibrosa is a 3-year-old Caucasian girl who is diagnosed with cystic fibrosis (CF). Her growth rate has been in the lower 30th percentile over the last year. Since birth, she has had occasional episodes of spontaneously reversible and minor small-bowel obstruction. These episodes are superimposed on gastrointestinal symptoms that suggest a degree of dietary fat malabsorption, such as bulky, glistening, foul-smelling stools two or three times per day. She has experienced recurrent flare-ups of bacterial bronchitis in the last 10 months, each time caused by *Pseudomonas aeruginosa*. A quantitative sweat test was unequivocally positive (excessive sodium and chloride were found in her sweat on two occasions). Based on these findings, the pediatrician informed Sissy's parents that Sissy probably has CF. A sample of her blood was sent to a DNA testing laboratory to confirm the diagnosis and to determine specifically which one of the many potential genetic mutations known to cause CF was present in her cells.

Cystic fibrosis is a disease caused by an inherited deficiency in the cystic fibrosis transmembrane conductance regulator (CFTR) protein, which is a chloride channel (see Chapter 10, Fig. 10.9). In the absence of chloride secretion, dried mucus blocks the pancreatic duct, resulting in decreased secretion of digestive enzymes into the intestinal lumen. The resulting malabsorption of fat and other foodstuffs decreases growth and may lead to varying degrees of small-bowel obstruction. Liver and gallbladder secretions may be similarly affected. Eventually, atrophy of the secretory organs or ducts may occur. Dried mucus also blocks the airways, markedly diminishing air exchange and predisposing the patient to stasis of secretions, diminished immune defenses, and increased secondary infections. Defects in the CFTR chloride channel also affect sweat composition, increasing the sodium and chloride content of the sweat, thereby providing a diagnostic tool.

Carrie Sichel, Will Sichel's 19-year-old sister, is considering marriage. Her growth and development have been normal, and she is free of symptoms of sickle cell anemia. Because a younger sister, Amanda, was tested and found to have sickle cell trait (expressing one normal β-globin gene and one sickle β-globin gene), and because of Will's repeated sickle crises, Carrie wants to know whether she also has sickle cell trait (see Chapters 6 and 7 for **Will Sichel's** history). A hemoglobin electrophoresis is performed that shows the composition of her hemoglobin to be 58% HbA, 39% HbS, 1% HbF, and 2% HbA_2, a pattern consistent with the presence of sickle cell trait. The hematologist who saw her in the clinic on her first visit is studying the genetic mutations of sickle cell trait and asks Carrie for permission to draw additional blood for more sophisticated analysis of the genetic disturbance that causes her to produce HbS. Carrie informed her fiancé that she has sickle cell trait and that she wants to delay their marriage until he is tested.

Vicky Tim was a 21-year-old woman who was the victim of a rape and murder. She left her home and drove to the local convenience store. When she had not returned home an hour later, her father drove to the store, looking for Vicky. He found her car still parked in front of the store and called the police. They searched the area around the store and found **Vicky Tim's** body in a wooded area behind the building. She had been sexually assaulted and strangled. Medical technologists from the police laboratory collected a semen sample from vaginal fluid and took samples of dried blood from under the victim's fingernails. Witnesses identified three men who spoke to **Vicky Tim** while she was at the convenience store. DNA samples were obtained from these suspects to determine whether any of them was the perpetrator of the crime.

Ivy Sharer's cough is slightly improved on a multidrug regimen for pulmonary tuberculosis, but she continues to have night sweats. She is tolerating her current AIDS therapy well but complains of weakness and fatigue.

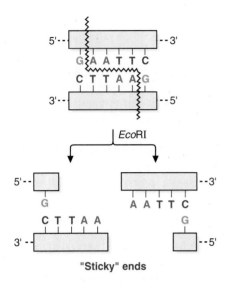

FIG. 17.1. Action of restriction enzymes. Note that the DNA sequence shown is a palindrome: Each strand of the DNA, when read in a 5'-to-3' direction, has the same sequence. Cleavage of this sequence by *Eco*RI produces single-stranded (or "sticky") ends or tails. Not shown is an example of an enzyme that generates blunt ends (see Table 17.1).

The man with whom she has shared "dirty" needles to inject drugs accompanies Ivy to the clinic and requests that he be tested for the presence of HIV.

I. RECOMBINANT DNA TECHNIQUES

Techniques for joining DNA sequences into new combinations (recombinant DNA) were originally developed as research tools to explore and manipulate genes but are now also being used to identify defective genes associated with disease and to correct genetic defects. Even a cursory survey of the current literature demonstrates that these techniques will soon replace many current clinical testing procedures. At least a basic appreciation of recombinant DNA techniques is required to understand the ways in which genetic variations among individuals are determined and how these differences can be used to diagnose disease. The first steps in determining individual variations in genes involve isolating the genes (or fragments of DNA) that contain variable sequences and obtaining adequate quantities for study.

A. Strategies for Obtaining Fragments of DNA and Copies of Genes

1. RESTRICTION FRAGMENTS

Enzymes called *restriction endonucleases* enable molecular biologists to cleave segments of DNA from the genome of various types of cells or to fragment DNA obtained from other sources. A restriction enzyme is an endonuclease that specifically recognizes a short sequence of DNA, usually 4 to 6 base pairs (bp) in length, and cleaves a phosphodiester bond in both DNA strands within this sequence (Fig. 17.1). A key feature of restriction enzymes is their specificity. A restriction enzyme always cleaves at the same DNA sequence and cleaves only at that particular sequence. Most of the DNA sequences recognized by restriction enzymes are palindromes; that is, both strands of DNA have the same base sequence when read in a 5'-to-3' direction. The cuts made by these enzymes are usually "sticky" (i.e., the products are single-stranded at the ends, with one strand overhanging the other). However, sometimes they are blunt (the products are double-stranded at the ends, with no overhangs). Hundreds of restriction enzymes with different specificities have been isolated (Table 17.1).

Which of the following sequences is most likely to be a restriction enzyme recognition sequence? All the sequences are written in standard notation, with the top strand going 5' to 3', left to right.

A. GTCCTG
    CAGGAC
B. TACGAT
    ATGCTA
C. CTGAG
    GACTC
D. ATCCTA
    TAGGAT

Table 17.1   Sequences Cleaved by Selected Restriction Enzymes[a]

Restriction Enzyme	Source	Cleavage Site
*Alu*I (blunt ends)	*Arthrobacter luteus*	5'–AG CT–3' 3'–TC GA–5'
*Bam*HI	*Bacillus amyloliquefaciens* H	5'–G GATCC–3' 3'–CCTAG G–5'
*Eco*RI	*Escherichia coli* RY13	5'–G AATTC–3' 3'–CTTAA G–5'
*Hae*III (blunt ends)	*Haemophilus aegyptius*	5'–GG CC–3' 3'–CC GG–5'
*Hind*III	*Haemophilus influenzae* R$_d$	5'–A AGCTT–3' 3'–TTCGA A–5'
*Msp*I	*Moraxella* species	5'–C CGG–3' 3'–GGC C–5'
*Mst*II	*Microcoleus*	5'–CC TNAGG–3' 3'–GGANT CC–5'
*Not*I	*Nocardia otitidis*	5'–GC GGCCGC–3' 3'–CGCCGG CG–5'
*Pst*I	*Providencia stuartii* 164	5'–CTGCA G–3' 3'–G ACGTC–5'
*Sma*I (blunt ends)	*Serratia marcescens* S$_b$	5'–CCC GGG–3' 3'–GGG CCC–5'

[a]Restriction enzymes are named for the bacterium from which they were isolated (e.g., *Eco* is from *Escherichia coli*). Unless otherwise indicated, they all create "sticky" overhanging ends. N stands for any base.

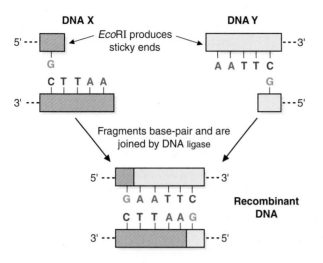

FIG. 17.2. Production of recombinant DNA molecules with restriction enzymes and DNA ligase. The *dashes* at the 5′- and 3′-ends indicate that this sequence is part of a longer DNA molecule.

A: The answer is C. C follows the palindromic sequence CTNAG, where N can be any base. None of the other sequences are this close to a palindrome. Although most restriction enzymes recognize a "perfect" palindrome, in which the sequence of bases in each strand are the same, others may have intervening bases between the regions of identity, as in this example. Note also the specificity of the enzyme *Mst*II in Table 17.1.

Restriction endonucleases were discovered in bacteria in the late 1960s and 1970s. These enzymes were named for the fact that bacteria use them to "restrict" the growth of viruses (bacteriophage) that infect the bacterial cells. They cleave the phage DNA into smaller pieces so the phage cannot reproduce in the bacterial cells. However, they do not cleave the bacterial DNA because its bases are methylated at the restriction sites by DNA methylases. Restriction enzymes also restrict uptake of DNA from the environment, and they restrict mating with nonhomologous species.

Restriction fragments of DNA can be used to identify variations in base sequence in a gene. However, they also can be used to synthesize a recombinant DNA (also called *chimeric DNA*), which is composed of molecules of DNA from different sources that have been recombined in vitro (outside the organism, e.g., in a test tube). The sticky ends of two unrelated DNA fragments can be joined to each other if they have sticky ends that are complementary. Complementary ends are obtained by cleaving the unrelated DNAs with the same restriction enzyme (Fig. 17.2). After the sticky ends of the fragments base-pair with each other, the fragments can be attached covalently by the action of DNA ligase.

In sickle cell anemia, the point mutation that converts a glutamate residue to a valine residue (G**A**G to G**T**G) occurs in a site that is cleaved by the restriction enzyme *Mst*II (recognition sequence CCTNAGG, where N can be any base) within the normal β-globin gene. The sickle cell mutation causes the β-globin gene to lose this *Mst*II restriction site. Therefore, because **Will Sichel** is homozygous for the sickle cell gene, neither of the two alleles of his β-globin gene will be cleaved at this site.

2. DNA PRODUCED BY REVERSE TRANSCRIPTASE

If messenger RNA (mRNA) transcribed from a gene is isolated, this mRNA can be used as a template by the enzyme reverse transcriptase (see Chapter 12, "Biochemical Comments"), which produces a DNA copy (cDNA) of the RNA. In contrast to DNA fragments cleaved from the genome by restriction enzymes, DNA produced by reverse transcriptase does not contain introns because mRNA, which has no introns, is used as a template. cDNA also lacks the regulatory regions of a gene, as those sequences (promoter, promoter-proximal elements, and enhancers) are not transcribed into mRNA.

3. CHEMICAL SYNTHESIS OF DNA

Automated machines can synthesize oligonucleotides (short molecules of single-stranded DNA) up to 150 nucleotides in length. These machines can be programmed to produce oligonucleotides with a specified base sequence. Although entire genes cannot yet be synthesized in one piece, appropriate overlapping pieces of genes can be made and then ligated together to produce a fully synthetic gene. Additionally, oligonucleotides can be prepared that will base-pair with segments of genes. These oligonucleotides can be used in the process of identifying, isolating, and amplifying genes.

Double-stranded
DNA

Heat or alkali

Single-stranded
DNA

Label
Probe

Probe hybridizes only with
complementary sequence on DNA

FIG. 17.3.   Use of probes to identify DNA sequences. The probe can be either DNA or RNA.

B. Techniques for Identifying DNA Sequences

1. PROBES

A probe is a single-stranded polynucleotide of DNA or RNA that is used to identify a complementary sequence on a larger single-stranded DNA or RNA molecule (Fig. 17.3). Formation of base pairs with a complementary strand is called *annealing* or *hybridization*. Probes can be composed of cDNA (produced from mRNA by reverse transcriptase), fragments of genomic DNA (cleaved by restriction enzymes from the genome), chemically synthesized oligonucleotides, or, occasionally, RNA.

The conditions of hybridization can be manipulated to provide different degrees of stringency. *Stringency* refers to how exact a match the probe must have to the DNA to which it is hybridizing in order for significant hybridization to occur. Low-stringency conditions allow a number of mismatches between the two nucleic acid strands to be tolerated (nonstandard base pairs); high stringency requires an exact match of the complementary sequences before hybridization can take place. Stringency can be manipulated by raising or lowering the temperature (increased temperature increases stringency) and raising or lowering the salt concentration in the hybridization reaction (high salt concentration reduces the stringency as it negates the electrostatic repulsion between the phosphates in the DNA backbone of two mismatched DNA strands). Thus, a high-stringency hybridization (looking for an exact match) will be performed at high temperature and low salt concentrations.

To identify the target sequence, the probe must carry a label (see Fig. 17.3). If the probe has a radioactive label such as ^{32}P, it can be detected by autoradiography. An autoradiogram is produced by covering the material containing the probe with a sheet of X-ray film. Electrons (β-particles) emitted by disintegration of the radioactive atoms expose the film in the region directly over the probe. Several techniques can be used to introduce labels into these probes. Not all probes are radioactive. Some are chemical adducts (compounds that bind covalently to DNA) that can be identified by, for example, fluorescence microscopy.

2. GEL ELECTROPHORESIS

Gel electrophoresis is a technique that uses an electrical field to separate molecules on the basis of size. Because DNA contains negatively charged phosphate groups, it will migrate in an electrical field toward the positive electrode (Fig. 17.4). Shorter molecules migrate more rapidly through the pores of a gel than do longer molecules, so separation is based on length. Gels composed of polyacrylamide, which can separate DNA molecules that differ in length by only one nucleotide, are used to determine the base sequence of DNA. Agarose gels are used to separate longer DNA fragments that have larger size differences.

The bands of DNA in the gel can be visualized by various techniques. Staining with dyes such as ethidium bromide allows direct visualization of DNA bands under ultraviolet light. Specific sequences are generally detected by means of a labeled probe.

A. Electrophoresis

DNA sample

Gel

Direction of migration

B. After electrophoresis and treatment with stain

Larger molecules

Smaller molecules

FIG. 17.4. Gel electrophoresis of DNA. **A.** DNA samples are placed into depressions ("wells") at one end of a gel, and an electrical field is applied. The DNA migrates toward the positive electrode at a rate that depends on the size of the DNA molecules. Shorter molecules migrate more rapidly than longer molecules. **B.** The gel is removed from the apparatus. The bands are not visible until techniques are performed to visualize them (see Fig. 17.6).

3. DETECTION OF SPECIFIC DNA SEQUENCES

To detect specific sequences, DNA is usually transferred to a solid support, such as a sheet of nitrocellulose paper. For example, if bacteria are growing on an agar plate, cells from each colony will adhere to a nitrocellulose sheet pressed against the agar, and an exact replica of the bacterial colonies can be transferred to the nitrocellulose paper (Fig. 17.5). A similar technique is used to transfer bands of DNA from electrophoretic gels to nitrocellulose sheets. After bacterial colonies or bands of DNA are transferred to nitrocellulose paper, the paper is treated with an alkaline solution and then heated. Alkaline solutions denature DNA (i.e., separate the two strands of each double helix), and the heating fixes the DNA on the filter paper (so it will not move from its position during the rest of the blotting procedure). The single-stranded DNA is then hybridized with a probe, and the regions on the nitrocellulose blot containing DNA that base-pairs with the probe are identified.

E. M. Southern developed the technique, which bears his name, for identifying DNA sequences on gels. *Southern blots* are produced when DNA on a nitrocellulose blot of an electrophoretic gel is hybridized with a DNA probe. Molecular biologists decided to continue with this geographic theme as they named two additional techniques. *Northern blots* are produced when RNA on a nitrocellulose blot is hybridized with a DNA probe. A slightly different but related technique, known as *Western blot*, involves separating proteins by gel electrophoresis and probing with labeled antibodies for specific proteins (Fig. 17.6).

4. DNA SEQUENCING

The most common procedure for determining the sequence of nucleotides in a DNA strand was developed by Frederick Sanger and involves the use of dideoxynucleotides. Dideoxynucleotides (see Chapter 13) lack a 3'-hydroxyl group (in addition to lacking the 2'-hydroxyl group that is normally absent from DNA deoxynucleotides). Thus, once they are incorporated into a replicating DNA chain, the next nucleotide cannot add, and polymerization is terminated. In this procedure, only one of the four dideoxynucleotides (ddATP, ddTTP, ddGTP, or ddCTP) is added to a tube containing all four normal deoxynucleotides, DNA polymerase, a primer, and the template strand for the DNA that is being sequenced (Fig. 17.7). As DNA polymerase catalyzes the sequential addition of complementary bases to the 3'-end, the dideoxynucleotide competes with its corresponding normal nucleotide

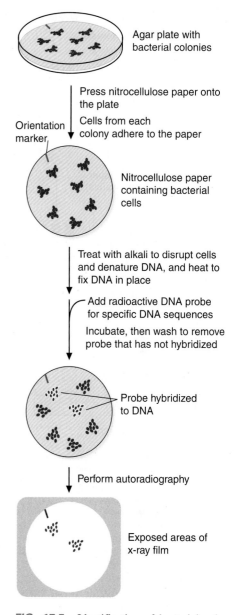

Agar plate with bacterial colonies

Press nitrocellulose paper onto the plate

Cells from each colony adhere to the paper

Orientation marker

Nitrocellulose paper containing bacterial cells

Treat with alkali to disrupt cells and denature DNA, and heat to fix DNA in place

Add radioactive DNA probe for specific DNA sequences

Incubate, then wash to remove probe that has not hybridized

Probe hybridized to DNA

Perform autoradiography

Exposed areas of x-ray film

FIG. 17.5. Identification of bacterial colonies containing specific DNA sequences. The autoradiogram can be used to identify bacterial colonies on the original agar plate that contain the desired DNA sequence. Note that an orientation marker is placed on the nitrocellulose and the agar plate so the results of the autoradiogram can be properly aligned with the original plate of bacteria.

 Western blots are one of the tests for the AIDS virus. Viral proteins in the blood are detected by antibodies. Tests performed on **Ivy Sharer's** friend showed that he was HIV positive. Unlike Ivy, however, he has not yet developed the symptoms of AIDS.

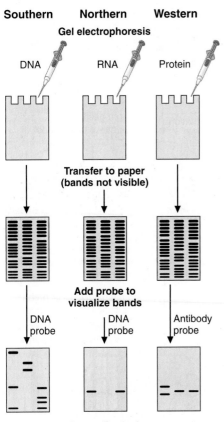

FIG. 17.6. Southern, Northern, and Western blots. For Southern blots, DNA molecules are separated by electrophoresis, denatured, transferred to nitrocellulose paper (by "blotting"), and hybridized with a DNA probe. For Northern blots, RNA is electrophoresed and treated similarly except that alkali is not used (first, because alkali hydrolyzes RNA, and second, because RNA is already single-stranded). For Western blots, proteins are electrophoresed, transferred to nitrocellulose, and probed with a specific antibody.

for insertion. Whenever the dideoxynucleotide is incorporated, further polymerization of the strand cannot occur, and synthesis is terminated. Some of the chains will terminate at each of the locations in the template strand that is complementary to the dideoxynucleotide. Consider, for example, a growing polynucleotide strand in which adenine (A) should add at positions 10, 15, and 17. Competition between ddATP and dATP for each position results in some chains terminating at position

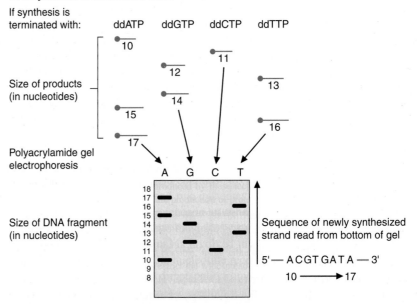

FIG. 17.7. The Sanger method. **A.** Reaction mixtures contain one of the dideoxynucleotides, such as ddATP, and some of the normal nucleotide, dATP, which compete for incorporation into the growing polypeptide chain. When a T is encountered on the template strand (position 10), some of the molecules will incorporate a ddATP and the chain will be terminated. Those that incorporate a normal dATP will continue growing until position 15 is reached, where they will incorporate either a ddATP or the normal dATP. Only those that incorporate a dATP will continue growing to position 17. Thus, strands of different length from the 5'-end are produced, corresponding to the position of a T in the template strand. **B.** DNA sequencing by the dideoxynucleotide method. Four tubes are used. Each one contains DNA polymerase; a DNA template hybridized to a primer; plus dATP, dGTP, dCTP, and dTTP. Either the primer or the nucleotides must have a radioactive label, so bands can be visualized on the gel by autoradiography. Only one of the four dideoxyribonucleotides (ddNTPs) is added to each tube. Termination of synthesis occurs where the ddNTP is incorporated into the growing chain. The template is complementary to the sequence of the newly synthesized strand. Automated DNA sequencers use fluorescent-labeled ddNTPs and a column to separate the oligonucleotides by size. As samples leave the column, their fluorescence is analyzed to determine which base has terminated synthesis of that fragment.

10, some at 15, and some at 17. Thus, DNA strands of varying lengths are produced from a template. The shortest strands are closest to the 5′-end of the growing DNA strand because the strand is synthesized in a 5′-to-3′ direction.

Four separate reactions are performed, each with only one of the dideoxynucleotides present (ddATP, ddTTP, ddGTP, ddCTP), plus a complete mixture of normal nucleotides (see Fig. 17.7B.). In each tube, some strands are terminated whenever the complementary base for that dideoxynucleotide is encountered. If these strands are subjected to gel electrophoresis, the sequence 5′ → 3′ of the DNA strand complementary to the template can be determined by "reading" from the bottom to the top of the gel, that is, by noting the lanes (A, G, C, or T) in which bands appear, starting at the bottom of the gel and moving sequentially toward the top.

C. Techniques for Amplifying DNA Sequences

To study genes or other DNA sequences, adequate quantities of material must be obtained. It is often difficult to isolate significant quantities of DNA from the original source. For example, an individual cannot usually afford to part with enough tissue to provide the amount of DNA required for clinical testing. Therefore, the available quantity of DNA has to be amplified.

1. CLONING OF DNA

The first technique developed for amplifying the quantity of DNA is known as *cloning* (Fig. 17.8). The DNA that you want amplified (the "foreign" DNA) is attached to a vector (a carrier DNA), which is introduced into a host cell that makes multiple copies of the DNA. The foreign DNA and the vector DNA are usually cleaved with the same restriction enzyme, which produces complementary sticky ends in both DNAs. The foreign DNA is then added to the vector. Base pairs form between the complementary single-stranded regions, and DNA ligase joins the molecules to produce a chimera, or recombinant DNA. As the host cells divide, they replicate their own DNA, and they also replicate the DNA of the vector, which includes the foreign DNA.

If the host cells are bacteria, commonly used vectors are *bacteriophage* (viruses that infect bacteria), *plasmids* (extrachromosomal pieces of circular DNA that are taken up by bacteria), or *cosmids* (plasmids that contain DNA sequences from the lambda phage). When eukaryotic cells are used as the host, the vectors are often retroviruses, adenoviruses, free DNA, or DNA coated with a lipid layer (liposomes). The foreign DNA sometimes integrates into the host cell genome or it exists as episomes (extrachromosomal fragments of DNA) (see Section III.D).

Host cells that contain recombinant DNA are called *transformed cells* if they are bacteria, or *transfected cells* if they are eukaryotes. Markers in the vector DNA are used to identify cells that have been transformed, and probes for the foreign DNA can be used to determine that the host cells actually contain the foreign DNA. If the host cells that contain the foreign DNA are incubated under conditions in which they replicate rapidly, large quantities of the foreign DNA can be isolated from the cells. With the appropriate vector and growth conditions that permit expression of the foreign DNA, large quantities of the protein produced from this DNA can be isolated.

2. LIBRARIES

Specific collections of DNA fragments are known as *libraries*. A *genomic library* is a set of host cells (or phage) that collectively contain all of the DNA sequences from the genome of another organism. A *cDNA library* is a set of host cells that collectively contain all the DNA sequences produced by reverse transcription of mRNA isolated from the cell (or tissue) type of interest. Therefore, a cDNA library contains complementary DNA for all the genes expressed in that cell type, corresponding to the particular stage of differentiation of the cell.

One of the drugs with which **Ivy Sharer** is being treated is didanosine, another nucleotide reverse transcriptase inhibitor (NRTI). This drug is a purine nucleoside composed of the base hypoxanthine linked to dideoxyribose. In cells, didanosine is phosphorylated to form a nucleotide that adds to growing DNA strands. Because dideoxynucleotides lack both 2′- and 3′-hydroxyl groups, DNA synthesis is terminated. Reverse transcriptase has a higher affinity for dideoxynucleotides than does the cellular DNA polymerase, so the use of this drug will affect reverse transcriptase to a greater extent than the cellular enzyme.

In the early studies on CF, DNA sequencing was used to determine the type of defect in patients. Buccal cells were obtained from washes of the mucous membranes of the mouth, DNA isolated from these cells was amplified by polymerase chain reaction (PCR), and DNA sequencing of the CF gene was performed. A sequencing gel for the region in which the normal gene differs from the mutant gene is shown in the following figure.

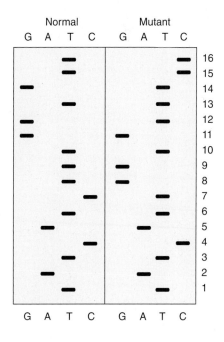

What is the difference between the normal and the mutant CF gene sequence shown on the gel, and what effect would this difference have on the protein produced from this gene?

A: In individuals of northern European descent, 70% of the cases of CF are caused by a deletion of three bases in the CF gene. In the region of the gene shown on the gels, the base sequence (read from the bottom to the top of the gel) is the same for the normal and mutant gene for the first 6 positions, and the bases in positions 10 through 16 of the normal gene are the same as the bases in positions 7 through 13 of the mutant gene. Therefore, a three-base deletion in the mutant gene corresponds to bases 7 through 9 of the normal gene.

```
                    Ile    Ile   Phe   Gly
                     |      |     |     |
Normal sequence:  T A T C A T C T T T G G T
CF sequence:      T A T C A T - - - T G G T
                     |      |         |
                    Ile    Ile       Gly
```

Loss of 3 bp (indicated by the *dashes*) maintains the reading frame, so only the single amino acid phenylalanine (F) is lost. Phenylalanine would normally appear as residue 508 in the protein. Therefore, the deletion is referred to as ΔF_{508}. The rest of the amino acid sequence of the normal and the mutant proteins is identical.

FIG. 17.8. Simplified scheme for cloning of DNA in bacteria. A plasmid is a specific type of vector, or carrier, which can contain inserts of foreign DNA of up to 2.0 kb in size. For clarity, the sizes of the pieces of DNA are not drawn to scale (e.g., the bacterial chromosomal DNA should be much larger than the plasmid DNA).

The DNA fragments that are used to construct genomic libraries are much larger than those needed to construct cDNA libraries (for humans, a genomic library would need to represent all 3 billion bp in the haploid genome; the average mRNA is about 2,500 bases in size). Thus, different vectors are used to construct genomic libraries compared to cDNA libraries. Bacteriophage (which can handle up to 20 kilobase pairs [kb] of foreign DNA), bacterial artificial chromosomes (BACs, which can handle up to 150 kb of foreign DNA), and yeast artificial chromosomes (YACs, which can handle up to 1,000 kb of foreign DNA) are often used in construction of genomic libraries. For cDNA libraries, plasmids (which can accept up to 2 kb of foreign DNA) are usually the vector of choice.

To clone a gene, a suitable probe must be developed (derived from either an amino acid sequence within a protein or from a similar DNA sequence obtained from another species); the library is then screened with the probe (using techniques described previously) to find host cells that harbor DNA sequences complementary to the probe. Obtaining sufficient clones enables the complete cDNA, or gene, to be obtained and sequenced.

3. POLYMERASE CHAIN REACTION

Polymerase chain reaction (PCR) is an in vitro method that can be used for rapid production of very large amounts of specific segments of DNA. It is particularly suited for amplifying regions of DNA for clinical or forensic testing procedures because only a very small sample of DNA is required as the starting material. Regions of DNA can be amplified by PCR from a single strand of hair or a single drop of blood or semen.

First, a sample of DNA containing the segment to be amplified must be isolated. Large quantities of primers, the four deoxyribonucleoside triphosphates, and a heat-stable DNA polymerase are added to a solution in which the DNA is heated to separate the strands (Fig. 17.9). The primers are two synthetic oligonucleotides: One oligonucleotide is complementary to a short sequence in one strand of the DNA to be amplified, and the other is complementary to a sequence in the other DNA strand. As the solution is cooled, the oligonucleotides form base pairs with the DNA and serve as primers for the synthesis of DNA strands by the heat-stable DNA polymerase (this polymerase is isolated from *Thermus aquaticus*, a bacterium that grows in hot springs). The process of heating, cooling, and new DNA synthesis is repeated many times until a large number of copies of the DNA is obtained. The process is automated, so each round of replication takes only a few minutes, and in 20 heating and cooling cycles, the DNA is amplified over a millionfold.

 Although only small amounts of semen were obtained from **Vicky Tim's** body, the quantity of DNA in these specimens could be amplified by PCR. This technique provided sufficient amounts of DNA for comparison with DNA samples from the three suspects.

FIG. 17.9. Polymerase chain reaction (PCR). Strand 1 and strand 2 are the original DNA strands. The *short dark blue fragments* are the primers. After multiple heating and cooling cycles, the original strands remain, but most of the DNA consists of amplified copies of the segment (shown in *lighter blue*) synthesized by the heat-stable DNA polymerase.

The mutation that causes sickle cell anemia abolishes a restriction site for the enzyme *Mst*II in the β-globin gene. The consequence of this mutation is that the restriction fragment produced by *Mst*II that includes the 5'-end of the β-globin gene is larger (1.3 kb) for individuals with sickle cell anemia than for normal individuals (1.1 kb). Analysis of restriction fragments provides a direct test for the mutation. In **Will Sichel's** case, both alleles for β-globin lack the *Mst*II site and produce 1.3-kb restriction fragments; thus, only one band is seen in a Southern blot.

A

Gene A (normal) — C C T G A G G —

↑ *Mst II* site

Gene S (sickle) — C C T G T G G —

(no *Mst II* site)

B

Restriction site absent in sickle cell β-globin

β-Globin gene

Mst II   *Mst II* *Mst II*

Gene A ├——1.1 kb——┤

Gene S ├———1.3 kb———┤

C

Southern blot of DNA cut with *Mst II* and hybridized with β-globin probe

βS (1.3 kb)

βA (1.1 kb)

Sickle cell control
Normal control
Carrie Sichel
Will Sichel

Carriers have both a normal and a mutant allele. Therefore, their DNA will produce both the larger and the smaller *Mst*II restriction fragments. When **Will Sichel's** sister, **Carrie Sichel**, was tested, she was found to have both the small and the large restriction fragments, and her status as a carrier of sickle cell anemia, initially made on the basis of protein electrophoresis, was confirmed.

II. USE OF RECOMBINANT DNA TECHNIQUES FOR DIAGNOSIS OF DISEASE

A. DNA Polymorphisms

Polymorphisms are variations among individuals of a species in DNA sequences of the genome. They serve as the basis for using recombinant DNA techniques in the diagnosis of disease. The human genome probably contains millions of different polymorphisms. Some polymorphisms involve point mutations, the substitution of one base for another. Deletions and insertions are also responsible for variations in DNA sequences. Some polymorphisms occur within the coding region of genes. Others are found in noncoding regions that are closely linked to genes involved in the cause of inherited disease, in which case they can be used as a marker for the disease. As only about 1.5% of the human genome codes for genes, most polymorphisms are present in noncoding regions of the genome.

B. Detection of Polymorphisms

1. RESTRICTION FRAGMENT LENGTH POLYMORPHISMS

Occasionally, a point mutation occurs in a recognition site for one of the restriction enzymes. The restriction enzyme, therefore, can cut at this restriction site in DNA from most individuals but not in DNA from individuals with this mutation. Consequently, the restriction fragment that binds a probe for this region of the genome will be larger for a person with the mutation than for most members of the population. Mutations also can create restriction sites that are not commonly present. In this case, the restriction fragment from this region of the genome will be smaller for a person with the mutation than for most individuals. These variations in the length of restriction fragments are known as *restriction fragment length polymorphisms* (RFLPs).

In some cases, the mutation that causes a disease affects a restriction site within the coding region of a gene. However, in many cases, the mutation affects a restriction site that is outside the coding region but tightly linked (i.e., physically close on the DNA molecule) to the abnormal gene that causes the disease. This RFLP can still serve as a biologic marker for the disease. Both types of RFLPs can be used for genetic testing to determine whether an individual has the disease.

2. DETECTION OF MUTATIONS BY ALLELE-SPECIFIC OLIGONUCLEOTIDE PROBES

Other techniques have been developed to detect mutations because many mutations associated with genetic diseases do not occur within restriction enzyme recognition sites or cause detectable restriction fragment length differences when digested with restriction enzymes. For example, oligonucleotide probes (containing 15 to 20 nucleotides) can be synthesized that are complementary to a DNA sequence that includes a mutation. Different probes are produced for alleles that contain mutations and for those that have a normal DNA sequence. The region of the genome that contains the abnormal gene is amplified by PCR, and the samples of DNA are placed in narrow bands on nitrocellulose paper ("slot blotting"). The paper is then treated with the radioactive probe for either the normal or the mutant sequence. Appropriate manipulation of the hybridization conditions (e.g., high temperature and low salt concentration) will allow probes with only a one base difference to distinguish between normal and mutant alleles, making this test a very sensitive technique. Autoradiograms indicate whether the normal or mutant probe has preferentially base-paired (hybridized) with the DNA—that is, whether the alleles are normal or mutated. Carriers, of course, have two different alleles—one that binds to the normal probe and one that binds to the mutant probe.

3. TESTING FOR MUTATIONS BY POLYMERASE CHAIN REACTION

If an oligonucleotide that is complementary to a DNA sequence containing a mutation is used as a primer for PCR, the DNA sample used as the template will be amplified only if it contains the mutation. If the DNA is normal, the primer will not hybridize, because of the one-base difference, and the DNA will not be amplified. This concept is extremely useful for clinical testing. In fact, several oligonucleotides, each specific for a different mutation and each containing a different label, can be used as primers in a single PCR reaction. This procedure results in rapid and relatively inexpensive testing for multiple mutations.

4. DETECTION OF POLYMORPHISMS CAUSED BY REPETITIVE DNA

Human DNA contains many sequences that are repeated in tandem a variable number of times at certain loci in the genome. These regions are called *highly variable regions* because they contain a variable number of tandem repeats (VNTR). Digestion with restriction enzymes that recognize sites that flank the VNTR region produces fragments containing these loci, which differ in size from one individual to another, depending on the number of repeats that are present. Probes used to identify these restriction fragments bind to or near the sequence that is repeated (Fig. 17.10).

The restriction fragment patterns produced from these loci can be used to identify individuals as accurately as the traditional fingerprint. In fact, this restriction fragment technique has been called "DNA fingerprinting" and is gaining widespread use in forensic analysis. Family relationships can be determined by this method, and it can be used to help acquit or convict suspects in criminal cases.

Individuals who are closely related genetically will have restriction fragment patterns (DNA fingerprints) that are more similar than those who are more distantly related. Only monozygotic twins will have identical patterns.

 So how does one determine the DNA sequence of a gene that contains a mutation to develop specific probes to that mutation? First, the gene that causes the disease must be identified. This is done by a process known as *positional cloning*, which involves linking polymorphic markers to the disease. Individuals who express the disease will have a specific variant of these polymorphic markers, whereas individuals who do not express the disease will not have these markers. Once such polymorphic markers are identified, they are used as probes to screen a human genomic library. This will identify pieces of human DNA that contain the polymorphic marker. These pieces of DNA can then be used as probes to expand the region of the genome surrounding this marker (chromosome walking). Potential genes within this region are identified (using data available from the sequencing of the human genome), and the sequence of bases within each gene is compared with the sequence of bases in the genes of individuals who have the disease. The one gene that shows an altered sequence in disease-carrying individuals compared with normal individuals is the tentative disease gene. Through the sequencing of genes from many people afflicted with the disease, the types of mutations that lead to this disease can be characterized and specific tests are developed to determine whether individuals express these particular mutations.

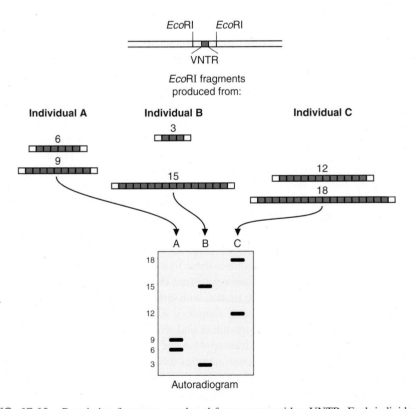

FIG. 17.10. Restriction fragments produced from a gene with a VNTR. Each individual has two homologs of every somatic chromosome and thus two genes each containing this region with a VNTR. Cleavage of each individual's genomic DNA with a restriction enzyme produces two fragments containing this region. The length of the fragments depends on the number of repeats they contain. Electrophoresis separates the fragments, and a labeled probe that binds to the fragments allows them to be visualized. Each *short blue block* represents one repeat.

Testing for CF by DNA sequencing is time consuming and expensive. Therefore, another technique that uses allele-specific oligonucleotide probes has been developed. **Sissy Fibrosa** and her family were tested by this method. Oligonucleotide probes, complementary to the region where the three-base deletion is located, have been synthesized. One probe binds to the mutant (ΔF_{508}) gene and the other to the normal gene.

DNA was isolated from Sissy, her parents, and two siblings and amplified by PCR. Samples of the DNA were spotted on nitrocellulose paper, treated with the oligonucleotide probes, and the following results were obtained. (*Dark spots* indicate binding of the probe.)

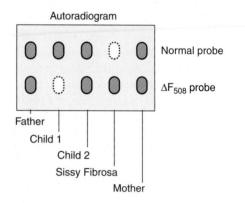

Which members of Sissy's family have CF, which are normal, and which are carriers?

Gene chips have been used to answer the question of whether there are changes in gene expression during dieting. Gene chips containing approximately 47,000 unique genes were used, and the probes were complementary DNA (cDNA) prepared from adipose tissue of control and calorie-restricted overweight women. Upon caloric restriction, 334 transcripts were upregulated, whereas 342 transcripts were reduced in expression, as compared to the control group. As expected, many of the genes corresponded to those involved in metabolism and metabolic regulation. Increased use of these techniques will, in the future, enable development of pharmaceutical agents that specifically target transcripts involved in weight regulation, with the goal being the development and implementation of new and improved weight loss drugs.

5. DNA CHIPS (MICROARRAYS)

Over the past 10 years, a technique has been developed that permits screening many genes simultaneously to determine which alleles of these genes are present in samples obtained from patients. The surface of a small chip is dotted with thousands of pieces of single-stranded DNA, each representing a different gene or segment of a gene. The chip is then incubated with a sample of a patient's DNA, and the pattern of hybridization is determined by computer analysis. The results of the hybridization analysis can be used, for example, to determine which one of the many known mutations for a particular genetic disease is the specific defect underlying a patient's problem. An individual's gene chip also may be used to determine which alleles of drug-metabolizing enzymes are present and, therefore, the likelihood of that individual having an adverse reaction to a particular drug.

Another use for a DNA chip is to determine which genes are being expressed. If the mRNA from a tissue specimen is used to produce cDNA by reverse transcriptase, the cDNA will hybridize with only those genes being expressed in that tissue. In the case of a cancer patient, this technique could be used to determine the classification of the cancer much more rapidly and more accurately than the methods traditionally used by pathologists. The treatment then could be tailored more specifically to the individual patient. This technique also can be used to identify the genes required for tissue specificity (e.g., the difference between a muscle cell and a liver cell) and differentiation (the conversion of precursor cells into the different cell types). Experiments using gene chips are helping us to understand differentiation and may open the opportunity to artificially induce differentiation and tissue regeneration in the treatment of disease.

As another example of the myriad uses of gene chips, a gene chip has been developed for the diagnosis of infectious disease. This gene chip contains 29,445 distinct oligonucleotides (60 bases long) that correspond to vertebrate viruses, bacteria, fungi, and parasites. Patient samples (nose aspirates, urine, blood, or tissue samples) are used as a source of RNA, which is converted to cDNA. Specific regions of the cDNA are amplified by PCR (the products of the PCR are fluorescent because of the incorporation of fluorescent primers in the procedure). Hybridization of the fluorescent probe with the chip allows identification of the infectious agent. The possibilities for gene chip applications in the future are virtually limitless.

The huge amount of information now available from the sequencing of the human genome, and the results available from gene chip experiments, has greatly expanded the field of bioinformatics. *Bioinformatics* can be defined as the gathering, processing, data storage, data analysis, information extraction, and visualization of biologic data. Bioinformatics also provides scientists with the capability to organize vast amounts of data in a manageable form that allows easy access and retrieval. Powerful computers are required to perform these analyses. As an example of an experiment that requires these tools, suppose you want to compare the effects of two different immunosuppressant drugs on gene expression in lymphocytes. Lymphocytes would be treated with either nothing (the control) or with the drugs individually (experimental samples). RNA would be isolated from the cells both before and after drug treatment and would be converted to fluorescent cDNA using the enzyme reverse transcriptase and a fluorescent nucleotide analog. The cDNA produced from your three samples would be used as probes for a gene chip containing DNA fragments from more than 5,000 human genes. The samples would be allowed to hybridize to the chips, and you would then have 15,000 results to interpret (the extent of hybridization of each cDNA sample with each of the 5,000 genes on the chip). Computers are used to analyze the fluorescent spots on the chips and to compare the levels of fluorescent intensity from one chip to another. In this way, you could group genes showing similar levels of stimulation or inhibition in the presence of the drugs and compare the two drugs with respect to which genes have had their levels of expression altered by drug treatment.

III. USE OF RECOMBINANT DNA TECHNIQUES FOR THE PREVENTION AND TREATMENT OF DISEASE

A. Vaccines

Before the advent of recombinant DNA technology, vaccines were made exclusively from infectious agents that had been either killed or attenuated (altered so that they can no longer multiply in an inoculated individual). Both types of vaccines were potentially dangerous because they could be contaminated with the live, infectious agent. In fact, in a small number of instances, disease has actually been caused by vaccination. The human immune system responds to antigenic proteins on the surface of an infectious agent. Using recombinant DNA techniques, these antigenic proteins can be produced, completely free of the infectious agent, and used in a vaccine. Thus, any risk of infection is eliminated. The first successful recombinant DNA vaccine to be produced was for the hepatitis B virus.

More recently, DNA vaccines have been used to achieve similar results. The theory behind DNA vaccines is to allow DNA to enter cells within a tissue, which then transcribe and translate the protein product encoded by the gene. This protein is an antigen from the organism against which antibody production is desired. The host then generates an immune response to the antigen, generating protection for the host. Although this therapy has been successful in rats, it has not yet evolved to the point of being successful in humans, perhaps as a result of insufficient cells accepting and expressing the DNA vaccine. Ongoing research is geared toward increasing the number of cells that receive the DNA, thereby enhancing immunogenicity.

B. Production of Therapeutic Proteins

1. INSULIN AND GROWTH HORMONE

Recombinant DNA techniques are used to produce proteins that have therapeutic properties. One of the first such proteins to be produced was human insulin. Recombinant DNA corresponding to the A chain of human insulin was prepared and inserted into plasmids that were used to transform *Escherichia coli* cells. The bacteria then synthesized the insulin chain, which was purified. A similar process was used to obtain B chains. The A and B chains were then mixed and allowed to fold and form disulfide bonds, producing active insulin molecules (Fig. 17.11). Insulin is not glycosylated, so there was no problem with differences in glycosyltransferase activity between *E. coli* and human cell types.

Human growth hormone has also been produced in *E. coli* and is used to treat children with growth hormone deficiencies. Before production of recombinant growth hormone, growth hormone isolated from cadaver pituitary tissue was used, which was in short supply.

2. COMPLEX HUMAN PROTEINS

More complex proteins have been produced in mammalian cell culture using recombinant DNA techniques. The gene for Factor VIII, a protein involved in blood clotting, is defective in individuals with hemophilia. Before genetically engineered Factor VIII became available, several hemophiliac patients died of AIDS or hepatitis that they contracted from transfusions of contaminated blood or from Factor VIII isolated from contaminated blood.

Tissue plasminogen activator (TPA) is a protease in blood that converts plasminogen to plasmin. *Plasmin* is a protease that cleaves *fibrin* (a major component of blood clots), so administered TPA dissolves blood clots. Recombinant TPA, produced in mammalian cell cultures, is frequently administered during or immediately after a heart attack to dissolve the thrombi that occlude coronary arteries and prevent oxygen from reaching the heart muscle.

Hematopoietic growth factors also have been produced in mammalian cell cultures by recombinant DNA techniques. Erythropoietin can be used in certain types of anemias to stimulate the production of red blood cells. Colony-stimulating factors (CSFs)

Individuals to which both probes hybridize are carriers (as they contain one normal allele and one mutant allele). Thus, the father and mother are both carriers of the defective allele, as is one of the two siblings *(Child 2)*. Sissy has the disease (expressing only the mutant allele), and the other sibling *(Child 1)* is normal (expressing only the normal allele).

A current method for forensic analysis of DNA samples is to take advantage of the presence of short tandem repeat (STR) sequences in the DNA. The number of repeats differs among alleles, so an analysis of 8 to 16 STRs is usually sufficient for a statistically valid match. The DNA to be analyzed is amplified in a PCR reaction with all of the primers (for all 8 to 16 STR regions) simultaneously (a process known as *multiplexing*). The primers are labeled with a fluorescent nucleotide, and they have been designed such that each STR amplification will yield a different-sized amplification product. After the PCR reaction has been completed, the fluorescent DNA samples are analyzed by size via capillary electrophoresis and a fluorescent detector. The sizes of the fragments are determined using time of elution from the column (and comparison to known size standards). If the multiplex PCR analyzed 8 STR regions, it is possible for 16 different-sized bands (two alleles for each STR) to be generated from each individual donating DNA. These products are compared with the products obtained from the unknown sample, and matches or nonmatches can be determined. These procedures are now automated and very precise.

DNA samples were obtained from each of the three suspects in **Vicky Tim's** rape and murder case, and these samples were compared with the victim's DNA by using DNA fingerprinting. Because **Vicky Tim's** sample size was small, PCR was used to amplify the regions containing the VNTRs. The results, using a probe for one of the repeated sequences in human DNA, are shown in the following figure to illustrate the process. For more positive identification, several different restriction enzymes and probes were used. The DNA from *suspect 2* produced the same restriction pattern as the DNA from the semen obtained from the victim. If the other restriction enzymes and probes corroborate this finding, *suspect 2* can be identified by DNA fingerprinting as the rapist and murderer.

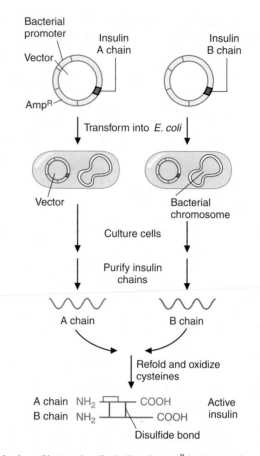

FIG. 17.11. Production of human insulin in *E. coli*. *Amp*^{R} is the gene for ampicillin resistance. The presence of *Amp*^{R} allows bacterial cells that contain the vector to grow in the presence of ampicillin. Cells that lack the *Amp*^{R} gene die in the presence of ampicillin. Because *E. coli* cannot process preproinsulin, a synthetic scheme was developed, whereby each individual chain of insulin was expressed, produced, and purified, and then the two chains were linked together in a test tube.

and interleukins (ILs) can be used after bone marrow transplants and after chemotherapy to stimulate white blood cell production and decrease the risk of infection.

Recombinant β-interferon is the first drug known to decrease the frequency and severity of episodes resulting from the effects of demyelination in patients with multiple sclerosis.

A method for producing human proteins that has proven to be succesful involves transgenic animals. These animals (usually goat or sheep) have been genetically engineered to produce human proteins in the mammary gland and secrete them into milk. The gene of interest is engineered to contain a promoter that is only active in the mammary glands under lactating conditions. The vector containing the gene and promoter is inserted into the nucleus of a freshly fertilized egg, which is then implanted into a foster mother. The female animal progeny are tested for the presence of this transgene, and milk from the positive animals is collected. Large quantities of the protein of interest can then be isolated from the relatively small number of proteins present in milk.

C. Small, Interfering RNA

In several disorders, it would be advantageous to reduce the expression of a particular gene. This has, in the past, been very difficult to do, but a recently discovered series of reactions will allow this to occur, and the technique is already showing promise as a therapeutic tool. One way to reduce expression of a particular protein is to reduce the level of mRNA within the cell that codes for the protein. This can occur by either specifically degrading this mRNA or by blocking translation from the mRNA of interest. It turns out that eukaryotic cells have a built-in system to silence gene expression via reduction of mRNA levels, a process known as *gene silencing*. Gene silencing comes about via the transcription of genes known as *microRNAs* (miRNA, see Chapter 16); the miRNAs are processed to form a small (21 to 24 bp) double-stranded RNA molecule. The double-stranded RNA is separated into single strands, and the strand that is complementary to a specific mRNA is guided to the mRNA, which is either degraded or inhibited from participation in translation, depending on the miRNA. If the miRNA pairing is exact with its target, mRNA degradation is initiated. If the miRNA pairing with the target is inexact, inhibition of translation results (see Fig. 16.22).

Since this expression ablation pathway was first discovered, it has been shown that the introduction of chemically synthesized double-stranded RNA molecules into cells will generate small, interfering RNAs (siRNAs) to inhibit production of a cellular protein. Although this technique holds great promise for antiviral and anticancer therapies, a great deal of work still needs to be done to optimize delivery of the double-stranded RNA to the target tissue and to optimize the stability of the agent. Alternative approaches include the induction, or inhibition, of certain miRNA genes.

D. Genetic Counseling

One means of preventing disease is to avoid passing defective genes to offspring. If individuals are tested for genetic diseases, particularly members of families who are known to carry a defective gene, genetic counselors can inform the individuals of their risks and options. With this information, people can decide in advance whether to have children.

Screening tests, based on the recombinant DNA techniques outlined in this chapter, have been developed for many inherited diseases. Although these tests are currently rather expensive, particularly if entire families have to be screened, the cost may be trivial compared with the burden of raising children with severe disabilities. Obviously, ethical considerations must be taken into account, but recombinant DNA technology has provided individuals with the ability to make choices.

Screening can be performed on the prospective parents before conception. If they decide to conceive, the fetus can be tested for the genetic defect. In some cases, if the fetus has the defect, treatment can be instituted at an early stage, even in utero. For certain diseases, early therapy leads to a more positive outcome.

E. Gene Therapy

The ultimate cure for genetic diseases is to introduce normal genes into individuals who have defective genes. Currently, gene therapy is being attempted in animals, cell cultures, and human subjects. It is not possible at present to replace a defective gene with a normal gene at its usual location in the genome of the appropriate cells. However, as long as the gene is expressed at the appropriate time and produces adequate amounts of protein to return the person to a normal state, the gene does not have to integrate into the precise place in the genome. Sometimes, the gene does not even have to be in the cells that normally contain it.

Retroviruses were the first vectors used to introduce genes into human cells. Normally, retroviruses enter target cells, their RNA genome is copied by reverse transcriptase, and the double-stranded cDNA is integrated into the host cell genome (see Fig. 14.22). If the retroviral genes (e.g., *gag*, *pol*, and *env*) are first removed and replaced with the therapeutic gene, the retroviral genes integrated into the host cell genome will produce the therapeutic protein rather than the viral proteins (Fig. 17.12). This process works only when the human host cells are undergoing division, so it has limited applicability. Other problems with this technique are that it can only be used with small genes (≤8 kb), and it may disrupt other genes because the insertion point is random, thereby possibly resulting in cancer.

Adenoviruses, which are natural human pathogens, can also be used as vectors. As in retroviral gene therapy, the normal viral genes required for synthesis of viral particles are replaced with the therapeutic genes. The advantages to using an adenovirus are that the introduced gene can be quite large (~36 kb), and infection

When **Erna Nemdy** began working with patients, she received the hepatitis B vaccine. The hepatitis B virus (HBV) infects the liver, causing severe damage. The virus contains a surface antigen (HBsAg) or coat protein for which the gene has been isolated. However, because the protein is glycosylated, it could not be produced in *E. coli*. (Bacteria, because they lack subcellular organelles, cannot produce glycosylated proteins.) Therefore, a yeast (eukaryotic) expression system was used that produced a glycosylated form of the protein. The viral protein, separated from the small amount of contaminating yeast protein, is used as a vaccine for immunization against HBV infection.

Di Abietes is using recombinant human insulin called lispro (Humalog) (see Chapter 6, Fig. 6.13). Lispro was genetically engineered so that lysine is at position 28 and proline is at position 29 of the B chain (the reverse of their positions in normal human insulin). Di injects a Humalog mixture that contains 75% lispro protamine suspension (intermediate acting) and 25% lispro solution (rapid acting). The switch of position of the two amino acids leads to a faster-acting insulin homolog. The lispro is absorbed from the site of injection much more quickly than other forms of insulin, and it acts to lower blood glucose levels much more rapidly than the other insulin forms.

Carrie Sichel's fiancé decided to be tested for the sickle cell gene. He was found to have both the 1.3-kb and the 1.1-kb *Mst*II restriction fragments that include a portion of the β-globin gene. Therefore, like Carrie, he also is a carrier of the sickle cell gene.

A defect in the adenosine deaminase (ADA) gene causes severe combined immunodeficiency syndrome (SCID). When ADA is defective, deoxyadenosine and dATP accumulate in rapidly dividing cells, such as lymphocytes, and prove toxic to these cells. Cells of the immune system cannot proliferate at a normal rate, and children with SCID usually die at an early age because they cannot combat infections. To survive, they must be confined to a sterile, environmental "bubble." When an appropriate donor is available, bone marrow transplantation can be performed with a reasonable degree of success.

In 1990, a 4-year-old girl, for whom no donor was available, was treated with infusions of her own lymphocytes that had been treated with a retrovirus containing a normal ADA gene. Although she had not responded to previous therapy, she improved significantly after this attempt at gene therapy. This disease is still being treated with gene therapy, in combination with replacement enzyme infusion.

FIG. 17.12. Use of retroviruses for gene therapy. The retrovirus carries an RNA copy of the therapeutic gene into the cell. The endosome that contains the virus dissolves, and the RNA and viral reverse transcriptase are released. This enzyme copies the RNA, making a double-stranded DNA that integrates into the host cell genome. Transcription and translation of this DNA (the therapeutic gene) produces the therapeutic protein. (The virus does not multiply because its genes were removed and replaced by the RNA copy of the therapeutic gene.)

does not require division of host cells. The disadvantage is that genes carried by the adenovirus do not integrate stably into the host genome, resulting in only transient expression of the therapeutic proteins (but preventing disruption of host genes and the complications that may arise from it). Thus, the treatment must be repeated periodically. Another problem with adenoviral gene therapy is that the host can mount an immune response to the pathogenic adenovirus, causing complications.

To avoid the problems associated with viral vectors, researchers are employing treatment with DNA alone or with DNA coated with a layer of lipid (i.e., in liposomes). Adding a ligand for a receptor located on the target cells could aid delivery of the liposomes to the appropriate host cells. Many problems still plague the field of gene therapy. In many instances, the therapeutic genes must be targeted to the cells where they normally function—a difficult task at present. Deficiencies in dominant genes are more difficult to treat than those in recessive genes, and the expression of the therapeutic genes often needs to be carefully regulated. Although the field is moving forward, progress is slow. As mentioned previously, current research is exploring the use of siRNA to block expression of oncogenes in tumor cells, although significant clinical impact is most likely years away.

F. Transgenic Animals

The introduction of normal genes into somatic cells with defective genes corrects the defect only in the treated individuals, not in their offspring. To eliminate the defect for future generations, the normal genes must be introduced into the germ cell line (the cells that produce sperm in males or eggs in females). Experiments with animals indicate that gene therapy in germ cells is feasible. Genes can be introduced into fertilized eggs from which transgenic animals develop, and these transgenic animals can produce apparently normal offspring.

In fact, if the nucleus isolated from the cell of one animal is injected into the enucleated egg from another animal of the same species and the egg is implanted in a foster mother, the resulting offspring is a "clone" of the animal from which the nucleus was derived. Clones of sheep and pigs have been produced, and similar techniques could be used to clone humans. Obviously, these experiments raise many ethical questions that will be difficult to answer.

IV. PROTEOMICS

The techniques described previously have concentrated on nucleic acid identification, but there have also been rapid advances in analyzing all proteins expressed by a cell at a particular stage of development. The techniques are sophisticated enough to allow comparisons between two different samples, such as normal cells and cancer cells from the same tissue. An abbreviated view of this technique is shown in Figure 17.13. Proteins from the two different cell types (A and B) are isolated

Another form of SCID is X-linked and is known as *X-SCID*. This disease results from mutations in a common subunit protein of multiple cytokine receptors. The cDNA corresponding to this subunit was delivered to the patient's lymphocytes using a retroviral vector, and the success rate of reconstituting the immune system was high for patients who received this gene therapy. The enthusiasm concerning the treatment was tempered, however, by the development of leukemia in three of the patients who were part of the initial trial. Retroviruses randomly insert their DNA copy of their genome into the host chromosome. In the patients who developed leukemia, it has been determined that the vector inserted near the LMO2 gene, a known proto-oncogene (see Chapter 18). The insertional event triggered activation (or overexpression) of LMO2, leading to uncontrolled cell proliferation. Current research is now directed to attempt to target areas of insertion for vectors used in gene therapy.

Adenoviral vectors have been used in an aerosol spray to deliver normal copies of the cystic fibrosis transmembrane conductance regulator (CFTR) gene to cells of the lung. Some cells took up this gene, and the patients experienced moderate improvement. However, stable integration of the gene into the genome did not occur, and cells affected by the disease other than those in the lung (e.g., pancreatic cells) did not benefit. Nevertheless, this approach marked a significant forward step in the development of gene therapy. Adenoviral vectors were also used in an attempt to treat ornithine transcarbamylase deficiency (a disorder of nitrogen metabolism). In this trial, a volunteer died of a severe immune response to the adenoviral vector. This unfortunate result has led to a reevaluation of the safety of viral vectors for gene therapy.

FIG. 17.13.   Using proteomics to determine if a protein is upregulated or downregulated. See text for more details.

and labeled with different fluorescent dyes. The proteins are then separated by two-dimensional gel electrophoresis (the first dimension, or separation, is by charge, and the second dimension is by size), which generates a large number of spots that can be viewed under a fluorescent imaging device, each of these spots corresponding to an individual protein. A computer aligns the spots from the two samples and can determine, by the level of fluorescence expressed at each protein spot, if a protein has been upregulated or downregulated in one sample compared to the other. Proteins whose expression levels change can then be identified by sensitive techniques involving protein mass spectrometry.

The proteomics approach holds great promise in molecularly fingerprinting particular tumors, and for discovering novel targets for drug development that are only expressed in the cancerous state. A physician's knowledge of the markers expressed by a particular tumor should allow for specific drug regimens to be used; no longer will one treatment be the norm for a particular tumor. Depending on a patient's proteome, treatments for the patient's specific tumor can be devised and prescribed.

CLINICAL COMMENTS

 Erna Nemdy. In reading about development of the hepatitis B vaccine, **Erna Nemdy** learned that the first vaccine available for hepatitis B virus (HBV), marketed in 1982, was a purified and "inactivated" vaccine containing HBV that had been chemically killed. The virus was derived from the blood of known HBV carriers. Later, "attenuated" vaccines were used, in which the virus remained live but was altered so that it no longer multiplied in the inoculated host. Both the inactivated and the attenuated vaccines are potentially dangerous because they can be contaminated with live infectious HBV.

The modern "subunit" vaccines, first marketed in 1987, were made by recombinant DNA techniques described earlier in this chapter. Because this vaccine consists solely of the viral surface protein or antigen to which the immune system responds, there is no risk of infection with HBV.

 The most common CF mutation is a 3-bp deletion that causes the loss of phenylalanine at position 508 (Δ508). This mutation is present in more than 70% of CFTR patients. The defective protein is synthesized in the endoplasmic reticulum but is misfolded. It is therefore not transported to the Golgi but is degraded by a proteolytic enzyme complex called the *proteasome*. Other mutations responsible for CF generate an incomplete mRNA because of premature stop signals, frame shifts, or abnormal splice sites, or create a CFTR channel in the membrane that does not function properly.

Sissy Fibrosa. Cystic fibrosis (CF) is a genetically determined autosomal recessive disease that can be caused by various mutations within the CF gene located on chromosome 7. **Sissy Fibrosa** was found to have a 3-bp deletion at residue 508 of the CF gene (the mutation present in approximately 70% of Caucasian patients with CF in the United States). This mutation is generally associated with a more severe clinical course than many other mutations that cause the disease. However, other genes and environmental factors may modify the clinical course of the disease, so it is not currently possible to counsel patients accurately about prognosis based on their genotype.

CF is a relatively common genetic disorder in the United States, with a carrier rate of approximately 5% in Caucasians. The disease occurs in 1 per 1,600 to 2,000 Caucasian births in the country (1 per 17,000 in African Americans and 1 per 100,000 in Asian Americans).

Carrie Sichel. After learning the results of their tests for the sickle cell gene, **Carrie Sichel** and her fiancé consulted a genetic counselor. The counselor informed them that because they were both carriers of the sickle cell gene, their chance of having a child with sickle cell anemia was fairly high (approximately 1 in 4). She told them that prenatal testing was available with fetal DNA obtained from cells by amniocentesis or chorionic villus sampling. If these tests indicated that the fetus had sickle cell disease, abortion was a possibility. Carrie, because of her religious background, was not sure that abortion was an option for her. But having witnessed her brother's sickle cell crises for many years, she also was not sure that she wanted to risk having a child with the disease.

Her fiancé also felt that, at 25 years of age, he was not ready to deal with such difficult problems. They mutually agreed to cancel their marriage plans.

 Vicky Tim. DNA fingerprinting represents an important advance in forensic medicine. Before the development of this technique, identification of criminals was far less scientific. The suspect in the rape and murder of **Vicky Tim** was arrested and convicted mainly on the basis of the results of DNA fingerprint analysis.

This technique has been challenged in some courts on the basis of technical problems in statistical interpretation of the data and sample collection. It is absolutely necessary for all of the appropriate controls to be run, including samples from the victim's DNA as well as the suspect's DNA. Another challenge to the fingerprinting procedure has been raised because polymerase chain reaction (PCR) is such a powerful technique that it can amplify minute amounts of contaminating DNA from a source unrelated to the case.

BIOCHEMICAL COMMENTS

 Mapping of the Human Genome. The Human Genome Project began in 1990, and by the summer of 2000, the entire human genome had been mapped. This feat was accomplished in far less than the expected time as a result of both cooperative and competitive interactions of laboratories in private as well as public sectors.

The human genome contains $>3 \times 10^9$ (3 billion) bp. A large percentage of this genome (<95%) does not code for the amino acid sequences of proteins or for functional RNA (such as ribosomal RNA [rRNA] or transfer RNA [tRNA]) but is composed of repetitive sequences, introns, and other noncoding elements of unknown function. The human genome is estimated to contain only about 25,000 to 30,000 genes; however, significantly more proteins are produced than there are genes. This arises from alternative splicing and various posttranslational modifications. Further analysis of the proteome may prove to be more informative than the genome.

Analysis of the genome has led to the identification of a large number of single nucleotide polymorphisms (SNPs), which refer to a single nucleotide change within a given DNA sequence as compared between individuals. For such a change to be considered an SNP (as opposed to a random mutation), the polymorphism must be present within 1% of the population. SNPs are plentiful in the human genome, occurring every 100 to 300 bp. SNPs are therefore useful tools for mapping disease genes within the chromosome. SNPs are also being used in place of short tandem repeat (STR) sequences in forensic DNA analysis.

When identification of a wayward gene is announced on the morning news, the average citizen may expect a cure for a genetic disease to be available that evening. Although knowledge of the chromosomal location and the sequence of genes will result in the rapid development of tests to determine whether an individual carries a defective gene, the development of a treatment for a genetic disease caused by a defective gene is not that easy or that rapid. As outlined in the section on gene therapy, many technical problems need to be solved before gene therapy becomes common. In addition to solving the molecular puzzles involved in gene therapy, we will also have to deal with many difficult ethical as well as technical questions.

Is it appropriate to replace defective genes in somatic cells to relieve human suffering? Many people may agree with this goal. But there is a related question: Is it appropriate to replace defective genes *in the germ cell line* to relieve human suffering? Fewer people may agree with this goal. Genetic manipulation of somatic cells affects only one generation; these cells die with the individual. Germ cells, however, live on, producing each successive generation.

 What are the statistical issues relating to DNA fingerprinting? Through the analysis of a large number of individuals of different ethnicities, one can determine the frequency of a particular DNA polymorphism within that distinct population. By matching 8 to 16 polymorphisms (using multiplexed PCR for polymorphic STRs) from DNA at the crime scene with DNA from a suspect, one can determine the odds of that match happening by chance. For example, let us assume that a suspect's DNA was compared with DNA found at the crime scene for four unique polymorphisms within the suspect's ethnic group. The frequency of polymorphism A in that population is 1 in 20; of polymorphism B, 1 in 30; of polymorphism C, 1 in 50; and of polymorphism D, 1 in 100. The odds of the suspect's DNA matching the DNA found at the crime scene for all four polymorphisms would be the product of each individual probability, or (1/20) × (1/30) × (1/50) × (1/100). This comes out to a 1 in 3 million chance that an individual would have the same polymorphisms in his or her DNA as that found at the crime scene. The question left to the courts is whether the 1 in 3 million match is sufficient to convict the suspect of the crime. Given that there may be 30 million individuals in the United States within the same ethnic group as the suspect, there would then be 30 people within the country who would match the DNA polymorphisms found at the scene of the crime. Can the court be sure that the suspect is the correct individual? Clearly, the use of DNA fingerprinting is much clearer when a match is not made, for that immediately indicates that the suspect was not at the scene of the crime.

Table 17.2   Diseases Discussed in Chapter 17

Disorder or Condition	Genetic or Environmental	Comments
Cystic fibrosis	Genetic	Cystic fibrosis is due to a mutation in the cystic fibrosis transmembrane conductance regulator (CFTR) protein, which is a chloride channel. The most common mutation in the CFTR gene is Δ508, a triplet deletion, which removes codon 508 from the primary sequence. The disease leads to pancreatic duct blockage as well as clogged airways.
Hepatitis B	Environmental	Vaccine development for hepatitis B using molecular genetic techniques to produce recombinant virus
Sickle cell disease	Genetic	The development of genetic testing for sickle cell disease, based on understanding the base change in DNA, which leads to the disease.

The techniques developed to explore the human genome could be used for many purposes. What are the limits for the application of the knowledge gained by advances in molecular biology? Who should decide what the limits are, and who should serve as the "genetic police"? If we permit experiments that involve genetic manipulation of the human germ cell line, however nobly conceived, could we, in our efforts to "improve" ourselves, genetically engineer the human race into extinction?

Key Concepts

- Techniques for isolating and amplifying genes and studying and manipulating DNA sequences are currently being used in the diagnosis, prevention, and treatment of disease.
- These techniques require an understanding of the following tools and processes:
  - Restriction enzymes
  - Cloning vectors
  - Polymerase chain reaction
  - Dideoxy DNA sequencing
  - Gel electrophoresis
  - Nucleic acid hybridization
  - Expression vectors
- Recombinant DNA molecules produced by these techniques can be used as diagnostic probes, in gene therapy, or for the large-scale production of proteins for the treatment of disease.
- Identified genetic polymorphisms, inherited differences in DNA base sequences between individuals, can be used for both diagnosis of disease and the generation of an individual's molecular fingerprint.
- Genetic treatment of disease is possible, using either gene therapy or gene ablation techniques. Technical difficulties currently restrict the widespread use of these treatments.
- Proteomics is the study of proteins expressed by a cell. Differences in protein expression between normal and cancer cells can be used to identify potential targets for future therapy.
- Diseases discussed in this chapter are summarized in Table 17.2.

REVIEW QUESTIONS—CHAPTER 17

1. Electrophoresis resolves double-stranded DNA fragments based on which one of the following?

   A. Sequence
   B. Molecular weight
   C. Isoelectric point
   D. Frequency of CTG repeats
   E. Secondary structure

2. If a restriction enzyme recognizes a six-base sequence, how frequently, on average, will this enzyme cut a large piece of DNA?

   A. Once every 16 bases
   B. Once every 64 bases
   C. Once every 256 bases
   D. Once every 1,024 bases
   E. Once every 4,096 bases

3. Which of the following sets of reagents is required for dideoxy chain DNA synthesis in the Sanger technique for DNA sequencing? (The lists are not meant to be all-inclusive.)

    A. Deoxyribonucleotides, Taq polymerase, DNA primer
    B. Dideoxyribonucleotides, deoxyribonucleotides, template DNA
    C. Dideoxyribonucleotides, DNA primer, reverse transcriptase
    D. Two DNA primers, template DNA, Taq polymerase
    E. mRNA, dideoxynucleotides, reverse transcriptase

4. Certain diseases, such as fragile X syndrome, are caused by an expansion of triplet repeats within the gene. Which of the following sets of techniques would best enable a rapid determination if such a repeat were present within a gene?

    A. PCR, RFLP analysis, but not SNP analysis
    B. PCR, RFLP analysis, and SNP analysis
    C. RFLP analysis, but not PCR or SNP analysis
    D. PCR, but not RFLP analysis or SNP analysis
    E. SNP analysis, but not PCR or RFLP analysis

5. The best method to determine whether albumin is transcribed in the liver of a mouse model of hepatocarcinoma is which one of the following?

    A. Genomic library screening
    B. Genomic Southern blot
    C. Tissue Northern blot
    D. Tissue Western blot
    E. VNTR analysis

18 The Molecular Biology of Cancer

Normal cells

Mutation in proto-oncogene or tumor-suppressor gene

Proliferation of mutated cell

Multiple mutations in proto-oncogenes; mutations in tumor-suppressor genes

Invasion of surrounding tissue

Invasion of blood vessel

Metastasis

FIG. 18.1. Development of cancer. Accumulation of mutations in several genes results in transformation. Cancer cells change morphologically, proliferate, invade other tissues, and metastasize.

*The term **cancer** applies to a group of diseases in which **cells grow abnormally** and form a **malignant tumor**. Malignant cells can invade nearby tissues and **metastasize** (i.e., travel to other sites in the body where they establish secondary areas of growth). This aberrant growth pattern results from **mutations in genes that regulate proliferation, differentiation, and survival of cells** in a multicellular organism. Because of these genetic changes, cancer cells no longer respond to the signals that govern growth of normal cells (Fig. 18.1).*

*   **Oncogenes and Tumor Suppressor Genes.** The genes involved in the development of cancer are classified as **oncogenes** or **tumor suppressor genes**. **Oncogenes** are mutated derivatives of normal genes (**proto-oncogenes**) whose function is to promote proliferation or cell survival. These genes can code for **growth factors, growth factor receptors, signal transduction proteins, intracellular kinases, and transcription factors**. The process of transformation into a malignant cell may begin with a **gain-of-function** mutation in only one copy of a proto-oncogene. As the mutated cell proliferates, additional mutations can occur. **Tumor suppressor genes** (normal growth suppressor genes) encode proteins that **inhibit proliferation, promote cell death**, or **repair DNA**; both alleles need to be inactivated for transformation (**a loss of function**). Growth suppressor genes have been called the guardians of the cell.*

*   **Cell Cycle Suppression and Apoptosis.** Normal cell growth depends on a balanced regulation of **cell cycle** progression and **apoptosis** (programmed cell death) by proto-oncogenes and growth suppressor genes. At **checkpoints** in the **cell cycle**, products of **tumor suppressor genes** slow growth in response to signals from the cell's environment, including external growth-inhibitory factors, or to allow time for repair of damaged DNA, or in response to other adverse circumstances in cells. Alternatively, cells with damaged DNA are targeted for **apoptosis** so that they will not proliferate. Many growth stimulatory pathways involving proto-oncogenes, and growth inhibitory controls involving a variety of tumor suppressor genes, converge to regulate the activity of some key protein kinases, the **cyclin-dependent kinases**. These kinases act to control progression at specific points in the cell growth cycle. Apoptosis is initiated by either **death receptor activation** or intracellular signals leading to release of the **mitochondrial protein, cytochrome c**.*

*   **Mutations.** Mutations in DNA that give rise to cancer may be **inherited** or may be caused by **chemical carcinogens, radiation, viruses**, and **replication errors** that are not repaired. A cell population must accumulate **multiple mutations** for transformation to malignancy.*

THE WAITING ROOM

Mannie Weitzels has chronic myelogenous leukemia (CML), a disease in which a single line of myeloid cells in the bone marrow proliferates abnormally, causing a large increase in the number of nonlymphoid white blood cells (see Chapter 16). His myeloid cells contain the abnormal Philadelphia chromosome, which increases their proliferation. He has recently complained of pain and tenderness in various areas of his skeleton, possibly stemming from the expanding mass of myeloid cells within his bone marrow. He also reports various hemorrhagic signs, including bruises (ecchymoses), bleeding gums, and the appearance of small red spots (petechiae caused by release of red cells into the skin).

Nick O'Tyne was diagnosed with a poorly differentiated adenocarcinoma of the lungs (see Chapter 13). He underwent procedures to determine the location and severity of the tumor. As a result of these tests, he was considered a candidate for surgical resection of the primary tumor, aimed at cure. He survived the surgery and was recovering uneventfully until 6 months later, when he complained of an increasingly severe right temporal headache. A computerized tomography (CT) scan of his brain was performed. Results indicated that the cancer, which had originated in his lungs, had metastasized to his brain.

Colin Tuma has had an intestinal adenocarcinoma resected, but there were several metastatic nodules in his liver (see Chapters 12 and 13). He completed his second course of chemotherapy with 5-fluorouracil (5-FU) and had no serious side effects. He assured his physician at his most recent checkup that, this time, he intended to comply with any instructions his physicians gave him. He ruefully commented that he wished he had returned for regular examinations after his first colonoscopy.

Mel Anoma returned to his physician after observing a brownish black irregular mole on his forearm (see Chapter 13). His physician thought the mole looked suspiciously like a malignant melanoma and so performed an excision biopsy (surgical removal for cytologic analysis).

I. CAUSES OF CANCER

Cancer is the term applied to a group of diseases in which cells no longer respond to normal restraints on growth. Normal cells in the body respond to signals, such as cell–cell contact (contact inhibition), that direct them to stop proliferating. Cancer cells do not require growth-stimulatory signals, and they are resistant to growth-inhibitory signals. They are also resistant to apoptosis, the programmed cell death process whereby unwanted or irreparably damaged cells self-destruct. They have an infinite proliferative capacity and do not become senescent (i.e., they are immortalized). Furthermore, they can grow independent of structural support, such as the extracellular matrix (loss of anchorage dependence).

The study of cells in culture was, and continues to be, a great impetus for the study of cancer. Tumor development in animals can take months, and it was difficult to do experiments with tumor growth in animals. Once cells could be removed from an animal and propagated in a tissue culture dish, the onset of transformation (the normal cell becoming a cancer cell) could be seen in days.

Once cells were available to study, it was important to determine the criteria that distinguish transformed cells from normal cells in culture. Three criteria were

Determination of abnormal chromosome structures is done by karyotype analysis (see Fig. 12.14). Karyotypes are created by arresting cells in *mitotic metaphase*, a stage at which the chromosomes are condensed and visible under the light microscope. Nuclei are isolated, placed on a microscope slide, and the chromosomes are stained. Pictures of the chromosomes through the microscope are obtained, and the homologous chromosomes are paired. Through this type of analysis, translocations between chromosomes can be determined, as can trisomies and monosomies. As seen in the figure, this karyotype indicates a translocation between chromosomes 9 and 22 (a piece of chromosome 22 is now attached to chromosome 9; note the *arrows* in the figure). This is known as the Philadelphia chromosome, and it gives rise to CML, the disease exhibited by **Mannie Weitzels**.

Patients with leukemia experience various hemorrhagic (bleeding) manifestations caused by a decreased number of platelets. Platelets are small cells that initiate clot formation at the site of endothelial injury. Because of the uncontrolled proliferation of white cells within the limited space of the marrow, the normal platelet precursor cells (the megakaryocytes) in the marrow are "squeezed" or crowded and fail to develop into mature platelets. Consequently, the number of mature platelets (thrombocytes) in the circulation falls, and a thrombocytopenia develops. Because there are fewer platelets to contribute to clot formation, bleeding problems are common.

Malignant neoplasms (new growth, a tumor) of epithelial cell origin (including the intestinal lining, cells of the skin, and cells lining the airways of the lungs) are called *carcinomas*. If the cancer grows in a glandlike pattern, it is an *adenocarcinoma*. Thus, **Nick O'Tyne** and **Colin Tuma** have adenocarcinomas. **Mel Anoma** had a carcinoma arising from melanocytes, which is technically a melanocarcinoma but is usually referred to as a *melanoma*.

Moles (also called *nevi*) are tumors of the skin. They are formed by melanocytes that have been transformed from highly dendritic single cells interspersed among other skin cells to round oval cells that grow in aggregates or "nests." (Melanocytes produce the dark pigment melanin, which protects against sunlight by absorbing ultraviolet [UV] light.) Additional mutations may transform the mole into a malignant melanoma.

The first experiments to show that oncogenes were mutant forms of proto-oncogenes in human tumors involved cells cultured from a human bladder carcinoma. The DNA sequence of the *ras* oncogene cloned from these cells differed from the normal c-*ras* proto-oncogene. Similar mutations were subsequently found in the *ras* gene of lung and colon tumors. **Colin Tuma's** malignant polyp had a mutation in the *ras* proto-oncogene.

established. The first is the requirement for serum in the cell culture medium to stimulate cell growth. *Serum* is the liquid fraction of clotted blood and contains many factors that stimulate cell proliferation. Transformed cells have, in general, a reduced requirement for serum, approximately 10% that required for normal cells to grow. The second criterion is the ability to grow without attachment to a supporting matrix (anchorage dependence). Normal cells (such as fibroblasts or smooth muscle cells) require adherence to a substratum (in this case, the bottom of the plastic dish) and will not grow if suspended in a soft agar mixture. Transformed cells, however, have lost this anchorage dependence. The third and most stringent criterion used to demonstrate that cells are truly transformed is the ability of cells to form tumors when they are injected into mice that lack an immune system. Transformed cells will do so, whereas normal cells will not.

Drs. Michael Bishop and Harold Varmus demonstrated that cancer is not caused by unusual and novel genes but rather by mutation within existing cellular genes, and that for every gene that causes cancer (an oncogene), there is a corresponding cellular gene called the *proto-oncogene*. Although this concept seems straightforward today, it was a significant finding when it was first announced and, in 1989, Drs. Bishop and Varmus were awarded the Nobel Prize in Medicine.

A single cell that divides abnormally eventually forms a mass called a *tumor*. A tumor can be benign and harmless; the common wart is a benign tumor formed from a slowly expanding mass of cells. In contrast, a malignant neoplasm (malignant tumor) is a proliferation of rapidly growing cells that progressively infiltrate, invade, and destroy surrounding tissue. Tumors develop angiogenic potential, which is the capacity to form new blood vessels and capillaries. Thus, tumors can generate their own blood supply to bring in oxygen and nutrients. Cancer cells also can metastasize, separating from the growing mass of the tumor and traveling through the blood or lymph to unrelated organs where they establish new growths of cancer cells.

The transformation of a normal cell to a cancer cell begins with damage to DNA (base changes or strand breaks) caused by chemical carcinogens, ultraviolet (UV) light, viruses, or replication errors (see Chapter 13). Mutations result from the damaged DNA if it is not repaired properly or if it is not repaired before replication occurs. A mutation that can lead to transformation also may be inherited. When a cell with one mutation proliferates, this clonal expansion (proliferation of cells arising from a single cell) results in a substantial population of cells containing this one mutation, from which one cell may acquire a second mutation relevant to control of cell growth or death. With each clonal expansion, the probability of another transforming mutation increases. Because mutations accumulate in genes that control proliferation, subsequent mutations occur even more rapidly until the cells acquire the multiple mutations (in the range of four to seven) necessary for full transformation.

The transforming mutations occur in genes that regulate cellular proliferation and differentiation (proto-oncogenes), suppress growth (tumor suppressor genes), target irreparably damaged cells for apoptosis, or repair damaged DNA. The genes that regulate cellular growth are called *proto-oncogenes*, and their mutated forms are called *oncogenes*. The term *oncogene* is derived from the Greek word *onkos*, meaning bulk or tumor. A transforming mutation in a proto-oncogene increases the activity or amount of the gene product (a gain-of-function mutation). Tumor suppressor genes (normal growth suppressor genes) and repair enzymes protect against uncontrolled cell proliferation. A transforming mutation in these protective genes results in a loss of activity or a decreased amount of the gene product.

In summary, cancer is caused by the accumulation of mutations in the genes involved in normal cellular growth and differentiation. These mutations give rise to cancer cells that are capable of unregulated, autonomous, and infinite proliferation. As these cancer cells proliferate, they impinge on normal cellular functions, leading to the symptoms exhibited by individuals with the tumors.

II. DAMAGE TO DNA LEADING TO MUTATIONS
A. Chemical and Physical Alterations in DNA

An alteration in the chemical structure of DNA, or of the sequence of bases in a gene, is an absolute requirement for the development of cancer. The function of DNA depends on the presence of various polar chemical groups in DNA bases, which are capable of forming hydrogen bonds between DNA strands or other chemical reactions. The oxygen and nitrogen atoms in DNA bases are targets for various electrophiles (electron-seeking chemical groups). A typical sequence of events leading to a mutation is shown for dimethylnitrosamine in Figure 18.2. Chemical carcinogens (compounds that can cause transforming mutations) found in the environment and ingested in foods are generally stable lipophilic compounds that, like dimethylnitrosamine, must be activated by metabolism in the body to react with DNA (see also benz[o]pyrene, "Action of Mutagens," Chapter 13, Section III.A, and Fig. 13.12). Many chemotherapeutic agents, which are designed to kill proliferating cells by interacting with DNA, may also act as carcinogens and cause new mutations and tumors while eradicating the old. Structural alterations in DNA also occur through radiation and through UV light, which causes the formation of pyrimidine dimers. More than 90% of skin cancers occur in sunlight-exposed areas. UV rays derived from the sun induce an increased incidence of all skin cancers, including squamous cell carcinoma, basal cell carcinoma, and malignant melanoma of the skin. The wavelength of UV light that is most associated with skin cancer is UVB (280 to 320 nm), which forms pyrimidine dimers in DNA. This type of DNA damage is repaired by nucleotide excision repair pathways that require products of at least 20 genes. With excessive exposure to the sun, the nucleotide excision repair pathway is overwhelmed, and some damage remains unrepaired.

Each chemical carcinogen or reactant creates a characteristic modification in a DNA base. The DNA damage, if not repaired, introduces a mutation into the next generation when the cell proliferates.

B. Gain-of-Function Mutations in Proto-oncogenes

Proto-oncogenes are converted to oncogenes by mutations in the DNA that cause a gain in function; that is, the protein can now function better in the absence of the normal activating events. Several mechanisms that lead to the conversion of proto-oncogenes to oncogenes are known.

- Radiation and chemical carcinogens act (1) by causing a mutation in the regulatory region of a gene, increasing the rate of production of the proto-oncogene protein; or (2) by producing a mutation in the coding portion of the oncogene that results in the synthesis of a protein of slightly different amino acid composition capable of transforming the cell (Fig. 18.3A).
- The entire proto-oncogene or a portion of it may be transposed or translocated, that is, moved from one position in the genome to another (see Fig. 18.3B). In its new location, the proto-oncogene may be under the control of a promoter that is regulated differently than the promoter that normally regulates this gene. This may allow the gene to be expressed in a tissue where it is not normally expressed or at higher-than-normal levels of expression. If only a portion of the proto-oncogene is translocated, it may be expressed as a truncated protein with altered properties, or it may fuse with another gene and produce a fusion protein containing portions of what are normally two separate proteins. The truncated or fusion protein may be hyperactive and cause inappropriate cell growth.
- The proto-oncogene may be amplified (see Fig. 18.3C) so that multiple copies of the gene are produced in a single cell. If more genes are active, more proto-oncogene protein will be produced, increasing the growth rate of the cells. As examples, the oncogene N-*myc* (a cell proliferation transcription factor, related to c-*myc*) is amplified in some neuroblastomas, and amplification of the *erb*-b2 oncogene (a growth factor receptor) is associated with several breast carcinomas.

FIG. 18.2. Mutations in DNA caused by nitrosamines. Nitrosamines are consumed in many natural products and are produced in the stomach from nitrites used as preservatives and secondary amines found in foods such as fish. They are believed to be responsible for the high incidence of gastric cancer in Japan and Iceland where salt-preserved fish is a major dietary item. Nitrosamine metabolites methylate guanine (the transferred methyl group is shown in *red*).

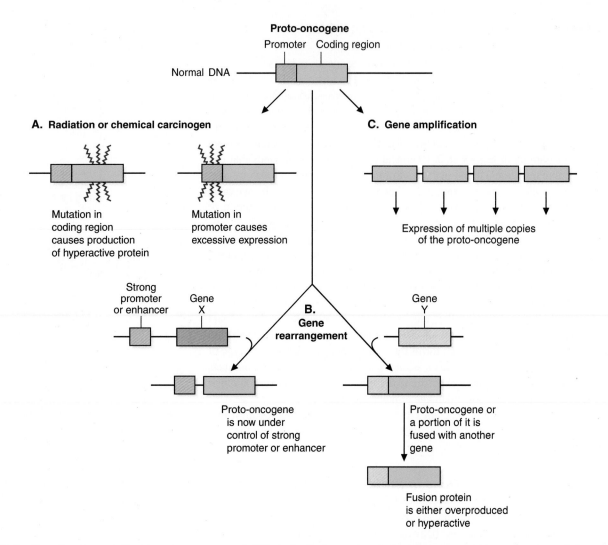

FIG. 18.3. Transforming mutations in proto-oncogenes. **A.** Effect of radiation or chemical carcinogens on proto-oncogenes or their promoters. The mutations may be point mutations, deletions, or insertions. **B.** Gene rearrangements as caused by transposition or translocation of a proto-oncogene or proto-oncogene fragment. **C.** Amplification of a proto-oncogene allows more protein to be produced.

 Burkitt lymphoma, a general name for several types of B-cell malignancies, results from a translocation between chromosomes 8 and 14. The translocation of genetic material moves the proto-oncogene transcription factor c-*myc* (normally found on chromosome 8) to chromosome 14. The translocated gene is now under the control of the promoter region for the immunoglobulin heavy-chain gene, which leads to inappropriate and overexpression of c-*myc*. The result may be uncontrolled cell proliferation and tumor development. All subtypes of Burkitt lymphoma contain this translocation. Epstein-Barr virus infection of B cells is also associated with certain types of Burkitt lymphoma.

• If an oncogenic virus infects a cell, its oncogene may integrate into the host cell genome, permitting production of the abnormal oncogene protein. The cell may be transformed and exhibit an abnormal pattern of growth. Rather than inserting an oncogene, a virus may simply insert a strong promoter into the host cell genome. This promoter may cause increased or untimely expression of a normal proto-oncogene.

The important point to remember is that transformation results from abnormalities in the normal growth-regulatory program caused by gain-of-function mutations in proto-oncogenes. However, loss-of-function mutations also occur in the tumor suppressor genes, repair enzymes, or activators of apoptosis, and a combination of both types of mutations is usually required for full transformation to a cancer cell.

C. Mutations in Repair Enzymes

Repair enzymes are the first line of defense preventing conversion of chemical damage in DNA to a mutation (see Chapter 13, Section III.B). DNA repair enzymes are tumor suppressor genes in the sense that errors repaired before replication do not become mutagenic. DNA damage is constantly occurring from exposure to sunlight, background radiation, toxins, and replication errors. If DNA repair enzymes are absent, mutations accumulate much more rapidly, and once a mutation develops in a growth-regulatory gene, a cancer may arise. As an example, inherited mutations in the tumor suppressor genes *BRCA1* and *BRCA2* predispose women to the development of breast cancer (see "Biochemical Comments"). The protein products of these genes play roles in DNA repair, recombination, and regulation of transcription. A second example, HNPCC (*h*ereditary *n*on*p*olyposis *c*olorectal *c*ancer), was introduced in Chapter 13. It results from inherited mutations in enzymes involved in the DNA mismatch repair system.

III. ONCOGENES

Proto-oncogenes control normal cell growth and division. These genes encode proteins that are growth factors, growth factor receptors, signal transduction proteins, transcription factors, cell cycle regulators, and regulators of apoptosis (Table 18.1). (The name representing the gene of an oncogene is referred to in lowercase letters and italics [e.g., *myc*], but the name of the protein product is capitalized and italics are not used [e.g., Myc]). The mutations in oncogenes that give rise to transformation are usually gain-of-function mutations; either a more active protein is produced or an increased amount of the normal protein is synthesized.

MicroRNAs (miRNAs) can also behave as oncogenes. If a miRNA is overexpressed (increased function), it can act as an oncogene if its target (which would exhibit reduced expression under these conditions) is a protein that is involved in inhibiting, or antagonizing, cell proliferation.

A. Oncogenes and Signal Transduction Cascades

All of the proteins in growth factor signal transduction cascades are proto-oncogenes (Fig. 18.4).

1. GROWTH FACTORS AND GROWTH FACTOR RECEPTORS

The genes for both growth factors and growth factor receptors are proto-oncogenes.

Growth factors generally regulate growth by serving as ligands that bind to cellular receptors located on the plasma membrane (cell surface receptors) (see Chapter 11). Binding of ligands to these receptors stimulates a signal transduction pathway in the cell that activates the transcription of certain genes. If too much of a growth factor or a growth factor receptor is produced, the target cells may respond by proliferating inappropriately. Growth factor receptors may also become oncogenic through translocation or point mutations in domains that affect binding of the growth factor, dimerization, kinase activity, or some other aspect of their signal transmission. In such cases, the receptor transmits a proliferative signal even though the growth factor normally required to activate the receptor is absent. In other words, the receptor is stuck in the "on" position.

2. SIGNAL TRANSDUCTION PROTEINS

The genes that encode proteins involved in growth factor signal transduction cascades may also be proto-oncogenes. Consider, for example, the monomeric G protein Ras. Binding of growth factor leads to the activation of Ras (see Fig. 11.11). When Ras binds guanosine triphosphate (GTP), it is active, but Ras slowly inactivates itself by hydrolyzing its bound GTP to guanosine diphosphate (GDP) and inorganic phosphate (P_i). This controls the length of time that Ras is active. Ras is converted to an oncogenic form by point mutations that decrease the activity of the GTPase domain of Ras, thereby increasing the length of time it remains in the active form.

Ras, when it is active, activates the serine–threonine kinase Raf (a mitogen-activated protein [MAP] kinase kinase kinase), which activates MEK (a MAP kinase kinase), which activates MAP kinase (Fig. 18.5). Activation of MAP kinase

Mannie Weitzels's bone marrow cells contain the Philadelphia chromosome, typical of CML. The Philadelphia chromosome results from a reciprocal translocation between the long arms of chromosome 9 and 22. As a consequence, a fusion protein is produced that contains the N-terminal region of the Bcr protein from chromosome 22 and the C-terminal region of the Abl protein from chromosome 9. *Abl* is a proto-oncogene, and the resulting fusion protein (Bcr-Abl) has lost its regulatory region and is constitutively active, resulting in deregulated tyrosine kinase activity. When it is active, Abl stimulates the Ras pathway of signal transduction, leading to cell proliferation.

The gene for the human epidermal growth factor receptor (*HER2, c-erbB-2*) is overexpressed in 10% to 20% of breast cancer cases. When this gene is overexpressed, the prognosis for recovery is poor because the patients display shorter disease-free intervals, increased risks for metastasis, and resistance to therapy. A drug has been developed that recognizes and blocks the receptor's action (herceptin, a monoclonal antibody with specificity to the HER2 protein). Preliminary results are encouraging in that use of this drug, either alone or in combination with others, appears to control the growth of some tumors that overexpress the *HER2* gene. However, not all tumors that overexpress *HER2* are responsive to herceptin. Thus, it appears that a complete genotyping of breast cancer cells may be necessary (using the microarray techniques described in Chapter 17) to develop an effective therapy for each patient with the disease, leading to individualized therapy.

Table 18.1   Classes of Oncogenes, Mechanism of Activation, and Associated Human Tumors

Class	Proto-oncogene	Activation Mechanism	Location	Disease
Growth factors				
Platelet-derived growth factor β-chain	*sis*	Overexpression	Secreted	Glioma Fibrosarcoma
Fibroblast growth factors	*int-2*	Amplification	Secreted	Breast cancer Bladder cancer Melanoma
	hst	Overexpression	Secreted	Stomach carcinoma
Growth factor receptors				
Epidermal growth factor receptor family	*erb-b1*	Overexpression	Cell membrane	Squamous cell carcinoma of the lung
	erb-b2	Amplification	Cell membrane	Breast, ovarian, lung, stomach cancers
Platelet-derived growth factor receptor	*PDGFR*	Translocation	Cell membrane	Chronic myelomonocytic leukemia
Hedgehog receptor	*SMO*	Point mutation	Cell membrane	Basal cell carcinoma
Signal transduction proteins				
G proteins	*ras*	Point mutation	Cytoplasm	Multiple cancers, including lung, colon, thyroid, pancreas, many leukemias
Serine–threonine kinase	*akt2*	Amplification	Cytoplasm	Ovarian carcinoma
	raf	Overexpression	Cytoplasm	Myeloid leukemia
Tyrosine kinase	*abl*	Translocation	Cytoplasm	Chronic myeloid leukemia Acute lymphoblastic leukemia
	src	Overexpression	Cytoplasm	Colon carcinoma
Hormone receptors				
Retinoid receptor	*RARα*	Translocation	Nucleus	Acute promyelocytic leukemia
Transcription factors				
	Hox11	Translocation	Nucleus	Acute T-cell leukemia
	myc	Translocation	Nucleus	Burkitt lymphoma
		Amplification	Nucleus	Neuroblastoma, small cell carcinoma of the lung
	fos, jun	Phosphorylation	Nucleus	Osteosarcoma, sarcoma
Apoptosis regulators				
	Bcl-2	Translocation	Mitochondria	Follicular B-cell lymphoma
Cell cycle regulators				
Cyclins	Cyclin D	Translocation	Nucleus	Lymphoma
		Amplification	Nucleus	Breast, liver, esophageal cancers
Cyclin-dependent kinase	CDK4	Amplification	Nucleus	Glioblastoma, sarcoma
		Point mutation	Nucleus	Melanoma

Note. The table is not meant to be all-inclusive; only examples of each class of gene are presented.

results in the phosphorylation of cytoplasmic and nuclear proteins, followed by increased transcription of the transcription factor proto-oncogenes *myc* and *fos* (see the following sections). Note that mutations in the genes for any of the proteins that regulate MAP kinase activity, as well as those proteins induced by MAP kinase activation, can lead to uncontrolled cell proliferation.

3.   TRANSCRIPTION FACTORS

Many transcription factors, such as Myc and Fos, are proto-oncoproteins (the products of proto-oncogenes). MAP kinase, in addition to inducing *myc* and *fos*, also directly activates the activator protein-1 (AP-1) transcription factor through phosphorylation (see Fig. 18.5). AP-1 is a heterodimer formed by the protein products of the *fos* and *jun* families of proto-oncogenes. The targets of AP-1 activation are genes involved in cellular proliferation and progression through the cell cycle, as are the targets of the *myc* transcription factor. The synthesis of the transcription factor C-*myc* is tightly regulated in normal cells, and it is expressed only during the

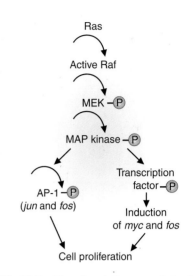

FIG. 18.5. Phosphorylation cascade leading to activation of proto-oncogene transcription factors *myc*, *fos*, and *jun*.

FIG. 18.4. Proto-oncogene sites for transforming mutations in growth factor signaling pathways. *(I)* The amount of growth factor. *(II)* The receptor, which normally must bind the growth factor to dimerize and activate a kinase domain. *(III)* Signal transduction proteins. Some, such as PI-3 kinase, form second messengers. *(IV)* G proteins, and their regulators, which are also signal transduction proteins. *(V)* Nonreceptor protein kinase cascades, which lead to phosphorylation of transcription factors. *(VI)* Nuclear transcription factors that are normally activated through phosphorylation or binding of a ligand.

S phase of the cell cycle. In a large number of tumor types, this regulated expression is lost, and c-*myc* becomes inappropriately expressed or overexpressed throughout the cell cycle, driving cells continuously to proliferate.

The net result of alterations in the expression of transcription factors is the increased production of the proteins that carry out the processes required for proliferation.

B. Oncogenes and the Cell Cycle

The growth of human cells, involving DNA replication and cell division in the cell cycle, is activated by growth factors, hormones, and other messengers. These activators work through cyclins and cyclin-dependent kinases (CDKs) that control progression from one phase of the cycle to another (Fig. 18.6). For quiescent cells to proliferate, they must leave G_0 and enter the G_1 phase of the cell cycle (see Chapter 13, Fig. 13.7). If the proper sequence of events occurs during G_1, the cells enter the S phase and are committed to DNA replication and cell division. Similarly, during G_2, cells make a commitment to mitotic division. CDKs are made constantly throughout the cell cycle but require binding of a specific cyclin to be active. Different cyclins made at different times in the cell cycle control each of the transitions (G_1/S, S/G_2, G_2/M).

The activity of the cyclin–CDK complex is further regulated through phosphorylation and through inhibitory proteins called *cyclin-dependent kinase inhibitors* (CKIs) (Fig. 18.7). CKIs slow cell cycle progression by binding and inhibiting the cyclin–CDK complexes. CDKs are also controlled through activating phosphorylation by cyclin-activating kinases (CAKs) and inhibitory hyperphosphorylation kinases.

Cell cycle

FIG. 18.6. Cyclin synthesis during different phases of the cell cycle.

FIG. 18.7. CKI inhibition of cyclin–CDK activity.

To illustrate the role of these proteins, consider some of the events that occur at the G_1/S checkpoint (Fig. 18.8). Because the cell is committed to DNA replication and division once it enters the S phase, multiple regulatory proteins are involved in determining whether the cell is ready to pass this checkpoint. These regulatory proteins include cdk4 and cdk6 (which are constitutively produced throughout the cell cycle), cyclin D (whose synthesis is induced only after growth factor stimulation of a quiescent cell), the retinoblastoma gene product (Rb), and a class of transcription factors known collectively as *E2 transcription factor* (*E2F*). In quiescent cells, Rb is complexed with E2F, resulting in inhibition of these transcription factors. Upon growth factor stimulation, the cyclin Ds are induced (there are three types of cyclin D: D1, D2, and D3). They bind to cdk4 and cdk6, converting them to active protein kinases. One of the targets of cyclin/CDK phosphorylation is the Rb protein. Phosphorylation of Rb releases it from E2F, and E2F is then free to activate the transcription of genes required for entry into S. The Rb protein is a tumor suppressor gene (more discussions in the following sections).

The proteins induced by E2F include cyclin E, cyclin A, cdc25A (an activating protein phosphatase), and proteins required to bind at origins of replication to initiate DNA synthesis. The synthesis of cyclin E allows it to complex with cdk2, forming another active cyclin complex that retains activity into S phase (see Fig. 18.6). One of the major functions of the cyclin E1–cdk2 complex is hyperphosphorylation of the Rb protein, thereby keeping Rb in its inactive state. Cyclin A also complexes with Cdk2, and it phosphorylates and inactivates the E2F family of transcription factors. This ensures that the signals are not present for extended periods of time. Thus, each phase of the cell cycle activates the next through cyclin synthesis. The cyclins are removed by regulated proteolysis.

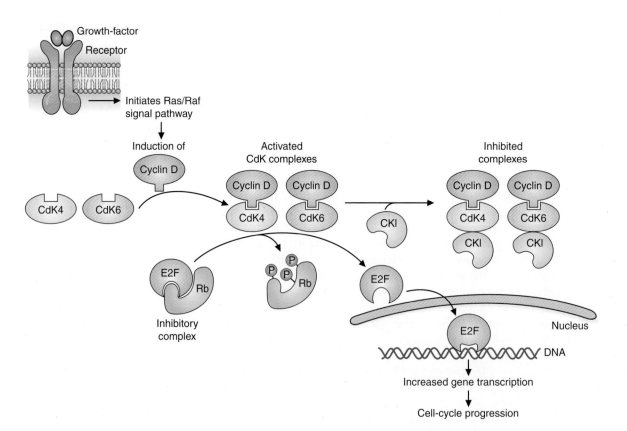

FIG. 18.8. Control of the G_1/S transition in the cell cycle. The genes that encode cyclins and CDKs are oncogenes, and the gene that encodes the retinoblastoma protein (Rb) is a tumor suppressor gene. *CKI*, cyclin-dependent kinase inhibitor.

Progression through the cell cycle is opposed by the CKIs (see Fig. 18.8). The CKIs regulating cyclin/CDK expression in the G_1 phase of the cell cycle fall into two categories: the Cip/Kip family and the INK4 family. The Cip/Kip family members (p21, p27, and p57) have a broad specificity and inhibit all cyclin–CDK complexes. The INK4 family, which consists of p15, p16, p18, and p19, are specific for the cyclin D–cdk4/6 family of complexes (*in*hibitors of cyclin-dependent *k*inase-*4*). The regulation of synthesis of different CKIs is complex but some are induced by DNA damage to the cell and halt cell cycle progression until the damage can be repaired. For example, the CKI p21 (a protein of 21,000 Da) is a key member of this group that responds to specific signals to block cell proliferation. If the damage cannot be repaired, an apoptotic pathway is selected and the cell dies.

IV. TUMOR SUPPRESSOR GENES

Like the oncogenes, the tumor suppressor genes encode molecules involved in the regulation of cell proliferation. Table 18.2 provides several examples. The normal function of tumor suppressor proteins is generally to inhibit proliferation in response to certain signals such as DNA damage. The signal is removed when the cell is fully equipped to proliferate; the effect of the elimination of tumor suppressor genes is to remove the brakes on cell growth. They affect cell cycle regulation, signal transduction, transcription, and cell adhesion. The products of tumor suppressor genes frequently modulate pathways that are activated by the products of proto-oncogenes.

Tumor suppressor genes contribute to the development of cancer when both copies of the gene are inactivated. This is different from the case of proto-oncogene mutations because only one allele of a proto-oncogene needs to be converted to an oncogene to initiate transformation. As with the oncogenes, this is also applicable to miRNAs. If the expression of a particular miRNA is lost, the mRNA it regulates would be overexpressed, which could lead to enhanced cellular proliferation. Thus, miRNAs can be classified as either oncogenes (overexpression) or tumor suppressors (loss of function) depending on the genes that they regulate.

A. Tumor Suppressor Genes that Regulate the Cell Cycle Directly

The two best understood cell cycle regulators that are also tumor suppressors are the retinoblastoma (*rb*) and p53 genes.

1. THE RETINOBLASTOMA (*rb*) GENE

As discussed previously, the retinoblastoma gene product, Rb, functions in the transition from G_1 to S phase and regulates the activation of members of the E2F family of transcription factors (see Fig. 18.8). If an individual inherits a mutated

 In addition to sunlight and a preexisting nevus, hereditary factors also play a role in the development of malignant melanoma. Ten percent of melanomas tend to run in families. Some of the suspected melanoma-associated genes include the tumor suppressor gene p16 (an inhibitor of cdk4) and CDK4. **Mel Anoma** was the single child of parents who had died of a car accident in their 50s, and thus a familial tendency could not be assessed.

Table 18.2 Tumor Suppressors

Class	Protein	Location	Associated Diseases
Adhesion protein receptor	E-cadherin	Cell membrane	Stomach cancer
	Patched	Cell membrane	Basal cell carcinoma
	TGF-β receptor	Cell membrane	Colon cancer
Signal transduction	NF-1	Under cell membrane	Neurofibrosarcoma
	Smad4/DPC	Cytoplasm/nucleus	Pancreatic and colorectal cancers
Transcription factor cell cycle regulator	WT-1	Nucleus	Wilms tumor
	p16(INK4)	Nucleus	Melanoma, lung, pancreatic cancers
	Retinoblastoma	Nucleus	Retinoblastoma, sarcomas
Cell cycle/apoptosis	p53	Nucleus	Most cancers
DNA repair	*BRCA1*	Nucleus	Breast cancer

FIG. 18.9. Mutations in the retinoblastoma (Rb) gene. **A.** Sporadic retinoblastoma. **B.** Familial retinoblastoma.

 Inheritance of a mutation in p53 leads to Li-Fraumeni syndrome, which is characterized by multiple types of tumors. Mutations in p53 are present in more than 50% of human tumors. These are secondary mutations within the cell, and if p53 is mutated, the overall rate of cellular mutation will increase because there is no p53 to check for DNA damage, to initiate the repair of the damaged DNA, or to initiate apoptosis if the damage is not repaired. Thus, damaged DNA is replicated, and the frequency of additional mutations within the same cell increases remarkably.

copy of the *rb* allele, there is a 100% chance of that individual developing retinoblastoma, because of the high probability that the second allele of *rb* will gain a mutation (Fig. 18.9). This is considered familial retinoblastoma. Individuals who do not inherit mutations in *rb* but who develop retinoblastoma are said to have sporadic retinoblastoma and acquire two specific mutations, one in each *rb* allele of the retinoblastoma, during their lifetime.

2. p53, THE GUARDIAN OF THE GENOME

The p53 protein is a transcription factor that regulates the cell cycle and apoptosis, programmed cell death. Loss of both p53 alleles is found in more than 50% of human tumors. p53 acts as the "guardian of the genome" by halting replication in cells that have suffered DNA damage and targeting unrepaired cells to apoptosis.

In response to DNA-damaging mutagens, ionizing radiation, or UV light, the level of p53 rises (Fig. 18.10, circle 1). p53, acting as a transcription factor, stimulates transcription of p21 (a member of the Cip/Kip family of CKIs), as shown in Figure 18.10, circle 2. The p21 gene product inhibits the cyclin–CDK complexes, which prevents the phosphorylation of Rb and release of E2F proteins. The cell is thus prevented from entering S phase. p53 also stimulates the transcription of a number of DNA repair enzymes (including GADD45, growth *a*rrest and *D*NA *da*mage) (see Fig. 18.10, circle 3). If the DNA is successfully repaired, p53 induces its own downregulation through the activation of the *mdm2* gene. If the DNA repair was not successful, p53 activates several genes involved in apoptosis, including *Bax* (discussed subsequently) and *insulinlike growth factor–binding protein 3* (*IGF-BP3*) (see Fig. 18.10, circle 4). The IGF-BP3 protein product binds the receptor for insulinlike growth factor, which presumably induces apoptosis by blocking the antiapoptotic signaling by growth factors, and the cell enters a growth factor deprivation mode.

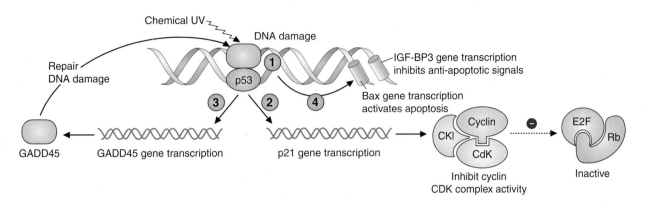

FIG. 18.10. p53 and cell cycle arrest. Mechanisms that recognize DNA damage stop p53 degradation and modify the p53 protein (*circle 1*). p53 stimulates the transcription of p21 (*circle 2*) and GADD45 (*circle 3*). p21 blocks the cyclin/CDK phosphorylation of Rb, which continues to inhibit the E2F family of transcription factors, thereby blocking cell progression through the cell cycle. GADD45 allows the DNA damage to be repaired. If the damage is not repaired, apoptotic genes are activated (*circle 4*).

B. Tumor Suppressor Genes that Affect Receptors and Signal Transduction

Tumor suppressor genes may encode receptors, components of the signaling transduction pathway, or transcription factors.

1. REGULATORS OF RAS

The Ras family of proteins is involved in signal transduction for many hormones and growth factors (see previous discussion) and is therefore oncogenic. The activity of these pathways is interrupted by GAPs (*GTPase-activating proteins*; see Chapter 9, Section III.C.2), which vary among cell types. *Neurofibromin*, the product of the tumor suppressor gene *NF-1*, is a nervous system–specific GAP that regulates the activity of Ras in neuronal tissues (Fig. 18.11). The growth signal is transmitted so long as the Ras protein binds GTP. Binding of NF-1 to Ras activates the GTPase domain of Ras, which hydrolyzes GTP to GDP, thereby inactivating Ras. Without a functional neurofibromin molecule, Ras is perpetually active.

2. PATCHED AND SMOOTHENED

A good example of tumor suppressors and oncogenes working together is provided by the coreceptor genes *patched* and *smoothened*, which encode the receptor for the hedgehog class of signaling peptides. (The strange names of some of the tumor suppressor genes arose because they were first discovered in *Drosophila* [fruit fly], and the names of *Drosophila* mutations are often based on the appearance of a fly that expresses the mutation. Once the human homolog was found, it was given the same name as the *Drosophila* gene.) These coreceptors normally function to control growth during embryogenesis and illustrate the importance of maintaining a balance between oncogenes and tumor suppressor genes. The patched receptor protein inhibits smoothened, its coreceptor protein. Binding of a hedgehog ligand to patched releases the inhibition of smoothened, which then transmits an activating signal to the nucleus, stimulating new gene transcription (Fig. 18.12). *Smoothened* is a proto-oncogene, and *patched* is a tumor suppressor gene. If patched loses its function (definition of a tumor suppressor), then smoothened can signal the cell to proliferate, even in the absence of a hedgehog signal. Conversely, if smoothened undergoes a gain-of-function mutation (definition of an oncogene), it can signal in the absence of the hedgehog signal, even in the presence of patched. Inherited mutations in either smoothened or patched will lead to an increased incidence of basal cell carcinoma.

FIG. 18.11. NF-1 (neurofibromin) binds to Ras and activates its guanosine triphosphatase (GTPase) activity, thereby decreasing cell proliferation. A mutation in neurofibromin leads to prolonged GTP binding and activation of Ras.

 An inherited mutation in *NF-1* can lead to neurofibromatosis, a disease primarily of numerous benign, but painful, tumors of the nervous system. The movie *Elephant Man* was based on an individual who was believed to have this disease. Recent analysis of the patient's remains, however, indicates that he may have suffered from the rare Proteus syndrome, not neurofibromatosis.

A. Catenins and cadherins in cell attachment

B. β-Catenin and APC in gene transcription

FIG. 18.13. **A.** Catenins and cadherins. E-cadherin molecules form intercellular, calcium-dependent homodimers with cadherins from another cell, resulting in cell–cell adhesion. The cytoplasmic portion of E-cadherin is complexed to various catenins, which anchor the cadherin to the actin cytoskeleton. **B.** β-Catenin and adenomatous polyposis coli (APC) in transcription. The APC complex activates β-catenin for proteolytic degradation. If APC is inactivated, β-catenin levels increase. It acts as a transcription factor that increases synthesis of *myc* and other genes that regulate cell cycle progression.

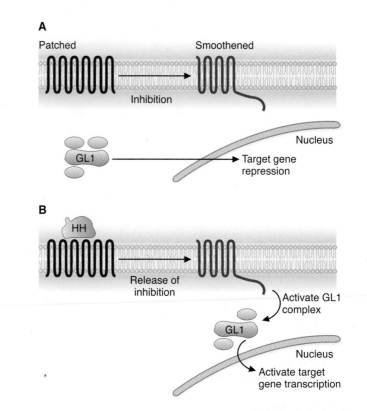

FIG. 18.12. The patched/smoothened signaling system. **A.** In the absence of a hedgehog (HH) signal, smoothened is inactive because of inhibition by the HH receptor patched, and the GL1 transcription factor complex acts as a repressor of transcription. **B.** When a ligand binds to the patched receptor, the inhibition of smoothened is repressed, leading to an activation of the GL1 complex, and active transcription of the target genes.

C. Tumor Suppressor Genes that Affect Cell Adhesion

The cadherin family of glycoproteins mediates calcium-dependent cell–cell adhesion. Cadherins form intercellular complexes that bind cells together (Fig. 18.13A). They are anchored intracellularly by catenins, which bind to actin filaments. Loss of E-cadherin expression may contribute to the ability of cancer cells to detach and migrate in metastasis. Individuals who inherit a mutation in E-cadherin (this mutation is designated CDH1) are sharply predisposed to developing diffuse-type gastric cancer.

The catenin proteins have two functions: In addition to anchoring cadherins to the cytoskeleton, they act as transcription factors (see Fig. 18.13B). β-Catenin also binds to a complex that contains the regulatory protein APC (*a*denomatous *p*olyposis *c*oli), which activates it for degradation. When the appropriate signal inactivates APC, β-catenin levels increase, and it travels to the nucleus where it activates *myc* and *cyclin D1* transcription, leading to cell proliferation. APC is a tumor suppressor gene. If it is inactivated, it cannot bind β-catenin and inhibit cell proliferation. Mutations in APC or proteins that interact with it are found in most sporadic human colon cancers. Inherited mutations in APC lead to the most common form of hereditary colon cancer, familial adenomatous polyposis (FAP).

V. CANCER AND APOPTOSIS

In the body, superfluous or unwanted cells are destroyed by a pathway called *apoptosis*, or *programmed cell death*. Apoptosis is a regulated energy-dependent sequence of events by which a cell self-destructs. In this suicidal process, the cell shrinks, the chromatin condenses, and the nucleus fragments. The cell membrane forms blebs (outpouches), and the cell breaks up into membrane-enclosed apoptotic vesicles (apoptotic bodies) containing varying amounts of cytoplasm, organelles, and DNA fragments. Phosphatidylserine, a lipid on the inner leaflet of the cell membrane, is exposed on the external surface of these apoptotic vesicles. It is one of the phagocytic markers recognized by macrophages and other nearby phagocytic cells that engulf the apoptotic bodies.

Apoptosis is a normal part of multiple processes in complex organisms: embryogenesis, the maintenance of proper cell number in tissues, the removal of infected or otherwise injured cells, the maintenance of the immune system, and aging. It can be initiated by injury, radiation, free radicals, or other toxins; withdrawal of growth factors or hormones; binding of proapoptotic cytokines; or interactions with cytotoxic T cells in the immune system. Apoptosis can protect organisms from the negative effects of mutations by destroying cells with irreparably damaged DNA before they proliferate. Just as an excess of a growth signal can produce an excess of unwanted cells, the failure of apoptosis to remove excess or damaged cells can contribute to the development of cancer.

A. Normal Pathways to Apoptosis

Apoptosis can be divided into three general phases: an initiation phase, a signal integration phase, and an execution phase. Apoptosis can be initiated by external signals that work through death receptors, such as tumor necrosis factor (TNF), or deprivation of growth hormones (Fig. 18.14). It can also be initiated by intracellular events that affect mitochondrial integrity (e.g., oxygen deprivation, radiation), and irreparably damaged DNA. In the signal integration phase, these proapoptotic signals are balanced against antiapoptotic cell survival signals by several pathways, including members of the Bcl-2 family of proteins. The execution phase is carried out by proteolytic enzymes called *caspases*.

1. CASPASES

Caspases are cysteine proteases that cleave peptide bonds next to an aspartate residue. They are present in the cell as procaspases, zymogen-type enzyme precursors that are activated by proteolytic cleavage of the inhibitory portion of their polypeptide chain. The different caspases are generally divided into two groups according to their function: initiator caspases, which specifically cleave other procaspases; and execution caspases, which cleave other cellular proteins involved in maintaining cellular integrity (see Fig. 18.14). The initiator caspases are activated through two major signaling pathways: the death receptor pathway and the mitochondrial integrity pathway. They activate the execution caspases, which cleave protein kinases involved in cell adhesion, lamins that form the inner lining of the nuclear envelope, actin and other proteins required for cell structure, and DNA repair enzymes. They also cleave an inhibitor protein of the endonuclease CAD (*c*aspase-*a*ctivated *D*Nase), thereby activating CAD to initiate the degradation of cellular DNA. With destruction of the nuclear envelope, additional endonucleases (Ca^{2+}- and Mg^{2+}-dependent) also become activated.

2. THE DEATH RECEPTOR PATHWAY TO APOPTOSIS

The death receptors are a subset of TNF-1 receptors, which includes Fas/CD95, TNF-receptor 1 (TNF-R1), and death receptor 3 (DR3). These receptors form a trimer that binds TNF-1 or another death ligand on its external domain and binds adaptor proteins to its intracellular domain (Fig. 18.15). The activated TNF–receptor complex forms the scaffold for binding two molecules of procaspase 8 (or procaspase 10), which autocatalytically cleave each other to form active caspase 8 (or caspase 10). Caspases 8 and 10 are initiator caspases that activate execution caspases 3, 6, and 7. Caspase 3 also cleaves a Bcl-2 protein, Bid, to a form that activates the mitochondrial integrity pathway to apoptosis.

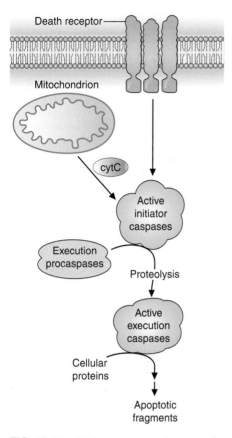

FIG. 18.14. Major components in apoptosis. The release of cytochrome c from mitochondria or activation of death receptors can both lead to the initiation of apoptosis.

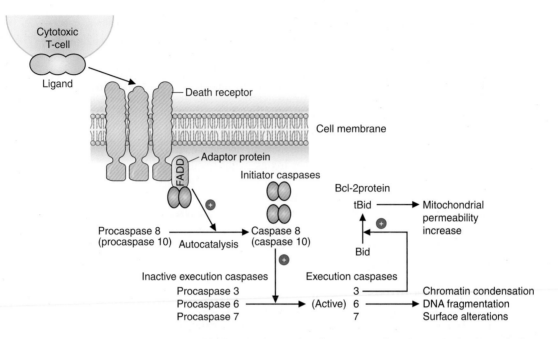

FIG. 18.15. The death receptor pathway to apoptosis. The ligand (either a free ligand or a cell surface–associated protein from another cell) binds to the death receptor, which makes a scaffold for autocatalytic activation of caspases 8 (and sometimes 10). Active caspases 8 (and sometimes 10) cleave apoptotic execution caspases directly. However, the pathway also activates Bid, which acts on mitochondrial membrane integrity.

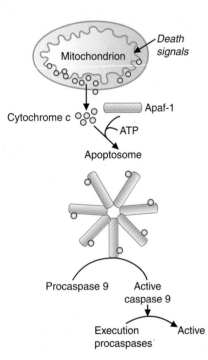

FIG. 18.16. The mitochondrial integrity pathway releases cytochrome c, which binds to Apaf and forms a multimeric complex called the *apoptosome.* The apoptosome converts procaspase 9 to active caspase 9, an initiator caspase, which is released by the apoptosome into the cytosol.

3. THE MITOCHONDRIAL INTEGRITY PATHWAY TO APOPTOSIS

Apoptosis is also induced by intracellular signals indicating that cell death should occur. Examples of these signals include growth factor withdrawal, cell injury, the release of certain steroids, and an inability to maintain low levels of intracellular calcium. All of these treatments or changes lead to release of cytochrome c from the mitochondria (Fig. 18.16). Cytochrome c is a necessary protein component of the mitochondrial electron-transport chain that is loosely bound to the outside of the inner mitochondrial membrane. Its release initiates apoptosis.

In the cytosol, cytochrome c binds Apaf (pro*a*poptotic *p*rotease-*a*ctivating *f*actor). The Apaf/cytochrome c complex binds caspase 9, an initiator caspase, to form an active complex called the *apoptosome.* The apoptosome, in turn, activates execution caspases (3, 6, and 7) by zymogen cleavage.

4. INTEGRATION OF PROAPOPTOTIC AND ANTIAPOPTOTIC SIGNALS BY THE BCL-2 FAMILY OF PROTEINS

The Bcl-2 family members are decision makers that integrate prodeath and antideath signals to determine whether the cell should commit suicide. Both proapoptotic and antiapoptotic members of the Bcl-2 family exist (Table 18.3). Bcl-2 family members contain regions of homology, known as Bcl-2 homology (BH) domains. There are four such domains. The antiapoptotic factors contain all four domains (BH1–BH4). The channel-forming proapoptotic factors contain just three domains (BH1–BH3), whereas the proapoptotic BH3-only family members contain just one BH domain (BH3).

The antiapoptotic Bcl-2–type proteins (including Bcl-2, Bcl-L, and Bcl-w) have at least two ways of antagonizing death signals. They insert into the outer mitochondrial membrane to antagonize channel-forming proapoptotic factors, thereby decreasing cytochrome c release. They may also bind cytoplasmic Apaf so that it cannot form the apoptosome complex (Fig. 18.17).

These antiapoptotic Bcl-2 proteins are opposed by proapoptotic family members that fall into two categories: ion channel–forming members and BH3-only members. The prodeath ion channel–forming members, such as Bax, are very similar to the antiapoptotic family members, except that they do not contain the binding domain for Apaf. They have the other structural domains, however, and when they dimerize with proapoptotic BH3-only members in the outer mitochondrial membrane, they form an ion channel that promotes cytochrome c release rather than inhibiting it (see Fig. 18.17). The prodeath BH3-only proteins (e.g., Bim and Bid) contain only the structural domain that allows them to bind to other Bcl-2 family members (the BH3 domain) and not the domains for binding to the membrane, forming ion channels, or binding to Apaf. Their binding activates the prodeath family members and inactivates the antiapoptotic members. When the cell receives a signal from a prodeath agonist, a BH3 protein like Bid is activated (see Fig. 18.17). The BH3 protein activates Bax (an ion channel–forming proapoptotic channel member), which stimulates release of cytochrome c. Normally, Bcl-2 acts as a death antagonist by binding Apaf and keeping it in an inactive state. However, at the same time that Bid is activating Bax, Bid also binds to Bcl-2, thereby disrupting the Bcl-2/Apaf complex and freeing Apaf to bind to released cytochrome c to form the apoptosome.

B. Cancer Cells Bypass Apoptosis

Apoptosis should be triggered by several stimuli, such as withdrawal of growth factors, elevation of p53 in response to DNA damage, monitoring of DNA damage by repair enzymes, or release of TNF or other immune factors. However, mutations in oncogenes can create apoptosis-resistant cells.

One of the ways this occurs is through activation of growth factor–dependent signaling pathways that inhibit apoptosis, such as the PDGF/Akt/BAD pathway. Nonphosphorylated BAD acts like Bid in promoting apoptosis (see Fig. 18.17). Binding of the platelet-derived growth factor to its receptor activates PI-3 kinase, which phosphorylates and activates the serine–threonine kinase Akt (protein kinase B, see Chapter 11, Section III.B.3). Activation of Akt results in the phosphorylation of the proapoptotic BH3-only protein BAD, which inactivates it. The PDGF/Akt/BAD pathway illustrates the requirement of normal cells for growth factor stimulation to prevent cell death. One of the features of neoplastic transformation is the loss of growth factor dependence for survival. The MAP kinase pathway is also involved in regulating apoptosis and sends cell survival signals. MAP kinase kinase phosphorylates and activates another protein kinase known as RSK. Like Akt, RSK phosphorylates BAD and inhibits its activity. Thus, BAD acts as a site

Table 18.3 Examples of Bcl-2 Family Members

Antiapoptotic
Bcl-2
Bcl-x
Bcl-w
Proapoptotic
Channel forming
Bax
Bak
Bok
Proapoptotic
BH3 only
Bad
Bid
Bim

Roughly 30 Bcl-2 family members are currently known. These proteins play tissue-specific as well as signal pathway–specific roles in regulating apoptosis. The tissue specificity is overlapping. For example, Bcl-2 is expressed in hair follicles, kidney, small intestines, neurons, and the lymphoid system, whereas Bcl-x is expressed in the nervous system and hematopoietic cells.

 When Bcl-2 is mutated, and oncogenic, it is usually overexpressed, for example, in follicular lymphoma and CML. Overexpression of Bcl-2 disrupts the normal regulation of proapoptotic and antiapoptotic factors and tips the balance to an antiapoptotic stand. This leads to an inability to destroy cells with damaged DNA, such that mutations can accumulate within the cell. Bcl-2 is also a multidrug-resistant transport protein and if it is overexpressed, it will block the induction of apoptosis by antitumor agents by rapidly removing them from the cell. Thus, strategies are being developed to reduce Bcl-2 levels in tumors that overexpress it before initiating drug or radiation treatment.

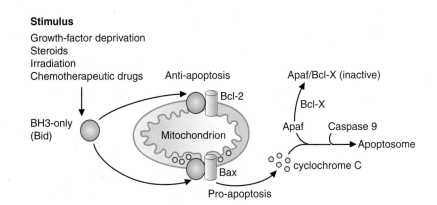

Stimulus

Growth-factor deprivation
Steroids
Irradiation
Chemotherapeutic drugs

FIG. 18.17. Roles of the Bcl-2 family members in regulating apoptosis. Bcl-2, which is antiapoptotic, binds Bid (or tBid) and blocks formation of channels that allow cytochrome c release from the mitochondria. Death signals result in activation of a BH3-only protein such as Bid, which can lead to mitochondrial pore formation, swelling, and release of cytochrome c. Bid binds to and activates the membrane ion channel proapoptotic protein Bax, activating cytochrome c release, which binds to Apaf and leads to formation of the apoptosome.

of convergence for the PI-3 kinase/Akt and MAP kinase pathways in signaling cell survival. Gain-of-function mutations in the genes that control these pathways, such as *ras*, create apoptosis-resistant cells.

C. MicroRNAs and Apoptosis

Recent work has identified several miRNAs that regulate apoptotic factors. Bcl-2, for example, is regulated by at least 2 miRNAs, designated as miR-15 and miR-16. Expression of these miRNAs will control Bcl-2 (an antiapoptotic factor) levels in the cell. If, for any reason, the expression of these miRNAs is altered, Bcl-2 levels will also be altered, promoting either apoptosis (if Bcl-2 levels decrease) or cell proliferation (if Bcl-2 levels increase). Loss of both of these miRNAs is found in 68% of chronic lymphocytic leukemia (CLL) cells, most often caused by a deletion on chromosome 13q14. Loss of miR-15 and miR-16 expression would lead to an increase in Bcl-2 levels, favoring increased cell proliferation.

Other miRNA species have been identified, which regulate factors involved in apoptosis. miR-21 regulates the expression of the programmed cell death 4 gene (PDCD4). PDCD4 is upregulated during apoptosis and functions to block translation. Loss of miR-21 activity would lead to cell death, as PDCD4 would be overexpressed. However, overexpression of miR-21 would be antiapoptotic, as PDCD4 expression would be ablated.

The miR-17 cluster regulates the protein kinase B/akt pathway by regulating the levels of PTEN (the enzyme that converts PIP_3 to PIP_2), as well as the levels of the E2F family of transcription factors. An upregulation of miR-17, acting as an oncogene, would decrease PTEN levels such that cellular proliferation is favored over apoptosis because of the constant activation of the akt pathway.

VI. CANCER REQUIRES MULTIPLE MUTATIONS

Cancer takes a long time to develop in humans because multiple genetic alterations are required to transform normal cells into malignant cells (see Fig. 18.1). A single change in one oncogene or tumor suppressor gene in an individual cell is not adequate for transformation. For example, if cells derived from biopsy specimens of normal cells are not already "immortalized," that is, able to grow in culture indefinitely, addition of the *ras* oncogene to the cells is not sufficient for transformation. However, additional mutations in a combination of oncogenes, for example, *ras* and *myc*, can result in transformation (Fig. 18.18). Epidemiologists have estimated that four to seven mutations are required for normal cells to be transformed.

Cells accumulate multiple mutations through clonal expansion. When DNA damage occurs in a normally proliferative cell, a population of cells with that mutation is produced. Expansion of the mutated population enormously increases the probability of a second mutation in a cell containing the first mutation. After one or more mutations in proto-oncogenes or tumor suppressor genes, a cell may proliferate more rapidly in the presence of growth stimuli and with further mutations grow autonomously, that is, independent of normal growth controls. Enhanced growth increases the probability of further mutations. Some families have a strong predisposition to cancer. Individuals in these families have inherited a mutation or deletion of one allele of a tumor suppressor gene, and as progeny of that cell proliferate, mutations can occur in the second allele, leading to a loss of control of cellular proliferation. These familial cancers include familial retinoblastoma, familial adenomatous polyps of the colon, and multiple endocrine neoplasia (MEN), one form of which involves tumors of the thyroid, parathyroid, and adrenal medulla (MEN type II).

Studies of benign and malignant polyps of the colon show that these tumors have several different genetic abnormalities. The incidence of these mutations increases with the level of malignancy. In the early stages, normal cells of the intestinal epithelium proliferate, develop mutations in the APC gene, and develop polyps

Cell type   Gene alteration

Normal
epithelium
        Loss of APC
Hyperproliferative
epithelium

Early
adenoma
        Activation
        of Ras
Intermediate
adenoma
        Loss of a tumor-
        suppressor gene
Late
adenoma
        Loss of p53
        activity
Carcinoma
        Other
        alterations
Metastasis

FIG. 18.18. Possible steps in the development of colon cancer. The changes do not always occur in this order, but the most benign tumors have the lowest frequency of mutations, and the most malignant have the highest frequency.

(see Fig. 18.18). This change is associated with a mutation in the *ras* proto-oncogene that converts it to an active oncogene. Progression to the next stage is associated with a deletion or alteration of a tumor suppressor gene on chromosome 5. Subsequently, mutations occur in chromosome 18, inactivating a gene that may be involved in cell adhesion, and in chromosome 17, inactivating the p53 tumor suppressor gene. The cells become malignant, and further mutations result in growth that is more aggressive and metastatic. This sequence of mutations is not always followed precisely, but an accumulation of mutations in these genes is found in a large percentage of colon carcinomas.

VII. AT THE MOLECULAR LEVEL, CANCER IS MANY DIFFERENT DISEASES

More than 20% of the deaths in the United States each year are caused by cancer, with tumors of the lung, the large intestine, and the breast being the most common (Fig. 18.19). Different cell types typically use different mechanisms through which they lose the ability to control their own growth. An examination of the genes involved in the development of cancer shows that a particular type of cancer can arise in multiple ways. For example, patched and smoothened are the receptor and coreceptor for the signaling peptide, sonic hedgehog. Either mutation of smoothened, an oncogene, or inactivation of patched, a tumor suppressor gene, can give rise to basal cell carcinoma. Similarly, transforming growth factor *β* and its signal transduction proteins Smad4/DPC are part of the same growth-inhibiting pathway, and either may be absent in colon cancer. Thus, treatments that are successful for one patient with colon cancer may not be successful in a second patient with colon cancer because of the differences in the molecular basis of each individual's disease (this now appears to be the case with breast cancer as well). Medical practice in the future will require identifying the molecular lesions involved in a particular disease and developing appropriate treatments accordingly. The use of proteomics and gene chip technology (see Chapter 17) to genotype tumor tissues, and to understand which proteins they express, will aid greatly in allowing patient-specific treatments to be developed.

 Nick O'Tyne had been smoking for 40 years before he developed lung cancer. The fact that cancer takes so long to develop has made it difficult to prove that the carcinogens in cigarette smoke cause lung cancer. Studies in England and Wales show that cigarette consumption by men began to increase in the early 1900s. Followed by a 20-year lag, the incidence in lung cancer in men also began to rise. Women began smoking later, in the 1920s. Again, the incidence of lung cancer began to increase after a 20-year lag.

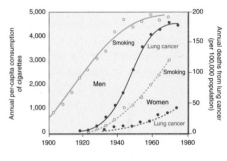

A treatment for CML based on rational drug design has been developed. The fusion protein Bcr-Abl is found only in transformed cells that express the Philadelphia chromosome and not in normal cells. Once the structure of Bcr-Abl was determined, the drug Gleevec was designed to specifically bind to and inhibit only the active site of the fusion protein and not the normal protein. Gleevec was successful in blocking Bcr-Abl function, thereby stopping cell proliferation, and in some cells inducing apoptosis, so the cells would die. Because normal cells do not express the hybrid protein, they were not affected by the drug. The problem with this treatment is that some patients suffered relapses, and when their Bcr-Abl proteins were studied, it was found that in some patients, the fusion protein had a single amino acid substitution near the active site that prevented Gleevec from binding to the protein. Other patients had an amplification of the Bcr-Abl gene product. Other tyrosine kinase inhibitors (such as dasatinib and nilotinib) can also be used in treating CML if a resistance to Gleevec is encountered.

FIG. 18.19. Estimated cancer deaths by site and sex. Data from the American Cancer Society, Inc., *Cancer Facts and Figures*, 2006.

VIII. VIRUSES AND HUMAN CANCER

Three RNA retroviruses are associated with the development of cancer in humans: HTLV-1, HIV, and hepatitis C. There are also DNA viruses associated with cancer, such as hepatitis B, Epstein-Barr virus (EBV), human papillomavirus (HPV), and herpesvirus (HHV-8).

HTLV-1 causes adult T-cell leukemia. The HTLV-1 genome encodes a protein Tax, which is a transcriptional coactivator. The cellular proto-oncogenes c-*sis* and c-*fos* are activated by Tax, thereby altering the normal controls on cellular proliferation and leading to malignancy. Thus, *tax* is a viral oncogene without a counterpart in the host cell genome.

Infection with HIV, the virus that causes AIDS, leads to the development of neoplastic disease through several mechanisms. HIV infection leads to immunosuppression and, consequently, loss of immune-mediated tumor surveillance. HIV-infected individuals are predisposed to non-Hodgkin lymphoma, which results from an overproduction of T-cell lymphocytes. The HIV genome encodes a protein, Tat, a transcription factor that activates transcription of the *interleukin-6* (IL-6) and *interleukin-10* (IL-10) genes in infected T cells. IL-6 and IL-10 are growth factors that promote proliferation of T cells, and thus their increased production may contribute to the development of non-Hodgkin lymphoma. Tat can also be released from infected cells and act as an angiogenic (blood vessel–forming) growth factor. This property is thought to contribute to the development of Kaposi sarcoma.

DNA viruses also cause human cancer but by different mechanisms. Chronic hepatitis B infections will lead to hepatocellular carcinoma. A vaccine currently is available to prevent hepatitis B infections. EBV is associated with B- and T-cell lymphomas, Hodgkin disease, and other tumors. The EBV encodes a Bcl-2 protein that restricts apoptosis of the infected cell. HHV-8 has been associated with Kaposi sarcoma. Certain strains of papillomavirus have been shown to be a major cause of cervical cancer, and a vaccine has been developed against the specific papillomavirus strains that often lead to cancer development.

CLINICAL COMMENTS

 Mannie Weitzels. The treatment of a symptomatic patient with chronic myelogenous leukemia (CML) whose white blood cell count is in excess of 50,000 cells/mL is usually initiated with a tyrosine kinase inhibitor. If the patient is intolerant to the tyrosine kinase inhibitor, then busulfan, a DNA-alkylating agent, may be used. Other alkylating agents, such as cyclophosphamide, have also been used alone or in combination with busulfan. Purine and pyrimidine antagonists and hydroxyurea (an inhibitor of the enzyme ribonucleotide reductase, which converts ribonucleotides to deoxyribonucleotides for DNA synthesis) are sometimes effective in CML as well. In addition, past experience with both γ- and β-interferon has shown promise in increasing survival in these patients if they are intolerant to the tyrosine kinase inhibitors. Interestingly, the interferons have been associated with the disappearance of the Philadelphia chromosome in dividing marrow cells of some patients treated in this way.

 Nick O'Tyne. Surgical resection of the primary lung cancer with an attempt at cure was justified in **Nick O'Tyne** who had a good prognosis with a T1N0M0 staging classification preoperatively. Without some evidence of spread to the central nervous system at that time, a preoperative CT scan of the brain would not have been justified. This conservative approach would require scanning of all of the potential sites for metastatic disease from a non–small-cell cancer of the lung in all patients who present in this way. In an era of runaway costs of health care delivery, such an approach could not be considered cost-effective.

Unfortunately, Mr. O'Tyne developed a metastatic lesion in the right temporal cortex of his brain. Because metastases were almost certainly present in other organs, Mr. O'Tyne's brain tumor was not treated surgically. In spite of palliative radiation therapy to the brain, Mr. O'Tyne succumbed to his disease just 9 months after its discovery, an unusually virulent course for this malignancy. On postmortem examination, it was found that his body was riddled with metastatic disease.

The TNM system standardizes the classification of tumors. The T stands for the stage of tumor (the higher the number, the worse the prognosis), the N stands for the number of lymph nodes that are affected by the tumor (again, the higher the number, the worse the prognosis), and M stands for the presence of metastasis (0 for none, 1 for the presence of metastatic cells).

Colin Tuma. **Colin Tuma** requires regular colonoscopies to check for new polyps in his intestinal tract. Because the development of a metastatic adenoma requires several years (because of the large numbers of mutations that must occur), frequent checks will enable new polyps to be identified and removed before malignant tumors develop.

Mel Anoma. The biopsy of **Mel Anoma's** excised mole showed that it was not malignant. The most important clinical sign of a malignant melanoma is a change in color in a pigmented lesion. Unlike benign (nondysplastic) nevi, melanomas exhibit striking variations in pigmentation, appearing in shades of black, brown, red, dark blue, and gray. Additional clinical warning signs of a melanoma are enlargement of a preexisting mole, itching or pain in a preexisting mole, development of a new pigmented lesion during adult life, and irregularity of the borders of a pigmented lesion. **Mel Anoma** was advised to conduct a monthly self-examination, to have a clinical skin examination once or twice yearly, to avoid sunlight, and to use appropriate sunscreens.

Mutations associated with malignant melanomas include *ras* (gain of function in growth signal transduction oncogene), p53 (loss of function of tumor suppressor gene), p16 (loss of function in Cdk inhibitor tumor suppressor gene), Cdk4 (gain of function in a cell cycle progression oncogene), and cadherin/β-catenin regulation (loss of regulation that requires attachment).

BIOCHEMICAL COMMENTS

Hereditary nonpolyposis colorectal cancer (HNPCC) and hereditary breast cancer both result from inherited mutations in genes involved in DNA repair.

HNPCC is estimated to account for between 5% and 6% of all colon cancer cases. These syndromes are heterogeneous, caused, most likely, by the finding that mutations in any of five genes could lead to the finding of right-sided colon cancer. The disease genes include hMSH2, hMLH1, hPMS1, hPMS2, and hMSH6. These genes all play a role in DNA mismatch repair, and all act as tumor suppressors (a loss of function is required for the tumor to develop).

It is important to understand that the lack of a DNA mismatch repair enzyme actually does not directly lead to cancer (such as an activating mutation in *myc* would do, for example). However, the lack of a functional mismatch repair system increases the frequency at which new mutations are introduced into somatic cells (particularly rapidly proliferating cells, such as the colonic epithelium), such that eventually a mutation will result in a gene necessary for proper growth control. Once that mutation occurs, tumors can begin to develop.

Familial breast cancer results in only 10% of all breast cancer cases and has been traced to inherited mutations in either one of two genes, *BRCA1* and *BRCA2*. *BRCA1* maps to chromosome 17 and acts as a tumor suppressor. The biochemical function of *BRCA1* is to participate in the response to DNA damage. *BRCA1* is phosphorylated by various kinases, each of which is activated by a different form of DNA damage. *BRCA1* is primarily involved in repairing double-strand breaks in DNA and in transcription-coupled repair. Once *BRCA1* is phosphorylated, it will signal for cell cycle arrest to allow the DNA damage to be repaired.

Women who carry a *BRCA1* mutation have an 80% risk of developing breast cancer, and a 40% risk of ovarian cancer, by the age of 70 years. Men who carry *BRCA1* mutations do not develop breast cancer, and there is mixed data in the literature whether these men have an increased risk of prostate cancer. *BRCA1* mutations are correlated with 40% to 50% of all hereditary breast cancer cases.

The other gene involved in hereditary breast cancer is *BRCA2* located on chromosome 13. *BRCA2* is required for DNA double-strand break repair, which is usually caused by ionizing radiation. As such, loss of *BRCA2* activity is required for cancer to develop, classifying *BRCA2* as a tumor suppressor. *BRCA2* is also required for homologous recombination between sister chromatids during meiosis and mitosis. *BRCA2* mutations have been liked to increased incidence of breast and ovarian cancer in women and breast cancer in men.

An understanding of the roles of *BRCA1* and *BRCA2* in repairing double-strand breaks in DNA has led to the development of poly-ADP ribose polymerase (PARP-1) inhibitors for the treatment of *BRCA1*- or *BRCA2*-induced breast cancers. Double-strand break repair occurs either by homologous recombination (requiring the activities of *BRCA1* and *BRCA2* proteins) or through nonhomologous end-joining (NHEJ), which is an error-prone process, caused by trimming of the DNA ends before ligation.

Single-strand breaks in DNA are more common than double-strand breaks. The cellular mechanism for repairing single-strand breaks is dependent on PARP-1. PARP-1 produces large branched chains of poly (ADP-ribose) (derived from NAD^+) at the site of damage, which acts as a docking station for proteins involved in repairing the single-strand break. Inhibiting PARP-1 would lead to an accumulation of single-strand breaks in the DNA.

PARP-1 inhibitors are effective in killing *BRCA1* or *BRCA2* mutated cells in that when single-strand breaks are not repaired, they often are converted to double-strand breaks when the replisome tries to replicate through the break. In a cell lacking *BRCA1* or *BRCA2* activity, the only way the DNA can be repaired is by NHEJ, which is an error-prone process. This leads to the cells accumulating a large number of mutations, eventually leading to cell death. Cells with functional *BRCA1* or *BRCA2* activity will not undergo that fate. Drugs that inhibit PARP-1 activity in cell culture are now in clinical trials with very promising results.

Key Concepts

- *Cancer* is the term applied to a group of diseases in which cells no longer respond to normal constraints on growth.
- Cancer arises because of mutations in the genome (either inherited or formed in somatic cells).
- The mutations that lead to cancer occur in certain classes of genes, including
  - Those that regulate cellular proliferation and differentiation
  - Those that suppress growth
  - Those that target cells for apoptosis
  - Those that repair damaged DNA
- Mutations that lead to cancer can be either gain-of-function mutations or loss of activity of a protein.
  - Gain-of-function mutations occur in proto-oncogenes, resulting in oncogenes.
  - Loss-of-function mutations occur in tumor suppressor genes.
- Examples of proto-oncogenes are those involved in signal transduction and cell cycle progression.
  - Growth factors and growth factor receptors
  - Ras (a GTP-binding protein)
  - Transcription factors
  - Cyclins and proteins that regulate them
  - MicroRNAs, which regulate growth-inhibitory proteins
- Examples of tumor suppressor genes include
  - Retinoblastoma gene product (Rb), which regulates the G_1 to S phase of the cell cycle
  - p53, which monitors DNA damage and arrests cell cycle progression until the damage has been repaired
  - Regulators of *ras*
  - MicroRNAs, which regulate growth-promoting signals
- Apoptosis, programmed cell death, leads to the destruction of damaged cells that cannot be repaired.
- Apoptosis consists of three phases:
  - Initiation phase (external signals or mitochondrial release of cytochrome c)
  - Signal integration phase
  - Execution phase

Table 18.4 Diseases Discussed in Chapter 18

Disease or Disorder	Environmental or Genetic	Comments
Chronic myelogenous leukemia	Environmental	Chromosomal translocation leading to the novel Bcr-Abl protein being produced, leading to uncontrolled cell growth. Rational drug design has led to Bcr-Abl targeted agents such as Gleevec, which have a high rate of initial success in controlling tumor cell proliferation.
Lung adenocarcinoma	Environmental	Lung tumor caused by inhalation of mutagenic compounds over several years. Longitudinal data indicates a 20-year lag from the initiation of smoking and a rise in cancer incidence in such individuals.
Intestinal adenocarcinoma	Both	Colon tumors may result from environmental insult, leading to mutations, or an inherited mutation in a tumor suppressor gene, such as APC. HNPCC is caused by inherited mutations in proteins involved in DNA mismatch repair.
Melanoma	Environmental	Tumor of the melanocyte, leading to uncontrolled cell growth. Mutations associated with malignant melanomas include Ras, p53, p16 (a regulator of cdk4), cdk4, and cadherin/β-catenin regulation.
Burkitt lymphoma	Environmental	Disorder caused by a chromosomal translocation, in this case chromosomes 8 and 14, leading to the transcription factor *myc* being moved from chromosome 8 to 14. This leads to inappropriate and overexpression of c-*myc*, leading to uncontrolled cell proliferation.
Li-Fraumeni syndrome	Genetic	An inherited mutation in the protein p53, which is responsible for protecting the genome against environmental damage. Loss of p53 activity will lead to an increased mutation rate, eventually leading to a mutation in a gene which regulates cell proliferation.
Neurofibromatosis (NF-1)	Genetic	A mutation in a protein (neurofibromin-1) that regulates the GTPase activity of ras, which leads to numerous, benign tumors of the nervous system.

APC, adenomatous polyposis coli; GTPase, guanosine triphosphatase; HNPCC, hereditary nonpolyposis colorectal cancer.

- Apoptosis is regulated by a group of proteins of the Bcl-2 family, which consists of both proapoptotic and antiapoptotic factors.
- Cancer cells have developed mechanisms to avoid apoptosis.
- Multiple mutations are required for a tumor to develop in a patient, acquired over several years.
- Both RNA and DNA viruses can cause a normal cell to become transformed.
- Exploitation of DNA repair mechanisms may provide a novel means for regulating tumor cell growth.
- The diseases discussed in this chapter are summarized in Table 18.4.

REVIEW QUESTIONS—CHAPTER 18

1. The *ras* oncogene in **Colin Tuma's** malignant polyp differs from the c-*ras* proto-oncogene only in the region that encodes the N-terminus of the protein. This portion of the normal and mutant sequences is

```
            10            20          30
Normal  ATGACGGAATATAAGCTGGTGGTGGTGGGCGCCGGCGGT
Mutant  ATGACGGAATATAAGCTGGTGGTGGTGGGCGCCGTCGGT
```

This mutation is similar to the mutation found in the *ras* oncogene in various tumors. What type of mutation converts the *ras* proto-oncogene to an oncogene?

A. An insertion that disrupts the reading frame of the protein
B. A deletion that disrupts the reading frame of the protein
C. A missense mutation that changes one amino acid within the protein
D. A silent mutation that produces no change in amino acid sequence of the protein
E. An early termination that creates a stop codon in the reading frame of the protein

2. The mechanism through which Ras becomes an oncogenic protein is which of the following?

A. Ras remains bound to GAP.
B. Ras can no longer bind cAMP.
C. Ras has lost its GTPase activity.
D. Ras can no longer bind GTP.
E. Ras can no longer be phosphorylated by MAP kinase.

3. Which of the following statements best describes a characteristic of oncogenes?

A. All retroviruses contain at least one oncogene.
B. Retroviral oncogenes were originally obtained from a cellular host chromosome.
C. Proto-oncogenes are genes, found in retroviruses, which have the potential to transform normal cells when expressed inappropriately.
D. The oncogenes that lead to human disease are different from those that lead to tumors in animals.
E. Oncogenes are mutated versions of normal viral gene products.

4. When p53 increases in response to DNA damage, which of the following events occurs?

   A. p53 induces transcription of cdk4.
   B. p53 induces transcription of cyclin D.
   C. p53 binds E2F to activate transcription.
   D. p53 induces transcription of p21.
   E. p53 directly phosphorylates the transcription factor *jun*.

5. A tumor suppressor gene is best described by which of the following?

   A. A gain-of-function mutation leads to uncontrolled proliferation.
   B. A loss-of-function mutation leads to uncontrolled proliferation.
   C. When it is expressed, the gene suppresses viral genes from being expressed.
   D. When it is expressed, the gene specifically blocks the G_1/S checkpoint.
   E. When it is expressed, the gene induces tumor formation.

SECTION FOUR

Fuel Oxidation and the Generation of Adenosine Triphosphate

All physiologic processes in living cells require energy transformation. Cells convert the chemical bond energy in foods into other forms, such as an electrochemical gradient across the plasma membrane, the movement of muscle fibers in an arm, or the assembly of complex molecules such as DNA (Fig. IV.1). These energy transformations can be divided into three principal phases: (1) oxidation of fuels (fat, carbohydrate, and protein), (2) conversion of energy from fuel oxidation into the high-energy phosphate bonds of adenosine triphosphate (ATP), and (3) use of ATP phosphate bond energy to drive energy-requiring processes.

The first two phases of energy transformation are part of *cellular respiration*, the overall process of using O_2 and energy derived from oxidizing fuels to generate ATP. We need to breathe principally because our cells require O_2 to generate adequate amounts of ATP from the oxidation of fuels to CO_2. Cellular respiration uses >90% of the O_2 we inhale.

In phase 1 of respiration, energy is conserved from fuel oxidation by enzymes that transfer electrons from the fuels to the electron-accepting coenzymes nicotinamide adenine dinucleotide (NAD^+) and flavin adenine dinucleotide (FAD), which are reduced to NADH and FAD(2H), respectively (Fig. IV.2). The pathways for the oxidation of most fuels (glucose, fatty acids, ketone bodies, and many amino acids) converge in the generation of the activated 2-carbon acetyl group in acetyl coenzyme A (acetyl-CoA). The complete oxidation of the acetyl group to CO_2 occurs in the tricarboxylic acid (TCA) cycle, which collects the energy mostly as NADH and FAD(2H).

In phase 2 of cellular respiration, the energy derived from fuel oxidation is converted to the high-energy phosphate bonds of ATP by the process of oxidative phosphorylation (see Fig. IV.2). Electrons are transferred from NADH and FAD(2H) to O_2 by the *electron-transport chain*, a series of electron-transfer proteins that are located in the inner mitochondrial membrane. Oxidation of NADH and FAD(2H) by O_2 generates an electrochemical potential across the inner mitochondrial membrane in the form of a transmembrane proton gradient (Δp). This electrochemical potential drives the synthesis of ATP from adenosine diphosphate (ADP) and inorganic phosphate (P_i) by a transmembrane enzyme called *ATP synthase* (or $F_0F_1ATPase$).

In phase 3 of cellular respiration, the high-energy phosphate bonds of ATP are used for processes such as muscle contraction (mechanical work), maintaining low intracellular Na^+ concentrations (transport work), synthesis of larger molecules such as DNA in anabolic pathways (biosynthetic work), or detoxification (biochemical work). As a consequence of these processes, ATP is either directly or indirectly hydrolyzed to ADP and P_i or to adenosine monophosphate (AMP) and pyrophosphate (PP_i).

Cellular respiration occurs in mitochondria (Fig. IV.3). The mitochondrial matrix, which is the compartment enclosed by the inner mitochondrial membrane, contains almost all of the enzymes for the TCA cycle and oxidation of fatty acids,

FIG. IV.1. Energy transformations in fuel metabolism. When ATP energy is transformed into cellular responses, such as muscle contraction, ATP is cleaved to ADP and P_i. In cellular respiration, O_2 is used for regenerating ATP from oxidation of fuels to CO_2.

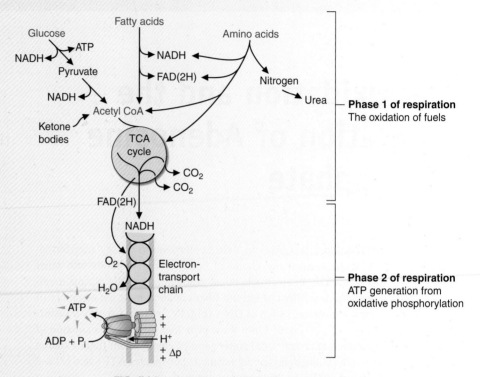

FIG. IV.2. Cellular respiration. Δp, proton gradient.

FIG. IV.3. Oxidative metabolism in mitochondria. The inner mitochondrial membrane forms infoldings, called *cristae*, which enclose the mitochondrial matrix. Most of the enzymes for the TCA cycle, the β-oxidation of fatty acids, and for mitochondrial DNA synthesis are found in the matrix. ATP synthase and the protein complexes of the electron-transport chain are embedded in the inner mitochondrial membrane. The outer mitochondrial membrane is permeable to small ions, but the inner mitochondrial membrane is impermeable.

ketone bodies, and most amino acids. The inner mitochondrial membrane contains the protein complexes of the electron-transport chain and *ATP synthase*, the enzyme complex that generates ATP from ADP and P_i. Some of the subunits of these complexes are encoded by mitochondrial DNA, which resides in the matrix. ATP is generated in the matrix, but most of the energy-using processes in the cell occur outside of the mitochondrion. As a consequence, newly generated ATP must be continuously transported to the cytosol by protein transporters in the impermeable inner mitochondrial membrane and by diffusion through pores in the more permeable outer mitochondrial membrane.

The rates of fuel oxidation and ATP use are tightly coordinated through feedback regulation of the electron-transport chain and the pathways of fuel oxidation. Thus, if less energy is required for work, more fuel is stored as glycogen or fat in adipose tissue. The basal metabolic rate (BMR), caloric balance, and ΔG (the change in Gibbs free energy, which is the amount of energy available to do useful work) are quantitative ways of describing energy requirements and the energy that can be derived from fuel oxidation. The various types of enzyme regulation described in Chapter 9 are all used to regulate the rate of oxidation of different fuels to meet energy requirements.

Fatty acids are a major fuel in the body. After eating, we store excess fatty acids and carbohydrates that are not oxidized as fat (triacylglycerols) in adipose tissue. Between meals, these fatty acids are released and circulate in blood bound to albumin. In muscle, liver, and other tissues, fatty acids are oxidized to acetyl-CoA in the pathway of β-oxidation. NADH and FAD(2H) generated from β-oxidation are reoxidized by O_2 in the electron-transport chain, thereby generating ATP (see Fig. IV.2). Small amounts of certain fatty acids are oxidized through other pathways that convert them to either oxidizable fuels or urinary excretion products (e.g., peroxisomal β-oxidation).

Not all acetyl-CoA generated from β-oxidation enters the TCA cycle. In the liver, acetyl-CoA generated from β-oxidation of fatty acids can also be converted to the ketone bodies acetoacetate and β-hydroxybutyrate. Ketone bodies are taken up by muscle and other tissues, which convert them back to acetyl-CoA for oxidation in the TCA cycle. They become a major fuel for the brain during prolonged fasting.

Amino acids derived from dietary or body proteins are also potential fuels that can be oxidized to acetyl-CoA or converted to glucose and then oxidized (see Fig. IV.2). These oxidation pathways, like those of fatty acids, generate NADH or FAD(2H). Ammonia, which can be formed during amino acid oxidation, is toxic. It is therefore converted to urea in the liver and excreted in the urine. There are more than 20 different amino acids, each with a somewhat different pathway for oxidation of the carbon skeleton and conversion of its nitrogen to urea. Because of the complexity of amino acid metabolism, use of amino acids as fuels is considered separately in Section VII.

Glucose is a universal fuel used to generate ATP in every cell type in the body (Fig. IV.4). In glycolysis, 1 mol of glucose is converted to 2 mol of pyruvate and 2 mol of NADH by cytosolic enzymes. Small amounts of ATP are generated when high-energy pathway intermediates transfer phosphate to ADP in a process termed *substrate-level phosphorylation*. In aerobic glycolysis, the NADH produced from glycolysis is reoxidized by O_2 via the electron-transport chain, and pyruvate enters the TCA cycle. In anaerobic glycolysis, the NADH is reoxidized by conversion of pyruvate to lactate, which enters the blood. Although anaerobic glycolysis has a low ATP yield, it is important for tissues with a low oxygen supply and few mitochondria (e.g., the kidney medulla) or tissues that are experiencing diminished blood flow (ischemia).

All cells continuously use ATP and require a constant supply of fuels to provide energy for the generation of ATP. Chapters 1 through 3 of this text outlined the basic patterns of fuel use in the human and provided information about dietary components.

The pathologic consequences of metabolic problems in fuel oxidation can be grouped into one of two categories: (1) lack of a required product or (2) excess of a substrate or pathway intermediate. The product of fuel oxidation is ATP, and an inadequate rate of ATP production occurs under a wide variety of medical conditions. Extreme conditions that interfere with ATP generation from oxidative phosphorylation, such as complete oxygen deprivation (anoxia) or cyanide poisoning, are fatal. A myocardial infarction is caused by a lack of adequate blood flow to regions of the heart (ischemia), thereby depriving cardiomyocytes of oxygen and fuel. Hyperthyroidism is associated with excessive heat generation from fuel oxidation, and in hypothyroidism, ATP generation can decrease to a fatal level. Conditions such as malnutrition, anorexia nervosa, or excessive alcohol consumption may decrease availability of thiamine, Fe^{2+}, and other vitamins and minerals required by the enzymes of fuel oxidation. Mutations in mitochondrial DNA or nuclear DNA result in deficient ATP generation from oxidative metabolism.

In contrast, problems arising from an excess of substrate or fuel are seen in diabetes mellitus, which may result in a potentially fatal ketoacidosis. Lactic acidosis occurs with a reduction in oxidative metabolism.

FIG. IV.4. Glycolysis. In glycolysis, glucose is converted to pyruvate. If the pyruvate is reduced to lactate, the pathway does not require O_2 and is called *anaerobic glycolysis* (in *red*). If this pyruvate is converted instead to acetyl-CoA and oxidized in the TCA cycle, glycolysis requires O_2 and is aerobic (in *black*).

Definitions of prefixes and suffixes used in describing clinical conditions:

an-	without
-emia	blood
hyper-	excessive, above normal
hypo-	deficient, below normal
-osis	abnormal or diseased state
-uria	urine

19 Cellular Bioenergetics: ATP and O_2

FIG. 19.1. The ATP–ADP cycle.

*Bioenergetics refers to **cellular energy transformations.***

The ATP–ADP Cycle.** In cells, the **chemical bond energy** of fuels is transformed into the physiologic responses that are necessary for life. The central role of the **high-energy phosphate bonds of adenosine triphosphate (ATP)** in these processes is summarized in the **ATP–ADP (adenosine diphosphate) cycle** (Fig. 19.1). To generate ATP through cellular respiration, fuels are degraded by oxidative reactions that transfer most of their **chemical bond energy** to NAD^+ and FAD to generate the reduced form of these coenzymes: **NADH** and **FAD(2H)**. When NADH and FAD(2H) are oxidized by O_2 in the electron-transport chain, the energy is used to regenerate ATP in the process of **oxidative phosphorylation.** Energy available from cleavage of the high-energy phosphate bonds of ATP can be used directly for **mechanical work** (e.g., muscle contraction) or for **transport work** (e.g., a Na^+ gradient generated by Na^+,K^+-**ATPase**). It can also be used for **biochemical work** (energy-requiring chemical reactions), such as **anabolic pathways** (biosynthesis of large molecules such as proteins) or detoxification reactions. **Phosphoryl transfer** reactions, **protein conformational changes**, and the formation of **activated intermediates** containing **high-energy bonds** (e.g., nucleotide-sugars) facilitate these energy transformations. Energy released from foods that is not used for work against the environment is transformed into **heat.

***ATP Homeostasis.** Fuel oxidation is regulated to maintain **ATP homeostasis** ("homeo," same; "stasis," state). Regardless of whether the level of cellular fuel utilization is high (with increased ATP consumption) or low (with decreased ATP consumption), the available ATP within the cell is maintained at a constant level by appropriate increases or decreases in the rate of fuel oxidation. Problems in ATP homeostasis and energy balance occur in obesity, hyperthyroidism, and myocardial infarction.*

***Energy from Fuel Oxidation.** Fuel oxidation is **exergonic**: It releases energy. The maximum quantity of energy released that is available for useful work (e.g., ATP synthesis) is called $\Delta G^{0'}$, the **change in Gibbs free energy** at pH 7.0 under standard conditions. Fuel oxidation has a **negative** $\Delta G^{0'}$; that is, the products have a lower chemical bond energy than the reactants and their formation is energetically favored. ATP synthesis from ADP and inorganic phosphate is **endergonic**: It requires energy and has a positive $\Delta G^{0'}$. To proceed in our cells, all pathways must have a negative $\Delta G^{0'}$. How is this accomplished for anabolic pathways such as glycogen synthesis? These metabolic pathways incorporate reactions that expend high-energy bonds to compensate for the energy-requiring steps. Because the $\Delta G^{0'}$ values for a sequence of reactions **are additive**, the overall pathway becomes energetically favorable.*

*Fuels are oxidized principally by donating electrons to NAD^+ and FAD, which then donate electrons to O_2 in the electron-transport chain. The **caloric value** of a fuel is related to its $\Delta G^{0'}$ for transfer of electrons to O_2 and its **reduction potential**, $E^{0'}$ (a measure of its willingness to donate or accept electrons). Because fatty acids are more reduced than carbohydrates, they have a higher caloric value. The high affinity of oxygen for electrons* *(a high positive reduction potential) drives fuel oxidation forward, with release of energy that can be used for ATP synthesis in oxidative phosphory- lation. However, smaller amounts of ATP can be generated without the use of O_2 in* **anaerobic glycolysis***.*

Fuel oxidation can also generate **NADPH***, which usually donates electrons to biosynthetic pathways and detoxification reactions. For example, in some reactions catalyzed by* **oxygenases***, NADPH is the electron donor and O_2 is the electron acceptor.*

THE WAITING ROOM

 Otto Shape is a 26-year-old medical student who has completed his first year of medical school. He is 70 in tall and began medical school weigh- ing 154 lb—within his ideal weight range (see Chapter 1). By the time he finished his last examination in his first year, he weighed 187 lb. He had calculated his basal metabolic rate (BMR) at approximately 1,680 kcal and his energy expen- diture for physical exercise equal to 30% of his BMR. He planned on returning to his premedical school weight in 6 weeks over the summer by eating 576 kcal less each day and playing 7 hours of tennis every day. However, he did a summer internship instead of playing tennis. When Otto started his second year of medical school, he weighed 210 lb.

 X. S. Teefore is a 26-year-old man who noted heat intolerance, with heavy sweating, heart palpitations, and tremulousness. Over the past 4 months, he has lost weight in spite of a good appetite. He is sleeping poorly and describes himself as feeling "jittery inside."

On physical examination, his heart rate is rapid (116 beats/minute) and he appears restless and fidgety. His skin feels warm, and he is perspiring profusely. A fine hand tremor is observed as he extends his arms in front of his chest. His thy- roid gland appears to be diffusely enlarged and, on palpation, is approximately three times normal size. Thyroid function tests confirm that Mr. Teefore's thyroid gland is secreting excessive amounts of the thyroid hormones T_4 (tetraiodothyronine) and T_3 (triiodothyronine), the major thyroid hormones present in the blood.

Cora Nari is a 64-year-old woman who had a myocardial infarction 8 months ago. Although she has managed to lose 6 lb since that time, she remains overweight and has not reduced the fat content of her diet adequately. The graded aerobic exercise program she started 5 weeks after her infarction is now followed irregularly, falling far short of the cardiac conditioning intensity prescribed by her cardiologist. She is readmitted to the hospital cardiac care unit (CCU) after experiencing a severe "viselike pressure" in the midchest area while cleaning ice from the windshield of her car. The electrocardiogram (ECG) shows evidence of a new posterior wall myocardial infarction. Signs and symptoms of left ventricular failure are present.

I. ENERGY AVAILABLE TO DO WORK

The basic principle of the ATP–ADP cycle is that fuel oxidation generates adenos- ine triphosphate (ATP), and hydrolysis of ATP to adenosine diphosphate (ADP) provides the energy to perform most of the work required in the cell. ATP has,

 To assess for thyroid function, one must understand how the hormones T_3 and T_4 are released from the thyroid (see Chapter 43). The hypothalamus and the pituitary gland both monitor the level of free T_3 in the blood bathing them. When the concentration of free T_3 in the blood drops, the pituitary releases thyroid-stimulating hor- mone (TSH), which stimulates the thyroid to release T_3 and T_4. The pituitary is under the control of the hypothalamus, which releases TSH-releasing hormone (TSHRH) under the appropriate conditions. Thus, if one notices low serum T_3 or T_4 levels, it may represent a thyroid or pituitary problem. Understanding the physiology enables the appropriate tests to be run to determine where the defect lies.

T_3 and T_4 are measured using sensitive techniques that involve antibody recognition (radioimmunoassay; see Chapter 43). TSH levels can be determined in a similar fashion, using a sandwich technique (which requires the use of two distinct antibodies that recognize TSH).

Through the appropriate interpretation of these tests, one can determine if thyroid or pituitary function is impaired, and design treat- ment accordingly.

 Cora Nari suffered a heart attack 8 months ago and had a significant loss of functional heart muscle. The pain she is experiencing is called *angina pecto- ris* and is a crushing or constricting pain located in the center of the chest, often radiating to the neck or arms (see **Ann Jeina**, Chapters 6 and 7). The most common cause of angina pectoris is partial blockage of coronary arteries from atherosclerosis. The heart muscle cells beyond the block receive an inadequate blood flow and oxygen, and they die when ATP production falls too low.

The heart is a specialist in the transformation of ATP chemical bond energy into mechanical work. Each single heartbeat uses approximately 2% of the ATP in the heart. If the heart were not able to regenerate ATP, all its ATP would be hydrolyzed in less than 1 minute. Because the amount of ATP required by the heart is so high, it must rely on the pathway of oxidative phosphorylation for generation of this ATP. In **Cora Nari's** heart, hypoxia is affecting her ability to generate ATP.

therefore, been called the energy currency of the cells. Like the $1 bill, it has a defined value, is required to obtain goods and services, and disappears before we know it. To keep up with the demand, we must constantly replenish our ATP supply through the use of O_2 for fuel oxidation.

The amount of energy from ATP cleavage available to do useful work is related to the difference in energy levels between the products and substrates of the reaction and is called the change in *Gibbs free energy*, ΔG (Δ, difference; G, Gibbs free energy). In cells, the ΔG for energy production from fuel oxidation must be greater than the ΔG of energy-requiring processes, such as protein synthesis and muscle contraction, for life to continue.

A. The High-Energy Phosphate Bonds of ATP

The amount of energy released or required by bond cleavage or formation is determined by the chemical properties of the substrates and products. The bonds between the phosphate groups in ATP are called *phosphoanhydride bonds* (Fig. 19.2). When these bonds are hydrolyzed, energy is released because the products of the reaction (ADP and phosphate) are more stable, with lower bond energies, than the reactants (ATP and water [H_2O]). The instability of the phosphoanhydride bonds arises from their negatively charged phosphate groups, which repel each other and strain the bonds between them. It takes energy to make the phosphate groups stay together. In contrast, there are fewer negative charges in ADP to repel each other. The phosphate group, as a free anion, is more stable than it is in ATP because of an increase in resonance structures (i.e., the electrons of the oxygen double bond are shared by all the oxygen atoms). As a consequence, ATP hydrolysis is energetically favorable and proceeds with release of energy as heat.

In the cell, ATP is not hydrolyzed directly. Energy released as heat from ATP hydrolysis cannot be transferred efficiently into energy-requiring processes such as biosynthetic reactions or maintaining an ion gradient. Instead, cellular enzymes transfer the phosphate group directly to a metabolic intermediate or protein that is part of the energy-requiring process (a phosphoryl transfer reaction).

B. Change in Free Energy (ΔG) during a Reaction

How much energy can be obtained from ATP hydrolysis to do the work required in the cell? The maximum amount of useful energy that can be obtained from a reaction

FIG. 19.2. Hydrolysis of ATP to ADP and inorganic phosphate (P_i). Cleavage of the phosphoanhydride bonds between either the β- and γ-phosphates or between the α- and β-phosphates releases the same amount of energy, approximately 7.3 kcal/mol. However, hydrolysis of the phosphate–adenosine bond (a phosphoester bond) releases less energy (≈3.4 kcal/mol), and consequently, this bond is not considered a high-energy phosphate bond. During ATP hydrolysis, the change in disorder during the reaction is small and so ΔG values at physiologic temperature (37°C) are similar to those at standard temperature (25°C). ΔG is affected by pH, which alters the ionization state of the phosphate groups of ATP and by the intracellular concentration of Mg^{2+} ions, which bind to the β- and γ-phosphate groups of ATP.

Table 19.1   Thermodynamic Expressions, Laws, and Constants

Definitions

ΔG	Change in free energy, or Gibbs free energy
ΔG^0	Standard free-energy change, ΔG starting with 1 M concentrations of substrates and products
$\Delta G^{0\prime}$	Standard free-energy change at 25°C, pH 7.0
ΔH	Change in enthalpy, or heat content
ΔS	Change in entropy, or increase in disorder
K'_{eq}	Equilibrium constant at 25°C, pH 7.0, incorporating $[H_2O] = 55.5$ M and $[H^+] = 10^{-7}$ M in the constant
$\Delta E^{0\prime}$	Change in reduction potential
P	Biochemical symbol for a high-energy phosphate bond (i.e., a bond that is hydrolyzed with the release of more than about 7 kcal/mol of heat)

Laws of Thermodynamics

First law of thermodynamics, the conservation of energy: In any physical or chemical change, the total energy of a system, including its surroundings, remains constant.
Second law of thermodynamics: The universe tends toward disorder. In all natural processes, the total entropy of a system always increases.

Constants

Units of ΔG and ΔH = cal/mol or J/mol: 1 cal = 4.18 J
T, absolute temperature: K, kelvin = 273 + °C (25°C = 298 K)
R, universal gas constant: 1.99 cal/mol-K or 8.31 J/mol-K
F, Faraday constant: F = 23 kcal/mol-V or 96,500 J/V-mol
Units of $E^{0\prime}$, V

Formulas

$\Delta G = \Delta H - T \Delta S$
$\Delta G^{0\prime} = -RT \ln K_{eq}'$
$\Delta G^{0\prime} = -n F \Delta E^{0\prime}$
$\ln = 2.303 \log_{10}$

is called ΔG—the change in Gibbs free energy. The value of ΔG for a reaction can be influenced by the initial concentration of substrates and products, temperature, pH, and pressure. The ΔG^0 for a reaction refers to the energy change for a reaction starting at 1 M substrate and product concentrations and proceeding to equilibrium (equilibrium, by definition, occurs when there is no change in substrate and product concentrations with time). $\Delta G^{0\prime}$ is the value for ΔG^0 under standard conditions (pH = 7.0, $[H_2O]$ = 55 M, and 25°C), as well as standard concentrations (Table 19.1).

$\Delta G^{0\prime}$ is equivalent to the chemical bond energy of the products minus that of the reactants, corrected for energy that has gone into entropy (an increase in amount of molecular disorder). This correction for change in entropy is very small for most reactions that occur in cells and, thus, the $\Delta G^{0\prime}$ for hydrolysis of various chemical bonds reflects the amount of energy available from that bond.

The value -7.3 kcal/mol (-30.5 kJ/mol) that is generally used for the $\Delta G^{0\prime}$ of ATP hydrolysis is thus the amount of energy available from hydrolysis of ATP under standard conditions that can be spent on energy-requiring processes; it defines the "monetary value" of our "ATP currency." Although the difference between cellular conditions (pH 7.3, 37°C) and standard conditions is very small, the difference between cellular concentrations of ATP, ADP, and inorganic phosphate (P_i) and the standard 1 M concentrations is huge and greatly affects the availability of energy in the cell.

C. Exothermic and Endothermic Reactions

The value of $\Delta G^{0\prime}$ tells you whether the reaction requires or releases energy, the amount of energy involved, and the ratio of products to substrates at equilibrium. The negative value for the $\Delta G^{0\prime}$ of ATP hydrolysis indicates that, if you begin with equimolar (1 M) concentrations of substrates and products, the reaction proceeds in the forward direction with the release of energy. From initial concentrations of 1 M, the ATP concentration will decrease, and ADP and P_i will increase until equilibrium is reached.

 The reaction catalyzed by phosphoglucomutase (PGM) is reversible and functions in the synthesis of glycogen from glucose as well as the degradation of glycogen back to glucose. If the $\Delta G^{0\prime}$ for conversion of glucose 6-phosphate to glucose 1-phosphate is $+1.65$ kcal/mol, what is the $\Delta G^{0\prime}$ of the reverse reaction?

A: The $\Delta G^{0'}$ for the reverse reaction is −1.65 kcal. The change in free energy is the same for the forward and reverse directions but has opposite sign. Because negative $\Delta G^{0'}$ values indicate favorable reactions, this reaction under standard conditions favors the conversion of glucose 1-P to glucose 6-P.

Glucose 6-phosphate (G6P)

PGM

Glucose 1-phosphate (G1P)

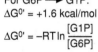

For G6P → G1P:
$\Delta G^{0'} = +1.6$ kcal/mol

$\Delta G^{0'} = -RT \ln \dfrac{[G1P]}{[G6P]}$

FIG. 19.3. The phosphoglucomutase reaction. The forward direction (formation of glucose 1-phosphate) is involved in converting glucose to glycogen, and the reverse direction in converting glycogen to glucose 6-phosphate. *PGM*, phosphoglucomutase.

Q: The $\Delta G^{0'}$ for the conversion of glucose 6-P to glucose 1-P is +1.65 kcal/mol. What is the ratio of [glucose 1-P] to [glucose 6-P] at equilibrium?

For a reaction in which a substrate S is converted to a product P, the ratio of the product concentration to the substrate concentration at equilibrium is given by

Equation 19.1:
$$\Delta G^{0'} = -RT \ln[P]/[S]$$

(see Table 19.2 for a more general form of this equation; R is the gas constant [1.99 cal/mol °K], and T is the temperature in degrees Kelvin).

Thus, the difference in chemical bond energies of the substrate and product ($\Delta G^{0'}$) determines the concentration of each at equilibrium.

Reactions such as ATP hydrolysis are exergonic (release energy) or exothermic (release heat). They have a negative $\Delta G^{0'}$ and release energy while proceeding in the forward direction to equilibrium. Endergonic or endothermic reactions have a positive $\Delta G^{0'}$ for the forward direction (the direction shown), and the backward direction is favored. For example, in the pathway of glycogen synthesis, phosphoglucomutase converts glucose 6-phosphate (glucose 6-P) to glucose 1-phosphate (glucose 1-P). Glucose 1-P has a higher phosphate bond energy than glucose 6-P because the phosphate is on the aldehyde carbon (Fig. 19.3). The $\Delta G^{0'}$ for the forward direction (glucose 1-P → glucose 6-P) is therefore positive. Beginning at equimolar concentrations of both compounds, there is a net conversion of glucose 1-P back to glucose 6-P and, at equilibrium, the concentration of glucose 6-P is higher than glucose 1-P. The exact ratio is determined by the $\Delta G^{0'}$ for the reaction.

It is often said that a reaction with a negative $\Delta G^{0'}$ proceeds spontaneously in the forward direction, meaning that products accumulate at the expense of reactants. However, $\Delta G^{0'}$ is not an indicator of the velocity of the reaction or of the rate at which equilibrium can be reached. In the cell, the velocity of the reaction depends on the efficiency and amount of enzyme available to catalyze the reaction (see Chapter 9), so a reaction proceeding "spontaneously" in this context can be misleading.

The equations for calculating ΔG are based on the first law of thermodynamics (see Table 19.1). The change in chemical bond energy that occurs during a reaction is ΔH—the change in enthalpy of the reaction. At constant temperature and pressure, ΔH is equivalent to the chemical bond energy of the products minus that of the reactants. ΔG—the maximum amount of useful work available from a reaction—is equal to $\Delta H - T\Delta S$. $T\Delta S$ is a correction for the amount of energy that has gone into an increase in the entropy (disorder in arrangement of molecules) of the system. Thus, $\Delta G = \Delta H - T\Delta S$, where ΔH is the change in enthalpy, T is the temperature of the system in kelvin, and ΔS is the change in entropy, or increased disorder of the system. ΔS is often negligible in reactions such as ATP hydrolysis, in which the numbers of substrates (H_2O, ATP) and products (ADP, P_i) are equal and no gas is formed. Under these conditions, the values for ΔG at physiologic temperature (37°C) are similar to those at standard temperature (25°C).

Table 19.2   A General Expression for ΔG

To generalize the expression for ΔG, consider a reaction in which
$aA + bB \leftrightarrows cC + dD$
The lowercase letters denote that a moles of A will combine with b moles of B to produce c moles of C and d moles of D.

$$\Delta G^{0'} = -RT \ln K_{eq} = -RT \ln \frac{[C]^c_{eq}[D]^d_{eq}}{[A]^a_{eq}[B]^b_{eq}}$$

And

$$\Delta G = \Delta G^{0'} + RT \ln \frac{[C]^c[D]^d}{[A]^a[B]^b}$$

II. ENERGY TRANSFORMATIONS TO DO MECHANICAL AND TRANSPORT WORK

To do work in the cell, a mechanism must be available for converting the chemical bond energy of ATP into another form, such as a Na^+ gradient across a membrane. These energy transformations usually involve intermediate steps in which ATP is bound to a protein, and cleavage of the bound ATP results in a conformational change of the protein.

A. Mechanical Work

In mechanical work, the high-energy phosphate bond of ATP is converted into movement by changing the conformation of a protein (Fig. 19.4). For example, in contracting muscle fibers, the hydrolysis of ATP while it is bound to myosin ATPase changes the conformation of myosin so that it is in a "cocked" position—ready to associate with the sliding actin filament. Thus, exercising muscle fibers have almost a 100-fold higher rate of ATP utilization and caloric requirements than resting muscle fibers. Motor proteins, such as kinesins that transport chemicals along fibers, provide another example of mechanical work in a cell.

B. Transport Work

In transport work, called *active transport*, the high-energy phosphate bond of ATP is used to transport compounds against a concentration gradient (see Chapter 10, Fig. 10.10). In plasma membrane ATPases (P-ATPases) and vesicular ATPases (V-ATPases), the chemical bond energy of ATP is used to reversibly phosphorylate the transport protein and change its conformation. For example, as Na^+,K^+-ATPase binds and cleaves ATP, it becomes phosphorylated and changes its conformation to release 3 Na^+ ions to the outside of the cell, thereby building up a higher extracellular than intracellular concentration of Na^+. Na^+ reenters the cell on cotransport proteins that drive the uptake of amino acids and many other compounds into the

 As shown in Table 19.2, $\Delta G^{0'} = -RT \ln K_{eq}$. For this reaction, $K_{eq} =$ [glucose 1-phosphate] / [glucose 6-phosphate]. The constant R is 1.99×10^{-3} kcal/mol-K, and T is $(273 + 25)$ K, so RT $= -0.593$ kcal/mol. Substituting in the previous equation then gives $1.65 = -0.593 \ln$[glucose 1-P] / [glucose 6-P]. Thus, $\ln$[glucose 1-P] / [glucose 6-P] $= -2.78$, and [glucose 1-P] / [glucose 6-P] $= e^{-2.78}$, or 0.062. So the ratio of [glucose 1-P] to [glucose 6-P] at equilibrium is 0.062.

FIG. 19.4. A simplified diagram of myosin ATPase. Muscle fiber is made of thick filaments composed of bundles of the protein myosin, and thin filaments composed of the protein actin (which is activated by Ca^{2+} binding). At many positions along the actin filament, a terminal domain of a myosin molecule, referred to as the "head," binds to a specific site on the actin. The myosin head has an ATP-binding site and is an ATPase; it can hydrolyze ATP to ADP and P_i. *(1)* As ATP binds to myosin, the conformation of myosin changes, and it dissociates from the actin. *(2)* Myosin hydrolyzes the ATP, again changing conformation. *(3)* When P_i dissociates, the myosin head reassociates with activated actin at a new position (position 2 in the figure). *(4)* As ADP dissociates, the myosin again changes conformation, or tightens. This change of conformation at multiple association points between actin and myosin slides the actin filament forward.

Otto Shape has not followed his proposed diet and exercise regimen and has been gaining weight. He has a positive caloric balance, because his daily energy expenditure is less than his daily energy intake (see Chapter 2). Although the energy expenditure for physical exercise is only approximately 30% of the BMR in a sedentary individual, it can be 100% or more of the BMR in a person who exercises strenuously for several hours or more each day. The large increase in ATP utilization for muscle contraction during exercise accounts for its contribution to the daily energy expenditure.

In the thermodynamic perspective of energy expenditure, when energy intake to the body exceeds energy expended, the difference is effectively stored as fat.

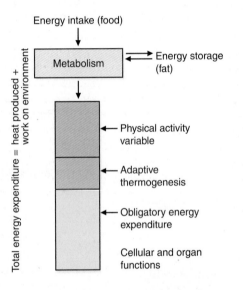

The portion of food that is metabolized is regulated to match the total energy expenditure of the body. A certain amount of the energy is obligatory (the amount of energy expended to do the work of the cells; the BMR). Some energy is also expended for adaptive thermogenesis, which is heat generated in response to cold or diet. An additional amount of energy is used for physical exercise (work against the environment). To voluntarily store less energy as fat, we can vary our caloric intake through dietary changes or our energy expenditures through changes in our physical exercise.

cell. Thus, Na^+ must be continuously transported back out. The expenditure of ATP for Na^+ transport occurs even while we sleep and is estimated to account for 10% to 30% of our basal metabolic rate (BMR).

A large number of other active transporters also convert ATP chemical bond energy into an ion gradient (membrane potential). V-ATPases pump protons into lysosomes. Ca^{2+}-ATPases in the plasma membrane move Ca^{2+} out of the cell against a concentration gradient. Similar Ca^{2+}-ATPases pump Ca^{2+} into the lumen of the endoplasmic reticulum and the sarcoplasmic reticulum (in muscle). Thus, a considerable amount of energy is expended in maintaining a low cytoplasmic Ca^{2+} level.

III. BIOCHEMICAL WORK

The high-energy phosphate bonds of ATP are also used for biochemical work. Biochemical work occurs in anabolic pathways, which are pathways that synthesize large molecules (e.g., DNA, glycogen, triacylglycerols, and proteins) from smaller compounds. Biochemical work also occurs when toxic compounds are converted to nontoxic compounds that can be excreted (e.g., the liver converts NH_4^+ ions to urea in the urea cycle). In general, formation of chemical bonds between two organic molecules (e.g., C–C bonds in fatty acid synthesis or C–N bonds in protein synthesis) requires energy and is, therefore, biochemical work. How do our cells get these necessary energy-requiring reactions to occur?

To answer this question, the next sections consider how energy is used to synthesize glycogen from glucose (Fig. 19.5). Glycogen is a storage polysaccharide consisting of glucosyl units linked together through glycosidic bonds. If an anabolic pathway, such as glycogen synthesis, were to have an overall positive $\Delta G^{0'}$, the cell would be full of glucose and intermediates of the pathway, but very little glycogen would be formed. To avoid this, cells do biochemical work and spend enough of their ATP currency to give anabolic pathways an overall negative $\Delta G^{0'}$.

A. ΔG^0 Values Are Additive

Reactions in which chemical bonds are formed between two organic molecules are usually catalyzed by enzymes that transfer energy from cleavage of ATP in a phosphoryl transfer reaction or by enzymes that cleave a high-energy bond in an activated intermediate of the pathway. Because the $\Delta G^{0'}$ values in a reaction sequence are additive, the pathway acquires an overall negative $\Delta G^{0'}$, and the reactions in the pathway will occur to move toward an equilibrium state in which the concentration of final products is greater than that of the initial reactants.

1. PHOSPHORYL TRANSFER REACTIONS

One of the characteristics of Gibbs free energy is that ΔG^0 values for consecutive steps or reactions in a sequence can be added together to obtain a single value for the overall process. Thus, the high-energy phosphate bonds of ATP can be used to drive a reaction forward that would otherwise be highly unfavorable energetically. Consider, for example, synthesis of glucose 6-P from glucose, the first step in glycolysis and glycogen synthesis (see Fig. 19.5, circle 2). If the reaction were to proceed by addition of inorganic phosphate to glucose, glucose 6-P synthesis would have a positive $\Delta G^{0'}$ value of 3.3 kcal/mol (Table 19.3). However, when this reaction is coupled to cleavage of the high-energy ATP bond through a phosphoryl transfer reaction, the $\Delta G^{0'}$ for glucose 6-P synthesis acquires a net negative value of −4.0 kcal/mol, which can be calculated from the sum of the two reactions. Glucose 6-P cannot be transported back out of the cell and, therefore, the net negative $\Delta G^{0'}$ for glucose 6-P synthesis helps the cell to trap glucose for its own metabolic needs.

The net value for synthesis of glucose 6-P from glucose and ATP would be the same whether the two reactions were catalyzed by the same enzyme, were catalyzed by two separate enzymes, or were not catalyzed by an enzyme at all because it is dictated by the amount of energy in the chemical bonds being broken and formed.

Table 19.3 ΔG⁰′ for the Transfer of a Phosphate from Adenosine
Triphosphate to Glucose

Glucose + P$_i$ → glucose 6-P + H$_2$O	ΔG$^{0'}$ = +3.3 kcal/mol
ATP + H$_2$O → ADP + P$_i$	ΔG$^{0'}$ = −7.3 kcal/mol
Sum: glucose + ATP → glucose 6-P + ADP	ΔG$^{0'}$ = −4.0 kcal/mol

2. ACTIVATED INTERMEDIATES IN GLYCOGEN SYNTHESIS

To synthesize glycogen from glucose, energy is provided by the cleavage of three high-energy phosphate bonds in ATP, uridine triphosphate (UTP), and pyrophosphate (PP$_i$) (see Fig. 19.5, Steps 2, 5, and 6). Energy transfer is facilitated by phosphoryl group transfer and by the formation of an activated intermediate (UDP-glucose). Step 4—the conversion of glucose 6-P to glucose 1-P—has a positive ΔG$^{0'}$. This step is pulled and pushed in the desired direction by the accumulation of substrate and removal of product in reactions that have a negative ΔG$^{0'}$ from cleavage of high-energy bonds. In Step 5, the UTP high-energy phosphate bond is cleaved to form the activated sugar, UDP-glucose (Fig. 19.6). This reaction is further facilitated by cleavage of the high-energy bond in the PP$_i$ (Step 6) that is released in Step 5 (approximately −7.7 kcal). In Step 7, cleavage of the bond between UDP and glucose in the activated intermediate provides the energy for attaching the glucose moiety to the end of the glycogen molecule (approximately −3.3 kcal). In general, the amount of ATP phosphate bond energy used in an anabolic pathway, or detoxification pathway, must provide the pathway with an overall negative ΔG$^{0'}$, so that the concentration of products is favored over that of reactants.

B. ΔG Depends on Substrate and Product Concentrations

ΔG$^{0'}$ reflects the energy difference between reactants and products at specific concentrations (each at 1 M) and standard conditions (pH 7.0, 25°C). However, these are not the conditions that prevail in cells, in which variations from "standard conditions" are relevant to determining actual free-energy changes and, hence, the direction in which reactions are likely to occur. One aspect of free-energy changes contributing to the forward direction of anabolic pathways is the dependence of ΔG, the free-energy change of a reaction, on the initial substrate and product concentrations. Reactions in the cell with a positive ΔG$^{0'}$ can proceed in the forward direction if the concentration of substrate is raised to a high enough level, or if the concentration of product is decreased to a very low level. Product concentrations can be very low if, for example, the product is rapidly used in a subsequent energetically favorable reaction, or if the product diffuses or is transported away.

FIG. 19.5. Energetics of glycogen synthesis. Compounds containing high-energy bonds are shown in *red*. *(1)* Glucose is transported into the cell. *(2)* Glucose phosphorylation uses the high-energy phosphate bond (~P) of ATP in a phosphoryl transfer step. *(4)* Conversion of glucose 6-phosphate to glucose 1-phosphate by phosphoglucomutase. *(5)* UDP-glucose pyrophosphorylase cleaves a ~P bond in UTP, releasing pyrophosphate (PP$_i$) and forming UDP-glucose, an activated intermediate. *(6)* The PP$_i$ is hydrolyzed, releasing additional energy. *(7)* The phosphoester bond of UDP-glucose is cleaved during the addition of a glucosyl unit to the end of a glycogen polysaccharide chain. The UDP acts as the leaving group in this reaction. Glucose 6-phosphate also can be metabolized via glycolysis *(3)* when energy is required.

Uridine diphosphate glucose
(UDP-glucose)

FIG. 19.6. UDP-glucose contains a high-energy pyrophosphate (PP$_i$) bond, shown in the *green box.*

Q: Given a ΔG$^{0'}$ of +1.65 kcal/mol for the conversion of glucose 6-P to glucose 1-P and a ΔG$^{0'}$ of −4.0 kcal/mol for the conversion of glucose + ATP to glucose 6-P + ADP, what is the value of ΔG$^{0'}$ for the conversion of glucose to glucose 1-P?

X. S. Teefore has increased blood levels of thyroid hormones, which accelerate basal metabolic processes that use ATP in our organs (e.g., Na^+,K^+-ATPase), thereby increasing the BMR. An increased BMR was used for a presumptive diagnosis of hyperthyroidism before development of the tests to measure T_3 and T_4. Because **X. S. Teefore** did not fully compensate for his increased ATP requirements with an increased caloric intake, he was in negative caloric balance and lost weight.

Approximately 70% of our resting daily energy requirement arises from work carried out by our largest organs: the heart, brain, kidneys, and liver. Using their rate of oxygen consumption and a P/O ratio of 2.5 (see Chapter 21), it can be estimated that each of these organs is using and producing several times its own weight in ATP each day.

Estimated Daily Use of ATP (g ATP/g Tissue)

Heart	16
Brain	6
Kidneys	24
Liver	6
Skeletal muscle (rest)	0.3
Skeletal muscle (running)	23.6

The heart, which contracts rhythmically, is using this ATP for mechanical work. In contrast, skeletal muscles in a resting individual use far less ATP per gram of tissue. The kidney has an ATP consumption per gram of tissue similar to that of the heart and uses this ATP largely for transport work to recover usable nutrients and to maintain pH and electrolyte balance. The brain, likewise, uses most of its ATP for transport work, maintaining the ion gradients necessary for conduction of nerve impulses. The liver, in contrast, has a high rate of ATP consumption and utilization to carry out metabolic work (biosynthesis and detoxification). **Otto Shape** realizes that his resting daily energy requirement will remain constant, and for him to lose weight, he will have to eat less, exercise more, or both.

1. THE DIFFERENCE BETWEEN ΔG AND $\Delta G^{0'}$

The driving force toward equilibrium starting at any concentration of substrate and product is expressed by ΔG, and not by $\Delta G^{0'}$, which is the free-energy change to reach equilibrium starting with 1 M concentration of substrate and product. For a reaction in which the substrate S is converted to the product P,

Equation 19.2:
$$\Delta G = \Delta G^{0'} + RT \ln[P]/[S]$$

(see Table 19.2, for the general form of this equation).

The expression for ΔG has two terms: $\Delta G^{0'}$, the energy change to reach equilibrium starting at equal and 1 M concentrations of substrates and products; and the second term, the energy change to reach equal concentrations of substrate and product starting from any initial concentration. (When $[P] = [S]$ and $[P] / [S] = 1$, $\ln [P] / [S] = 0$, and $\Delta G = \Delta G^{0'}$.) The second term will be negative for all concentrations of substrate greater than the product, and the greater the substrate concentration, the more negative this term will be. Thus, if the substrate concentration is suddenly raised high enough or the product concentration is decreased low enough, ΔG (the sum of the first and second terms) will also be negative, and conversion of substrate to product becomes thermodynamically favorable.

2. THE REVERSIBILITY OF THE PHOSPHOGLUCOMUTASE REACTION IN THE CELL

The effect of substrate and product concentration on ΔG and the direction of a reaction in the cell can be illustrated with conversion of glucose 6-P to glucose 1-P, the reaction catalyzed by phosphoglucomutase in the pathway of glycogen synthesis (see Fig. 19.3). The reaction has a small positive $\Delta G^{0'}$ for glucose 1-P synthesis (+1.65. kcal/mol), and at equilibrium, the ratio [glucose 1-P] / [glucose 6-P] is approximately 6/94 (which was determined in Question 2). However, if another reaction uses glucose 1-P such that this ratio suddenly becomes 3/94, there is now a driving force for converting more glucose 6-P to glucose 1-P and restoring the equilibrium ratio. Substitution in Equation 19.2 gives ΔG, the driving force to equilibrium, as $+1.65 + RT$ ln[glucose 1-P] / [glucose 6-P] $= 1.65 + (-2.06) = -0.41$, which is a negative value. Thus, a decrease in the ratio of product to substrate has converted the synthesis of glucose 1-P from a thermodynamically unfavorable to a thermodynamically favorable reaction that will proceed in the forward direction until equilibrium is reached.

C. Activated Intermediates with High-Energy Bonds

Many biochemical pathways form activated intermediates containing high-energy bonds to facilitate biochemical work. The term *high-energy bond* is a biologic term defined by the $\Delta G^{0'}$ for ATP hydrolysis; any bond that can be hydrolyzed with the release of approximately as much—or more—energy than ATP is called a high-energy bond. The high-energy bonds in activated intermediates, such as UDP-glucose in glycogen synthesis, facilitate energy transfer.

1. ATP, UTP, GTP, AND CTP

Cells use guanosine triphosphate (GTP) and cytidine triphosphate (CTP), as well as UTP and ATP, to form activated intermediates. Different anabolic pathways generally use different nucleotides as their direct source of high phosphate-bond energy: UTP is used for combining sugars, CTP for lipid synthesis, and GTP for protein synthesis.

The high-energy phosphate bonds of UTP, GTP, and CTP are energetically equivalent to ATP and are synthesized from ATP by nucleoside diphosphokinases and nucleoside monophosphokinases. For example, UTP is formed from UDP by a nucleoside diphosphokinase in the reaction

$$ATP + UDP \leftrightarrow UTP + ADP$$

ADP is converted back to ATP by the process of oxidative phosphorylation, using energy supplied by fuel oxidation.

Energy-requiring reactions often generate the nucleoside diphosphate ADP. *Adenylate kinase*, an important enzyme in cellular energy balance, is a nucleoside monophosphate kinase that transfers a phosphate from one ADP to another ADP to form ATP and adenosine monophosphate (AMP):

$$ADP + ADP \leftrightarrow AMP + ATP$$

This enzyme can thus regenerate ATP under conditions in which ATP use is required.

2. OTHER COMPOUNDS WITH HIGH-ENERGY BONDS

In addition to the nucleoside triphosphates, other compounds containing high-energy bonds are formed to facilitate energy transfer in anabolic and catabolic pathways (e.g., 1,3-bisphosphoglycerate in glycolysis and acetyl coenzyme A in the tricarboxylic acid cycle) (Fig. 19.7). Creatine phosphate contains a high-energy phosphate bond that allows it to serve as an energy reservoir for ATP synthesis and transport in muscle cells, neurons, and spermatozoa. All of these high-energy bonds are "unstable," and their hydrolysis yields substantial free energy because the products are much more stable, because of electron resonance within their structures.

IV. THERMOGENESIS

According to the first law of thermodynamics, energy cannot be destroyed. Thus, energy from oxidation of a fuel (its caloric content) must be equal to the amount of heat released, the work performed against the environment, and the increase in order of molecules in our bodies. Some of the energy from fuel oxidation is converted into heat as the fuel is oxidized and some heat is generated as ATP is used to do work. If we become less efficient in converting energy from fuel oxidation into ATP, or if we use an additional amount of ATP for muscular contraction, we will oxidize an additional amount of fuel to maintain ATP homeostasis (constant cellular ATP levels). With the oxidation of additional fuel, we release additional heat. Thus, heat production is a natural consequence of "burning fuel."

The term *thermogenesis* refers to energy expended for the purpose of generating heat in addition to that expended for ATP production. To maintain the body at 37°C despite changes in environmental temperature, it is necessary to regulate fuel oxidation and its efficiency (as well as heat dissipation). In shivering thermogenesis, we respond to sudden cold with asynchronous muscle contractions (shivers) that increase ATP utilization and, therefore, fuel oxidation and the release of energy as heat. In nonshivering thermogenesis (adaptive thermogenesis), the efficiency of converting energy from fuel oxidation into ATP is decreased. More fuel needs to be oxidized to maintain constant ATP levels and, thus, more heat is generated.

V. ENERGY FROM FUEL OXIDATION

Fuel oxidation provides energy for bodily processes principally through generation of the reduced coenzymes NADH and FAD(2H). They are used principally to generate ATP in oxidative phosphorylation. However, fuel oxidation also generates NADPH, which is most often used directly in energy-requiring processes. Carbohydrates also may be used to generate ATP through a nonoxidative pathway, called *anaerobic glycolysis.*

A. Energy Transfer from Fuels through Oxidative Phosphorylation

Fuel oxidation is our major source of ATP and our major means of transferring energy from the chemical bonds of the fuels to cellular energy-requiring

$\Delta G^{0'}$ for the overall reaction is the sum of the individual reactions, or -2.35 kcal. The individual reactions are

Glucose + ATP → glucose 6-P + ADP
$$\Delta G^{0'} = -4.0 \text{ kcal/mol}$$
Glucose 6-P → glucose 1-P
$$\Delta G^{0'} = +1.65 \text{ kcal/mol}$$

Therefore,

Glucose + ATP → glucose 1-P + ADP $\Delta G^{0'}$
$$= -2.35 \text{ kcal/mol}$$

Thus, the cleavage of ATP has made the synthesis of glucose 1-P from glucose energetically favorable.

FIG. 19.7. Some compounds with high-energy bonds. 1,3-bisphosphoglycerate and phosphoenolpyruvate are intermediates of glycolysis. Creatine phosphate is a high-energy phosphate reservoir and shuttle in brain, muscle, and spermatozoa. Acetyl coenzyme A (acetyl-CoA) is a precursor of the TCA cycle. The high-energy bonds are shown in *red*.

X. S. Teefore has increased thyroid hormone levels that increase his rate of ATP utilization and fuel oxidation. An excess of thyroid hormones may also affect the efficiency of ATP production, resulting in fewer ATP produced for a given level of O_2 consumption. The increased rate of ATP utilization and diminished efficiency stimulate oxidative metabolism, resulting in a much greater rate of heat production. The hyperthyroid patient, therefore, complains of constantly feeling hot (heat intolerance) and sweaty. (Perspiration allows dissipation of excess heat through evaporation from the skin surface.)

FIG. 19.8. Overview of energy transformations in oxidative phosphorylation. The electrochemical potential gradient across the mitochondrial membrane (Δp) is represented by two components: the ΔpH, the proton gradient; and $\Delta\psi$, the membrane potential. The role of the electrochemical potential in oxidative phosphorylation is discussed in more depth in Chapter 21.

processes. The amount of energy available from a fuel is equivalent to the amount of heat that is generated when a fuel is burned. To conserve this energy for the generation of ATP, the process of cellular respiration transforms the energy from the chemical bonds of fuels into the reduction state of electron-accepting coenzymes: NAD^+ and FAD (circle 1, Fig. 19.8). As these compounds transfer electrons to O_2 in the electron-transport chain, most of this energy is transformed into an electrochemical gradient across the inner mitochondrial membrane (circle 2, Fig. 19.8). Much of the energy in the electrochemical gradient is used to regenerate ATP from ADP in oxidative phosphorylation (phosphorylation that requires O_2).

1. OXIDATION–REDUCTION REACTIONS

Oxidation–reduction reactions always involve a pair of chemicals: an electron donor, which is oxidized in the reactions; and an electron acceptor, which is reduced in the reaction. In fuel metabolism, the fuel donates electrons and is oxidized, and NAD^+ and FAD accept electrons and are reduced.

To remember this, think of the acronym LEO GER: *L*oss of *E*lectrons = *O*xidation; *G*ain of *E*lectrons = *R*eduction. Compounds are oxidized in the body in essentially three ways: (1) the transfer of electrons from the compound as a hydrogen atom or a hydride ion, (2) the direct addition of oxygen from O_2, and (3) the direct donation of electrons (e.g., $Fe^{2+} \rightarrow Fe^{3+}$) (see Chapter 5). Fuel oxidation involves the transfer of electrons as a hydrogen atom or a hydride ion and, thus, reduced compounds have more hydrogen relative to oxygen than the oxidized compounds. Consequently, aldehydes are more reduced than acids, and alcohols are more reduced than aldehydes.

When is NAD^+, rather than FAD, used in a particular oxidation–reduction reaction? It depends on the chemical properties of the electron donor and the enzyme that catalyzes the reaction. In oxidation reactions, NAD^+ accepts two electrons as a hydride ion to form NADH, and a proton (H^+) is released into the medium (Fig. 19.9). It is generally used for metabolic reactions involving oxidation of alcohols and aldehydes. In contrast, FAD accepts two electrons as hydrogen atoms, which are donated singly from separate atoms (e.g., formation of a double bond or a disulfide) (Fig. 19.10).

FIG. 19.9. Reduction of NAD⁺ and NADP⁺. These structurally related coenzymes are reduced by accepting two electrons as H⁻, the hydride ion.

As the reduced coenzymes donate these electrons to O_2 through the electron-transport chain, they are reoxidized. The energy derived from reoxidation of NADH and FAD(2H) is available for the generation of ATP by oxidative phosphorylation. In our analogy of ATP as a currency, the reduced coenzymes are our "paychecks" for oxidizing fuels. Because our cells spend ATP so fast, we must immediately convert our paychecks into ATP cash.

FIG. 19.10. Reduction of FAD. FAD accepts two electrons as two hydrogen atoms and is reduced. The reduced coenzyme is denoted in this text as FAD(2H) because it often accepts a total of two electrons one at a time, never going to the fully reduced form—FADH₂. Flavin mononucleotide (FMN) consists of riboflavin with one phosphate group attached.

Otto Shape decided to lose weight by decreasing his intake of fat and alcohol (ethanol) and increasing his intake of carbohydrates. Compare the structure of ethanol with that of glucose and fatty acids. Based on their oxidation states, which compound provides the most energy (calories) per gram?

$$HOH_2C-(HC-OH)_4-\overset{\overset{\displaystyle O}{\|}}{C}-H$$

Glucose

$$CH_3CH_2OH$$

Ethanol

$$CH_3-(CH_2)_{16}-\overset{\overset{\displaystyle O}{\|}}{C}-OH$$

A fatty acid

2. REDUCTION POTENTIAL

Each oxidation–reduction reaction makes or takes a fixed amount of energy, ($\Delta G^{0'}$), which is directly proportional to the $\Delta E^{0'}$ (the difference in reduction potentials of the oxidation–reduction pair). The reduction potential of a compound, $E^{0'}$, is a measure in volts of the energy change when that compound accepts electrons (becomes reduced); $-\Delta E^{0'}$ is the energy change when the compound donates electrons (becomes oxidized). $E^{0'}$ can be considered an expression of the willingness of the compound to accept electrons. Some examples of reduction potentials are shown in Table 19.4. Oxygen, which is the best electron acceptor, has the largest positive reduction potential (i.e., is the most willing to accept electrons and be reduced). As a consequence, the transfer of electrons from all compounds to O_2 is energetically favorable and occurs with energy release.

The more negative the reduction potential of a compound, the greater is the energy available for ATP generation when that compound passes its electrons to oxygen. The $\Delta G^{0'}$ for transfer of electrons from NADH to O_2 is greater than the transfer from FAD(2H) to O_2 (see the reduction potential values for NADH and FAD[2H] in Table 19.4). Thus, the energy available for ATP synthesis from NADH is approximately -53 kcal, and approximately -41 kcal from the FAD-containing flavoproteins in the electron-transport chain.

To calculate the free-energy change of an oxidation–reduction reaction, the reduction potential of the electron donor (NADH) is added to that of the acceptor (O_2). The $\Delta E^{0'}$ for the net reaction is calculated from the sum of the half-reactions. For NADH donation of electrons, it is $+0.320$ V, opposite of that shown in Table 19.4 (remember, Table 19.4 shows the $E^{0'}$ for accepting electrons), and for O_2 acceptance it is $+0.816$ V. The number of electrons being transferred is 2 (so, $n = 2$). The direct relationship between the energy changes in oxidation–reduction reactions and $\Delta G^{0'}$ is expressed by the Nernst equation

Equation 19.3:
$$\Delta G^{0'} = -n\,F\,\Delta E^{0'}$$

where n is the number of electrons transferred and F is Faraday's constant (23 kcal/mol-V). Thus, a value of approximately -53 kcal/mol is obtained for the energy available for ATP synthesis by transferring two electrons from NADH to oxygen. The $\Delta E^{0'}$ for FAD(2H) to donate electrons to O_2 is 1.016 V compared to a $\Delta E^{0'}$ of 1.136 V for electron transfer from NADH to O_2.

3. CALORIC VALUES OF FUELS

The caloric value of a food is related directly to its oxidation state, which is a measure of $\Delta G^{0'}$ for transfer of electrons from that fuel to O_2. The electrons donated by the fuel are from its C–H and C–C bonds. Fatty acids such as palmitate [$CH_3(CH_2)_{14}COOH$] have a caloric value of roughly 9 kcal/g. Glucose is already

Table 19.4 Reduction Potentials of Some Oxidation–Reduction Half-Reactions

Reduction Half-Reactions	*E^0 at pH 7.0*
$\frac{1}{2}O_2 + 2H^+ + 2e^- \rightarrow H_2O$	0.816
Cytochrome a-Fe^{3+} + $1e^- \rightarrow$ cytochrome a-Fe^{2+}	0.290
$CoQ + 2H^+ + 2e^- \rightarrow CoQ\text{-}H_2$	0.060
Fumarate + $2H^+ + 2e^- \rightarrow$ succinate	0.030
Oxalacetate + $2H^+ + 2e^- \rightarrow$ malate	-0.102
Acetaldehyde + $2H^+ + 2e^- \rightarrow$ ethanol	-0.163
Pyruvate + $2H^+ + 2e^- \rightarrow$ lactate	-0.190
Riboflavin + $2H^+ + 2e^- \rightarrow$ riboflavin-H_2	-0.200
FAD + $2H^+ + 2e^- \rightarrow$ FAD(2H)	-0.219^a
$NAD^+ + 2H^+ + 2e^- \rightarrow$ NADH + H^+	-0.320
Acetate + $2H^+ + 2e^- \rightarrow$ acetaldehyde	-0.468

^{a}This is the value for free FAD; when FAD is bound to a protein, its value can be altered in either direction.

partially oxidized and has a caloric value of only about 4 kcal/g. The carbons, on average, contain fewer C–H bonds from which to donate electrons.

The caloric value of a food is applicable in humans only if our cells have enzymes that can oxidize that fuel by transferring electrons from the fuel to NAD⁺, NADP⁺, or FAD. When we burn wood in a fireplace, electrons are transferred from cellulose and other carbohydrates to O₂, releasing energy as heat. However, wood has no caloric content for humans; we cannot digest it and convert cellulose to a form that can be oxidized by our enzymes. Cholesterol, although it is a lipid, also has no caloric value for us because we cannot oxidize the carbons in its complex ring structure in reactions that generate NADH, FAD(2H), or NADPH.

B. NADPH in Oxidation–Reduction Reactions

NADP⁺ is similar to NAD⁺ and has the same reduction potential. However, NADP⁺ has an extra phosphate group on the ribose, which affects its enzyme binding (see Fig. 19.9). Consequently, most enzymes use either NAD⁺ or NADP⁺, but seldom both. In certain reactions, fuels are oxidized by transfer of electrons to NADP⁺ to form NADPH. For example, glucose 6-P dehydrogenase, in the pentose phosphate pathway, transfers electrons from glucose 6-P to NADP⁺ instead of NAD⁺. NADPH usually donates electrons to biosynthetic reactions such as fatty acid synthesis, and to detoxification reactions that use oxygen directly. Consequently, the energy in its reduction potential is usually used in energy-requiring reactions without first being converted to ATP currency.

C. Anaerobic Glycolysis

Not all ATP is generated by fuel oxidation. In anaerobic glycolysis, glucose is degraded in reactions that form high-energy phosphorylated intermediates of the pathway (Fig. 19.11). These activated high-energy intermediates provide the energy for the generation of ATP from ADP without involving electron transfer to O₂. Therefore, this pathway is called anaerobic glycolysis, and ATP is generated from substrate-level phosphorylation rather than from oxidative phosphorylation (see Chapter 22). Anaerobic glycolysis is a critical source of ATP for cells that have a decreased O₂ supply, either because they are physiologically designed that way (e.g., cells in the kidney medulla, rapidly working muscle), or because their supply of O₂ has been pathologically decreased (e.g., coronary artery disease).

VI. OXYGENASES AND OXIDASES NOT INVOLVED IN ATP GENERATION

Approximately 90% to 95% of the oxygen we consume is used by the terminal oxidase in the electron-transport chain for ATP generation via oxidative phosphorylation. The remainder of the O₂ is used directly by oxygenases and other oxidases, enzymes that oxidize a compound in the body by transferring electrons directly to O₂ (Fig. 19.12). The large positive reduction potential of O₂ makes all of these reactions extremely favorable thermodynamically, but the electronic structure of O₂ slows the speed of electron transfer. These enzymes, therefore, contain a metal ion that facilitates reduction of O₂.

A. Oxidases

Oxidases transfer electrons from the substrate to O₂, which is reduced to water (H₂O) or to hydrogen peroxide (H₂O₂). The terminal protein complex in the electron-transport chain, called *cytochrome oxidase*, is an oxidase because it accepts electrons donated to the chain by NADH and FAD(2H) and uses these to reduce O₂ to H₂O. Most of the other oxidases in the cell form H₂O₂ instead of H₂O and are called *peroxidases*. Peroxidases are generally confined to peroxisomes to protect DNA and other cellular components from toxic free radicals (compounds containing single electrons in an outer orbital) generated by hydrogen peroxide.

A: In palmitate and other fatty acids, most carbons are more reduced than those in glucose or ethanol (more of the carbons have electrons in C–H bonds). Therefore, fatty acids have the greatest caloric content per gram, 9 kcal. In glucose, the carbons have already formed bonds with oxygen, and fewer electrons in C–H bonds are available to generate energy. Thus, the complete oxidation of glucose provides roughly 4 kcal/g. In ethanol, one carbon is a methyl group with C–H bonds, and one has an –OH group. Therefore, the oxidation state is intermediate between those of glucose and fatty acids, and ethanol thus has 7 kcal/g.

FIG. 19.11. Anaerobic glycolysis. Phosphate is transferred from high-energy intermediates of the pathway to ADP. Because NADH from the pathway is reoxidized by reduction of pyruvate to lactate, no oxygen is required.

Oxidases

$$O_2 + 4e^-, 4H^+ \longrightarrow 2H_2O$$

$$O_2 + SH_2 \longrightarrow S + H_2O_2$$

Mono-oxygenases

$$O_2 + S + \text{Electron} \longrightarrow$$
$$\text{donor–}XH_2$$

$$H_2O + \text{Electron} + S–OH$$
$$\text{donor–}X$$

Dioxygenases

$$S + O_2 \longrightarrow SO_2$$

FIG. 19.12. Oxidases and oxygenases. The fate of O₂ is shown in *red*. *S* represents an organic substrate.

FIG. 19.13. Cytochrome P450 monooxygenases. Electrons are donated by NADPH to O_2 and the substrate. The flavin coenzymes FAD and FMN in one protein subunit participate in the transfer of single electrons to cytochrome P450, which is an Fe-heme–containing protein that absorbs light at a wavelength of 450 nm. The iron in the heme group aids in facilitating electron transfer to oxygen. The enzyme is embedded in a membrane, usually the endoplasmic reticulum.

B. Oxygenases

Oxygenases, in contrast to oxidases, incorporate one or both of the atoms of oxygen into the organic substrate (see Fig. 19.12). *Monooxygenases*, enzymes that incorporate one atom of oxygen into the substrate and the other into H_2O, are often named *hydroxylases* (e.g., phenylalanine hydroxylase, which adds a hydroxyl group to phenylalanine to form tyrosine) or mixed-function oxidases. Monooxygenases require an electron-donor substrate such as NADPH, a coenzyme such as FAD, which can transfer single electrons, and a metal or similar compound that can form a reactive oxygen complex (Fig. 19.13). They are usually found in the endoplasmic reticulum and occasionally in mitochondria. Dioxygenases, enzymes that incorporate both atoms of oxygen into the substrate, are used in the pathways for converting arachidonate into prostaglandins, thromboxanes, and leukotrienes.

VII. ENERGY BALANCE

Our total energy expenditure is equivalent to our oxygen consumption (Fig. 19.14). The resting metabolic rate (energy expenditure of a person at rest, at 25°C, after an overnight fast) accounts for approximately 60% to 70% of our total energy expenditure and O_2 consumption, and physical exercise accounts for the remainder. Of the resting metabolic rate, approximately 90% to 95% of O_2 consumption is used by the mitochondrial electron-transport chain, and only 5% to 10% is required for nonmitochondrial oxidases and oxygenases and is not related to ATP synthesis. Approximately 20% to 30% of the energy from this mitochondrial O_2 consumption is lost by proton leak back across the mitochondrial membrane, which dissipates the electrochemical gradient without ATP synthesis. The remainder of our O_2 consumption is used for ATPases that maintain ion gradients and for biosynthetic pathways.

ATP homeostasis refers to the ability of our cells to maintain constant levels of ATP despite fluctuations in the rate of use. Thus, increased use of ATP for exercise or biosynthetic reactions increases the rate of fuel oxidation. The major mechanism employed is feedback regulation; all of the pathways of fuel oxidation that lead to

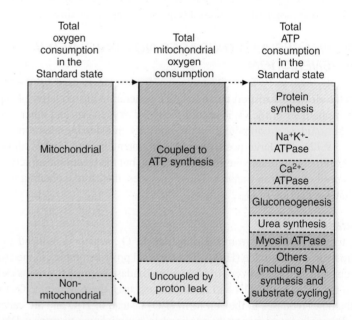

FIG. 19.14. Estimated contribution of processes to energy use in standard state. (Reproduced, with permission, from Rolfe DFS, Brown GC. Cellular energy utilization and molecular origin of standard metabolic rate in mammals. *Physiol Rev.* 1997;77:731–758.)

generation of ATP are feedback-regulated by ATP levels, or by compounds related to the concentration of ATP. In general, the less ATP used, the less fuel will be oxidized to generate ATP.

According to the first law of thermodynamics, the energy (in calories) in our consumed fuel can never be lost. Consumed fuel is either oxidized to meet the energy demands of the BMR + exercise, or it is stored as fat. Thus, an intake of calories in excess of those expended results in weight gain. The simple statement, "If you eat too much and don't exercise, you will get fat," is really a summary of the bioenergetics of the ATP–ADP cycle.

CLINICAL COMMENTS

Otto Shape. Otto Shape visited his physician, who noted his increased weight. The physician recommended several diet modifications to Otto that would decrease the caloric content of his diet, and he pointed out the importance of exercise for weight reduction. He reminded Otto that the American Heart Association and the American Cancer Society recommended 45 to 60 minutes of moderate to vigorous exercise 5 to 7 days per week. He also reminded Otto that he would want to be a role model for his patients. Otto decided to begin an exercise regimen that included an hour of running each day.

X. S. Teefore. Mr. Teefore exhibited the classical signs and symptoms of hyperthyroidism (increased secretion of the thyroid hormones T_3 and T_4; see Fig. 11.8 for the structure of T_3), including a goiter (enlarged thyroid gland). T_3 is the more active form of the hormone. T_4 is synthesized and secreted in approximately 10 times greater amounts than T_3. Liver and other cells contain an enzyme (a deiodinase) that removes one of the iodines from T_4, converting it to T_3. Thyroid function tests confirmed this diagnosis.

Thyroid hormones (principally T_3) modulate cellular energy production and utilization through their ability to increase the gene transcription (see Fig. 16.13) of many proteins involved in intermediary metabolism, including enzymes in the tricarboxylic acid (TCA) cycle and oxidative phosphorylation. They increase the rate of adenosine triphosphate (ATP) use by the Na^+,K^+-ATPase and other enzymes. They also affect the efficiency of energy transformations, so that either more fuel must be oxidized to maintain a given level of ATP or more ATP must be expended to achieve the desired physiologic response. The loss of weight experienced by **X. S. Teefore**, in spite of a very good appetite, reflects his increased caloric requirements and less efficient use of fuels. The result is enhanced oxidation of adipose tissue stores as well as a catabolic effect on muscle and other protein-containing tissues. Through mechanisms that are not well understood, increased levels of thyroid hormone in the blood also increase the activity or "tone" of the sympathetic (adrenergic) nervous system. An activated sympathetic nervous system leads to a more rapid and forceful heartbeat (tachycardia and palpitations), increased nervousness (anxiety and insomnia), tremulousness (a sense of shakiness or jitteriness), and other symptoms.

Cora Nari. Cora Nari was in left ventricular heart failure (LVF) when she presented to the hospital with her second heart attack in 8 months. The symptoms consistent with LVF were her rapid heart rate (104 beats/minute) and respiratory rate. On examining her lungs, her physician heard respiratory rales, caused by inspired air bubbling in fluid that had filled her lung air spaces secondary to LVF. This condition is referred to as *congestive heart failure*.

Congestive heart failure occurs when the weakened pumping action of the ischemic left ventricular heart muscle leads to a reduced blood flow from the heart to the rest of the body. This leads to an increase in blood volume in the vessels that bring oxygenated blood from the lungs to the left side of the heart. The pressure inside these pulmonary vessels eventually reaches a critical level, greater than which water from the blood moves down a "pressure gradient" from the capillary lumen into alveolar air spaces of the lung (transudation). The patient experiences shortness of breath as the fluid in the air spaces interferes with oxygen exchange from the inspired air into arterial blood, causing hypoxia. The hypoxia then stimulates the respiratory center in the central nervous system, leading to a more rapid respiratory rate in an effort to increase the oxygen content of the blood. As the patient inhales deeply, the physician hears gurgling/crackling sounds (known as *inspiratory rales*) with a stethoscope placed over the posterior lung bases. These sounds represent the bubbling of inspired air as it enters the fluid-filled pulmonary alveolar air spaces.

Cora's rapid heart rate (tachycardia) resulted from a reduced capacity of her ischemic, failing left ventricular muscle to eject a normal amount of blood into the arteries leading away from the heart with each contraction. The resultant drop in intra-arterial pressure signaled a reflex response in the central nervous system that, in turn, caused an increase in heart rate in an attempt to bring the total amount of blood leaving the left ventricle each minute (the cardiac output) back toward a more appropriate level to maintain systemic blood pressure.

Initial treatment of Cora's congestive heart failure will include efforts to reduce the workload of the heart with diuretics and other "load reducers," attempts to improve the force of left ventricular contraction with digitalis, and the administration of oxygen by nasal cannula to increase the oxygen levels to the viable heart tissue in the vicinity of the infarction.

BIOCHEMICAL COMMENTS

Active Transport and Cell Death. Most of us cannot remember when we first learned that we would die if we stopped breathing. However, exactly how cells die from a lack of oxygen is an intriguing question. Hypoxia leads to both physical and transcriptional changes. Pathologists generally describe two histologically distinct types of cell death: necrosis and apoptosis (programmed cell death). Cell death from a lack of O_2, such as that occurs during a myocardial infarction, can be very rapid, and is considered necrosis. The lack of adenosine triphosphate (ATP) for the active transport of Na^+ and Ca^{2+} triggers some of the death cascades that lead to necrosis (Fig. 19.15).

The influx of Na^+ and loss of the Na^+ gradient across the plasma membrane is an early event accompanying ATP depletion during interruption of the O_2 supply. One consequence of the increased intracellular Na^+ concentration is that other transport processes driven by the Na^+ gradient are impaired. For example, the Na^+/H^+ exchanger, which normally pumps out H^+ generated from metabolism in exchange for extracellular Na^+, can no longer function, and intracellular pH may drop. The increased intracellular H^+ may impair ATP generation from anaerobic glycolysis. As a consequence of increased intracellular ion concentrations, water enters the cells and hydropic swelling occurs. Swelling is accompanied by the release of creatine kinase MB subunits, troponin I, and troponin C into the blood. These enzymes are measured in the blood as indicators of a myocardial infarction (see Chapters 6 and 7). Swelling is an early event and is considered a reversible stage of cell injury.

Normally, intracellular Ca^{2+} concentration is carefully regulated to fluctuate at low levels (intracellular Ca^{2+} concentration is $<10^7$ M, compared to approximately 10^3 M in extracellular fluid). Fluctuations of Ca^{2+} concentration at these low levels regulate myofibrillar contraction, energy metabolism, and other cellular processes. However, when Ca^{2+} concentration is increased greater than this normal range, it triggers cell death (necrosis). High Ca^{2+} concentrations activate a phospholipase that increases membrane permeability, resulting in further loss of ion gradients across the cell membrane. They also trigger opening of the mitochondrial permeability transition pore, which results in loss of mitochondrial function and further impairs oxidative phosphorylation.

Intracellular Ca^{2+} levels may increase because of cell swelling, the lack of ATP for ATP-dependent Ca^{2+} pumps, or the loss of the Na^+ gradient. Normally, Ca^{2+}-ATPases located in the plasma membrane pump Ca^{2+} out of the cell. Ca^{2+}-ATPases in the endoplasmic reticulum, and in the sarcoplasmic reticulum of heart and other muscles, sequester Ca^{2+} within the membranes, where it is

FIG. 19.15. Hypoxia, Ca^{2+}, Na^+, and cell death. Without an adequate O_2 supply, decreased ATP synthesis from oxidative phosphorylation results in an increase of cytoplasmic Na^+ and Ca^{2+} ions. Increased ion levels can trigger death cascades that involve increased permeability of the plasma membrane, loss of ion gradients, decreased cytosolic pH, mitochondrial Ca^{2+} overload, and a change in mitochondrial permeability called the *mitochondrial permeability transition*. The *solid lines* show the first sequence of events; the *dashed lines* show how these events feed back to accelerate the mitochondrial deterioration, making recovery of oxidative phosphorylation impossible.

bound by a low-affinity binding protein. Ca^{2+} is released from the sarcoplasmic reticulum in response to a nerve impulse, which signals contraction, and the increase of Ca^{2+} stimulates both muscle contraction and the oxidation of fuels. Within the heart, another Ca^{2+} transporter protein, the Na^+/Ca^{2+} exchange transporter, coordinates the efflux of Ca^{2+} in exchange for Na^+, so that Ca^{2+} is extruded with each contraction.

Hypoxia also induces the transcription of genes in an attempt to compensate for the hypoxic conditions. A family of transcription factors, known as *hypoxia-inducible factors* (HIFs), is activated under hypoxic conditions. These factors bind to hypoxia-responsive elements (promoter-proximal elements) in the regulatory region of target genes. More than 70 target genes are regulated by HIFs, including the gene for erythropoietin, which stimulates increased red blood cell production. Induction of these genes allows cells to adapt to and survive for some time under these hypoxic conditions.

Key Concepts

- Bioenergetics refers to cellular energy transformations.
- The high-energy phosphate bonds of ATP are a cell's primary source of energy.
- ATP is generated through cellular respiration—the oxidation of fuels to carbon dioxide and water.
- ATP can also be generated, at reduced levels, via anaerobic glycolysis (in the absence of O_2).
- The electrons captured from fuel oxidation generate NADH and FAD(2H), which are used to regenerate ATP via the process of oxidative phosphorylation.
- The energy available from ATP hydrolysis can be used for:
  - Mechanical work (muscle contraction)
  - Transport work (establishment of ion gradients across membranes)
  - Biochemical work (energy-requiring chemical reactions, including detoxification reactions)
- Energy released from fuel oxidation that is not used for work is transformed into and released as heat.
- The many pathways of fuel oxidation are coordinately regulated to maintain ATP homeostasis.
- $\Delta G^{0'}$ is the change in Gibbs free energy at pH 7.0 under standard conditions between the substrates and products of a reaction.
- Fuel oxidation has a negative $\Delta G^{0'}$; the products formed have less chemical energy than the reactants (an exergonic reaction pathway).
- ATP synthesis has a positive $\Delta G^{0'}$ and is endergonic; the reaction requires energy.
- Metabolic pathways have an overall negative $\Delta G^{0'}$, which is obtained by summing all of the $\Delta G^{0'}$ values for each reaction in the pathway.
- Oxidation–reduction reactions can be related to changes in free energy, the use of $E^{0'}$, the chemical's affinity for electrons. Compounds with higher $E^{0'}$ values have greater affinity for electrons than those with lower $E^{0'}$ values.
- Diseases discussed in this chapter are summarized in Table 19.5.

Table 19.5   Diseases Presented in this Chapter

Disease or Disorder	Environmental or Genetic	Comments
Obesity	Both	Understanding daily caloric needs can enable one to gain or lose weight through alterations in exercise and eating habits.
Hyperthyroidism	Environmental	Thyroid hormone is important in regulating energy metabolism; excessive T_3 and T_4 release enhance metabolism, leading to weight loss and a greater rate of heat production.
Heart attack	Both	The heart requires a constant level of energy, derived primarily from lactate, glucose, and fatty acids. This is necessary so that the rate of contraction can remain constant, or increase during appropriate periods. Interference of oxygen flow to certain areas of the heart will reduce energy generation, leading to a myocardial infarction.

1. The highest energy phosphate bond in ATP is located between which of the following groups:

    A. Adenosine and phosphate
    B. Ribose and phosphate
    C. Ribose and adenine
    D. Two hydroxyl groups in the ribose ring
    E. Two phosphate groups

2. Which of the following bioenergetic terms or phrases is defined correctly?

    A. The first law of thermodynamics states that the universe tends toward a state of increased order.
    B. The second law of thermodynamics states that the total energy of a system remains constant.
    C. The change in enthalpy of a reaction is a measure of the total amount of heat that can be released from changes in the chemical bonds.
    D. $\Delta G^{0'}$ of a reaction is the standard free-energy change measured at 37°C and a pH of 7.4.
    E. A high-energy bond is a bond that releases more than 3 kcal/mol of heat when it is hydrolyzed.

3. Which statement best describes the direction a chemical reaction will follow?

    A. A reaction with positive free energy will proceed in a forward direction if the substrate concentration is raised high enough.
    B. Under standard conditions, a reaction will proceed in a forward direction if the free energy $\Delta G^{0'}$ is positive.

    C. The direction of a reaction is independent of the initial substrate and product concentrations, because the direction is determined by the change in free energy.
    D. The concentration of all of the substrates must be higher than that of all of the products for the reaction to proceed in a forward direction.
    E. The enzyme for the reaction must be working at >50% of its maximum efficiency for the reaction to proceed in a forward direction.

4. A patient, Mr. Perkins, has just suffered a heart attack. As a consequence, his heart will display which of the following changes?

    A. Increased intracellular O_2 concentration
    B. Increased intracellular ATP concentration
    C. Increased intracellular H^+ concentration
    D. Decreased intracellular Ca^{2+} concentration
    E. Decreased intracellular Na^+ concentration

5. Which of the following statements correctly describes reduction of one of the electron carriers, NAD^+ or FAD?

    A. NAD^+ accepts two electrons as hydrogen atoms to form NAD(2H).
    B. NAD^+ accepts two electrons that are each donated from a separate atom of the substrate.
    C. NAD^+ accepts two electrons as a hydride ion to form NADH.
    D. FAD releases a proton as it accepts two electrons.
    E. FAD must accept two electrons at a time.

The **tricarboxylic acid cycle** (**TCA cycle**) accounts for more than two-thirds of the adenosine triphosphate (ATP) generated from fuel oxidation. The pathways for oxidation of fatty acids, glucose, amino acids, acetate, and ketone bodies all generate **acetyl coenzyme A** (**acetyl-CoA**), which is the substrate for the TCA cycle. As the activated two-carbon acetyl group is oxidized to two molecules of CO_2, energy is conserved as **NADH, FAD(2H)**, and guanosine triphosphate (**GTP**) (Fig. 20.1). NADH and FAD(2H) subsequently donate electrons to O_2 via the electron-transport chain, with the generation of ATP from oxidative phosphorylation. Thus, the TCA cycle is central to energy generation from **cellular respiration**.

Within the TCA cycle, the oxidative decarboxylation of α-ketoglutarate is catalyzed by the multisubunit α-**ketoglutarate dehydrogenase complex**, which contains the coenzymes **thiamine pyrophosphate (TTP)**, **lipoate**, and **flavin adenine dinucleotide (FAD)**. A similar complex, the **pyruvate dehydrogenase complex (PDC)**, catalyzes the oxidation of pyruvate to acetyl-CoA, thereby providing a link between the pathways of glycolysis and the TCA cycle (see Fig. 20.1).

The two-carbon acetyl group is the ultimate source of the electrons that are transferred to nicotinamide adenine dinucleotide (NAD^+) and FAD and also the carbon in the two CO_2 molecules that are produced. Oxaloacetate is used and regenerated in each turn of the cycle (see Fig. 20.1). However, when cells use intermediates of the TCA cycle for biosynthetic reactions, the carbons of oxaloacetate must be replaced by **anaplerotic** (filling-up) reactions, such as the **pyruvate carboxylase reaction**.

The TCA cycle occurs in the mitochondrion, where its flux is tightly coordinated with the rate of the electron-transport chain and oxidative phosphorylation through **feedback regulation that reflects the demand for ATP**. The rate of the TCA cycle is increased when ATP utilization in the cell is increased through the response of several enzymes to adenosine diphosphate (**ADP**) **levels, the NADH/NAD^+ ratio**, the rate of FAD(2H) oxidation, or the Ca^{2+} **concentration**. For example, **isocitrate dehydrogenase is allosterically activated by ADP**.

There are two general consequences to impaired functioning of the TCA cycle: (1) an inability to generate ATP from fuel oxidation and (2) an accumulation of TCA cycle precursors. For example, inhibition of pyruvate oxidation in the TCA cycle results in its reduction to lactate, which can cause **lactic acidosis**. The most common situation leading to an impaired function of the TCA cycle is a relative lack of oxygen to accept electrons in the electron-transport chain.

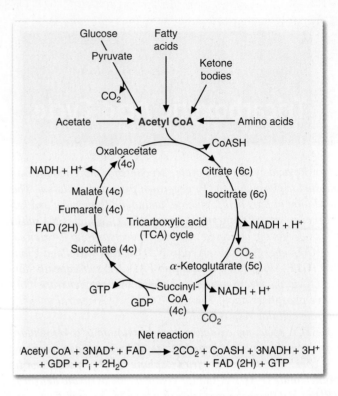

Net reaction
$$Acetyl\ CoA + 3NAD^+ + FAD \longrightarrow 2CO_2 + CoASH + 3NADH + 3H^+$$
$$+\ GDP + P_i + 2H_2O \qquad\qquad + FAD\ (2H) + GTP$$

FIG. 20.1. Summary of the tricarboxylic acid (TCA) cycle. The number of carbons in each intermediate of the cycle is indicated in *parentheses* by the name of the compound.

THE WAITING ROOM

 Confirmation of a suspected thiamine deficiency requires measuring thiamine levels. A standard assay for determining if thiamine levels are sufficient for metabolic processes is to use the enzyme transketolase, which requires thiamine pyrophosphate (TPP) for activity (see Chapter 29). Transketolase can be obtained from red blood cells, making sample collection relatively straightforward. The measurement of transketolase activity is done in the absence and presence of exogenous TPP. If the difference in activity levels is >25%, then a thiamine deficiency is confirmed. Other more time-consuming assays for thiamine include high-performance liquid chromatography (HPLC) analysis to quantify the levels of both free thiamine and the active form, TPP, in biologic fluids, and microbiologic assays that measure bacterial cell growth in the presence of a sample that contains thiamine. Because the bacteria require thiamine for growth, samples with more thiamine will stimulate more cell growth than samples that contain lesser levels of the vitamin.

Otto Shape, a 26-year-old medical student, has faithfully followed his diet and aerobic exercise program of daily tennis and jogging (see Chapter 19). He has lost a total of 33 lb and is just 23 lb from his college weight of 154 lb. His exercise capacity has markedly improved; he can run for a longer time at a faster pace before noting shortness of breath or palpitations of his heart. Even his test scores in his medical school classes have improved.

Ann O'Rexia suffers from anorexia nervosa (see Chapters 1, 3, and 9). In addition to a low body weight, decreased muscle mass, glycogen, and fat stores, she has iron deficiency anemia (see Chapter 16). She has started to gain weight and is trying a daily exercise program. However, she constantly feels weak and tired. When she walks, she feels pain in her calf muscles. On this visit to her nutritionist, they discuss the vitamin content of her diet and its role in energy metabolism.

Al Martini has been hospitalized for congestive heart failure (see Chapter 8) and for head injuries sustained while driving under the influence of alcohol (Chapters 9 and 10). He completed an alcohol detoxification program, enrolled in a local Alcoholics Anonymous (AA) group, and began seeing a psychologist. During this time, his alcohol-related neurologic and cardiac manifestations of thiamine deficiency partially cleared. However, in spite of the support he was receiving, he began drinking excessive amounts of alcohol again while eating poorly. Three weeks later, he was readmitted with symptoms of "high-output" heart failure.

I. OVERVIEW OF THE TRICARBOXYLIC ACID CYCLE

The tricarboxylic acid (TCA) cycle is frequently called the Krebs cycle because Sir Hans Krebs first formulated its reactions into a cycle. It is also called the *citric acid cycle* because citrate was one of the first compounds known to participate. The most common name for this pathway, the *tricarboxylic acid* or *TCA cycle*, denotes the involvement of the tricarboxylates citrate and isocitrate.

In order for the body to generate large amounts of adenosine triphosphate (ATP), the major pathways of fuel oxidation generate acetyl coenzyme A (acetyl-CoA), which is the substrate for the TCA cycle. In the first step of the TCA cycle, the acetyl portion of acetyl-CoA combines with the four-carbon intermediate oxaloacetate to form citrate (six carbons), which is rearranged to form isocitrate. In the next two oxidative decarboxylation reactions, electrons are transferred to nicotinamide adenine dinucleotide (NAD$^+$) to form NADH, and two molecules of electron-depleted CO_2 are released. Subsequently, a high-energy phosphate bond in guanosine triphosphate (GTP) is generated from substrate-level phosphorylation. In the remaining portion of the TCA cycle, succinate is oxidized to oxaloacetate with the generation of one FAD(2H) and one NADH. The *net* reaction of the TCA cycle, which is the sum of the equations for individual steps, shows that the two carbons of the acetyl group have been oxidized to two molecules of CO_2, with conservation of energy as three molecules of NADH, one of FAD(2H), and one of GTP.

The TCA cycle requires a large number of vitamins and minerals to function. These include niacin (NAD$^+$), riboflavin (flavin adenine dinucleotide [FAD] and flavin mononucleotide [FMN]), pantothenic acid (coenzyme A), thiamine, Mg^{2+}, Ca^{2+}, Fe^{2+}, and phosphate.

II. REACTIONS OF THE TRICARBOXYLIC ACID CYCLE

In the TCA cycle, the two-carbon acetyl group of acetyl-CoA is oxidized to two CO_2 molecules (see Fig. 20.1). The function of the cycle is to conserve the energy from this oxidation, which it accomplishes principally by transferring electrons from intermediates of the cycle to NAD$^+$ and FAD. The eight electrons donated by the acetyl group eventually end up in three molecules of NADH and one of FAD(2H) (Fig. 20.2). As a consequence, ATP can be generated from oxidative phosphorylation when NADH and FAD(2H) donate these electrons to O_2 via the electron-transport chain.

Initially, the acetyl group is incorporated into citrate, an intermediate of the TCA cycle (Fig. 20.3). As citrate progresses through the cycle to oxaloacetate, it is oxidized by four dehydrogenases (isocitrate dehydrogenase, α-ketoglutarate dehydrogenase, succinate dehydrogenase, and malate dehydrogenase), which remove electron-containing hydrogen or hydride atoms from a substrate and transfer them to electron-accepting coenzymes such as NAD$^+$ or FAD. The isomerase aconitase rearranges electrons in citrate, thereby forming isocitrate to facilitate an electron transfer to NAD$^+$. An iron cofactor in aconitase facilitates the isomerization.

Although no O_2 is introduced into the TCA cycle, the two molecules of CO_2 produced have more oxygen than the acetyl group. These oxygen atoms are ultimately derived from the carbonyl group of acetyl-CoA, two molecules of water added by fumarase and citrate synthase and the PO_4^{2-} added to guanosine diphosphate (GDP).

The overall yield of energy-containing compounds from the TCA cycle is three NADH, one FAD(2H), and one GTP. The high-energy phosphate bond of GTP is generated from substrate-level phosphorylation catalyzed by succinate thiokinase (succinyl-CoA synthetase). As the NADH and FAD(2H) are reoxidized in the electron-transport chain, approximately 2.5 ATP are generated for each NADH and 1.5 ATP for the FAD(2H). Consequently, the net energy yield from the TCA cycle and oxidative phosphorylation is about 10 high-energy phosphate bonds for each acetyl group oxidized.

FIG. 20.2. The acetyl group of acetyl-CoA. Acetyl-CoA donates eight electrons to the TCA cycle, which are shown in *red*, and two carbons. The high-energy bond is shown by a ~. The acetyl group is the ultimate source of the carbons in the two molecules of CO_2 that are produced and the source of electrons in the one molecule of FAD(2H) and three molecules of NADH, which have each accepted two electrons. However, the same carbon atoms and electrons that enter from one molecule of acetyl-CoA do not leave as CO_2, NADH, or FAD(2H) within the same turn of the cycle.

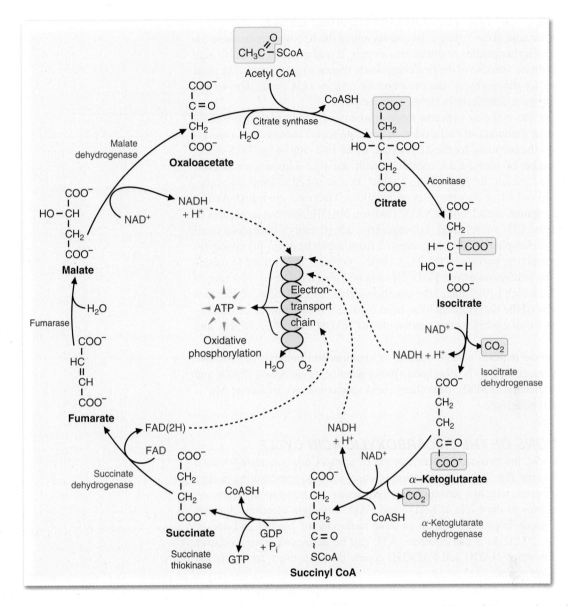

FIG. 20.3. Reactions of the TCA cycle. The oxidation–reduction enzymes and coenzymes are shown in *red*. Entry of the two carbons of acetyl-CoA into the TCA cycle are indicated with the *green box*. The carbons released as CO_2 are shown with *yellow boxes*.

Otto Shape's exercise program increases his rate of ATP utilization and his rate of fuel oxidation in the TCA cycle. The TCA cycle generates NADH and FAD(2H), and the electron-transport chain transfers electrons from NADH and FAD(2H) to O_2, thereby creating the electrochemical potential that drives ATP synthesis from ADP. As ATP is used in the cell, the rate of the electron-transport chain increases. The TCA cycle and other fuel oxidative pathways respond by increasing their rates of NADH and FAD(2H) production.

A. Formation and Oxidation of Isocitrate

The TCA cycle begins with condensation of the activated acetyl group and oxaloacetate to form the six-carbon intermediate citrate, a reaction that is catalyzed by the enzyme citrate synthase (see Fig. 20.3). Synthases, in general, catalyze the condensation of two organic molecules to form a carbon–carbon bond in the absence of high-energy phosphate bond energy. A synthetase catalyzes the same type of reaction, but requires high-energy phosphate bonds to complete the reaction. Because oxaloacetate is regenerated with each turn of the cycle, it is not really considered a substrate of the cycle or a source of electrons or carbon.

In the next step of the TCA cycle, the hydroxyl (alcohol) group of citrate is moved to an adjacent carbon so that it can be oxidized to form a keto group. The isomerization of citrate to isocitrate is catalyzed by the enzyme aconitase, which is named for an intermediate of the reaction. The enzyme isocitrate dehydrogenase catalyzes the oxidation of the alcohol group and the subsequent cleavage

of the carboxyl group to release CO_2 (an oxidation followed by a decarboxylation) forming α-ketoglutarate.

B. α-Ketoglutarate to Succinyl Coenzyme A

The next step of the TCA cycle is the oxidative decarboxylation of α-ketoglutarate to succinyl-CoA, catalyzed by the α-ketoglutarate dehydrogenase complex (see Fig. 20.3). The dehydrogenase complex contains the coenzymes thiamine pyrophosphate (TPP), lipoic acid, and FAD.

In this reaction, one of the carboxyl groups of α-ketoglutarate is released as CO_2, and the adjacent keto group is oxidized to the level of an acid, which then combines with CoASH to form succinyl-CoA (see Fig. 20.3). Energy from the reaction is conserved principally in the reduction state of NADH, with a smaller amount present in the high-energy thioester bond of succinyl-CoA.

C. Generation of Guanosine Triphosphate

Energy from the succinyl-CoA thioester bond is used to generate GTP from GDP and inorganic phosphate (P_i) in the reaction catalyzed by succinate thiokinase (also known as *succinyl-CoA synthetase*, for the reverse reaction) (see Fig. 20.3). This reaction is an example of substrate-level phosphorylation. By definition, *substrate-level phosphorylation* is the formation of a high-energy phosphate bond where none previously existed without the use of molecular O_2 (in other words, *not* oxidative phosphorylation). The high-energy phosphate bond of GTP is energetically equivalent to that of ATP and can be used directly for energy-requiring reactions such as protein synthesis.

D. Oxidation of Succinate to Oxaloacetate

Up to this stage of the TCA cycle, two carbons have been stripped of their available electrons and released as CO_2. Two pairs of these electrons have been transferred to two NAD^+, and one GTP has been generated. However, two additional pairs of electrons arising from acetyl-CoA still remain in the TCA cycle as part of succinate. The remaining steps of the TCA cycle transfer these two pairs of electrons to FAD and NAD^+ and add H_2O, thereby regenerating oxaloacetate.

The sequence of reactions that converts succinate to oxaloacetate begins with the oxidation of succinate to fumarate (see Fig. 20.3). Single electrons are transferred from the two adjacent $-CH_2-$ methylene groups of succinate to an FAD bound to succinate dehydrogenase, thereby forming the double bond of fumarate. From the reduced enzyme-bound FAD, the electrons are passed into the electron-transport chain. An $-OH^-$ group and a proton from water add to the double bond of fumarate, converting it to malate. In the last reaction of the TCA cycle, the alcohol group of malate is oxidized to a keto group through the donation of electrons to NAD^+.

With regeneration of oxaloacetate, the TCA cycle is complete; the chemical bond energy, carbon, and electrons donated by the acetyl group have been converted to CO_2, NADH, FAD(2H), GTP, and heat.

The succinate-to-oxaloacetate sequence of reactions—oxidation through formation of a double bond, addition of water to the double bond, and oxidation of the resultant alcohol to a ketone—is found in many oxidative pathways in the cell, such as the pathways for the oxidation of fatty acids and oxidation of the branched-chain amino acids.

III. COENZYMES OF THE TRICARBOXYLIC ACID CYCLE

The enzymes of the TCA cycle rely heavily on coenzymes for their catalytic function. Isocitrate dehydrogenase and malate dehydrogenase use NAD^+ as a coenzyme, and succinate dehydrogenase uses FAD. Citrate synthase catalyzes a reaction that uses a CoA derivative, acetyl-CoA. The α-ketoglutarate dehydrogenase complex uses TPP, lipoate, and FAD as bound coenzymes, and NAD^+ and CoASH as

Q: From Figure 20.3, which enzymes in the TCA cycle release CO_2? How many moles of oxaloacetate are consumed in the TCA cycle for each mole of CO_2 produced?

Ann O'Rexia has been malnourished for some time and has developed subclinical deficiencies of many vitamins, including riboflavin. The coenzymes FAD and FMN are synthesized from the vitamin riboflavin. Riboflavin is actively transported into cells where the enzyme flavokinase adds a phosphate to form FMN. FAD synthetase then adds AMP to form FAD. FAD is the major coenzyme in tissues and is generally found tightly bound to proteins, with about 10% being covalently bound. Its turnover in the body is very slow, and people can live for long periods on low intakes without displaying any signs of a riboflavin deficiency.

**Flavin adenine dinucleotide (FAD) and
flavin mononucleotide (FMN)**

FIG. 20.4. One-electron steps in the reduction of FAD. When FAD and FMN accept single electrons, they are converted to the half-reduced *semiquinone*, a semistable free-radical form. They can also accept two electrons to form the fully reduced form, FADH$_2$. However, in most dehydrogenases, FADH$_2$ is never formed. Instead, the first electron is shared with a group on the protein as the next electron is transferred. Therefore, in this text, overall acceptance of two electrons by FAD has been denoted by the more general abbreviation, FAD(2H).

 Isocitrate dehydrogenase releases the first CO_2, and α-ketoglutarate dehydrogenase releases the second CO_2. There is no net consumption of oxaloacetate in the TCA cycle—the first step uses an oxaloacetate, and the last step produces one. The use and regeneration of oxaloacetate is the "cycle" part of the TCA cycle.

 One of **Otto Shape's** tennis partners told him that he had heard about a health food designed for athletes that contained succinate. The advertisement made the claim that succinate would provide an excellent source of energy during exercise because it could be metabolized directly without oxygen. Do you see anything wrong with this statement?

substrates. Each of these coenzymes has unique structural features that enable it to fulfill its role in the TCA cycle.

A. Flavin Adenine Dinucleotide and Nicotinamide Adenine Dinucleotide

Both FAD and NAD$^+$ are electron-accepting coenzymes. Why is FAD used in some reactions and NAD$^+$ in others? Their unique structural features enable FAD and NAD$^+$ to act as electron acceptors in different types of reactions and to play different physiologic roles in the cell. FAD is able to accept single electrons (H•) and forms a half-reduced single-electron intermediate (Fig. 20.4). It thus participates in reactions in which single electrons are transferred independently from two different atoms, which occurs in double-bond formation (e.g., succinate to fumarate) and disulfide bond formation (e.g., lipoate to lipoate disulfide in the α-ketoglutarate dehydrogenase reaction). In contrast, NAD$^+$ accepts a pair of electrons as the hydride ion (H$^-$), which is attracted to the carbon opposite the positively charged pyridine ring (Fig. 20.5). This occurs, for example, in the oxidation of alcohols to ketones by malate dehydrogenase and isocitrate dehydrogenase. The nicotinamide ring accepts a hydride ion from the C–H bond, and the alcoholic hydrogen is released into the medium as a positively charged proton, H$^+$.

The free radical, single-electron forms of FAD are very reactive, and FADH can lose its electron through exposure to water or the initiation of chain reactions. As a consequence, FAD must remain very tightly, sometimes covalently, attached to its enzyme while it accepts and transfers electrons to another group bound on the

Isocitrate

α-**Ketoglutarate**

NAD⁺

NADH

FIG. 20.5. Oxidation and decarboxylation of isocitrate. The alcohol group (C–OH) is oxidized to a ketone, with the C–H electrons donated to NAD⁺ as the hydride ion. Subsequent electron shifts in the pyridine ring remove the positive charge. The H of the −OH group dissociates into water as a proton, H⁺. NAD⁺, the electron acceptor, is reduced.

enzyme (Fig. 20.6). Because FAD interacts with many functional groups on amino acid side chains in the active site, the $E^{0'}$ for enzyme-bound FAD varies greatly and can be greater or much less than that of NAD⁺. In contrast, NAD⁺ and NADH are more like substrate and product than coenzymes.

NADH plays a regulatory role in balancing energy metabolism that FAD(2H) cannot because FAD(2H) remains attached to its enzyme. Free NAD⁺ binds to a dehydrogenase and is reduced to NADH that is then released into the medium where it can bind and inhibit a different dehydrogenase. Consequently, oxidative enzymes are controlled by the NADH/NAD⁺ ratio and do not generate NADH faster than it can be reoxidized in the electron-transport chain. The regulation of the TCA cycle and other pathways of fuel oxidation by the NADH/NAD⁺ ratio is part of the mechanism for coordinating the rate of fuel oxidation to the rate of ATP use.

B. Role of Coenzyme A in the Tricarboxylic Acid Cycle

CoASH, the acylation coenzyme, participates in reactions through the formation of a thioester bond between the sulfur (S) of CoASH and an acyl group (e.g., acetyl-CoA, succinyl-CoA) (Fig. 20.7). The complete structure of CoASH and its vitamin

Succinate   Fumarate

His-FAD

Fe-S

Inner mitochondrial membrane

CoQ
ETC acceptor
CoQH₂

Succinate dehydrogenase

The claim that succinate oxidation can produce energy without oxygen is wrong. It is probably based on the fact that succinate is oxidized to fumarate by the donation of electrons to FAD. However, ATP can be generated from this process only when these electrons are donated to oxygen in the electron-transport chain. The energy generated by the electron-transport chain is used for ATP synthesis in the process of oxidative phosphorylation. After the covalently bound FAD(2H) is oxidized back to FAD by the electron-transport chain, succinate dehydrogenase can oxidize another succinate molecule.

FIG. 20.6. Succinate dehydrogenase contains covalently bound FAD. As a consequence, succinate dehydrogenase and similar flavoproteins reside in the inner mitochondrial membrane where they can transfer electrons directly into the electron-transport chain. The electrons are transferred from the covalently bound FAD to an Fe–S complex on the enzyme, and then to coenzyme Q in the electron-transport chain (see Chapter 21). Thus, FAD does not have to dissociate from the enzyme to transfer its electrons. All the other enzymes of the TCA cycle are found in the mitochondrial matrix.

A

OAA   HS-CoA

$CH_3-C\overset{O}{\sim}SCoA$

Acetyl CoA

Citrate synthase

$HO-C-CH_2-C-O^-$

Citrate

B

GDP   GTP

Succinyl CoA   Pi   CoASH   **Succinate**

FIG. 20.7. Utilization of the high-energy thioester bond of acyl-CoAs. Energy transformations are shown in *red*. **A.** The energy released by hydrolysis of the thioester bond of acetyl coenzyme A (acetyl-CoA) in the citrate synthase reaction contributes a large negative $\Delta G^{0'}$ to the forward direction of the TCA cycle. **B.** The energy of the succinyl-CoA thioester bond is used for the synthesis of the high-energy phosphate bond of GTP.

CoASH is synthesized from the vitamin pantothenate in a sequence of reactions that phosphorylate pantothenate, add the sulfhydryl portion of CoA from cysteine, and then add AMP and an additional phosphate group from ATP (see Fig. 8.12A). Pantothenate is widely distributed in foods ("pantos" means everywhere), so it is unlikely that **Ann O'Rexia** has developed a pantothenate deficiency. Although CoA is required in approximately 100 different reactions in mammalian cells, no Recommended Daily Allowance (RDA) has been established for pantothenate, in part, because indicators have not yet been found that specifically and sensitively reflect a deficiency of this vitamin in the human. The reported symptoms of pantothenate deficiency (fatigue, nausea, and loss of appetite) are characteristic of vitamin deficiencies in general.

precursor, pantothenate, is shown in Figure 8.12A. A thioester bond differs from a typical oxygen ester bond because S, unlike O, does not share its electrons and participate in resonance formations. One of the consequences of this feature of sulfur chemistry is that the carbonyl carbon, the α-carbon, and the β-carbon of the acyl group in a CoA thioester can be activated for participation in different types of reactions (e.g., in the citrate synthase reaction, the α-carbon methyl group is activated for condensation with oxaloacetate; see Figs. 20.3 and 20.7A). Another consequence is that the thioester bond is a high-energy bond that has a large negative $\Delta G^{0'}$ of hydrolysis (approximately -13 kcal/mol).

The energy from cleavage of the high-energy thioester bonds of succinyl-CoA and acetyl-CoA is used in two different ways in the TCA cycle. When the succinyl-CoA thioester bond is cleaved by succinate thiokinase, the energy is used directly for activating an enzyme-bound phosphate that is transferred to GDP (see Fig. 20.7B). In contrast, when the thioester bond of acetyl-CoA is cleaved in the citrate synthase reaction, the energy is released, giving the reaction a large negative $\Delta G^{0'}$ of -7.7 kcal/mol. The large negative $\Delta G^{0'}$ for citrate formation helps to keep the TCA cycle going in the forward direction.

C. The α-Keto Acid Dehydrogenase Complexes

The α-ketoglutarate dehydrogenase complex is one of a three-member family of similar α-keto acid dehydrogenase complexes. The other members of this family are the pyruvate dehydrogenase complex (PDC) and the branched-chain amino acid α-keto acid dehydrogenase complex. Each of these complexes is specific for a different α-keto acid structure. In the sequence of reactions catalyzed by the complexes, the α-keto acid is decarboxylated (i.e., releases the carboxyl group as CO_2) (Fig. 20.8). The keto group is oxidized to the level of a carboxylic acid and then combined with CoASH to form an acyl-CoA thioester (e.g., succinyl-CoA).

FIG. 20.8. Oxidative decarboxylation of α-ketoglutarate. The α-ketoglutarate dehydrogenase complex oxidizes α-ketoglutarate to succinyl-CoA. The carboxyl group is released as CO_2. The keto group on the α-carbon is oxidized and then forms the acyl-CoA thioester, succinyl-CoA. The α, β, γ, and δ on succinyl-CoA refer to the sequence of atoms in α-ketoglutarate.

FIG. 20.9. Mechanism of α-keto acid dehydrogenase complexes (including α-ketogluta-rate dehydrogenase, pyruvate dehydrogenase, and the branched-chain α-keto acid dehydro-genase complex). *R* represents the portion of the α-keto acid that begins with the β-carbon. In α-ketoglutarate, R is CH₂–CH₂–COOH. In pyruvate, R is –CH₃. The individual steps in the oxidative decarboxylation of α-keto acids are catalyzed by three different subunits: *E₁*, α-keto acid decarboxylase (α-ketoglutarate decarboxylase); *E₂*, transacylase (*trans*-succinylase); and *E₃*, dihydrolipoyl dehydrogenase. *(1)* Thiamine pyrophosphate (TPP) on E₁ decarboxylates the α-keto acid and forms a covalent intermediate with the remaining portion. *(2)* The acyl portion of the α-keto acid is transferred by TPP on E₁ to lipoate on E₂, which is a transacylase. *(3)* E₂ transfers the acyl group from lipoate to CoASH. Note how lipoate is reduced during this conversion. The lipoyl disulfide bond has been reduced to sulfhydral groups (dihydrolipoate). *(4)* E₃, dihydrolipoyl dehydrogenase (DH) transfers the electrons from reduced lipoate to its tightly bound FAD molecule, thereby oxidizing lipoate back to its original disulfide form. *(5)* The electrons are then transferred from FAD(2H) to NAD⁺ to form NADH.

Q: The $E^{0'}$ for FAD accepting electrons is -0.219 (see Table 19.4). The $E^{0'}$ for NAD⁺ accepting electrons is -0.32. Thus, transfer of electrons from FAD(2H) to NAD⁺ is energetically unfavorable. How do the α-keto acid dehydrogenase complexes allow this electron transfer to occur?

All of the α-keto acid dehydrogenase complexes are huge enzyme complexes composed of multiple subunits of three different enzymes, designated as E₁, E₂, and E₃ (Fig. 20.9). *E₁* is an α-keto acid decarboxylase that contains TPP; it cleaves off the carboxyl group of the α-keto acid. *E₂* is a transacylase-containing lipoate; it transfers the acyl portion of the α-keto acid from thiamine to CoASH. *E₃* is dihydrolipoyl dehydrogenase, which contains FAD; it transfers electrons from reduced lipoate to NAD⁺. The collection of three enzyme activities into one huge complex enables the product of one enzyme to be transferred to the next enzyme without loss of energy. Complex formation also increases the rate of catalysis because the substrates for E₂ and E₃ remain bound to the enzyme complex.

1. THIAMINE PYROPHOSPHATE IN THE α-KETOGLUTARATE DEHYDROGENASE COMPLEX

TPP is synthesized from the vitamin thiamine by the addition of pyrophosphate (see Fig. 8.11). The pyrophosphate group binds magnesium, which binds to amino acid side chains on the enzyme. This binding is relatively weak for a coenzyme, so thiamine turns over rapidly in the body, and a deficiency can develop rapidly in individuals who are on thiamine-free or low-thiamine diets.

The general function of TPP is the cleavage of a carbon–carbon bond next to a keto group. In the α-ketoglutarate, pyruvate, and branched-chain α-keto acid dehy-drogenase complexes, the functional carbon on the thiazole ring forms a covalent bond with the α-keto carbon, thereby cleaving the bond between the α-keto carbon and the adjacent carboxylic acid group (see Fig. 8.11 for the mechanism of this reaction). TPP is also a coenzyme for transketolase in the pentose phosphate path-way, where it similarly cleaves the carbon–carbon bond next to a keto group. In thiamine deficiency, α-ketoglutarate, pyruvate, and other α-keto acids accumulate in the blood.

In **Al Martini's** heart failure, which is caused by a dietary deficiency of the vitamin thiamine, pyruvate dehydrogenase, α-ketoglutarate dehydroge-nase, and the branched-chain α-keto acid dehydrogenase complexes are less functional than normal. Because heart muscle, skeletal muscle, and nervous tissue have high rates of ATP production from the NADH produced by the oxidation of pyruvate to acetyl-CoA and of acetyl-CoA to CO₂ in the TCA cycle, these tissues present with the most obvious signs of thiamine deficiency.

In Western societies, gross thiamine defi-ciency is most often associated with alcohol-ism. The mechanism for active absorption of thiamine is strongly and directly inhibited by alcohol. Subclinical deficiency of thiamine from malnutrition or anorexia may be common in the general population and is usually associ-ated with multiple vitamin deficiencies.

The $E^{0'}$ values were calculated in a test tube under standard conditions. When FAD is bound to an enzyme, as it is in the α-keto acid dehydrogenase complexes, amino acid side chains can alter its $E^{0'}$ value. Thus, the transfer of electrons from the bound FAD(2H) to NAD^+ in dihydrolipoyl dehydrogenase is actually energetically favorable.

Lipoamide (oxidized)

— TPP intermediate

FIG. 20.10. Function of lipoate. Lipoate is attached to the ε-amino group of a lysine side chain of the transacylase enzyme (E_2). The oxidized lipoate disulfide form is reduced as it accepts the acyl group from thiamine pyrophosphate (TPP) attached to E_1. The example shown is for the α-ketoglutarate dehydrogenase complex.

2. LIPOATE

Lipoate is a coenzyme found only in α-keto acid dehydrogenase complexes. It is synthesized in the human from carbohydrate and amino acids, and it does not require a vitamin precursor. Lipoate is attached to the transacylase enzyme through its carboxyl group, which is covalently bound to the terminal $-NH_2$ of a lysine in the protein (Fig. 20.10). At its functional end, lipoate contains a disulfide group that accepts electrons when it binds the acyl fragment of α-ketoglutarate. It can thus act like a long, flexible $-CH_2-$ arm of the enzyme that reaches over to the decarboxylase to pick up the acyl fragment from thiamine and transfer it to the active site containing bound CoASH. It then swings over to dihydrolipoyl dehydrogenase to transfer electrons from the lipoyl sulfhydryl groups to FAD.

3. FLAVIN ADENINE DINUCLEOTIDE AND DIHYDROLIPOYL DEHYDROGENASE

FAD on dihydrolipoyl dehydrogenase accepts electrons from the lipoyl sulfhydryl groups and transfers them to bound NAD^+. FAD thus accepts and transfers electrons without leaving its binding site on the enzyme. The direction of the reaction is favored by interactions of FAD with groups on the enzyme, which change its reduction potential, and by the overall release of energy from cleavage and oxidation of α-ketoglutarate.

IV. ENERGETICS OF THE TRICARBOXYLIC ACID CYCLE

Like all metabolic pathways, the TCA cycle operates with an overall net negative $\Delta G^{0'}$ (Fig. 20.11). The conversion of substrates to products is, therefore, energetically favorable. However, some of the reactions, such as the malate dehydrogenase reaction, have a positive value.

The net standard free-energy change for the TCA cycle, $\Delta G^{0'}$, can be calculated from the sum of the $\Delta G^{0'}$ values for the individual reactions. The $\Delta G^{0'}$, -13 kcal, is the amount of energy lost as heat. It can be considered the amount of energy spent to ensure that oxidation of the acetyl group to CO_2 goes to completion. This value

Arsenic poisoning is caused by the presence of a large number of different arsenious compounds that are effective metabolic inhibitors. Acute accidental or intentional arsenic poisoning requires high doses and involves arsenate (AsO_4^{2-}) and arsenite (AsO_3^{2-}). Arsenite, which is 10 times more toxic than arsenate, binds to neighboring sulfhydryl groups, such as those in dihydrolipoate and in nearby cysteine pairs (vicinal) found in α-keto acid dehydrogenase complexes and in succinic dehydrogenase. Arsenate weakly inhibits enzymatic reactions involving phosphate, including the enzyme glyceraldehyde 3-P dehydrogenase in glycolysis (see Chapter 22). Thus, both aerobic and anaerobic ATP production can be inhibited. The low doses of arsenic compounds found in water supplies are a major public health concern but are associated with increased risk of cancer rather than direct toxicity.

is surprisingly small. However, oxidation of NADH and FAD(2H) in the electron-transport chain helps to make acetyl oxidation more energetically favorable and pulls the TCA cycle forward.

A. Overall Efficiency of the Tricarboxylic Acid Cycle

The reactions of the TCA cycle are extremely efficient in converting energy in the chemical bonds of the acetyl group to other forms. The total amount of energy available from the acetyl group is about 228 kcal/mol (the amount of energy that could be released from complete combustion of 1 mol of acetyl groups to CO_2 in a bomb calorimeter). The products of the TCA cycle (NADH, FAD[2H], and GTP) contain about 207 kcal (Table 20.1). Thus, the TCA cycle reactions are able to conserve about 90% of the energy available from the oxidation of acetyl-CoA.

B. Thermodynamically and Kinetically Reversible and Irreversible Reactions

Three reactions in the TCA cycle have large negative values for $\Delta G^{0'}$ that strongly favor the forward direction: the reactions catalyzed by citrate synthase, isocitrate dehydrogenase, and α-ketoglutarate dehydrogenase (see Fig. 20.11). Within the TCA cycle, these reactions are physiologically irreversible for two reasons: The products do not rise to high enough concentrations under physiologic conditions to overcome the large negative $\Delta G^{0'}$ values; and the enzymes involved catalyze the reverse reaction very slowly. These reactions make the major contribution to the overall negative $\Delta G^{0'}$ for the TCA cycle and keep it going in the forward direction.

In contrast to these irreversible reactions, the reactions catalyzed by aconitase and malate dehydrogenase have a positive $\Delta G^{0'}$ for the forward direction and are thermodynamically and kinetically reversible. Because aconitase is rapid in both directions, equilibrium values for the concentration ratio of products to substrates is maintained, and the concentration of citrate is about 20 times that of isocitrate. The accumulation of citrate instead of isocitrate facilitates transport of excess citrate to the cytosol, where it can provide a source of acetyl-CoA for pathways such as fatty acid and cholesterol synthesis. It also allows citrate to serve as an inhibitor of

Table 20.1   Energy Yield of the Tricarboxylic Acid Cycle

kcal/mol		
3: NADH 3×53	=	159
1 FAD(2H)	=	41
1 GTP	=	7
Sum	=	207

The values given for energy yield from NADH and FAD(2H) are based on the equation $\Delta G = -n\,F\,\Delta E^{0'}$, explained in Chapter 19.
GTP, guanosine triphosphate.

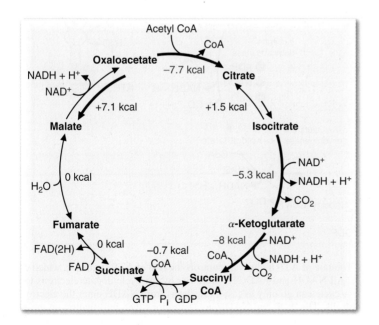

FIG. 20.11.   Approximate $\Delta G^{0'}$ values for the reactions in the TCA cycle, given for the forward direction. The reactions with _large_ negative $\Delta G^{0'}$ values are shown in _red_. See Chapter 19 for a discussion of the meaning of $\Delta G^{0'}$ values.

Otto Shape had difficulty losing weight because human fuel utilization is too efficient. His adipose tissue fatty acids are being converted to acetyl-CoA, which is being oxidized in the TCA cycle, thereby generating NADH and FAD(2H). The energy in these compounds is used for ATP synthesis from oxidative phosphorylation. If his fuel utilization were less efficient and his ATP yield were lower, he would have to oxidize much greater amounts of fat to get the ATP he needs for exercise.

citrate synthase when flux through isocitrate dehydrogenase is decreased. Likewise, the equilibrium constant of the malate dehydrogenase reaction favors the accumulation of malate over oxaloacetate, resulting in a low oxaloacetate concentration that is influenced by the NADH/NAD$^+$ ratio. Thus, there is a net flux of oxaloacetate toward malate in the liver during fasting (as a result of fatty acid oxidation, which raises the NADH/NAD$^+$ ratio), and malate can then be transported out of the mitochondria to provide a substrate for gluconeogenesis.

V. REGULATION OF THE TRICARBOXYLIC ACID CYCLE

The oxidation of acetyl-CoA in the TCA cycle and the conservation of this energy as NADH and FAD(2H) is essential for generation of ATP in almost all tissues in the body. In spite of changes in the supply of fuels, type of fuels in the blood, or rate of ATP utilization, cells maintain ATP homeostasis (a constant level of ATP). The rate of the TCA cycle, like that of all fuel oxidation pathways, is principally regulated to correspond to the rate of the electron-transport chain, which is regulated by the ATP/ADP ratio and the rate of ATP utilization (see Chapter 21). The major sites of regulation are shown in Figure 20.12.

Two major messengers feed information on the rate of ATP utilization back to the TCA cycle: (1) the phosphorylation state of ATP, as reflected in ATP and ADP levels; and (2) the reduction state of NAD$^+$, as reflected in the ratio of NADH/NAD$^+$. Within the cell, even within the mitochondrion, the total adenine nucleotide

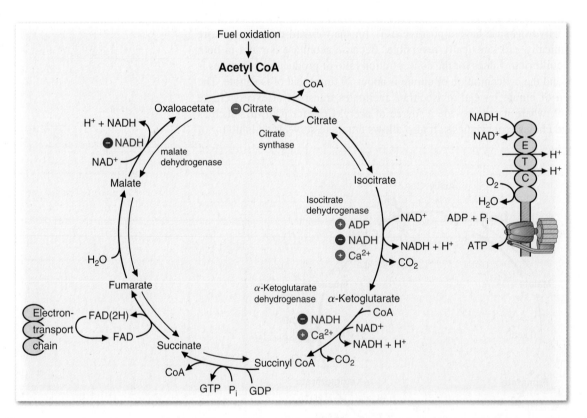

FIG. 20.12.   Major regulatory interactions in the TCA cycle. The rate of ATP hydrolysis controls the rate of ATP synthesis, which controls the rate of NADH oxidation in the electron-transport chain (ETC). All NADH and FAD(2H) produced by the cycle donate electrons to this chain (shown on the **right**). Thus, oxidation of acetyl-CoA in the TCA cycle can go only as fast as electrons from NADH enter the electron-transport chain, which is controlled by the ATP and ADP content of the cells. The ADP and NADH concentrations feed information on the rate of oxidative phosphorylation back to the TCA cycle. Isocitrate dehydrogenase (DH), α-ketoglutarate DH, and malate DH are inhibited by increased NADH concentration. The NADH/NAD$^+$ ratio changes the concentration of oxaloacetate. Citrate is a product inhibitor of citrate synthase. ADP is an allosteric activator of isocitrate DH. During muscular contraction, increased Ca^{2+} concentrations activate isocitrate DH and α-ketoglutarate DH (as well as pyruvate DH).

Table 20.2 Generalizations on the Regulation of Metabolic Pathways

1. Regulation matches function. The type of regulation use depends on the function of the pathway. Tissue-specific isozymes may allow the features of regulatory enzymes to match somewhat different functions of the pathway in different tissues.
2. Regulation of metabolic pathways occurs at rate-limiting steps, the slowest steps, in the pathway. These are reactions in which a small change of rate will affect the flux through the whole pathway.
3. Regulation usually occurs at the first committed step of a pathway or at metabolic branch points. In human cells, most pathways are interconnected with other pathways and have regulatory enzymes for every branch point.
4. Regulatory enzymes often catalyze physiologically irreversible reactions. These are also the steps that differ in biosynthetic and degradative pathways.
5. Many pathways have feedback regulation; that is, the end product of the pathway controls the rate of its own synthesis. Feedback regulation may involve inhibition of an early step in the pathway (feedback inhibition) or regulation of gene transcription.
6. Human cells use compartmentation to control access of substrate and activators or inhibitors to different enzymes.
7. Hormonal regulation integrates responses in pathways requiring more than one tissue. Hormones generally regulate fuel metabolism by:
    a. Changing the phosphorylation state of enzymes
    b. Changing the amount of enzyme present by changing its rate of synthesis (often induction or repression of mRNA synthesis) or degradation
    c. Changing the concentration of an activator or inhibitor

pool (AMP, ADP, plus ATP) and the total NAD pool (NAD^+ plus NADH) are relatively constant. Thus, an increased rate of ATP utilization results in a small decrease of ATP concentration and an increase of ADP. Likewise, increased NADH oxidation to NAD^+ by the electron-transport chain increases the rate of pathways that produce NADH. Under normal physiologic conditions, the TCA cycle and other oxidative pathways respond so rapidly to increased ATP demand that the ATP concentration does not change significantly.

A. Regulation of Citrate Synthase

The principles of pathway regulation are summarized in Table 20.2. In pathways that are subject to feedback regulation, the first step of the pathway must be regulated so that precursors flow into alternative pathways if product is not needed. *Citrate synthase*, which is the first enzyme of the TCA cycle, is a simple enzyme that has no allosteric regulators. Its rate is controlled principally by the concentration of oxaloacetate, its substrate, and the concentration of citrate, a product inhibitor that is competitive with oxaloacetate (see Fig. 20.12). The malate–oxaloacetate equilibrium favors malate, so the oxaloacetate concentration is very low inside the mitochondrion and is below the apparent K_m (see Chapter 9, Section I.A.4) of citrate synthase. When the $NADH/NAD^+$ ratio decreases, the ratio of oxaloacetate to malate increases. When isocitrate dehydrogenase is activated, the concentration of citrate decreases, thus relieving the product inhibition of citrate synthase. Thus, both increased oxaloacetate and decreased citrate levels regulate the response of citrate synthase to conditions established by the electron-transport chain and oxidative phosphorylation. In the liver, the $NADH/NAD^+$ ratio helps determine whether acetyl-CoA enters the TCA cycle or goes into the alternative pathway for ketone body synthesis.

B. Allosteric Regulation of Isocitrate Dehydrogenase

Another generalization that can be made about regulation of metabolic pathways is that it occurs at the enzyme that catalyzes the rate-limiting (slowest) step in a pathway (see Table 20.2). Isocitrate dehydrogenase is considered one of the rate-limiting steps of the TCA cycle, and it is allosterically activated by ADP and inhibited by NADH (Fig. 20.13). In the absence of ADP, the enzyme exhibits positive cooperativity; as isocitrate binds to one subunit, other subunits are converted to an active conformation (see Chapter 9, Section III.A, on allosteric enzymes). In the presence of ADP, all of the subunits are in their active conformation, and isocitrate

As **Otto Shape** exercises, his myosin ATPase hydrolyzes ATP to provide the energy for movement of myofibrils. The decrease of ATP and increase of ADP stimulates the electron-transport chain to oxidize more NADH and FAD(2H). The TCA cycle is stimulated to provide more NADH and FAD(2H) to the electron-transport chain. The activation of the TCA cycle occurs through a decrease of the $NADH/NAD^+$ ratio, an increase of ADP concentration, and an increase of Ca^{2+}. Although regulation of the transcription of genes for TCA cycle enzymes is too slow to respond to changes of ATP demands during exercise, the number and size of mitochondria increase during training. Thus, **Otto Shape** is increasing his capacity for fuel oxidation as he trains.

FIG. 20.13. Allosteric regulation of isocitrate dehydrogenase (ICDH). Isocitrate, NAD^+, and NADH bind in the active site; ADP and Ca^{2+} are activators and bind to separate allosteric sites. **A.** A graph of velocity versus isocitrate concentration shows positive cooperativity (sigmoid curve) in the absence of ADP. The allosteric activator ADP changes the curve into one closer to a rectangular hyperbola and decreases the K_m ($S_{0.5}$) for isocitrate. **B.** The allosteric activation by ADP is not an all-or-nothing response. The extent of activation by ADP depends on its concentration. **C.** Increases in the concentration of product, NADH, decrease the velocity of the enzyme through effects on the allosteric activation.

binds more readily. Consequently, the apparent K_m (the $S_{0.5}$) shifts to a much lower value. Thus, at the concentration of isocitrate found in the mitochondrial matrix, a small change in the concentration of ADP can produce a large change in the rate of the isocitrate dehydrogenase reaction. Small changes in the concentration of the product, NADH, and of the cosubstrate, NAD^+, also affect the rate of the enzyme more than they would a nonallosteric enzyme.

C. Regulation of α-Ketoglutarate Dehydrogenase

The α-ketoglutarate dehydrogenase complex, although it is not an allosteric enzyme, is product inhibited by NADH and succinyl-CoA and may also be inhibited by GTP (see Fig. 20.12). Thus, both α-ketoglutarate dehydrogenase and isocitrate dehydrogenase respond directly to changes in the relative levels of ADP and, hence, the rate at which NADH is oxidized by electron transport. Both of these enzymes are also activated by Ca^+. In contracting heart muscle and possibly other muscle tissues, the release of Ca^+ from the sarcoplasmic reticulum during muscle contraction may provide an additional activation of these enzymes when ATP is being rapidly hydrolyzed.

D. Regulation of Tricarboxylic Acid Cycle Intermediates

Regulation of the TCA cycle serves two functions: (1) It ensures that NADH is generated fast enough to maintain ATP homeostasis, and (2) it regulates the concentration of TCA cycle intermediates. For example, in the liver, a decreased rate of isocitrate dehydrogenase increases citrate concentration, which stimulates citrate efflux to the cytosol. Several regulatory interactions occur in the TCA cycle, in addition to those mentioned previously, that control the levels of TCA intermediates and their flux into pathways that adjoin the TCA cycle.

VI. PRECURSORS OF ACETYL COENZYME A

Compounds enter the TCA cycle as acetyl-CoA or as an intermediate that can be converted to malate or oxaloacetate. Compounds that enter as acetyl-CoA are oxidized to CO_2. Compounds that enter as TCA cycle intermediates replenish intermediates that have been used in biosynthetic pathways, such as gluconeogenesis or heme synthesis, but cannot be fully oxidized to CO_2.

A. Sources of Acetyl Coenzyme A

Acetyl-CoA serves as a common point of convergence for the major pathways of fuel oxidation. It is generated directly from the β-oxidation of fatty acids and degradation of the ketone bodies β-hydroxybutyrate and acetoacetate (Fig. 20.14). It is also formed from acetate, which can arise from the diet or from ethanol oxidation. Glucose and other carbohydrates enter glycolysis, a pathway common to all cells, and are oxidized to pyruvate. The amino acids alanine and serine are also converted to pyruvate. Pyruvate is oxidized to acetyl-CoA by the PDC. Several amino acids such as leucine and isoleucine are also oxidized to acetyl-CoA. Thus, the final oxidation of acetyl-CoA to CO_2 in the TCA cycle is the last step in all the major pathways of fuel oxidation.

B. Pyruvate Dehydrogenase Complex

The PDC oxidizes pyruvate to acetyl-CoA, thus linking glycolysis and the TCA cycle. In the brain, which is dependent on the oxidation of glucose to CO_2 to fulfill its ATP needs, regulation of the PDC is a life-and-death matter.

1. STRUCTURE OF THE PYRUVATE DEHYDROGENASE COMPLEX

PDC belongs to the α-keto acid dehydrogenase complex family and thus shares structural and catalytic features with the α-ketoglutarate dehydrogenase complex and the branched-chain α-keto acid dehydrogenase complex (Fig. 20.15). It contains the same three basic types of catalytic subunits: (1) pyruvate decarboxylase

FIG. 20.14. Origin of the acetyl group from various fuels. Acetyl coenzyme A (acetyl-CoA) is derived from the oxidation of fuels. The portions of fatty acids, ketone bodies, glucose, pyruvate, the amino acid alanine, and ethanol that are converted to the acetyl group of acetyl coenzyme A (acetyl-CoA) are shown in *boxes*.

FIG. 20.15. PDC catalyzes oxidation of the α-keto acid pyruvate to acetyl-CoA.

subunits that bind TPP (E_1), (2) transacetylase subunits that bind lipoate (E_2), and (3) dihydrolipoyl dehydrogenase subunits that bind FAD (E_3) (see Fig. 20.9). Although the E_1 and E_2 enzymes in PDC are relatively specific for pyruvate, the same dihydrolipoyl dehydrogenase participates in all of the α-keto acid dehydrogenase complexes. In addition to these three types of subunits, the PDC complex contains one additional subunit, an E_3-binding protein (E_3-BP). Each functional component of the PDC complex is present in multiple copies (e.g., bovine heart PDC has 30 subunits of E_1, 60 subunits of E_2, and 6 subunits each of E_3 and E_3-BP). The E_1 enzyme is itself a tetramer of two different types of subunits, α and β.

2. REGULATION OF THE PYRUVATE DEHYDROGENASE COMPLEX

PDC activity is controlled principally through phosphorylation by pyruvate dehydrogenase kinase, which inhibits the enzyme and dephosphorylation by pyruvate dehydrogenase phosphatase, which activates it (Fig. 20.16). Pyruvate dehydrogenase kinase and pyruvate dehydrogenase phosphatase are regulatory subunits within the PDC complex and act only on the complex. PDC kinase transfers a phosphate from ATP to specific serine hydroxyl (ser-OH) groups on pyruvate decarboxylase (E_1). PDC phosphatase removes these phosphate groups by hydrolysis. Phosphorylation of just one serine on the PDC E_1 α-subunit can decrease its activity by >99%. PDC kinase is present in complexes as tissue-specific isozymes that vary in their regulatory properties.

PDC kinase is itself inhibited by ADP and pyruvate. Thus, when rapid ATP utilization results in an increase of ADP or when activation of glycolysis increases pyruvate levels, PDC kinase is inhibited and PDC remains in an active, nonphosphorylated form. PDC phosphatase requires Ca^{2+} for full activity. In the heart, increased intramitochondrial Ca^{2+} during rapid contraction activates the phosphatase, thereby increasing the amount of active, nonphosphorylated PDC.

PDC is also regulated through inhibition by its products, acetyl-CoA and NADH. This inhibition is stronger than regular product inhibition because their binding to PDC stimulates its phosphorylation to the inactive form. The substrates of the enzyme, CoASH and NAD^+, antagonize this product inhibition. Thus, when an ample supply of acetyl-CoA for the TCA cycle is already available from fatty acid oxidation, acetyl-CoA and NADH build up and dramatically decrease their own further synthesis by PDC.

 Deficiencies of the PDC are among the most common inherited diseases leading to lactic acidemia and, similar to pyruvate carboxylase deficiency, are grouped into the category of Leigh disease (subacute necrotizing encephalopathy). In its severe form, PDC deficiency presents with overwhelming lactic acidosis at birth, with death in the neonatal period. In a second form of presentation, the lactic acidemia is moderate, but there is profound psychomotor retardation with increasing age. In many cases, concomitant damage to the brainstem and basal ganglia lead to death in infancy. The neurologic symptoms arise because the brain has a very limited ability to use fatty acids as a fuel and is, therefore, dependent on glucose metabolism for its energy supply.

The most common PDC genetic defects are in the gene for the α-subunit of E_1. The E_1 α-gene is X-linked. Because of its importance in central nervous system metabolism, pyruvate dehydrogenase deficiency is a problem in both males and females, even if the female is a carrier. For this reason, it is classified as an X-linked dominant disorder.

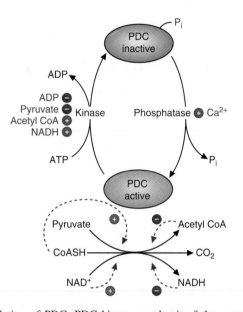

FIG. 20.16. Regulation of PDC. PDC kinase, a subunit of the enzyme, phosphorylates PDC at a specific serine residue, thereby converting PDC to an inactive form. The kinase is inhibited by adenosine diphosphate (ADP) and pyruvate. PDC phosphatase, another subunit of the enzyme, removes the phosphate, thereby activating PDC. The phosphatase is activated by Ca^{2+}. When the substrates pyruvate and CoASH are bound to PDC, the kinase activity is inhibited and PDC is active. When the products acetyl-CoA and NADH bind to PDC, the kinase activity is stimulated, and the enzyme is phosphorylated to the inactive form. E_1 and the kinase exist as tissue-specific isozymes with overlapping tissue specificity and somewhat different regulatory properties.

PDC can also be activated rapidly through a mechanism involving insulin, which plays a prominent role in adipocytes. In many tissues, insulin may, over time, slowly increase the amount of PDC present.

The rate of other fuel oxidation pathways that feed into the TCA cycle is also increased when ATP utilization increases. Insulin, other hormones, and diet control the availability of fuels for these oxidative pathways.

VII. TCA CYCLE INTERMEDIATES AND ANAPLEROTIC REACTIONS

A. TCA Cycle Intermediates Are Precursors for Biosynthetic Pathways

The intermediates of the TCA cycle serve as precursors for a variety of different pathways present in different cell types (Fig. 20.17). This is particularly important in the central metabolic role of the liver. The TCA cycle in the liver is often called an "open cycle" because there is such a high efflux of intermediates. After a high-carbohydrate meal, citrate efflux and cleavage to acetyl-CoA provides acetyl units for cytosolic fatty acid synthesis. During fasting, gluconeogenic precursors are converted to malate, which leaves the mitochondria for cytosolic gluconeogenesis. The liver also uses TCA cycle intermediates to synthesize carbon skeletons of amino acids. Succinyl-CoA may be removed from the TCA cycle to form heme in cells of the liver and bone marrow. In the brain, α-ketoglutarate is converted to glutamate and then to γ-aminobutyric acid (GABA), a neurotransmitter. In skeletal muscle, α-ketoglutarate is converted to glutamine, which is transported through the blood to other tissues.

Pyruvate, citrate, α-ketoglutarate and malate, ADP, ATP, and phosphate (as well as many other compounds) have specific transporters in the inner mitochondrial membrane that transport compounds between the mitochondrial matrix and cytosol in exchange for a compound of similar charge. In contrast, CoASH, acetyl-CoA,

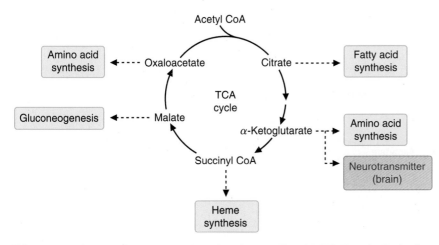

FIG. 20.17. Efflux of intermediates from the tricarboxylic acid (TCA) cycle. In the liver, TCA cycle intermediates are continuously withdrawn into the pathways of fatty acid synthesis, amino acid synthesis, gluconeogenesis, and heme synthesis. In the brain, α-ketoglutarate is converted to glutamate and γ-aminobutyric acid (GABA), both of which are neurotransmitters.

other CoA derivatives, NAD^+ and NADH, and oxaloacetate are not transported at a metabolically significant rate. To obtain cytosolic acetyl-CoA, many cells transport citrate to the cytosol, where it is cleaved to acetyl-CoA and oxaloacetate by citrate lyase.

B. Anaplerotic Reactions

Removal of any of the intermediates from the TCA cycle removes the four carbons that are used to regenerate oxaloacetate during each turn of the cycle. With depletion of oxaloacetate, it is impossible to continue oxidizing acetyl-CoA. To enable the TCA cycle to keep running, cells have to supply enough four-carbon intermediates from degradation of carbohydrate or certain amino acids to compensate for the rate of removal. Pathways or reactions that replenish the intermediates of the TCA cycle are referred to as *anaplerotic* ("filling up").

1. PYRUVATE CARBOXYLASE IS A MAJOR ANAPLEROTIC ENZYME

Pyruvate carboxylase is one of the major anaplerotic enzymes in the cell. It catalyzes the addition of CO_2 to pyruvate to form oxaloacetate (Fig. 20.18). Like most carboxylases, pyruvate carboxylase contains biotin (a vitamin), which forms a covalent intermediate with CO_2 in a reaction that requires ATP and Mg^{2+} (see Fig. 8.12). The activated CO_2 is then transferred to pyruvate to form the carboxyl group of oxaloacetate.

Pyruvate carboxylase is found in many tissues such as liver, brain, adipocytes, and fibroblasts where its function is anaplerotic. Its concentration is high in liver and kidney cortex where there is a continuous removal of oxaloacetate and malate from the TCA cycle to enter the gluconeogenic pathway.

Pyruvate carboxylase is activated by acetyl-CoA and inhibited by high concentrations of many acyl-CoA derivatives. As the concentration of oxaloacetate is depleted through the efflux of TCA cycle intermediates, the rate of the citrate synthase reaction decreases and acetyl-CoA concentration rises. The acetyl-CoA then activates pyruvate carboxylase to synthesize more oxaloacetate.

2. AMINO ACID DEGRADATION FORMS TCA CYCLE INTERMEDIATES

The pathways for oxidation of many amino acids convert their carbon skeletons into five- and four-carbon intermediates of the TCA cycle that can regenerate oxaloacetate

FIG. 20.18. Pyruvate carboxylase reaction. Pyruvate carboxylase adds a carboxyl group from bicarbonate (which is in equilibrium with CO_2) to pyruvate to form oxaloacetate. Biotin is used to activate and transfer the CO_2. The energy to form the covalent biotin–CO_2 complex is provided by the high-energy phosphate bond of ATP, which is cleaved in the reaction. The enzyme is activated by acetyl coenzyme A (acetyl-CoA).

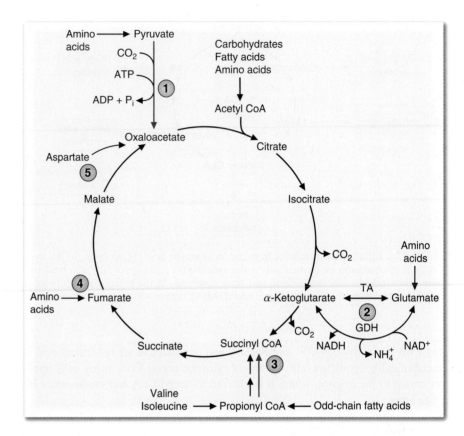

FIG. 20.19. Major anaplerotic pathways of the tricarboxylic acid (TCA) cycle. (1) and (3) (red arrows) are the two major anaplerotic pathways. (1) Pyruvate carboxylase. (2) Glutamate is reversibly converted to α-ketoglutarate by transaminases (TA) and glutamate dehydrogenase (GDH) in many tissues. (3) The carbon skeletons of valine and isoleucine, a three-carbon unit from odd-chain fatty acid oxidation, and a number of other compounds enter the TCA cycle at the level of succinyl-CoA. Other amino acids are also degraded to fumarate (4) and oxaloacetate (5), principally in the liver.

 Pyruvate carboxylase deficiency is one of the genetic diseases grouped together under the clinical manifestations of Leigh disease. In the mild form, the patient presents early in life with delayed development and a mild-to-moderate lactic acidemia. Patients who survive are severely mentally retarded, and there is a loss of cerebral neurons. In the brain, pyruvate carboxylase is present in the astrocytes, which use TCA cycle intermediates to synthesize glutamine. This pathway is essential for neuronal survival. The major cause of the lactic acidemia is that cells dependent on pyruvate carboxylase for an anaplerotic supply of oxaloacetate cannot oxidize pyruvate in the TCA cycle (because of low oxaloacetate levels), and the liver cannot convert pyruvate to glucose (because the pyruvate carboxylase reaction is required for this pathway to occur), so the excess pyruvate is converted to lactate.

(Fig. 20.19). Alanine and serine carbons can enter through pyruvate carboxylase (see Fig. 20.19, circle 1). In all tissues with mitochondria (except for, surprisingly, the liver), oxidation of the two branched-chain amino acids isoleucine and valine to succinyl-CoA forms a major anaplerotic route (see Fig. 20.19, circle 3). In the liver, other compounds that form propionyl-CoA (e.g., methionine, threonine, and odd-chain-length or branched fatty acids) also enter the TCA cycle as succinyl-CoA. In most tissues, glutamine is taken up from the blood, converted to glutamate, and then oxidized to α-ketoglutarate, forming another major anaplerotic route (see Fig. 20.19, circle 2). However, the TCA cycle cannot be resupplied with intermediates by even-chain-length fatty acid oxidation or by ketone body oxidation, which forms only acetyl-CoA. In the TCA cycle, two carbons are lost from citrate before succinyl-CoA is formed, so there is no net conversion of acetyl carbon to oxaloacetate.

CLINICAL COMMENTS

Otto Shape. **Otto Shape** is experiencing the benefits of physical conditioning. A variety of functional adaptations in the heart, lungs, vascular system, and skeletal muscle occur in response to regular graded exercise. The pumping efficiency of the heart increases, allowing greater cardiac output with fewer beats per minute and at a lower rate of oxygen utilization. The lungs extract a greater percentage of oxygen from the inspired air, allowing fewer respirations per unit of activity. The vasodilatory capacity of the arterial beds in skeletal muscle increases, promoting greater delivery of oxygen and fuels to exercising muscle. Concurrently, the venous drainage capacity in muscle is enhanced, ensuring that lactic acid will not accumulate in contracting tissues. These adaptive changes in physiologic responses are accompanied by increases in the number, size, and activity of skeletal muscle mitochondria along with the content of TCA cycle enzymes and components of the electron-transport chain. These changes markedly enhance the oxidative capacity of exercising muscle.

In skeletal muscle and other tissues, ATP is generated by anaerobic glycolysis when the rate of aerobic respiration is inadequate to meet the rate of ATP utilization. Under these circumstances, the rate of pyruvate production exceeds the cell's capacity to oxidize NADH in the electron-transport chain and, hence, to oxidize pyruvate in the TCA cycle. The excess pyruvate is reduced to lactate. Because lactate is an acid, its accumulation affects the muscle and causes pain and swelling.

 Ann O'Rexia. **Ann O'Rexia** is experiencing fatigue for several reasons. She has iron deficiency anemia, which affects iron-containing hemoglobin in her red blood cells, iron in aconitase and succinic dehydrogenase, as well as iron in the heme proteins of the electron-transport chain. She may also be experiencing the consequences of multiple vitamin deficiencies, including thiamine, riboflavin, and niacin (the vitamin precursor of NAD^+). It is less likely, but possible, that she also has subclinical deficiencies of pantothenate (the precursor of CoA) or biotin. As a result, Ann's muscles must use glycolysis as their primary source of energy, which results in sore muscles.

Riboflavin deficiency generally occurs in conjunction with other water-soluble vitamin deficiencies. The classic deficiency symptoms are *cheilosis* (inflammation of the corners of the mouth), *glossitis* (magenta tongue), and *seborrheic* ("greasy") dermatitis. It is also characterized by sore throat, edema of the pharyngeal and oral mucus membranes, and normochromic, normocytic anemia associated with pure red cell cytoplasia of the bone marrow. However, it is not known whether the glossitis and dermatitis are actually due to multiple vitamin deficiencies.

Riboflavin has a wide distribution in foods, and small amounts are present as coenzymes in most plant and animal tissues. Eggs, lean meats, milk, broccoli, and enriched breads and cereals are especially good sources. A portion of our niacin requirement can be met by synthesis from tryptophan. Meat (especially red meat), liver, legumes, milk, eggs, alfalfa, cereal grains, yeast, and fish are good sources of niacin and tryptophan.

 Al Martini. **Al Martini** presents a second time with an alcohol-related high-output form of heart failure that is sometimes referred to as *wet beriberi* or as the *beriberi heart* (see Chapter 9). The word *wet* refers to the fluid retention that may eventually occur when left ventricular contractility is so compromised that cardiac output, although initially relatively "high," cannot meet the "demands" of the peripheral vascular beds, which have dilated in response to the thiamine deficiency.

The cardiomyopathy is related directly to a reduction in the normal biochemical function of the vitamin thiamine in heart muscle. Inhibition of the α-keto acid dehydrogenase complexes causes accumulation of α-keto acids in heart muscle (and in blood), resulting in a chemically induced cardiomyopathy. Impairment of two other functions of thiamine may also contribute to the cardiomyopathy. Thiamine pyrophosphate (TPP) serves as the coenzyme for transketolase in the pentose phosphate pathway, and pentose phosphates accumulate in thiamine deficiency. In addition, thiamine triphosphate (a different coenzyme form) may function in Na^+ conductance channels.

 Beriberi, now known to be caused by thiamine deficiency, was attributed to lack of a nitrogenous component in food by Takaki, a Japanese surgeon, in 1884. In 1890, Eijkman, a Dutch physician working in Java, noted that the polyneuritis associated with beriberi could be prevented by rice bran that had been removed during polishing. Thiamine is present in the bran portion of grains, and it is abundant in pork and legumes. In contrast to most vitamins, milk and milk products, seafood, fruits, and vegetables are *not* good sources of thiamine.

Immediate treatment with large doses (50 to 100 mg) of intravenous thiamine may produce a measurable decrease in cardiac output and increase in peripheral vascular resistance as early as 30 minutes after the initial injection. Dietary supplementation of thiamine is not as effective because ethanol consumption interferes with thiamine absorption. Because ethanol also affects the absorption of most water-soluble vitamins or their conversion to the coenzyme form, **Al Martini** was also given a bolus containing a multivitamin supplement.

BIOCHEMICAL COMMENTS

Compartmentation of Mitochondrial Enzymes. The mitochondrion forms a structural, functional, and regulatory compartment within the cell. The inner mitochondrial membrane is impermeable to anions and cations, and compounds can cross the membrane only on specific transport proteins. The enzymes of the tricarboxylic acid (TCA) cycle, therefore, have more direct access to products of the previous reaction in the pathway than they would if these products were able to diffuse throughout the cell. Complex formation between enzymes also restricts access to pathway intermediates. Malate dehydrogenase and citrate synthase may form a loosely associated complex. The multienzyme pyruvate dehydrogenase and α-ketoglutarate dehydrogenase complexes are examples of substrate channeling by tightly bound enzymes; only the transacylase enzyme has access to the thiamine-bound intermediate of the reaction, and only lipoamide dehydrogenase has access to reduced lipoic acid.

Compartmentation plays an important role in regulation. The close association between the rate of the electron-transport chain and the rate of the TCA cycle is maintained by their mutual access to the same pool of NADH and NAD$^+$ in the mitochondrial matrix. NAD$^+$, NADH, CoASH, and acyl-CoA derivatives have no transport proteins and cannot cross the mitochondrial membrane. Thus, all of the dehydrogenases compete for the same NAD$^+$ molecules and are inhibited when NADH rises. Likewise, accumulation of acyl-CoA derivatives (e.g., acetyl-CoA) within the mitochondrial matrix affects other CoA-using reactions, either by competing at the active site or by limiting CoASH availability.

Import of Nuclear-Encoded Proteins. All mitochondrial matrix proteins, such as the TCA cycle enzymes, are encoded by the nuclear genome. They are imported into the mitochondrial matrix as unfolded proteins that are pushed and pulled through channels in the outer and inner mitochondrial membranes (Fig. 20.20). Proteins destined for the mitochondrial matrix have either a targeting N-terminal presequence of about 20 amino acids that includes several positively charged amino acid residues or an internal mitochondrial localizing signal. The mitochondrial matrix proteins are synthesized on free ribosomes in the cytosol and maintain an unfolded conformation by binding to hsp70 chaperonins. This basic presequence binds to a receptor in a *t*ranslocases of the *o*uter *m*embrane (TOM) complex (see Fig. 20.20, step 1). The TOM complexes consist of channel proteins, assembly proteins, and receptor proteins with different specificities (e.g., TOM20 binds the matrix protein presequence). Negatively charged acidic residues on the receptors and in the channel pore assist in translocation of the matrix protein through the channel, presequence first.

The matrix preprotein is translocated across the inner membrane through a *t*ranslocases of the *i*nner *m*embrane (TIM) complex (see Fig. 20.20, step 2). Insertion of the preprotein into the TIM channel is driven by the potential difference across the membrane, $\Delta\psi$. Mitochondrial hsp70 (mthsp70), which is bound to the matrix side of the TIM complex, binds the incoming preprotein and may "ratchet" it through the membrane. Adenosine triphosphate (ATP) is required for binding of mthsp70 to the TIM complex and again for the subsequent dissociation of the mthsp70 and

FIG. 20.20. Model for the import of nuclear-encoded proteins into the mitochondrial matrix. The matrix preprotein with its positively charged N-terminal presequence is shown in *red. hsp*, heat-shock protein; *OM*, outer mitochondrial membrane; *IMS*, intermembrane space; *IM*, inner mitochondrial membrane; *TOM*, translocases of the outer mitochondrial membrane; *TIM*, translocases of the inner mitochondrial membrane; *mthsp70*, mitochondrial heat-shock protein 70.

the matrix preprotein. In the matrix, the preprotein may require another heat-shock protein, hsp60, for proper folding. The final step in the import process is cleavage of the signal sequence by a matrix-processing protease (see Fig. 20.20, step 3).

Proteins of the inner mitochondrial membrane are imported through a similar process, using TOM and TIM complexes containing different protein components.

Key Concepts

- The tricarboxylic acid (TCA) cycle accounts for more than two-thirds of the adenosine triphosphate (ATP) generated from fuel oxidation.
- All of the enzymes required for the TCA cycle are in the mitochondria.
- Acetyl coenzyme A (acetyl-CoA), generated from fuel oxidation, is the substrate for the TCA cycle.
- Acetyl-CoA, when oxidized via the cycle, generates CO_2, reduced electron carriers, and guanosine triphosphate (GTP).
- The reduced electron carriers [NADH, FAD(2H)] donate electrons to O_2 via the electron-transport chain, which leads to ATP generation from oxidative phosphorylation.
- The cycle requires several cofactors to function properly, some of which are derived from vitamins. These include thiamine pyrophosphate (TTP) (derived from vitamin B_1), flavin adenine dinucleotide (FAD) (derived from vitamin B_2, riboflavin), and coenzyme A (derived from pantothenic acid).
- Intermediates of the TCA cycle are used for many biosynthetic reactions and are replaced by anaplerotic (refilling) reactions within the cell.
- The cycle is carefully regulated within the mitochondria by energy and the levels of reduced electron carriers. As energy levels decrease, the rate of the cycle increases.
- Impaired functioning of the TCA cycle leads to an inability to generate ATP from fuel oxidation and an accumulation of TCA cycle precursors.
- Diseases discussed in this chapter are summarized in Table 20.3

Table 20.3   Diseases Discussed in Chapter 20

Disease or Disorder	Environmental or Genetic	Comments
Obesity	Both	Increased physical activity without increasing caloric intake will lead to weight loss and increased exercise capacity. One effect of increased aerobic exercise is increasing the number and size of mitochondria in the muscle cells.
Anorexia nervosa	Both	Patients who have been malnourished for some time may exhibit subclinical deficiencies in many vitamins, including riboflavin and niacin, factors required for energy generation.
Congestive heart failure linked to alcoholism	Both	Thiamine deficiency brought about by chronic alcohol ingestion leads to inefficient energy production by the heart and failure to adequately pump blood throughout the body. The vitamin B1 deficiency reduces the activity of pyruvate dehydrogenase and the TCA cycle, severely restricting ATP generation.
Arsenic poisoning	Environmental	Arsenite inhibits enzymes and cofactors with free adjacent sulfhydral groups (lipoic acid is a target of arsenite), whereas arsenate acts as a phosphate analog and inhibits substrate-level phosphorylation reactions.
Leigh disease (subacute necrotizing encephalopathy)	Genetic	Deficiencies of the pyruvate dehydrogenase complex (PDC) as well as of pyruvate carboxylase are inherited disorders leading to lactic acidemia. In its most severe form, PDC deficiency presents with overwhelming lactic acidosis at birth, with death in the neonatal period. Even in less severe forms, neurologic symptoms arise due to the brain's dependence on glucose metabolism for energy. The most common PDC deficiency is X-linked, in the α-subunit of the pyruvate decarboxylase (E_1) subunit. Pyruvate carboxylase deficiency also leads to mental retardation.

TCA, tricarboxylic acid; ATP, adenosine triphosphate.

1. Which of the following coenzymes is unique to α-keto acid dehydrogenase complexes?

    A. NAD^+
    B. FAD
    C. GDP
    D. H_2O
    E. Lipoic acid

2. A patient diagnosed with thiamine deficiency exhibited fatigue and muscle cramps. The muscle cramps have been related to an accumulation of metabolic acids. Which of the following metabolic acids is most likely to accumulate in a thiamine deficiency?

    A. Isocitric acid
    B. Pyruvic acid
    C. Succinic acid
    D. Malic acid
    E. Oxaloacetic acid

3. Succinate dehydrogenase differs from all other enzymes in the TCA cycle in that it is the only enzyme that displays which of the following characteristics?

    A. It is embedded in the inner mitochondrial membrane.
    B. It is inhibited by NADH.
    C. It contains bound FAD.
    D. It contains Fe–S centers.
    E. It is regulated by a kinase.

4. During exercise, stimulation of the TCA cycle results principally from which of the following?

    A. Allosteric activation of isocitrate dehydrogenase by increased NADH
    B. Allosteric activation of fumarase by increased ADP
    C. A rapid decrease in the concentration of four-carbon intermediates
    D. Product inhibition of citrate synthase
    E. Stimulation of the flux through a number of enzymes by a decreased $NADH/NAD^+$ ratio

5. Coenzyme A is synthesized from which of the following vitamins?

    A. Niacin
    B. Riboflavin
    C. Vitamin A
    D. Pantothenate
    E. Vitamin C

21 Oxidative Phosphorylation and Mitochondrial Function

*Energy from fuel oxidation is converted to the high-energy phosphate bonds of adenosine triphosphate (ATP) by the process of **oxidative phosphorylation (OXPHOS)**. Most of the energy from oxidation of fuels in the tricarboxylic acid (TCA) cycle and other pathways is conserved in the form of the reduced electron-accepting coenzymes, NADH and FAD(2H). The **electron-transport chain** oxidizes **NADH** and **FAD(2H)** and donates the electrons to O_2, which is reduced to H_2O (Fig. 21.1). Energy from reduction of O_2 is used for phosphorylation of adenosine diphosphate (ADP) to ATP by **ATP synthase (F_0F_1 ATPase)**. The net yield of OXPHOS is approximately 2.5 mol of ATP per mole of NADH oxidized or 1.5 mol of ATP per mole of FAD(2H) oxidized.*

*__Chemiosmotic Model of ATP Synthesis.__ The **chemiosmotic model** explains how energy from transport of electrons to O_2 is transformed into the high-energy phosphate bond of ATP (see Fig. 21.1). Basically, the electron-transport chain contains three large **protein complexes (I, III, and IV)** that span the inner mitochondrial membrane. As electrons pass through these complexes in a series of oxidation–reduction reactions, protons are transferred from the mitochondrial matrix to the cytosolic side of the inner mitochondrial membrane. The pumping of protons generates an **electrochemical gradient (Δp)** across the membrane composed of the membrane potential and the proton gradient. ATP synthase contains a proton pore that spans the inner mitochondrial membrane and a catalytic headpiece that protrudes into the matrix. As protons are driven into the matrix through the pore, they change the conformation of the headpiece, which releases ATP from one site and catalyzes formation of ATP from ADP and inorganic phosphate (P_i) at another site.*

*__Deficiencies of Electron Transport.__ In cells, complete transfer of electrons from NADH and FAD(2H) through the chain to O_2 is necessary for ATP generation. Impaired transfer through any complex can have pathologic consequences. Fatigue can result from iron deficiency **anemia**, which decreases **Fe** for **Fe–S centers** and **cytochromes**. **Cytochrome c_1 oxidase**, which contains the O_2-binding site, is inhibited by **cyanide**. **Mitochondrial DNA (mtDNA)**, which is maternally inherited, encodes some of the subunits of the electron-transport chain complexes and ATP synthase. **OXPHOS diseases** are caused by **mutations** in **nuclear DNA** or **mtDNA** that decrease mitochondrial capacity for OXPHOS.*

*__Regulation of Oxidative Phosphorylation.__ The rate of the electron-transport chain is **coupled** to the rate of ATP synthesis by the transmembrane electrochemical gradient. As ATP is used for energy-requiring processes and ADP levels increase, proton influx through the ATP synthase pore generates more ATP, and the electron-transport chain responds to restore Δp. In **uncoupling**, protons return to the matrix by a mechanism that bypasses the ATP synthase pore, and the energy is released as heat. **Proton leakage, chemical***

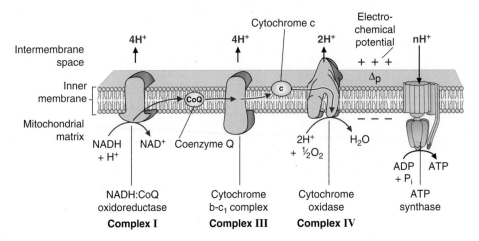

FIG. 21.1. Oxidative phosphorylation. *Red arrows* show the path of electron transport from NADH to O_2. As electrons pass through the chain, protons are pumped from the mitochondrial matrix to the intermembrane space, thereby establishing an electrochemical potential gradient, Δp, across the inner mitochondrial membrane. The positive and negative charges on the membrane denote the membrane potential ($\Delta\psi$). Δp drives protons into the matrix through a pore in ATP synthase, which uses the energy to form ATP from ADP and P_i.

uncouplers, and regulated **uncoupling proteins** *increase our metabolic rate and heat generation.*

   Mitochondria and Cell Death. *Although OXPHOS is a mitochondrial process, most ATP use occurs outside of the mitochondrion. ATP synthesized from OXPHOS is actively transported from the matrix to the intermembrane space by* **adenine nucleotide translocase (ANT).** ***Porins form voltage-dependent anion channels (VDACs)*** *through the outer mitochondrial membrane for the diffusion of H_2O, ATP metabolites, and other ions. Under certain types of stress, ANT, VDACs, and other proteins form a nonspecific open channel known as the* **mitochondrial permeability transition pore.** *This pore is associated with events that lead rapidly to* **necrotic cell death.**

THE WAITING ROOM

Cora Nari was recovering uneventfully from her heart attack 1 month earlier (see Chapter 19) when she won the Georgia State Lottery. When she heard her number announced over television, she experienced crushing chest pain, grew short of breath, and passed out. She regained consciousness as she was being rushed to the hospital emergency room.

   On initial examination, her blood pressure was extremely high and her heart rhythm was irregular. Her blood levels of creatine kinase muscle–brain (CK-MB) and troponin I (TnI) were elevated. An electrocardiogram showed unequivocal evidence of severe lack of oxygen (ischemia) in the muscles of the anterior and lateral walls of her heart. Life-support measures including nasal oxygen were initiated. An intravenous drip of nitroprusside, a vasodilating agent, was started in an effort to reduce her hypertension. After her blood pressure was well controlled, and because the hospital did not have a cardiac catheterization laboratory, a decision was made to administer intravenous tissue plasminogen activator (tPA) in an attempt to break up any intracoronary artery blood clots in vessels supplying the ischemic myocardium (thrombolytic therapy).

Cora Nari is experiencing a second myocardial infarction. Ischemia (low blood flow) has caused hypoxia (low levels of oxygen) in the threatened area of her heart muscle, resulting in inadequate generation of ATP for the maintenance of low intracellular Na^+ and Ca^{2+} levels (see Chapter 19). As a consequence, the myocardial cells in that specific location have become swollen and the cytosolic proteins creatine kinase (MB isoform) and troponin (heart isoform) have leaked into the blood. (See **Ann Jeina**, Chapters 6 and 7).

A ^{123}I thyroid uptake and scan performed on **X. S. Teefore** confirmed that his hyperthyroidism was the result of Graves disease (see Chapter 19). *Graves disease*, also known as *diffuse toxic goiter*, is an autoimmune genetic disorder caused by the generation of human thyroid-stimulating immunoglobulins. These immunoglobulins stimulate growth of the thyroid gland (goiter) and excess secretion of the thyroid hormones, T_3 and T_4. Because heat production is increased under these circumstances, Mr. Teefore's heat intolerance and sweating were growing worse with time.

Ivy Sharer, an intravenous drug user, appeared to be responding well to her multidrug regimens to treat pulmonary tuberculosis and AIDS (see Chapters 11, 12, 15, and 16). In the past 6 weeks, however, she has developed increasing weakness in her extremities, to the point that she has difficulty carrying light objects or walking. Physical examination indicates a diffuse proximal and distal muscle weakness associated with muscle atrophy. The muscles are neither painful on motion nor tender to compression. The blood level of the muscle enzymes, creatine phosphokinase (CPK) and aldolase, are normal. An electromyogram (EMG) revealed a generalized reduction in the muscle action potentials, suggestive of a primary myopathic process. Proton spectroscopy of her brain and upper spinal cord showed no anatomic or biochemical abnormalities. The diffuse and progressive skeletal muscle weakness was out of proportion to that expected from her AIDS or her tuberculosis. This information led her physicians to consider the possibility that her skeletal muscle dysfunction might be drug induced.

 An electromyogram measures the electrical potential of muscle cells both at rest and while contracting. Electrodes are inserted through the skin and into the muscle, and baseline recordings (no contraction) are obtained, followed by measurements of electrical activity when the muscle contracts. The electrode is retracted in a small amount, and the measurements are repeated. This occurs for up to 10 to 20 measurements, thereby sampling many distinct areas of the muscle. Under normal conditions, muscles at rest will have minimal electrical activity, which increases significantly as the muscle contracts. Electromyograms that deviate from the norm suggest an underlying pathology interfering with membrane polarization–depolarization as the nerve cells instruct the muscle cells to contract.

I. OXIDATIVE PHOSPHORYLATION

Generation of ATP from oxidative phosphorylation requires an electron donor (NADH or FAD[2H]), an electron acceptor (O_2), an intact inner mitochondrial membrane that is impermeable to protons, all the components of the electron-transport chain, and ATP synthase. It is regulated by the rate of ATP use.

Most cells are dependent on oxidative phosphorylation for ATP homeostasis. During oxygen deprivation from ischemia (low blood flow), an inability to generate energy from the electron-transport chain results in increased permeability of this membrane and mitochondrial swelling. Mitochondrial swelling is a key element in the pathogenesis of irreversible cell injury leading to cell lysis and death (necrosis).

A. Overview of Oxidative Phosphorylation

Our understanding of oxidative phosphorylation is based on the chemiosmotic hypothesis, which proposes that the energy for ATP synthesis is provided by an electrochemical gradient across the inner mitochondrial membrane. This electrochemical gradient is generated by the components of the electron-transport chain, which pump protons across the inner mitochondrial membrane as they sequentially accept and donate electrons (see Fig. 21.1). The final acceptor is O_2, which is reduced to H_2O.

1. ELECTRON TRANSFER FROM NADH TO OXYGEN

In the electron-transport chain, electrons donated by NADH or FAD(2H) are passed sequentially through a series of electron carriers embedded in the inner mitochondrial membrane. Each of the components of the electron-transfer chain is reduced as it accepts an electron and then oxidized as it passes the electrons to the next member of the chain. From NADH, electrons are transferred sequentially through NADH:CoQ oxidoreductase (complex I), coenzyme Q (CoQ), the cytochrome b–c_1 complex (complex III), cytochrome c, and finally, cytochrome c oxidase (complex IV). NADH:CoQ oxidoreductase, the cytochrome b–c_1 complex, and cytochrome c oxidase are each multisubunit protein complexes that span the inner

 Arlyn Foma, who has a follicular-type non-Hodgkin lymphoma was being treated with the anthracycline drug doxorubicin (see Chapter 16). During the course of his treatment, he developed biventricular heart failure. Although doxorubicin is a highly effective anticancer agent against a wide variety of human tumors, its clinical use is limited by a specific, cumulative, dose-dependent cardiotoxicity. Impairment of mitochondrial function may play a major role in this toxicity. Doxorubicin binds to cardiolipin, a lipid component of the inner membrane of mitochondria, where it might directly affect components of oxidative phosphorylation. Doxorubicin inhibits succinate oxidation, inactivates cytochrome oxidase, interacts with CoQ, adversely affects ion pumps, and inhibits ATP synthase, resulting in decreased ATP levels and mildly swollen mitochondria. It decreases the ability of the mitochondria to sequester Ca^{2+} and increases free radicals (highly reactive single-electron forms), leading to damage of the mitochondrial membrane (see Chapter 24). It also might affect heart function indirectly through other mechanisms.

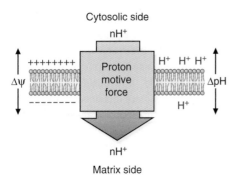

FIG. 21.2. Proton motive force (electrochemical gradient) across the inner mitochondrial membrane. The proton motive force consists of a membrane potential, $\Delta\psi$, and a proton gradient, denoted by ΔpH for the difference in pH across the membrane. The electrochemical potential is called the *proton motive force* because it represents the potential energy driving protons to return to the more negatively charged alkaline matrix.

mitochondrial membrane. CoQ is a lipid-soluble quinone that is not protein bound and is free to diffuse in the lipid membrane. It transports electrons from complex I to complex III and is an intrinsic part of the proton pump for each of these complexes. Cytochrome c is a small protein in the intermembrane space that transfers electrons from the b–c_1 complex to cytochrome oxidase. The terminal complex, cytochrome c oxidase, contains the binding site for O_2. As O_2 accepts electrons from the chain, it is reduced to H_2O.

2. THE ELECTROCHEMICAL POTENTIAL GRADIENT

At each of the three large membrane-spanning complexes in the chain, electron transfer is accompanied by proton pumping across the membrane. There is an energy drop of approximately 16 kcal in reduction potential as electrons pass through each of these complexes, which provides the energy required to move protons against a concentration gradient. The membrane is impermeable to protons, so they cannot diffuse through the lipid bilayer back into the matrix. Thus, in actively respiring mitochondria, the intermembrane space and cytosol may be approximately 0.75 pH unit lower than the matrix.

The transmembrane movement of protons generates an electrochemical gradient with two components: the membrane potential (the external face of the membrane is charged positive relative to the matrix side) and the proton gradient (the intermembrane space has a higher proton concentration and is, therefore, more acidic than the matrix) (Fig. 21.2). The electrochemical gradient is sometimes called the *proton motive force* because it is the energy that pushes the protons to reenter the matrix to equilibrate on both sides of the membrane. The protons are attracted to the more negatively charged matrix side of the membrane, where the pH is more alkaline.

3. ADENOSINE TRIPHOSPHATE SYNTHASE

ATP synthase (F_0F_1 ATPase), the enzyme that generates ATP, is a multisubunit enzyme that contains an inner membrane portion (F_0) and a stalk and headpiece (F_1) that project into the matrix (Fig. 21.3). The 12 c-subunits in the membrane form a rotor that is attached to a central asymmetric shaft composed of the ε- and γ-subunits. The headpiece is composed of three $\alpha\beta$-subunit pairs. Each β-subunit

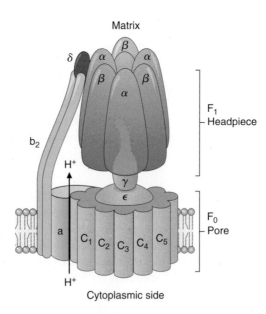

FIG. 21.3. ATP synthase (F_0F_1 ATPase). Note that the matrix side of the mitochondrial inner membrane is at the top of the figure.

contains a catalytic site for ATP synthesis. The headpiece is held stationary by a δ-subunit attached to a long b-subunit connected to a-subunit in the membrane.

The influx of protons through the proton channel turns the rotor. The proton channel is formed by the c-subunit on one side and the a-subunit on the other side. Although the channel is continuous, it has two offset portions: one portion open directly to the intermembrane space and one portion open directly to the matrix. In the current model, each c-subunit contains a glutamyl carboxyl group that extends into the proton channel. Because this carboxyl group accepts a proton from the intermembrane space, the c-subunit rotates into the hydrophobic lipid membrane. The rotation exposes a different proton-containing c-subunit to the portion of the channel that is open directly to the matrix side. Because the matrix has a lower proton concentration, the glutamyl carboxylic acid group releases a proton into the matrix portion of the channel. Rotation is completed by an attraction between the negatively charged glutamyl residue and a positively charged arginyl group on the a-subunit.

According to the binding-change mechanism, as the asymmetric shaft rotates to a new position, it forms different binding associations with the $\alpha\beta$-subunits (Fig. 21.4). The new position of the shaft alters the conformation of one β-subunit so that it releases a molecule of ATP and another subunit spontaneously catalyzes synthesis of ATP from inorganic phosphate, one proton, and adenosine diphosphate (ADP). Thus, energy from the electrochemical gradient is used to change the conformation of the ATP synthase subunits so that the newly synthesized ATP is released. Twelve c-subunits are hypothesized, and it takes 12 protons to complete one turn of the rotor and synthesize three ATPs.

B. Oxidation–Reduction Components of the Electron-Transport Chain

Electron transport to O_2 occurs via a series of oxidation–reduction steps in which each successive component of the chain is reduced as it accepts electrons and oxidized as it passes electrons to the next component of the chain. The oxidation–reduction components of the chain include flavin mononucleotide (FMN), iron–sulfur (Fe–S) centers, CoQ, and Fe in cytochromes b, c_1, c, a, and a_3. Copper (Cu) is also a component of cytochromes a and a_3 (Fig. 21.5). With the exception of CoQ, all of these electron acceptors are tightly bound to the protein subunits of the carriers. FMN, like flavin adenine dinucleotide (FAD), is synthesized from the vitamin riboflavin (see Fig. 19.10).

The reduction potential of each complex of the chain is at a lower energy level than the previous complex, so energy is released as electrons pass through each complex. This energy is used to move protons against their concentration gradient, so they become concentrated on the cytosolic side of the inner membrane.

1. NADH:COQ OXIDOREDUCTASE

NADH:CoQ oxidoreductase (also named *NADH dehydrogenase*) is an enormous 42-subunit complex that contains a binding site for NADH, several FMN and Fe–S center-binding proteins, and binding sites for CoQ (see Fig. 21.5). An FMN accepts two electrons from NADH and is able to pass single electrons to the Fe–S centers (Fig. 21.6). Fe–S centers, which are able to delocalize single electrons into large orbitals, transfer electrons to and from CoQ. Fe–S centers are also present in other enzyme systems, such as proteins within the cytochrome b–c_1 complex, which transfer electrons to CoQ and in aconitase in the TCA cycle.

2. SUCCINATE DEHYDROGENASE AND OTHER FLAVOPROTEINS

In addition to NADH:CoQ oxidoreductase, succinate dehydrogenase and other flavoproteins in the inner mitochondrial membrane also pass electrons to CoQ (see Fig. 21.5). Succinate dehydrogenase is part of the TCA cycle and also a component

FIG. 21.4. Binding-change mechanism for ATP synthesis. The three $\alpha\beta$-subunit pairs of the ATP synthase headpiece have binding sites that can exist in three different conformations, depending on the position of the γ-stalk subunit. *(1)* When ADP + P_i bind to an open site and the proton influx rotates the γ-spindle *(white arrow)*, the conformation of the subunits change and ATP is released from one site. (ATP dissociation is thus the energy-requiring step). Bound ADP and P_i combine to form ATP at another site. *(2)* As the ADP + P_i bind to the new open site, and the γ-shaft rotates, the conformations of the sites change again, and ATP is released. ADP and P_i combine to form another ATP.

FIG. 21.5. Components of the electron-transport chain. NADH:CoQ oxidoreductase (complex I) spans the membrane and has a proton-pumping mechanism involving CoQ. The electrons go from CoQ to cytochrome b–c_1 complex (complex III); electron transfer does *not* involve complex II. Succinate dehydrogenase (complex II), glycerol-3-phosphate dehydrogenase, and ETF:Q oxidoreductase all transfer electrons to CoQ, but they do not span the membrane and do not have proton-pumping mechanisms. As CoQ accepts electrons and protons from the matrix side, it is converted to QH_2. Electrons are transferred from complex III to complex IV (cytochrome c oxidase) by cytochrome c, a small cytochrome in the intermembrane space that has reversible binding sites on the b–c_1 complex and cytochrome c oxidase.

FIG. 21.6. Fe_4S_4 centers. In Fe–S centers, the Fe is chelated to free sulfur (S) atoms and to cysteine sulfhydryl groups on proteins (indicated by Pr). Other Fe–S centers contain Fe_2S_2. The protein subunits are sometimes called *non–heme iron proteins*. When these proteins are treated with acid, the free sulfur produces hydrogen sulfide (H_2S)—the familiar smell of rotten eggs.

of complex II of the electron-transport chain. ETF-CoQ oxidoreductase accepts electrons from ETF (*e*lectron-*t*ransferring *f*lavoprotein), which acquires them from fatty acid oxidation and other pathways. Both of these flavoproteins have Fe–S centers. Glycerol-3-phosphate dehydrogenase is a flavoprotein that is part of a shuttle for reoxidizing cytosolic NADH.

The free-energy drop in electron transfer between NADH and CoQ of approximately −13 to −14 kcal is able to support movement of four protons. However, the FAD in succinate dehydrogenase (as well as ETF-CoQ oxidoreductase and glycerol-3-phosphate dehydrogenase) is at roughly the same redox potential as CoQ, and no energy is released as they transfer electrons to CoQ. These proteins (complex II) do not span the membrane and consequently do not have a proton-pumping mechanism.

3. COENZYME Q

CoQ is the only component of the electron-transport chain that is not protein bound. The large hydrophobic side chain of 10 isoprenoid units (50 carbons) confers lipid solubility, and CoQ is able to diffuse through the lipids of the inner mitochondrial membrane (Fig. 21.7). When the oxidized quinone form accepts a single electron, it forms a free radical (a compound with a single electron in an orbital). The transfer of single electrons makes it the major site for generation of toxic oxygen free radicals in the body (see Chapter 24).

The semiquinone can accept a second electron and two protons from the matrix side of the membrane to form the fully reduced quinone. The mobility of CoQ in the membrane, its ability to accept one or two electrons, and its ability to accept

FIG. 21.7. Coenzyme Q contains a quinone with a long lipophilic side chain comprising 10 isoprenoid units (thus, it is sometimes called *CoQ10*). CoQ can accept one electron (e^-) to become the half-reduced form or two e^- to become fully reduced.

and donate protons enable it to participate in the proton pumps for both complexes I and III as it shuttles electrons between them (see Section I.C). CoQ is also called *ubiquinone* (the ubiquitous quinone) because quinones with similar structures are found in all plants and animals.

4. CYTOCHROMES

The remaining components in the electron-transport chain are cytochromes (see Fig. 21.5). Each cytochrome is a protein that contains a bound heme (i.e., an Fe atom bound to a porphyrin nucleus similar in structure to the heme in hemoglobin) (Fig. 21.8).

Because of differences in the protein component of the cytochromes and small differences in the heme structure, each heme has a different reduction potential. The cytochromes of the $b-c_1$ complex have a higher energy level than those of cytochrome oxidase (a and a_3). Thus, energy is released by electron transfer between complexes III and IV. The iron atoms in the cytochromes are in the Fe^{3+} state. As they accept an electron, they are reduced to Fe^{2+}. As they are reoxidized to Fe^{3+}, the electrons pass to the next component of the electron-transport chain.

5. COPPER (CU⁺) AND THE REDUCTION OF OXYGEN

The last cytochrome complex is cytochrome oxidase, which passes electrons from cytochrome c to O_2 (see Fig. 21.5). It contains cytochromes a and a_3 and the oxygen-binding site. A whole oxygen molecule, O_2, must accept four electrons to be reduced to two H_2O molecules. Bound copper (Cu^+) ions in the cytochrome oxidase complex facilitate the collection of the four electrons and the reduction of O_2.

Cytochrome oxidase has a much lower K_m for O_2 than myoglobin (the heme-containing intracellular oxygen carrier) or hemoglobin (the heme-containing oxygen transporter in the blood). Thus, O_2 is "pulled" from the erythrocyte to myoglobin and from myoglobin to cytochrome oxidase, where it is reduced to H_2O.

C. Pumping of Protons

One of the tenets of the chemiosmotic theory is that energy from the oxidation–reduction reactions of the electron-transport chain is used to transport protons from

 Although iron deficiency anemia is characterized by decreased levels of hemoglobin and other iron-containing proteins in the blood, the iron-containing cytochromes and Fe–S centers of the electron-transport chain in tissues such as skeletal muscle are affected as rapidly. Fatigue in iron deficiency anemia, in patients such as **Ann O'Rexia** (see Chapter 16), results, in part, from the lack of electron transport for ATP production.

 The iron in the heme in hemoglobin, unlike the iron in the heme of cytochromes, never changes its oxidation state (it is Fe^{2+} in hemoglobin). If the iron in hemoglobin were to become oxidized (Fe^{3+}), the oxygen-binding capacity of the molecule would be lost. What accounts for this difference in iron oxidation states between hemoglobin and cytochromes?

FIG. 21.8.   Heme A. Heme A is found in cytochromes a and a_3. Cytochromes are proteins that contain a heme chelated with an iron atom. Hemes are derivatives of protoporphyrin IX. Each cytochrome has a heme with different modifications of the side chains *(indicated with dashed lines)*, resulting in a slightly different reduction potential and, consequently, a different position in the sequence of electron transfer.

A: Normally, the protein structures binding the heme either protect the iron from oxidation (such as the globin proteins) or allow oxidation to occur (such as happens in the cytochromes). However, in hemoglobin M, a rare hemoglobin variant found in the human population, a tyrosine is substituted for the histidine at position F8 in the normal hemoglobin A. This tyrosine stabilizes the Fe^{3+} form of heme, and these subunits cannot bind oxygen. This is a lethal condition if it is homozygous.

the matrix to the intermembrane space. This proton pumping is generally facilitated by the vectorial arrangement of the membrane-spanning complexes. Their structure allows them to pick up electrons and protons on one side of the membrane and release protons on the other side of the membrane as they transfer an electron to the next component of the chain. The direct physical link between proton movement and electron transfer can be illustrated by an examination of the Q cycle for the b–c_1 complex (Fig. 21.9). The Q cycle involves a double cycle of CoQ reduction and oxidation. CoQ accepts two protons at the matrix side together with two electrons; it then releases protons into the intermembrane space while donating one electron back to another component of the cytochrome b–c_1 complex and one to cytochrome c.

The mechanism for pumping protons at the NADH:CoQ oxidoreductase complex is not well understood, but it involves a Q cycle in which the Fe–S centers and FMN might participate. However, transmembrane proton movement at cytochrome c oxidase probably involves direct transport of the proton through a series of bound water molecules or amino acid side chains in the protein, a mechanism that has been described as a *proton wire*.

The significance of the direct link between the electron transfer and proton movement is that one cannot occur without the other. Thus, when protons are not being used for ATP synthesis, the proton gradient and the membrane potential buildup. This "proton back pressure" controls the rate of proton pumping, which controls electron transport and O_2 consumption.

D. Energy Yield from the Electron-Transport Chain

The overall free-energy release from oxidation of NADH by O_2 is approximately −53 kcal, and from FAD(2H) it is approximately −41 kcal. This ΔG^0 is so negative that the chain is never reversible; we never synthesize oxygen from H_2O. It is so negative that it drives NADH and FAD(2H) formation from the pathways of fuel oxidation, such as the TCA cycle and glycolysis, to completion.

FIG. 21.9. The proton motive Q cycle for the b–c_1 complex. *(1)* From $2QH_2$, electrons go down two different paths: One path is through an Fe–S center protein (ISP) toward cytochrome c *(red arrows)*. Another path is "backward" to one of the b cytochromes *(dashed arrows)*. *(2)* Electrons are transferred from ISP through cytochrome c_1. Cytochrome c, which is in the intermembrane space, binds to the b–c_1 complex to accept an electron. *(3)* Returning electrons go through another b cytochrome and are directed toward the matrix. *(4)* At the matrix side, electrons and $2H^+$ are accepted by Q. Q, coenzyme Q; $Q^{\cdot-}$, CoQ semiquinone; QH_2, CoQ hydroquinone.

Overall, each NADH donates two electrons, equivalent to the reduction of one-half of an O_2 molecule. A generally (but not universally) accepted estimate of the stoichiometry of ATP synthesis is that four protons are pumped at complex I, four protons at complex III, and two protons at complex IV. With four protons translocated for each ATP synthesized, an estimated 2.5 ATPs are formed for each NADH oxidized, and 1.5 ATPs are formed for each of the other FAD(2H)-containing flavoproteins that donate electrons to CoQ. (This calculation neglects proton requirements for the transport of phosphate and substrates from the cytosol, as well as the basal proton leak.) Thus, only approximately 30% of the energy available from NADH and FAD(2H) oxidation by O_2 is used for ATP synthesis. Some of the remaining energy in the electrochemical potential is used for the transport of anions and Ca^{2+} into the mitochondrion. The remainder of the energy is released as heat. Consequently, the electron-transport chain is also our major source of heat.

E. Respiratory Chain Inhibition and Sequential Transfer
In the cell, electron flow in the electron-transport chain must be sequential from NADH or a flavoprotein all the way to O_2 to generate ATP (see Fig. 21.5). In the absence of O_2, no ATP is generated from oxidative phosphorylation because electrons back up in the chain. Even complex I cannot pump protons to generate the electrochemical gradient because every molecule of CoQ already has electrons that it cannot pass down the chain without an O_2 to accept them at the end. The action of the respiratory chain inhibitor cyanide, which binds to cytochrome oxidase, is similar to that of anoxia: It prevents proton pumping by all three complexes. Complete inhibition of the b–c_1 complex prevents pumping at cytochrome oxidase because there is no donor of electrons; it prevents pumping at complex I because there is no electron acceptor. Although complete inhibition of any one complex inhibits proton pumping at all of the complexes, partial inhibition of proton pumping can occur when only a fraction of the molecules of a complex contains bound inhibitor. The partial inhibition results in a partial decrease of the maximal rate of ATP synthesis. Table 21.1 lists chemical inhibitors of oxidative phosphorylation and indicates the steps within either electron transport or ATP synthesis at which they act.

II. OXIDATIVE PHOSPHORYLATION DISEASES
Clinical diseases involving components of oxidative phosphorylation (referred to as *OXPHOS diseases*) are among the most commonly encountered degenerative diseases. The clinical pathology may be caused by gene mutations in either mitochondrial DNA (mtDNA) or nuclear DNA (nDNA) that encodes proteins required for normal oxidative phosphorylation.

 Cora Nari has a lack of oxygen in the anterior and lateral walls of her heart caused by severe ischemia (lack of blood flow), resulting from clots formed within certain coronary arteries at the site of ruptured atherosclerotic plaques. The limited availability of O_2 to act as an electron acceptor will decrease proton pumping and generation of an electrochemical potential gradient across the inner mitochondrial membrane of ischemic cells. As a consequence, the rate of ATP generation in these specific areas of her heart will decrease, thereby triggering events that lead to irreversible cell injury.

 Intravenous nitroprusside rapidly lowers elevated blood pressure through its direct vasodilating action. Fortunately, it was required in **Cora Nari's** case only for several hours. During prolonged infusions of 24 to 48 hours or more, nitroprusside is converted to cyanide, an inhibitor of the cytochrome c oxidase complex. Because small amounts of cyanide are detoxified in the liver by conversion to thiocyanate, which is excreted in the urine, the conversion of nitroprusside to cyanide can be monitored by following blood thiocyanate levels.

Table 21.1   Inhibitors of Oxidative Phosphorylation

Inhibitor	Site of Inhibition
Rotenone, Amytal	Transfer of electrons from complex I to coenzyme Q
Antimycin C	Transfer of electrons from complex III to cytochrome c
Carbon monoxide (CO)	Transfer of electrons from complex IV to oxygen
Cyanide (CN)	Transfer of electrons from complex IV to oxygen
Atractyloside	Inhibits the adenine nucleotide translocase (ANT)
Oligomycin	Inhibits proton flow through the F_0 component of the ATP synthase
Dinitrophenol	An uncoupler; facilitates proton transfer across the inner mitochondrial membrane
Valinomycin	A potassium ionophore; facilitates potassium ion transfer across the inner mitochondrial membrane

ATP, adenosine triphosphate.

Cyanide binds to the Fe^{3+} in the heme of the cytochrome aa_3 component of cytochrome c oxidase and prevents electron transport to O_2. Mitochondrial respiration and energy production cease, and cell death rapidly occurs. The central nervous system is the primary target for cyanide toxicity. Acute inhalation of high concentrations of cyanide (e.g., smoke inhalation during a fire) provokes a brief central nervous system stimulation followed rapidly by convulsion, coma, and death. Acute exposure to lower amounts can cause light-headedness, breathlessness, dizziness, numbness, and headaches.

Cyanide is present in the air as hydrogen cyanide (HCN), in soil and water as cyanide salts (e.g., NaCN), and in foods as cyanoglycosides. Most of the cyanide in the air usually comes from automobile exhaust. Examples of populations with potentially high exposures include active and passive smokers, people who are exposed to house or other building fires, residents who live near cyanide- or thiocyanate-containing hazardous waste sites, and workers involved in several manufacturing processes (e.g., photography or pesticide application).

Cyanoglycosides such as amygdalin are present in edible plants such as almonds, pits from stone fruits (e.g., apricots, peaches, plums, cherries), sorghum, cassava, soybeans, spinach, lima beans, sweet potatoes, maize, millet, sugar cane, and bamboo shoots.

Amygdalin, a cyanoglycoside

HCN is released from cyanoglycosides by β-glucosidases present in the plant or in intestinal bacteria. Small amounts are inactivated in the liver principally by rhodanase, which converts it to thiocyanate.

In the United States, toxic amounts of cyanoglycosides have been ingested as ground apricot pits, either as a result of their promotion as a health food or as a treatment for cancer. The drug Laetrile (amygdalin) was used as a cancer therapeutic agent, although it was banned in the United States because it was ineffective and potentially toxic. Commercial fruit juices made from unpitted fruit could provide toxic amounts of cyanide, particularly in infants or children. In countries in which cassava is a dietary staple, improper processing results in retention of its high cyanide content at potentially toxic levels.

A. Mitochondrial DNA and Oxidative Phosphorylation Diseases

The mtDNA is a small, 16,569 nucleotide-pair, double-stranded, circular DNA. It encodes 13 subunits of the complexes involved in oxidative phosphorylation: 7 of the 42 subunits of complex I (NADH:CoQ oxidoreductase complex), 1 of the 11 subunits of complex III (cytochrome b–c_1 complex), 3 of the 13 subunits of complex IV (cytochrome oxidase), and 2 subunits of the F_0 portion ATP–synthase complex. In addition, mtDNA encodes the necessary components for translation of its mRNA: a large and small ribosomal RNA (rRNA) and 22 transfer RNAs (tRNAs). Mutations in mtDNA have been identified as deletions, duplications, or point mutations (Table 21.2).

The genetics of mutations in mtDNA are defined by maternal inheritance, replicative segregation, threshold expression, a high mtDNA mutation rate, and the accumulation of somatic mutations with age. The maternal inheritance pattern reflects the exclusive transmission of mtDNA from the mother to her children. The egg contains approximately 300,000 molecules of mtDNA packaged into mitochondria. These are retained during fertilization, whereas those of the sperm do not enter the egg or are lost. Usually, some mitochondria are present that have the mutant mtDNA and some have normal (wild-type) DNA. As cells divide during mitosis and meiosis, mitochondria replicate by fission, but various amounts of mitochondria with mutant and wild-type DNA are distributed to each daughter cell (replicative segregation). Thus, any cell can have a mixture of mitochondria, each with mutant or wild-type mtDNAs (heteroplasmy). The mitotic and meiotic segregation of the heteroplasmic mtDNA mutation results in variable oxidative phosphorylation deficiencies between patients with the same mutation and even among a patient's own tissues.

The disease pathology usually becomes worse with age because a small amount of normal mitochondria might confer normal function and exercise capacity while the patient is young. As the patient ages, somatic (spontaneous) mutations in mtDNA accumulate from the generation of free radicals within the mitochondria (see Chapter 24). These mutations frequently become permanent, partly because

 Decreased activity of the electron-transport chain can result from inhibitors as well as from mutations in mtDNA and nuclear DNA. Why does an impairment of the electron-transport chain result in lactic acidosis?

Oxidative phosphorylation (OXPHOS) is responsible for producing most of the ATP that our cells require. The genes responsible for the polypeptides that comprise the OXPHOS complexes within the mitochondria are located within either the nuclear DNA (nDNA) or the mitochondrial DNA (mtDNA). A broad spectrum of human disorders (the OXPHOS diseases) may result from genetic mutations or nongenetic alterations (spontaneous mutations) in either the nDNA or the mtDNA. Increasingly, such changes appear to be responsible for at least some aspects of common disorders, such as Parkinson disease, dilated and hypertrophic cardiomyopathies, diabetes mellitus, Alzheimer disease, depressive disorders, and a host of less well-known clinical entities.

Table 21.2   Examples of OXPHOS Diseases Arising from mtDNA Mutations

Syndrome	Characteristic Symptoms	mtDNA Mutation
I. mtDNA rearrangements in which genes are deleted or duplicated		
Kearns-Sayre syndrome	Onset before 20 years of age, characterized by ophthalmoplegia, atypical retinitis pigmentosa, mitochondrial myopathy, and one of the following: cardiac conduction defect, cerebellar syndrome, or elevated CSF proteins	Deletion of contiguous segments of tRNA and OXPHOS polypeptides, or duplication mutations consisting of tandemly arranged normal mtDNA and an mtDNA with a deletion mutation
Pearson syndrome	Systemic disorder of oxidative phosphorylation that predominantly affects bone marrow	Deletion of contiguous segments of tRNA and OXPHOS polypeptides, or duplication mutations consisting of tandemly arranged normal mtDNA and a mtDNA with a deletion mutation
II. mtDNA point mutations in tRNA or ribosomal RNA genes		
MERRF (*myoclonic epilepsy and ragged red fiber disease*)	Progressive myoclonic epilepsy, a mitochondrial myopathy with ragged red fibers, and a slowly progressive dementia. Onset of symptoms: late childhood to adult	$tRNA^{Lys}$
MELAS (mitochondrial *myopathy, encephalomyopathy, lactic acidosis, and strokelike episodes*)	Progressive neurodegenerative disease characterized by strokelike episodes first occurring between 5 and 15 years of age and a mitochondrial myopathy	80%–90% mutations in $tRNA^{Leu}$
III. mtDNA missense mutations in OXPHOS polypeptides		
Leigh disease (subacute necrotizing encephalopathy)	Mean age of onset, 1.5–5 years; clinical manifestations include optic atrophy, ophthalmoplegia, nystagmus, respiratory abnormalities, ataxia, hypotonia, spasticity, and developmental delay or regression	7%–20% of cases have mutations in F_0 subunits of F_0F_1 ATPase.
LHON (*Leber hereditary optic neuropathy*)	Late onset, acute optic atrophy	90% of European and Asian cases result from mutation in NADH dehydrogenase

mtDNA, mitochondrial DNA; CSF, cerebrospinal fluid; tRNA, transfer RNA; OXPHOS, oxidative phosphorylation; rRNA, ribosomal RNA.

mtDNA does not have access to the same repair mechanisms available for nDNA (high mutation rate). Even in normal individuals, somatic mutations result in a decline of oxidative phosphorylation capacity with age (accumulation of somatic mutations with age). At some stage, the ATP-generating capacity of a tissue falls below the tissue-specific threshold for normal function (threshold expression). In general, symptoms of these defects appear in one or more of the tissues with the highest ATP demands: nervous tissue, heart, skeletal muscle, and kidney.

B. Other Genetic Disorders of Oxidative Phosphorylation

Genetic mutations also have been reported for mitochondrial proteins that are encoded by nDNA. Most of the estimated 1,000 proteins required for oxidative phosphorylation are encoded by nDNA, whereas mtDNA encodes only 13 subunits of the oxidative phosphorylation complexes (including ATP synthase). Nuclear DNA encodes the additional 70 or more subunits of the oxidative phosphorylation complexes, as well as the adenine nucleotide translocase (ANT) and other anion translocators. Coordinate regulation of expression of nDNA and mtDNA,

A patient experienced spontaneous muscle jerking (myoclonus) in her midteens, and her condition progressed over 10 years to include debilitating myoclonus, neurosensory hearing loss, dementia, hypoventilation, and mild cardiomyopathy. Energy metabolism was affected in the central nervous system, heart, and skeletal muscle, resulting in lactic acidosis. A history indicated that the patient's mother, her grandmother, and two maternal aunts had symptoms involving either nervous or muscular tissue (clearly a case of maternal inheritance). However, no other relatives had identical symptoms. The symptoms and history of the patient are those of myoclonic epileptic ragged red fiber disease (MERRF). The affected tissues (central nervous system and muscle) are two of the tissues with the highest ATP requirements. Most cases of MERRF are caused by a point mutation in mitochondrial $tRNA^{Lys}$ (m$tRNA^{Lys}$). The mitochondria, obtained by muscle biopsy, are enlarged and show abnormal patterns of cristae. The muscle tissue also shows ragged red fibers.

The effect of inhibition of electron transport is an impaired oxidation of pyruvate, fatty acids, and other fuels. In many cases, the inhibition of mitochondrial electron transport results in higher than normal levels of lactate and pyruvate in the blood and an increased lactate:pyruvate ratio. NADH oxidation requires the complete transfer of electrons from NADH to O_2, and a defect anywhere along the chain will result in the accumulation of NADH and a decrease of NAD^+. The increase in NADH/NAD^+ inhibits pyruvate dehydrogenase and causes the accumulation of pyruvate. It also increases the conversion of pyruvate to lactate, and elevated levels of lactate appear in the blood. A large number of genetic defects of the proteins in respiratory chain complexes have, therefore, been classified together as "congenital lactic acidosis."

How does shivering generate heat?

FIG. 21.10. The concentration of ADP (or the phosphate potential, [ATP]/[ADP][P_i]) controls the rate of oxygen consumption. *(1)* ADP is phosphorylated to ATP by ATP synthase. *(2)* The release of the ATP requires proton flow through ATP synthase into the matrix. *(3)* The use of protons from the intermembrane space for ATP synthesis decreases the proton gradient. *(4)* As a result, the electron-transport chain pumps more protons, and oxygen is reduced to H_2O. *(5)* As NADH donates electrons to the electron-transport chain, NAD^+ is regenerated and returns to the TCA cycle or other NADH-producing pathways.

importation of proteins into the mitochondria, assembly of the complexes, and regulation of mitochondrial fission are nuclear encoded. The nuclear respiratory factors (NRF-1 and NRF-2) are nuclear transcription factors that bind to and activate promoter regions of the nuclear genes that encode subunits of the respiratory chain complexes, including cytochrome c. They also activate the transcription of the nuclear gene for the mitochondrial transcription factor (mTF)-A. The protein product of this gene translocates into the mitochondrial matrix, where it stimulates transcription and replication of the mitochondrial genome.

Nuclear DNA mutations differ from mtDNA mutations in several important respects. These mutations do not show a pattern of maternal inheritance but are usually autosomal recessive. The mutations are uniformly distributed to daughter cells and therefore are expressed in all tissues that contain the allele for a particular tissue-specific isoform. However, phenotypic expression will still be most apparent in tissues with high ATP requirements.

III. COUPLING OF ELECTRON TRANSPORT AND ADENOSINE TRIPHOSPHATE SYNTHESIS

The electrochemical gradient couples the rate of the electron-transport chain to the rate of ATP synthesis. Because electron flow requires proton pumping, electron flow cannot occur faster than protons are used for ATP synthesis (coupled oxidative phosphorylation) or returned to the matrix by a mechanism that short-circuits the ATP synthase pore (uncoupling).

A. Regulation through Coupling

As ATP chemical bond energy is used by energy-requiring reactions, ADP and P_i concentrations increase. The more ADP is present to bind to the ATP synthase, the greater will be proton flow through the ATP synthase pore, from the intermembrane space to the matrix. Thus, as ADP levels rise, proton influx increases, and the electrochemical gradient decreases (Fig. 21.10). The proton pumps of the electron-transport chain respond with increased proton pumping and electron flow to maintain the electrochemical gradient. The result is increased O_2 consumption. The increased oxidation of NADH in the electron-transport chain and the increased concentration of ADP stimulate the pathways of fuel oxidation, such as the TCA cycle, to supply more NADH and FAD(2H) to the electron-transport chain. For example, during exercise we use more ATP for muscle contraction, consume more oxygen, oxidize more fuel (which means burn more calories), and generate more heat from the electron-transport chain. If we rest, and the rate of ATP use decreases, proton influx decreases, the electrochemical gradient increases, and proton "back pressure" decreases the rate of the electron-transport chain. NADH and FAD(2H) cannot be oxidized as rapidly in the electron-transport chain, and consequently, their buildup inhibits the enzymes that generate them.

The system is poised to maintain very high levels of ATP at all times. In most tissues, the rate of ATP use is nearly constant over time. However, in skeletal muscles, the rates of ATP hydrolysis change dramatically as the muscle goes from rest to rapid contraction. Even under these circumstances, ATP concentration decreases by only approximately 20% because it is so rapidly regenerated. In the heart, Ca^{2+} activation of TCA cycle enzymes provides an extra push to NADH generation, so that neither ATP nor NADH levels fall as ATP demand is increased. The electron-transport chain has a very high capacity and can respond very rapidly to any increase in ATP use.

B. Uncoupling Adenosine Triphosphate Synthesis from Electron Transport

When protons leak back into the matrix without going through the ATP synthase pore, they dissipate the electrochemical gradient across the membrane without generating ATP. This phenomenon is called *uncoupling* oxidative phosphorylation. It occurs with chemical compounds, known as *uncouplers*, and it occurs physiologically with uncoupling proteins that form proton conductance channels through the membrane. Uncoupling of oxidative phosphorylation results in increased oxygen consumption and heat production as electron flow and proton pumping attempt to maintain the electrochemical gradient.

1. CHEMICAL UNCOUPLERS OF OXIDATIVE PHOSPHORYLATION

Chemical uncouplers, also known as *proton ionophores*, are lipid-soluble compounds that rapidly transport protons from the cytosolic to the matrix side of the inner mitochondrial membrane (Fig. 21.11). Because the proton concentration is higher in the intermembrane space than in the matrix, uncouplers pick up protons from the intermembrane space. Their lipid solubility enables them to diffuse through the inner mitochondrial membrane while carrying protons and to release these protons on the matrix side. The rapid influx of protons dissipates the electrochemical potential gradient; therefore, the mitochondria are unable to synthesize ATP. Eventually, mitochondrial integrity and function are lost.

2. UNCOUPLING PROTEINS AND THERMOGENESIS

Uncoupling proteins (UCPs) form channels through the inner mitochondrial membrane that are able to conduct protons from the intermembrane space to the matrix, thereby short-circuiting ATP synthase.

UCP1 (thermogenin) is associated with heat production in brown adipose tissue. The major function of brown adipose tissue is nonshivering thermogenesis, whereas the major function of white adipose tissue is the storage of triacylglycerols in white lipid droplets. The brown color arises from the large number of mitochondria that participate. Human infants, who have little voluntary control over their environment and may kick their blankets off at night, have brown fat deposits along the neck, the breastplate, between the scapulae, and around the kidneys to protect them from cold. However, there is very little brown fat in most adults.

In response to cold, sympathetic nerve endings release norepinephrine, which activates a lipase in brown adipose tissue that releases fatty acids from triacylglycerols (Fig. 21.12). Fatty acids serve as a fuel for the tissue (i.e., are oxidized to generate the electrochemical potential gradient and ATP) and participate directly in the proton

Shivering results from muscular contraction, which increases the rate of ATP hydrolysis. As a consequence of proton entry for ATP synthesis, the electron-transport chain is stimulated. Oxygen consumption increases, as does the amount of energy lost as heat by the electron-transport chain.

A skeletal muscle biopsy performed on **Ivy Sharer** indicated proliferation of subsarcolemmal mitochondria with degeneration of muscle fibers (ragged red fibers) in approximately 55% of the total fibers observed. An analysis of mitochondrial DNA (mtDNA) indicated no genetic mutations but did show a moderate quantitative depletion of mtDNA.

Ivy Sharer's AIDS was being treated with zidovudine (azidothymidine [AZT]), which also can act as an inhibitor of the mtDNA polymerase (polymerase γ). A review of the drug's potential adverse effects showed that, rarely, it may cause varying degrees of mtDNA depletion in different tissues, including skeletal muscle. The depletion may cause a severe mitochondrial myopathy, including "ragged red fiber" accumulation within the skeletal muscle cells associated with ultrastructural abnormalities in their mitochondria.

FIG. 21.11. Dinitrophenol (DNP) is lipid-soluble and can, therefore, diffuse across the membrane. It has a dissociable proton with a pK_a near 7.2. Thus, in the intermembrane space where [H$^+$] is high (pH low), DNP picks up a proton, which it carries across the membrane. At the lower proton concentration of the matrix, the H$^+$ dissociates. As a consequence, cells cannot maintain their electrochemical gradient or synthesize ATP. DNP was once recommended in the United States as a weight-loss drug, based on the principle that decreased [ATP] and increased electron transport stimulate fuel oxidation. However, several deaths resulted from its use.

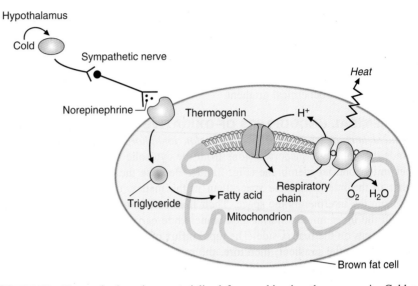

FIG. 21.12. Brown fat is a tissue specialized for nonshivering thermogenesis. Cold or excessive food intake stimulates the release of norepinephrine from the sympathetic nerve endings. As a result, a lipase is activated that releases fatty acids for oxidation. The proton conductance protein, thermogenin, is activated, and protons are brought into the matrix. This stimulates the electron-transport chain, which increases its rate of NADH and FAD(2H) oxidation and produces more heat.

 Salicylate, which is a degradation product of aspirin in humans, is lipid-soluble and has a dissociable proton. In high concentrations, as in salicylate poisoning, salicylate is able to partially uncouple mitochondria. The decline of ATP concentration in the cell and consequent increase of AMP in the cytosol stimulates glycolysis. The overstimulation of the glycolytic pathway (see Chapter 22) results in increased levels of lactic acid in the blood and a metabolic acidosis. Fortunately, **Dennis Veere** did not develop this consequence of aspirin poisoning (see Chapter 4).

conductance channel by activating UCP1 along with reduced CoQ. When UCP1 is activated by fatty acids, it transports protons from the cytosolic side of the inner mitochondrial membrane back into the mitochondrial matrix without ATP generation. Thus, it partially uncouples oxidative phosphorylation and generates additional heat.

The uncoupling proteins exist as a family of proteins: *UCP1* (thermogenin) is expressed in brown adipose tissue, *UCP2* is found in most cells, *UCP3* is found principally in skeletal muscle, and *UCP4* and *UCP5* are found in the nervous system. These are highly regulated proteins that, when activated, increase the amount of energy from fuel oxidation that is being released as heat. However, recent data indicate that this may not be the primary role of *UCP2* and *UCP3*. It has been hypothesized that *UCP3* acts as a transport protein to remove fatty acid anions and lipid peroxides from the mitochondria, thereby reducing the risk of forming oxygen free radicals (see Chapter 24) and thus decreasing the occurrence of mitochondrial and cell injury.

3. PROTON LEAK AND RESTING METABOLIC RATE
A low level of proton leak across the inner mitochondrial membrane occurs in our mitochondria all the time, and our mitochondria, thus, are normally partially uncoupled. It has been estimated that more than 20% of our resting metabolic rate is the energy expended to maintain the electrochemical gradient dissipated by our basal proton leak (also referred to as *global proton leak*). Some of the proton leak results from permeability of the membrane associated with proteins embedded in the lipid bilayer. An unknown amount may result from uncoupling proteins.

IV. TRANSPORT THROUGH INNER AND OUTER MITOCHONDRIAL MEMBRANES
Most of the newly synthesized ATP that is released into the mitochondrial matrix must be transported out of the mitochondria, where it is used for energy-requiring processes such as active ion transport, muscle contraction, or biosynthetic reactions. Likewise, ADP, phosphate, pyruvate, and other metabolites must be transported into the matrix. This requires transport of compounds through both the inner and outer mitochondrial membranes.

A. Transport through the Inner Mitochondrial Membrane

The inner mitochondrial membrane forms a tight permeability barrier to all polar molecules, including ATP; ADP; P_i; anions such as pyruvate; and cations such as Ca^{2+}, H^+, and K^+. Yet, the process of oxidative phosphorylation depends on rapid and continuous transport of many of these molecules across the inner mitochondrial membrane (Fig. 21.13). Ions and other polar molecules are transported across the inner mitochondrial membrane by specific protein translocases that nearly balance charge during the transport process. Most of the exchange transport is a form of active transport that generally uses energy from the electrochemical potential gradient, either the membrane potential or the proton gradient.

ATP–ADP translocase (also called ANT, for *a*denine *n*ucleotide *t*ranslocase) transports ATP formed in the mitochondrial matrix to the intermembrane space in a specific 1:1 exchange for ADP produced from energy-requiring reactions outside of the mitochondria (see Fig. 21.13). Because ATP contains four negative charges and ADP contains only three, the exchange is promoted by the electrochemical potential gradient because the net effect is the transport of one negative charge from the matrix to the cytosol. Similar antiports exist for most metabolic anions. In contrast, inorganic phosphate and pyruvate are transported into the mitochondrial matrix on specific transporters called *symports* together with a proton. A specific transport protein for Ca^{2+} uptake, called the *Ca^{2+} uniporter*, is driven by the electrochemical potential gradient, which is negatively charged on the matrix side of the membrane relative to the cytosolic side. Other transporters include the dicarboxylate transporter (phosphate–malate exchange), the tricarboxylate transporter (citrate–malate exchange), the aspartate–glutamate transporter, and the malate–α-ketoglutarate transporter.

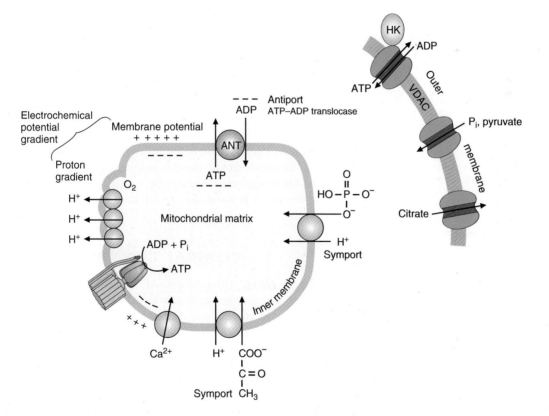

FIG. 21.13. Transport of compounds across the inner and outer mitochondrial membranes. The electrochemical potential gradient drives the transport of ions across the inner mitochondrial membrane on specific translocases. Each translocase is composed of specific membrane-spanning helices that bind only specific compounds (adenine nucleotide translocase [ANT]). In contrast, the outer membrane contains relatively large unspecific pores called voltage-dependent anion channels (VDACs) through which a wide range of ions diffuse. These bind cytosolic proteins such as hexokinase (HK), which enables HK to have access to newly exported ATP.

Q: Investigators reported finding antibodies against cardiac ATP–ADP translocase in an individual who died of a viral cardiomyopathy. How could these antibodies result in death?

B. Transport through the Outer Mitochondrial Membrane

Whereas the inner mitochondrial membrane is highly impermeable, the outer mitochondrial membrane is permeable to compounds with a molecular weight up to approximately 6,000 Da because it contains large nonspecific pores called voltage-dependent anion channels (VDACs) that are formed by mitochondrial porins (see Fig. 21.13). Unlike most transport proteins, which are membrane-spanning helices with specific binding sites, VDACs are composed of porin homodimers that form a β-barrel with a relatively large nonspecific water-filled pore through the center. These channels are "open" at low transmembrane potential, with a preference for anions such as phosphate, chloride, pyruvate, citrate, and adenine nucleotides. VDACs thus facilitate translocation of these anions between the intermembrane space and the cytosol. Several cytosolic kinases, such as the hexokinase that initiates glycolysis, bind to the cytosolic side of the channel where they have ready access to newly synthesized ATP.

C. The Mitochondrial Permeability Transition Pore

The mitochondrial permeability transition involves the opening of a large nonspecific pore (called MPTP, the *m*itochondrial *p*ermeability *t*ransition *p*ore) through the inner mitochondrial membrane and outer membranes at sites where they form a junction (Fig. 21.14). In one model of the MPTP, the basic components of the pore are ANT, the VDAC, and cyclophilin D (CD) (which is a *cis-trans* isomerase for the proline peptide bond). Normally, ANT is a closed pore that functions specifically in a 1:1 exchange of matrix ATP for ADP in the intermembrane space. However, increased mitochondrial matrix Ca^{2+}, excess phosphate, or reactive oxygen species (ROS), which form oxygen or oxygen–nitrogen radicals, can activate opening of the pore. Conversely, ATP on the cytosolic side of the pore (and possibly a pH <7.0) and a membrane potential across the inner membrane protect against pore opening. Opening of the MPTP can be triggered by ischemia (hypoxia), which results in a temporary lack of O_2 for maintaining the proton gradient and ATP synthesis. When the proton gradient is not being generated by the electron-transport chain, ATP synthase runs backward and hydrolyzes ATP in an attempt to restore the gradient, thus rapidly depleting cellular levels of ATP. As ATP is hydrolyzed to ADP, the ADP is converted to adenine, and the nucleotide pool is no longer able to protect against pore opening. This can lead to a downward spiral of cellular events. A lack of ATP for maintaining the low intracellular Ca^{2+} can contribute to pore opening. When the MPTP opens, protons flood in and maintaining a proton gradient becomes impossible. Anions and cations enter the matrix, mitochondrial swelling ensues, and the mitochondria become irreversibly damaged. The result is cell lysis and death (necrosis).

FIG. 21.14. The mitochondrial permeability transition pore (MPTP). In the MPTP, ANT is thought to complex with VDAC. The conformation of ANT is regulated by cyclophilin D (CD), and Ca^{2+}. The change to an open pore is activated by Ca^{2+}, depletion of adenine nucleotides, and reactive oxygen species (ROS) that alter SH groups. It is inhibited by the electrochemical potential gradient (Δp), by cytosolic ATP, and by a low cytosolic pH. VDACs bind several proteins, including Bcl-2 and Bax, which regulate apoptosis. Binding of proapoptotic members of the Bcl-2 family to VDAC may change the permeability of the outer membrane so as to either favor or block events leading to apoptosis.

CLINICAL COMMENTS

Cora Nari. Thrombolysis stimulated by intravenous recombinant tissue plasminogen activator (tPA) restored O_2 to Cora Nari's heart muscle and successfully decreased the extent of ischemic damage. The rationale for the use of tPA within 4 to 6 hours after the onset of a myocardial infarction relates to the function of the normal intrinsic fibrinolytic system (see Chapter 45). This system is designed to dissolve unwanted intravascular clots through the action of the enzyme plasmin, a protease that digests the fibrin matrix within the clot. tPA stimulates the conversion of plasminogen to its active form, plasmin. The result is a lysis of the thrombus and improved blood flow through the previously obstructed vessel, allowing fuels and oxygen to reach the heart cells. The human tPA protein administered to Mrs. Nari is produced by recombinant DNA technology (see Chapter 17). This treatment rapidly restored oxygen supply to her heart.

X. S. Teefore. Mr. Teefore could be treated with antithyroid drugs, by subtotal resection of the thyroid gland, or with radioactive iodine. Successful treatment normalizes thyroid hormone secretion, and all of the signs, symptoms, and metabolic alterations of hyperthyroidism quickly subside.

Ivy Sharer. In the case of **Ivy Sharer**, a diffuse myopathic process was superimposed on her AIDS and her pulmonary tuberculosis, either of which could have caused progressive weakness. In addition, she could have been suffering from a congenital mtDNA myopathy, symptomatic only as she ages. A systematic diagnostic process, however, finally led her physician to conclude that her myopathy was caused by a disorder of oxidative phosphorylation induced by her treatment with zidovudine (AZT). Fortunately, when AZT was discontinued, Ivy's myopathic symptoms gradually subsided. A repeat skeletal muscle biopsy performed 4 months later showed that her skeletal muscle cell mtDNA had been restored to normal and that she had experienced a reversible drug-induced disorder of oxidative phosphorylation.

BIOCHEMICAL COMMENTS

Mitochondria and Apoptosis. The loss of mitochondrial integrity is a major route initiating apoptosis (see Chapter 18, Section V). The intermembrane space contains procaspases 2, 3, and 9, which are proteolytic enzymes that are in the zymogen form (i.e., they must be proteolytically cleaved to be active). It also contains apoptosis-initiating factor (AIF) and caspase-activated DNAase (CAD). AIF has a nuclear-targeting sequence and is transported into the nucleus under appropriate conditions. Once AIF is inside the nucleus, it initiates chromatin condensation and degradation. Cytochrome c, which is loosely bound to the inner mitochondrial membrane, may also enter the intermembrane space when the electrochemical potential gradient is lost. The release of cytochrome c and the other proteins into the cytosol initiates apoptosis (see Chapter 18).

What is the trigger for the release of cytochrome c and the other proteins from the mitochondria? The VDAC pore is not large enough to allow the passage of proteins. Several theories have been proposed, each supported and contradicted by experimental evidence. One is that Bax (a member of the Bcl-2 family of proteins that forms an ion channel in the outer mitochondrial membrane) allows the entry of ions into the intermembrane space, causing swelling of this space and rupture of the outer mitochondrial membrane. Another theory is that Bax and VDAC (which is known to bind Bax and other Bcl-2 family members) combine to form an extremely large pore, much larger than is formed by either alone. Finally, it is possible that the MPTP or ANT participate in rupture of the outer membrane, but that they close in a way that still provides the energy for apoptosis.

 As ATP is hydrolyzed during muscular contraction, ADP is formed. This ADP must exchange into the mitochondria on ATP–ADP translocase to be converted back to ATP. Inhibition of ATP–ADP translocase results in rapid depletion of the cytosol ATP levels and loss of cardiac contractility.

 As infusion of tPA lysed the clot blocking blood flow to **Cora Nari's** heart, oxygenated blood was reintroduced into the ischemic heart. Although oxygen may rapidly restore the capacity to generate ATP, it often increases cell death, a phenomenon called *ischemia–reperfusion injury.*

During ischemia, several factors may protect heart cells against irreversible injury and cell death until oxygen is reintroduced. The stimulation of anaerobic glycolysis in the cytosol generates ATP without oxygen because glucose is converted to lactic acid. Lactic acid decreases cytosolic pH. Both cytosolic ATP and a lowering of the pH protect against opening of the MPTP. In addition, Ca^{2+} uptake by mitochondria requires a membrane potential, and it is matrix Ca^{2+} that activates opening of the MPTP. Thus, depending on the severity of the ischemic insult, the MPTP may not open, or may open and reseal, until oxygen is reintroduced. Then, depending on the sequence of events, reestablishment of the proton gradient, mitochondrial uptake of Ca^{2+}, or an increase of pH above 7.0 may activate the MPTP before the cell has recovered. In addition, the reintroduction of O_2 generates oxygen free radicals, particularly through free radical forms of CoQ in the electron-transport chain. These also may open the MPTP. The role of free radicals in ischemia–reperfusion injury is discussed in more detail in Chapter 24.

Key Concepts

- The reduced cofactors generated during fuel oxidation donate their electrons to the mitochondrial electron-transport chain.
- The electron-transport chain transfers the electrons to O_2, which is reduced to water.
- As electrons travel through the electron-transport chain, protons are transferred from the mitochondrial matrix to the cytosolic side of the inner mitochondrial membrane.
- The asymmetric distribution of protons across the inner mitochondrial membrane generates an electrochemical gradient across the membrane.
- The electrochemical gradient consists of a change in pH (ΔpH) across the membrane and also a difference in charge ($\Delta\psi$) across the membrane.
- Proton entry into the mitochondrial matrix is energetically favorable and drives the synthesis of ATP via the ATP synthase.

In addition to increased transcription of genes that encode TCA cycle enzymes and certain other enzymes of fuel oxidation, thyroid hormones increase the level of UCP2 and UCP3. In hyperthyroidism, the efficiency with which energy is derived from the oxidation of these fuels is significantly less than normal. As a consequence of the increased rate of the electron-transport chain, hyperthyroidism results in increased heat production. Patients with hyperthyroidism, such as **X. S. Teefore**, complain of constantly feeling hot and sweaty.

- Respiration (oxygen consumption) is normally coupled to ATP synthesis; if one process is inhibited, the other is also inhibited.
- Uncouplers allow respiration to continue in the absence of ATP synthesis because the energy inherent in the proton gradient is released as heat.
- OXPHOS diseases are caused by mutations in either nuclear or mitochondrial DNA that lead to a decrease in mitochondrial capacity for synthesizing ATP via oxidative phosphorylation.
- Because the inner mitochondrial membrane is impermeable to virtually all biochemical compounds, transport systems exist to allow entry and exit of appropriate metabolites.
- Under appropriate stress, mitochondria will generate a nonspecific channel across both the inner and outer membranes that is known as the *mitochondrial permeability transition pore*. The opening of the pore is associated with events that lead to necrotic cell death.
- Diseases discussed in this chapter are summarized in Table 21.3.

Table 21.3   Diseases Discussed in Chapter 21

Disease or Disorder	Environmental or Genetic	Comments
Myocardial infarction	Both	The lack of oxygen in the anterior and lateral walls of the heart is caused by severe ischemia because of clots formed within certain coronary arteries at the site of ruptured atherosclerotic plaques. The limited availability of oxygen to act as an electron acceptor decreases the proton motive force across the inner mitochondrial membrane of ischemic cells. This leads to reduced ATP generation, triggering events that lead to irreversible cell injury.
Hyperthyroidism	Both	Graves disease is an autoimmune genetic disorder caused by the generation of human thyroid stimulating immunoglobulins. These immunoglobulins stimulate growth of the thyroid gland and excess secretion of the thyroid hormones T_3 and T_4.
AIDS treatment	Environmental	AZT, a component of AIDS treatment cocktails, can act as an inhibitor of mitochondrial DNA polymerase. Under rare conditions, it can lead to a depletion of mitochondrial DNA in cells, leading to a severe mitochondrial myopathy.
Iron deficiency anemia	Environmental	Lack of iron for heme synthesis, leading to reduced oxygen delivery to cells, and reduced iron in the electron-transfer chain, leading to muscle weakness.
Cyanide poisoning	Environmental	Cyanide binds to the Fe^{3+} in the heme of cytochrome aa_3, a component of cytochrome oxidase. Mitochondrial respiration and energy production cease, and cell death rapidly occurs.
Mitochondrial disorders	Genetic	Many types of mutations, leading to altered mitochondrial function, and reduced energy production, due to mutations in the mitochondrial DNA. See Table 21.2 for a full listing of these disorders.

ATP, adenosine triphosphate; AZT, azidothymidine.

REVIEW QUESTIONS—CHAPTER 21

1. Consider the following experiment. Carefully isolated liver mitochondria are incubated in the presence of a limiting amount of malate. Three minutes after adding the substrate, cyanide is added, and the reaction is allowed to proceed for another 7 minutes. At this point, which of the following components of the electron-transfer chain will be in an oxidized state?

    A. Complex I
    B. Complex II
    C. Complex III
    D. Coenzyme Q
    E. Cytochrome C

2. Consider the following experiment. Carefully isolated liver mitochondria are placed in a weakly buffered solution. Malate is added as an energy source, and an increase in oxygen consumption confirms that the electron-transport chain is functioning properly within these organelles. Valinomycin and potassium are then added to the mitochondrial suspension. *Valinomycin* is a drug that allows potassium ions to freely cross the inner mitochondrial membrane. What is the effect of valinomycin on the proton motive force that had been generated by the oxidation of malate?

    A. The proton motive force will be reduced to a value of zero.
    B. There will be no change in the proton motive force.
    C. The proton motive force will be increased.
    D. The proton motive force will be decreased but to a value greater than zero.
    E. The proton motive force will be decreased to a value less than zero.

3. Dinitrophenol acts as an uncoupler of oxidative phosphorylation by which of the following mechanisms?

    A. Activating the H^+-ATPase
    B. Activating coenzyme Q

    C. Blocking proton transport across the inner mitochondrial membrane
    D. Allowing for proton exchange across the inner mitochondrial membrane
    E. Enhancing oxygen transport across the inner mitochondrial membrane

4. A 25-year-old woman presents with chronic fatigue. A series of blood tests is ordered, and the results suggest that her red blood cell count is low because of iron deficiency anemia. Such a deficiency would lead to fatigue because of which of the following?

    A. Her decrease in Fe–S centers is impairing the transfer of electrons in the electron-transport chain.
    B. She is not producing enough H_2O in the electron-transport chain, leading to dehydration, which has resulted in fatigue.
    C. Iron forms a chelate with NADH and FAD(2H) that is necessary for them to donate their electrons to the electron-transport chain.
    D. Iron acts as a cofactor for α-ketoglutarate DH in the TCA cycle, a reaction required for the flow of electrons through the electron-transport chain.
    E. Iron accompanies the protons that are pumped from the mitochondrial matrix to the cytosolic side of the inner mitochondrial membrane. Without iron, the proton gradient cannot be maintained to produce adequate ATP.

5. Which of the following would be expected for a patient with an OXPHOS disease?

    A. A high ATP:ADP ratio in the mitochondria
    B. A high $NADH:NAD^+$ ratio in the mitochondria
    C. A deletion on the X chromosome
    D. A high activity of complex II of the electron-transport chain
    E. A defect in the integrity of the inner mitochondrial membrane

22 Generation of Adenosine Triphosphate from Glucose: Glycolysis

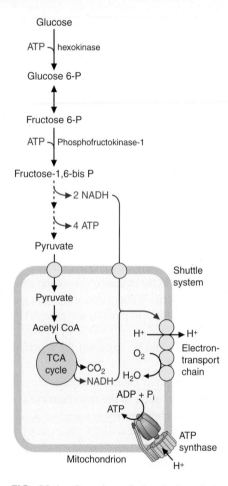

FIG. 22.1. Overview of glycolysis and the TCA cycle.

Glucose is the universal fuel for human cells. Every cell type in the human is able to generate adenosine triphosphate (ATP) from glycolysis, the pathway in which glucose is oxidized and cleaved to form pyruvate. The importance of glycolysis in our fuel economy is related to the availability of glucose in the blood, as well as the ability of glycolysis to generate ATP in both the presence and absence of O_2. Glucose is the major sugar in our diet and the sugar that circulates in the blood to ensure that all cells have a continuous fuel supply. The brain uses glucose almost exclusively as a fuel.

Glycolysis begins with the phosphorylation of glucose to glucose 6-phosphate (**glucose 6-P**) by **hexokinase**. In subsequent steps of the pathway, one glucose 6-P molecule is oxidized to two **pyruvate** molecules with generation of two molecules of **nicotinamide adenine dinucleotide (NADH)** (Fig. 22.1). A net generation of two molecules of ATP occurs through direct transfer of **high-energy phosphate** from intermediates of the pathway to adenosine diphosphate (ADP) (**substrate-level phosphorylation**).

Glycolysis occurs in the **cytosol** and generates cytosolic NADH. Because NADH cannot cross the inner mitochondrial membrane, its reducing equivalents are transferred to the electron-transport chain by either the **malate–aspartate shuttle** or the **glycerol 3-phosphate shuttle** (see Fig. 22.1). Pyruvate is then oxidized completely to CO_2 by pyruvate dehydrogenase and the tricarboxylic acid (TCA) cycle. Complete **aerobic oxidation** of glucose to CO_2 can generate approximately **30 to 32 mol of ATP per mole of glucose**.

When cells have a limited supply of oxygen (e.g., the kidney medulla), or few or no mitochondria (e.g., the red cell), or greatly increased demands for ATP (e.g., skeletal muscle during high-intensity exercise), they rely on **anaerobic glycolysis** for generation of ATP. In anaerobic glycolysis, **lactate dehydrogenase** oxidizes the NADH generated from glycolysis by reducing pyruvate to **lactate** (Fig. 22.2). Because O_2 is not required to reoxidize the NADH, the pathway is referred to as anaerobic. The energy yield from anaerobic glycolysis (2 mol ATP per mole of glucose) is much lower than the yield from aerobic oxidation. The lactate (lactic acid) is released into the blood. Under pathologic conditions that cause **hypoxia**, tissues may generate enough lactic acid to cause **lactic acidemia**.

In each cell, glycolysis is regulated to ensure that **ATP homeostasis** is maintained, without using more glucose than necessary. In most cell types, **hexokinase**, the first enzyme of glycolysis, is inhibited by glucose 6-P (see Fig. 22.1). Thus, glucose is not taken up and phosphorylated by a cell unless glucose 6-P enters a metabolic pathway, such as glycolysis or glycogen synthesis. The control of glucose 6-P entry into glycolysis occurs at phosphofructokinase-1 (**PFK-1**), the rate-limiting enzyme of the pathway.

*PFK-1 is **allosterically inhibited** by **ATP** and **allosterically activated** by adenosine monophosphate (**AMP**). AMP increases in the cytosol as ATP is hydrolyzed by energy-requiring reactions.*

*Glycolysis has functions in addition to ATP production. For example, in liver and adipose tissue, this pathway generates pyruvate as a precursor for **fatty acid biosynthesis**. Glycolysis also provides precursors for the synthesis of compounds such as amino acids and five-carbon sugar phosphates.*

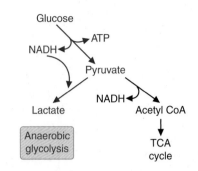

FIG. 22.2. Anaerobic glycolysis (shown in *red*). The conversion of glucose to lactate generates 2 ATP molecules from substrate-level phosphorylation. Because there is no net generation of NADH, there is no need for O_2, and thus the pathway is anaerobic.

THE WAITING ROOM

 Lopa Fusor is a 68-year-old woman who is admitted to the hospital emergency department with very low blood pressure (80/40 mm Hg) caused by an acute hemorrhage from a previously diagnosed ulcer of the stomach. Lopa's bleeding stomach ulcer has reduced her effective blood volume severely enough to compromise her ability to perfuse (deliver blood to) her tissues. She is also known to have chronic obstructive pulmonary disease (COPD) as a result of 42 years of smoking two packs of cigarettes per day. Her respiratory rate is rapid and labored, her skin is cold and clammy, and her lips are slightly blue (cyanotic). She appears anxious and moderately confused.

As appropriate emergency measures are taken to stabilize her and elevate her blood pressure, blood is sent for immediate blood typing and crossmatching so that blood transfusions can be started. A battery of laboratory tests is ordered, including venous hemoglobin, hematocrit, lactate levels, and an arterial blood gas, which includes an arterial pH, partial pressures of oxygen (Po_2) and carbon dioxide (Pco_2), bicarbonate, and oxygen saturation. Results show that the hemorrhaging and COPD have resulted in hypoxemia, with decreased oxygen delivery to her tissues, and both a respiratory and metabolic acidosis.

 Otto Shape, a 26-year-old medical student, had gained weight during his first sedentary year in medical school. During his second year, he began watching his diet, jogging for an hour four times each week, and playing tennis twice a week. He has decided to compete in a 5-km race. To prepare for the race, he begins training with wind sprints, bouts of alternately running and walking.

Ivan Applebod is a 56-year-old morbidly obese accountant (see Chapters 1 through 3). He decided to see his dentist because he felt excruciating pain in his teeth when he ate ice cream. He really likes sweets and keeps hard candy in his pocket. The dentist noted from Mr. Applebod's history that he had numerous cavities as a child in his baby teeth. At this visit, the dentist found cavities in two of Mr. Applebod's teeth.

I. GLYCOLYSIS

Glycolysis is one of the principal pathways for generating ATP in cells and is present in all cell types. The central role of glycolysis in fuel metabolism is related to its ability to generate ATP with, and without, oxygen. The oxidation of glucose to pyruvate generates ATP from substrate-level phosphorylation (the transfer of phosphate from high-energy intermediates of the pathway to ADP) and NADH. Subsequently, the pyruvate may be oxidized to CO_2 in the TCA cycle and ATP generated from electron transfer to oxygen in oxidative phosphorylation. However, if the pyruvate

 The hematocrit (the percentage of the volume of blood occupied by packed red blood cells) and hemoglobin content (grams of hemoglobin in 100 mL of blood) are measured to determine whether the oxygen-carrying capacity of the blood is adequate. Both values can be decreased by conditions that interfere with erythropoiesis (the synthesis of red blood cells in bone marrow), such as iron deficiency. They also can be decreased during chronic bleeding but not during immediate acute hemorrhage, if interstitial fluid replaces the lost blood volume and dilutes out the red blood cells. The Pco_2 and Po_2 are the partial pressures of carbon dioxide and oxygen, respectively, in the blood. The Po_2 and oxygen saturation determine whether adequate oxygen is available for tissues. Measurement of the Pco_2 and bicarbonate can distinguish between a metabolic and a respiratory acidosis (see Chapter 4).

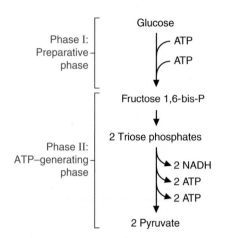

FIG. 22.3.   Phases of the glycolytic pathway.

and NADH from glycolysis are converted to lactate (anaerobic glycolysis), ATP can be generated in the absence of oxygen, via substrate-level phosphorylation.

Glucose is readily available from our diet, internal glycogen stores, and the blood. Carbohydrate provides 50% or more of the calories in most diets, and glucose is the major carbohydrate. Other dietary sugars, such as fructose and galactose, are oxidized by conversion to intermediates of glycolysis. Glucose is stored in cells as glycogen, which can provide an internal source of fuel for glycolysis in emergency situations (e.g., decreased supply of fuels and oxygen during ischemia, a low blood flow). Insulin and other hormones maintain blood glucose in a relatively constant range (glucose homeostasis), thereby ensuring that glucose is always available to cells that depend on glycolysis for generation of ATP.

After a high-carbohydrate meal, glucose is the major fuel for almost all tissues. Exceptions include intestinal mucosal cells, which transport glucose from the gut into the blood, and cells in the proximal convoluted tubule of the kidney, which return glucose from the renal filtrate to the blood. During fasting, the brain continues to oxidize glucose because it has a limited capacity for the oxidation of fatty acids or other fuels. Cells also continue to use glucose for the portion of their ATP generation that must be met by anaerobic glycolysis, due to either a limited oxygen supply or a limited capacity for oxidative phosphorylation (e.g., the red blood cell).

In addition to serving as an anaerobic and aerobic source of ATP, glycolysis is an anabolic pathway that provides biosynthetic precursors. For example, in liver and adipose tissue, this pathway generates pyruvate as a precursor for fatty acid biosynthesis. Glycolysis also provides precursors for the synthesis of compounds such as amino acids and ribose 5-phosphate, the precursor of nucleotides. The integration of glycolysis with other anabolic pathways is discussed in Chapter 36.

A. The Reactions of Glycolysis

The glycolytic pathway, which cleaves 1 mol of glucose to 2 mol of the three-carbon compound pyruvate, consists of a preparative phase and an ATP-generating phase. In the initial preparative phase of glycolysis, glucose is phosphorylated twice by ATP and cleaved into two triose phosphates (Fig. 22.3). The ATP expenditure in the beginning of the preparative phase is sometimes called "priming the pump," because this initial utilization of 2 mol of ATP per mole of glucose results in the production of 4 mol of ATP per mole of glucose in the ATP-generating phase.

In the ATP-generating phase, glyceraldehyde 3-phosphate (glyceraldehyde 3-P) (a triose phosphate) is oxidized by NAD^+ and phosphorylated using inorganic phosphate. The high-energy phosphate bond generated in this step is transferred to ADP to form ATP. The remaining phosphate is also rearranged to form another high-energy phosphate bond that is transferred to ADP. Because 2 mol of triose phosphate were formed, the yield from the ATP-generating phase is 4 mol of ATP and 2 mol of NADH. The result is a net yield of 2 mol of ATP, 2 mol of NADH, and 2 mol of pyruvate per mole of glucose.

1.   CONVERSION OF GLUCOSE TO GLUCOSE 6-PHOSPHATE

Glucose metabolism begins with transfer of a phosphate from ATP to glucose to form glucose 6-P (Fig. 22.4). Phosphorylation of glucose commits it to metabolism within the cell because glucose 6-P cannot be transported back across the plasma membrane. The phosphorylation reaction is irreversible under physiologic conditions because the reaction has a high-negative $\Delta G^{0'}$. Phosphorylation does not, however, commit glucose to glycolysis.

Glucose 6-P is a branch point in carbohydrate metabolism. It is a precursor for almost every pathway that uses glucose, including glycolysis, the pentose phosphate pathway, and glycogen synthesis. From the opposite point of view, it also can be generated from other pathways of carbohydrate metabolism, such as glycogenolysis

FIG. 22.4.   Glucose 6-phosphate metabolism.

(breakdown of glycogen), the pentose phosphate pathway, and gluconeogenesis (the synthesis of glucose from noncarbohydrate sources).

Hexokinases, the enzymes that catalyze the phosphorylation of glucose, are a family of tissue-specific isoenzymes that differ in their kinetic properties. The isoenzyme found in liver and β-cells of the pancreas has a much higher K_m than other hexokinases and is called *glucokinase*. In many cells, some of the hexokinase is bound to porins in the outer mitochondrial membrane (voltage-dependent anion channels; see Chapter 21), which gives these enzymes first access to newly synthesized ATP as it exits the mitochondria.

2. CONVERSION OF GLUCOSE 6-PHOSPHATE TO THE TRIOSE PHOSPHATES

In the remainder of the preparative phase of glycolysis, glucose 6-P is isomerized to fructose 6-phosphate (fructose 6-P), again phosphorylated, and subsequently cleaved into two three-carbon fragments (Fig. 22.5). The isomerization, which positions a keto group next to carbon 3, is essential for the subsequent cleavage of the bond between carbons 3 and 4.

The next step of glycolysis, phosphorylation of fructose 6-P to fructose 1,6-bisphosphate (fructose 1,6-bisP) by phosphofructokinase-1 (PFK-1), is generally considered the first committed step of the pathway. This phosphorylation requires ATP and is thermodynamically and kinetically irreversible. Therefore, PFK-1 irrevocably commits glucose to the glycolytic pathway. PFK-1 is a regulated enzyme in cells, and its regulation controls the entry of glucose into glycolysis. Like hexokinase, it exists as tissue-specific isoenzymes whose regulatory properties match variations in the role of glycolysis in different tissues.

Fructose 1,6-bisP is cleaved into two phosphorylated three-carbon compounds (triose phosphates) by aldolase (see Fig. 22.5). Dihydroxyacetone phosphate (DHAP) is isomerized to glyceraldehyde 3-P, which is a triose phosphate. Aldolase is named for the mechanism of the forward reaction, which is an aldol cleavage, and the mechanism of the reverse reaction, which is an aldol condensation. The enzyme exists as tissue-specific isoenzymes, which all catalyze the cleavage of fructose 1,6-bisP but differ in their specificities for fructose 1-P. The enzyme uses a lysine residue at the active site to form a covalent bond with the substrate during the course of the reaction. Inability to form this covalent linkage inactivates the enzyme.

Thus, at this point in glycolysis, for every mole of glucose that enters the pathway, 2 mol of glyceraldehyde 3-P are produced and continue through the pathway.

3. OXIDATION AND SUBSTRATE-LEVEL PHOSPHORYLATION

In the next part of the glycolytic pathway, glyceraldehyde 3-P is oxidized and phosphorylated so that subsequent intermediates of glycolysis can donate phosphate to ADP to generate ATP. The first reaction in this sequence, catalyzed by glyceraldehyde 3-P dehydrogenase, is really the key to the pathway (see Fig. 22.5). This enzyme oxidizes the aldehyde group of glyceraldehyde 3-P to an enzyme-bound carboxyl group and transfers the electrons to NAD^+ to form NADH. The oxidation step is dependent on a cysteine residue at the active site of the enzyme, which forms a high-energy thioester bond during the course of the reaction. The high-energy intermediate immediately accepts an inorganic phosphate to form the high-energy acyl phosphate bond in 1,3-bisphosphoglycerate, releasing the product from the cysteine residue on the enzyme. This high-energy phosphate bond is the start of substrate-level phosphorylation (the formation of a high-energy phosphate bond where none previously existed, without the use of oxygen).

In the next reaction, the phosphate in this bond is transferred to ADP to form ATP by phosphoglycerate kinase. The energy of the acyl phosphate bond is high enough ($\sim$10 kcal/mol) so that transfer to ADP is an energetically favorable process. Another product of this reaction is 3-phosphoglycerate.

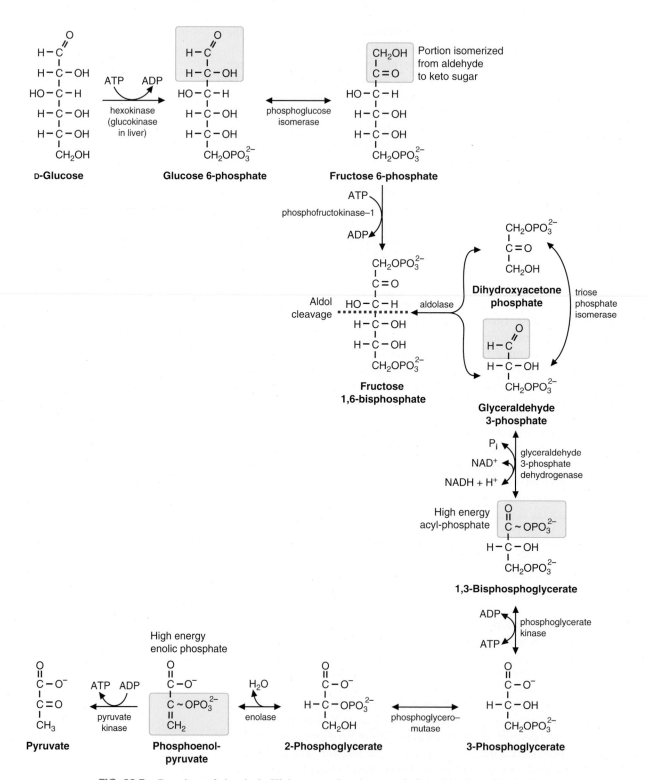

FIG. 22.5. Reactions of glycolysis. High-energy phosphates are indicated by the *red squiggles*.

To transfer the remaining low-energy phosphoester on 3-phosphoglycerate to ADP, it must be converted into a high-energy bond. This conversion is accomplished by moving the phosphate to the second carbon (forming 2-phosphoglycerate) and then removing water to form phosphoenolpyruvate (PEP). The enolphosphate bond is a high-energy bond (its hydrolysis releases approximately 14 kcal/mol of energy), so the transfer of phosphate to ADP by pyruvate kinase is energetically favorable (see Fig. 22.5). This final reaction converts PEP to pyruvate.

4. SUMMARY OF THE GLYCOLYTIC PATHWAY

The overall net reaction in the glycolytic pathway is

Glucose + 2 NAD^+ + 2 P_i + 2 ADP → 2 pyruvate + 2 NADH + 4 H^+ + 2 ATP + 2 H_2O

The pathway occurs with an overall negative $\Delta G^{0'}$ of approximately -22 kcal/mol. Therefore, it cannot be reversed without the expenditure of energy.

B. Oxidative Fates of Pyruvate and Nicotinamide Adenine Dinucleotide

The NADH produced from glycolysis must be continuously reoxidized back to NAD^+ to provide an electron acceptor for the glyceraldehyde 3-P dehydrogenase reaction and prevent product inhibition. Without oxidation of this NADH, glycolysis cannot continue. There are two alternate routes for oxidation of cytosolic NADH (Fig. 22.6). One route is aerobic, involving shuttles that transfer reducing equivalents across the mitochondrial membrane and ultimately to the electron-transport chain and oxygen (see Fig. 22.6A). The other route is anaerobic (without the use of oxygen). In anaerobic glycolysis, NADH is reoxidized in the cytosol by lactate dehydrogenase (LDH), which reduces pyruvate to lactate (see Fig. 22.6B).

The fate of pyruvate depends on the route used for NADH oxidation. If NADH is reoxidized in a shuttle system, pyruvate can be used for other pathways, one of which is oxidation to acetyl coenzyme A (acetyl-CoA) and entry into the TCA cycle for complete oxidation. Alternatively, in anaerobic glycolysis, pyruvate is reduced to lactate and diverted away from other potential pathways. Thus, the use of the shuttle systems allows for more ATP to be generated than by anaerobic glycolysis, by both oxidizing the cytoplasmically derived NADH in the electron-transport chain and by allowing pyruvate to be oxidized completely to CO_2.

The reason that shuttles are required for the oxidation of cytosolic NADH by the electron-transport chain is that the inner mitochondrial membrane is impermeable to NADH, and no transport protein exists that can translocate NADH across this membrane directly. Consequently, NADH is reoxidized to NAD^+ in the cytosol by

 The confusion experienced by **Lopa Fusor** in the emergency department is caused by an inadequate delivery of oxygen to the brain. Neurons have very high ATP requirements, and most of this ATP is provided by aerobic oxidation of glucose to pyruvate in glycolysis and by pyruvate oxidation to CO_2 in the TCA cycle. The brain has little or no capacity to oxidize fatty acids so its glucose consumption is high (approximately 125 to 150 g/day in the adult). Its oxygen demands are also high. If cerebral oxygen supply were completely interrupted, the brain would last only 10 seconds. The only reason that consciousness lasts longer during anoxia or asphyxia is that there is still some oxygen in the lungs and in circulating blood. A decrease of blood flow to approximately one-half of the normal rate results in a loss of consciousness.

FIG. 22.6.   Alternate fates of pyruvate. **A.** The pyruvate produced by glycolysis enters mitochondria and is oxidized to CO_2 and H_2O. The reducing equivalents in NADH enter mitochondria via a shuttle system. **B.** Pyruvate is reduced to lactate in the cytosol, thereby using the reducing equivalents in NADH.

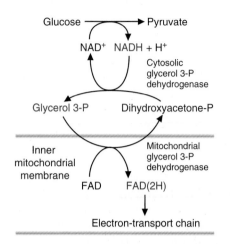

FIG. 22.7. Glycerol 3-P shuttle. Because NAD$^+$ and NADH cannot cross the mitochondrial membrane, shuttles transfer the reducing equivalents into mitochondria. DHAP is reduced to glycerol 3-P by cytosolic glycerol 3-P dehydrogenase, using cytosolic NADH produced in glycolysis. Glycerol 3-P then reacts in the inner mitochondrial membrane with mitochondrial glycerol 3-P dehydrogenase, which transfers the electrons to FAD and regenerates DHAP, which returns to the cytosol. The electron-transport chain transfers the electrons to O$_2$, which generates approximately 1.5 ATP molecules for each FAD(2H) that is oxidized.

a reaction that transfers the electrons to DHAP in the glycerol 3-phosphate (glycerol 3-P) shuttle and oxaloacetate in the malate–aspartate shuttle. The NAD$^+$ that is formed in the cytosol returns to glycolysis, whereas glycerol 3-P or malate carries the reducing equivalents that are ultimately transferred across the inner mitochondrial membrane. Thus, these shuttles transfer electrons and not NADH per se.

1.   GLYCEROL 3-PHOSPHATE SHUTTLE

The *glycerol 3-P shuttle* is the major shuttle in most tissues. In this shuttle, cytosolic NAD$^+$ is regenerated by cytoplasmic glycerol 3-P dehydrogenase, which transfers electrons from NADH to DHAP to form glycerol 3-P (Fig. 22.7). Glycerol 3-P then diffuses through the outer mitochondrial membrane to the inner mitochondrial membrane, where the electrons are donated to a membrane-bound flavin adenine dinucleotide (FAD)–containing glycerophosphate dehydrogenase. This enzyme, like succinate dehydrogenase, ultimately donates electrons to coenzyme Q (CoQ), resulting in an energy yield of approximately 1.5 ATP from oxidative phosphorylation. DHAP returns to the cytosol to continue the shuttle. The sum of the reactions in this shuttle system is simply

$$NADH_{cytosol} + H^+ + FAD_{mitochondria} \rightarrow NAD^+_{cytosol} + FAD(2H)_{mitochondria}$$

2.   MALATE–ASPARTATE SHUTTLE

Many tissues contain both the glycerol 3-P shuttle and the malate–aspartate shuttle. In the malate–aspartate shuttle (Fig. 22.8), cytosolic NAD$^+$ is regenerated by cytosolic malate dehydrogenase, which transfers electrons from NADH to cytosolic oxaloacetate to form malate. Malate is transported across the inner mitochondrial membrane by a specific translocase, which exchanges malate for α-ketoglutarate. In the matrix, malate is oxidized back to oxaloacetate by mitochondrial malate dehydrogenase, and NADH is generated. This NADH can donate electrons to the electron-transport chain with generation of approximately 2.5 mol of ATP per mole of NADH. The newly formed oxaloacetate cannot pass back through the inner mitochondrial membrane under physiologic conditions, so aspartate is used to return the oxaloacetate carbon skeleton to the cytosol. In the matrix, transamination reactions transfer an amino group to oxaloacetate to form aspartate, which is transported out to the cytosol (using an aspartate–glutamate exchange translocase) and converted back to oxaloacetate through another transamination reaction. The sum of all the reactions of this shuttle system is simply

$$NADH_{cytosol} + NAD^+_{matrix} \rightarrow NAD^+_{cytosol} + NADH_{matrix}$$

FIG. 22.8.   Malate–aspartate shuttle. NADH produced by glycolysis reduces oxaloacetate (OAA) to malate, which crosses the mitochondrial membrane and is reoxidized to OAA. The mitochondrial NADH donates electrons to the electron-transport chain, with 2.5 ATP molecules generated for each NADH. To complete the shuttle, OAA must return to the cytosol, although it cannot be transported directly on a translocase. Instead, it is transaminated to aspartate, which is then transported out to the cytosol, where it is transaminated back to OAA. The translocators exchange compounds in such a way that the shuttle is completely balanced. *TA,* transamination reaction; *α-KG,* α-ketoglutarate.

C. Anaerobic Glycolysis

When the oxidative capacity of a cell is limited (e.g., in the red blood cell, which has no mitochondria), the pyruvate and NADH produced from glycolysis cannot be oxidized aerobically. The NADH is therefore oxidized to NAD^+ in the cytosol by reduction of pyruvate to lactate. This reaction is catalyzed by LDH (Fig. 22.9). The net reaction for anaerobic glycolysis is

$$Glucose + 2\ ADP + 2\ P_i \rightarrow 2\ lactate + 2\ ATP + 2\ H_2O + 2\ H^+$$

1. ENERGY YIELD OF AEROBIC VERSUS ANAEROBIC GLYCOLYSIS

In both aerobic and anaerobic glycolysis, each mole of glucose generates 2 mol of ATP, 2 mol of NADH, and 2 mol of pyruvate. The energy yield from anaerobic glycolysis (1 mol of glucose to 2 mol of lactate) is only 2 mol of ATP per mole of glucose, as the NADH is recycled to NAD^+ by reducing pyruvate to lactate. Neither the NADH nor the pyruvate produced is thus used for further energy generation. However, when oxygen is available and cytosolic NADH can be oxidized via a shuttle system, pyruvate can also enter the mitochondria and be completely oxidized to CO_2 via pyruvate dehydrogenase (PDH) and the TCA cycle. The oxidation of pyruvate via this route generates roughly 12.5 mol of ATP per mole of pyruvate. If the cytosolic NADH is oxidized by the glycerol 3-P shuttle, approximately 1.5 mol of ATP are produced per NADH. If, instead, the NADH is oxidized by the malate–aspartate shuttle, approximately 2.5 mol are produced. Thus, the two NADH molecules produced during glycolysis can lead to 3 to 5 mol of ATP being produced, depending on which shuttle system is used to transfer the reducing equivalents. Because each pyruvate produced can give rise to 12.5 mol of ATP, altogether, 30 to 32 mol of ATP can be produced from 1 mol of glucose oxidized to carbon dioxide.

To produce the same amount of ATP per unit time from anaerobic glycolysis as from the complete aerobic oxidation of glucose to CO_2, anaerobic glycolysis must occur approximately 15 times faster and use approximately 15 times more glucose. Cells achieve this high rate of glycolysis by expressing high levels of glycolytic enzymes. In certain skeletal muscles and in most cells during hypoxic crises, high rates of glycolysis are associated with rapid degradation of internal glycogen stores to supply the required glucose 6-P.

2. ACID PRODUCTION IN ANAEROBIC GLYCOLYSIS

Anaerobic glycolysis results in acid production in the form of H^+. Glycolysis forms pyruvic acid, which is reduced to lactic acid. At an intracellular pH of 7.35, lactic acid dissociates to form the carboxylate anion, lactate, and H^+ (the pK_a for lactic acid is 3.85). Lactate and the H^+ are both transported out of the cell into interstitial fluid by a transporter on the plasma membrane and eventually diffuse into the blood. If the amount of lactate generated exceeds the buffering capacity of the blood, the pH drops below the normal range, resulting in lactic acidosis (see Chapter 4).

3. TISSUES DEPENDENT ON ANAEROBIC GLYCOLYSIS

Many tissues, including red and white blood cells, the kidney medulla, the tissues of the eye, and skeletal muscles, rely on anaerobic glycolysis for at least a portion of their ATP requirements (Table 22.1). Tissues (or cells) that are heavily dependent on anaerobic glycolysis usually have a low ATP demand, high levels of glycolytic enzymes, and few capillaries, such that oxygen must diffuse over a greater distance to reach target cells. The lack of mitochondria, or the increased rate of glycolysis, is often related to some aspect of cell function. For example, the mature red blood cell has no mitochondria because oxidative metabolism might interfere with its function in transporting oxygen bound to hemoglobin. Some of the lactic acid generated by anaerobic glycolysis in skin is secreted in sweat, where it acts as an antibacterial

Glycolysis

Pyruvate   **Lactate**

FIG. 22.9. Lactate dehydrogenase reaction. Pyruvate, which may be produced by glycolysis, is reduced to lactate. The reaction, which occurs in the cytosol, requires NADH and is catalyzed by lactate dehydrogenase. This reaction is readily reversible.

 What are the energy-generating steps as pyruvate is completely oxidized to carbon dioxide to generate 12.5 molecules of ATP per pyruvate?

The dental caries in **Ivan Applebod's** mouth were caused principally by the low pH generated from lactic acid production by oral bacteria. Below a pH of 5.5, decalcification of tooth enamel and dentine occurs. Lactobacilli and *S. mutans* are major contributors to this process because almost all of their energy is derived from the conversion of glucose or fructose to lactic acid, and they are able to grow well at the low pH generated by this process. Mr. Applebod's dentist explained that bacteria in his dental plaque could convert all the sugar in his candy into acid in less than 20 minutes. The acid is buffered by bicarbonate and other buffers in saliva, but saliva production decreases in the evening. Thus, the acid could dissolve the hydroxyapatite in his tooth enamel during the night.

A: In the complete oxidation of pyruvate to carbon dioxide, four steps generate NADH (pyruvate dehydrogenase, isocitrate dehydrogenase, α-ketoglutarate dehydrogenase, and malate dehydrogenase). One step generates FAD(2H) (succinate dehydrogenase) and one substrate-level phosphorylation (succinate thiokinase). Thus, because each NADH generates 2.5 ATP molecules, the overall contribution by NADH is 10 ATP molecules. The FAD(2H) generates an additional 1.5 ATP molecules, and the substrate-level phosphorylation provides one more. Therefore, 10 + 1.5 + 1 = 12.5 molecules of ATP.

In response to the hypoxemia caused by **Lopa Fusor's** COPD, she has increased hypoxia-inducible factor-1 (HIF-1) in her tissues. HIF-1 is a gene transcription factor found in tissues throughout the body (including the brain, heart, kidneys, lungs, liver, pancreas, skeletal muscles, and white blood cells) that plays a homeostatic role in coordinating tissue responses to hypoxia. Each tissue will respond with a subset of the following changes. HIF-1 increases transcription of the genes for many of the glycolytic enzymes, including PFK-1, enolase, phosphoglycerate kinase, and lactate dehydrogenase. HIF-1 also increases synthesis of several proteins that enhance oxygen delivery to tissues, including erythropoietin, which increases the generation of red blood cells in bone marrow; vascular endothelial growth factor, which regulates angiogenesis (formation of blood vessels); and inducible nitric oxide synthase, which synthesizes nitric oxide, a vasodilator. As a consequence, Mrs. Fusor was able to maintain hematocrit and hemoglobin levels that were on the high side of the normal range, and her tissues had an increased capacity for anaerobic glycolysis.

Table 22.1 Major Tissue Sites of Lactate Production in a Resting Man (An Average 70-kg Man Consumes about 300 g of Carbohydrate per Day)

Daily Lactate Production (g/d)	
Total lactate production	115
Red blood cells	29
Skin	20
Brain	17
Skeletal muscles	16
Renal medulla	15
Intestinal mucosa	8
Other tissues	10

agent. Many large tumors use anaerobic glycolysis for ATP production and lack capillaries in their core.

In tissues with some mitochondria, both aerobic and anaerobic glycolysis occur simultaneously. The relative proportion of the two pathways depends on the mitochondrial oxidative capacity of the tissue and its oxygen supply and may vary among cell types within the same tissue because of cell distance from the capillaries. When a cell's energy demand exceeds the capacity of the rate of the electron-transport chain and oxidative phosphorylation to produce ATP, glycolysis is activated, and the increased $NADH/NAD^+$ ratio directs excess pyruvate into lactate. Because under these conditions—the PDH, the TCA cycle, and the electron-transport chain are operating as fast as they can—anaerobic glycolysis is meeting the need for additional ATP.

4. FATE OF LACTATE

Lactate released from cells that undergo anaerobic glycolysis is taken up by other tissues (primarily the liver, heart, and skeletal muscle) and oxidized back to pyruvate. In the liver, the pyruvate is used to synthesize glucose (gluconeogenesis), which is returned to the blood. The cycling of lactate and glucose between peripheral tissues and liver is called the *Cori cycle* (Fig. 22.10).

In many other tissues, lactate is oxidized to pyruvate, which is then oxidized to CO_2 in the TCA cycle. Although the equilibrium of the LDH reaction favors lactate production, flux occurs in the opposite direction if NADH is being rapidly oxidized in the electron-transport chain (or is being used for gluconeogenesis):

$$\text{Lactate} + NAD^+ \rightarrow \text{pyruvate} + NADH + H^+$$

The heart, with its huge mitochondrial content and oxidative capacity, is able to use lactate released from other tissues as a fuel. During exercise such as bicycle riding, lactate released into the blood from skeletal muscles in the leg might be used by

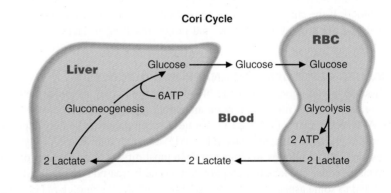

Cori Cycle

FIG. 22.10. The Cori cycle. Glucose, produced in the liver by gluconeogenesis, is converted to lactate by glycolysis in muscles, red blood cells, and many other cells. Lactate returns to the liver and is reconverted to glucose by gluconeogenesis.

resting skeletal muscles in the arm. In the brain, glial cells and astrocytes produce lactate, which is used by neurons or released into the blood.

LDH is a tetramer composed of A-subunits (also called M-subunits, for skeletal muscle form) and B-subunits (also called H-subunits, for heart). Different tissues produce different amounts of the two subunits, which then combine randomly to form five different tetramers (M4, M3H1, M2H2, M1H3, and H4). These isoenzymes differ only slightly in their properties, but the kinetic properties of the M4 form facilitate conversion of pyruvate to lactate in skeletal muscle, whereas the kinetic properties of H4 form facilitate conversion of lactate to pyruvate in the heart for energy generation.

II. OTHER FUNCTIONS OF GLYCOLYSIS

Glycolysis, in addition to providing ATP, generates precursors for biosynthetic pathways (Fig. 22.11). Intermediates of the pathway can be converted to ribose 5-phosphate, the sugar incorporated into nucleotides such as ATP. Other sugars, such as UDP-glucose, mannose, and sialic acid, are also formed from intermediates of glycolysis. Serine is synthesized from 3-phosphoglycerate, and alanine from pyruvate. The backbone of triacylglycerols, glycerol 3-P, is derived from DHAP in the glycolytic pathway.

The liver is the major site of biosynthetic reactions in the body. In addition to those pathways mentioned previously, the liver synthesizes fatty acids from the pyruvate generated by glycolysis. It also synthesizes glucose from lactate, glycerol 3-P, and amino acids in the gluconeogenic pathway, which is basically a reversal of glycolysis. Consequently, in liver, many of the glycolytic enzymes exist as isoenzymes with properties suited for these functions.

The bisphosphoglycerate shunt is a "side reaction" of the glycolytic pathway in which 1,3-bisphosphoglycerate is converted to 2,3-bisphosphoglycerate (2,3-BPG). Red blood cells form 2,3-BPG to serve as an allosteric inhibitor of oxygen

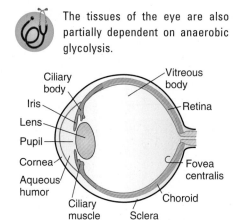

The tissues of the eye are also partially dependent on anaerobic glycolysis.

The eye contains cells that transmit or focus light, and these cells, therefore, cannot be filled with opaque structures such as mitochondria or densely packed capillary beds. The corneal epithelium generates most of its ATP aerobically from its few mitochondria but still metabolizes some glucose anaerobically. Oxygen is supplied by diffusion from the air. The lens of the eye is composed of fibers that must remain birefringent to transmit and focus light, so mitochondria are nearly absent. The small amount of ATP required (principally for ion balance) can readily be generated from anaerobic glycolysis even though the energy yield is low. The lens is able to pick up glucose and release lactate into the vitreous body and aqueous humor. It does not need oxygen and has no use for capillaries.

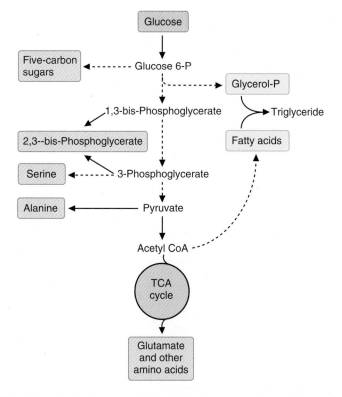

FIG. 22.11.   Biosynthetic functions of glycolysis. Compounds formed from intermediates of glycolysis are shown in the *boxes*. These pathways are discussed in later chapters. *Dotted lines* indicate that more than one step is required for the conversion shown in the figure.

binding to heme (see Chapter 44). 2,3-BPG reenters the glycolytic pathway via dephosphorylation to 3-phosphoglycerate. It also functions as a coenzyme in the conversion of 3-phosphoglycerate to 2-phosphoglycerate by the glycolytic enzyme phosphoglyceromutase. Because 2,3-BPG is not depleted by its role in this catalytic process, most cells need only very small amounts.

III. REGULATION OF GLYCOLYSIS BY THE NEED FOR ADENOSINE TRIPHOSPHATE

One of the major functions of glycolysis is the generation of ATP, so the pathway is regulated to maintain ATP homeostasis in all cells. PFK-1 and PDH, which links glycolysis and the TCA cycle, are both major regulatory sites that respond to feedback indicators of the rate of ATP utilization (Fig. 22.12). The supply of glucose 6-P for glycolysis is tissue-dependent and can be regulated at the steps of glucose

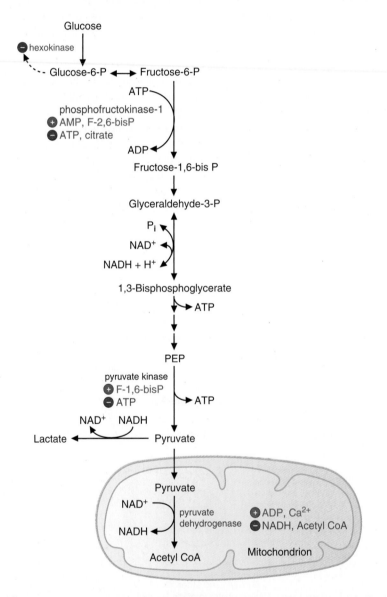

FIG. 22.12.   Major sites of regulation in the glycolytic pathway. Hexokinase and phosphofructokinase-1 are the major regulatory enzymes in skeletal muscle. The activity of pyruvate dehydrogenase in the mitochondrion determines whether pyruvate is converted to lactate or to acetyl coenzyme A (acetyl-CoA). The regulation shown for pyruvate kinase occurs only for the liver (L) isoenzyme.

transport into cells, glycogenolysis (the degradation of glycogen to form glucose), or the rate of glucose phosphorylation by hexokinase isoenzymes. Other regulatory mechanisms integrate the ATP-generating role of glycolysis with its anabolic roles.

All of the regulatory enzymes of glycolysis exist as tissue-specific isoenzymes, which alter the regulation of the pathway to match variations in conditions and needs in different tissues. For example, in the liver, an isoenzyme of pyruvate kinase introduces an additional regulatory site in glycolysis that contributes to the inhibition of glycolysis when the reverse pathway, gluconeogenesis, is activated.

A. Relationships among ATP, ADP, and AMP Concentrations

The AMP levels within the cytosol provide a better indicator of the rate of ATP utilization than the ATP concentration itself (Fig. 22.13). The concentration of AMP in the cytosol is determined by the equilibrium position of the adenylate kinase reaction, which catalyzes the following reaction:

$$2 \text{ ADP} \leftrightarrow \text{AMP} + \text{ATP}$$

The equilibrium is such that hydrolysis of ATP to ADP in energy-requiring reactions increases both the ADP and AMP contents of the cytosol. However, ATP is present in much higher quantities than AMP or ADP, so a small decrease of ATP concentration in the cytosol causes a much larger percentage increase in the small AMP pool. In skeletal muscles, for instance, ATP levels are approximately 5 mM and decrease by no more than 20% during strenuous exercise (see Fig. 22.13). At the same time, ADP levels may increase by 50%, and AMP levels, which are in the micromolar range, may increase by 300%. AMP activates several metabolic pathways, including glycolysis, glycogenolysis, and fatty acid oxidation (particularly in muscle tissues), to ensure that ATP homeostasis is maintained.

B. Regulation of Hexokinases

Hexokinases exist as tissue-specific isoenzymes whose regulatory properties reflect the role of glycolysis in different tissues. In most tissues, hexokinase is a low-K_m enzyme with a high affinity for glucose (see Chapter 9). It is inhibited by physiologic concentrations of its product, glucose 6-P (see Fig. 22.12). If glucose 6-P does not enter glycolysis or another pathway, it accumulates and decreases the activity of hexokinase. In the liver, the isoenzyme glucokinase is a high-K_m enzyme that is not readily inhibited by glucose 6-P. Thus, glycolysis can continue in the liver even when energy levels are high, so that anabolic pathways, such as the synthesis of the major energy storage compounds, glycogen, and fatty acids, can occur.

C. Regulation of Phosphofructokinase-1

PFK-1 is the rate-limiting enzyme of glycolysis and controls the rate of glucose 6-P entry into glycolysis in most tissues. PFK-1 is an allosteric enzyme that has a total of six binding sites: two are for substrates (MgATP and fructose 6-P) and four are allosteric regulatory sites (see Fig. 22.12). The allosteric regulatory sites occupy a physically different domain on the enzyme than the catalytic site. When an allosteric effector binds, it changes the conformation at the active site and may activate or inhibit the enzyme (see also Chapter 9). The allosteric sites for PFK-1 include an inhibitory site for MgATP, an inhibitory site for citrate and other anions, an allosteric activation site for AMP, and an allosteric activation site for fructose 2,6-bisphosphate (fructose 2,6-bisP) and other bisphosphates. Several different tissue-specific isoforms of PFK-1 are affected in different ways by the concentration of these substrates and allosteric effectors but all contain these four allosteric sites.

Three different types of PFK-1 isoenzyme subunits exist: M (muscle), L (liver), and C (other tissues). The three subunits show variable expression in different tissues, with some tissues having more than one type. For example, mature human

FIG. 22.13. Changes in ATP, ADP, and AMP concentrations in skeletal muscles during exercise. The concentration of ATP decreases by only approximately 20% during exercise, and the concentration of ADP rises. The concentration of AMP, produced by the adenylate kinase reaction, increases manyfold and serves as a sensitive indicator of decreasing ATP levels.

A

B

FIG. 22.14. Regulation of PFK-1 by AMP, ATP, and fructose 2,6-bisP. **A.** AMP and fructose 2,6-bisP activate PFK-1. **B.** ATP, as a substrate, increases the rate of the reaction at low concentrations but allosterically inhibits the enzyme at high concentrations.

muscle expresses only the M-subunit, the liver expresses principally the L-subunit, and erythrocytes express both the M- and the L-subunits. The C-subunit is present in highest levels in platelets, placenta, kidney, and fibroblasts but is relatively common to most tissues. Both the M- and L-subunits are sensitive to AMP and ATP regulation, but the C-subunits are much less so. Active PFK-1 is a tetramer, composed of four subunits. Within muscle, the M4 form predominates; but within tissues that express multiple isoenzymes of PFK-1, heterotetramers can form that have full activity.

1. ALLOSTERIC REGULATION OF PFK-1 BY AMP AND ATP

ATP binds to two different sites on the enzyme: the substrate-binding site and an allosteric inhibitory site. Under physiologic conditions in the cell, the ATP concentration is usually high enough to saturate the substrate-binding site and inhibit the enzyme by binding to the ATP allosteric site. This effect of ATP is opposed by AMP, which binds to a separate allosteric activator site (Fig. 22.14). For most of the PFK-1 isoenzymes, the binding of AMP increases the affinity of the enzyme for fructose 6-P (e.g., it shifts the kinetic curve to the left). Thus, increases in AMP concentration can greatly increase the rate of the enzyme (see Fig. 22.14), particularly when fructose 6-P concentrations are low.

2. REGULATION OF PFK-1 BY FRUCTOSE 2,6-BISPHOSPHATE

Fructose 2,6-bisP is also an allosteric activator of PFK-1 that opposes ATP inhibition. Its effect on the rate of activity of PFK-1 is qualitatively similar to that of AMP, but it has a separate binding site. Fructose 2,6-bisP is *not* an intermediate of glycolysis but is synthesized by an enzyme that phosphorylates fructose 6-P at the 2-position. The enzyme is therefore named phosphofructokinase-2 (PFK-2); it is a bifunctional enzyme with two separate domains: a kinase domain and a phosphatase domain. At the kinase domain, fructose 6-P is phosphorylated to fructose 2,6-bisP; and at the phosphatase domain, fructose 2,6-bisP is hydrolyzed back to fructose 6-P. PFK-2 is regulated through changes in the ratio of activity of the two domains. For example, in skeletal muscles, high concentrations of fructose 6-P activate the kinase and inhibit the phosphatase, thereby increasing the concentration of fructose 2,6-bisP and activating glycolysis.

PFK-2 can also be regulated through phosphorylation by serine–threonine protein kinases. The liver isoenzyme contains a phosphorylation site near the amino terminal that decreases the activity of the kinase and increases the phosphatase activity. This site is phosphorylated by the cyclic adenosine monophosphate (cAMP)–dependent protein kinase (protein kinase A) and is responsible for decreased levels of liver fructose 2,6-bisP during fasting conditions (as modulated by circulating glucagon levels, which is discussed in detail in Chapters 26 and 31). The cardiac isoenzyme contains a phosphorylation site near the carboxy terminal that can be phosphorylated in response to adrenergic activators of contraction (such as norepinephrine) and by increased AMP levels. Phosphorylation at this site

Otto Shape has started high-intensity exercise that will increase the production of lactate in his exercising skeletal muscles. In skeletal muscles, the amount of aerobic versus anaerobic glycolysis that occurs varies with the intensity of the exercise, with the duration of the exercise, with the type of skeletal muscle fiber involved, and with the level of training. Human skeletal muscles are usually combinations of type I fibers (called *fast glycolytic fibers* or *white muscle fibers*) and type IIb fibers (called *slow oxidative fibers* or *red muscle fibers*). The designation "fast" or "slow" refers to the fibers' rate of shortening, which is determined by the level of the isoenzyme of myosin ATPase present. Compared with glycolytic fibers, oxidative fibers have a higher content of mitochondria and myoglobin, which gives them a red color. The gastrocnemius, a muscle in the leg used for running, has a high content of type IIb fibers. However, these fibers will still produce lactate during sprints when the ATP demand exceeds their oxidative capacity.

increases the kinase activity and increases fructose 2,6-bisP levels, thereby contributing to the activation of glycolysis.

3. ALLOSTERIC INHIBITION OF PFK-1 AT THE CITRATE SITE

The function of the citrate-anion allosteric site is to integrate glycolysis with other pathways. For example, the inhibition of PFK-1 by citrate may play a role in decreasing glycolytic flux in the heart during the oxidation of fatty acids.

D. Regulation of Pyruvate Kinase

Pyruvate kinase exists as tissue-specific isoenzymes, designated as R (red blood cells), L (liver), and M1/M2 (muscle and other tissues). The M1 form present in brain, heart, and muscle contains no allosteric sites, and pyruvate kinase does not contribute to the regulation of glycolysis in these tissues (these tissues also do not undergo significant gluconeogenesis). However, the liver isoenzyme can be inhibited through phosphorylation by the cAMP-dependent protein kinase and by several allosteric effectors that contribute to the inhibition of glycolysis during fasting conditions. These allosteric effectors include activation by fructose 1,6-bisP, which ties the rate of pyruvate kinase to that of PFK-1, and inhibition by ATP, which signifies high energy levels.

E. Pyruvate Dehydrogenase Regulation and Glycolysis

PDH is also regulated principally by the rate of ATP utilization (see Chapter 20) through rapid phosphorylation to an inactive form. Thus, in a normally respiring cell, with an adequate supply of O_2, glycolysis and the TCA cycle are activated together, and glucose can be completely oxidized to CO_2. However, when tissues do not have an adequate supply of O_2 to meet their ATP demands, the increased $NADH/NAD^+$ ratio inhibits PDH, but AMP activates glycolysis. A proportion of the pyruvate is then reduced to lactate to allow glycolysis to continue.

IV. LACTIC ACIDEMIA

Lactate production is a normal part of metabolism. In the absence of disease, elevated lactate levels in the blood are associated with anaerobic glycolysis during exercise. In lactic acidosis, lactic acid accumulates in blood to levels that significantly affect the pH (lactate levels >5 mM and a decrease of blood pH below 7.2).

Lactic acidosis generally results from a greatly increased $NADH/NAD^+$ ratio in tissues (Fig. 22.15). The increased NADH concentration prevents pyruvate oxidation in the TCA cycle and directs pyruvate to lactate. To compensate for the decreased ATP production from oxidative metabolism, PFK-1, and therefore the entire glycolytic pathway, is activated. For example, consumption of large amounts of alcohol, which is rapidly oxidized in the liver and increases NADH levels, can result in lactic acidosis. Hypoxia in any tissue increases lactate production as cells attempt to compensate for a lack of O_2 for oxidative phosphorylation.

Several other problems that interfere with either the electron-transport chain or pyruvate oxidation in the TCA cycle result in lactic acidemia (see Fig. 22.15). For

Under ischemic conditions, AMP levels within the heart increase rapidly because of the lack of ATP production via oxidative phosphorylation. The increase in AMP levels activates the AMP-activated protein kinase, which phosphorylates the heart isoenzyme of PFK-2 to activate its kinase activity. This results in increased levels of fructose 2,6-bisP, which activates PFK-1 along with AMP so that the rate of glycolysis can increase to compensate for the lack of ATP production via aerobic means.

During **Cora Nari's** myocardial infarction (see Chapter 20), the ischemic area in her heart had a limited supply of oxygen and blood-borne fuels. The absence of oxygen for oxidative phosphorylation would decrease the levels of ATP and increase those of AMP, an activator of PFK-1 and the AMP-dependent protein kinase, resulting in a compensatory increase of anaerobic glycolysis and lactate production. However, obstruction of a vessel leading to her heart would decrease lactate removal, resulting in a decrease of intracellular pH. Under these conditions, at very low pH levels, glycolysis is inhibited and unable to compensate for the lack of oxidative phosphorylation.

Several methods can be used to determine lactate levels in blood. Two of the most commonly used enzymatic methods are given. The first is the conversion of lactate to pyruvate (which also converts NAD^+ to NADH) in the presence of lactate dehydrogenase. Because NADH has considerable light absorption at 340 nm (and NAD^+ does not), one can follow the increase in absorbance at this wavelength as the reaction proceeds and determine the levels of lactate that were initially present in the sample. To ensure that all of the lactate is measured, hydrazine is added to the reaction; hydrazine reacts with pyruvate to remove the product of the LDH reaction, which forces the reaction to go to completion. The second enzymatic procedure that is commonly used employs lactate oxidase, which converts lactate, in the presence of oxygen, to pyruvate and hydrogen peroxide. In this case, a second enzymatic reaction measures the amount of hydrogen peroxide produced (which removes the product of the lactate oxidase reaction, ensuring completion of the reaction). This second reaction uses peroxidase and a chromagen, which is converted to a colored product as the hydrogen peroxide is removed. The amount of colored product produced allows lactate levels to be determined accurately. Both procedures have been automated for use in the clinical laboratory.

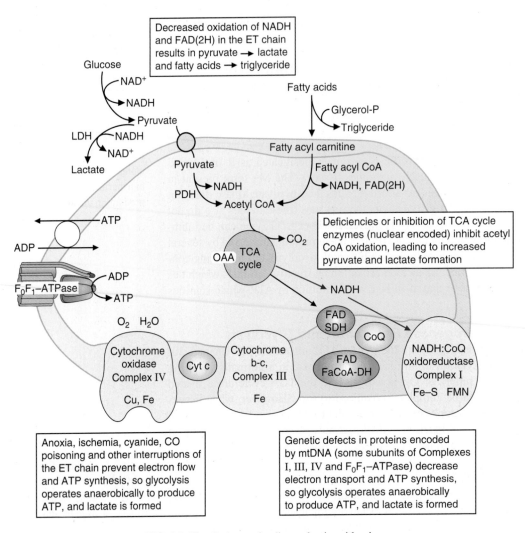

FIG. 22.15. Pathways leading to lactic acidemia.

example, oxidative phosphorylation diseases (inherited deficiencies in subunits of complexes in the electron-transport chain, such as myoclonic epilepsy with ragged red fibers [MERFF]) increase the NADH/NAD$^+$ ratio and inhibit PDH (see Chapter 21). Pyruvate accumulates and is converted to lactate to allow glycolytic ATP production to proceed. Similarly, impaired PDH activity from an inherited deficiency of E$_1$ (the decarboxylase subunit of the complex), or from severe thiamine deficiency, increases blood lactate levels (see Chapter 20). Pyruvate carboxylase deficiency also can result in lactic acidosis (see Chapter 20), also because of an accumulation of pyruvate.

Lactic acidosis can also result from inhibition of lactate utilization in gluconeogenesis (e.g., hereditary fructose intolerance, which is caused by a defective aldolase gene). If other pathways that use glucose 6-P are blocked, glucose 6-P can be shunted into glycolysis and lactate production (e.g., glucose 6-P deficiency).

CLINICAL COMMENTS

Lopa Fusor. Lopa Fusor was admitted to the hospital with severe hypotension caused by an acute hemorrhage. Her plasma lactic acid level was elevated and her arterial pH was low. The underlying mechanism for Ms. Fusor's derangement in acid–base balance is a severe reduction in the amount of oxygen delivered to her tissues for cellular respiration (hypoxemia). Several

Lopa Fusor had a decreased arterial Po$_2$ and elevated arterial Pco$_2$ caused by underperfusion of her lungs. The elevated CO$_2$ content resulted in an increase of H$_2$CO$_3$ and acidity of the blood (see Chapter 4). The decreased O$_2$ delivery to tissues resulted in increased lactate production from anaerobic glycolysis and an elevation of serum lactate to 10 times normal levels. The reduction in her arterial pH to 7.18 (reference range, 7.35 to 7.45), therefore, resulted from both a mild respiratory acidosis (elevated Pco$_2$) and a more profound metabolic acidosis (elevated serum lactate level).

concurrent processes contributed to this lack of oxygen. The first was her severely reduced blood pressure caused by a brisk hemorrhage from a bleeding gastric ulcer. The blood loss led to hypoperfusion and therefore reduced delivery of oxygen to her tissues. The marked reduction in the number of red blood cells in her circulation caused by blood loss further compromised oxygen delivery. Her preexisting chronic obstructive pulmonary disease (COPD) added to her hypoxemia by decreasing her ventilation and therefore the transfer of oxygen to her blood (low P_{O_2}). In addition, her COPD led to retention of carbon dioxide (high P_{CO_2}), which caused a respiratory acidosis because the retained CO_2 interacted with water to form carbonic acid (H_2CO_3), which dissociates to H^+ and bicarbonate.

 Otto Shape. In skeletal muscles, lactate production occurs when the need for ATP exceeds the capacity of the mitochondria for oxidative phosphorylation. Thus, increased lactate production accompanies an increased rate of the TCA cycle. The extent to which skeletal muscles use aerobic versus anaerobic glycolysis to supply ATP varies with the intensity of exercise. During low-intensity exercise, the rate of ATP use is lower, and fibers can generate this ATP from oxidative phosphorylation, with the complete oxidation of glucose to CO_2. However, when **Otto Shape** sprints, a high-intensity exercise, the ATP demand exceeds the rate at which the electron-transport chain and the TCA cycle can generate ATP from oxidative phosphorylation. The increased AMP level signals the need for additional ATP and stimulates PFK-1. The NADH/NAD$^+$ ratio directs the increase in pyruvate production toward lactate. The fall in pH causes muscle fatigue and pain. As Otto trains, the amounts of mitochondria and myoglobin in his skeletal muscle fibers increase, and these fibers rely less on anaerobic glycolysis.

 Ivan Applebod. Ivan Applebod had two sites of dental caries: one on a smooth surface and one in a fissure. The decreased pH resulting from lactic acid production by lactobacilli, which grow anaerobically within the fissure, is a major cause of fissure caries. *Streptococcus mutans* plays a major role in smooth-surface caries because it secretes dextran, an insoluble polysaccharide, which forms the base for plaque. *S. mutans* contains dextransucrase, a glucosyltransferase that transfers glucosyl units from dietary sucrose (the glucose–fructose disaccharide in sugar and sweets) to form the $\alpha(1{\rightarrow}6)$ and $\alpha(1{\rightarrow}3)$ linkages between the glucosyl units in dextran (Fig. 22.16). Dextransucrase is specific for sucrose and does not catalyze the polymerization of free glucose or glucose from other disaccharides or polysaccharides. Thus, sucrose is responsible for the cariogenic potential of candy. The sticky, water-insoluble dextran mediates the attachment of *S. mutans* and other bacteria to the tooth surface. This also keeps the acids produced from these bacteria close to the enamel surface. Fructose from sucrose is converted to intermediates of glycolysis and is rapidly metabolized to lactic acid. Other bacteria present in the plaque produce different acids from anaerobic metabolism, such as acetic acid and formic acid. The decrease in pH that results initiates demineralization of the hydroxyapatite of the tooth enamel. **Ivan Applebod's** caries in his baby teeth could have been caused by sucking on bottles containing fruit juice. The sugar in fruit juice is also sucrose, and babies who fall asleep with a bottle of fruit juice in their mouth may develop caries. Rapid decay of these baby teeth can harm the development of their permanent teeth.

FIG. 22.16. General structure of dextran. Glucosyl residues are linked by α-1,3-; α-1,6-; and some α-1,4-bonds.

BIOCHEMICAL COMMENTS

 The Mechanism of Glyceraldehyde 3-Phosphate Dehydrogenase. How is the first high-energy bond created in the glycolytic pathway? This is the work of the glyceraldehyde 3-P dehydrogenase reaction, which converts glyceraldehyde 3-P to 1,3-bisphosphoglycerate. This reaction

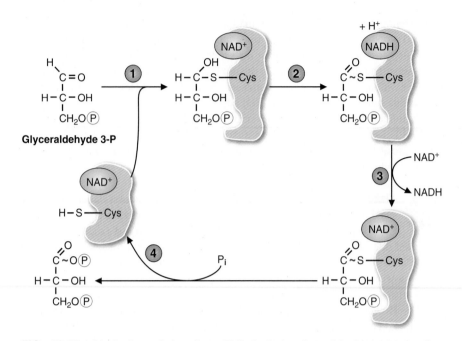

FIG. 22.17. Mechanism of the glyceraldehyde 3-phosphate dehydrogenase reaction. *(1)* The enzyme forms a covalent linkage with the substrate, using a cysteine group at the active site. The enzyme also contains bound NAD^+ close to the active site. *(2)* The substrate is oxidized, forming a high-energy thioester linkage (in *red*) and NADH. *(3)* NADH has a low affinity for the enzyme and is replaced by a new molecule of NAD^+. *(4)* Inorganic phosphate attacks the thioester linkage, releasing the product 1,3-bisphosphoglycerate and regenerating the active enzyme in a form ready to initiate another reaction.

can be considered to be two separate half-reactions: the first being the oxidation of glyceraldehyde 3-P to 3-phosphoglycerate, and the second being the addition of inorganic phosphate to 3-phosphoglycerate to produce 1,3-bisphosphoglycerate. The $\Delta G^{0'}$ for the first reaction is approximately -12 kcal/mol; for the second reaction, it is approximately $+12$ kcal/mol. Thus, although the first half-reaction is extremely favorable, the second half-reaction is unfavorable and does not proceed under cellular conditions. So how does the enzyme help this reaction to proceed? This is accomplished through the enzyme forming a covalent bond with the substrate, using an essential cysteine residue at the active site to form a high-energy thioester linkage during the course of the reaction (Fig. 22.17). Thus, the energy that would be released as heat in the oxidation of glyceraldehyde 3-P to 3-phosphoglycerate is conserved in the thioester linkage that is formed (such that the $\Delta G^{0'}$ of the formation of the thioester intermediate from glyceraldehyde 3-P is close to zero). Then, replacement of the sulfur with inorganic phosphate to form the final product, 1,3-bisphosphoglycerate, is relatively straightforward, as the $\Delta G^{0'}$ for that conversion is also close to zero, and the acylphosphate bond retains the energy from the oxidation of the aldehyde. This is one example of how covalent catalysis by an enzyme can result in the conservation of energy between different bond types.

Key Concepts

- Glycolysis is the pathway in which glucose is oxidized and cleaved to form pyruvate.
- The enzymes of glycolysis are in the cytosol.
- Glucose is the major sugar in our diet; all cells can use glucose for energy.
- Glycolysis generates two molecules of ATP through substrate-level phosphorylation, and two molecules of NADH.
- The cytosolic NADH generated via glycolysis transfers its reducing equivalents to mitochondrial NAD^+ via shuttle systems across the inner mitochondrial membrane.

Table 22.2   Diseases Discussed in Chapter 22

Disease or Disorder	Environmental Genetic or	Comments
Chronic obstructive pulmonary disease	Both	Can lead to inefficient energy production in the nervous systems due to reduced oxygen delivery to the tissue
Obesity	Both	Lactate production via anaerobic glycolysis in the muscle occurs during vigorous exercise
Dental caries	Environmental	Effects of carbohydrate metabolism on oral flora and acid production
Lactic acidemia	Both	Elevated lactic acid due to mutations in a variety of enzymes involved in carbohydrate and energy metabolism

- The pyruvate generated during glycolysis can enter the mitochondria and be oxidized completely to CO_2 by PDH and the TCA cycle.
- Anaerobic glycolysis generates energy in cells with a limited supply of oxygen or few mitochondria.
- Under anaerobic conditions, pyruvate is reduced to lactate by NADH, thereby regenerating the NAD^+ required for glycolysis to continue.
- Glycolysis is regulated to ensure that ATP homeostasis is maintained.
- The key regulated enzymes of glycolysis are hexokinase, phosphofructokinase-1, and pyruvate kinase.
- Mutations in the TCA cycle, or proteins involved in oxidative phosphorylation, can lead to an accumulation of pyruvate, which will lead to lactic acidemia.
- Diseases discussed in this chapter are summarized in Table 22.2.

REVIEW QUESTIONS—CHAPTER 22

1. A major role of glycolysis is which of the following?

    A. To synthesize glucose
    B. To generate energy
    C. To produce FAD(2H)
    D. To synthesize glycogen
    E. To use ATP to generate heat

2. Starting with glyceraldehyde 3-phosphate and synthesizing one molecule of pyruvate, the net yield of ATP and NADH would be which of the following?

    A. 1 ATP, 1 NADH
    B. 1 ATP, 2 NADH
    C. 1 ATP, 4 NADH
    D. 2 ATP, 1 NADH
    E. 2 ATP, 2 NADH
    F. 2 ATP, 4 NADH
    G. 3 ATP, 1 NADH
    H. 3 ATP, 2 NADH
    I. 3 ATP, 4 NADH

3. When glycogen is degraded, glucose 1-phosphate is formed. Glucose 1-phosphate can then be isomerized to glucose 6-phosphate. Starting with glucose 1-phosphate and ending with two molecules of pyruvate, what is the net yield of glycolysis in terms of ATP and NADH formed?

    A. 1 ATP, 1 NADH
    B. 1 ATP, 2 NADH

    C. 1 ATP, 3 NADH
    D. 2 ATP, 1 NADH
    E. 2 ATP, 2 NADH
    F. 2 ATP, 3 NADH
    G. 3 ATP, 1 NADH
    H. 3 ATP, 2 NADH
    I. 3 ATP, 3 NADH

4. Which of the following statements correctly describes an aspect of glycolysis?

    A. ATP is formed by oxidative phosphorylation.
    B. Two molecules of ATP are used in the beginning of the pathway.
    C. Pyruvate kinase is the rate-limiting enzyme.
    D. One molecule of pyruvate and three molecules of CO_2 are formed from the oxidation of one glucose molecule.
    E. The reactions take place in the matrix of the mitochondria.

5. How many moles of ATP are generated by the complete aerobic oxidation of 1 mol of glucose to 6 mol of CO_2?

    A. 2 to 4
    B. 10 to 12
    C. 18 to 22
    D. 30 to 32
    E. 60 to 64

Fatty acids are a major fuel for humans and supply our energy needs between meals and during periods of increased demand, such as exercise. During overnight fasting, fatty acids become the major fuel for cardiac muscle, skeletal muscle, and liver. The liver converts fatty acids to ketone bodies (acetoacetate and β-hydroxybutyrate), which also serve as major fuels for tissues (e.g., the gut). The brain, which does not have a significant capacity for fatty acid oxidation, can use ketone bodies as a fuel during prolonged fasting.

*The route of metabolism for a fatty acid depends somewhat on its chain length. Fatty acids are generally classified as **very long-chain-length fatty acids** (>C20), **long-chain fatty acids** (C12 to C20), **medium-chain fatty acids** (C6 to C12), and **short-chain fatty acids** (C4).*

*Adenosine Triphosphate (ATP) is generated from oxidation of fatty acids in the pathway of β-oxidation. Between meals and during overnight fasting, **long-chain fatty acids** are released from adipose tissue triacylglycerols. They circulate through blood bound to **albumin** (Fig. 23.1). In cells, they are converted to **fatty acyl coenzyme A** (**fatty acyl-CoA**) derivatives by **acyl-CoA synthetases**. The activated acyl group is transported into the mitochondrial matrix bound to **carnitine**, where fatty acyl-CoA is regenerated. In the pathway of **β-oxidation**, the fatty acyl group is sequentially oxidized to yield FAD(2H), NADH, and acetyl-CoA. Subsequent oxidation of NADH and FAD(2H) in the electron-transport chain, and oxidation of acetyl-CoA to CO_2 in the tricarboxylic acid (TCA) cycle, generates ATP from oxidative phosphorylation.*

*Many fatty acids have structures that require variations of this basic pattern. Long-chain fatty acids that are **unsaturated fatty acids** generally require additional isomerization and oxidation–reduction reactions to rearrange their double bonds during β-oxidation. Metabolism of water-soluble **medium-chain-length fatty acids** does not require carnitine and occurs only in the liver. **Odd-chain-length fatty acids** undergo β-oxidation to the terminal three-carbon **propionyl-CoA**, which enters the TCA cycle as succinyl-CoA.*

*Fatty acids that do not readily undergo mitochondrial β-oxidation are oxidized first by alternate routes that convert them to a more suitable substrates or to urinary excretion products. **Excess fatty acids** may undergo microsomal **ω-oxidation**, which converts them to **dicarboxylic acids** that appear in urine. **Very long-chain fatty acids** (both straight-chain and **branched fatty acids** such as phytanic acid) are whittled down to size in peroxisomes. **Peroxisomal α- and β-oxidation** generates hydrogen peroxide (H_2O_2), NADH, acetyl-CoA, or propionyl-CoA and a short- to medium-chain-length acyl-CoA. The acyl-CoA products are transferred to mitochondria to complete their metabolism.*

*In the liver, much of the acetyl-CoA generated from fatty acid oxidation is converted to the ketone bodies, **acetoacetate** and **β-hydroxybutyrate**, which enter the blood (see Fig. 23.1). In other tissues, these ketone bodies are converted to acetyl-CoA, which is oxidized in the TCA cycle. The liver synthesizes ketone bodies but cannot use them as a fuel.*

FIG. 23.1. Overview of mitochondrial long-chain fatty acid metabolism. *(1)* Fatty acid–binding proteins (FaBP) transport fatty acids across the plasma membrane and bind them in the cytosol. *(2)* Fatty acyl-CoA synthetase activates fatty acids to fatty acyl-CoAs. *(3)* Carnitine transports the activated fatty acyl group into mitochondria. *(4)* β-Oxidation generates NADH, FAD(2H), and acetyl-CoA. *(5)* In the liver, acetyl-CoA is converted to ketone bodies.

The **rate of fatty acid oxidation** is linked to the rate of NADH, FAD(2H), and acetyl-CoA oxidation and, thus, to the rate of oxidative phosphorylation and **ATP use**. Additional regulation occurs through **malonyl-CoA**, which inhibits formation of the fatty acyl carnitine derivatives. Fatty acids and ketone bodies are used as fuel when their level increases in the blood, which is determined by hormonal regulation of adipose tissue **lipolysis**.

THE WAITING ROOM

Otto Shape was disappointed that he did not place in his 5-km race and decided that short-distance running is probably not right for him. After careful consideration, he decides to train for the marathon by running 12 miles three times per week. He is now 13 lb over his ideal weight, and he plans on losing this weight while studying for his pharmacology finals. He considers a variety of dietary supplements to increase his endurance and selects one that contains carnitine, coenzyme Q (CoQ), pantothenate, riboflavin, and creatine.

The liver transaminases measured in the blood are aspartate aminotransferase (AST), which was previously designated serum glutamate-oxaloacetate transaminase (SGOT), and alanine aminotransferase (ALT), which was previously designated serum glutamate pyruvate transaminase (SGPT). Elevation of these enzymes in the serum reflects damage of the liver cell plasma membrane. Transaminases catalyze the transfer of the nitrogen group of an amino acid to an acceptor α-keto acid. For AST, aspartate donates the nitrogen to α-ketoglutarate, forming oxaloacetate (the corresponding α-keto acid to aspartate) and glutamate. For ALT, alanine donates the nitrogen to α-ketoglutarate, forming pyruvate and glutamate. Transaminase activity is measured using a coupled reaction: Both oxaloacetate and pyruvate can be reduced by NADH to form, respectively—malate and lactate—in the presence of the appropriate secondary enzyme (malate dehydrogenase and lactate dehydrogenase). Thus, automated procedures that follow the loss of NADH in the reaction mix (by measuring the decrease in absorbance at 340 nm) can be used to measure the activity of AST and ALT in serum samples.

 During **Otto Shape's** distance running (a moderate-intensity exercise), decreases in insulin and increases in insulin counterregulatory hormones, such as epinephrine and norepinephrine, increase adipose tissue lipolysis. Thus, his muscles are being provided with a supply of fatty acids in the blood that can be used as a fuel.

 Lofata Burne developed symptoms during fasting when adipose tissue lipolysis was elevated. Under these circumstances, muscle tissue, liver, and many other tissues are oxidizing fatty acids as a fuel. After overnight fasting, approximately 60% to 70% of our energy supply is derived from the oxidation of fatty acids.

 Lofata Burne is a 16-year-old girl. Since age 14 months, she has experienced recurrent episodes of profound fatigue associated with vomiting and increased perspiration, which required hospitalization. These episodes occurred only if she fasted for more than 8 hours. Because her mother gave her food late at night and woke her early in the morning for breakfast, Lofata's physical and mental development had progressed normally.

On the day of admission for this episode, Lofata had missed breakfast, and by noon, she was extremely fatigued, nauseated, sweaty, and limp. She was unable to hold any food in her stomach and was rushed to the hospital, where an infusion of glucose was started intravenously. Her symptoms responded dramatically to this therapy.

Her initial serum glucose level was low at 38 mg/dL (reference range for fasting serum glucose levels, 70 to 100 mg/dL). Her blood urea nitrogen (BUN) level was slightly elevated at 26 mg/dL (reference range, 8 to 25 mg/dL) because of vomiting, which led to a degree of dehydration. Her blood levels of liver transaminases were slightly elevated, although her liver was not palpably enlarged. Despite elevated levels of free fatty acids (4.3 mM) in the blood, blood ketone bodies were lower than normal.

 Di Abietes, a 27-year-old woman with type 1 diabetes mellitus, had been admitted to the hospital in a ketoacidotic coma a year ago (see Chapter 4). She had been feeling drowsy and had been vomiting for 24 hours before that admission. At the time of admission, she was clinically dehydrated, her blood pressure was low, and her breathing was deep and rapid (Kussmaul breathing). Her pulse was rapid, and her breath had the odor of acetone. Her arterial blood pH was 7.08 (reference range, pH 7.36 to 7.44), and her blood ketone body levels were 15 mM (normal is approximately 0.2 mM for a person on a normal diet).

I. FATTY ACIDS AS FUELS

The fatty acids oxidized as fuels are principally long-chain fatty acids released from adipose tissue triacylglycerol stores between meals, during overnight fasting, and during periods of increased fuel demand (e.g., during exercise). Adipose tissue triacylglycerols are derived from two sources: dietary lipids and triacylglycerols synthesized in the liver. The major fatty acids oxidized are the long-chain fatty acids, palmitate, oleate, and stearate, because they are highest in dietary lipids and are also synthesized in the human.

Between meals, a decreased insulin level and increased levels of insulin counterregulatory hormones (e.g., glucagon) activate lipolysis, and free fatty acids are transported to tissues bound to serum albumin. Within tissues, energy is derived from oxidation of fatty acids to acetyl-CoA in the pathway of β-oxidation. Most of the enzymes involved in fatty acid oxidation are present as two or three isoenzymes, which have different but overlapping specificities for the chain length of the fatty acid. Metabolism of unsaturated fatty acids, odd-chain-length fatty acids, and medium-chain-length fatty acids requires variations of this basic pattern. The acetyl-CoA produced from fatty acid oxidation is principally oxidized in the tricarboxylic acid (TCA) cycle or converted to ketone bodies in the liver.

A. Characteristics of Fatty Acids Used as Fuels

Fat constitutes approximately 38% of the calories in the average North American diet. Of this, more than 95% of the calories are present as triacylglycerols (three fatty acids esterified to a glycerol backbone). During ingestion and absorption, dietary triacylglycerols are broken down into their constituents and then reassembled for transport to adipose tissue in chylomicrons (see Chapter 2). Thus, the fatty acid composition of adipose triacylglycerols varies with the type of food consumed.

The most common dietary fatty acids are the saturated long-chain fatty acids palmitate (C16) and stearate (C18), the monounsaturated fatty acid oleate (C18:1), and the polyunsaturated essential fatty acid linoleate (C18:2) (to review fatty acid nomenclature, consult Chapter 5). Animal fat contains, principally, saturated and monounsaturated long-chain fatty acids, whereas vegetable oils contain linoleate and some longer chain and polyunsaturated fatty acids. They also contain smaller amounts of branched-chain and odd-chain-length fatty acids. Medium-chain-length fatty acids are present principally in dairy fat (e.g., milk, butter), maternal milk, and vegetable oils.

Adipose tissue triacylglycerols also contain fatty acids synthesized in the liver, principally from excess calories ingested as glucose. The pathway of fatty acid synthesis generates palmitate, which can be elongated to form stearate or can be unsaturated to form oleate. These fatty acids are assembled into triacylglycerols and transported to adipose tissues as the lipoprotein very low-density lipoprotein (VLDL).

B. Transport and Activation of Long-Chain Fatty Acids

Long-chain fatty acids are hydrophobic and, therefore, water insoluble. In addition, they are toxic to cells because they can disrupt the hydrophobic bonding between amino acid side chains in proteins. Consequently, they are transported in the blood and in cells bound to proteins.

1. CELLULAR UPTAKE OF LONG-CHAIN FATTY ACIDS

During fasting and other conditions of metabolic need, long-chain fatty acids are released from adipose tissue triacylglycerols by lipases. They travel in the blood bound in the hydrophobic binding pocket of albumin: the major serum protein (see Fig. 23.1).

Fatty acids enter cells both by a saturable transport process and by diffusion through the lipid plasma membrane. A fatty acid–binding protein in the plasma membrane facilitates transport. An additional fatty acid–binding protein binds the fatty acid intracellularly and may facilitate its transport to the mitochondrion. The free fatty acid concentration in cells is, therefore, extremely low.

2. ACTIVATION OF LONG-CHAIN FATTY ACIDS

Fatty acids must be activated to acyl-CoA derivatives before they can participate in β-oxidation and other metabolic pathways (Fig. 23.2). The process of activation involves an acyl-CoA synthetase (also called a *thiokinase*) that uses ATP energy to form the fatty acyl-CoA thioester bond. In this reaction, the β-bond of ATP is cleaved to form a fatty acyl adenosine monophosphate (AMP) intermediate and pyrophosphate (PP$_i$). Subsequent cleavage of PP$_i$ helps to drive the reaction.

The acyl-CoA synthetase that activates long-chain fatty acids—12 to 20 carbons in length—is present in three locations in the cell: the endoplasmic reticulum, outer mitochondrial membranes, and peroxisomal membranes (Table 23.1). This enzyme has no activity toward C22 or longer fatty acids, and has little activity below C12. In contrast, the synthetase for activation of very long-chain fatty acids is present in peroxisomes, and the medium-chain-length fatty acid–activating enzyme is present only in the mitochondrial matrix of liver and kidney cells.

3. FATES OF FATTY ACYL-COAS

Fatty acyl-CoA formation, like the phosphorylation of glucose, is a prerequisite to metabolism of the fatty acid in the cell (Fig. 23.3). The multiple locations of the long-chain acyl-CoA synthetase reflect the location of different metabolic routes taken by fatty acyl-CoA derivatives in the cell (e.g., triacylglycerol and phospholipid synthesis in the endoplasmic reticulum, oxidation and plasmalogen synthe-

FIG. 23.2. Activation of a fatty acid by a fatty acyl-CoA synthetase. The fatty acid is activated by reacting with ATP to form a high-energy fatty acyl AMP and pyrophosphate. The AMP is then exchanged for CoA. Pyrophosphate is cleaved by a pyrophosphatase.

Table 23.1   Chain-Length Specificity of Fatty Acid Activation and Oxidation Enzymes

Enzyme	Chain Length	Comments
Acyl-CoA synthetases		
Very long chain	14–26	Found only in peroxisomes.
Long chain	12–20	Enzyme present in membranes of endoplasmic reticulum, mitochondria, and peroxisomes to facilitate different metabolic routes of acyl-CoAs.
Medium chain	6–12	Exists as many variants, present only in mitochondrial matrix of kidney and liver. Also involved in xenobiotic metabolism.
Acetyl	2–4	Present in cytoplasm and possibly mitochondrial matrix.
Acyltransferases		
CPTI	12–16	Although maximum activity is for fatty acids 12–16 carbons long, it also acts on many smaller acyl-CoA derivatives.
Medium chain (octanoylcarnitine transferase)	6–12	Substrate is medium-chain acyl-CoA derivatives generated during peroxisoma oxidation.
Carnitine:acetyl transferase	2	High level in skeletal muscle and heart to facilitate use of acetate as a fuel.
Acyl-CoA dehydrogenases		
VLCAD	14–20	Present in inner mitochondrial membrane.
LCAD	12–18	Members of same enzyme family, which also includes acyl-CoA dehydrogenases for carbon skeleton of branched-chain amino acids.
MCAD	4–12	
SCAD	4–6	
Other enzymes		
Enoyl-CoA hydratase, short-chain	>4	Also called crotonase. Activity decreases with increasing chain length.
L-3-Hydroxyacyl-CoA dehydrogenase, short-chain	4–16	Activity decreases with increasing chain length.
Acetoacetyl-CoA thiolase	4	Specific for acetoacetyl-CoA.
Trifunctional protein	12–16	Complex of long-chain enoyl hydratase, acyl-CoA dehydrogenase, and a thiolase with broad specificity. Most active with longer chains.

CPTI, carnitine palmitoyl transferase I; VLCAD, very long-chain acyl-CoA dehydrogenase; LCAD, long-chain acyl-CoA dehydrogenase; MCAD, medium acyl-CoA dehydrogenase; SCAD, short-chain acyl-CoA dehydrogenase deficiency.

FIG. 23.3. Major metabolic routes for long-chain fatty acyl-CoAs. Fatty acids are activated to acyl-CoA compounds for degradation in mitochondrial β-oxidation or incorporation into triacylglycerols or membrane lipids. When β-oxidation is blocked through an inherited enzyme deficiency or metabolic regulation, excess fatty acids are diverted into triacylglycerol synthesis.

sis in the peroxisome, β-oxidation in mitochondria). In the liver and some other tissues, fatty acids that are not being used for energy generation are reincorporated (reesterified) into triacylglycerols.

4. TRANSPORT OF LONG-CHAIN FATTY ACIDS INTO MITOCHONDRIA

Carnitine serves as the carrier that transports activated long-chain fatty acyl groups across the inner mitochondrial membrane (Fig. 23.4). Carnitine acyl transferases are able to reversibly transfer an activated fatty acyl group from CoA to the hydroxyl group of carnitine to form an acylcarnitine ester. The reaction is reversible, so the fatty acyl-CoA derivative can be regenerated from the carnitine ester.

Carnitine palmitoyl transferase I (CPTI; also called *carnitine acyltransferase* I, CATI), the enzyme that transfers long-chain fatty acyl groups from CoA to carnitine, is located on the outer mitochondrial membrane (Fig. 23.5). Fatty acylcarnitine crosses the inner mitochondrial membrane with the aid of a translocase. The fatty acyl group is transferred back to CoA by a second enzyme, carnitine palmitoyl transferase II (CPTII or CATII). The carnitine released in this reaction returns to the cytosolic side of the mitochondrial membrane by the same translocase that brings fatty acylcarnitine to the matrix side. Long-chain fatty acyl-CoA, now located within the mitochondrial matrix, is a substrate for β-oxidation.

Carnitine is obtained from the diet or synthesized from the side chain of lysine by a pathway that begins in skeletal muscle and is completed in the liver. The reactions use *S*-adenosylmethionine to donate methyl groups, and vitamin C (ascorbic acid) is also required for these reactions. Skeletal muscles have a high-affinity uptake system for carnitine, and most of the carnitine in the body is stored in skeletal muscle.

Fatty acylcarnitine

FIG. 23.4. Structure of fatty acylcarnitine. Carnitine palmitoyl transferases catalyze the reversible transfer of a long-chain fatty acyl group from the fatty acyl-CoA to the hydroxyl group of carnitine. The atoms in the *green box* originate from the fatty acyl-CoA.

 Several inherited diseases in the metabolism of carnitine or acylcarnitines have been described. These include defects in the following enzymes or systems: the transporter for carnitine uptake into muscle, CPTI, carnitine acylcarnitine translocase, and CPTII. Classical CPTII deficiency, the most common of these diseases, is characterized by adolescent-to-adult onset of recurrent episodes of acute myoglobinuria precipitated by prolonged exercise or fasting. During these episodes, the patient is weak and may be somewhat hypoglycemic with diminished ketosis (hypoketosis), but metabolic decompensation is not severe. Lipid deposits are found in skeletal muscles. Both creatine phosphokinase (CPK) and long-chain acylcarnitines are elevated in the blood. CPTII levels in fibroblasts are approximately 25% of normal. The remaining CPTII activity probably accounts for the mild effect on liver metabolism. In contrast, when CPTII deficiency presents in infants, CPTII levels are <10% of normal, the hypoglycemia and hypoketosis are severe, hepatomegaly occurs from triacylglycerol deposits, and cardiomyopathy is also present.

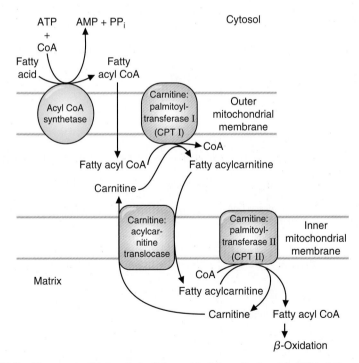

FIG. 23.5. Transport of long-chain fatty acids into mitochondria. The fatty acyl-CoA crosses the outer mitochondrial membrane. Carnitine palmitoyl transferase I in the outer mitochondrial membrane transfers the fatty acyl group to carnitine and releases CoASH. The fatty acyl carnitine is translocated into the mitochondrial matrix as carnitine moves out. Carnitine palmitoyl transferase II on the inner mitochondrial membrane transfers the fatty acyl group back to CoASH to form fatty acyl-CoA in the matrix.

Otto Shape's power supplement contains carnitine. However, his body can synthesize enough carnitine to meet his needs, and his diet contains carnitine. Carnitine deficiency has been found only in infants fed a soy-based formula that was not supplemented with carnitine. His other supplements likewise probably provide no benefit but are designed to facilitate fatty acid oxidation during exercise. Riboflavin is the vitamin precursor of FAD, which is required for acyl-CoA dehydrogenases and electron-transfer flavoproteins (ETFs). Coenzyme Q (CoQ) is synthesized in the body, but it is the recipient in the electron-transport chain for electrons passed from complexes I and II and the ETFs. Some reports suggest that supplementation with pantothenate—the precursor of CoA—improves performance.

C. β-Oxidation of Long-Chain Fatty Acids

The oxidation of fatty acids to acetyl-CoA in the β-oxidation spiral conserves energy as FAD(2H) and NADH. FAD(2H) and NADH are oxidized in the electron-transport chain, generating ATP from oxidative phosphorylation. Acetyl-CoA is oxidized in the TCA cycle or converted to ketone bodies.

1. THE β-OXIDATION SPIRAL

The fatty acid β-oxidation pathway sequentially cleaves the fatty acyl group into two-carbon acetyl-CoA units, beginning with the carboxyl end attached to CoA (Fig. 23.6). Before cleavage, the β-carbon is oxidized to a keto group in two reactions that generate NADH and FAD(2H); thus, the pathway is called β-oxidation. As each acetyl group is released, the cycle of β-oxidation and cleavage begins again, but each time the fatty acyl group is two carbons shorter.

There are four types of reactions in the β-oxidation pathway (Fig. 23.7). In the first step, a double bond is formed between the β- and α-carbons by an acyl-CoA dehydrogenase that transfers electrons to FAD. The double bond is in the *trans* configuration (a Δ^2-*trans* double bond). In the next step, an −OH from water is added to the β-carbon, and an −H from water is added to the α-carbon. The enzyme is called an *enoyl hydratase* (hydratases add the elements of water, and "-ene" in a name denotes a double bond). In the third step of β-oxidation, the hydroxyl group on the

FIG. 23.6. Overview of β-oxidation. Oxidation at the β-carbon is followed by cleavage of the α–β bond, releasing acetyl-CoA and a fatty acyl-CoA that is two carbons shorter than the original. The carbons cleaved to form acetyl-CoA are shown in *red*. Successive spirals of β-oxidation completely cleave an even-chain fatty acyl-CoA to acetyl-CoA.

FIG. 23.7. Steps of β-oxidation. The four steps are repeated until an even-chain fatty acid is completely converted to acetyl-CoA. The FAD(2H) and NADH are reoxidized by the electron-transport chain—producing ATP.

β-carbon is oxidized to a ketone by a hydroxyacyl-CoA dehydrogenase. In this reaction, as in the conversion of most alcohols to ketones, the electrons are transferred to NAD⁺ to form NADH. In the last reaction of the sequence, the bond between the β- and α-carbons is cleaved by a reaction that attaches Coenzyme A (CoASH) to the β-carbon, and acetyl-CoA is released. This is a thiolytic reaction (*lysis* refers to breakage of the bond, and *thio* refers to the sulfur) catalyzed by enzymes called β-ketothiolases. The release of two carbons from the carboxyl end of the original fatty acyl-CoA produces acetyl-CoA and a fatty acyl-CoA that is two carbons shorter than the original. It is of interest to note that the β-oxidation spiral uses the same reaction types seen in the TCA cycle in the conversion of succinate to oxaloacetate.

The shortened fatty acyl-CoA repeats these four steps until all of its carbons are converted to acetyl-CoA. β-Oxidation is thus a spiral rather than a cycle. In the last spiral, cleavage of the four-carbon fatty acyl-CoA (butyryl-CoA) produces two acetyl-CoAs. Thus, an even-chain fatty acid such as palmitoyl-CoA, which has 16 carbons, is cleaved seven times, producing 7 FAD(2H)s, 7 NADHs, and 8 acetyl-CoAs.

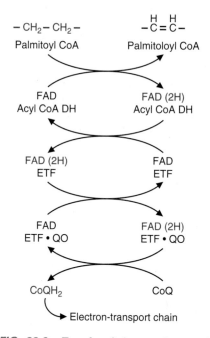

FIG. 23.8. Transfer of electrons from acyl-CoA dehydrogenase to the electron-transport chain. An FAD is tightly bound to each protein in these three electron-transfer reactions. *ETF*, electron-transfer flavoprotein; *ETF-QO*, electron-transferring flavoprotein–coenzyme Q (CoQ) oxidoreductase.

2. ENERGY YIELD OF β-OXIDATION

Like the FAD in all flavoproteins, FAD(2H) bound to the acyl-CoA dehydrogenases is oxidized back to FAD without dissociating from the protein (Fig. 23.8). Electron-transfer flavoproteins (ETF) in the mitochondrial matrix accept electrons from the enzyme-bound FAD(2H) and transfer these electrons to ETF–coenzyme Q (CoQ) oxidoreductase (ETF-QO) in the inner mitochondrial membrane. ETF-QO, also a flavoprotein, transfers the electrons to CoQ in the electron-transport chain. Oxidative phosphorylation thus generates approximately 1.5 ATP for each FAD(2H) produced in the β-oxidation spiral.

The total energy yield from the oxidation of 1 mol of palmityl-CoA to 8 mol of acetyl-CoA is 28 mol of ATP: 1.5 for each of the 7 FAD(2H), and 2.5 for each of the 7 NADH. To calculate the energy yield from oxidation of 1 mol of palmitate, two ATP need to be subtracted from the total because two high-energy phosphate bonds are cleaved when palmitate is activated to palmityl-CoA.

3. CHAIN-LENGTH SPECIFICITY IN β-OXIDATION

The four reactions of β-oxidation are catalyzed by sets of enzymes that are each specific for fatty acids with different chain lengths (see Table 23.1). The acyl-CoA dehydrogenases, which catalyze the first step of the pathway, are part of an enzyme family that has four different ranges of specificity. The subsequent steps of the spiral use enzymes that are specific for long- or short-chain enoyl-CoAs. Although these enzymes are structurally distinct, their specificities overlap to some extent. As the fatty acyl chains are shortened by consecutive cleavage of two acetyl units, they are transferred from enzymes that act on longer chains to those that act on shorter chains. Medium- or short-chain fatty acyl-CoA that may be formed from dietary fatty acids, or transferred from peroxisomes, enters the spiral at the enzyme that is most active for fatty acids of its chain length.

4. OXIDATION OF UNSATURATED FATTY ACIDS

Approximately one-half of the fatty acids in the human diet are unsaturated, containing *cis* double bonds, with oleate (C18:1, Δ^9) and linoleate (18:2, $\Delta^{9,12}$) being the most common. In β-oxidation of saturated fatty acids, a *trans* double bond is created between the second and third (α- and β-) carbons. For unsaturated fatty acids to undergo the β-oxidation spiral, their *cis* double bonds must be isomerized to *trans* double bonds that will end up between the second and third carbons during β-oxidation, or the double bond must be reduced. The process is illustrated for the polyunsaturated fatty acid linoleate in Figure 23.9. Linoleate is obtained from the diet and cannot be synthesized in the human; thus, it is considered an essential fatty acid. Therefore, only that portion of linoleate that is not needed for other

What is the total ATP yield for the oxidation of 1 mol of palmitic acid to carbon dioxide and water?

Palmitic acid is 16 carbons long with no double bonds, so it requires seven oxidation spirals to be completely converted to acetyl-CoA. After seven spirals, there are 7 FAD(2H)s, 7 NADHs, and 8 acetyl-CoAs. Each NADH yields 2.5 ATP, each FAD(2H) yields 1.5 ATP, and each acetyl-CoA yields 10 ATP as it is processed around the TCA cycle. This then yields 17.5 + 10.5 + 80 = 108 ATP. However, activation of palmitic acid to palmityl-CoA requires two high-energy bonds, so the net yield is 108 − 2 or 106 mol of ATP.

After reviewing **Lofata Burne's** previous hospital records, a specialist suspected that Lofata's medical problems were caused by a disorder in fatty acid metabolism. A battery of tests showed that Lofata's blood contained elevated levels of several partially oxidized medium-chain fatty acids, such as octanoic acid (8:0) and 4-decenoic acid (10:1, Δ^4). A urine specimen showed an increase in organic acid metabolites of medium-chain fatty acids containing 6 to 10 carbons, including medium-chain acylcarnitine derivatives. The profile of acylcarnitine species in the urine was characteristic of a genetically determined medium-chain acyl-CoA dehydrogenase (MCAD) deficiency. In this disease, long-chain fatty acids are metabolized by β-oxidation to a medium-chain-length acyl-CoA, such as octanoyl-CoA. Because further oxidation of this compound is blocked in MCAD deficiency, the medium-chain acyl group is transferred back to carnitine. These acylcarnitines are water-soluble and appear in blood and urine. The specific enzyme deficiency was demonstrated in cultured fibroblasts from Lofata's skin as well as in her circulating monocytic leukocytes.

In long-chain acyl-CoA dehydrogenase (LCAD) deficiency, fatty acylcarnitines accumulate in the blood. Those containing 14 carbons predominate. However, these do not appear in the urine.

FIG. 23.9. Oxidation of linoleate. After three spirals of β-oxidation (*dashed lines*), there is now a 3,4-*cis* double bond and a 6,7-*cis* double bond. The 3,4-*cis* double bond is isomerized to a 2,3-*trans* double bond, which is in the proper configuration for the normal enzymes to act. One spiral of β-oxidation occurs, plus the first step of a second spiral. A reductase that uses NADPH now converts these two double bonds (between carbons 2 and 3 and between carbons 4 and 5) to one double bond between carbons 3 and 4 in a *trans* configuration. The isomerase (which can act on double bonds that are in either the *cis* or the *trans* configuration) moves this double bond to the 2,3-*trans* position, and β-oxidation can resume.

processes will be oxidized. Linoleate undergoes β-oxidation until one double bond is between carbons 3 and 4 near the carboxyl end of the fatty acyl chain and the other is between carbons 6 and 7. An isomerase moves the double bond from the 3,4-position so that it is *trans* and in the 2,3-position, and β-oxidation continues. When a conjugated pair of double bonds is formed (two double bonds separated by one single bond) at positions 2 and 4, an NADPH-dependent reductase reduces the pair to one *trans* double bond at position 3. Then isomerization and β-oxidation resume.

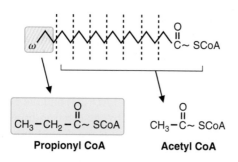

FIG. 23.10. Formation of propionyl-CoA from odd-chain fatty acids. Successive spirals of β-oxidation cleave each of the bonds marked with dashed lines, producing acetyl-CoA except for the three carbons at the ω-end, which produce propionyl-CoA.

In oleate (C18:1, Δ^9), there is only one double bond between carbons 9 and 10. It is handled by an isomerization reaction similar to that shown for the double bond at position 9 of linoleate.

5. ODD-CHAIN-LENGTH FATTY ACIDS

Fatty acids that contain an odd number of carbon atoms undergo β-oxidation, producing acetyl-CoA until the last spiral—when five carbons remain in the fatty acyl-CoA. In this case, cleavage by thiolase produces acetyl-CoA and a three-carbon fatty acyl-CoA, propionyl-CoA (Fig. 23.10). Carboxylation of propionyl-CoA yields methylmalonyl-CoA, which is ultimately converted to succinyl-CoA in a vitamin B_{12}–dependent reaction (Fig. 23.11). Propionyl-CoA also arises from the oxidation of branched-chain amino acids.

The propionyl-CoA to succinyl-CoA pathway is a major anaplerotic route for the TCA cycle and is used in the degradation of valine, isoleucine, and several other compounds. In the liver, this route provides precursors of oxaloacetate, which is converted to glucose. Thus, this small proportion of the odd-carbon-number fatty acid chain can be converted to glucose. In contrast, the acetyl-CoA formed from β-oxidation of even-chain-number fatty acids in the liver either enters the TCA cycle, where it is principally oxidized to CO_2, or it is converted to ketone bodies.

D. Oxidation of Medium-Chain-Length Fatty Acids

Dietary medium-chain-length fatty acids are more water-soluble than long-chain fatty acids and are not stored in adipose triacylglycerol. After a meal, they enter the blood and pass into the portal vein to the liver. In the liver, they enter the mitochondrial matrix by the monocarboxylate transporter and are activated to acyl-CoA derivatives in the mitochondrial matrix (see Fig. 23.1). Medium-chain-length acyl-CoAs, such as long-chain acyl-CoAs, are oxidized to acetyl-CoA via the β-oxidation spiral. Medium-chain acyl-CoAs also can arise from the peroxisomal oxidation pathway.

The medium-chain-length acyl-CoA synthetase has a broad range of specificity for compounds of approximately the same size that contain a carboxyl group, such as drugs (salicylate—from aspirin metabolism—and valproate, which is used to treat epileptic seizures) or benzoate, a common component of plants. Once the drug-CoA derivative is formed, the carboxyl group is conjugated with glycine to form a urinary excretion product. With certain disorders of fatty acid oxidation, medium- and short-chain fatty acylglycines may appear in the urine, together with acylcarnitines or dicarboxylic acids. Octanoylglycine, for example, will appear in the urine of a patient with medium-chain acyl-CoA dehydrogenase (MCAD) deficiency.

FIG. 23.11. Conversion of propionyl-CoA to succinyl-CoA. Succinyl-CoA, an intermediate of the TCA cycle, can form malate, which can be converted to glucose in the liver through the process of gluconeogenesis. Certain amino acids also form glucose by this route (see Chapter 39).

The unripe fruit of the ackee tree produces a toxin—hypoglycin—which causes a condition known as *Jamaican vomiting sickness*. The victims of the toxin are usually unwary children who eat this unripe fruit and develop a severe hypoglycemia, which is often fatal.

Although hypoglycin causes hypoglycemia, it acts by inhibiting an acyl-CoA dehydrogenase involved in β-oxidation that has specificity for short- and medium-chain fatty acids. Because more glucose must be oxidized to compensate for the decreased ability of fatty acids to serve as fuel, blood glucose levels may fall to extremely low levels. Fatty acid levels, however, rise because of decreased β-oxidation. Because of the increased fatty acid levels, ω-oxidation increases, and dicarboxylic acids are excreted in the urine. The diminished capacity to oxidize fatty acids in liver mitochondria results in decreased levels of acetyl-CoA, the substrate for ketone body synthesis.

 As **Otto Shape** runs, his skeletal muscles increase their use of ATP and their rate of fuel oxidation. Fatty acid oxidation is accelerated by the increased rate of the electron-transport chain. As ATP is used and AMP increases, the AMP-PK acts to facilitate fuel use and maintain ATP homeostasis. Phosphorylation of acetyl-CoA carboxylase results in a decreased level of malonyl-CoA and increased activity of carnitine palmitoyl-CoA transferase I. At the same time, AMP-PK facilitates the recruitment of glucose transporters into the plasma membrane of skeletal muscle, thereby increasing the rate of glucose uptake. AMP and hormonal signals also increase the supply of glucose 6-phosphate from glycogenolysis. Thus, his muscles are supplied with more fuel, and all the oxidative pathways are accelerated.

E. Regulation of β-Oxidation

Fatty acids are used as fuels principally when they are released from adipose tissue triacylglycerols in response to hormones that signal fasting or increased demand. Many tissues, such as muscle and kidney, oxidize fatty acids completely to CO_2 and H_2O. In these tissues, the acetyl-CoA produced by β-oxidation enters the TCA cycle. The FAD(2H) and the NADH from β-oxidation and the TCA cycle are reoxidized by the electron-transport chain, and ATP is generated. The process of β-oxidation is regulated by the cells' requirements for energy (i.e., by the levels of ATP and NADH), because fatty acids cannot be oxidized any faster than NADH, and FAD(2H) are reoxidized in the electron-transport chain.

Fatty acid oxidation also may be restricted by the mitochondrial CoASH pool size. Acetyl CoASH units must enter the TCA cycle or another metabolic pathway to regenerate CoASH required for formation of the fatty acyl-CoA derivative from fatty acyl carnitine.

An additional type of regulation occurs at CPTI. CPTI is inhibited by malonyl-CoA, which is synthesized in the cytosol of many tissues by acetyl-CoA carboxylase (Fig. 23.12). Acetyl-CoA carboxylase is regulated by several different mechanisms, some of which are tissue dependent. In skeletal muscles and liver, it is inhibited when it is phosphorylated by the AMP-activated protein kinase (AMP-PK). Thus, during exercise—when AMP levels increase—AMP-PK is activated, and phosphorylates acetyl-CoA carboxylase, which becomes inactive. Consequently, malonyl-CoA levels decrease, CPTI is activated, and the β-oxidation of fatty acids is able to restore ATP homeostasis and decrease AMP levels. In liver, in addition to the negative regulation by the AMP-PK, acetyl-CoA carboxylase is activated by insulin-dependent mechanisms leading to elevated cytoplasmic citrate, an allosteric activator, which promotes the conversion of malonyl-CoA to palmitate in the fatty acid synthesis pathway. Thus, in the liver, malonyl-CoA inhibition of CPTI prevents newly synthesized fatty acids from being oxidized.

β-Oxidation is strictly an aerobic pathway, dependent on oxygen, a good blood supply, and adequate levels of mitochondria. Tissues that lack mitochondria, such as red blood cells, cannot oxidize fatty acids by β-oxidation. Fatty acids also do not serve as a significant fuel for the brain. They are not used by adipocytes, whose function is to store triacylglycerols to provide a fuel for other tissues. Those tissues that do not use fatty acids as a fuel, or use them only to a limited extent, are able to use ketone bodies instead.

FIG. 23.12. Regulation of β-oxidation. *(1)* Hormones control the supply of fatty acids in the blood. *(2)* Carnitine palmitoyl transferase I is inhibited by malonyl-CoA, which is synthesized by acetyl-CoA carboxylase (ACC). AMP-PK is the AMP-activated protein kinase. *(3)* The rate of ATP use controls the rate of the electron-transport chain, which regulates the oxidative enzymes of β-oxidation and the TCA cycle.

II. ALTERNATIVE ROUTES OF FATTY ACID OXIDATION

Fatty acids that are not readily oxidized by the enzymes of β-oxidation enter alternative pathways of oxidation, including peroxisomal β- and α-oxidation and microsomal ω-oxidation. The function of these pathways is to convert as much as possible the unusual fatty acids to compounds that can be used as fuels or biosynthetic precursors, and to convert the remainder to compounds that can be excreted in bile or urine. During prolonged fasting, fatty acids released from adipose triacylglycerols may enter the ω-oxidation or peroxisomal β-oxidation pathway, even though they have a normal composition. These pathways not only use fatty acids, they act on *xenobiotic* (a term used to cover all organic compounds that are foreign to an organism) carboxylic acids that are large hydrophobic molecules resembling fatty acids.

A. Peroxisomal Oxidation of Fatty Acids

A small proportion of our diet consists of very long-chain fatty acids (20 or more carbons) or branched-chain fatty acids arising from degradative products of chlorophyll. Very long-chain fatty acid synthesis also occurs within the body, especially in cells of the brain and nervous system, which incorporate them into the sphingolipids of myelin. These fatty acids are oxidized by peroxisomal β- and α-oxidation pathways, which are essentially chain-shortening pathways.

1. VERY LONG-CHAIN FATTY ACIDS

Very long-chain fatty acids of 24 to 26 carbons are oxidized exclusively in peroxisomes by a sequence of reactions similar to mitochondrial β-oxidation in that they generate acetyl-CoA and NADH. However, the peroxisomal oxidation of straight-chain fatty acids stops when the chain reaches 4 to 6 carbons in length. Some of the long-chain fatty acids also may be oxidized by this route.

The long-chain fatty acyl-CoA synthetase is present in the peroxisomal membrane, and the acyl-CoA derivatives enter the peroxisome by a transporter that does not require carnitine. The first enzyme of peroxisomal β-oxidation is an oxidase, which donates electrons directly to molecular oxygen and produces hydrogen peroxide (H_2O_2) (Fig. 23.13). (In contrast, the first enzyme of mitochondrial β-oxidation is a dehydrogenase that contains FAD and transfers the electrons to the electron-transport chain via ETF.) Thus, the first enzyme of peroxisomal oxidation is not linked to energy production. The three remaining steps of β-oxidation are catalyzed by enoyl-CoA hydratase, hydroxyacyl-CoA dehydrogenase, and thiolase—enzymes with activities similar to those found in mitochondrial β-oxidation but coded for by different genes. Thus, one NADH and one acetyl-CoA are generated for each turn of the spiral. The peroxisomal β-oxidation spiral continues generating acetyl-CoA until a medium-chain acyl-CoA, which may be as short as butyryl-CoA, is produced (Fig. 23.14).

Within the peroxisome, the acetyl groups can be transferred from CoA to carnitine by an acetylcarnitine transferase, or they can enter the cytosol. A similar reaction converts medium-chain-length acyl-CoAs and the short-chain butyryl-CoA to acyl carnitine derivatives. These acylcarnitines diffuse from the peroxisome to the mitochondria, pass through the outer mitochondrial membrane, and are transported through the inner mitochondrial membrane via the carnitine translocase system. They are converted back to acyl-CoAs by carnitine:acyltransferases appropriate for their chain length and enter the normal pathways for β-oxidation and acetyl-CoA metabolism. The electrons from NADH and acetyl-CoA can also pass from the peroxisome to the cytosol. The export of NADH-containing electrons occurs through use of a shuttle system similar to those described for NADH electron transfer into the mitochondria.

FIG. 23.13. Oxidation of fatty acids in peroxisomes. The first step of β-oxidation is catalyzed by an FAD-containing oxidase. The electrons are transferred from FAD(2H) to O_2, which is reduced to hydrogen peroxide (H_2O_2).

Several inherited deficiencies of peroxisomal enzymes have been described. Zellweger syndrome, which results from defective peroxisomal biogenesis, leads to complex developmental and metabolic phenotypes that affect, principally, the liver and the brain. One of the metabolic characteristics of these diseases is an elevation of C26:0 and C26:1 fatty acid levels in plasma. Refsum disease is caused by a deficiency in a single peroxisomal enzyme, the phytanoyl-CoA hydroxylase that carries out α-oxidation of phytanic acid. Symptoms include retinitis pigmentosa, cerebellar ataxia, and chronic polyneuropathy. Because phytanic acid is obtained solely from the diet, placing patients on a low-phytanic acid diet has resulted in marked improvement.

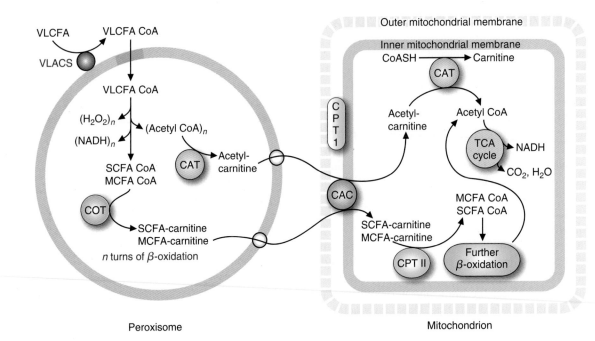

FIG. 23.14. Chain shortening by peroxisomal β-oxidation. Very long-chain fatty acyl-CoAs and some long-chain fatty acyl-CoAs are oxidized in peroxisomes through *n* cycles of β-oxidation to the stage of a short- to medium-chain fatty acyl-CoA. These short- to medium-chain fatty acyl-CoAs are converted to carnitine derivatives by COT or CAT in the peroxisomes. In the mitochondria, SCFA-carnitine is converted back to acyl-CoA derivatives by either CPTII or CAT. *VLCFA*, very long-chain fatty acyl; *VLACS*, very long-chain acyl-CoA synthetase; *MCFA*, medium-chain fatty acyl; *SCFA*, short-chain fatty acyl; *CAT*, carnitine acetyltransferase; *COT*, carnitine octanoyltransferase; *CAC*, carnitine acylcarnitine carrier; *CPTI*, carnitine palmitoyltransferase I; *CPTII*, carnitine palmitoyltransferase II; *OMM*, outer mitochondrial membrane; *IMM*, inner mitochondrial membrane.

Peroxisomes are present in almost every cell type and contain many degradative enzymes, in addition to fatty acyl-CoA oxidase, that generate hydrogen peroxide. H_2O_2 can generate toxic free radicals. Thus, these enzymes are confined to peroxisomes, where the H_2O_2 can be neutralized by the free-radical defense enzyme, catalase. Catalase converts H_2O_2 to water and O_2 (see Chapter 24).

2. LONG-CHAIN BRANCHED-CHAIN FATTY ACIDS

Two of the most common branched-chain fatty acids in the diet are phytanic acid and pristanic acid, which are degradation products of chlorophyll and, thus, are consumed in green vegetables. Animals do not synthesize branched-chain fatty acids. These two multimethylated fatty acids are oxidized in peroxisomes to the level of a branched C8 fatty acid, which is then transferred to mitochondria. The pathway thus is similar to that for the oxidation of straight very long-chain fatty acids.

Phytanic acid, a multimethylated C20 fatty acid, is first oxidized to pristanic acid using the α-oxidation pathway (Fig. 23.15). Phytanic acid hydroxylase introduces a hydroxyl group on the α-carbon, which is then oxidized to a carboxyl group with release of the original carboxyl group as CO_2. By shortening the fatty acid by one carbon, the methyl groups will appear on the α-carbon rather than the β-carbon during the β-oxidation spiral and, therefore, can no longer interfere with oxidation of the β-carbon. Peroxisomal β-oxidation thus can proceed normally, releasing propionyl-CoA and acetyl-CoA with alternate turns of the spiral. When a medium-chain length of approximately eight carbons is reached, the fatty acid is transferred to the mitochondrion as a carnitine derivative and β-oxidation is resumed.

FIG. 23.15. Oxidation of phytanic acid. A peroxisomal α-hydroxylase oxidizes the α-carbon, and its subsequent oxidation to a carboxyl group releases the carboxyl carbon as CO_2. Subsequent spirals of peroxisomal β-oxidation alternately release propionyl and acetyl-CoA. At a chain length of approximately eight carbons, the remaining branched fatty acid is transferred to mitochondria as a medium-chain carnitine derivative.

FIG. 23.16.   ω-Oxidation of fatty acids converts them to dicarboxylic acids.

B. ω-Oxidation of Fatty Acids

Fatty acids also may be oxidized at the ω-carbon of the chain (the terminal methyl group) by enzymes in the endoplasmic reticulum (Fig. 23.16). The ω-methyl group is first oxidized to an alcohol by an enzyme that uses cytochrome P450, molecular oxygen, and NADPH. Dehydrogenases convert the alcohol group to a carboxylic acid. The dicarboxylic acids produced by ω-oxidation can undergo β-oxidation, forming compounds with 6 to 10 carbons that are water-soluble. Such compounds may then enter the blood, be oxidized as medium-chain fatty acids, or be excreted in urine as medium-chain dicarboxylic acids.

The pathways of peroxisomal α- and β-oxidation, and microsomal ω-oxidation, are not feedback regulated. These pathways function to decrease levels of water-insoluble fatty acids or of xenobiotic compounds with a fatty acid–like structure that would become toxic to cells at high concentrations. Thus, their rate is regulated by the availability of substrate.

III. METABOLISM OF KETONE BODIES

Overall, fatty acids released from adipose triacylglycerols serve as the major fuel for the body during fasting. These fatty acids are completely oxidized to CO_2 and H_2O by some tissues. In the liver, much of the acetyl-CoA generated from β-oxidation of fatty acids is used for synthesis of the ketone bodies acetoacetate and β-hydroxybutyrate, which enter the blood (Fig. 23.17). In skeletal muscles and other tissues, these ketone bodies are converted back to acetyl-CoA, which is oxidized in the TCA cycle with generation of ATP. An alternate fate of acetoacetate in tissues is the formation of cytosolic acetyl-CoA.

 Normally, ω-oxidation is a minor process. However, in conditions that interfere with β-oxidation (such as carnitine deficiency or deficiency in an enzyme of β-oxidation), ω-oxidation produces dicarboxylic acids in increased amounts. These dicarboxylic acids are excreted in the urine.

Lofata Burne was excreting dicarboxylic acids in her urine, particularly adipic acid (which has six carbons) and suberic acid (which has eight carbons):

$$^-OOC—CH_2—CH_2—CH_2—CH_2—COO^- \quad \text{Adipic acid}$$
$$^-OOC–CH_2—CH_2—CH_2—CH_2—CH_2—CH_2—COO^- \quad \text{Suberic acid}$$

Octanoylglycine was also found in the urine.

FIG. 23.17.   The ketone bodies, acetoacetate and β-hydroxybutyrate, are synthesized in the liver. Their principal fate is conversion back to acetyl-CoA and oxidation in the TCA cycle in other tissues.

A. Synthesis of Ketone Bodies

In the liver, ketone bodies are synthesized in the mitochondrial matrix from acetyl-CoA generated from fatty acid oxidation (Fig. 23.18). The thiolase reaction of fatty acid oxidation, which converts one molecule of acetoacetyl-CoA to two molecules of acetyl-CoA, is a reversible reaction, although formation of acetoacetyl-CoA is not the favored direction. Thus, when acetyl-CoA levels are high, it can generate acetoacetyl-CoA for ketone body synthesis. The acetoacetyl-CoA will react with acetyl-CoA to produce 3-hydroxy-3-methylglutaryl-CoA (HMG-CoA). The enzyme that catalyzes this reaction is HMG-CoA synthase. In the next reaction of the pathway, HMG-CoA lyase catalyzes the cleavage of HMG-CoA to form acetyl-CoA and acetoacetate.

Acetoacetate can enter the blood directly or can be reduced by β-hydroxybutyrate dehydrogenase to β-hydroxybutyrate, which enters the blood (see Fig. 23.18). This dehydrogenase reaction is readily reversible and interconverts these two ketone bodies, which exist in an equilibrium ratio determined by the NADH/NAD$^+$ ratio of the mitochondrial matrix. Under normal conditions, the ratio of β-hydroxybutyrate to acetoacetate in the blood is approximately 1:1.

An alternative fate of acetoacetate is spontaneous decarboxylation—a nonenzymatic reaction that cleaves acetoacetate into CO_2 and acetone (see Fig. 23.18). Because acetone is volatile, it is expired by the lungs. A small amount of acetone may be further metabolized in the body.

B. Oxidation of Ketone Bodies as Fuels

Acetoacetate and β-hydroxybutyrate can be oxidized as fuels in most tissues, including skeletal muscle, brain, certain cells of the kidney, and cells of the intestinal mucosa. Cells transport both acetoacetate and β-hydroxybutyrate from the circulating blood into the cytosol and into the mitochondrial matrix. Here, β-hydroxybutyrate is oxidized back to acetoacetate by β-hydroxybutyrate

FIG. 23.18. Synthesis of the ketone bodies acetoacetate, β-hydroxybutyrate, and acetone. The portion of HMG-CoA shown in the *tinted box* is released as acetyl-CoA, and the remainder of the molecule forms acetoacetate. Acetoacetate is reduced to β-hydroxybutyrate or decarboxylated to acetone. Note that the dehydrogenase that interconverts acetoacetate and β-hydroxybutyrate is specific for the D-isomer. Thus, it differs from the dehydrogenases of β-oxidation, which act on 3-hydroxyacyl-CoA derivatives and is specific for the L-isomer.

dehydrogenase. This reaction produces NADH. Subsequent steps convert acetoacetate to acetyl-CoA (Fig. 23.19).

In mitochondria, acetoacetate is activated to acetoacetyl-CoA by succinyl-CoA: acetoacetate-CoA transferase. As the name suggests, CoA is transferred from succinyl-CoA—a TCA-cycle intermediate—to acetoacetate. Although the liver produces ketone bodies, it does not use them, because this thiotransferase enzyme is not present in sufficient quantity.

One molecule of acetoacetyl-CoA is cleaved to two molecules of acetyl-CoA by acetoacetyl-CoA thiolase, the same enzyme as is involved in β-oxidation. The principal fate of this acetyl-CoA is oxidation in the TCA cycle.

Ketogenic diets, which are high-fat diets with a 3:1 ratio of lipid to carbohydrate, are being used to reduce the frequency of epileptic seizures in children. The reason for its effectiveness in the treatment of epilepsy is not known. Ketogenic diets are also used to treat children with pyruvate dehydrogenase deficiency. Ketone bodies can be used as a fuel by the brain in the absence of pyruvate dehydrogenase. They also can provide a source of cytosolic acetyl-CoA for acetylcholine synthesis. They often contain medium-chain triglycerides, which induce ketosis more effectively than long-chain triglycerides.

FIG. 23.19. Oxidation of ketone bodies. β-Hydroxybutyrate is oxidized to acetoacetate, which is activated by accepting a CoA group from succinyl-CoA. Acetoacetyl-CoA is cleaved to two acetyl-CoA, which enter the TCA cycle and are oxidized.

The energy yield from oxidation of acetoacetate is equivalent to the yield for oxidation of two molecules of acetyl-CoA in the TCA cycle (20 ATP) minus the energy for activation of acetoacetate (1 ATP). The energy of activation is calculated at one high-energy phosphate bond, because succinyl-CoA is normally converted to succinate in the TCA cycle, with generation of one molecule of guanosine triphosphate (GTP) (the energy equivalent of ATP). However, when the high-energy thioester bond of succinyl-CoA is transferred to acetoacetate, succinate is produced without the generation of this GTP. Oxidation of β-hydroxybutyrate generates one additional NADH. Therefore, the net energy yield from one molecule of β-hydroxybutyrate is approximately 21.5 molecules of ATP.

C. Alternative Pathways of Ketone Body Metabolism

Although fatty acid oxidation is usually the major source of ketone bodies, they also can be generated from the catabolism of certain amino acids: leucine, isoleucine, lysine, tryptophan, phenylalanine, and tyrosine. These amino acids are called *ketogenic amino acids* because their carbon skeleton is catabolized to acetyl-CoA or acetoacetyl-CoA, which may enter the pathway of ketone body synthesis in liver. Leucine and isoleucine also form acetyl-CoA and acetoacetyl-CoA in other tissues as well as the liver.

Acetoacetate can be activated to acetoacetyl-CoA in the cytosol by an enzyme similar to the acyl-CoA synthetases. This acetoacetyl-CoA can be used directly in cholesterol synthesis. It also can be cleaved to two molecules of acetyl-CoA by a cytosolic thiolase. Cytosolic acetyl-CoA is required for processes such as acetylcholine synthesis in neuronal cells.

IV. THE ROLE OF FATTY ACIDS AND KETONE BODIES IN FUEL HOMEOSTASIS

Fatty acids are used as fuels whenever fatty acid levels are elevated in the blood—that is, during fasting and starvation; because of a high-fat, low-carbohydrate diet; or during long-term low- to mild-intensity exercise. Under these conditions, a decrease in insulin and increased levels of glucagon, epinephrine, or other hormones stimulate adipose tissue lipolysis. Fatty acids begin to increase in the blood approximately 3 to 4 hours after a meal and progressively increase with time of fasting up to approximately 2 to 3 days (Fig. 23.20). In the liver, the rate of ketone body synthesis increases as the supply of fatty acids increases. However, the blood level of ketone bodies continues to increase, presumably because their utilization by skeletal muscles decreases.

After 2 to 3 days of starvation, ketone bodies rise to a level in the blood that enables them to enter brain cells, where they are oxidized, thereby reducing the amount of glucose required by the brain. During prolonged fasting, they may supply as much as two-thirds of the energy requirements of the brain. The reduction in glucose requirements spares skeletal muscle protein, which is a major source of amino acid precursors for hepatic glucose synthesis from gluconeogenesis.

A. Preferential Use of Fatty Acids

As fatty acids increase in the blood, they are used by skeletal muscles and certain other tissues in preference to glucose. Fatty acid oxidation generates NADH and FAD(2H) through both β-oxidation and the TCA cycle, resulting in relatively high NADH/NAD$^+$ ratios, acetyl-CoA concentrations, and ATP/ADP or ATP/AMP levels. In skeletal muscles, the AMP-PK (see Section I.E) adjusts the concentration of malonyl-CoA so that CPTI and β-oxidation operate at a rate that is able to sustain ATP homeostasis. With adequate levels of ATP obtained from fatty acid (or ketone body) oxidation, the rate of glycolysis is decreased. The activity of the regulatory enzymes in glycolysis and the TCA cycle (pyruvate dehydrogenase and phosphofructokinase-1 [PFK-1])

FIG. 23.20. Levels of ketone bodies in the blood at various times during fasting. Glucose levels remain relatively constant, as do levels of fatty acids. Ketone body levels, however, increase markedly, rising to levels at which they can be used by the brain and other nervous tissue. (From Cahill GF Jr, Aoki TT. How metabolism affects clinical problems. *Med Times.* 1970;98[10]:106.)

Children are more prone to ketosis than adults are, because their bodies enter the fasting state more rapidly. Their bodies use more energy per unit mass (because their muscle-to-adipose tissue ratio is higher), and liver glycogen stores are depleted faster (the ratio of their brain mass to liver mass is higher). In children, blood ketone body levels reach 2 mM in 24 hours; in adults, it takes more than 3 days to reach this level. Mild pediatric infections that cause anorexia and vomiting are the most common causes of ketosis in children. Mild ketosis is observed in children after prolonged exercise, perhaps attributable to an abrupt decrease in muscular use of fatty acids liberated during exercise. The liver then oxidizes these fatty acids and produces ketone bodies.

are decreased by the changes in concentration of their allosteric regulators (ADP—an activator of PDH—decreases in concentration; NADH and acetyl-CoA—inhibitors of PDH—are increased in concentration under these conditions; and ATP and citrate—inhibitors of PFK-1—are increased in concentration). As a consequence, glucose 6-phosphate (glucose 6-P) accumulates. Glucose 6-P inhibits hexokinase, thereby decreasing the rate of entry of glucose into glycolysis and its uptake from the blood. In skeletal muscles, this pattern of fuel metabolism is facilitated by the decrease in insulin concentration (see Chapter 36). Preferential use of fatty acids does not, however, restrict the ability of glycolysis to respond to an increase in AMP or ADP levels, such as what might occur during exercise or oxygen limitation.

B. Tissues that Use Ketone Bodies

Skeletal muscles, the heart, the liver, and many other tissues use fatty acids as their major fuel during fasting and under other conditions that increase fatty acids in the blood. However, several other tissues (or cell types), such as the brain, use ketone bodies to a greater extent. For example, cells of the intestinal mucosa, which transport fatty acids from the intestine to the blood, use ketone bodies and amino acids rather than fatty acids during starvation. Adipocytes, which store fatty acids in triacylglycerols, do not use fatty acids as a fuel during fasting but can use ketone bodies. Ketone bodies cross the placenta and can be used by the fetus. Almost all tissues and cell types, with the exception of liver and red blood cells, are able to use ketone bodies as fuel.

C. Regulation of Ketone Body Synthesis

Several events, in addition to the increased supply of fatty acids from adipose triacylglycerols, promote hepatic ketone body synthesis during fasting. The decreased insulin/glucagon ratio results in inhibition of acetyl-CoA carboxylase and decreased malonyl-CoA levels, which activates CPTI, thereby allowing fatty acyl-CoA to enter the pathway of β-oxidation (Fig. 23.21). When oxidation of fatty acyl-CoA to acetyl-CoA generates enough NADH and FAD(2H) to supply the ATP needs of the liver, acetyl-CoA is diverted from the TCA cycle into ketogenesis and oxaloacetate in the TCA cycle is diverted toward malate and into glucose synthesis (gluconeogenesis). This pattern is regulated by the NADH/NAD$^+$ ratio, which is relatively high during β-oxidation. As the length of time of fasting continues, increased transcription of

The level of total ketone bodies in **Di Abietes'** blood greatly exceeds normal fasting levels and the mild ketosis produced during exercise. In a person on a normal mealtime schedule, total blood ketone bodies rarely exceed 0.2 mM. During prolonged fasting, they may rise to 4 to 5 mM. Levels >7 mM are considered evidence of ketoacidosis, because the acid produced must reach this level to exceed the bicarbonate buffer system in the blood and compensatory respiration (Kussmaul respiration) (see Chapter 4).

Why can red blood cells not use ketone bodies for energy?

A: Red blood cells lack mitochondria, which is the site of ketone body use.

FIG. 23.21. Regulation of ketone body synthesis. *(1)* The supply of fatty acids is increased. *(2)* The malonyl-CoA inhibition of CPTI is lifted by inactivation of acetyl-CoA carboxylase. *(3)* β-Oxidation supplies NADH and FAD(2H), which are used by the electron-transport chain for oxidative phosphorylation. As ATP levels increase, less NADH is oxidized, and the NADH/NAD$^+$ ratio is increased. *(4)* Oxaloacetate is converted into malate because of the high NADH levels, and the malate enters the cytoplasm for gluconeogenesis. *(5)* Acetyl-CoA is diverted from the TCA cycle into ketogenesis, in part because of low oxaloacetate levels, which reduces the rate of the citrate synthase reaction.

the gene for mitochondrial HMG-CoA synthase facilitates high rates of ketone body production. Although the liver has been described as "altruistic" because it provides ketone bodies for other tissues, it is simply getting rid of fuel that it does not need.

CLINICAL COMMENTS

Otto Shape. As **Otto Shape** runs, he increases the rate at which his muscles oxidize all fuels. The increased rate of ATP use stimulates the electron-transport chain, which oxidizes NADH and FAD(2H) much faster, thereby increasing the rate at which fatty acids are oxidized. During exercise, he also uses muscle glycogen stores, which contribute glucose to glycolysis. In some of the fibers, the glucose is used anaerobically, thereby producing lactate. Some of the lactate will be used by his heart, and some will be taken up by the liver to be converted to glucose. As he trains, he increases his mitochondrial capacity, as well as his oxygen delivery, resulting in an increased ability to oxidize fatty acids and ketone bodies. As he runs, he increases fatty acid release from adipose tissue triacylglycerols. In the liver, fatty acids are being converted to ketone bodies, providing his muscles with another fuel. As a consequence, he experiences mild ketosis after his 12-mile run.

More than 25 enzymes and specific transport proteins participate in mitochondrial fatty acid metabolism. At least 15 of these have been implicated in inherited diseases in the human.

Lofata Burne. Recently, medium-chain acyl-CoA dehydrogenase (MCAD) deficiency, the cause of **Lofata Burne's** problems, has emerged as one of the most common of the inborn errors of metabolism, with a carrier frequency ranging from 1 in 40 in northern European populations to <1 in 100 in Asians. Overall, the predicted disease frequency for MCAD deficiency is 1 in 15,000 persons.

MCAD deficiency is an autosomal recessive disorder caused by the substitution of a T for an A at position 985 of the MCAD gene. This mutation causes a lysine to replace a glutamate residue in the protein, resulting in the production of an unstable dehydrogenase.

The most frequent manifestation of MCAD deficiency is intermittent hypoketotic hypoglycemia during fasting (low levels of ketone bodies and low levels of glucose in the blood). Fatty acids normally would be oxidized to CO_2 and H_2O under these conditions. In MCAD deficiency, however, fatty acids are oxidized only until they reach medium-chain length. As a result, the body must rely more on oxidation of blood glucose to meet its energy needs.

However, hepatic gluconeogenesis appears to be impaired in MCAD. Inhibition of gluconeogenesis may be caused by the lack of hepatic fatty acid oxidation to supply the energy required for gluconeogenesis, or by the accumulation of unoxidized fatty acid metabolites that inhibit gluconeogenic enzymes. As a consequence, liver glycogen stores are depleted more rapidly, and hypoglycemia results. The decrease in hepatic fatty acid oxidation results in less acetyl-CoA for ketone body synthesis and, consequently, a hypoketotic hypoglycemia develops.

Some of the symptoms once ascribed to hypoglycemia are now believed to be caused by the accumulation of toxic fatty acid intermediates, especially in patients with only mild reductions in blood glucose levels. **Lofata Burne's** mild elevation in the blood of liver transaminases may reflect an infiltration of her liver cells with unoxidized medium-chain fatty acids.

The management of MCAD-deficient patients includes the intake of a relatively high-carbohydrate diet and the avoidance of prolonged fasting.

 LCAD deficiency, a reduced activity of the long-chain 3-hydroxyacyl-CoA dehydrogenase, is a rare disorder with a poor outcome. LCAD activity is contained within the mitochondrial trifunctional protein, which is a hetero-octamer of four α- and four β-subunits. This complex catalyzes three steps in the oxidation of long-chain fatty acids: the long-chain enoyl-CoA hydratase activity, the LCAD activity, and the long-chain ketothiolase activity. Mutations in LCAD are located in the α-subunit. Although an intact protein is produced, LCAD activity is significantly reduced, and the other two activities of the complex are reduced approximately 40%. Generalized mitochondrial trifunctional protein deficiency, with a significant reduction in all three activities, can result from mutations in either the α- or β-chain. Patients with generalized trifunctional protein deficiency exhibit a wide clinical spectrum of disease—from severe to mild.

 Di Abietes. A 26-year-old woman with type 1 diabetes mellitus, was admitted to the hospital in diabetic ketoacidosis. In this complication of diabetes mellitus, an acute deficiency of insulin, coupled with a relative excess of glucagon, results in a rapid mobilization of fuel stores from muscle (amino acids) and adipose tissue (fatty acids). Some of the amino acids are converted to glucose, and fatty acids are converted to ketones (acetoacetate, β-hydroxybutyrate, and acetone). The high glucagon:insulin ratio promotes the hepatic production of ketones. In response to the metabolic "stress," the levels of insulin-antagonistic hormones, such as catecholamines, glucocorticoids, and growth hormone are increased in the blood. The insulin deficiency further reduces the peripheral use of glucose and ketones. Because of this interrelated dysmetabolism, plasma glucose levels reach 500 mg/dL (27.8 mmol/L) or more (normal fasting levels are 70 to 100 mg/dL or 3.9 to 5.5 mmol/L), and plasma ketones rise to levels of 8 to 15 mmol/L or more (normal is in the range of 0.2 to 2 mmol/L, depending on the fed state of the individual).

The increased glucose presented to the renal glomeruli induces an osmotic diuresis, which further depletes intravascular volume, further reducing the renal excretion of hydrogen ions and glucose. As a result, the metabolic acidosis worsens, and the hyperosmolarity of the blood increases, at times exceeding 330 mOsm/kg (normal is in the range of 285 to 295 mOsm/kg). The severity of the hyperosmolar state correlates closely with the degree of central nervous system dysfunction and may end in coma and even death if left untreated.

BIOCHEMICAL COMMENTS

 Acetylation and Regulation of Fatty Acid Oxidation. Previously in Chapter 16, *acetylation of histones* was described as a mechanism of regulating gene expression. Histone acetyltransferases (HATs) would catalyze histone acetylation on lysine side chains, leading to histone dissociation from the DNA. This freed the DNA to bind factors important for transcription to occur. Recent work has indicated that acetylation of long-chain acyl-CoA dehydrogenase (LCAD) regulates the activity of the enzyme and offers more complexity to the regulation of fatty acid oxidation. Acetylation of LCAD reduces enzymatic activity, whereas deacetylation will restore activity.

A family of proteins known as the *sirtuins* (SIRT) are NAD^+-dependent protein deacetylases. There are seven forms in humans, designated SIRT1 through SIRT7, all of which affect certain areas of metabolism. The sirtuins catalyze the reaction shown in Figure 23.22, in which NAD^+ is split into nicotinamide and 2-O-acetyl-ADP-ribose, and the protein target is deacetylated (the acetate group is transferred from the target to the 2′-hydroxy group of the ribose attached to the nicotinamide in NAD^+).

Sirtuin 3 is localized to the mitochondrial matrix, and recent evidence indicates that it is a key regulator for fatty acid oxidation within the mitochondria. Using mice as a model system, it was demonstrated that SIRT3 expression is upregulated during fasting in the liver. A primary target of SIRT3 deacetylation activity is LCAD, which is hyperacetylated on lysine-42. When hyperacetylated, LCAD activity is

FIG. 23.22.   Generalized sirtuin reaction.

reduced. Because LCAD will initiate fatty acid oxidation, regulating LCAD activity will regulate overall use of long-chain fatty acids by liver mitochondria. Fasting will upregulate the sirtuins leading to activation of LCAD, and increased fatty acid oxidation by the liver. Mice lacking SIRT3 activity were deficient in fatty acid oxidation during fasting conditions, accumulating long-chain intermediates and triglyceride in the liver. Human LCAD was also demonstrated to be acetylated and SIRT3 would deacetylate the enzyme in a test tube.

The recent finding of acetylation as a regulatory tool for fatty acid oxidation provides another avenue for complex regulation between various aspects of metabolism and provides fertile ground for further research in this area.

Key Concepts

- Fatty acids are a major fuel for humans.
- During overnight fasting, fatty acids become the major fuel for cardiac muscle, skeletal muscle, and liver.
- The nervous system has a limited ability to use fatty acids directly as fuel. The liver converts fatty acids to ketone bodies, which can be used by the nervous system as a fuel during prolonged periods of fasting.
- Fatty acids are released from adipose tissue triacylglycerols under appropriate hormonal stimulation.
- In cells, fatty acids are activated to fatty acyl-CoA derivatives by acyl-CoA synthetases.
- Acyl-CoAs are transported into the mitochondria for oxidation via carnitine.
- ATP is generated from fatty acids by the pathway of β-oxidation.
- In β-oxidation, the fatty acyl group is sequentially oxidized to yield FAD(2H), NADH, and acetyl-CoA. Although the reactions are similar, enzyme specificity is determined by the acyl chain length of the substrate.
- Unsaturated and odd-chain-length fatty acids require additional reactions for their metabolism.
- β-Oxidation is regulated by the levels of FAD(2H), NADH, and acetyl-CoA.
- The entry of fatty acids into mitochondria is regulated by malonyl-CoA levels.
- Alternative pathways for very long-chain and branched-chain fatty acid oxidation occur within peroxisomes.
- If β-oxidation is impaired, other pathways of oxidation will be used, such as α- and ω-oxidation.
- Table 23.2 summarizes the diseases discussed in this chapter.

Table 23.2   Diseases Discussed in Chapter 23

Disease or Disorder	Environmental or Genetic	Comments
Obesity	Both	The contribution of fatty acids to overall energy metabolism and energy storage.
MCAD deficiency	Genetic	Lack of medium-chain acyl-CoA dehydrogenase activity, leading to hypoglycemia and reduced ketone body formation under fasting conditions.
Type 1 diabetes	Environmental	Ketoacidosis; overproduction of ketone bodies because of lack of insulin and metabolic dysregulation in the liver.
Carnitine deficiency	Both	A primary carnitine deficiency is the lack of a membrane transporter for carnitine; a secondary carnitine deficiency is because of other metabolic disorders.
Zellweger syndrome	Genetic	A defect in peroxisome biogenesis, leading to a lack of peroxisomes, inability to synthesize plasmalogens, or oxidize very long-chain fatty acids.
LCAD deficiency	Genetic	A lack of long-chain acyl-CoA dehydrogenase activity, leading to hypoglycemia.
Jamaican vomiting disorder	Environmental	Inhibition of carnitine activity by hypoglycin; can lead to death because of severe hypoglycemia.

MCAD, medium acyl-CoA dehydrogenase; LCAD, long-chain acyl-CoA dehydrogenase.

1. A lack of the enzyme ETF-QO oxidoreductase leads to death. This is caused by which of the following reasons?

   A. The energy yield from glucose use is dramatically reduced.

   B. The energy yield from alcohol use is dramatically reduced.

   C. The energy yield from ketone body use is dramatically reduced.

   D. The energy yield from fatty acid use is dramatically reduced.

   E. The energy yield from glycogen use is dramatically reduced.

2. The ATP yield from the complete oxidation of 1 mol of a C18:0 fatty acid to carbon dioxide and water would be closest to which one of the following?

   A. 105

   B. 115

   C. 120

   D. 125

   E. 130

3. The oxidation of fatty acids is best described by which of the following sets of reactions?

   A. Oxidation, hydration, oxidation, carbon–carbon bond breaking

   B. Oxidation, dehydration, oxidation, carbon–carbon bond breaking

   C. Oxidation, hydration, reduction, carbon–carbon bond breaking

   D. Oxidation, dehydration, reduction, oxidation, carbon–carbon bond breaking

   E. Reduction, hydration, oxidation, carbon–carbon bond breaking

4. An individual with a deficiency of an enzyme in the pathway for carnitine synthesis is not eating adequate amounts of carnitine in the diet. Which of the following effects would you expect during fasting as compared with an individual with an adequate intake and synthesis of carnitine?

   A. Fatty acid oxidation is increased.

   B. Ketone body synthesis is increased.

   C. Blood glucose levels are increased.

   D. Levels of dicarboxylic acids in the blood are increased.

   E. Levels of very long-chain fatty acids in the blood are increased.

5. In which one of the following periods will fatty acids be the major source of fuel for the tissues of the body?

   A. Immediately after breakfast

   B. Minutes after a snack

   C. Immediately after dinner

   D. While running the first mile of a marathon

   E. While running the last mile of a marathon

24 Oxygen Toxicity and Free Radical Injury

O_2 is both essential to human life and **toxic**. We are dependent on O_2 for oxidation reactions in the pathways of adenosine triphosphate (ATP) generation, detoxification, and biosynthesis. However, when O_2 accepts single electrons, it is transformed into highly reactive **oxygen radicals** that damage cellular lipids, proteins, and DNA. Damage by reactive oxygen radicals contributes to cellular death and degeneration in a wide range of diseases (Table 24.1).

Radicals are compounds that contain a single electron, usually at an outside orbital. Oxygen is a **biradical**, a molecule that has two unpaired electrons in separate orbitals (Fig. 24.1). Through several enzymatic and nonenzymatic processes that routinely occur in cells, O_2 accepts **single electrons to form reactive oxygen species (ROS)**. ROS are highly reactive oxygen radicals or compounds that are readily converted in cells to these reactive radicals. The ROS formed by reduction of O_2 are the radical **superoxide (O_2^-)**, the nonradical **hydrogen peroxide (H_2O_2)**, and the **hydroxyl radical (OH•)**.

ROS may be generated nonenzymatically or enzymatically as accidental by-products or major products of reactions. Superoxide may be generated nonenzymatically from coenzyme Q (CoQ) or from metal-containing enzymes (e.g., **cytochrome P450, xanthine oxidase**, and **NADPH oxidase**). The highly toxic hydroxyl radical is formed nonenzymatically from superoxide in the presence of Fe^{2+} or Cu^+ by the **Fenton reaction** and from hydrogen peroxide in the **Haber-Weiss reaction**.

Oxygen radicals and their derivatives can be deadly to cells. The hydroxyl radical causes oxidative damage to proteins and DNA. It also forms **lipid peroxides** and **malondialdehyde** from membrane lipids containing **polyunsaturated fatty acids**. In some cases, free radical damage is the direct cause of a disease state (e.g., tissue damage initiated by exposure to ionizing radiation). In **neurodegenerative diseases**, such as Parkinson disease, or in ischemia-reperfusion injury, ROS may perpetuate the cellular damage caused by another process.

Oxygen radicals are joined in their destructive damage by the free radical **nitric oxide (NO)** and the ROS **hypochlorous acid (HOCl)**. NO combines with O_2 or superoxide to form **reactive nitrogen–oxygen species (RNOS)**, such as the nonradical peroxynitrite or the radical **nitrogen dioxide**. RNOS are

FIG. 24.1. O_2 is a biradical. It has two antibonding electrons with parallel spins, (*parallel arrows*). It has a tendency to form toxic ROS, such as superoxide (O_2^-), the nonradical hydrogen peroxide (H_2O_2), and the hydroxyl radical (OH•).

Table 24.1 Some Disease States Associated with Free Radical Injury

Atherogenesis	Cerebrovascular disorders
Emphysema bronchitis	Ischemia/reperfusion injury
Duchenne-type muscular dystrophy	Neurodegenerative disorders
Pregnancy/preeclampsia	Amyotrophic lateral sclerosis (Lou Gehrig disease)
Retrolental fibroplasia	
Cervical cancer	Alzheimer disease
Alcohol-induced liver disease	Down syndrome
Hemodialysis	Ischemia-reperfusion injury following stroke
Diabetes	OXPHOS diseases (mitochondrial DNA disorders)
Acute renal failure	Multiple sclerosis
Aging	Parkinson disease

FIG. 24.2. Oxidative stress. Oxidative stress occurs when the rate of ROS and RNOS production overbalances the rate of their removal by cellular defense mechanisms. These defense mechanisms include a number of enzymes and antioxidants. Antioxidants usually react nonenzymatically with ROS.

The basal ganglia are part of a neuronal feedback loop that modulates and integrates the flow of information from the cerebral cortex to the motor neurons of the spinal cord. The neostriatum is the major input structure from the cerebral cortex. The substantia nigra pars compacta consists of neurons that provide integrative input to the neostriatum through pigmented neurons that use dopamine as a neurotransmitter (the nigrastriatal pathway). Integrated information feeds back to the basal ganglia and to the cerebral cortex to control voluntary movement. In Parkinson disease, a decrease in the amount of dopamine reaching the basal ganglia results in the movement disorder.

In ventricular fibrillation, rapid premature beats from an irritative focus in ventricular muscle occur in runs of varying duration. Persistent fibrillation compromises cardiac output, leading to death. This arrythmia can result from severe ischemia (lack of blood flow) in the ventricular muscle of the heart caused by clots forming at the site of a ruptured atherosclerotic plaque. However, **Cora Nari's** rapid beats began during the infusion of tissue plasminogen activator (TPA) as the clot was lysed. Thus, they probably resulted from reperfusing a previously ischemic area of her heart with oxygenated blood. This phenomenon is known as *ischemia-reperfusion injury*, and it is caused by cytotoxic ROS derived from oxygen in the blood that reperfuses previously hypoxic cells. Ischemic-reperfusion injury also may occur when tissue oxygenation is interrupted during surgery or transplantation.

*present in the environment (e.g., cigarette smoke) and are generated in cells. During phagocytosis of invading microorganisms, cells of the immune system produce O_2^-, HOCl, and NO through the actions of **NADPH oxidase**, **myeloperoxidase**, and **inducible nitric oxide synthase**, respectively. In addition to killing phagocytosed invading microorganisms, these toxic metabolites may damage surrounding tissue components.*

*Cells **protect** themselves against damage by ROS and other radicals through **repair processes**, **compartmentalization** of free radical production, **defense enzymes**, and **endogenous and exogenous antioxidants (free radical scavengers)**. The defense enzyme **superoxide dismutase (SOD)** removes the superoxide free radical. Catalase and glutathione peroxidase remove hydrogen peroxide and lipid peroxides. **Vitamin E**, **vitamin C**, and **plant flavonoids** act as **antioxidants**. **Oxidative stress** occurs when the rate of ROS generation exceeds the capacity of the cell for their removal (Fig. 24.2).*

THE WAITING ROOM

Two years ago, **Les Dopaman**, a 62-year-old man, noted an increasing tremor of his right hand when sitting quietly (resting tremor). The tremor disappeared if he actively used this hand to do purposeful movement. As this symptom progressed, he also complained of stiffness in his muscles that slowed his movements (bradykinesia). His wife noticed a change in his gait; he had begun taking short, shuffling steps and leaned forward as he walked (postural imbalance). He often appeared to be staring ahead with a rather immobile facial expression. She noted a tremor of his eyelids when he was asleep and, recently, a tremor of his legs when he was at rest. Because of these progressive symptoms and some subtle personality changes (anxiety and emotional lability), she convinced Les to see their family doctor.

The doctor suspected that her patient probably had primary or idiopathic parkinsonism (Parkinson disease) and referred Mr. Dopaman to a neurologist. In Parkinson disease, neurons of the substantia nigra pars compacta, containing the pigment melanin and the neurotransmitter dopamine, degenerate.

Cora Nari had done well since the successful lysis of blood clots in her coronary arteries with the use of intravenous recombinant tissue plasminogen activator (TPA) (see Chapters 19 and 21). This therapy quickly relieved the crushing chest pain (angina) she experienced when she won the lottery. At her first office visit after her discharge from the hospital, Cora's cardiologist told her she had developed multiple premature contractions of the ventricular muscle of her heart as the clots were being lysed. This process could have led to a life-threatening arrhythmia known as *ventricular fibrillation*. However, Cora's arrhythmia responded quickly to pharmacologic suppression and did not recur during the remainder of her hospitalization.

I. O_2 AND THE GENERATION OF REACTIVE OXYGEN SPECIES

The generation of reactive oxygen species (ROS) from O_2 in our cells is a natural, everyday occurrence. ROS are formed as accidental products of nonenzymatic and enzymatic reactions. Occasionally, they are deliberately synthesized in enzyme-catalyzed reactions. Ultraviolet radiation and pollutants in the air can increase formation of toxic oxygen-containing compounds.

A. The Radical Nature of O_2

A *radical*, by definition, is a molecule that has a single unpaired electron in an orbital. A *free radical* is a radical that is capable of independent existence. (Radicals formed in an enzyme active site during a reaction, for example, are not considered free radicals unless they can dissociate from the protein to interact with other molecules.) Radicals are highly reactive and initiate chain reactions by extracting an electron from a neighboring molecule to complete their own orbitals. Although the transition metals (e.g., Fe, Cu, Mo) have single electrons in orbitals, they are not usually considered free radicals because they are relatively stable, do not initiate chain reactions, and are bound to proteins in the cell.

The oxygen molecule is a biradical, which means it has two single electrons in different orbitals. These electrons cannot both travel in the same orbital because they have parallel spins (they spin in the same direction). Although oxygen is very reactive from a thermodynamic standpoint, its single electrons cannot react rapidly with the paired electrons found in the covalent bonds of organic molecules. As a consequence, O_2 reacts slowly through the acceptance of single electrons in reactions that require a catalyst (such as a metal-containing enzyme).

Because the two unpaired electrons in oxygen have the same (parallel) spin, they are called *antibonding electrons*. In contrast, carbon–carbon and carbon–hydrogen bonds each contain two electrons, which have antiparallel spins and form a thermodynamically stable pair. As a consequence, O_2 cannot readily oxidize a covalent bond because one of its electrons would have to flip its spin around to make new pairs. The difficulty in changing spins is called *spin restriction*. Without spin restriction, organic life forms could not have developed in the oxygen atmosphere on earth because they would be spontaneously oxidized by O_2.

O_2 is capable of accepting a total of four electrons, which reduces it to water (Fig. 24.3). When O_2 accepts one electron, superoxide is formed. Superoxide is still a radical because it has one unpaired electron remaining. This reaction is not thermodynamically favorable and requires a moderately strong reducing agent that can donate single electrons (e.g., the radical form of coenzyme Q [CoQH•] in the electron-transport chain). When superoxide accepts an electron, it is reduced to hydrogen peroxide, which is not a radical. The hydroxyl radical is formed in the next one-electron reduction step in the reduction sequence. Finally, acceptance of the last electron reduces the hydroxyl radical to H_2O.

B. Characteristics of Reactive Oxygen Species

ROS are oxygen-containing compounds that are highly reactive free radicals or compounds that are readily converted to these oxygen free radicals in the cell. The major oxygen metabolites produced by one-electron reduction of oxygen (superoxide, hydrogen peroxide, and the hydroxyl radical) are classified as ROS (Table 24.2).

Reactive free radicals extract electrons (usually as hydrogen atoms) from other compounds to complete their own orbitals, thereby initiating free radical chain reactions. The hydroxyl radical is probably the most potent of the ROS. It initiates chain reactions that form lipid peroxides and organic radicals and adds directly to compounds. The superoxide anion is also highly reactive, but it has limited lipid solubility and cannot diffuse far. However, it can generate the more reactive hydroxyl and hydroperoxy radicals by reacting nonenzymatically with hydrogen peroxide in the Haber-Weiss reaction (Fig. 24.4).

Hydrogen peroxide is not actually a radical; it is a weak oxidizing agent that is classified as a ROS because it can generate the hydroxyl radical (OH•). Transition metals, such as Fe^{2+} or Cu^+, catalyze formation of the hydroxyl radical from

 Catecholamine (epinephrine, norepinephrine, dopamine) measurements use either serum or a 24-hour urine collection as samples for assay. After appropriate removal of cells and/or particulate matter, the sample is placed over an ion-exchange high-pressure liquid chromatography (HPLC) column and the eluate from the column is analyzed by sensitive electrochemical detection. Through comparison with retention times of standard catecholamines on the column, the various catecholamine species can be clearly resolved from each other. The electrochemical detection uses electrodes that are oxidized by the samples, and the amplitude current that is generated via the redox reaction allows one to determine the concentration of catecholamines in the specimen.

FIG. 24.3. Reduction of oxygen by four one-electron steps. The four one-electron reduction steps for O_2 progressively generate superoxide, hydrogen peroxide (H_2O_2), and the hydroxyl radical plus water. Superoxide is sometimes written O_2^- to better illustrate its single unpaired electron. H_2O_2, the half-reduced form of O_2, has accepted two electrons and is therefore not an oxygen radical.

Table 24.2   Reactive Oxygen Species and Reactive Nitrogen–Oxygen Species

Reactive Species	Properties
Superoxide anion (O_2^-)	Produced by the electron-transport chain and at other sites. Cannot diffuse far from the site of origin. Generates other ROS.
Hydrogen peroxide (H_2O_2)	Not a free radical but can generate free radicals by reaction with a transition metal (e.g., Fe^{2+}). Can diffuse into and through cell membranes.
Hydroxyl radical (OH•)	The most reactive species in attacking biologic molecules. Produced from H_2O_2 in the Fenton reaction in the presence of Fe^{2+} or Cu^+.
RO•, R•, R–S organic radicals	Organic free radicals (R denotes the remainder of the compound). Produced from ROH, RH (e.g., at the carbon of a double bond in a fatty acid) or RSH OH• attack.
RCOO• peroxyl radical	An organic peroxyl radical, such as occurs during lipid degradation (also denoted LOO•).
Hypochlorous acid (HOCl)	Produced in neutrophils during the respiratory burst to destroy invading organisms. Toxicity is through halogenation and oxidation reactions. Attacking species is OCl^-.
$O_2^{\downarrow\uparrow}$ Singlet oxygen	Oxygen with antiparallel spins. Produced at high oxygen tensions from absorption of UV light. Decays so fast that it is probably not a significant in vivo source of toxicity.
Nitric oxide (NO)	RNOS. A free radical produced endogenously by nitric oxide synthase. Binds to metal ions. Combines with O_2 or other oxygen-containing radicals to produce additional RNOS.
Peroxynitrite ($ONOO^-$)	RNOS. A strong oxidizing agent that is not a free radical. It can generate nitrogen dioxide (NO_2), which is a radical.

The Haber-Weiss reaction

The Fenton reaction

FIG. 24.4. Generation of the hydroxyl radical by the nonenzymatic Haber-Weiss and Fenton reactions. In the simplified versions of these reactions shown here, the transfer of single electrons generates the hydroxyl radical. ROS are shown in the boxes. In addition to Fe^{2+}, Cu^+ and many other metals can also serve as single-electron donors in the Fenton reaction.

hydrogen peroxide in the nonenzymatic Fenton reaction (see Fig. 24.4.). Because hydrogen peroxide is lipid soluble, it can diffuse through membranes and generate OH• at localized Fe^{2+}- or Cu^+-containing sites, such as the electron-transport chain within the mitochondria. Hydrogen peroxide is also the precursor of *hypochlorous acid* (HOCl), a powerful oxidizing agent that is produced endogenously and enzymatically by phagocytic cells. To decrease occurrence of the Fenton reaction, accessibility to transition metals, such as Fe^{2+} and Cu^+, are highly restricted in cells or in the body as a whole. Events that release iron from cellular storage sites, such as a crushing injury, are associated with increased free radical injury.

Organic radicals are generated when superoxide or the hydroxyl radical indiscriminately extract electrons from other molecules. Organic peroxy radicals are intermediates of chain reactions, such as lipid peroxidation. Other organic radicals, such as the ethoxy radical, are intermediates of enzymatic reactions that escape into solution (see Table 24.2).

An additional group of oxygen-containing radicals, termed *reactive nitrogen–oxygen species (RNOS)*, contains nitrogen as well as oxygen. These radicals are derived principally from the free radical *nitric oxide* (NO), which is produced endogenously by the enzyme nitric oxide synthase. Nitric oxide combines with O_2 or superoxide to produce additional RNOS.

C. Major Sources of Primary Reactive Oxygen Species in the Cell

ROS are constantly being formed in the cell; approximately 3% to 5% of the oxygen we consume is converted to oxygen free radicals. Some are produced as accidental by-products of normal enzymatic reactions that escape from the active site of metal-containing enzymes during oxidation reactions. Others, such as hydrogen peroxide, are physiologic products of oxidases in peroxisomes. Deliberate production of toxic free radicals occur during the inflammatory response. Drugs, natural radiation, air pollutants, and other chemicals also can increase formation of free radicals in cells.

1. COENZYME Q GENERATES SUPEROXIDE

One of the major sites of superoxide generation is coenzyme Q (CoQ) in the mitochondrial electron-transport chain (Fig. 24.5). The one-electron reduced form of CoQ (CoQH•) is free within the membrane and can accidentally transfer an electron to dissolved O_2, thereby forming superoxide. In contrast, when O_2 binds to cytochrome oxidase and accepts electrons, none of the O_2 radical intermediates are released from the enzyme, and no ROS are generated.

2. OXIDASES, OXYGENASES, AND PEROXIDASES

Most of the oxidases, peroxidases, and oxygenases in the cell bind O_2 and transfer single electrons to it via a metal. Free radical intermediates of these reactions may be accidentally released before the reduction is complete.

Cytochrome P450 enzymes are a major source of free radicals "leaked" from reactions. Because these enzymes catalyze reactions in which single electrons are transferred to O_2 and an organic substrate, the possibility of accidentally generating and releasing free radical intermediates is high (see Chapters 19 and 25). Induction of P450 enzymes by alcohol, drugs, or chemical toxicants leads to increased cellular injury. As an example, carbon tetrachloride (CCl_4), which is used as a solvent in the dry cleaning industry, is converted by cytochrome P450 to a highly reactive free radical that has caused hepatocellular necrosis in workers in that industry. When the enzyme-bound CCl_4 accepts an electron, it dissociates into CCl_3• and Cl. The CCl_3• radical, which cannot continue through the P450 reaction sequence, "leaks" from the enzyme active site and initiates chain reactions in the surrounding polyunsaturated lipids of the endoplasmic reticulum. These reactions spread into the plasma membrane and to proteins, eventually resulting in cell swelling, accumulation of lipids, and cell death. When substrates for cytochrome P450 enzymes are not present, its potential for destructive damage is diminished by repression of gene transcription.

Hydrogen peroxide and lipid peroxides are generated enzymatically as major reaction products by several oxidases present in peroxisomes, mitochondria, and the endoplasmic reticulum. For example, monoamine oxidase, which oxidatively degrades the neurotransmitter dopamine, generates H_2O_2 at the mitochondrial membrane of certain neurons. Peroxisomal fatty acid oxidase generates H_2O_2 rather than FAD(2H) during the oxidation of very long-chain fatty acids (see Chapter 23). *Xanthine oxidase*, an enzyme of purine degradation that can reduce O_2 to O_2^-or H_2O_2 in the cytosol, is thought to be a major contributor to ischemia-reperfusion injury, especially in intestinal mucosal and endothelial cells. Lipid peroxides are also formed enzymatically as intermediates in the pathways for synthesis of many eicosanoids, including leukotrienes and prostaglandins.

3. IONIZING RADIATION

Cosmic rays that continuously bombard the earth, radioactive chemicals, and X-rays are forms of ionizing radiation. Ionizing radiation has a high enough energy level that it can split water into hydroxyl and hydrogen radicals, thus leading to radiation damage to the skin, mutations, cancer, and cell death (Fig. 24.6). It also may generate organic radicals through direct collision with organic cellular components.

II. OXYGEN RADICAL REACTIONS WITH CELLULAR COMPONENTS

Oxygen radicals produce cellular dysfunction by reacting with lipids, proteins, carbohydrates, and DNA to extract electrons (summarized in Fig. 24.7). Evidence of free radical damage has been described in >100 disease states. In some of these diseases, free radical damage is the primary cause of the disease; in others, it enhances complications of the disease.

FIG. 24.5.   Generation of superoxide by CoQ in the electron-transport chain. In the process of transporting electrons to O_2, some of the electrons escape when CoQH• accidentally interacts with O_2 to form superoxide. Fe-H represents the Fe-heme center of the cytochromes.

 With insufficient oxygen, **Cora Nari's** ischemic heart muscle mitochondria were unable to maintain cellular adenosine triphosphate (ATP) levels, resulting in high intracellular Na^+ and Ca^{2+} levels. The reduced state of the electron carriers in the absence of oxygen and loss of mitochondrial ion gradients or membrane integrity leads to increased superoxide production once oxygen becomes available during reperfusion. The damage can be self-perpetuating, especially if iron bound to components of the electron-transport chain becomes available for the Fenton reaction or the mitochondrial permeability transition is activated.

 Les Dopaman, who is in the early stages of Parkinson disease, is treated with a monoamine oxidase B inhibitor. *Monoamine oxidase* is a copper-containing enzyme that inactivates dopamine in neurons, producing hydrogen peroxide (H_2O_2). The drug was originally administered to inhibit dopamine degradation. However, current theory suggests that the effectiveness of the drug is also related to a decrease of free radical formation within the cells of the basal ganglia. The dopaminergic neurons involved are particularly susceptible to the cytotoxic effects of ROS and reactive nitrogen–oxygen species (RNOS) that may arise from H_2O_2.

FIG. 24.6. Generation of free radicals from radiation.

Production of ROS by xanthine oxidase in endothelial cells may be enhanced during ischemia-reperfusion in **Cora Nari's** heart. In undamaged tissues, xanthine oxidase exists as a dehydrogenase that uses NAD^+ rather than O_2 as an electron acceptor in the pathway for degradation of purines (hypoxanthine → xanthine → uric acid; see Chapter 41). When O_2 levels decrease, phosphorylation of adenosine diphosphate (ADP) to adenosine triphosphate (ATP) decreases, and degradation of ADP and adenine through xanthine oxidase increases. In the process, xanthine dehydrogenase is converted to an oxidase. As long as O_2 levels are below the high K_m of the enzyme for O_2, little damage is done. However, during reperfusion, when O_2 levels return to normal, xanthine oxidase generates H_2O_2 and O_2^- at the site of injury.

The appearance of lipofuscin granules in many tissues increases during aging. The pigment lipofuscin (from the Greek *lipos*, for lipids, and the Latin *fuscus*, for dark) consists of a heterogeneous mixture of cross-linked polymerized lipids and protein formed by reactions between amino acid residues and lipid peroxidation products such as malondialdehyde. These cross-linked products are probably derived from peroxidatively damaged cell organelles that were autophagocytized by lysosomes but could not be digested. When these dark pigments appear on the skin of the hands in aged individuals, they are referred to as "liver spots," a traditional hallmark of aging. In **Les Dopaman** and other patients with Parkinson disease, lipofuscin appears as Lewy bodies in degenerating neurons.

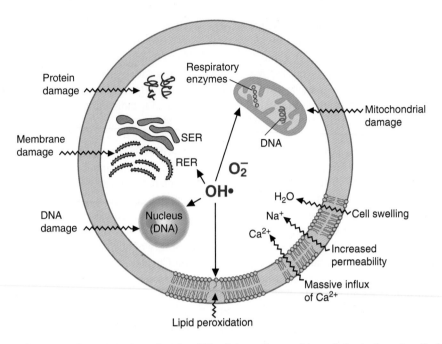

FIG. 24.7. Free radical–mediated cellular injury. Superoxide and the hydroxyl radical initiate lipid peroxidation in the cellular, mitochondrial, nuclear, and endoplasmic reticulum membranes. The increase in cellular permeability results in an influx of Ca^{2+}, which causes further mitochondrial damage. The cysteine sulfhydryl groups and other amino acid residues on proteins are oxidized and degraded. Nuclear and mitochondrial DNA can be oxidized, resulting in strand breaks and other types of damage. RNOS (NO, NO_2, and peroxynitrite) have similar effects.

A. Membrane Attack: Formation of Lipid and Lipid Peroxy Radicals

Chain reactions that form lipid free radicals and lipid peroxides in membranes make a major contribution to ROS-induced injury (Fig. 24.8). An initiator (such as a hydroxyl radical produced locally in the Fenton reaction) begins the chain reaction. It extracts a hydrogen atom, preferably from the double bond of a polyunsaturated fatty acid in a membrane lipid. The chain reaction is propagated when O_2 adds to form lipid peroxyl radicals and lipid peroxides. Eventually, lipid degradation occurs, forming such products as malondialdehyde (from fatty acids with three or more double bonds) and ethane and pentane (from the ω-terminal carbons of three- and six-carbon fatty acids, respectively). Malondialdehyde appears in the blood and urine and is used as an indicator of free radical damage.

Peroxidation of lipid molecules invariably changes or damages lipid molecular structure. In addition to the self-destructive nature of membrane lipid peroxidation, the aldehydes that are formed can cross-link proteins. When the damaged lipids are the constituents of biologic membranes, the cohesive lipid bilayer arrangement and stable structural organization is disrupted (see Fig. 24.7). Disruption of mitochondrial membrane integrity may result in further free radical production.

B. Proteins and Peptides

In proteins, the amino acids proline, histidine, arginine, cysteine, and methionine are particularly susceptible to hydroxyl-radical attack and oxidative damage. As a consequence of oxidative damage, the protein may fragment or residues cross-link with other residues. Free radical attack on protein cysteine residues can result in cross-linking and formation of aggregates that prevents their degradation. However, oxidative damage increases the susceptibility of other proteins to proteolytic digestion.

Free radical attack and oxidation of the cysteine sulfhydryl residues of the tripeptide glutathione (γ-glutamylcysteinylglycine; see Section V.A.3) increases oxidative damage throughout the cell. Glutathione is a major component of cellular defense against free radical injury, and its oxidation reduces its protective effects.

 Evidence of protein damage shows up in many diseases, particularly those associated with aging. In patients with cataracts, proteins in the lens of the eye exhibit free radical damage and contain methionine sulfoxide residues and tryptophan degradation products.

FIG. 24.8. Lipid peroxidation: a free radical chain reaction. **A.** Lipid peroxidation is initiated by a hydroxyl or other radical that extracts a hydrogen atom from a polyunsaturated lipid (*LH*), thereby forming a lipid radical (*L•*). **B.** The free radical chain reaction is propagated by reaction with O_2, forming the lipid peroxy radical (*LOO•*) and lipid peroxide (*LOOH*). **C.** Rearrangements of the single electron result in degradation of the lipid. Malondialdehyde, one of the compounds formed, is soluble and appears in blood. **D.** The chain reaction can be terminated by reduced vitamin E and other lipid-soluble antioxidants that donate single electrons. Two subsequent reduction steps form a stable, oxidized antioxidant.

Guanine

•OH

8-Hydroxyguanine

FIG. 24.9. Conversion of guanine to 8-hydroxy-guanine by the hydroxy radical. The amount of 8-hydroxyguanosine present in cells can be used to estimate the amount of oxidative damage they have sustained. The addition of the hydroxyl group to guanine allows it to mispair with A residues at a low frequency, leading to the creation of a daughter molecule with an A–T base pair in this position.

Nitroglycerin, in tablet form, is often given to patients with coronary artery disease who experience ischemia-induced chest pain (angina). The nitroglycerin decomposes in the blood, forming *nitric oxide* (NO), a potent vasodilator, which increases blood flow to the heart and relieves the angina.

Arginine

NADPH

O_2

NO synthase
(Fe-Heme, FAD,
FMN, BH_4)

NO

Nitric oxide

$NADP^+$

Citrulline

FIG. 24.10. Nitric oxide synthase (NOS) synthesizes the free radical NO. Like cyto-chrome P450 enzymes, NOS uses Fe-heme, flavin adenine dinucleotide (FAD), and flavin mononucleotide (FMN) to transfer single electrons from NADPH to O_2. NOS also requires the cofactor tetrahydrobiopterin (BH_4).

C. DNA

Oxygen-derived free radicals are also a major source of DNA damage. Approximately 20 types of oxidatively altered DNA molecules have been identified. The nonspecific binding of Fe^{2+} to DNA facilitates localized production of the hydroxyl radical, which can cause base alterations in the DNA (Fig. 24.9). It also can attack the deoxyribose backbone and cause strand breaks. This DNA damage can be repaired to some extent by the cell (see Chapter 12) or minimized by apoptosis of the cell.

III. NITRIC OXIDE AND REACTIVE NITROGEN–OXYGEN SPECIES

NO is an oxygen-containing free radical that, like O_2, is both essential to life and toxic. NO has a single electron and therefore binds to other compounds that contain single electrons, such as Fe^{3+}. As a gas, NO diffuses through the cytosol and lipid membranes and into cells. At low concentrations, it functions physiologically as a neurotransmitter and as a hormone that causes vasodilation. At high concentrations, however, it combines with O_2 or with superoxide to form additional reactive and toxic species that contain both nitrogen and oxygen (RNOS). RNOS are involved in neurodegenerative diseases, such as Parkinson disease, and in chronic inflammatory diseases, such as rheumatoid arthritis.

A. Nitric Oxide Synthase

At low concentrations, NO serves as a neurotransmitter or as a hormone. It is synthesized from arginine by NO synthases (Fig. 24.10). As a gas, it is able to diffuse through water and lipid membranes and into target cells. In the target cell, it exerts its physiologic effects by high-affinity binding to Fe-heme in the enzyme guanylyl cyclase, thereby activating a signal transduction cascade. However, NO is rapidly inactivated by nonspecific binding to many molecules, and therefore, cells that produce NO need to be close to the target cells.

The body has three different tissue-specific isoforms of NO synthase, each encoded by a different gene: neuronal nitric oxide synthase (nNOS, isoform I), inducible nitric oxide synthase (iNOS, isoform II), and endothelial nitric oxide synthase (eNOS, isoform III). nNOS and eNOS are tightly regulated by Ca^{2+} concentration to produce the small amounts of NO required for its role as a neurotransmitter and hormone. In contrast, iNOS is present in many cells of the immune system and cell types with a similar lineage, such as macrophages and brain astroglia. This isoenzyme of NO synthase is regulated principally by induction of gene transcription and not by changes in Ca^{2+} concentration. It produces high and toxic levels of NO to assist in killing invading microorganisms. It is these very high levels of NO that are associated with generation of RNOS and NO toxicity.

B. Nitric Oxide Toxicity

The toxic actions of NO can be divided into two categories: direct toxic effects resulting from binding to Fe-containing proteins and indirect effects mediated by compounds formed when NO combines with O_2 or with superoxide to form RNOS.

1. DIRECT TOXIC EFFECTS OF NITRIC OXIDE

NO, as a radical, exerts direct toxic effects by combining with Fe-containing compounds that also have single electrons. Major destructive sites of attack include Fe–S centers (e.g., electron-transport chain complexes I through III, aconitase) and Fe-heme proteins (e.g., hemoglobin and electron-transport chain cytochromes). However, there is usually little damage because NO is present in low concentrations and Fe-heme compounds are present in excess capacity. NO can cause serious damage, however, through direct inhibition of respiration in cells that are already compromised through oxidative phosphorylation diseases or ischemia.

2. REACTIVE NITROGEN–OXYGEN SPECIES TOXICITY

When NO is present in very high concentrations (e.g., during inflammation), it combines nonenzymatically with superoxide to form peroxynitrite ($ONOO^-$) or with O_2 to form N_2O_3 (Fig. 24.11). *Peroxynitrite*, although it is not a free radical, is a strong oxidizing agent that is stable and directly toxic. It can diffuse through the cell and lipid membranes to interact with a wide range of targets, including the methionine side chain in proteins and –SH groups (e.g., Fe–S centers in the electron-transport chain). It also breaks down to form additional RNOS, including the free radical *nitrogen dioxide* (NO_2), which is an effective initiator of lipid peroxidation. Peroxynitrite products also react (nitration) with aromatic rings, forming compounds such as nitrotyrosine or nitroguanosine. N_2O_3, which can be derived from either NO_2 or nitrite, is the agent of nitrosative stress, and it nitrosylates sulfhydryl and similarly reactive groups in the cell. Nitrosylation usually interferes with the proper functioning of the protein or lipid that has been modified. Thus, RNOS can do as much oxidative and free radical damage as non–nitrogen-containing ROS as well as nitrating and nitrosylating compounds. The result is widespread and includes inhibition of a large number of enzymes, mitochondrial lipid peroxidation, inhibition of the electron-transport chain and energy depletion, single-stranded or double-stranded breaks in DNA, and modification of bases in DNA.

FIG. 24.11. Formation of RNOS from nitric oxide. RNOS are shown in *red*. The type of damage caused by each RNOS is shown in parentheses. Of all the nitrogen–oxygen-containing compounds shown, only nitrate is relatively nontoxic. NO_2 is one of the toxic agents present in smog, automobile exhaust, gas ranges, pilot lights, cigarette smoke, and smoke from forest fires or burning buildings.

In patients with chronic granulomatous disease, phagocytes have genetic defects in NADPH oxidase. NADPH oxidase, of which there are several isozymes, generally has six different subunits (two in the cell membrane, α and β, which together form flavoprotein b_{558}, and four recruited from the cytosol, which include the small GTPase Rac, as well as a complex of $p47^{phox}$, $p67^{phox}$, and $p40^{phox}$), and the genetic defect may be in any of four of the genes that encode these subunits. The membrane catalytic β-subunit of NADPH oxidase is a 91-kDa flavocytochrome glycoprotein. It transfers electrons from bound NADPH to flavin adenine dinucleotide (FAD), which transfers them to the Fe-heme components. The membranous α-subunit (p22) is required for stabilization. The cytosolic proteins are required for assembly of the complex. The 91-kDa β-subunit is affected most often in X-linked chronic granulatomous disease, whereas the α-subunit is affected in a rare autosomal recessive form. The cytosolic subunits p47 and p67 are affected most often in patients with the autosomal recessive form of granulomatous disease. In addition to their enhanced susceptibility to bacterial and fungal infections, these patients suffer from an apparent dysregulation of normal inflammatory responses.

IV. FORMATION OF FREE RADICALS DURING PHAGOCYTOSIS AND INFLAMMATION

In response to infectious agents and other stimuli, phagocytic cells of the immune system (neutrophils, eosinophils, and monocytes/macrophages) exhibit a rapid consumption of O_2 called the *respiratory burst*. The respiratory burst is a major source of superoxide, H_2O_2, the hydroxyl radical, HOCl, and RNOS. The generation of free radicals is part of the human antimicrobial defense system and is intended to destroy invading microorganisms, tumor cells, and other cells targeted for removal.

A. NADPH Oxidase

The respiratory burst results from the activity of NADPH oxidase, which catalyzes the transfer of an electron from NADPH to O_2 to form superoxide (Fig. 24.12). NADPH oxidase is assembled from cytosolic as well as membranous proteins recruited into the phagolysosome membrane as it surrounds an invading microorganism.

Superoxide is released into the intramembranous space of the phagolysosome, where it is generally converted to H_2O_2 and other ROS that are effective against bacteria and fungal pathogens. H_2O_2 is formed by superoxide dismutase (SOD), which may come from the phagocytic cell or from the invading microorganism.

B. Myeloperoxidase and Hypochlorous Acid

The formation of HOCl from H_2O_2 is catalyzed by *myeloperoxidase*, a heme-containing enzyme that is present only in phagocytic cells of the immune system (predominantly neutrophils). The HOCl rapidly dissociates and loses a proton.

$$\text{Myeloperoxidase} \qquad \text{Dissociation:}$$

$$H_2O_2 + Cl^- + H^+ \rightarrow HOCl + H_2O \rightarrow {}^-OCl + H^+ + H_2O$$

Myeloperoxidase contains two Fe-hemelike centers, which gives it the green color seen in pus. Hypochlorous acid is a powerful toxin that destroys bacteria within seconds through halogenation and oxidation reactions. It oxidizes many

FIG. 24.12. Production of reactive oxygen species during the phagocytic respiratory burst by activated neutrophils. **1.** Activation of NADPH oxidase on the outer side of the plasma membrane initiates the respiratory burst with the generation of superoxide. During phagocytosis, the plasma membrane invaginates, so superoxide is released into the vacuole space. **2.** Superoxide (either spontaneously or enzymatically via SOD) generates H_2O_2. **3.** Granules containing myeloperoxidase are secreted into the phagosome where myeloperoxidase generates HOCl and other halides. **4.** H_2O_2 can also generate the hydroxyl radical from the Fenton reaction. **5.** Inducible nitric oxide synthase may be activated and generate NO. **6.** Nitric oxide combines with superoxide to form peroxynitrite, which may generate additional RNOS. The result is an attack on the membranes and other components of phagocytosed cells and eventual lysis. The whole process is referred to as the respiratory burst because it lasts only 30 to 60 minutes and consumes O_2.

Fe- and S-containing groups (e.g., sulfhydryl groups, Fe–S centers, ferredoxin, heme proteins, methionine), oxidatively decarboxylates and deaminates proteins, and cleaves peptide bonds. Aerobic bacteria under attack rapidly lose membrane transport, possibly because of damage to ATP synthase or electron-transport chain components (which reside in the plasma membrane of bacteria).

C. Reactive Nitrogen–Oxygen Species and Inflammation

When human neutrophils of the immune system are activated to produce NO, NADPH oxidase is also activated. NO reacts rapidly with superoxide to generate peroxynitrite, which forms additional RNOS. NO also may be released into the surrounding medium to combine with superoxide in target cells.

In several disease states, free radical release by neutrophils or macrophages during an inflammation contributes to injury in the surrounding tissues. During stroke or myocardial infarction, phagocytic cells that move into the ischemic area to remove dead cells may increase the area and extent of damage. The self-perpetuating mechanism of radical release by neutrophils during inflammation and immune-complex formation may explain some of the features of chronic inflammation in patients with rheumatoid arthritis. As a result of free radical release, the immunoglobulin G (IgG) proteins present in the synovial fluid are partially oxidized, which improves their binding with the rheumatoid antibody. This binding, in turn, stimulates the neutrophils to release more free radicals.

V. CELLULAR DEFENSES AGAINST OXYGEN TOXICITY

Our defenses against oxygen toxicity fall into the categories of antioxidant defense enzymes, dietary and endogenous antioxidants (free radical scavengers), cellular compartmentation, metal sequestration, and repair of damaged cellular components. The antioxidant defense enzymes react with ROS and cellular products of free radical chain reactions to convert them to nontoxic products. Dietary antioxidants, such as vitamin E and flavonoids, and endogenous antioxidants, such as urate, can terminate free radical chain reactions. Defense through compartmentation refers to separation of species and sites involved in ROS generation from the rest of the cell (Fig. 24.13). For example, many of the enzymes that produce hydrogen peroxide

During **Cora Nari's** myocardial ischemia (decreased blood flow), the ability of her heart to generate ATP from oxidative phosphorylation was compromised. The damage appeared to accelerate when oxygen was first reintroduced (reperfused) into the tissue. During ischemia, coenzyme Q (CoQ) and the other single-electron components of the electron-transport chain become saturated with electrons. When oxygen is reintroduced (reperfusion), electron donation to O_2 to form superoxide is increased. The increase of superoxide results in enhanced formation of hydrogen peroxide and the hydroxyl radical. Macrophages in the area clean up cell debris from ischemic injury and produce nitric oxide, which may further damage mitochondria by generating RNOS that attack Fe–S centers and cytochromes in the electron-transport chain membrane lipids. Thus, the RNOS may increase the infarct size.

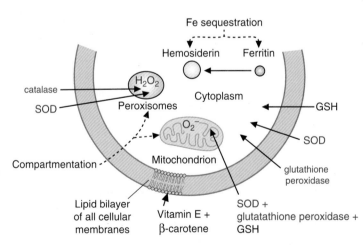

FIG. 24.13. Compartmentization of free radical defenses. Various defenses against ROS are found in the various subcellular compartments of the cell. The location of free radical defense enzymes (shown in *red*) matches the type and amount of ROS generated in each subcellular compartment. The highest activities of these enzymes are found in the liver, adrenal gland, and kidney where mitochondrial and peroxisomal contents are high, and cytochrome P450 enzymes are found in abundance in the smooth endoplasmic reticulum. The enzymes SOD and glutathione peroxidase are present as isozymes in the various compartments. Another form of compartmentization involves the sequestration of Fe, which is stored as mobilizable Fe in ferritin. Excess Fe is stored in nonmobilizable hemosiderin deposits. Glutathione (GSH) is a nonenzymatic antioxidant.

A

B

2 H_2O_2
Hydrogen peroxide

Catalase
(peroxisomes)

2 $H_2O + O_2$

FIG. 24.14. **A.** Superoxide dismutase converts superoxide to hydrogen peroxide, which is non-toxic unless it is converted to other ROS. **B.** Catalase reduces hydrogen peroxide. (ROS is shown in a *yellow box*.)

 The intracellular form of the Cu$^+$–Zn^{2+} superoxide dismutase is encoded by the superoxide dismutase 1 (SOD1) gene. To date, 58 mutations in this gene have been discovered in individuals affected by familial amyotrophic lateral sclerosis (ALS, Lou Gehrig disease). How a mutation in this gene leads to the symptoms of this disease has yet to be understood. It is important to note that only 5% to 10% of the total cases of diagnosed ALS are caused by the familial form. Recent work has indicated that mutations in enzymes involved in RNA processing also lead to familial and sporadic ALS.

are sequestered in peroxisomes with a high content of antioxidant enzymes. Metals are bound to a wide range of proteins within the blood and in cells, preventing their participation in the Fenton reaction. Iron, for example, is tightly bound to its storage protein, ferritin, and cannot react with hydrogen peroxide. Repair mechanisms for DNA and for removal of oxidized fatty acids from membrane lipids are available to the cell. Oxidized amino acids on proteins are continuously repaired through protein degradation and resynthesis of new proteins.

A. Antioxidant Scavenging Enzymes

The enzymatic defense against ROS includes SOD, catalase, and glutathione peroxidase.

1. SUPEROXIDE DISMUTASE

Conversion of superoxide anion to hydrogen peroxide and O_2 (dismutation) by SOD is often called the *primary defense against oxidative stress* because superoxide is such a strong initiator of chain reactions (Fig. 24.14A). SOD exists as three isoenzyme forms: a Cu$^+$–Zn^{2+} form present in the cytosol, a Mn^{2+} form present in mitochondria and a Cu$^+$–Zn^{2+} form found extracellularly. The activity of Cu$^+$–Zn^{2+} SOD is increased by chemicals or conditions (such as hyperbaric oxygen) that increase the production of superoxide.

2. CATALASE

Hydrogen peroxide, once formed, must be reduced to water to prevent it from forming the hydroxyl radical in the Fenton reaction or the Haber-Weiss reaction (see Fig. 24.4). One of the enzymes that is capable of reducing hydrogen peroxide is catalase (see Fig. 24.14B). Catalase is found principally in peroxisomes and, to a lesser extent, in the cytosol and microsomal fraction of the cell. The highest activities are found in tissues with a high peroxisomal content (kidney and liver). In cells of the immune system, catalase serves to protect the cell against its own respiratory burst.

3. GLUTATHIONE PEROXIDASE AND GLUTATHIONE REDUCTASE

Glutathione (γ-glutamylcysteinylglycine) is one of the body's principal means of protecting against oxidative damage (see also Chapter 29). Glutathione is a tripeptide composed of glutamate, cysteine, and glycine, with the amino group of cysteine joined in peptide linkage to the γ-carboxyl group of glutamate (Fig. 24.15). In reactions that are catalyzed by glutathione peroxidases, the reactive sulfhydryl groups reduce hydrogen peroxide to water and lipid peroxides to nontoxic

FIG. 24.15. Glutathione peroxidase reduces hydrogen peroxide to water. **A.** The structure of glutathione. The sulfhydryl group of glutathione, which is oxidized to a disulfide, is shown in *red*. **B.** Glutathione peroxidase transfers electrons from GSH to hydrogen peroxide. **C.** Glutathione redox cycle. Glutathione reductase regenerates reduced glutathione. (ROS is shown in the *yellow box*.)

alcohols. In these reactions, two glutathione molecules are oxidized to form a single molecule, glutathione disulfide. The sulfhydryl groups are also oxidized in nonenzymatic chain-terminating reactions with organic radicals.

Glutathione peroxidases exist as a family of selenium enzymes with somewhat different properties and tissue locations. Within cells, they are found principally in the cytosol and mitochondria and are the major means for removing H_2O_2 produced outside of peroxisomes. They contribute to our dietary requirement for selenium and account for the protective effect of selenium in the prevention of free radical injury.

Once oxidized glutathione (GSSG) is formed, it must be reduced back to the sulfhydryl form by glutathione reductase in a redox cycle (see Fig. 24.15C). Glutathione reductase contains a flavin adenine dinucleotide (FAD) and catalyzes transfer of electrons from NADPH to the disulfide bond of GSSG. NADPH is thus essential for protection against free radical injury. The major source of NADPH for this reaction is the pentose phosphate pathway (see Chapter 29).

B. Nonenzymatic Antioxidants (Free Radical Scavengers)

Free radical scavengers convert free radicals to a nonradical, nontoxic form in nonenzymatic reactions. Most free radical scavengers are antioxidants, compounds that neutralize free radicals by donating a hydrogen atom (with its one electron) to the radical. Antioxidants therefore reduce free radicals and are themselves oxidized in the reaction. Dietary free radical scavengers (e.g., vitamin E, ascorbic acid, carotenoids, flavonoids) as well as endogenously produced free radical scavengers (e.g., urate, melatonin) have a common structural feature, a conjugated double bond system that may be an aromatic ring.

1. VITAMIN E

Vitamin E (α-tocopherol), the most widely distributed antioxidant in nature, is a lipid-soluble antioxidant vitamin that functions principally to protect against lipid peroxidation in membranes (see Fig. 24.13). Vitamin E comprises several tocopherols that differ in their methylation pattern. Among these, α-tocopherol is the most potent antioxidant and is present in the largest amounts in our diet (Fig. 24.16).

Vitamin E is an efficient antioxidant and nonenzymatic terminator of free radical chain reactions, and it has little pro-oxidant activity. When vitamin E donates an electron to a lipid peroxy radical, it is converted to a free radical form that is stabilized by resonance. If this free radical form were to act as a pro-oxidant and abstract an electron from a polyunsaturated lipid, it would be oxidizing that lipid and actually propagate the free radical chain reaction. The chemistry of vitamin E is such that it has a much greater tendency to donate a second electron and go to the fully oxidized form.

2. ASCORBIC ACID

Although ascorbate (vitamin C) is an oxidation–reduction coenzyme that functions in collagen synthesis and other reactions, it also plays a role in free radical defense. Reduced ascorbate can regenerate the reduced form of vitamin E by donating electrons in a redox cycle (Fig. 24.17). It is water-soluble and circulates unbound in blood and extracellular fluid, where it has access to the lipid-soluble vitamin E present in membranes and lipoprotein particles.

3. CAROTENOIDS

Carotenoids is a term applied to β-carotene (the precursor of vitamin A) and similar compounds with functional oxygen-containing substituents on the rings, such as zeaxanthin and lutein (Fig. 24.18). These compounds can exert antioxidant effects as well as quench singlet O_2 (*singlet oxygen* is a highly ROS in which there are no unpaired electrons in the outer orbitals, but there is one orbital that is completely empty). Epidemiologic studies have shown a correlation between diets that are high in fruits and vegetables and health benefits, leading to the hypothesis that

Q: Why does the cell need a high content of SOD in mitochondria?

Premature infants with low levels of lung surfactant (see Chapter 33) require oxygen therapy. The level of oxygen must be closely monitored to prevent ROS-induced retinopathy and subsequent blindness (the retinopathy of prematurity) and to prevent bronchial pulmonary dysplasia. The tendency for these complications to develop is enhanced by the possibility of low levels of SOD and vitamin E in the premature infant.

Selenium (Se) is present in human proteins principally as selenocysteine (cysteine with the sulfur group replaced by Se, abbreviated sec). This amino acid functions in catalysis and has been found in 11 or more human enzymes, including the 4 enzymes of the glutathione peroxidase family. Selenium is supplied in the diet as selenomethionine from plants (methionine with the Se replacing the sulfur), selenocysteine from animal foods, and inorganic selenium. Se from all of these sources can be converted to selenophosphate. Selenophosphate reacts with a unique tRNA-containing bound serine to form a selenocysteine-tRNA, which incorporates selenocysteine into the appropriate protein as it is being synthesized. Se homeostasis in the body is controlled principally through regulation of its secretion as methylated Se. The current dietary requirement is approximately 70 μg/day for adult males and 55 μg/day for females. Deficiency symptoms reflect diminished antioxidant defenses and include symptoms of vitamin E deficiency.

Mitochondria are major sites for generation of superoxide from the interaction of CoQ and O_2. The Mn^{2+} superoxide dismutase present in mitochondria is not regulated through induction/repression of gene transcription, presumably because the rate of superoxide generation is always high. Mitochondria also have a high content of glutathione and glutathione peroxidase, and can thus convert H_2O_2 to H_2O and prevent lipid peroxidation.

Vitamin E is found in the diet in the lipid fractions of some vegetable oils and in liver, egg yolks, and cereals. It is absorbed together with lipids, and fat malabsorption results in symptomatic deficiencies. Vitamin E circulates in the blood in lipoprotein particles. Its deficiency causes neurologic symptoms, probably because the polyunsaturated lipids in myelin and other membranes of the nervous system are particularly sensitive to free radical injury. Epidemiologic evidence suggests that individuals with a higher intake of foods containing vitamin E, β-carotene, and vitamin C have a somewhat lower risk of cancer and certain other ROS-related diseases than do individuals on diets that are deficient in these vitamins. However, studies in which well-nourished populations were given supplements of these antioxidant vitamins found either no effects or harmful effects compared with the beneficial effects from eating foods containing a wide variety of antioxidant compounds. Of the pure chemical supplements tested, there is evidence only for the efficacy of vitamin E. In two clinical trials, β-carotene (or β-carotene + vitamin A) was associated with a higher incidence of lung cancer among smokers and higher mortality rates. In one study, vitamin E intake was associated with a higher incidence of hemorrhagic stroke (possibly because of vitamin K mimicry).

FIG. 24.16. Vitamin E (α-tocopherol) terminates free radical lipid peroxidation by donating single electrons to lipid peroxyl radicals (LOO•) to form the more stable lipid peroxide, LOOH. In so doing, the α-tocopherol is converted to the fully oxidized tocopheryl quinone.

FIG. 24.17. L-Ascorbate (the reduced form) donates single electrons to free radicals or disulfides in two steps as it is oxidized to dehydro-L-ascorbic acid. Its principal role in free radical defense is probably regeneration of vitamin E. However, it also may react with superoxide, hydrogen peroxide, hypochlorite, the hydroxyl and peroxyl radicals, and NO_2.

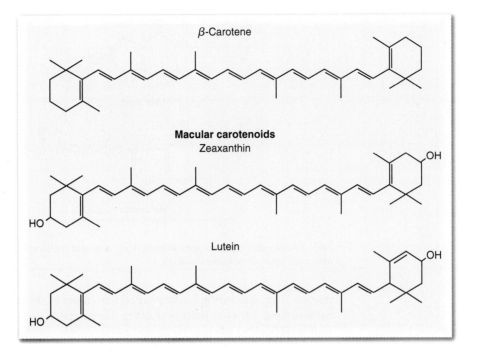

FIG. 24.18.   Carotenoids are compounds related in structure to β-carotene. Lutein and zeaxanthin (the macular carotenoids) are analogs that contain hydroxyl groups.

carotenoids might slow the progression of cancer, atherosclerosis, and other degenerative diseases by acting as chain-breaking antioxidants. However, in clinical trials, β-carotene supplements had either no effect or an undesirable effect. Its ineffectiveness may be caused by the pro-oxidant activity of the free radical form.

In contrast, epidemiologic studies relating the intake of lutein and zeaxanthin with decreased incidence of age-related macular degeneration have received progressive support. These two carotenoids are concentrated in the macula (the central portion of the retina) and are called the *macular carotenoids*.

4.   OTHER DIETARY ANTIOXIDANTS

Flavonoids are a group of structurally similar compounds that contain two spatially separate aromatic rings and are found in red wine, green tea, chocolate, and other plant-derived foods (Fig. 24.19). Flavonoids have been hypothesized to contribute to our free radical defenses in several ways. Some flavonoids inhibit enzymes responsible for superoxide anion production, such as xanthine oxidase. Others efficiently chelate Fe and Cu, making it impossible for these metals to participate in the Fenton

A flavonoid

FIG. 24.19.   The flavonoid quercetin. All flavonoids have the same ring structure, shown in *red*. They differ in ring substituents (=O, –OH, and –OCH₃). Quercetin is effective in Fe chelation and antioxidant activity. It is widely distributed in fruits (principally in the skins) and in vegetables (e.g., onions).

Age-related macular degeneration (AMD) is the leading cause of blindness in the United States among persons older than 50 years of age, and it affects 1.7 million people worldwide. In AMD, visual loss is related to oxidative damage to the retinal pigment epithelium (RPE) and the choriocapillaris epithelium. The photoreceptor/retinal pigment complex is exposed to sunlight, it is bathed in near-arterial levels of oxygen, and the membranes contain high concentrations of polyunsaturated fatty acids, all of which are conducive to oxidative damage. Lipofuscin granules, which accumulate in the RPE throughout life, may serve as photosensitizers, initiating damage by absorbing blue light and generating singlet oxygen (an energetically excited form of oxygen) that forms other radicals. Dark sunglasses are protective. Epidemiologic studies showed that the intake of lutein and zeaxanthin in dark green leafy vegetables (e.g., spinach, collard greens) also may be protective. Lutein and zeaxanthin accumulate in the macula and protect against free radical damage by absorbing blue light and quenching singlet oxygen.

FIG. 24.20. Endogenous antioxidants. Uric acid and melatonin both act to successively neutralize several molecules of ROS.

FIG. 24.21. A model for the role of ROS and RNOS in neuronal degradation in Parkinson disease. **1.** Dopamine levels are reduced by monoamine oxidase, which generates H_2O_2. **2.** Superoxide also can be produced by mitochondria, which superoxide dismutase (SOD) will convert to H_2O_2. Iron levels increase, which allows the Fenton reaction to proceed, generating hydroxyl radicals. **3.** NO, produced by inducible nitric oxide synthase, reacts with superoxide to form RNOS. **4.** The RNOS and hydroxyl radical lead to radical chain reactions that result in lipid peroxidation, protein oxidation, the formation of lipofuscin, and neuronal degeneration. The end result is a reduced production and release of dopamine, which leads to the clinical symptoms observed.

reaction. They also may act as free radical scavengers by donating electrons to superoxide or lipid peroxy radicals or stabilize free radicals by complexing with them.

It is difficult to tell how much dietary flavonoids contribute to our free radical defense system; they have a high pro-oxidant activity and are poorly absorbed. Nonetheless, we generally consume large amounts of flavonoids (approximately 800 mg/day), and there is evidence that they can contribute to the maintenance of vitamin E as an antioxidant.

5. ENDOGENOUS ANTIOXIDANTS

Several compounds that are synthesized endogenously for other functions, or as urinary excretion products, also function nonenzymatically as free radical antioxidants. Uric acid is formed from the degradation of purines and is released into extracellular fluids, including blood, saliva, and lung lining fluid (Fig. 24.20). Together with protein thiols, it accounts for the major free radical–trapping capacity of plasma. It is particularly important in the upper airways where there are few other antioxidants. It can directly scavenge hydroxyl radicals, oxyheme oxidants formed between the reaction of hemoglobin and peroxy radicals, and peroxyl radicals themselves. Having acted as a scavenger, uric acid produces a range of oxidation products that are subsequently excreted.

Melatonin, which is a secretory product of the pineal gland, is a neurohormone that functions in regulation of our circadian rhythm, light–dark signal transduction, and sleep induction. In addition to these receptor-mediated functions, it functions as a nonenzymatic free radical scavenger that donates an electron (as hydrogen) to "neutralize" free radicals. It also can react with ROS and RNOS to form additional products, thereby undergoing suicidal transformations. Its effectiveness is related to both its lack of pro-oxidant activity and its joint hydrophilic/hydrophobic nature, which allows it to pass through membranes and the blood–brain barrier.

CLINICAL COMMENTS

 Les Dopaman has "primary" parkinsonism. The pathogenesis of this disease is not well established and may be multifactorial (Fig. 24.21). Recent work has identified several genes, which, when mutated and inactive, lead to rare familial Parkinson disease. The major clinical disturbances in Parkinson disease are a result of dopamine depletion in the neostriatum, resulting from degeneration of dopaminergic neurons whose cell bodies reside in the substantia nigra pars compacta. The decrease in dopamine production is the result of severe degeneration of these nigrostriatal neurons. Although the agent that initiates the disease is unknown, various studies support a role for free radicals in Parkinson disease (mitochondrial dysfunction), along with alterations in the ubiquitin–proteasome pathway of protein degradation. Within these neurons, dopamine turnover is increased, dopamine levels are lower, glutathione is decreased, and lipofuscin (Lewy bodies) is increased. Iron levels are higher, and ferritin, the storage form of iron, is lower. Furthermore, the disease is mimicked by the compound 1-methyl-4-phenylpyridinium (MPP^+), an inhibitor of NADH:CoQ oxidoreductase that increases superoxide production in these neurons and decreases ATP production. Analysis of mitochondria from patients with Parkinson disease indicates a 30% to 40% reduction in complex I activity. The reduced ATP levels may affect the ubiquitin–proteasome pathway negatively, reducing protein degradation and linking these two pathways, which can lead to Parkinson disease. Even so, it is not known whether oxidative stress makes a primary or secondary contribution to the disease process.

Drug therapy is based on the severity of the disease. Several options are available. In the early phases of the disease, a monoamine oxidase B inhibitor can be used that inhibits dopamine degradation and decreases hydrogen peroxide formation. In later stages of the disease, patients are treated with levodopa (L-dopa), a precursor of dopamine, sometimes in combination with the monoamine oxidase B inhibitor.

 Cora Nari experienced angina caused by severe ischemia in the ventricular muscle of her heart. The ischemia was caused by clots that formed at the site of atherosclerotic plaques within the lumen of the coronary arteries. When tissue plasminogen activator (TPA) was infused to dissolve the clots, the ischemic area of her heart was reperfused with oxygenated blood, resulting in ischemia-reperfusion injury. In her case, the reperfusion injury resulted in ventricular fibrillation.

During ischemia, several events occur simultaneously in cardiomyocytes. A decreased O_2 supply results in decreased ATP generation from mitochondrial oxidative phosphorylation and inhibition of cardiac muscle contraction. As a consequence, cytosolic adenosine monophosphate (AMP) concentration increases, activating anaerobic glycolysis and lactic acid production. If ATP levels are inadequate to maintain Na^+,K^+-ATPase activity, intracellular Na^+ increases, resulting in cellular swelling, a further increase in H^+ concentration, and increases of cytosolic and subsequently mitochondrial Ca^{2+} levels. The decrease in ATP and increase in Ca^{2+} may open the mitochondrial permeability transition pore, resulting in permanent inhibition of oxidative phosphorylation. Damage to lipid membranes is further enhanced by Ca^{2+} activation of phospholipases.

Reperfusion with O_2 allows recovery of oxidative phosphorylation, provided that the mitochondrial membrane has maintained some integrity and the mitochondrial transition pore can close. However, it also increases generation of free radicals. The transfer of electrons from CoQ• to O_2 to generate superoxide is increased. Endothelial production of superoxide by xanthine oxidase also may increase. These radicals may go on to form the hydroxyl radical, which can enhance the damage to components of the electron-transport chain and mitochondrial lipids, as well as activate the mitochondrial permeability transition. As macrophages move into the area to clean up cellular debris, they may generate NO and superoxide, thus introducing peroxynitrite and other free radicals into the area. Depending on the route and timing involved, the acute results may be cell death through necrosis, with slower cell death through apoptosis in the surrounding tissue.

Currently, an intense study of ischemic insults to various animal organs is underway in an effort to discover ways of preventing reperfusion injury. These include methods designed to increase endogenous antioxidant activity, to reduce the generation of free radicals, and, finally, to develop exogenous antioxidants that, when administered before reperfusion, would prevent its injurious effects.

Preconditioning tissues to hypoxia is also a viable option to reducing reperfusion injury. Each of these approaches has met with some success, but their clinical application awaits further refinement. With the growing number of invasive procedures aimed at restoring arterial blood flow through partially obstructed coronary vessels, such as clot lysis, balloon or laser angioplasty, and coronary artery bypass grafting, development of methods to prevent ischemia-reperfusion injury will become increasingly urgent.

In **Cora Nari's** case, oxygen was restored before permanent impairment of oxidative phosphorylation had occurred and the stage of irreversible injury was reached. However, reintroduction of oxygen did induce ventricular fibrillation, from which she recovered.

BIOCHEMICAL COMMENTS

Protection against Ozone in Lung Lining Fluid. The *lung lining fluid*, a thin fluid layer extending from the nasal cavity to the most distal lung alveoli, protects the epithelial cells lining our airways from ozone and other pollutants. Although ozone is not a radical species, many of its toxic effects are mediated through generation of the classical reactive oxygen species (ROS), as well as generation of aldehydes and ozonides. Polyunsaturated fatty acids represent the primary target for ozone, and peroxidation of membrane lipids is the most important mechanism of ozone-induced injury. However, ozone also oxidizes proteins. Although most individuals are able to protect against small amounts of ozone in the atmosphere, even slightly elevated ozone concentrations produce respiratory symptoms in 10% to 20% of the healthy population.

The lung lining fluid has two phases: a gel phase that traps microorganisms and large particles and a soluble phase containing various ROS defense mechanisms that prevent pollutants from reaching the underlying lung epithelial cells (Fig. 24.22). When the ozone level of inspired air is low, ozone is neutralized principally by uric acid (UA) present in the fluid lining the nasal cavity. In the proximal and distal regions of the respiratory tract, glutathione (GSH) and

FIG. 24.22. Protection against ozone in the lung lining fluid. *GSH*, glutathione; *AA*, ascorbic acid (vitamin C); *UA*, uric acid; *CHO*, carbohydrate; α-*TOC*, vitamin E; *GSH-Px*, glutathione peroxidase; *EC-SOD*, extracellular superoxide dismutase.

ascorbic acid (AA), in addition to UA, react directly with ozone. Ozone that escapes this antioxidant screen may react directly with proteins, lipids, and carbohydrates (CHO–) to generate secondary oxidants, such as lipid peroxides, that can initiate chain reactions. A second layer of defense protects against these oxidation and peroxidation products: α-tocopherol (vitamin E) and glutathione react directly with lipid radicals, glutathione peroxidase reacts with hydrogen peroxide and lipid peroxides, and extracellular superoxide dismutase (EC-SOD) converts superoxide to hydrogen peroxide. However, oxidative stress may still overwhelm even this extensive defense network because ozone also promotes neutrophil migration into the lung lining fluid. Once they are activated, the neutrophils produce a second wave of ROS (superoxide, hypochlorous acid [HOCl], and nitric oxide [NO]), which can lead to oxidative damage of the epithelial cells lining the lung.

Key Concepts

- Oxygen radical generation contributes to cellular death and degeneration in various diseases.
- Radical damage occurs via electron extraction from a biologic molecule, creating a chain reaction of radical propagation.
- Reactive oxygen species (ROS) include superoxide, hydrogen peroxide, and the hydroxyl radical.
- ROS can be produced either enzymatically or nonenzymatically.
- ROS cause damage by oxidatively damaging DNA, proteins, and lipids, leading to mutations and cell death.
- Other radical species include nitric oxide (NO) and hypochlorous acid (HOCl).
- NO reacts with oxygen or superoxide to form a family of reactive nitrogen–oxygen species (RNOS).
- The immune response normally produces radical species (superoxide, HOCl, NO) to destroy invading microorganisms. Escape of radicals from the immune cells during this protective event can damage surrounding tissues.
- Cellular defense mechanisms against radical damage include defense enzymes, antioxidants, and compartmentalization of free radicals.
- Cellular defense enzymes include superoxide dismutase, catalase, and glutathione peroxidase.
- Antioxidants include vitamins E and C and plant flavonoids.
- Diseases discussed in this chapter are summarized in Table 24.3.

Table 24.3   Diseases Discussed in Chapter 24

Disease or Disorder	Environmental or Genetic	Comments
Free radical disease	Both	Damage caused to proteins and lipids caused by free radical generation may lead to cellular dysfunction.
Parkinson disease	Environmental	Inability to convert tyrosine to DOPA; DOPA treatment can temporarily reverse tremors and other symptoms.
Myocardial infarction	Both	Further damage to the heart muscle can occur because of free radical generation after oxygen is reintroduced to the cells, which were temporarily ischemic, a process known as *ischemic reperfusion injury*.
Chronic granulomatous disease	Genetic	This disorder occurs because of a reduced activity of NADPH oxidase, leading to a reduction in the oxidative burst by neutrophils, coupled with a dysregulated immune response to bacteria and fungi.
Respiratory distress syndrome	Both	Either mutations in surfactant or lack of surfactant production in newborns; lungs have difficulty inflating and compressing.
Amyotrophic lateral sclerosis (ALS)	Both	The genetic form of ALS is caused by mutations in superoxide dismutase, leading to difficulty in disposing of superoxide radicals, leading to cell damage caused by excessive ROS.
Age-related macular degeneration	Both	Oxidative damage occurs in the retinal pigment epithelium, leading to first, reduced vision, and second, to blindness.

REVIEW QUESTIONS—CHAPTER 24

1. Which of the following vitamins or enzymes is unable to protect against free radical damage?

    A. β-Carotene
    B. Glutathione peroxidase
    C. Superoxide dismutase
    D. Vitamin B_6
    E. Vitamin C
    F. Vitamin E

2. Superoxide dismutase catalyzes which of the following reactions?

    A. $O_2^- + e^- + 2H+ \rightarrow H_2O_2$
    B. $2O_2^- + 2H^+ \rightarrow H_2O_2 + O_2$
    C. $O_2^- + HO\bullet + H+ \rightarrow CO_2 + H_2O$
    D. $H_2O_2 + O_2 \rightarrow 4H_2O$
    E. $O_2^- + H_2O_2 + H+ \rightarrow 2H_2O + O_2$

3. The mechanism of vitamin E as an antioxidant is best described by which of the following?

    A. Vitamin E binds to free radicals and sequesters them from the contents of the cell.
    B. Vitamin E participates in the oxidation of the radicals.
    C. Vitamin E participates in the reduction of the radicals.
    D. Vitamin E forms a covalent bond with the radicals, thereby stabilizing the radical state.
    E. Vitamin E inhibits enzymes that produce free radicals.

4. An accumulation of hydrogen peroxide in a cellular compartment can be converted to dangerous radical forms in the presence of which metal?

    A. Selenium
    B. Iron
    C. Manganese
    D. Magnesium
    E. Molybdenum

5. The level of oxidative damage to mitochondrial DNA is ten times greater than that to nuclear DNA. This could be caused, in part, by which of the following?

    A. Superoxide dismutase is present in the mitochondria.
    B. The nucleus lacks glutathione.
    C. The nuclear membrane presents a barrier to reactive oxygen species.
    D. The mitochondrial membrane is permeable to reactive oxygen species.
    E. Mitochondrial DNA lacks histones.

Metabolism of Ethanol

Ethanol is a *dietary fuel* that is metabolized to acetate principally in the liver with the generation of NADH. The principal route for metabolism of ethanol is through hepatic *alcohol dehydrogenases* (ADHs), which oxidize ethanol to *acetaldehyde* in the cytosol (Fig. 25.1). Acetaldehyde is further oxidized by *acetaldehyde dehydrogenases* to *acetate*, principally in *mitochondria*. Acetaldehyde, which is toxic, also may enter the blood. *NADH* produced by these reactions is used for adenosine triphosphate (ATP) generation through oxidative phosphorylation. Most of the acetate enters the blood and is taken up by skeletal muscles and other tissues, where it is activated to *acetyl coenzyme A* (*acetyl-CoA*) and is oxidized in the tricarboxylic acid (TCA) cycle.

Approximately 10% to 20% of ingested ethanol is oxidized through a microsomal ethanol oxidizing system (*MEOS*), comprising *cytochrome P450* enzymes in the endoplasmic reticulum (especially *CYP2E1*). CYP2E1 has a high K_m for ethanol and is inducible by ethanol. Therefore, the proportion of ethanol metabolized through this route is greater at high ethanol concentrations and greater after chronic consumption of ethanol.

Acute effects of alcohol ingestion arise principally from the generation of NADH, which greatly increases the *NADH/NAD$^+$* ratio of the liver. As a consequence, *fatty acid oxidation is inhibited*, and *ketogenesis* may occur. The elevated *NADH/NAD$^+$* ratio may also cause *lactic acidosis* and inhibit *gluconeogenesis*.

Ethanol metabolism may result in *alchohol-induced liver disease*, including *hepatic steatosis* (fatty liver), *alcohol-induced hepatitis*, and *cirrhosis*. The principal toxic products of ethanol metabolism include *acetaldehyde* and *free radicals*. Acetaldehyde forms *adducts* with proteins and other compounds. The *hydroxyethyl radical* produced by the MEOS and other radicals produced during inflammation cause irreversible damage to the liver. Many other tissues are adversely affected by ethanol, acetaldehyde, or by the consequences of *hepatic dysmetabolism* and injury. *Genetic polymorphisms* in the enzymes of ethanol metabolism may be responsible for individual variations in the development of alcoholism or the development of liver cirrhosis.

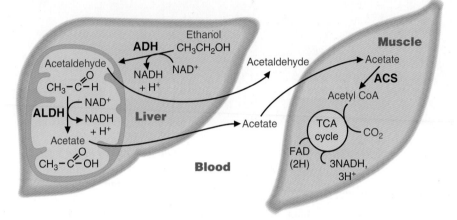

FIG. 25.1. The major route for metabolism of ethanol and use of acetate by the muscle. *ADH*, alcohol dehydrogenase; *ALDH*, acetaldehyde dehydrogenase; *ACS*, acetyl-CoA synthetase.

THE WAITING ROOM

A dietary history for **Ivan Applebod** showed that he had continued his habit of drinking scotch and soda each evening while watching TV, but he did not add the ethanol calories to his dietary intake. He justifies this calculation on the basis of a comment he heard on a radio program that calories from alcohol ingestion "don't count" because they are empty calories that do not cause weight gain.

Al Martini was found lying semiconscious at the bottom of the stairs by his landlady when she returned from an overnight visit with friends. His face had multiple bruises and his right forearm was grotesquely angulated. Nonbloody dried vomitus stained his clothing. Mr. Martini was rushed by ambulance to the emergency room at the nearest hospital. In addition to multiple bruises and the compound fracture of his right forearm, he had deep and rapid (Kussmaul) respirations and was moderately dehydrated.

Initial laboratory studies showed a relatively large anion gap of 34 mmol/L (reference range, 9 to 15 mmol/L). An arterial blood gas analysis (which measures pH in addition to the levels of dissolved O_2 and CO_2) confirmed the presence of a metabolic acidosis. Mr. Martini's blood alcohol level was only slightly elevated. His serum glucose was 68 mg/dL (low normal).

 Jean Ann Tonich, a 46-year-old commercial artist, recently lost her job because of absenteeism. Her husband of 24 years had left her 10 months earlier. She complains of loss of appetite, fatigue, muscle weakness, and emotional depression. She has had occasional pain in the area of her liver, at times accompanied by nausea and vomiting.

On physical examination, she appears disheveled and pale. The physician notes tenderness to light percussion over her liver and detects a small amount of ascites (fluid within the peritoneal cavity around the abdominal organs). The lower edge of her liver is palpable about 2 in below the lower margin of her right rib cage, suggesting liver enlargement. The edge feels somewhat more firm and nodular than normal. Jean Ann's spleen is not palpably enlarged. There is a suggestion of mild

The anion gap is calculated by subtracting the sum of the value for serum chloride and for the serum HCO_3^- content from the serum sodium concentration. If the gap is greater than normal, it suggests that acids such as the ketone bodies acetoacetate and β-hydroxybutyrate are present in the blood in increased amounts.

jaundice (yellow discoloration of her skin and mucus membranes). No obvious neurologic or cognitive abnormalities are present.

After detecting a hint of alcohol on Jean Ann's breath, the physician questions her about possible alcohol abuse, which she denies. With more intensive questioning, however, Jean Ann admits that for the last 5 or 6 years, she has been drinking gin on a daily basis (approximately 4 to 5 drinks or 68 to 85 g ethanol) and eating infrequently. Laboratory tests showed that her serum ethanol level on the initial office visit was 245 mg/dL (0.245%). A serum ethanol level >150 mg/dL (0.15%) is considered indicative of inebriation.

I. ETHANOL METABOLISM

Ethanol is a small molecule that is both lipid- and water-soluble. It is therefore readily absorbed from the intestine by passive diffusion. A small percentage of ingested ethanol (0% to 5%) enters the gastric mucosal cells of the upper gastrointestinal (GI) tract (tongue, mouth, esophagus, and stomach), where it is metabolized. The remainder enters the blood. Of this, 85% to 98% is metabolized in the liver, and only 2% to 10% is excreted through the lungs or kidneys.

The major route of ethanol metabolism in the liver is through liver alcohol dehydrogenase (ADH), a cytosolic enzyme that oxidizes ethanol to acetaldehyde with reduction of NAD^+ to NADH (Fig. 25.2). If it is not removed by metabolism, acetaldehyde exerts toxic actions in the liver and can enter the blood and exert toxic effects in other tissues.

Approximately 90% of the acetaldehyde that is generated is further metabolized to acetate in the liver. The major enzyme involved is a low K_m mitochondrial acetaldehyde dehydrogenase (ALDH), which oxidizes acetaldehyde to acetate with generation of NADH (see Fig. 25.2). Acetate, which has no toxic effects, may be activated to acetyl coenzyme A (acetyl-CoA) in the liver (where it can enter either the tricarboxylic acid [TCA] cycle or the pathway for fatty acid synthesis). However, most of the acetate that is generated enters the blood and is activated to acetyl-CoA in skeletal muscles and other tissues (see Fig. 25.1). Acetate is generally considered nontoxic and is a normal constituent of the diet.

The other principal route of ethanol oxidation in the liver is the microsomal ethanol oxidizing system (MEOS), which also oxidizes ethanol to acetaldehyde (Fig. 25.3). The principal microsomal enzyme involved is a cytochrome P450 mixed-function oxidase isozyme (CYP2E1), which uses NADPH as an additional electron donor and O_2 as an electron acceptor. This route accounts for only 10% to 20% of ethanol oxidation in a moderate drinker.

Each of the enzymes involved in ethanol metabolism (ADH, ALDH, and CYP2E1) exists as a family of isoenzymes. Individual variations in the quantity of these isoenzymes influence several factors such as the rate of ethanol clearance from the blood, the degree of inebriation exhibited by an individual, and differences in individual susceptibility to the development of alcohol-induced liver disease.

A. Alcohol Dehydrogenase

ADH exists as a family of isoenzymes with varying specificity for chain length of the alcohol substrate (Table 25.1). *Ethanol* is a small molecule that does not exhibit much in the way of unique structural characteristics and, at high concentrations, is nonspecifically metabolized by many members of the ADH family. The ADHs that exhibit the highest specificity for ethanol are members of the *ADH1* family. We have three genes for this family of ADHs, each of which exists as allelic variants (polymorphisms).

The *ADH1* alcohol dehydrogenases are present in high quantities in the liver, representing approximately 3% of all soluble protein. These ADHs, commonly referred

Jaundice is a yellow discoloration involving the sclerae (the "whites" of the eyes) and skin. It is caused by the deposition of *bilirubin*, a yellow degradation product of heme. Bilirubin accumulates in the blood under conditions of liver injury, bile duct obstruction, and excessive degradation of heme.

Jean Ann Tonich's admitted ethanol consumption exceeds the definition of moderate drinking. Moderate drinking is now defined as not more than two drinks per day for men, but only one drink per day for women. A drink is defined as 12 oz of regular beer, 5 oz of wine, or 1.5 oz distilled spirits (80 proof).

FIG. 25.2. The pathway of ethanol metabolism. *ADH*, alcohol dehydrogenase; *ALDH*, acetaldehyde dehydrogenase.

FIG. 25.3. The reaction catalyzed by the *MEOS* (which includes CYP2E1) in the endoplasmic reticulum (*ER*).

Table 25.1 Major Isozymes of Medium-Chain-Length Alcohol Dehydrogenases

Gene	Subunit	Tissue Distribution	Properties
ADH1A	α	Most abundant in liver and adrenal glands. Much lower levels in kidney, lung, colon, small intestine, eye, ovary, blood vessels. None in brain or heart.	K_m of 0.02 to 5 mM for ethanol. Active only with ethanol. High tissue capacity.
ADH1B	β		
ADH1C	γ		
ADH2	π	Primarily liver, lower levels in GI tract.	K_m of 23 mM for ethanol.
ADH3	χ	Ubiquitously expressed, but at higher levels in liver. The only isozyme present in germinal cells.	Relatively inactive toward ethanol (K_m = 3400 mM). Active mainly toward long-chain alcohols, and ω-OH fatty acids.
ADH4	σ	Present in highest levels in upper GI tract, gingiva and mouth, esophagus, down to the stomach. Not present in liver.	K_m of 58 mM. It is the most active of medium-chain alcohol dehydrogenases toward the substrate retinal.

GI, gastrointestinal.

to collectively as *liver alcohol dehydrogenase*, have a low K_m for ethanol between 0.02 and 5 mM (high affinities). Thus, the liver is the major site of ethanol metabolism and the major site at which the toxic metabolite acetaldehyde is generated.

Although the *ADH4* and *ADH2* enzymes make minor contributions to ethanol metabolism, they may contribute to its toxic effects. Ethanol concentrations can be quite high in the upper GI tract (e.g., beer is approximately 0.8 M ethanol), and acetaldehyde generated here by *ADH4* enzymes (gastric ADH) might contribute to the risk for cancer associated with heavy drinking. Class II ADH genes are expressed primarily in the liver and at lower levels in the lower GI tract.

The human has at least seven and possibly more genes that code for specific isoenzymes of medium-chain-length ADHs, the major enzyme responsible for the oxidation of ethanol to acetaldehyde in the human. These different ADHs have an approximately 60% to 70% identity and are assumed to have arisen from a common ancestral gene similar to the *ADH3* isoenzyme many millions of years ago. The *ADH1* alcohol dehydrogenases (*ADH1A*, *ADH1B*, and *ADH1C*) are all present in high concentration in the liver, and they have relatively high affinity and capacity for ethanol at low concentrations. (These properties are quantitatively reflected by their low K_m, a parameter discussed in Chapter 9). They have a 90% to 94% sequence identity and are able to form both homodimers and heterodimers among themselves (e.g., ββ or βγ). However, none of the *ADH1*s can form dimers with an ADH from *ADH2*, *ADH3*, or *ADH4*. The three genes for class I ADH are arranged in tandem, head to tail, on chromosome 4. The genes for the other classes of ADH are also on chromosome 4 in nearby locations.

B. Acetaldehyde Dehydrogenases

Acetaldehyde is oxidized to acetate with the generation of NADH by acetaldehyde dehydrogenases (see Fig. 25.2). More than 80% of acetaldehyde oxidation in the human liver is normally catalyzed by mitochondrial acetaldehyde dehydrogenase (*ALDH2*), which has a high affinity for acetaldehyde (K_m of 0.2 μM) and is highly specific. However, individuals with a common allelic variant of *ALDH2* (designated as *ALDH2*2*) have a greatly decreased capacity for acetaldehyde metabolism due to an increased K_m (46 μM) and a decreased V_{max} (0.017 units/mg vs. 0.60 units/mg).

Most of the remainder of acetaldehyde oxidation occurs through a cytosolic acetaldehyde dehydrogenase (*ALDH1*). Additional aldehyde dehydrogenases act on a variety of organic alcohols, toxins, and pollutants.

The accumulation of acetaldehyde causes nausea and vomiting, and therefore, inactive acetaldehyde dehydrogenases are associated with a distaste for alcoholic beverages and protection against alcoholism. In one of the common allelic variants of *ALDH2* (*ALDH2*2*), a single substitution increases the K_m for acetaldehyde 23-fold (lowers the affinity) and decreases the V_{max} 35-fold resulting in a very inactive enzyme. Homozygosity for the *ALDH2*2* allele affords absolute protection against alcoholism; no individual with this genotype has been found among alcoholics. Alcoholics are frequently treated with acetaldehyde dehydrogenase inhibitors (e.g., disulfiram) to help them abstain from alcohol intake. Unfortunately, alcoholics who continue to drink while taking this drug are exposed to the toxic effects of elevated acetaldehyde levels.

C. Fate of Acetate

Metabolism of acetate requires activation to acetyl-CoA by acetyl-CoA synthetase in a reaction similar to that catalyzed by fatty acyl-CoA synthetases (Fig. 25.4). In liver, the principal isoform of acetyl-CoA synthetase (ACS I) is a cytosolic enzyme that generates acetyl-CoA for the cytosolic pathways of cholesterol and fatty acid synthesis. Acetate entry into these pathways is under regulatory control by mechanisms involving cholesterol or insulin. Thus, most of the acetate generated enters the blood.

Acetate is taken up and oxidized by other tissues, notably heart and skeletal muscle, which have a high concentration of the mitochondrial acetyl-CoA synthetase isoform (ACS II). This enzyme is present in the mitochondrial matrix. It therefore generates acetyl-CoA that can enter the TCA cycle directly and be oxidized to CO_2.

FIG. 25.4. The activation of acetate to acetyl-CoA.

D. The Microsomal Ethanol Oxidizing System

Ethanol is also oxidized to acetaldehyde in the liver by the MEOS, which comprises members of the cytochrome P450 superfamily of enzymes. Ethanol and NADPH both donate electrons in the reaction, which reduces O_2 to $2H_2O$ (Fig. 25.5). The cytochrome P450 enzymes all have two major catalytic protein components: an electron-donating reductase system that transfers electrons from NADPH (cytochrome P450 reductase) and a cytochrome P450. The cytochrome P450 protein contains the binding sites for O_2 and the substrate (e.g., ethanol) and carries out the reaction. The enzymes are present in the endoplasmic reticulum, which on isolation from disrupted cells forms a membrane fraction after centrifugation that was formerly called *microsomes* by biochemists.

1. CYP2E1

The MEOS is part of the superfamily of cytochrome P450 enzymes, all of which catalyze similar oxidative reactions. Within the superfamily, at least 10 distinct gene families are found in mammals. More than 100 different cytochrome P450 isozymes exist within these 10-gene families. Each isoenzyme has a distinct classification according to its structural relationship with other isoenzymes. The isoenzyme that has the highest activity toward ethanol is called *CYP2E1*. CYP represents cytochrome P450. In CYP2E1, the "2" refers to the gene family (isozymes with >40% amino acid sequence identity), the "E" to the subfamily (isozymes with >55% sequence identity), and the "1" refers to the individual enzymes within this subfamily. A great deal of overlapping specificity exists among the various P450 isoenzymes, and ethanol is also oxidized by several other P450 isoenzymes. *MEOS* refers to the combined ethanol-oxidizing activity of all the P450 enzymes.

CYP2E1 has a much higher K_m for ethanol than the *ADH1* alcohol dehydrogenases (11 mM [51 mg/dL], compared with 0.02 to 5 mM [0.09 to 22.5 mg/dL]). Thus, a greater proportion of ingested ethanol is metabolized through CYP2E1 at high levels of ethanol consumption than at low levels.

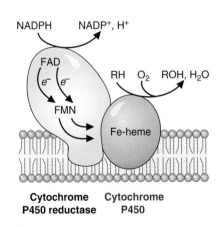

FIG. 25.5. General structure of cytochrome P450 enzymes. O_2 binds to the P450 Fe-heme in the active site and is activated to a reactive form by accepting electrons. The electrons are donated by the cytochrome P450 reductase, which contains a flavin adenine dinucleotide (*FAD*) plus a flavin mononucleotide (*FMN*) or Fe–S center to facilitate the transfer of single electrons from NADPH to O_2. The P450 enzymes involved in steroidogenesis have a somewhat different structure. For CYP2E1, RH is ethanol (CH_3CH_2OH) and ROH is acetaldehyde (CH_3CHO).

ADH1A and *ADH1C* are present as functional polymorphisms that differ in their properties. Genetic polymorphisms for ADH partially account for the observed differences in ethanol elimination rates among various individuals or populations. Although susceptibility to alcoholism is a complex function of genetics and socioeconomic factors, possession of the *ADH1B*2* allele, which encodes a relatively fast ADH (high V_{max}), is associated with a decreased susceptibility to alcoholism—presumably because of nausea and flushing caused by acetaldehyde accumulation (because the aldehyde dehydrogenase gene cannot keep up with the amount of acetaldehyde produced). This particular allele has a relatively high frequency in the East Asian population and a low frequency among white Europeans. In contrast, the *ADH1B*1/1B*1* genotype (homozygous for allele 1 of the *ADH1B* gene) is a risk factor for the development of *Wernicke-Korsakoff syndrome*, a neuropsychiatric syndrome that is commonly associated with alcoholism.

As blood ethanol concentration rises above 18 mM (the legal intoxication limit is now defined as 0.08% in most states of the United States, which is approximately 18 mM), the brain and central nervous system are affected. Induction of CYP2E1 increases the rate of ethanol clearance from the blood, thereby contributing to increased alcohol tolerance. However, the apparent ability of a chronic alcoholic to drink without appearing inebriated is partly a learned behavior.

2. INDUCTION OF P450 ENZYMES

The P450 enzymes are inducible both by their most specific substrate and by substrates for some of the other cytochrome P450 enzymes. Chronic consumption of ethanol increases hepatic CYP2E1 levels approximately five-fold to ten-fold. However, it also causes a twofold to fourfold increase in some of the other P450s from the same subfamily, from different subfamilies, and even from different gene families. The endoplasmic reticulum undergoes proliferation, with a general increase in the content of microsomal enzymes, including those that are not involved directly in ethanol metabolism.

The increase in CYP2E1 with ethanol consumption occurs through transcriptional, posttranscriptional, and posttranslational regulation. Increased levels of mRNA resulting from induction of gene transcription or stabilization of message are found in actively drinking patients. The protein is also stabilized against degradation. In general, the mechanism for induction of P450 enzymes by their substrates occurs through the binding of the substrate (or related compound) to an intracellular receptor protein, followed by binding of the activated receptor to a response element in the target gene. Ethanol induction of CYP2E1 appears to act via stabilization of the protein and protection against degradation (an increased half-life for the synthesized protein).

Although induction of CYP2E1 increases ethanol clearance from the blood, it has negative consequences. Acetaldehyde may be produced faster than it can be metabolized by ALDH, thereby increasing the risk of hepatic injury. An increased amount of acetaldehyde can enter the blood and can damage other tissues. In addition, cytochrome P450 enzymes are capable of generating free radicals, which also may lead to increased hepatic injury and cirrhosis (see Chapter 24).

Overlapping specificity in the catalytic activity of P450 enzymes and in their inducers is responsible for several types of drug interactions. For example, *phenobarbital*, a barbiturate long used as a sleeping pill or for treatment of epilepsy, is converted to an inactive metabolite by cytochrome P450 monooxygenases CYP2B1 and CYP2B2. After treatment with phenobarbital, CYP2B2 is increased 50- to 100-fold. Individuals who take phenobarbital for prolonged periods develop a drug tolerance as CYP2B2 is induced, and the drug is metabolized to an inactive metabolite more rapidly. Consequently, these individuals use progressively higher doses of phenobarbital.

Ethanol is an inhibitor of the phenobarbital-oxidizing P450 system. When large amounts of ethanol are consumed, the inactivation of phenobarbital is directly or indirectly inhibited. Therefore, when high doses of phenobarbital and ethanol are consumed at the same time, toxic levels of the barbiturate can accumulate in the blood.

E. Variations in the Pattern of Ethanol Metabolism

The routes and rates of ethanol oxidation vary from individual to individual. Differences in ethanol metabolism may influence whether an individual becomes a chronic alcoholic, develops alcohol-induced liver disease, or develops other diseases associated with increased alcohol consumption (such as hepatocarcinogenesis, lung cancer, or breast cancer). Factors that determine the rate and route of ethanol oxidation in individuals include

- Genotype—Polymorphic forms of ADHs and ALDHs can greatly affect the rate of ethanol oxidation and the accumulation of acetaldehyde. CYP2E1 activity may vary as much as 20-fold among individuals, partly because of differences in the inducibility of different allelic variants.
- Drinking history—The level of gastric ADH decreases and CYP2E1 increases with the progression from a naive, to a moderate, and to a heavy and chronic consumer of alcohol.

- Gender—Blood levels of ethanol after consuming a drink are normally higher for women than for men, partly because of lower levels of gastric ADH activity in women. After chronic consumption of ethanol, gastric ADH decreases in both men and women but the gender differences become even greater. Gender differences in blood alcohol levels also occur because women are normally smaller. Furthermore, in women, alcohol is distributed in a 12% smaller water space because a woman's body composition consists of more fat and less water than that of a man.

- Quantity—The amount of ethanol an individual consumes over a short period of time determines its metabolic route. Small amounts of ethanol are metabolized most efficiently through the low-K_m pathway of *ADH1* genes and *ALDH2* genes. Little accumulation of NADH occurs to inhibit ethanol metabolism via these dehydrogenases. However, when higher amounts of ethanol are consumed within a short period, a disproportionately greater amount is metabolized through the MEOS. The MEOS, which has a much higher K_m for ethanol, functions principally at high concentrations of ethanol. A higher activity of the MEOS may be expected to correlate with a tendency to develop alcohol-induced liver disease because both acetaldehyde and free radical levels will be increased.

F. The Energy Yield of Ethanol Oxidation

The adenosine triphosphate (ATP) yield from ethanol oxidation to acetate varies with the route of ethanol metabolism. If ethanol is oxidized by the major route of cytosolic ADH and mitochondrial ALDH, one cytosolic and one mitochondrial NADH are generated with a maximum yield of 5 ATP. Oxidation of acetyl-CoA in the TCA cycle and the electron-transport chain leads to the generation of 10 high-energy phosphate bonds. However, activation of acetate to acetyl-CoA requires two high-energy phosphate bonds (one in the cleavage of ATP to adenosine monophosphate (AMP)+ pyrophosphate and one in the cleavage of pyrophosphate to phosphate), which must be subtracted. Thus, the maximum total energy yield is 13 mol of ATP per mole of ethanol.

In contrast, oxidation of ethanol to acetaldehyde by CYP2E1 consumes energy in the form of NADPH, which is equivalent to 2.5 ATP. Thus, for every mole of ethanol metabolized by this route, only a maximum of 8.0 mol of ATP can be generated (10 ATP from acetyl-CoA oxidation through the TCA cycle, minus 2 for acetate activation; the NADH generated by aldehyde dehydrogenase is balanced by the loss of NADPH in the MEOS step).

II. TOXIC EFFECTS OF ETHANOL METABOLISM

Alcohol-induced liver disease, a common and sometimes fatal consequence of chronic ethanol abuse, may manifest itself in three forms: fatty liver, alcohol-induced hepatitis, and cirrhosis. Each may occur alone, or they may be present in any combination in a given patient. Alcohol-induced cirrhosis is discovered in up to 9% of all autopsies performed in the United States, with a peak incidence in patients 40 to 55 years of age.

However, ethanol ingestion also has acute effects on liver metabolism including inhibition of fatty acid oxidation and stimulation of triacylglycerol synthesis leading to a fatty liver. It also can result in ketoacidosis or lactic acidosis and cause hypoglycemia or hyperglycemia, depending on the dietary state. These effects are considered reversible.

In contrast, acetaldehyde and free radicals generated from ethanol metabolism can result in *alcohol-induced hepatitis*, a condition in which the liver is inflamed and cells become necrotic and die. Diffuse damage to hepatocytes results in cirrhosis, characterized by fibrosis (scarring), disturbance of the normal architecture and blood flow, loss of liver function, and, ultimately, hepatic failure.

At **Ivan Applebod's** low level of ethanol consumption, ethanol is oxidized to acetate via ADH and ALDH in the liver and the acetate is activated to acetyl-CoA and oxidized to CO_2 in skeletal muscle and other tissues. The overall energy yield of 13 ATP per ethanol molecule accounts for the caloric value of ethanol, approximately 7 kcal/g. However, chronic consumption of substantial amounts of alcohol does not have the effect on body weight expected from the caloric intake. This is partly attributable to induction of MEOS, resulting in a proportionately greater metabolism of ethanol through the MEOS with its lower energy yield (only approximately 8 ATP). In general, weight loss diets recommend no, or low, alcohol consumption because ethanol calories are "empty" in the sense that alcoholic beverages are generally low in vitamins, essential amino acids, and other required nutrients but not empty of calories.

A. Acute Effects of Ethanol Arising from the Increased NADH/NAD⁺ Ratio

Many of the acute effects of ethanol ingestion arise from the increased NADH/NAD⁺ ratio in the liver (Fig. 25.6). At lower levels of ethanol intake, the rate of ethanol oxidation is regulated by the supply of ethanol (usually determined by how much ethanol we consume) and the rate at which NADH is reoxidized in the electron-transport chain. NADH is not a very effective product inhibitor of ADH or ALDH, and there is no other feedback regulation by ATP, ADP, or AMP. As a consequence, NADH generated in the cytosol and mitochondria tends to accumulate, increasing the NADH/NAD⁺ ratio to high levels (see Fig. 25.6, circle 1). The increase is even greater as the mitochondria become damaged from acetaldehyde or free radical injury.

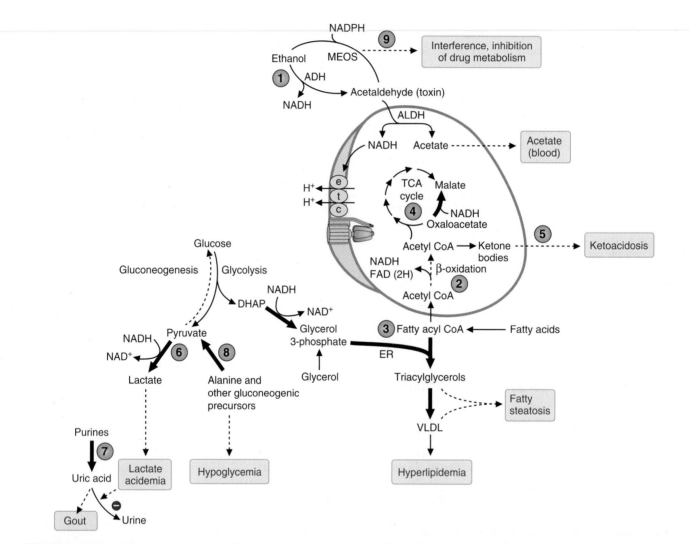

FIG. 25.6. Acute effects of ethanol metabolism on lipid metabolism in the liver. *(1)* Metabolism of ethanol generates a high NADH/NAD⁺ ratio. *(2)* The high NADH/NAD⁺ ratio inhibits fatty acid oxidation and the TCA cycle resulting in accumulation of fatty acids. *(3)* Fatty acids are reesterified to glycerol 3-phosphate by acyltransferases in the endoplasmic reticulum. Glycerol 3-phosphate levels are increased because a high NADH/NAD⁺ ratio favors its formation from dihydroxyacetone phosphate (an intermediate of glycolysis). Ethanol-stimulated increases of endoplasmic reticulum enzymes also favor triacylglycerol formation. *(4)* NADH generated from ethanol oxidation can meet the requirements of the cell for ATP generation from oxidative phosphorylation. Thus, acetyl-CoA oxidation in the TCA cycle is inhibited. *(5)* The high NADH/NAD⁺ ratio shifts oxaloacetate (OAA) toward malate, and acetyl-CoA is directed into ketone-body synthesis. Options *(6)* through *(8)* are discussed in the text.

1. CHANGES IN FATTY ACID METABOLISM

The high NADH/NAD$^+$ ratio generated from ethanol oxidation inhibits the oxidation of fatty acids, which accumulate in the liver (see Fig. 25.6, circles 2 and 3) These fatty acids are reesterified into triacylglycerols by combining with glycerol 3-phosphate (glycerol 3-P). The increased NADH/NAD$^+$ ratio increases the availability of glycerol 3-P by promoting its synthesis from intermediates of glycolysis. The triacylglycerols are incorporated into very low-density lipoproteins (VLDLs) that accumulate in the liver and enter the blood resulting in an ethanol-induced hyperlipidemia.

Although just a few drinks may result in hepatic fat accumulation, chronic consumption of alcohol greatly enhances the development of a fatty liver. Reesterification of fatty acids into triacylglycerols by fatty acyl transferases in the endoplasmic reticulum is enhanced (see Fig. 25.6). Because the transferases are microsomal enzymes, they are induced by ethanol consumption just as the MEOS is induced. The result is a fatty liver (hepatic steatosis).

The source of the fatty acids can be dietary fat, fatty acids synthesized in the liver, or fatty acids released from adipose tissue stores. Adipose tissue lipolysis increases after ethanol consumption, possibly because of a release of epinephrine.

2. ALCOHOL-INDUCED KETOACIDOSIS

Fatty acids that are oxidized are converted to acetyl-CoA and subsequently to ketone bodies (acetoacetate and β-hydroxybutyrate). Enough NADH is generated from oxidation of ethanol and fatty acids that there is no need to oxidize acetyl-CoA in the TCA cycle. The very high NADH/NAD$^+$ ratio shifts the oxaloacetate (OAA) in the TCA cycle to malate, leaving the OAA levels too low for citrate synthase to synhesize citrate (see Fig. 25.6, circle 4). The acetyl-CoA enters the pathway for ketone body synthesis instead of the TCA cycle.

Although ketone bodies are being produced at a high rate, their metabolism in other tissues is restricted by the supply of acetate, which is the preferred fuel. Thus, the blood concentration of ketone bodies may be much higher than is found under normal fasting conditions.

3. LACTIC ACIDOSIS, HYPERURICEMIA, AND HYPOGLYCEMIA

Another consequence of the very high NADH/NAD$^+$ ratio is that the balance in the lactate dehydrogenase reaction is shifted toward lactate, resulting in a lactic acidosis (see Fig. 25.6, circle 6). The elevation of blood lactate may decrease excretion of uric acid (see Fig. 25.6, circle 7) by the kidney. Consequently, patients with gout (which results from precipitated uric acid crystals in the joints) are advised not to drink excessive amounts of ethanol. Increased degradation of purines also may contribute to hyperuricemia.

The increased NADH/NAD$^+$ ratio also can cause hypoglycemia in a fasting individual who has been drinking and is dependent on gluconeogenesis to maintain blood glucose levels (Fig. 25.6, circles 6 and 8). Alanine and lactate are major gluconeogenic precursors that enter gluconeogenesis as pyruvate. The high NADH/NAD$^+$ ratio shifts the lactate dehydrogenase equilibrium to lactate, so that pyruvate formed from alanine is converted to lactate and cannot enter gluconeogenesis. The high NADH/NAD$^+$ ratio also prevents other major gluconeogenic precursors, such as OAA and glycerol, from entering the gluconeogenic pathway.

In contrast, ethanol consumption with a meal may result in a transient hyperglycemia, possibly because the high NADH/NAD$^+$ ratio inhibits glycolysis at the glyceraldehyde-3-phosphate dehydrogenase step.

B. Acetaldehyde Toxicity

Many of the toxic effects of chronic ethanol consumption result from accumulation of acetaldehyde, which is produced from ethanol by both ADHs and the MEOS.

Al Martini's admitting physician suspected an alcohol-induced ketoacidosis superimposed on a starvation ketoacidosis. Tests showed that his plasma-free fatty acid level was elevated, and his plasma β-hydroxybutyrate level was 40 times the upper limit of normal. The increased NADH/NAD$^+$ ratio from ethanol consumption inhibited the TCA cycle and shifted acetyl-CoA from fatty acid oxidation into the pathway of ketone-body synthesis.

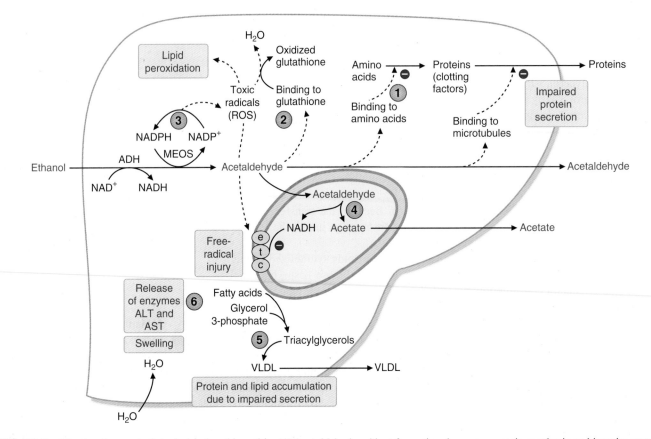

FIG. 25.7. The development of alcohol-induced hepatitis. *(1)* Acetaldehyde-adduct formation decreases protein synthesis and impairs protein secretion. *(2)* Free radical injury results partly from acetaldehyde-adduct formation with glutathione. *(3)* Induction of the *MEOS* increases formation of free radicals, which leads to lipid peroxidation and cell damage. *(4)* Mitochondrial damage inhibits the electron transport chain, which decreases acetaldehyde oxidation. *(5)* Microtubule damage increases *VLDL* and protein accumulation. *(6)* Cell damage leads to release of the hepatic enzymes alanine aminotransferase *(ALT)* and aspartate aminotransferase *(AST)*.

Acetaldehyde accumulates in the liver and is released into the blood after heavy doses of ethanol (Fig. 25.7). It is highly reactive and binds covalently to amino groups, sulfhydryl groups, nucleotides, and phospholipids to form "adducts."

1. ACETALDEHYDE AND ALCOHOL-INDUCED HEPATITIS

One of the results of acetaldehyde-adduct formation with amino acids is a general decrease in hepatic protein synthesis (see Fig. 25.7, circle 1). Calmodulin, ribonuclease, and tubulin are some of the proteins affected. Proteins in the heart and other tissues also may be affected by acetaldehyde that appears in the blood.

As a consequence of forming acetaldehyde adducts of tubulin, there is a diminished secretion of serum proteins and VLDL from the liver. The liver synthesizes many blood proteins, including serum albumin, blood coagulation factors, and transport proteins for vitamins, steroids, and iron. These proteins accumulate in the liver together with lipid. The accumulation of proteins results in an influx of water (see Fig. 25.7, circle 6) within the hepatocytes and a swelling of the liver that contributes to portal hypertension and a disruption of hepatic architecture.

2. ACETALDEHYDE AND FREE RADICAL DAMAGE

Acetaldehyde-adduct formation enhances free radical damage. Acetaldehyde binds directly to glutathione and diminishes its ability to protect against H_2O_2 and prevent lipid peroxidation (see Fig. 25.7, circle 2). It also binds to free radical defense enzymes.

Damage to mitochondria from acetaldehyde and free radicals perpetuates a cycle of toxicity (see Fig. 25.7, circles 3 and 4). With chronic consumption of ethanol, mitochondria become damaged, the rate of electron transport is inhibited, and oxidative phosphorylation tends to become uncoupled. Fatty acid oxidation is decreased even further, thereby enhancing lipid accumulation (see Fig. 25.7, circle 5). The mitochondrial changes further impair mitochondrial acetaldehyde oxidation, thereby initiating a cycle of progressively increasing acetaldehyde damage.

C. Ethanol and Free Radical Formation

Increased oxidative stress in the liver during chronic ethanol intoxication arises from increased production of free radicals, principally by CYP2E1. Flavin adenine dinucleotide (FAD) and flavin mononucleotide (FMN) in the reductase and heme in the cytochrome P450 system transfer single electrons, thus operating through a mechanism that can generate free radicals. The hydroxyethyl radical ($CH_3CH_2O\bullet$) is produced during ethanol metabolism and can be released as a free radical. Induction of CYP2E1 as well as other cytochrome P450 enzymes can increase the generation of free radicals from drug metabolism and from the activation of toxins and carcinogens (see Fig. 25.7, circle 3). These effects are enhanced by acetaldehyde-adduct damage.

Phospholipids, the major lipid in cellular membranes, are a primary target of peroxidation caused by free radical release. Peroxidation of lipids in the inner mitochondrial membrane may contribute to the inhibition of electron transport and uncoupling of mitochondria, leading to inflammation and cellular necrosis. Induction of CYP2E1 and other P450 cytochromes also increases formation of other radicals and the activation of hepatocarcinogens.

D. Hepatic Cirrhosis and Loss of Liver Function

Liver injury is irreversible at the stage that hepatic cirrhosis develops. Initially, the liver may be enlarged, full of fat, crossed with collagen fibers (fibrosis), and have nodules of regenerating hepatocytes ballooning between the fibers. As liver function is lost, the liver becomes shrunken (Laennec cirrhosis). During the development of cirrhosis, many of the normal metabolic functions of the liver are lost, including biosynthetic and detoxification pathways. Synthesis of blood proteins including blood coagulation factors and serum albumin is decreased. The capacity to incorporate amino groups into urea is decreased, resulting in the accumulation of toxic levels of ammonia in the blood. Conjugation and excretion of the yellow pigment bilirubin (a product of heme degradation) is diminished, and bilirubin accumulates in the blood. It is deposited in many tissues, including the skin and sclerae of the eyes, causing the patient to become visibly yellow. Such a patient is said to be jaundiced.

CLINICAL COMMENTS

 Ivan Applebod. When ethanol consumption is low (<15% of the calories in the diet), it is used efficiently to produce adenosine triphosphate (ATP), thereby contributing to **Ivan Applebod's** weight gain. However, in individuals with chronic consumption of large amounts of ethanol, the caloric content of ethanol is not converted to ATP as effectively. Some of the factors that may contribute to this decreased efficiency include mitochondrial damage (inhibition of oxidative phosphorylation and uncoupling) resulting in the loss of calories as heat, increased recycling of metabolites such as ketone bodies, and inhibition of the normal pathways of fatty acid and glucose oxidation. In addition, heavier drinkers metabolize an increased amount of alcohol through the microsomal ethanol oxidizing system (MEOS), which generates less ATP.

 Al Martini. **Al Martini** was suffering from acute effects of high ethanol ingestion in the absence of food intake. Both heavy ethanol consumption and low caloric intake increase adipose tissue lipolysis and elevate

 The noncaloric effect of heavy and chronic ethanol ingestion that led **Ivan Applebod** to believe ethanol has no calories may be partly attributable to uncoupling of oxidative phosphorylation. The hepatic mitochondria from tissues of chronic alcoholics may be partially uncoupled and unable to maintain the transmembrane proton gradient necessary for normal rates of ATP synthesis. Consequently, a greater proportion of the energy in ethanol is converted to heat. Metabolic disturbances such as the loss of ketone bodies in urine or futile cycling of glucose also might contribute to a diminished energy value for ethanol.

 Because of the possibility of mild alcoholic hepatitis and perhaps chronic alcohol-induced cirrhosis, the physician ordered liver function studies on **Jean Ann Tonich**. The tests indicated an alanine aminotransferase (ALT) level of 46 U/L (reference range, 5 to 30 U/L) and an aspartate aminotransferase (AST) level of 98 U/L (reference range, 10 to 30 U/L). The concentration of these enzymes is high in hepatocytes. When hepatocellular membranes are damaged in any way, these enzymes are released into the blood. Jean Ann's serum alkaline phosphatase level was 195 U/L (reference range, 56 to 155 U/L for an adult female). The serum total bilirubin level was 2.4 mg/dL (reference range, 0.2 to 1.0 mg/L). These tests show impaired capacity for normal liver function. Her blood hemoglobin and hematocrit levels were slightly below the normal range, consistent with a toxic effect of ethanol on red blood cell production by bone marrow. Serum folate and vitamin B_{12} levels were also slightly suppressed. Folate is dependent on the liver for its activation and recovery from the enterohepatic circulation. Vitamin B_{12} is dependent on the liver for synthesis of its blood carrier proteins. Thus, **Jean Ann Tonich** shows many of the consequences of hepatic damage.

In liver fibrosis, disruption of the normal liver architecture, including sinusoids, impairs blood from the portal vein. Increased portal vein pressure (portal hypertension) causes capillaries to anastomose (to meet and unite or run into each other) and form thin-walled dilated esophageal venous conduits known as *esophageal varices*. When these burst, there is hemorrhaging into the GI tract. The bleeding can be very profuse because of the high venous pressure within these varices in addition to the adverse effect of impaired hepatic function on the production of blood-clotting proteins.

Although the full spectrum of alcohol-induced liver disease may be present in a well-nourished individual, the presence of nutritional deficiencies enhances the progression of the disease. Ethanol creates nutritional deficiencies in several different ways. The ingestion of ethanol reduces the GI absorption of foods that contain essential nutrients including vitamins, essential fatty acids, and essential amino acids. For example, ethanol interferes with absorption of folate, thiamine, and other nutrients. Secondary malabsorption can occur through GI complications, pancreatic insufficiency, and impaired hepatic metabolism or impaired hepatic storage of nutrients such as vitamin A. Changes in the level of transport proteins produced by the liver also strongly affect nutrient status.

blood fatty acids. As a consequence of his elevated hepatic NADH/NAD$^+$ ratio, acetyl coenzyme A (acetyl-CoA) produced from fatty acid oxidation was diverted from the tricarboxylic acid (TCA) cycle into the pathway of ketone body synthesis. Because his skeletal muscles were using acetate as a fuel, ketone body use was diminished, resulting in ketoacidosis. Al's moderately low blood glucose level also suggests that his high hepatic NADH level prevented pyruvate and glycerol from entering the gluconeogenic pathway. Pyruvate is diverted to lactate, which may have contributed to his metabolic acidosis and anion gap.

Rehydration with intravenous fluids containing glucose and potassium was initiated. Al's initial potassium level was low, possibly secondary to vomiting. An orthopedic surgeon was consulted regarding the compound fracture of his right forearm.

Jean Ann Tonich. Jean Ann Tonich's signs and symptoms as well as her laboratory profile were consistent with the presence of mild reversible alcohol-induced hepatocellular inflammation (alcohol-induced hepatitis) superimposed on a degree of irreversible scarring of liver tissues known as *chronic alcoholic (Laennec) cirrhosis of the liver*. The chronic inflammatory process associated with long-term ethanol abuse in patients such as **Jean Ann Tonich** is accompanied by increases in the levels of serum alanine aminotransferase (ALT) and aspartate aminotransferase (AST). Her elevated bilirubin and alkaline phosphatase levels in the blood were consistent with hepatic damage. Her values for ALT and AST were significantly below those seen in acute viral hepatitis. In addition, the ratio of the absolute values for serum ALT and AST often differ in the two diseases tending to be >1 in acute viral hepatitis and <1 in chronic alcohol-induced cirrhosis. The reason for the difference in ratio of enzyme activities released is not fully understood, but a lower level of ALT in the serum may be attributable to an alcohol-induced deficiency of pyridoxal phosphate. In addition, serologic tests for viral hepatitis were nonreactive. Her serum folate and vitamin B$_{12}$ were also slightly suppressed indicating impaired nutritional status.

Jean Ann was strongly cautioned to abstain from alcohol immediately and to improve her nutritional status. In addition, she was referred to the hospital drug and alcohol rehabilitation unit for appropriate psychologic therapy and supportive social counseling. The physician also arranged for a follow-up office visit in 2 weeks.

BIOCHEMICAL COMMENTS

Fibrosis in Chronic Alcohol-Induced Liver Disease. *Fibrosis is the excessive accumulation of connective tissue in parenchymal organs.* In the liver, it is a frequent event following a repeated or chronic insult of sufficient intensity (such as chronic ethanol intoxication or infection by a hepatitis virus) to trigger a "wound healing–like" reaction. Regardless of the insult, the events are similar: An overproduction of extracellular matrix components occurs, with the tendency to progress to sclerosis, accompanied by a degenerative alteration in the composition of matrix components (Table 25.2). Some individuals (<20% of those who chronically consume alcohol) go on to develop cirrhosis.

The development of hepatic fibrosis after ethanol consumption is related to stimulation of the mitogenic development of stellate (Ito) cells into myofibroblasts, and stimulation of the production of collagen type I and fibronectin by these cells. The stellate cells are perisinusoidal cells lodged in the space of Disse that produce extracellular matrix protein. Normally, the space of Disse contains basement membrane–like collagen (collagen type IV) and laminin. As the stellate cells are activated, they change from a resting cell filled with lipids and vitamin A to one that proliferates, loses its vitamin A content, and secretes large quantities of extracellular matrix components.

Table 25.2   Hepatic Injury

Stage of Injury	Main Features
Fibrosis: increase of connective tissue	Accumulation of both fibrillar and basement membrane–like collagens Increase of laminin and fibronectin Thickening of connective tissue septae Capillary formation within the sinusoids
Sclerosis: aging of fibrotic tissue	Decrease of hyaluronic acid and heparan sulfate proteoglycans Increase of chondroitin sulfate proteoglycans Progressive fragmentation and disappearance of elastic fibers Distortion of sinusoidal architecture and parenchymal damage
Cirrhosis: end-stage process of liver fibrotic degeneration	Whole liver heavily distorted by thick bands of collagen surrounding nodules of hepatocytes with regenerative foci

One of the initial events in the activation and proliferation of stellate cells is the activation of Kupffer cells, which are macrophages that reside in the liver sinusoids (Fig. 25.8). The Kupffer cells are probably activated by a product of the damaged hepatocytes, such as necrotic debris, iron, reactive oxygen species (ROS), acetaldehyde, or aldehyde products of lipid peroxidation. Kupffer cells also may produce acetaldehyde from ethanol internally through their own microsomal ethanol oxidizing system (MEOS) pathway.

Activated Kupffer cells produce several products that contribute to activation of stellate cells. They generate additional ROS through NADPH oxidase during the oxidative burst and reactive nitrogen–oxygen species (RNOS) through inducible NO synthase (see Chapter 24). In addition, they secrete an impressive array of growth factors such as cytokines, chemokines, prostaglandins, and other reactive molecules. The cytokine transforming growth factor-β_1 (TGF-β_1), produced by both Kupffer cells and sinusoidal endothelial cells, is a major player in the activation of stellate cells. Once they are activated, the stellate cells produce collagen and proteases leading to an enhanced fibrotic network within the liver. Stellate cells may also be partially activated by hepatocyte release of ROS and acetaldehyde directly, with the involvement of Kupffer cells.

FIG. 25.8.   Proposed model for the development of hepatic fibrosis involving hepatocytes, Kupffer cells, and stellate (Ito) cells. *ROS*, reactive oxygen species; *NO*, nitric oxide; *TGF-β_1*, transforming growth factor β_1.

Table 25.3   Diseases Discussed in Chapter 25

Disease or Disorder	Environmental or Genetic	Comments
Obesity	Both	Ethanol is a nutrient, and its caloric content can contribute to obesity.
Alcoholism	Both	Alcohol addiction (alcoholism) may occur, leading to damage of internal organs by acetaldehyde production.
Jaundice	Environmental	Altered liver function leads to a reduced ability to conjugate and solubilize bilirubin, which leads to bilirubin deposition in the eyes and skin, giving them a yellow pallor. Jaundice is an indication of liver disease.
Liver fibrosis	Environmental	Excessive damage to liver due to alcohol metabolism, particularly acetaldehyde accumulation, leading to extensive collagen secretion and loss of liver function.

Key Concepts

- Ethanol metabolism occurs primarily in the liver, via a two-step oxidation sequence to acetate plus NADH.
- Acetate is activated to acetyl coenzyme A (acetyl-CoA) for energy generation by most tissues of the body.
- The alcohol dehydrogenase (ADH) family of enzymes catalyzes the first step of alcohol oxidation. The aldehyde dehydrogenase family of enzymes catalyzes the second step of the pathway.
- When ethanol levels are high, the microsomal ethanol oxidizing system (MEOS), consisting of CYP2E1, is induced.
- Acute effects of ethanol ingestion are due to the elevated NADH/NAD$^+$ ratio, which leads to the following:
  - Inhibition of fatty acid oxidation
  - Ketogenesis
  - Hyperlipidemia
  - Inhibition of gluconeogenesis
  - Lactic acidosis
  - Hyperuricemia
- Chronic effects of ethanol ingestion include the following:
  - Hepatic steatosis (fatty acid accumulation within the liver)
  - Hepatitis
  - Fibrosis (excessive collagen production within the liver)
  - Cirrhois (eventual liver death)
- The chronic effects of ethanol are caused by acetaldehyde and reactive oxygen species (ROS) production during ethanol metabolism.
- The diseases discussed in this chapter are summarized in Table 25.3.

REVIEW QUESTIONS—CHAPTER 25

1. The fate of acetate, the product of ethanol metabolism, is which of the following?

   A. It is taken up by other tissues and activated to acetyl-CoA.
   B. It is toxic to the tissues of the body and can lead to hepatic necrosis.
   C. It is excreted in bile.
   D. It enters the TCA cycle directly to be oxidized.
   E. It is converted into NADH by ADH.

2. Which of the following would be expected to occur after acute alcohol ingestion?

   A. The activation of fatty acid oxidation
   B. Lactic acidosis
   C. The inhibition of ketogenesis
   D. An increase in the NAD$^+$/NADH ratio
   E. An increase in gluconeogenesis

3. A chronic alcoholic is in treatment for alcohol abuse. The drug disulfiram is prescribed for the patient. This drug deters the consumption of alcohol by which of the following mechanisms?

   A. Inhibiting the absorption of ethanol so that an individual cannot become intoxicated, regardless of how much he or she drinks
   B. Inhibiting the conversion of ethanol to acetaldehyde, which cause the excretion of unmetabolized ethanol
   C. Blocking the conversion of acetaldehyde to acetate, which causes the accumulation of acetaldehyde
   D. Activating the excessive metabolism of ethanol to acetate, which causes inebriation with consumption of a small amount of alcohol
   E. Preventing the excretion of acetate, which causes nausea and vomiting

4. Induction of CYP2E1 would result in which of the following?

   A. A decreased clearance of ethanol from the blood
   B. A decrease in the rate of acetaldehyde production
   C. A low possibility of the generation of free radicals
   D. Protection from hepatic damage
   E. An increase of one's alcohol tolerance level

5. Which one of the following consequences of chronic alcohol consumption is irreversible?

   A. Inhibition of fatty acid oxidation
   B. Activation of triacylglycerol synthesis
   C. Ketoacidosis
   D. Lactic acidosis
   E. Liver cirrhosis

Carbohydrate Metabolism

Glucose is central to all of metabolism. It is the universal fuel for human cells and the source of carbon for the synthesis of most other compounds. Every human cell type uses glucose to obtain energy. The release of insulin and glucagon by the pancreas aids in the body's use and storage of glucose. Other dietary sugars (mainly fructose and galactose) are converted to glucose or to intermediates of glucose metabolism.

Glucose is the precursor for the synthesis of an array of other sugars that are required for the production of specialized compounds, such as lactose, cell surface antigens, nucleotides, or glycosaminoglycans. Glucose is also the fundamental precursor of noncarbohydrate compounds; it can be converted to lipids (including fatty acids, cholesterol, and steroid hormones), amino acids, and nucleic acids. Only those compounds that are synthesized from vitamins, essential amino acids, and essential fatty acids cannot be synthesized from glucose in humans.

More than 40% of the calories in the typical diet in the United States are obtained from starch, sucrose, and lactose. These dietary carbohydrates are converted to glucose, galactose, and fructose in the digestive tract (Fig. V.1). Monosaccharides are absorbed from the intestine, enter the blood, and travel to the tissues, where they are metabolized.

After glucose is transported into cells, it is phosphorylated by a hexokinase to form glucose 6-phosphate. Glucose 6-phosphate can then enter several metabolic pathways. The three that are common to all cell types are glycolysis, the pentose phosphate pathway, and glycogen synthesis (Fig. V.2). In tissues, fructose and galactose are converted to intermediates of glucose metabolism. Thus, the fate of these sugars parallels that of glucose (Fig. V.3).

The major fate of glucose 6-phosphate is oxidation via the pathway of glycolysis (see Chapter 22), which provides a source of adenosine triphosphate (ATP) for all cell types. Cells that lack mitochondria cannot oxidize other fuels. They produce ATP from anaerobic glycolysis (the conversion of glucose to lactic acid). Cells that contain mitochondria oxidize glucose to CO_2 and H_2O via glycolysis and the

FIG. V.1. Overview of carbohydrate digestion. The major carbohydrates of the diet (starch, lactose, and sucrose) are digested to produce monosaccharides (glucose, fructose, and galactose), which enter the blood.

FIG. V.2. Major pathways of glucose metabolism.

FIG. V.4. Conversion of glucose to lactate or to CO_2. *Acetyl-CoA*, acetyl coenzyme A; *ETC*, electron-transport chain.

FIG. V.3. Overview of fructose and galactose metabolism. Fructose and galactose are converted to intermediates of glucose metabolism.

tricarboxylic acid (TCA) cycle (Fig. V.4). Some tissues, such as the brain, depend on the oxidation of glucose to CO_2 and H_2O for energy because they have a limited capacity to use other fuels.

Glucose produces the intermediates of glycolysis and the TCA cycle that are used for the synthesis of amino acids and both the glycerol and fatty acid moieties of triacylglycerols (Fig. V.5).

Another important fate of glucose 6-phosphate is oxidation via the pentose phosphate pathway, which generates NADPH. The reducing equivalents of NADPH are used for biosynthetic reactions and for the prevention of oxidative damage to cells (see Chapter 24). In this pathway, glucose undergoes oxidation and decarboxylation to five-carbon sugars (pentoses), which may reenter the glycolytic pathway. They also may be used for nucleotide synthesis (Fig. V.6). There are also nonoxidative reactions, which can convert six- and five-carbon sugars.

FIG. V.5. Conversion of glucose to amino acids and to the glycerol and fatty acid (*FA*) moieties of triacylglycerols (*TG*). *Acetyl-CoA*, acetyl coenzyme A; *OAA*, oxaloacetate; *TCA*, tricarboxylic acid.

FIG. V.6. Overview of the pentose phosphate pathway. The oxidative reactions generate both NADPH and pentose phosphates. The nonoxidative reactions generate only pentose phosphates.

Glucose

Glucose 6-phosphate

Glucose 1-phosphate

Glucuronides

UDP-glucuronate

Glycogen

UDP-glucose

Glycoproteins
Glycolipids
Proteoglycans

UDP-galactose

Glucose

Lactose

FIG. V.7. Products derived from UDP-glucose.

Glucose 6-phosphate is also converted to UDP (uridine diphosphate)-glucose, which has many functions in the cell (Fig. V.7). The major fate of UDP-glucose is the synthesis of glycogen, the storage polymer of glucose. Although most cells have glycogen to provide emergency supplies of glucose, the largest stores are in muscle and liver. Muscle glycogen is used to generate ATP during muscle contraction. Liver glycogen is used to maintain blood glucose during fasting and during exercise or periods of enhanced need. UDP-glucose is also used for the formation of other sugars, and galactose and glucose are interconverted while attached to UDP. UDP-galactose is used for lactose synthesis in the mammary gland. In the liver, UDP-glucose is oxidized to UDP-glucuronate, which is used to convert bilirubin and other toxic compounds to glucuronides for excretion (see Fig. V.7).

Nucleotide sugars are also used for the synthesis of proteoglycans, glycoproteins, and glycolipids (see Fig. V.7). Proteoglycans are major carbohydrate components of the extracellular matrix, cartilage, and extracellular fluids (such as the synovial fluid of joints), and they are discussed in more detail in Chapter 49. Most extracellular proteins are glycoproteins; that is, they contain covalently attached carbohydrates. For both cell membrane glycoproteins and glycolipids, the carbohydrate portion extends into the extracellular space.

All cells are continuously supplied with glucose under normal circumstances; the body maintains a relatively narrow range of glucose concentration in the blood (approximately 80 to 100 mg/dL) in spite of the changes in dietary supply and tissue demand as we sleep and exercise. This process is called *glucose homeostasis*. Low blood glucose levels (hypoglycemia) are prevented by a release of glucose from the large glycogen stores in the liver (glycogenolysis); by synthesis of glucose from lactate, glycerol, and amino acids in the liver (gluconeogenesis) (Fig. V.8); and to a limited extent by a release of fatty acids from adipose tissue stores (lipolysis) to provide an alternate fuel when glucose is in short supply. High blood glucose levels (hyperglycemia) are prevented both by the conversion of glucose to glycogen and by its conversion to triacylglycerols in liver and adipose tissue. Thus, the pathways for glucose use as a fuel cannot

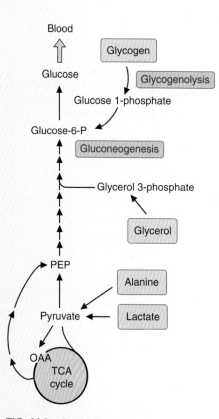

Blood

Glucose

Glycogen

Glycogenolysis

Glucose 1-phosphate

Glucose-6-P

Gluconeogenesis

Glycerol 3-phosphate

Glycerol

PEP

Alanine

Pyruvate

Lactate

OAA
TCA
cycle

FIG. V.8. Production of blood glucose from glycogen (by glycogenolysis) and from alanine, lactate, and glycerol (by gluconeogenesis). *PEP*, phosphoenolpyruvate; *OAA*, oxaloacetate; *TCA*, tricarboxylic acid.

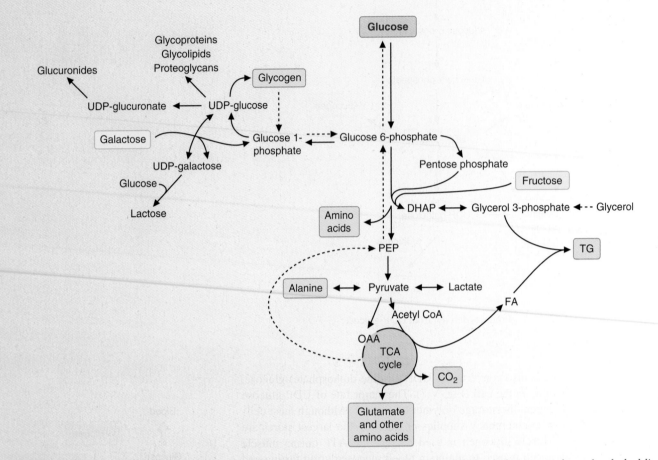

FIG. V.9. Overview of the major pathways of glucose metabolism. Pathways for production of blood glucose are shown by *dashed lines*. *Acetyl-CoA*, acetyl coenzyme A; *DHAP*, dihydroxyacetone phosphate; *FA*, fatty acids; *OAA*, oxaloacetate; *PEP*, phosphoenolpyruvate; *TCA*, tricarboxylic acid; *TG*, triacylglycerols.

be considered as totally separate from pathways involving amino acid and fatty acid metabolism (Fig. V.9).

Intertissue balance in the use and storage of glucose during fasting and feeding is accomplished principally by the actions of the hormones of metabolic homeostasis—insulin and glucagon (Fig. V.10). However, cortisol, epinephrine, norepinephrine, and other hormones are also involved in intertissue adjustments of supply and demand in response to changes of physiologic state.

FIG. V.10. Pathways regulated by the release of glucagon (in response to a lowering of blood glucose levels) and insulin (released in response to an elevation of blood glucose levels). Tissue-specific differences occur in the response to these hormones, as detailed in the chapters of this section.

26 Basic Concepts in the Regulation of Fuel Metabolism by Insulin, Glucagon, and Other Hormones

All cells use adenosine triphosphate (ATP) continuously and require a constant supply of fuels to provide energy for ATP generation. **Insulin** and **glucagon** are the two major hormones that regulate fuel mobilization and storage. Their function is to ensure that cells have a constant source of glucose, fatty acids, and amino acids for ATP generation and for cellular maintenance (Fig. 26.1).

Because most tissues are partially or totally dependent on glucose for generation of ATP and for production of precursors of other pathways, insulin and glucagon **maintain blood glucose** levels near 80 to 100 mg/dL (90 mg/dL is the same as 5 mM) despite the fact that carbohydrate intake varies considerably over the course of a day. The maintenance of constant blood glucose levels (**glucose homeostasis**) requires insulin and glucagon to regulate **carbohydrate, lipid,** and **amino acid metabolism** in accordance with the needs and capacities of individual tissues. Basically, the dietary intake of all fuels in excess of immediate need is stored, and the appropriate fuel is mobilized when a demand occurs. For example, when dietary glucose is not available to cells in sufficient quantities, fatty acids are mobilized and used by skeletal muscle as a fuel (see Chapters 2 and 23). Under these circumstances, the liver can also convert fatty acids to ketone bodies that can be used by the brain. The fatty acids that are mobilized under these conditions spare glucose for use by the brain and other glucose-dependent tissues (such as red blood cells).

Insulin and glucagon are important for the regulation of fuel storage and fuel mobilization (Fig. 26.2). Insulin, released from the β-cells of the pancreas in response to carbohydrate ingestion, promotes glucose utilization as a fuel and glucose storage as fat and glycogen. **Insulin, therefore, is a major anabolic hormone.** In addition to its storage function, insulin increases protein synthesis and cell growth. Blood insulin levels decrease as glucose is taken up by tissues and used. Glucagon, the major insulin **counterregulatory hormone**, is decreased in response to a carbohydrate meal and elevated during fasting. Its concentration in the blood increases as circulating levels of glucose fall, a response that promotes glucose production via **glycogenolysis** (glycogen degradation) and **gluconeogenesis** (glucose synthesis from amino acids and other noncarbohydrate precursors). Increased levels of circulating glucagon relative to insulin also stimulate the **mobilization of fatty acids** from adipose tissue. **Epinephrine** (the fight-or-flight hormone) and **cortisol** (a glucocorticoid released from the adrenal cortex in response to fasting and chronic stress) have effects on fuel metabolism that oppose those of insulin. Therefore, epinephrine and cortisol are considered to be insulin counterregulatory hormones.

Insulin and glucagon are polypeptide hormones synthesized as **prohormones** in the pancreatic β- and α-cells, respectively. **Proinsulin** is

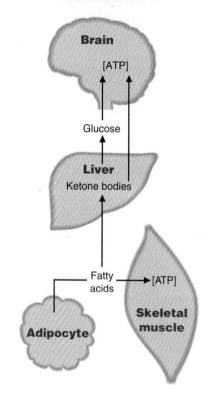

FIG. 26.1. Maintenance of fuel supplies to tissues. Glucagon release activates the pathways shown.

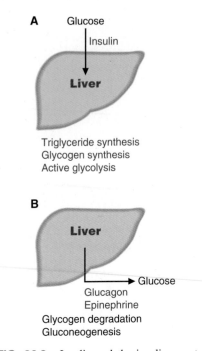

A Glucose
Insulin

Liver

Triglyceride synthesis
Glycogen synthesis
Active glycolysis

B

Liver

Glucose

Glucagon
Epinephrine

Glycogen degradation
Gluconeogenesis

FIG. 26.2. Insulin and the insulin counter-regulatory hormones. **A.** Insulin promotes glucose storage, as triglyceride (TG) or glycogen. **B.** Glucagon and epinephrine promote glucose release from the liver, activating glycogenolysis and gluconeogenesis. Cortisol will stimulate both glycogen synthesis and gluconeogenesis.

Pancreas

Low
blood
glucose

Glucagon

Cell
membrane

Receptor

Cytosol

Second messenger (cAMP)

Cellular response
(activation of protein kinase A)

FIG. 26.3. Cellular response to glucagon, which is released from the pancreas in response to a decrease in blood glucose levels.

*cleaved into mature insulin and a connection peptide (**C-peptide**) in storage vesicles and precipitated with Zn^{2+}. Insulin secretion is regulated principally by changes in blood glucose levels. Glucagon is also synthesized as a prohormone and cleaved into mature glucagon within storage vesicles. Its release is regulated principally through changes in the level of glucose and insulin bathing the α-cells located in the pancreatic islets of Langerhans.*

*Glucagon exerts its effects on cells by binding to a receptor located on the plasma membrane of target cells for this hormone. The binding to these specific receptors by glucagon stimulates the synthesis of the intracellular second messenger, cyclic adenosine monophosphate (**cAMP**) (Fig. 26.3). cAMP activates **protein kinase A (PKA)**, which phosphorylates key regulatory enzymes, thereby activating some while inhibiting others. Insulin, on the other hand, promotes the dephosphorylation of these key enzymes, leading to their activation or deactivation, depending on the enzyme. Changes of cAMP levels also induce or repress the synthesis of several enzymes.*

*Insulin binds to a receptor on the cell surface of insulin-sensitive tissues and initiates a cascade of intracellular events that differs from those stimulated by glucagon. Insulin binding activates both autophosphorylation of the receptor and the phosphorylation of other enzymes by the receptor's **tyrosine kinase** domain (see Chapter 11, Section III.B.3). The complete routes for **signal transduction** between this point and the final effects of insulin on the regulatory enzymes of fuel metabolism have not yet been fully established.*

THE WAITING ROOM

Ann Sulin returned to her physician for her monthly office visit. She has been seeing her physician for over a year because of obesity and elevated blood glucose levels. She still weighed 198 lb despite her insistence that she had adhered strictly to her hypocaloric diet. Her 2-hour postprandial blood glucose level was 180 mg/dL (reference range, 80 to 140 mg/dL).

Bea Selmass is a 46-year-old woman who 6 months earlier began noting episodes of fatigue and confusion as she finished her daily prebreakfast jog. These episodes were occasionally accompanied by blurred vision and an unusually urgent sense of hunger. The ingestion of food relieved all of her symptoms within 25 to 30 minutes. In the last month, these attacks have occurred more frequently throughout the day, and she has learned to reduce their severity by eating between meals. As a result of this increase in caloric intake, she has recently gained 8 lb.

A random serum glucose level done at 4:30 PM during her first office visit was subnormal at 46 mg/dL. Her physician, suspecting she had a form of fasting hypoglycemia, ordered a series of fasting serum glucose levels. In addition, he asked Bea to keep a careful diary of all of the symptoms that she experienced when her attacks were most severe.

I. METABOLIC HOMEOSTASIS

Living cells require a constant source of fuels from which to derive adenosine triphosphate (ATP) for the maintenance of normal cell function and growth. Therefore, a balance must be achieved among carbohydrate, fat, and protein intake;

their rates of oxidation; and their rates of storage when they are present in excess of immediate need. Alternatively, when the demands for these substrates increase, the rate of mobilization from storage sites and the rate of their de novo synthesis also require balanced regulation. The control of the balance between substrate need and substrate availability is referred to as *metabolic homeostasis* (Fig. 26.4). The intertissue integration required for metabolic homeostasis is achieved in three principal ways:

1. The concentration of nutrients or metabolites in the blood affects the rate at which they are used or stored in different tissues.
2. Hormones carry messages to their individual target tissues about the physiologic state of the body and the current level of nutrient supply or demand.
3. The central nervous system uses neural signals to control tissue metabolism, either directly or through the release of hormones.

Fatty acids provide an example of the influence that the level of a compound in the blood has on its own rate of metabolism. The concentration of fatty acids in the blood is the major factor determining whether skeletal muscles will use fatty acids or glucose as a fuel (see Chapter 23). In contrast, *hormones* are (by definition) intravascular carriers of messages between their sites of synthesis and their target tissues. *Epinephrine*, for example, is a flight-or-fight hormone that in times of stress signals an immediate need for increased fuel availability. Its level is regulated principally through the activation of the sympathetic nervous system.

Insulin and glucagon, however, are the two major hormones that regulate fuel storage and mobilization (see Fig. 26.2). Insulin is the major anabolic hormone of the body. It promotes the storage of fuels and the use of fuels for growth. Glucagon is the major hormone of fuel mobilization (Fig. 26.5). These hormones fluctuate continuously in response to our daily eating pattern.

Glucose has a special role in metabolic homeostasis. Many tissues (e.g., the brain, red blood cells, kidney medulla, exercising skeletal muscle) depend on glycolysis for all or a part of their energy needs. As a consequence, these tissues require uninterrupted access to glucose to meet their rapid rate of ATP use. In the adult, a minimum of 190 g glucose is required per day, approximately 150 g for the brain and 40 g for other tissues. Significant decreases of blood glucose lower than 60 mg/dL limit

FIG. 26.4. Metabolic homeostasis. The balance between fuel availability and the needs of tissues for different fuels is achieved by three types of messages: the level of the fuel or nutrients in the blood, the level of one of the hormones of metabolic homeostasis, or the nerve impulses that affect tissue metabolism or the release of hormones.

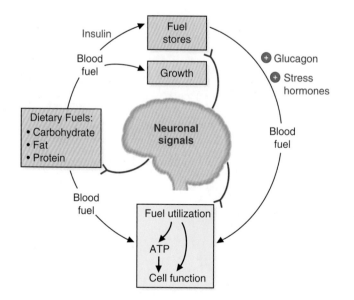

FIG. 26.5. Signals that regulate metabolic homeostasis. The major stress hormones are epinephrine and cortisol.

Hyperglycemia may cause a constellation of symptoms such as polyuria and subsequent polydipsia (increased thirst). These symptoms are caused by the osmotic diuresis that results from the high levels of glucose being excreted into the urine. This diuretic effect may decrease the effective plasma volume, thereby further increasing blood glucose levels. If this dehydration becomes severe, it may lead to cerebral dysfunction and even coma. The inability to move glucose into cells necessitates the oxidation of lipids as an alternative fuel. As a result, adipose stores are used, and a patient with poorly controlled diabetes mellitus loses weight in spite of a good appetite. Extremely high levels of serum glucose can cause nonketotic hyperosmolar coma in patients with type 2 diabetes mellitus (hyperosmolar hyperglycemic state [HHS] or nonketotic hyperglycemia). Such patients usually have sufficient insulin responsiveness to block fatty acid release and ketone body formation, but they are unable to significantly stimulate glucose entry into peripheral tissues. The severely elevated levels of glucose in the blood compared with those inside the cell lead to an osmotic effect that causes water to leave the cells and enter the blood. Chronic hyperglycemia also produces pathologic effects through the nonenzymatic glycosylation of a variety of proteins. Hemoglobin A (HbA), one of the proteins that becomes glycosylated, forms HbA1c (see Chapter 7). **Ann Sulin's** high levels of HbA1c (14% of the total HbA, compared with the reference range of 4.7% to 6.4%) indicate that her blood glucose has been significantly elevated over the last 12 to 14 weeks, the half-life of hemoglobin in the bloodstream.

All membrane and serum proteins exposed to high levels of glucose in the blood or interstitial fluid are candidates for nonenzymatic glycosylation. This process distorts protein structure and slows protein degradation, which leads to an accumulation of these products in various organs, thereby adversely affecting organ function. These events contribute to the long-term microvascular and macrovascular complications of diabetes mellitus, which include diabetic retinopathy, nephropathy, and neuropathy (microvascular), in addition to coronary artery, cerebral artery, peripheral artery disease, and atherosclerosis (macrovascular).

glucose metabolism in the brain and may elicit hypoglycemic symptoms (as experienced by **Bea Selmass**), presumably because the overall process of glucose flux through the blood–brain barrier, into the interstitial fluid, and subsequently into the neuronal cells is slow at low blood glucose levels because of the K_m values of the glucose transporters required for this to occur (see Chapter 27).

The continuous efflux of fuels from their storage depots during exercise, for example, is necessitated by the high amounts of fuel required to meet the need for ATP under these conditions. Disastrous results would occur if even a day's supply of glucose, amino acids, and fatty acids could not enter cells normally and were instead left circulating in the blood. Glucose and amino acids would be at such high concentrations in the circulation that the hyperosmolar effect would cause progressively severe neurologic deficits and even coma. The concentration of glucose and amino acids would rise above the renal tubular threshold for these substances (the maximal concentration in the blood at which the kidney can completely resorb metabolites), and some of these compounds would be wasted as they spilled over into the urine. Nonenzymatic glycosylation of proteins would increase at higher blood glucose levels, altering the function of tissues in which these proteins reside. Triacylglycerols, present primarily in chylomicrons and very low-density lipoproteins (VLDLs), would rise in the blood, increasing the likelihood of atherosclerotic vascular disease. These potential metabolic derangements emphasize the need to maintain a normal balance between fuel storage and fuel use.

II. MAJOR HORMONES OF METABOLIC HOMEOSTASIS

Insulin is the major anabolic hormone that promotes the storage of nutrients: glucose storage as glycogen in liver and muscle, conversion of glucose to triacylglycerols in liver and their storage in adipose tissue, and amino acid uptake and protein synthesis in skeletal muscle (Fig. 26.6). Insulin also increases the synthesis of albumin and other proteins by the liver. Insulin promotes the use of glucose as a fuel by facilitating its transport into muscle and adipose tissue. At the same time, insulin acts to inhibit fuel mobilization.

Glucagon acts to maintain fuel availability in the absence of dietary glucose by stimulating the release of glucose from liver glycogen (see Chapter 28);

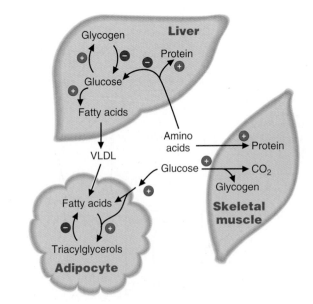

FIG. 26.6. Major sites of insulin action on fuel metabolism. *VLDL*, very low-density lipoprotein; ⊕, stimulated by insulin; ⊖, inhibited by insulin.

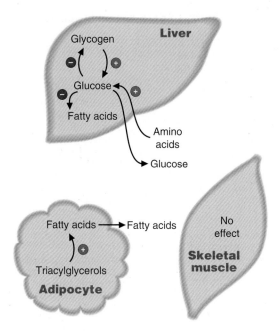

FIG. 26.7. Major sites of glucagon action in fuel metabolism. ⊕, pathways stimulated by glucagon; ⊖, pathways inhibited by glucagon.

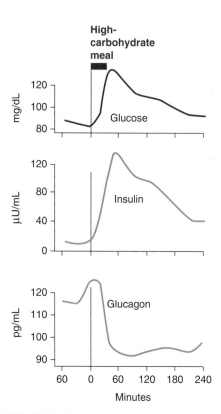

FIG. 26.8. Blood glucose, insulin, and glucagon levels after a high-carbohydrate meal.

by stimulating gluconeogenesis from lactate, glycerol, and amino acids (see Chapter 31); and, in conjunction with decreased insulin, by mobilizing fatty acids from adipose triacylglycerols to provide an alternate source of fuel (see Chapter 23 and Fig. 26.7). Its sites of action are principally the liver and adipose tissue; it has no influence on skeletal muscle metabolism because muscle cells lack glucagon receptors. The message carried by glucagon is that "glucose is gone"; that is, the current supply of glucose is inadequate to meet the immediate fuel requirements of the body.

The release of insulin from the β-cells of the pancreas is dictated primarily by the level of glucose in the blood bathing the β-cells in the islets of Langerhans. The highest levels of insulin occur approximately 30 to 45 minutes after a high-carbohydrate meal (Fig. 26.8). They return to basal levels as the blood glucose concentration falls, approximately 120 minutes after the meal. The release of glucagon from the α-cells of the pancreas, conversely, is controlled principally through a reduction of glucose and/or a rise in the concentration of insulin in the blood bathing the α-cells in the pancreas. Therefore, the lowest levels of glucagon occur after a high-carbohydrate meal. Because all of the effects of glucagon are opposed by insulin, the simultaneous stimulation of insulin release and suppression of glucagon secretion by a high-carbohydrate meal provides integrated control of carbohydrate, fat, and protein metabolism.

Insulin and glucagon are not the only regulators of fuel metabolism. The intertissue balance between the use and storage of glucose, fat, and protein is also accomplished by the circulating levels of metabolites in the blood, by neuronal signals, and by the other hormones of metabolic homeostasis (epinephrine, norepinephrine, cortisol, etc.) (Table 26.1). These hormones oppose the actions of insulin by mobilizing fuels. Like glucagon, they are insulin counterregulatory hormones (Fig. 26.9). Of all these hormones, only insulin and glucagon are synthesized and released in direct response to changing levels of fuels in the blood. The release of cortisol, epinephrine, and norepinephrine is mediated by neuronal signals. Rising levels of the insulin counterregulatory hormones in the blood reflect, for the most part, a current increase in the demand for fuel.

 Bea Selmass's studies confirmed that her fasting serum glucose levels were below normal. She continued to experience the fatigue, confusion, and blurred vision she had described on her first office visit. These symptoms are referred to as the *neuroglycopenic manifestations of severe hypoglycemia* (neurologic symptoms resulting from an inadequate supply of glucose to the brain for the generation of ATP).

Bea also noted the symptoms that are part of the adrenergic response to hypoglycemic stress. Stimulation of the sympathetic nervous system (because of the low levels of glucose reaching the brain) results in the release of epinephrine, a stress hormone, from the adrenal medulla. Elevated epinephrine levels cause tachycardia (rapid heart beat), palpitations, anxiety, tremulousness, pallor, and sweating.

In addition to the symptoms described by **Bea Selmass**, individuals may experience confusion, light-headedness, headache, aberrant behavior, blurred vision, loss of consciousness, or seizures. When severe and prolonged, death may occur.

Ms. Selmass's doctor explained that the general diagnosis of "fasting" hypoglycemia was now established and that a specific cause for this disorder must be found.

Table 26.1   Physiologic Actions of Insulin and Insulin Counterregulatory Hormones

Hormone	Function	Major Metabolic Pathways Affected
Insulin	Promotes fuel storage after a meal	Stimulates glucose storage as glycogen (muscle and liver)
	Promotes growth	Stimulates fatty acid synthesis and storage after a high-carbohydrate meal
		Stimulates amino acid uptake and protein synthesis
Glucagon	Mobilizes fuels	Activates gluconeogenesis and glycogenolysis (liver) during fasting
	Maintains blood glucose levels during fasting	Activates fatty acid release from adipose tissue
Epinephrine	Mobilizes fuels during acute stress	Stimulates glucose production from glycogen (muscle and liver)
		Stimulates fatty acid release from adipose tissue
Cortisol	Provides for changing requirements over the long-term	Stimulates amino acid mobilization from muscle protein
		Stimulates gluconeogenesis to produce glucose for liver glycogen synthesis
		Stimulates fatty acid release from adipose tissue

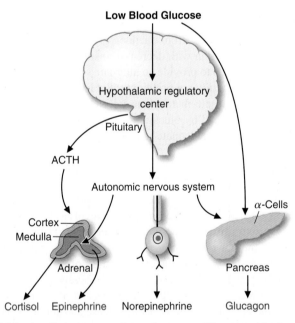

FIG. 26.9. Major insulin counterregulatory hormones. The stress of a low blood glucose level mediates the release of the major insulin counterregulatory hormones through neuronal signals. Hypoglycemia is one of the stress signals that stimulates the release of cortisol, epinephrine, and norepinephrine. Adrenocorticotropic hormone (ACTH) is released from the pituitary and stimulates the release of cortisol (a glucocorticoid) from the adrenal cortex. Neuronal signals stimulate the release of epinephrine from the adrenal medulla and norepinephrine from nerve endings. Neuronal signals also play a minor role in the release of glucagon. Although norepinephrine has counterregulatory actions, it is not a major counterregulatory hormone.

III. SYNTHESIS AND RELEASE OF INSULIN AND GLUCAGON

A. Endocrine Pancreas

Insulin and glucagon are synthesized in different cell types of the endocrine pancreas, which consists of microscopic clusters of small glands, the islets of Langerhans, scattered among the cells of the exocrine pancreas. The α-cells secrete glucagon and the β-cells secrete insulin into the hepatic portal vein via the pancreatic veins.

B. Synthesis and Secretion of Insulin

Insulin is a polypeptide hormone. The active form of insulin is composed of two polypeptide chains (the A-chain and the B-chain) linked by two interchain disulfide bonds. The A-chain has an additional intrachain disulfide bond (Fig. 26.10).

Insulin, like many other polypeptide hormones, is synthesized as a preprohormone that is converted in the rough endoplasmic reticulum (RER) to proinsulin. The "pre" sequence, a short hydrophobic signal sequence at the N-terminal end, is cleaved as it enters the lumen of the RER. Proinsulin folds into the proper conformation, and disulfide bonds are formed between the cysteine residues. It is then transported in microvesicles to the Golgi complex. It leaves the Golgi complex in storage vesicles, where a protease removes the biologically inactive "connecting peptide" (C-peptide) and a few small remnants, resulting in the formation of biologically active insulin (see Fig. 26.10). Zinc ions are also transported in these storage vesicles. Cleavage of the C-peptide decreases the solubility of the resulting insulin, which then coprecipitates with zinc. Exocytosis of the insulin storage vesicles from the cytosol of the β-cell into the blood is stimulated by rising levels of glucose in the blood bathing the β-cells.

The message that insulin carries to tissues is that glucose is plentiful and can be used as an immediate fuel or can be converted to storage forms such as triacylglycerol in adipocytes or glycogen in liver and muscle.

Because insulin stimulates the uptake of glucose into tissues where it may be immediately oxidized or stored for later oxidation, this regulatory hormone lowers blood glucose levels. Therefore, one of the possible causes of **Bea Selmass's** hypoglycemia is an insulinoma, a tumor that produces excessive insulin.

Whenever an endocrine gland continues to release its hormone in spite of the presence of signals that normally would suppress its secretion, this persistent inappropriate release is said to be "autonomous." Secretory neoplasms of endocrine glands generally produce their hormonal product autonomously in a chronic fashion.

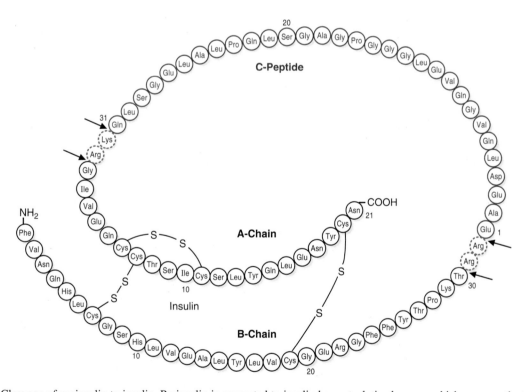

FIG. 26.10. Cleavage of proinsulin to insulin. Proinsulin is converted to insulin by proteolytic cleavage, which removes the C-peptide and a few additional amino acid residues. Cleavage occurs at the *arrows*. (From Murray RK, Granner DK, Mayer PA, et al. *Harper's Biochemistry.* 23rd ed. Stanford, CT: Appleton & Lange; 1993:560.)

Autonomous hypersecretion of insulin from a suspected pancreatic β-cell tumor (an insulinoma) can be demonstrated in several ways. The simplest test is to draw blood for the measurement of both glucose and insulin simultaneously, at a time when the patient is spontaneously experiencing the characteristic adrenergic or neuroglycopenic symptoms of hypoglycemia. During such a test, **Bea Selmass's** glucose levels fell to 45 mg/dL (normal, 80 to 100 mg/dL), and her ratio of insulin to glucose was far higher than normal. The elevated insulin levels markedly increased glucose uptake by the peripheral tissues, resulting in a dramatic lowering of blood glucose levels. In normal individuals, as blood glucose levels drop, insulin levels also drop. Insulin levels were determined by radioimmunoassay (see the Biochemical Comments in Chapter 43 for a description of this method).

Di Abietes has type 1 diabetes mellitus, formerly known as insulin-dependent diabetes mellitus (IDDM). This metabolic disorder is usually caused by antibody-mediated (autoimmune) destruction of the β-cells of the pancreas. Susceptibility to type 1 diabetes mellitus is, in part, conferred by a genetic defect in the human leukocyte antigen (HLA) region of β-cells that codes for the major histocompatibility complex II (MHC II). This protein presents an intracellular antigen to the cell surface for "self-recognition" by the cells involved in the immune response. Because of this defective protein, a cell-mediated immune response leads to varying degrees of β-cell destruction and eventually to dependence on exogenous insulin administration to control the levels of glucose in the blood.

FIG. 26.11. Release of insulin by the β-cells. Details are given in the text.

Glucose enters the β-cell via specific glucose transporter proteins known as GLUT 2 (see Chapter 27). Glucose is phosphorylated through the action of glucokinase to form glucose 6-phosphate, which is metabolized through glycolysis, the TCA cycle, and oxidative phosphorylation. These reactions result in an increase in ATP levels within the β-cell (*circle 1* in Fig. 26.11). As the β-cell [ATP]/[ADP] ratio increases, the activity of a membrane-bound, ATP-dependent K^+ channel (K^+_{ATP}) is inhibited (i.e., the channel is closed) (*circle 2* in Fig. 26.11). The closing of this channel leads to a membrane depolarization (*circle 3* in Fig. 26.11), which activates a voltage-gated Ca^{2+} channel that allows Ca^{2+} to enter the β-cell such that intracellular Ca^{2+} levels increase significantly (*circle 4* in Fig. 26.11). The increase in intracellular Ca^{2+} stimulates the fusion of insulin containing exocytotic vesicles with the plasma membrane, resulting in insulin secretion (*circle 5* in Fig. 26.11). Thus, an increase in glucose levels within the β-cells initiates insulin release.

Other intracellular metabolites, particularly NADPH, have been proposed to play important roles in insulin release in response to glucose. This will be discussed further in later chapters.

C. Stimulation and Inhibition of Insulin Release

The release of insulin occurs within minutes after the pancreas is exposed to a high glucose concentration. The threshold for insulin release is approximately 80 mg glucose/dL. Above 80 mg/dL, the rate of insulin release is not an all-or-nothing response but is proportional to the glucose concentration up to approximately 300 mg/dL. As insulin is secreted, the synthesis of new insulin molecules is stimulated, so that secretion is maintained until blood glucose levels fall. Insulin is rapidly removed from the circulation and degraded by the liver (and, to a lesser extent, by kidney and skeletal muscle), so blood insulin levels decrease rapidly once the rate of secretion slows.

Several factors other than the blood glucose concentration can modulate insulin release (Table 26.2). The pancreatic islets are innervated by the autonomic nervous system, including a branch of the vagus nerve. These neural signals help to coordinate insulin release with the secretory signals initiated by the ingestion of fuels. However, signals from the central nervous system are not required for insulin secretion. Certain amino acids also can stimulate insulin secretion, although the amount of insulin released during a high-protein meal is very much lower than that released by a high-carbohydrate meal. Gastric inhibitory polypeptide (GIP) and

Table 26.2   Regulators of Insulin Release

Regulator	Effect
Major regulators	
Glucose	+
Minor regulators	
Amino acids	+
Neural input	+
Gut hormones[a]	+
Epinephrine (adrenergic)	−

+, stimulates; −, inhibits.
[a]Gut hormones that regulate fuel metabolism are discussed in Chapter 43.

glucagon-like peptide 1 (GLP-1), gut hormones released after the ingestion of food, also aid in the onset of insulin release. Epinephrine, secreted in response to fasting, stress, trauma, and vigorous exercise, decreases the release of insulin. Epinephrine release signals energy use, which indicates that less insulin needs to be secreted, as insulin stimulates energy storage.

D. Synthesis and Secretion of Glucagon

Glucagon, a polypeptide hormone, is synthesized in the α-cells of the pancreas by cleavage of the much larger preproglucagon, a 160–amino acid peptide. Like insulin, preproglucagon is produced on the RER and is converted to proglucagon as it enters the lumen of the endoplasmic reticulum. Proteolytic cleavage at various sites produces the mature 29–amino acid glucagon (molecular weight 3,500 Da) and larger glucagon-containing fragments (named GLP-1 and GLP-2). Glucagon is rapidly metabolized, primarily in the liver and kidneys. Its plasma half-life is only about 3 to 5 minutes.

Glucagon secretion is regulated principally by circulating levels of glucose and insulin. Increasing levels of each inhibit glucagon release. Glucose probably has both a direct suppressive effect on secretion of glucagon from the α-cell as well as an indirect effect, the latter being mediated by its ability to stimulate the release of insulin. The direction of blood flow in the islets of the pancreas carries insulin from the β-cells in the center of the islets to the peripheral α-cells, where it suppresses glucagon secretion.

Conversely, certain hormones stimulate glucagon secretion. Among these are the catecholamines (including epinephrine) and cortisol (Table 26.3).

Many amino acids also stimulate glucagon release (Fig. 26.12). Thus, the high levels of glucagon that would be expected in the fasting state do not decrease after a high-protein meal. In fact, glucagon levels may increase, stimulating gluconeogenesis in the absence of dietary glucose. The relative amounts of insulin and glucagon in the blood after a mixed meal depend on the composition of the meal because glucose stimulates insulin release and amino acids stimulate glucagon release.

Table 26.3   Regulators of Glucagon Release

Regulator	Effect
Major regulators	
Glucose	−
Insulin	−
Amino acids	+
Minor regulators	
Cortisol	+
Neural (stress)	+
Epinephrine	+

+, stimulates; −, inhibits.

A form of diabetes known as *maturity-onset diabetes of the young* (*MODY*) results from mutations in either pancreatic glucokinase or specific nuclear transcription factors. MODY type 2 is caused by a glucokinase mutation that results in an enzyme with reduced activity because of either an elevated K_m for glucose or a reduced V_{max} for the reaction. Because insulin release depends on normal glucose metabolism within the β-cell that yields a critical [ATP]/[ADP] ratio in the β-cell, individuals with this glucokinase mutation cannot significantly metabolize glucose unless glucose levels are higher than normal. Thus, although these patients can release insulin, they do so at higher than normal glucose levels and are, therefore, almost always in a hyperglycemic state. Interestingly, however, these patients are somewhat resistant to the long-term complications of chronic hyperglycemia. The mechanism for this seeming resistance is not well understood.

Neonatal diabetes is an inherited disorder in which newborns develop diabetes within the first 3 months of life. The diabetes may be permanent, requiring life-long insulin treatment, or transient. The most common mutation leading to permanent neonatal diabetes is in the *KCNJ11* gene, which encodes a subunit of the K^+_{ATP} channel in various tissues, including the pancreas. This is an activating mutation, which keeps the K^+_{ATP} channel open, and less susceptible to ATP inhibition. If the K^+_{ATP} channel cannot be closed, activation of the Ca^{2+} channel will not occur, and insulin secretion will be impaired.

Ann Sulin is taking a sulfonylurea compound known as glipizide to treat her diabetes. The sulfonylureas act on the K^+_{ATP} channels on the surface of the pancreatic β-cells. The K^+_{ATP} channels contain pore-forming subunits (encoded by the *KCNJ11* gene) and regulatory subunits (the subunit to which sulfonylurea compounds bind, encoded by the *SUR1* gene). The binding of the drug to the sulfonylurea receptor closes K^+ channels (as do elevated ATP levels), which, in turn, increases Ca^{2+} movement into the interior of the β-cell. This influx of calcium modulates the interaction of the insulin storage vesicles with the plasma membrane of the β-cell, resulting in the release of insulin into the circulation.

Recently, a patient was discovered to have an activating mutation in the *SUR1* gene (which would make it difficult to close the K^+_{ATP} channel), and, among other symptoms, the patient displayed neonatal diabetes.

Measurements of proinsulin and the connecting peptide between the α- and β-chains of insulin (C-peptide) in **Bea Selmass's** blood during her hospital fast provided confirmation that she had an insulinoma. Insulin and C-peptide are secreted in approximately equal proportions from the β-cell, but C-peptide is not cleared from the blood as rapidly as insulin. Therefore, it provides a reasonably accurate estimate of the rate of insulin secretion. Plasma C-peptide measurements are also potentially useful in treating patients with diabetes mellitus because they provide a way to estimate the degree of endogenous insulin secretion in patients who are receiving exogenous insulin, which lacks the C-peptide.

Patients with type 1 diabetes mellitus, such as **Di Abietes**, have almost undetectable levels of insulin in their blood. Patients with type 2 diabetes mellitus, such as **Ann Sulin**, conversely, have normal or even elevated levels of insulin in their blood; however, the level of insulin in their blood is inappropriately low relative to their elevated blood glucose concentration. In type 2 diabetes mellitus, skeletal muscle, liver, and other tissues exhibit a resistance to the actions of insulin. As a result, insulin has a smaller than normal effect on glucose and fat metabolism in such patients. Levels of insulin in the blood must be higher than normal to maintain normal blood glucose levels. In the early stages of type 2 diabetes mellitus, these compensatory adjustments in insulin release may keep the blood glucose levels near the normal range. Over time, as the β-cells' capacity to secrete high levels of insulin declines, blood glucose levels increase, and exogenous insulin becomes necessary.

FIG. 26.12. Release of insulin and glucagon in response to a high-protein meal. This figure shows the increase in the release of insulin and glucagon into the blood after an overnight fast followed by the ingestion of 100 g protein (equivalent to a slice of roast beef). Insulin levels do not increase nearly as much as they do after a high-carbohydrate meal (see Fig. 26.8). The levels of glucagon, however, significantly increase above those present in the fasting state.

However, amino acids also induce insulin secretion, but not to the same extent that glucose does. Although this may seem paradoxical, it actually makes good sense. Insulin release stimulates amino acid uptake by tissues and enhances protein synthesis. However, because glucagon levels also increase in response to a protein meal, and the critical factor is the insulin-to-glucagon ratio, sufficient glucagon is released that gluconeogenesis is enhanced (at the expense of protein synthesis), and the amino acids that are taken up by the tissues serve as a substrate for gluconeogenesis. The synthesis of glycogen and TGs is also reduced when glucagon levels in the blood rise.

In fasting subjects, the average level of immunoreactive glucagon in the blood is 75 pg/mL and does not vary as much as insulin during the daily fasting–feeding cycle. However, only 30% to 40% of the measured immunoreactive glucagon is mature pancreatic glucagon. The rest is composed of larger immunoreactive fragments that are also produced in the pancreas or in the intestinal L-cells.

IV. MECHANISMS OF HORMONE ACTION

For a hormone to affect the flux of substrates through a metabolic pathway, it must be able to change the rate at which that pathway proceeds by increasing or decreasing the rate of the slowest step(s). Either directly or indirectly, hormones affect the activity of specific enzymes or transport proteins that regulate the flux through a pathway. Thus, ultimately, the hormone must either cause the amount of the substrate for the enzyme to increase (if substrate supply is a rate-limiting factor), change the conformation at the active site by phosphorylating the enzyme, change the concentration of an allosteric effector of the enzyme, or change the amount of the protein by inducing or repressing its synthesis or by changing its turnover rate or location. Insulin, glucagon, and other hormones use all of these regulatory mechanisms to determine the rate of flux in metabolic pathways. The effects mediated by phosphorylation or changes in the kinetic properties of an enzyme occur rapidly within minutes. In contrast, it may take hours for induction or repression of enzyme synthesis to change the amount of an enzyme in the cell.

The details of hormone action were described in Chapter 11 and are only summarized here.

A. Signal Transduction by Hormones that Bind to Plasma Membrane Receptors

Hormones initiate their actions on target cells by binding to specific receptors or binding proteins. In the case of polypeptide hormones (such as insulin and glucagon) and catecholamines (epinephrine and norepinephrine), the action of the hormone is mediated through binding to a specific receptor on the plasma membrane (see Chapter 11, Section III). The first message of the hormone is transmitted to intracellular enzymes by the activated receptor and an intracellular second messenger; the hormone does not need to enter the cell to exert its effects. (In contrast, steroid hormones such as cortisol and the thyroid hormone triiodothyronine [T_3] enter the cytosol and eventually move into the cell nucleus to exert their effects.)

The mechanism by which the message carried by the hormone that ultimately affects the rate of the regulatory enzyme in the target cell is called *signal transduction*. The three basic types of signal transduction for hormones binding to receptors on the plasma membrane are (1) receptor coupling to adenylate cyclase, which produces cyclic adenosine monophosphate (cAMP); (2) receptor kinase activity; and (3) receptor coupling to hydrolysis of phosphatidylinositol bisphosphate (PIP_2). The hormones of metabolic homeostasis each use one of these mechanisms to carry out their physiologic effect. In addition, some hormones and neurotransmitters act through receptor coupling to gated ion channels (described in Chapter 11).

1. SIGNAL TRANSDUCTION BY INSULIN

Insulin initiates its action by binding to a receptor on the plasma membrane of insulin's many target cells (see Fig. 11.13). The insulin receptor has two types of subunits: the α-subunits to which insulin binds, and the β-subunits, which span the membrane and protrude into the cytosol. The cytosolic portion of the β-subunit has tyrosine kinase activity. On binding of insulin, the tyrosine kinase phosphorylates tyrosine residues on the β-subunit (autophosphorylation), as well as on several other enzymes within the cytosol. A principal substrate for phosphorylation by the receptor, insulin receptor substrate 1 (IRS-1), then recognizes and binds to various signal transduction proteins in regions referred to as *SH_2 domains*. IRS-1 is involved in many of the physiologic responses to insulin through complex mechanisms that are the subject of intensive investigation. The basic tissue-specific cellular responses to insulin, however, can be grouped into five major categories: (1) insulin reverses glucagon-stimulated phosphorylation, (2) insulin works through a phosphorylation cascade that stimulates the phosphorylation of several enzymes, (3) insulin induces and represses the synthesis of specific enzymes, (4) insulin acts as a growth factor and has a general stimulatory effect on protein synthesis, and (5) insulin stimulates glucose and amino acid transport into cells (see Fig. V.10 in the introduction to Section Five).

Several mechanisms have been proposed for the action of insulin in reversing glucagon-stimulated phosphorylation of the enzymes of carbohydrate metabolism. From the student's point of view, the ability of insulin to reverse glucagon-stimulated phosphorylation occurs as if it were lowering cAMP and stimulating phosphatases that could remove those phosphates added by protein kinase A (PKA). In reality, the mechanism is more complex and still not fully understood.

The physiologic importance of insulin's usual action of mediating the suppressive effect of glucose on glucagon secretion is apparent in patients with types 1 and 2 diabetes mellitus. Despite the presence of hyperglycemia, glucagon levels in such patients initially remain elevated (near fasting levels), either because of the absence of insulin's suppressive effect or because of the resistance of the α-cells to insulin's suppressive effect even in the face of adequate insulin levels in type 2 patients. Thus, these patients have inappropriately high glucagon levels, leading to the suggestion that diabetes mellitus is actually a "bihormonal" disorder.

During the "stress" of hypoglycemia, the autonomic nervous system stimulates the pancreas to secrete glucagon, which tends to restore the serum glucose level to normal. The increased activity of the adrenergic nervous system (through epinephrine) also alerts a patient, such as **Bea Selmass**, to the presence of increasingly severe hypoglycemia. Hopefully, this will induce the patient to ingest simple sugars or other carbohydrates, which, in turn, will also increase glucose levels in the blood. **Bea Selmass** gained 8 lb before resection of her pancreatic insulin-secreting adenoma through this mechanism.

2. SIGNAL TRANSDUCTION BY GLUCAGON

The pathway for signal transduction by glucagon is one that is common to several hormones; the glucagon receptor is coupled to adenylate cyclase and cAMP production (see Fig. 11.10). Glucagon, through G-proteins, activates the membrane-bound adenylate cyclase, increasing the synthesis of the intracellular second messenger 3′,5′-cyclic AMP (cAMP) (see Fig. 11.18). cAMP activates PKA (cAMP-dependent protein kinase), which changes the activity of enzymes by phosphorylating them at specific serine residues. Phosphorylation activates some enzymes and inhibits others.

The *G-proteins*, which couple the glucagon receptor to adenylate cyclase, are proteins in the plasma membrane that bind guanosine triphosphate (GTP) and have dissociable subunits that interact with both the receptor and adenylate cyclase. In the absence of glucagon, the stimulatory G_s-protein complex binds guanosine diphosphate (GDP) but cannot bind to the unoccupied receptor or adenylate cyclase (see Fig. 11.17). Once glucagon binds to the receptor, the receptor also binds the G_s-complex, which then releases GDP and binds GTP. The α-subunit then dissociates from the $\beta\gamma$-subunits and binds to adenylate cyclase, thereby activating it. As the GTP on the α-subunit is hydrolyzed to GDP, the subunit dissociates and recomplexes with the β- and γ-subunits. Only continued occupancy of the glucagon receptor can keep adenylate cyclase active.

Although glucagon works by activating adenylate cyclase, a few hormones inhibit adenylate cyclase. In this case, the inhibitory G-protein complex is called a *G_i-complex*. cAMP is the intracellular second messenger for several hormones that regulate fuel metabolism. The specificity of the physiologic response to each hormone results from the presence of specific receptors for that hormone in target tissues. For example, glucagon activates glucose production from glycogen in liver but not in skeletal muscle because glucagon receptors are present in liver but absent in skeletal muscle. However, skeletal muscle has adenylate cyclase, cAMP, and PKA, which can be activated by epinephrine binding to the β_2-receptors in the membranes of muscle cells. Liver cells also have epinephrine receptors.

cAMP is very rapidly degraded to AMP by a membrane-bound phosphodiesterase. The concentration of cAMP is thus very low in the cell, so changes in its concentration can occur rapidly in response to changes in the rate of synthesis. The amount of cAMP present at any time is a direct reflection of hormone binding and the activity of adenylate cyclase. It is not affected by ATP, ADP (adenosine diphosphate), or AMP levels in the cell.

cAMP transmits the hormone signal to the cell by activating PKA (cAMP-dependent protein kinase). As cAMP binds to the regulatory subunits of PKA, these subunits dissociate from the catalytic subunits, which are thereby activated (see Chapter 9, Fig. 9.10). Activated PKA phosphorylates serine residues of key regulatory enzymes in the pathways of carbohydrate and fat metabolism. Some enzymes are activated and others are inhibited by this change in phosphorylation state. The message of the hormone is terminated by the action of semispecific protein phosphatases that remove phosphate groups from the enzymes. The activity of the protein phosphatases is also controlled through hormonal regulation.

Changes in the phosphorylation state of proteins that bind to cAMP response elements (CREs) in the promoter region of genes contribute to the regulation of gene transcription by several cAMP-coupled hormones (see Chapter 16). For instance, cAMP response element binding (CREB) protein is directly phosphorylated by PKA, a step essential for the initiation of transcription. Phosphorylation at other sites on CREB, by a variety of kinases, also may play a role in regulating transcription.

The mechanism for signal transduction by glucagon illustrates some of the important principles of hormonal signaling mechanisms. The first principle is that specificity of action in tissues is conferred by the receptor on a target cell for

Phosphodiesterase is inhibited by methylxanthines, a class of compounds that includes caffeine. Would the effect of a methylxanthine on fuel metabolism be similar to fasting or to a high-carbohydrate meal?

glucagon. In general, the major actions of glucagon occur in liver, adipose tissue, and certain cells of the kidney that contain glucagon receptors. The second principle is that signal transduction involves amplification of the first message. Glucagon and other hormones are present in the blood in very low concentrations. However, these minute concentrations of hormone are adequate to initiate a cellular response because the binding of one molecule of glucagon to one receptor ultimately activates many PKA molecules, each of which phosphorylates hundreds of downstream enzymes. The third principle involves integration of metabolic responses. For instance, the glucagon-stimulated phosphorylation of enzymes simultaneously activates glycogen degradation, inhibits glycogen synthesis, and inhibits glycolysis in the liver (see Fig. V.10 in the introduction to Section Five). The fourth principle involves augmentation and antagonism of signals. An example of augmentation involves the actions of glucagon and epinephrine (which is released during exercise). Although these hormones bind to different receptors, each can increase cAMP and stimulate glycogen degradation. The fifth principle is that of rapid signal termination. In the case of glucagon, both the termination of the G_s-protein activation and the rapid degradation of cAMP contribute to signal termination.

B. Signal Transduction by Cortisol and Other Hormones that Interact with Intracellular Receptors

Signal transduction by the glucocorticoid cortisol and other steroids that have glucocorticoid activity and by thyroid hormone involves hormone binding to intracellular (cytosolic) receptors or binding proteins, after which this hormone-binding protein complex, if not already in the nucleus, moves into the nucleus, where it interacts with chromatin. This interaction changes the rate of gene transcription in the target cells (see Chapter 16). The cellular responses to these hormones continue as long as the target cell is exposed to the specific hormones. Thus, disorders that cause a chronic excess in their secretion result in an equally persistent influence on fuel metabolism. For example, chronic stress such as that seen in prolonged sepsis may lead to varying degrees of glucose intolerance if high levels of epinephrine and cortisol persist.

The effects of cortisol on gene transcription are usually synergistic to those of certain other hormones. For instance, the rates of gene transcription for some of the enzymes in the pathway for glucose synthesis from amino acids (gluconeogenesis) are induced by glucagon as well as by cortisol.

C. Signal Transduction by Epinephrine and Norepinephrine

Epinephrine and norepinephrine are catecholamines (Fig. 26.13). They can act as neurotransmitters or as hormones. A neurotransmitter allows a neural signal to be transmitted across the juncture or synapse between the nerve terminal of a proximal nerve axon and the cell body of a distal neuron. A hormone, conversely, is released into the blood and travels in the circulation to interact with specific receptors on the plasma membrane or cytosol of cells of the target organ. The general effect of these catecholamines is to prepare us for fight or flight. Under these acutely stressful circumstances, these "stress" hormones increase fuel mobilization, cardiac output, blood flow, and so on, which enables us to meet these stresses. The catecholamines bind to adrenergic receptors (the term *adrenergic* refers to nerve cells or fibers that are part of the involuntary or autonomic nervous system, a system that employs norepinephrine as a neurotransmitter).

There are nine different types of adrenergic receptors: α_{1A}, α_{1B}, α_{1D}, α_{2A}, α_{2B}, α_{2C}, β_1, β_2, and β_3. Only the three β- and α_1-receptors are discussed here. The three β-receptors work through the adenylate cyclase–cAMP system, activating a G_s-protein, which activates adenylate cyclase, and eventually PKA. The β_1-receptor is the major adrenergic receptor in the human heart and is primarily stimulated by norepinephrine. On activation, the β_1-receptor increases the rate of muscle

 Inhibition of phosphodiesterase by methylxanthine would increase cAMP and have the same effects on fuel metabolism as would an increase of glucagon and epinephrine, as in the fasted state. Increased fuel mobilization would occur through glycogenolysis (the release of glucose from glycogen) and through lipolysis (the release of fatty acids from triacylglycerols).

 Ann O'Rexia, to stay thin, frequently fasts for prolonged periods, but she jogs every morning (see Chapter 2). The release of epinephrine and norepinephrine and the increase of glucagon and fall of insulin during her exercise provide coordinated and augmented signals that stimulate the release of fuels above the fasting levels. Fuel mobilization will occur, of course, only as long as she has fuel stored as triacylglycerols.

Epinephrine

Norepinephrine

FIG. 26.13. Structure of epinephrine and norepinephrine. Epinephrine and norepinephrine are synthesized from tyrosine and act as both hormones and neurotransmitters. They are catecholamines, the term *catechol* referring to a ring structure containing two hydroxyl groups.

Ann Sulin, a patient with type 2 diabetes mellitus, is experiencing insulin resistance. Her levels of circulating insulin are normal to high, although inappropriately low for her elevated level of blood glucose. However, her insulin target cells, such as muscle and fat, do not respond as those of a nondiabetic subject would to this level of insulin. For most type 2 patients, the site of insulin resistance is subsequent to binding of insulin to its receptor; that is, the number of receptors and their affinity for insulin is near normal. However, the binding of insulin at these receptors does not elicit most of the normal intracellular effects of insulin discussed earlier. Consequently, there is little stimulation of glucose metabolism and storage after a high-carbohydrate meal and little inhibition of hepatic gluconeogenesis.

contraction, in part because of PKA-mediated phosphorylation of phospholamban (see Chapter 47). The β_2-receptor is present in liver, skeletal muscle, and other tissues and is involved in the mobilization of fuels (such as the generation of glucose through glycogenolysis). It also mediates vascular, bronchial, and uterine smooth muscle contraction. Epinephrine is a much more potent agonist for this receptor than norepinephrine, whose major action is neurotransmission. The β_3-receptor is found predominantly in adipose tissue and to a lesser extent in skeletal muscle. Activation of this receptor stimulates fatty acid oxidation and thermogenesis, and agonists for this receptor may prove to be beneficial weight-loss agents. The a_1-receptors, which are postsynaptic receptors, mediate vascular and smooth muscle contraction. They work through the PIP_2 system (see Chapter 11, Section III.B.2) via activation of a G_q-protein, and phospholipase C-β. This receptor also mediates glycogenolysis in liver.

CLINICAL COMMENTS

Ann Sulin. Ann Sulin has type 2 diabetes mellitus (formerly called *non–insulin-dependent diabetes mellitus*), whereas Di Abietes has type 1 diabetes mellitus (formerly designated insulin-dependent diabetes mellitus [IDDM]). Although the pathogenesis differs for these major forms of diabetes mellitus, both cause varying degrees of hyperglycemia. In type 1 diabetes mellitus, the pancreatic β-cells are gradually destroyed by antibodies directed at a variety of proteins within the β-cells. As insulin secretory capacity by the β-cells gradually diminishes below a critical level, the symptoms of chronic hyperglycemia develop rapidly. In type 2 diabetes mellitus, these symptoms develop more subtly and gradually over the course of months or years. Eighty-five percent or more of type 2 patients are obese and, like **Ivan Applebod**, have a high waist–hip ratio with regard to adipose tissue disposition. This abnormal distribution of fat in the visceral (peri-intestinal) adipocytes is associated with reduced sensitivity of fat cells, muscle cells, and liver cells to the actions of insulin outlined previously. This insulin resistance can be diminished through weight loss, specifically in the visceral depots. The development of type 2 diabetes, coupled with obesity and high blood pressure, can lead to the metabolic syndrome, a common clinical entity that is discussed in more detail in the next section of the text.

Bea Selmass. Bea Selmass underwent a high-resolution ultrasonographic (ultrasound) study of her upper abdomen, which showed a 2.6-cm mass in the midportion of her pancreas. With this finding, her physicians decided that further noninvasive studies would not be necessary before surgical exploration of her upper abdomen was performed. At the time of surgery, a yellow-white 2.8-cm mass consisting primarily of insulin-rich β-cells was resected from her pancreas. No cytologic changes of malignancy were seen on microscopic examination of the surgical specimen, and no gross evidence of malignant behavior by the tumor (such as local metastases) was found. Bea had an uneventful postoperative recovery and no longer experienced the signs and symptoms of insulin-induced hypoglycemia.

BIOCHEMICAL COMMENTS

Actions of Insulin. One of the important cellular responses to insulin is the reversal of glucagon-stimulated phosphorylation of enzymes. Mechanisms proposed for this action include the inhibition of adenylate cyclase, a reduction of cAMP levels, the stimulation of phosphodiesterase, the production of a specific protein (insulin factor), the release of a second messenger from a bound glycosylated phosphatidylinositol, and the phosphorylation of enzymes at a site that antagonizes protein kinase A phosphorylation. Not all of these physiologic actions of insulin occur in each of the insulin-sensitive organs of the body.

Insulin is also able to antagonize the actions of glucagon at the level of specific induction or repression of key regulatory enzymes of carbohydrate metabolism. For instance, the rate of synthesis of messenger RNA (mRNA) for phosphoenol-pyruvate carboxykinase, a key enzyme of the gluconeogenic pathway, is increased severalfold by glucagon (via cAMP) and decreased by insulin. Thus, all of the effects of glucagon, even the induction of certain enzymes, can be reversed by insulin. This antagonism is exerted through an insulin-sensitive hormone response element (IRE) in the promoter region of the genes. Insulin causes repression of the synthesis of enzymes that are induced by glucagon.

The general stimulation of protein synthesis by insulin (its mitogenic or growth-promoting effect) appears to occur through a general increase in rates of mRNA translation for a broad spectrum of structural proteins. These actions result from a phosphorylation cascade initiated by autophosphorylation of the insulin receptor and ending in the phosphorylation of subunits of proteins that bind to and inhibit eukaryotic protein synthesis initiation factors (eIFs). When phosphorylated, the inhibitory proteins are released from the eIFs, allowing translation of mRNA to be stimulated. In this respect, the actions of insulin are similar to those of other hormones that act as growth factors and that also have receptors with tyrosine kinase activity.

In addition to signal transduction, activation of the insulin receptor mediates the internalization of receptor-bound insulin molecules, increasing their subsequent degradation. Although unoccupied receptors can be internalized and eventually recycled to the plasma membrane, the receptor can be irreversibly degraded after prolonged occupation by insulin. The result of this process, referred to as *receptor downregulation*, is an attenuation of the insulin signal. The physiologic importance of receptor internalization on insulin sensitivity is poorly understood but could lead eventually to chronic hyperglycemia.

Key Concepts

- Glucose homeostasis is directed toward the maintenance of constant blood glucose levels.
- Insulin and glucagon are the two major hormones that regulate the balance between fuel mobilization and storage. They maintain blood glucose levels near 80 to 100 mg/dL despite varying levels of carbohydrate intake during the day.
- If dietary intake of all fuels is in excess of immediate caloric requirements, those fuels are stored as either glycogen or fat. Conversely, stored fuels are mobilized when demand exceeds the quantity of calories ingested.
- Insulin is released in response to carbohydrate ingestion and promotes glucose utilization as a fuel and glucose storage as fat and glycogen. Insulin secretion is regulated principally by blood glucose levels.
- Glucagon promotes glucose production via glycogenolysis (glycogen degradation) and gluconeogenesis (glucose synthesis from amino acids and other noncarbohydrate precursors).
- Glucagon release is regulated principally through suppression by rising levels of glucose and rising levels of insulin. Glucagon levels decrease in response to a carbohydrate meal and increase during fasting. Increased levels of glucagon relative to insulin stimulate the release of fatty acids from adipose tissue.
- Glucagon acts by binding to a receptor on the cell surface, which stimulates the synthesis of the intracellular second messenger, cAMP.
- cAMP activates protein kinase A, which phosphorylates key regulatory enzymes, activating some and inhibiting others.
- Insulin acts via a receptor tyrosine kinase and leads to the dephosphorylation of the key enzymes phosphorylated in response to glucagon.
- Hormones that antagonize insulin action, known as *insulin counterregulatory hormones*, include glucagon, epinephrine, and cortisol.
- Diseases discussed in this chapter are summarized in Table 26.4.

Table 26.4   Diseases Discussed in Chapter 26

Disease or Disorder	Environmental or Genetic	Comments
Type 2 diabetes	Both	Emergence of insulin resistance, due to a wide variety of causes; tissues do not respond to insulin as they normally would.
Insulinoma	Environmental	Periodic release of insulin from a tumor of the β-cells, leading to hypoglycemic symptoms, which are accompanied by excessive appetite and weight gain.
Hyperglycemia	Both	Constantly elevated levels of glucose in the circulation due to a wide variety of causes. Hyperglycemia leads to protein glycation and potential loss of protein function in a variety of tissues.
Type 1 diabetes	Both	No production of insulin by the β-cells due to an autoimmune destruction of the β-cells. Hyperglycemia and ketoacidosis may result from the lack of insulin.
Maturity-onset diabetes of the young	Both	Form of diabetes caused by specific mutations, such as a mutation in pancreatic glucokinase, which alters the set point for insulin release from the β-cells.
Neonatal diabetes	Genetic	One cause of neonatal diabetes is a mutation in a subunit of the potassium channel in various tissues. Such a mutation in the pancreas leads to permanent opening of the potassium channel, keeping intracellular calcium levels low, and difficulty in releasing insulin from the β-cells.

REVIEW QUESTIONS—CHAPTER 26

1. A patient with type 1 diabetes mellitus takes an insulin injection before eating dinner but then gets distracted and does not eat. Approximately 3 hours later, the patient becomes shaky, sweaty, and confused. These symptoms have occurred because of which of the following?

   A. Increased glucagon release from the pancreas
   B. Decreased glucagon release from the pancreas
   C. High blood glucose levels
   D. Low blood glucose levels
   E. Elevated ketone body levels

2. Caffeine is a potent inhibitor of the enzyme cAMP phosphodiesterase. Which of the following consequences would you expect to occur in the liver after drinking two cups of strong espresso coffee?

   A. A prolonged response to insulin
   B. A prolonged response to glucagon
   C. An inhibition of protein kinase A
   D. An enhancement of glycolytic activity
   E. A reduced rate of glucose export to the circulation

3. Assume that an increase in blood glucose concentration from 5 to 10 mM would result in insulin release by the pancreas. A mutation in pancreatic glucokinase can lead to maturity-onset diabetes of the young (MODY) because of which of the following within the pancreatic β-cell?

   A. A reduced ability to raise cAMP levels
   B. A reduced ability to raise ATP levels
   C. A reduced ability to stimulate gene transcription
   D. A reduced ability to activate glycogen degradation
   E. A reduced ability to raise intracellular lactate levels

4. Which one of the following organs has the highest demand for glucose as a fuel?

   A. Brain
   B. Muscle (skeletal)
   C. Heart
   D. Liver
   E. Pancreas

5. Glucagon release does not alter muscle metabolism because of which of the following?

   A. Muscle cells lack adenylate cyclase.
   B. Muscle cells lack protein kinase A.
   C. Muscle cells lack G-proteins.
   D. Muscle cells lack guanosine triphosphate (GTP).
   E. Muscle cells lack the glucagon receptor.

27 Digestion, Absorption, and Transport of Carbohydrates

Carbohydrates are the largest source of dietary calories for most of the world's population. The major carbohydrates in the US diet are starch, lactose, and sucrose. The **starches amylose** and **amylopectin** are polysaccharides composed of hundreds to millions of glucosyl units linked together through α-1,4- and α-1,6-glycosidic bonds (Fig. 27.1). **Lactose** is a disaccharide composed of glucose and galactose, linked together through a β-1,4-glycosidic bond. **Sucrose** is a disaccharide composed of glucose and fructose, linked through an α-1,2-glycosidic bond. The digestive processes convert all of these dietary carbohydrates to their constituent monosaccharides by **hydrolyzing glycosidic bonds** between the sugars.

The digestion of starch begins in the mouth (Fig. 27.2). The **salivary gland** releases **α-amylase**, which converts starch to smaller polysaccharides called **α-dextrins**. Salivary α-amylase is inactivated by the acidity of the stomach (HCl). **Pancreatic α-amylase** and bicarbonate are secreted by the exocrine pancreas into the lumen of the small intestine, where bicarbonate neutralizes the gastric secretions. Pancreatic α-amylase continues the digestion of α-dextrins, converting them to disaccharides (**maltose**), trisaccharides (**maltotriose**), and oligosaccharides called **limit dextrins**. Limit dextrins usually contain four to nine glucosyl residues and an **isomaltose** branch (two glucosyl residues attached through an α-1,6-glycosidic bond).

The digestion of the disaccharides lactose and sucrose, as well as further digestion of maltose, maltotriose, and limit dextrins, occurs through **disaccharidases** attached to the membrane surface of the **brush border (microvilli)** of intestinal epithelial cells. **Glucoamylase** hydrolyzes the α-1,4-bonds of dextrins. The **sucrase–isomaltase complex** hydrolyzes sucrose, most of maltose, and almost all of the isomaltose formed by glucoamylase from limit dextrins. **Lactase-glycosylceramidase** (β-glycosidase) hydrolyzes the β-glycosidic bonds in **lactose** and **glycolipids**. A fourth disaccharidase complex, **trehalase**, hydrolyzes the bond (an α-1,1-glycosidic bond) between two glucosyl units in the sugar trehalose. The monosaccharides produced by these hydrolases (glucose, fructose, and galactose) are then transported into the intestinal epithelial cells.

Dietary fiber, composed principally of polysaccharides, cannot be digested by human enzymes in the intestinal tract. In the colon, dietary fiber and other nondigested carbohydrates may be converted to gases (H_2, CO_2, and methane) and short-chain fatty acids (principally acetic acid, propionic acid, and butyric acid) by bacteria in the colon.

Glucose, **galactose**, and **fructose** formed by the digestive enzymes are transported into the absorptive epithelial cells of the small intestine by protein-mediated Na^+**-dependent active transport** and **facilitative diffusion**. Monosaccharides are transported from these cells into the blood and circulate to the liver and peripheral tissues where they are taken up by facilitative transporters. Facilitative transport of glucose across epithelial cells and other cell membranes is mediated by a family of **tissue-specific glucose transport proteins (GLUT 1 to GLUT 5)**. The type of transporter found in each cell reflects the role of glucose metabolism in that cell.

FIG. 27.1.   The structures of common dietary carbohydrates. For disaccharides and higher, the sugars are linked through glycosidic bonds between the anomeric carbon of one sugar and a hydroxyl group on another sugar. The glycosidic bond may be either α- or β-, depending on its position above or below the plane of the sugar containing the anomeric carbon. (See Chapter 5, Section II.A, to review terms used in the description of sugars.) The starch amylose is a polysaccharide of glucose residues linked with α-1,4-glycosidic bonds. Amylopectin is amylose with the addition of α-1,6-glycosidic branch points. Dietary sugars may be monosaccharides (single sugar residues), disaccharides (two sugar residues), oligosaccharides (several sugar residues), or polysaccharides (hundreds of sugar residues). For clarity, the hydrogen atoms are not shown in the figure.

FIG. 27.2. Overview of carbohydrate digestion. Digestion of the carbohydrates occurs first, followed by absorption of monosaccharides. Subsequent metabolic reactions occur after the sugars are absorbed.

THE WAITING ROOM

Deria Voider is a 20-year-old exchange student from Nigeria who has noted gastrointestinal bloating, abdominal cramps, and intermittent diarrhea ever since arriving in the United States 6 months ago. A careful history shows that these symptoms occur most commonly about 45 minutes to 1 hour after eating breakfast but may occur after other meals as well. Dairy products, which were not a part of Deria's diet in Nigeria, were identified as the probable offending agent because her gastrointestinal symptoms disappeared when milk and milk products were eliminated from her diet.

The dietary sugar in fruit juice and other sweets is sucrose, a disaccharide composed of glucose and fructose joined through their anomeric carbons. **Nona Melos's** symptoms of pain and abdominal distension are caused by an inability to digest sucrose or absorb fructose, which are converted to gas by colonic bacteria. Nona's stool sample had a pH of 5 and gave a positive test for sugar. The possibility of carbohydrate malabsorption was considered, and a hydrogen breath test was recommended.

Ann Sulin's fasting and postprandial blood glucose levels are frequently above the normal range in spite of good compliance with insulin therapy. Her physician has referred her to a dietician skilled in training diabetic patients in the successful application of an appropriate American Diabetes Association diet. As part of the program, Ms. Sulin is asked to incorporate foods containing fiber into her diet, such as whole grains (e.g., wheat, oats, corn), legumes (e.g., peas, beans, lentils), tubers (e.g., potatoes, peanuts), and fruits.

Nona Melos is a 7-month-old baby girl, the second child born to unrelated parents. Her mother had a healthy, full-term pregnancy, and Nona's birth weight was normal. She did not respond well to breastfeeding and was changed entirely to a formula based on cows' milk at 4 weeks. Between 7 and 12 weeks of age, she was admitted to the hospital twice with a history of screaming after feeding, but she was discharged after observation without a specific diagnosis. Elimination of cows' milk from her diet did not relieve her symptoms; Nona's mother reported that the screaming bouts were worse after Nona drank juice and that Nona frequently had gas and a distended abdomen. At 7 months, she was still thriving (weight >97th percentile) with no abnormal findings on physical examination. A stool sample was taken.

I. DIETARY CARBOHYDRATES

Carbohydrates are the largest source of calories in the average US diet and usually constitute 40% to 45% of our caloric intake. The plant starches amylopectin and amylose, which are present in grains, tubers, and vegetables, constitute approximately 50% to 60% of the carbohydrate calories consumed. These starches are polysaccharides, containing 10,000 to 1 million glucosyl units. In amylose, the glucosyl residues form a straight chain linked via α-1,4-glycosidic bonds; in amylopectin, the α-1,4-chains contain branches connected via α-1,6-glycosidic bonds (see Fig. 27.1). The other major sugar found in fruits and vegetables is *sucrose*, a disaccharide of glucose and fructose (see Fig. 27.1). Sucrose and small amounts of the monosaccharides glucose and fructose are the major natural sweeteners found in fruit, honey, and vegetables. *Dietary fiber*, the part of the diet that cannot be digested by human enzymes of the intestinal tract, is also composed principally of plant polysaccharides and a polymer called *lignan*.

Most foods derived from animals, such as meat or fish, contain very little carbohydrate except for small amounts of glycogen (which has a structure similar to amylopectin) and glycolipids. The major dietary carbohydrate of animal origin is *lactose*, a disaccharide composed of glucose and galactose that is found exclusively in milk and milk products (see Fig. 27.1). Sweeteners, in the form of sucrose and high-fructose corn syrup (starch, partially hydrolyzed and isomerized to fructose), also appear in the diet as additives to processed foods. On average, a person in the United States consumes 65 lb of added sucrose and 40 lb of high-fructose corn syrup solids per year.

Although all cells require glucose for metabolic functions, neither glucose nor other sugars are specifically required in the diet. Glucose can be synthesized from many amino acids found in dietary protein. Fructose, galactose, xyulose, and all the other sugars required for metabolic processes in the human can be synthesized from glucose.

II. DIGESTION OF DIETARY CARBOHYDRATES

In the digestive tract, dietary polysaccharides and disaccharides are converted to monosaccharides by *glycosidases*, enzymes that hydrolyze the glycosidic bonds between the sugars. All of these enzymes exhibit some specificity for the sugar, the glycosidic bond (α- or β), and the number of saccharide units in the chain. The monosaccharides formed by glycosidases are transported across the intestinal mucosal cells into the interstitial fluid and subsequently enter the bloodstream. Undigested carbohydrates enter the colon, where they may be fermented by bacteria.

A. Salivary and Pancreatic α-Amylase

The digestion of starch (amylopectin and amylose) begins in the mouth, where chewing mixes the food with saliva. The salivary glands secrete approximately 1 L of liquid per day into the mouth, containing salivary α-amylase and other components. α-Amylase is an endoglucosidase, which means that it hydrolyzes internal α-1,4-bonds between glucosyl residues at random intervals in the polysaccharide chains (Fig. 27.3). The shortened polysaccharide chains that are formed are called α-*dextrins*. Salivary α-amylase is largely inactivated by the acidity of the stomach contents, which contain HCl secreted by the parietal cells.

The acidic gastric juice enters the *duodenum*, the upper part of the small intestine, where digestion continues. Secretions from the exocrine pancreas (approximately 1.5 L/day) flow down the pancreatic duct and also enter the duodenum. These secretions contain bicarbonate (HCO_3^-), which neutralizes the acidic pH of stomach contents, and digestive enzymes, including pancreatic α-amylase.

Pancreatic α-amylase continues to hydrolyze the starches and glycogen, forming the disaccharide maltose, the trisaccharide maltotriose, and oligosaccharides. These oligosaccharides, called *limit dextrins*, are usually four to nine glucosyl units long

Starch blockers were marketed many years ago as a means of losing weight without having to exercise or reduce your daily caloric intake. Starch blockers were based on a protein found in beans, which blocked the action of amylase. Thus, as the advertisements proclaimed, one could eat a large amount of starch during a meal, and as long as you took the starch blocker, the starch would pass through the digestive track without being metabolized. Unfortunately, this was too good to be true, and starch blockers were never shown to be effective in aiding weight loss. This was probably because of a combination of factors, such as inactivation of the inhibitor by the low pH in the stomach, and an excess of amylase activity as compared with the amount of starch blocker ingested. Recently, this issue has been revisited, as a starch blocker from wheat has been developed that may work as advertised, although much more work is required to determine whether this amylase inhibitor will be safe and effective in humans. Additionally, newer (and improved) preparations of the bean extract are also being readvertised.

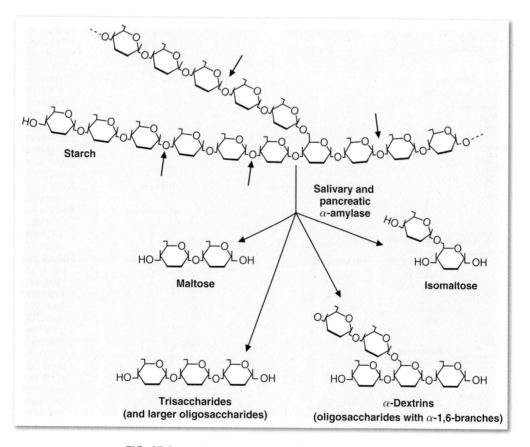

FIG. 27.3. Action of salivary and pancreatic α-amylases.

Amylase activity in the gut is abundant and is not normally rate limiting for the process of digestion. Alcohol-induced pancreatitis or surgical removal of part of the pancreas can decrease pancreatic secretion. Pancreatic exocrine secretion into the intestine also can be decreased as a result of cystic fibrosis (as in **Sissy Fibrosa**, see Chapter 18) in which mucus blocks the pancreatic duct, which eventually degenerates. However, pancreatic exocrine secretion can be decreased to 10% of normal and still not affect the rate of starch digestion because amylases are secreted in the saliva and pancreatic fluid in excessive amounts. In contrast, protein and fat digestion are more strongly affected in cystic fibrosis.

and contain one or more α-1,6-branches. The two glucosyl residues that contain the α-1,6-glycosidic bond eventually become the disaccharide isomaltose, but α-amylase does not cleave these branched oligosaccharides all the way down to isomaltose.

α-Amylase has no activity toward sugar-containing polymers other than glucose linked by α-1,4-bonds. α-Amylase displays no activity toward the α-1,6-bond at branch points and has little activity for the α-1,4-bond at the nonreducing end of a chain.

B. Disaccharidases of the Intestinal Brush Border Membrane

The dietary disaccharides lactose and sucrose, as well as the products of starch digestion, are converted to monosaccharides by glycosidases attached to the membrane in the brush border of absorptive cells (Fig. 27.4). The different glycosidase activities are found in four glycoproteins: *glucoamylase*, the sucrase–isomaltase complex, the smaller glycoprotein *trehalase*, and lactase-glucosylceramidase (Table 27.1). These glycosidases are collectively called the *small intestinal disaccharidases*, although glucoamylase is really an oligosaccharidase.

1. GLUCOAMYLASE

Glucoamylase and the sucrase–isomaltase complex have similar structures and exhibit a great deal of sequence homogeneity (Fig. 27.5). A membrane-spanning domain near the N-terminal attaches the protein to the luminal membrane. The long

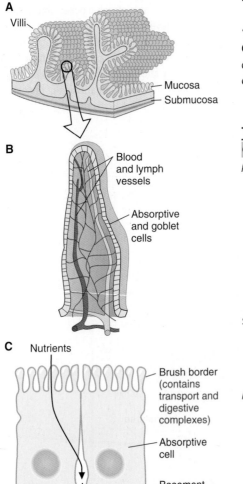

FIG. 27.4. Location of disaccharidase complexes in intestinal villi.

Table 27.1 The Different Forms of the Brush Border Glycosidases

Complex	Catalytic Sites	Principal Activities
β-Glucoamylase	α-Glucosidase	Split α-1,4-glycosidic bonds between glucosyl units, beginning sequentially with the residue at the tail end (nonreducing end) of the chain. This is an exoglycosidase. Substrates include amylose, amylopectin, glycogen, and maltose.
	β-Glucosidase	Same as above but with slightly different specificities and affinities for the substrates.
Sucrase–isomaltase	Sucrase–maltase	Splits sucrose, maltose, and maltotriose.
	Isomaltase–maltase	Splits α-1,-6-bonds in several limit dextrins, as well as the α-1,4-bonds in maltose and maltotriose.
β-Glycosidase	Glucosyl–ceramidase	Splits β-glycosidic bonds between (phlorizin hydrolase) glucose or galactose and hydrophobic residues, such as the glycolipids glucosylceramide and galactosylceramide.
	Lactase	Splits the β-1,4-bond between glucose and galactose. To a lesser extent also splits the β-1,4-bond between some cellulose disaccharides.
Trehalase	Trehalase	Splits bond in trehalose, which is two glucosyl units linked α-1,1 through their anomeric carbons.

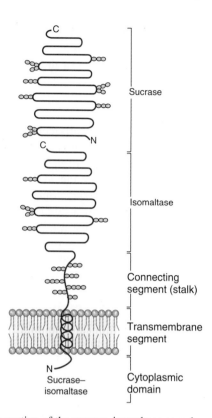

FIG. 27.5.   The major portion of the sucrase–isomaltase complex, containing the catalytic sites, protrudes from the absorptive cells into the lumen of the intestine. Other domains of the protein form a connecting segment (stalk) and an anchoring segment that extends through the membrane into the cell. The complex is synthesized as a single polypeptide chain that is split into its two enzyme subunits extracellularly. Each subunit is a domain with a catalytic site (distinct sucrase–maltase and isomaltase–maltase sites). In spite of their maltase activity, these catalytic sites are often called just *sucrase* and *isomaltase*.

Can the glycosidic bonds of the structure shown hereafter be hydrolyzed by α-amylose?

Acarbose is an FDA-approved drug that blocks the activities of pancreatic α-amylase and brush border α-glucosidases (with specificity for glucose). The drug is produced from a microorganism and is a unique tetrasaccharide. Acarbose is given to patients with type 2 diabetes, with the purpose of reducing the rate at which ingested carbohydrate reaches the bloodstream after a meal. This is one approach to better control blood glucose levels in such patients. Weight loss has not been associated with use of this drug, but flatulence and diarrhea (due to colonic bacterial metabolism of the sugars) are side effects of taking this drug.

polypeptide chain forms two globular domains, each with a catalytic site. In glucoamylase, the two catalytic sites have similar activities, with only small differences in substrate specificity. The protein is heavily glycosylated with oligosaccharides that protect it from digestive proteases.

Glucoamylase is an exoglucosidase that is specific for the α-1,4-bonds between glucosyl residues (Fig. 27.6). It begins at the nonreducing end of a polysaccharide or limit dextrin and sequentially hydrolyzes the bonds to release glucose monosaccharides. It will digest a limit dextrin down to isomaltose, the glucosyl disaccharide with an α-1,6-branch, which is subsequently hydrolyzed principally by the isomaltase activity in the sucrase–isomaltase complex.

2. SUCRASE–ISOMALTASE COMPLEX

The structure of the sucrase–isomaltase complex is very similar to that of glucoamylase, and these two proteins have a high degree of sequence homology. However, after the single polypeptide chain of sucrase–isomaltase is inserted through the membrane and the protein protrudes into the intestinal lumen, an intestinal protease clips it into two separate subunits that remain attached to each other. Each subunit has a catalytic site that differs in substrate specificity from the other through noncovalent interactions. The sucrase–maltase site accounts for approximately 100% of the intestine's ability to hydrolyze sucrose in addition to maltase activity; the isomaltase–maltase site accounts for almost all of the

FIG. 27.6.   *Glucoamylase* activity. Glucoamylase is an α-1,4-exoglycosidase that initiates cleavage at the nonreducing end of the sugar. Thus, for maltotriose, the bond labeled 1 is hydrolyzed first, which then allows the bond at position 2 to be the next one hydrolyzed.

A: No. This polysaccharide is cellulose, which contains β-1,4-glycosidic bonds. Pancreatic and salivary α-amylase cleave only α-1,4-bonds between glucosyl units.

FIG. 27.7. Isomaltase activity. *Arrows* indicate the α-1,6-bonds that are cleaved.

Individuals with genetic deficiencies of the sucrase–isomaltase complex show symptoms of sucrose intolerance but are able to digest normal amounts of starch in a meal without problems. The maltase activity in the glucoamylase complex, and residual activity in the sucrase–isomaltase complex (which is normally present in excess of need), is apparently sufficient to digest normal amounts of dietary starch.

Q: Which of the bonds in the structure shown hereafter are hydrolyzed by the sucrase–isomaltase complex? Which by glucoamylase?

intestine's ability to hydrolyze α-1,6-bonds (Fig. 27.7), in addition to maltase activity. Together, these sites account for approximately 80% of the maltase activity of the small intestine. The remainder of the maltase activity is found in the glucoamylase complex.

3. TREHALASE

Trehalase is only half as long as the other disaccharidases and has only one catalytic site. It hydrolyzes the glycosidic bond in *trehalose*, a disaccharide composed of two glucosyl units linked by an α-bond between their anomeric carbons (Fig. 27.8). Trehalose, which is found in insects, algae, mushrooms, and other fungi, is not currently a major dietary component in the United States. However, unwitting consumption of trehalose can cause nausea, vomiting, and other symptoms of severe gastrointestinal distress if consumed by an individual deficient in the enzyme. Trehalase deficiency was discovered when a woman became very sick after eating mushrooms and was initially thought to have α-amanitin poisoning.

4. β-GLYCOSIDASE COMPLEX (LACTASE-GLUCOSYLCERAMIDASE)

The β-glycosidase complex is another large glycoprotein found in the brush border that has two catalytic sites extending in the lumen of the intestine. However, its primary structure is very different from that of the other enzymes, and it is attached to the membrane through its carboxyl end by a phosphatidylglycan anchor (see Fig. 10.6). The lactase catalytic site hydrolyzes the β-bond connecting glucose and galactose in lactose (a β-galactosidase activity; Fig. 27.9). The major activity of the other catalytic site in humans is the β-bond between glucose or galactose and ceramide in glycolipids (this catalytic site is sometimes called *phlorizin hydrolase*, named for its ability to hydrolyze an artificial substrate).

5. LOCATION WITHIN THE INTESTINE

The production of maltose, maltotriose, and limit dextrins by pancreatic α-amylase occurs in the *duodenum*, the most proximal portion of the small intestine. Sucrase–isomaltase activity is highest in the jejunum, where the enzymes can hydrolyze sucrose and the products of starch digestion. β-Glycosidase activity is also highest in the jejenum. Glucoamylase activity increases progressively along the length of the small intestine, and its activity is highest in the ileum. Thus, it presents a final opportunity for digestion of starch oligomers that have escaped amylase and disaccharidase activities at the more proximal regions of the intestine.

FIG. 27.8. Trehalose. This disaccharide contains two glucose moieties linked by an unusual bond that joins their anomeric carbons. It is cleaved by trehalase.

FIG. 27.9. Lactase activity. Lactase is a β-galactosidase. It cleaves the β-galactoside lactose, the major sugar in milk, forming galactose and glucose.

C. Metabolism of Sugars by Colonic Bacteria

Not all of the starch ingested as part of foods is normally digested in the small intestine (Fig. 27.10). Starches that are high in amylose or are less well hydrated (e.g., starch in dried beans) are resistant to digestion and enter the colon. Dietary fiber and undigested sugars also enter the colon. Here, colonic bacteria rapidly metabolize the saccharides, forming gases, short-chain fatty acids, and lactate. The major short-chain fatty acids formed are acetic acid (two carbons), propionic acid (three carbons), and butyric acid (four carbons). The short-chain fatty acids are absorbed by the colonic mucosal cells and can provide a substantial source of energy for these cells. The major gases formed are hydrogen gas (H_2), carbon dioxide (CO_2), and methane (CH_4). These gases are released through the colon, resulting

 Bonds *(1)* and *(3)* would first be hydrolyzed by glucoamylase. Bond *(2)* requires isomaltase. Bonds *(4)* and *(5)* can then be hydrolyzed by the sucrase–isomaltase complex, or by the glucoamylase complex, all of which can convert maltotriose and maltose to glucose.

FIG. 27.10. Some indigestible carbohydrates. These compounds are components of dietary fiber.

Nona Melos was given a *hydrogen breath test,* a test measuring the amount of hydrogen gas released after consuming a test dose of sugar. In this test, the patient breathes into a portable meter or a collecting bag attached to a nonportable device. The larger, nonportable devices measure the hydrogen in the breath via gas chromatography. The portable devices measure the hydrogen gas produced using hydrogen-specific electrodes and measuring a current that is created when hydrogen comes into contact with the electrode. The association of Nona's symptoms with her ingestion of fruit juices suggests that she might have a problem resulting from low sucrase activity or an inability to absorb fructose. Her ability to thrive and her adequate weight gain suggest that any deficiencies of the sucrase–isomaltase complex must be partial and do not result in a functionally important reduction in maltase activity (maltase activity is also present in the glucoamylase complex). Her urine tested negative for sugar, suggesting the problem is in digestion or absorption, because only sugars that are absorbed and enter the blood can be found in urine. The basis of the hydrogen breath test is that if a sugar is not absorbed, it is metabolized in the intestinal lumen by bacteria that produce various gases, including hydrogen. The test is often accompanied by measurements of the amount of sugar that appear in the blood or feces and acidity of the feces.

in flatulence, or in the breath. Incomplete products of digestion in the intestines increase the retention of water in the colon, resulting in diarrhea.

D. Lactose Intolerance

Lactose intolerance refers to a condition of pain, nausea, and flatulence after the ingestion of foods containing lactose, most notably dairy products. Although lactose intolerance is often caused by low levels of lactase, it also can be caused by intestinal injury (defined subsequently).

1. NONPERSISTANT AND PERSISTANT LACTASE

Lactase activity increases in the human from about 6 to 8 weeks of gestation, and it rises during the late gestational period (27 to 32 weeks) through full term. It remains high for about 1 month after birth and then begins to decline. For most of the world's population, lactase activity decreases to adult levels at approximately 5 to 7 years of age. Adult levels are less than 10% of those present in infants. These populations have *adult hypolactasia* (formerly called *adult lactase deficiency*) and exhibit the lactase nonpersistence phenotype. In people who are derived mainly from Western Northern Europeans, and milk-dependent nomadic tribes of Saharan Africa, the levels of lactase remain at or only slightly below infant levels throughout adulthood (lactase persistence phenotype). Thus, adult hypolactasia is the normal condition for most of the world's population (Table 27.2). In contrast, *congenital lactase deficiency* is a severe autosomal recessive inherited disease in which lactase activity is significantly reduced, or totally absent. The disorder presents as soon as the newborn is fed breast milk or lactose-containing formula, resulting in watery diarrhea, weight loss, and dehydration. Treatment consists of removal of lactose from the diet, which allows for normal growth and development to occur.

2. INTESTINAL INJURY

Intestinal diseases that injure the absorptive cells of the intestinal villi diminish lactase activity along the intestine, producing a condition known as *secondary lactase deficiency.* Kwashiorkor (protein malnutrition), colitis, gastroenteritis, tropical and nontropical sprue, and excessive alcohol consumption fall into this category. These diseases also affect other disaccharidases, but sucrase, maltase, isomaltase, and glucoamylase activities are usually present at such excessive levels that there are no pathologic effects. Lactase is usually the first activity lost and the last to recover.

III. DIETARY FIBER

Dietary fiber is the portion of the diet that is resistant to digestion by human digestive enzymes. It consists principally of plant materials that are polysaccharide

Table 27.2   Prevalence of Late-Onset Lactase Deficiency

Group	Prevalence (%)
US population	
Asians	100
American Indians (Oklahoma)	95
Black Americans	81
Mexican Americans	56
White Americans	24
Other populations	
Ibo, Yoruba (Nigeria)	89
Italians	71
Aborigines (Australia)	67
Greeks	53
Danes	3
Dutch	0

Reproduced with permission from Büller HA, Grand RJ. Lactose intolerance. *Annu Rev Med.* 1990;41: 141–148. Copyright 1990 by Annual Reviews, Inc.

Table 27.3   Types of Fiber in the Diet

Classical Nomenclature	Classes of Compounds	Dietary Sources
Insoluble fiber		
Cellulose	Polysaccharide composed of glucosyl residues linked β-1,4	Whole wheat flour, unprocessed bran, cabbage, peas, green beans, wax beans, broccoli, brussel sprouts, cucumber with skin, green peppers, apples, carrots
Hemicelluloses	Polymers of arabinoxylans or galactomannans	Bran cereals, whole grains, brussel sprouts, mustard beans, beet root
Lignin	Noncarbohydrate, polymeric derivatives of phenylpropane	Bran cereals, unprocessed bran, strawberries, eggplant peas, green beans, radishes
Water-soluble fiber (or dispersible)		
Pectic substances	Galactouranans, arabinogalactans, β-glucans, arabinoxylans	Squash, apples, citrus fruits
Gums	Galactomannans, arabinogalactans	Oatmeal, dried beans, cauliflower, green beans, cabbage, carrots, dried peas, potatoes, strawberries
Mucilages	Wide range of branched and substituted galactans	Flax seed, psyllium, mustard seed

derivatives and lignan (see Fig. 27.10). The components of fiber are often divided into the categories of soluble and insoluble fiber, according to their ability to dissolve in water. Insoluble fiber consists of three major categories: cellulose, hemicellulose, and lignins. Soluble fiber categories include pectins, mucilages, and gums (Table 27.3). Although human enzymes cannot digest fiber, the bacterial flora in the normal human gut may metabolize the more soluble dietary fibers to gases and short-chain fatty acids, much as they do undigested starch and sugars. Some of these fatty acids may be absorbed and used by the colonic epithelial cells of the gut, and some may travel to the liver through the hepatic portal vein. We may obtain as much as 10% of our total calories from compounds produced by bacterial digestion of substances in our digestive tract.

In 2005, the Committee on Dietary Reference Intakes issued new guidelines for fiber ingestion—anywhere from 25 to 38 g/day, depending on the age and sex of the individual. It was also recommended that 14 g of fiber should accompany every 1,000 cal ingested. No distinction was made between soluble and insoluble fibers. Adult males between the ages of 19 and 49 years require 38 g of fiber per day. Males age 50 years or more are recommended to consume 30 g of fiber per day. Females from ages 4 to 8 years require 25 g/day; from ages 9 to 18 years, 26 g/day; and from ages 19 to 50 years, 25 g/day. Women older than 50 years of age

Lactose (1 glass of milk, about 200 mL)

Lactase-deficient cells

Intestinal lumen

Gas ← Bacterial fermentation

Lactic acid

Osmotic effect

↑Fluid load (1,000 mL) ← H₂O

Distention of gut walls

↑Peristalsis

Malabsorption Fats, Proteins, Drugs

Watery diarrhea (1L extracellular liquid lost per 9 g lactose in 1 glass of milk)

Lactose intolerance can either be the result of a primary deficiency of lactase production in the small bowel (as is the case for **Deria Voider**), or it can be secondary to an injury to the intestinal mucosa, where lactase is normally produced. The lactose that is not absorbed is converted by colonic bacteria to lactic acid, methane gas (CH_4), and H_2 gas (see accompanying figure). The osmotic effect of the lactose and lactic acid in the bowel lumen is responsible for the diarrhea that is often seen as part of this syndrome. Similar symptoms can result from sensitivity to milk proteins (milk intolerance) or from the malabsorption of other dietary sugars.

In adults suspected of having a lactase deficiency, the diagnosis is usually made inferentially when avoidance of all dairy products results in relief of symptoms and a rechallenge with these foods reproduces the characteristic syndrome. If the results of these measures are equivocal, however, the malabsorption of lactose can be determined more specifically by measuring the H_2 content of the patient's breath after a test dose of lactose has been consumed.

Deria Voider's symptoms did not appear if she took available over-the-counter tablets containing lactase when she ate dairy products.

Beans, peas, soybeans, and other leguminous plants contain oligosaccharides with (1,6)-linked galactose residues that cannot be hydrolyzed for absorption, including sucrose with one, two, or three galactose residues attached (see Fig. 27.10). What is the fate of these polysaccharides in the intestine?

The dietician explained to **Ann Sulin** the rationale for a person with diabetes to follow an American Diabetes Association diet plan. It is important for Ann to add a variety of fibers to her diet. The gel-forming, water-retaining pectins and gums delay gastric emptying and retard the rate of absorption of disaccharides and monosaccharides, thus reducing the rate at which blood glucose levels rise. The glycemic index of foods also needs to be considered for appropriate maintenance of blood glucose levels in persons with diabetes. Consumption of a low-glycemic-index diet results in a lower rise in blood glucose levels after eating, which can be more easily controlled by exogenous insulin. For example, Ms. Sulin is advised to eat pasta and rice (glycemic indices of 67 and 65, respectively) instead of potatoes (glycemic index of 80 to 120, depending on the method of preparation) and to incorporate breakfast cereals composed of wheat bran, barley, and oats into her morning routine.

are recommended to consume 21 g of fiber per day. These numbers are increased during pregnancy and lactation. One beneficial effect of fiber is seen in diverticular disease in which sacs or pouches may develop in the colon because of a weakening of the muscle and submucosal structures. Fiber is thought to "soften" the stool, thereby reducing pressure on the colonic wall and enhancing expulsion of feces.

Certain types of soluble fiber have been associated with disease prevention. For example, pectins may lower blood cholesterol levels by binding bile acids. β-Glucan (obtained from oats) has also been shown, in some studies, to reduce cholesterol levels through a reduction in bile acid resorption in the intestine (see Chapter 34). Pectins also may have a beneficial effect in the diet of individuals with diabetes mellitus by slowing the rate of absorption of simple sugars and preventing high blood glucose levels after meals. However, each of the beneficial effects that have been related to "fiber" is relatively specific for the type of fiber and the physical form of the food that contains the fiber. This factor, along with many others, has made it difficult to obtain conclusive results from studies of the effects of fiber on human health.

IV. ABSORPTION OF SUGARS

Once the carbohydrates have been split into monosaccharides, the sugars are transported across the intestinal epithelial cells and into the blood for distribution to all tissues. Not all complex carbohydrates are digested at the same rate within the intestine, and some carbohydrate sources lead to a near-immediate rise in blood glucose levels after ingestion, whereas others slowly raise blood glucose levels over an extended period after ingestion. The *glycemic index of a food* is an indication of how rapidly blood glucose levels rise after consumption. Glucose and maltose have the highest glycemic indices (142, with white bread defined as an index of 100). Table 27.4 indicates the glycemic index for a variety of food types. Although there is no need to memorize this table, note that cornflakes and potatoes have high glycemic indices, whereas yogurt and skim milk have particularly low glycemic indices.

The glycemic response to ingested foods depends not only on the glycemic index of the foods but also on the fiber and fat content of the food as well as its method of preparation. Highly glycemic carbohydrates can be consumed before and after exercise because their metabolism results in a rapid entry of glucose into the blood, where it is then immediately available for use by muscle cells. Low-glycemic carbohydrates enter the circulation slowly and can be used to best advantage if

Table 27.4 Glycemic Indices of Selected Foods, with Values Adjusted to White Bread of 100

Breads		Legumes	
Whole wheat	100	Baked beans (canned)	70
Pumpernickel (whole-grain rye)	88	Butter beans	46
Pasta		Garden peas (frozen)	85
Spaghetti, white, boiled	67	Kidney beans (dried)	43
Cereal grains		Kidney beans (canned)	74
Barley (pearled)	36	Peanuts	15
Rice (instant, boiled 1 min)	65	Fruit	
Rice, polished (boiled 10–25 min)	81	Apple	52
Sweet corn	80	Apple juice	45
Breakfast cereals		Orange	59
All bran	74	Raisins	93
Cornflakes	121	Sugars	
Muesli	96	Fructose	27
Cookies		Glucose	142
Oatmeal	78	Lactose	57
Plain water crackers	100	Sucrose	83
Root vegetables		Dairy products	
Potatoes (instant)	120	Ice cream	69
Potato (new, white, boiled)	80	Whole milk	44
Potato chips	77	Skim milk	46
Yam	74	Yogurt	52

consumed before exercise, such that as exercise progresses, glucose is slowly being absorbed from the intestine into the circulation in which it can be used to maintain blood glucose levels during the exercise period.

A. Absorption by the Intestinal Epithelium

Glucose is transported through the absorptive cells of the intestine by facilitated diffusion and by Na^+-dependent facilitated transport. (See Chapter 10 for a description of transport mechanisms.) The glucose molecule is extremely polar and cannot diffuse through the hydrophobic phospholipid bilayer of the cell membrane. Each hydroxyl group of the glucose molecule forms at least two hydrogen bonds with water molecules, and random movement would require energy to dislodge the polar hydroxyl groups from their hydrogen bonds and to disrupt the van der Waals forces between the hydrocarbon tails of the fatty acids in the membrane phospholipid. Glucose, therefore, enters the absorptive cells by binding to transport proteins, membrane-spanning proteins that bind the glucose molecule on one side of the membrane and release it on the opposite side (Fig. 27.11). Two types of glucose transport proteins are present in the intestinal absorptive cells: the Na^+-dependent glucose transporters and the facilitative glucose transporters (Fig. 27.12).

1. NA$^+$-DEPENDENT TRANSPORTERS

Na^+-dependent glucose transporters, which are located on the luminal side of the absorptive cells, enable these cells to concentrate glucose from the intestinal lumen.

 These sugars are not digested well by the human intestine but form good sources of energy for the bacteria of the gut. These bacteria convert the sugars to H_2, lactic acid, and short-chain fatty acids. The amount of gas released after a meal containing beans is especially notorious.

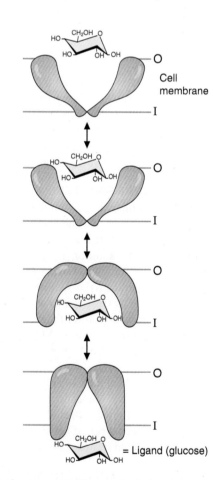

FIG. 27.11. Facilitative transport. Transport of glucose occurs without rotation of the glucose molecule. Multiple groups on the protein bind the hydroxyl groups of glucose and close behind it as it is released into the cell (i.e., the transporter acts like a "gated pore"). *O,* outside; *I,* inside.

FIG. 27.12. Na$^+$-dependent and facilitative transporters in the intestinal epithelial cells. Both glucose and fructose are transported by the facilitated glucose transporters on the luminal and serosal sides of the absorptive cells. Glucose and galactose are transported by the Na$^+$-glucose cotransporters on the luminal (mucosal) side of the absorptive cells.

A low intracellular Na$^+$ concentration is maintained by a Na$^+$,K$^+$-ATPase on the serosal (blood) side of the cell that uses the energy from adenosine triphosphate (ATP) cleavage to pump Na$^+$ out of the cell into the blood. Thus, the transport of glucose from a low concentration in the lumen to a high concentration in the cell is promoted by the cotransport of Na$^+$ from a high concentration in the lumen to a low concentration in the cell (secondary active transport).

2. FACILITATIVE GLUCOSE TRANSPORTERS

Facilitative glucose transporters, which do not bind Na$^+$, are located on the serosal side of the cells. Glucose moves via the facilitative transporters from the high concentration inside the cell to the lower concentration in the blood without the expenditure of energy. In addition to the Na$^+$-dependent glucose transporters, facilitative transporters for glucose also exist on the luminal side of the absorptive cells. The best characterized facilitative glucose transporters found in the plasma membranes of cells (referred to as *GLUT 1* to *GLUT 5*) are described in Table 27.5. One common structural theme to these proteins is that they all contain 12 membrane-spanning domains. Note that the sodium-linked transporter on the luminal side of the intestinal epithelial cell is not a member of the GLUT family.

The epithelial cells of the kidney, which reabsorb glucose from the lumen of the renal tubule back into the blood, have Na$^+$-dependent glucose transporters similar to those of intestinal epithelial cells. They are thus also able to transport glucose against its concentration gradient. Other types of cells use mainly facilitative glucose transporters that carry glucose down its concentration gradient.

3. GALACTOSE AND FRUCTOSE ABSORPTION THROUGH GLUCOSE TRANSPORTERS

Galactose is absorbed through the same mechanisms as glucose. It enters the absorptive cells on the luminal side via the Na$^+$-dependent glucose transporters and

Table 27.5   Properties of the GLUT 1 to GLUT 5 Isoforms of the Glucose Transport Proteins

Transporter	Tissue Distribution	Comments
GLUT 1	Human erythrocyte Blood–brain barrier Blood–retinal barrier Blood–placental barrier Blood–testis barrier	Expressed in cell types with barrier functions; a high-affinity glucose transport system
GLUT 2	Liver Kidney Pancreatic β-cell Serosal surface of intestinal mucosa cells	A high-capacity, low-affinity transporter May be used as the glucose sensor in the pancreas
GLUT 3	Brain (neurons)	Major transporter in the central nervous system; a high-affinity system
GLUT 4	Adipose tissue Skeletal muscle Heart muscle	Insulin-sensitive transporter. In the presence of insulin, the number of GLUT 4 transporters increases on the cell surface; a high-affinity system
GLUT 5	Intestinal epithelium Spermatozoa	This is actually a fructose transporter

Genetic techniques have identified additional GLUT transporters (GLUT 6 to GLUT 12), but the roles of these transporters have not yet been fully described.

facilitative glucose transporters and is transported through the serosal side on the facilitative glucose transporters.

Fructose both enters and leaves absorptive epithelial cells by facilitated diffusion, apparently via transport proteins that are part of the GLUT family. The transporter on the luminal side has been identified as GLUT 5. Although this transporter can transport glucose, it has a much higher activity with fructose (see Fig. 27.12). Other fructose transport proteins also may be present. For reasons yet unknown, fructose is absorbed at a much more rapid rate when it is ingested as sucrose than when it is ingested as a monosaccharide.

B. Transport of Monosaccharides into Tissues

The properties of the GLUT transport proteins differ among tissues, reflecting the function of glucose metabolism in each tissue. In most cell types, the rate of glucose transport across the cell membrane is not rate limiting for glucose metabolism. This is because the isoform of transporter present in these cell types has a relatively low K_m for glucose (i.e., a low concentration of glucose will result in half the maximal rate of glucose transport) or is present in relatively high concentration in the cell membrane so that the intracellular glucose concentration reflects that in the blood. Because the hexokinase isozyme present in these cells has an even lower K_m for glucose (0.05 to 0.10 mM), variations in blood glucose levels do not affect the intracellular rate of glucose phosphorylation. However, in several tissues, the rate of transport becomes rate limiting when the serum level of glucose is low or when low levels of insulin signal the absence of dietary glucose.

The *erythrocyte* (red blood cell) is an example of a tissue in which glucose transport is not rate limiting. Although the glucose transporter (GLUT 1) has a K_m of 1 to 7 mM, it is present in extremely high concentrations, constituting approximately 5% of all membrane proteins. Consequently, as the blood glucose levels fall from a postprandial level of 140 mg/dL (7.5 mM) to the normal fasting level of 80 mg/dL (4.5 mM), or even the hypoglycemic level of 40 mg/dL (2.2 mM), the supply of glucose is still adequate for the rates at which glycolysis and the pentose phosphate pathway operate.

In the liver, the K_m for the glucose transporter (GLUT 2) is relatively high compared with that of other tissues, probably 15 mM or higher. This is in keeping with

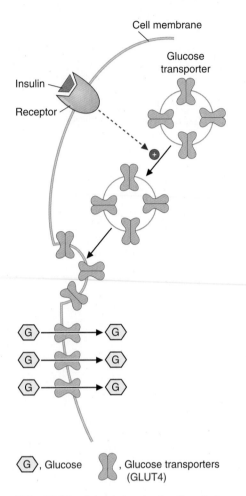

FIG. 27.13. Stimulation by insulin of glucose transport into muscle and adipose cells. Binding of insulin to its cell membrane receptor causes vesicles containing glucose transport proteins to move from inside the cell to the cell membrane.

the liver's role as the organ that maintains blood glucose levels. Thus, the liver will convert glucose into other energy storage molecules only when blood glucose levels are high, such as the time immediately after ingesting a meal. In muscle and adipose tissue, the transport of glucose is greatly stimulated by insulin. The mechanism involves the recruitment of glucose transporters (specifically, GLUT 4) from intracellular vesicles into the plasma membrane (Fig. 27.13). In adipose tissue, the stimulation of glucose transport across the plasma membrane by insulin increases its availability for the synthesis of fatty acids and glycerol from the glycolytic pathway. In skeletal muscle, the stimulation of glucose transport by insulin increases its availability for glycolysis and glycogen synthesis.

V. GLUCOSE TRANSPORT THROUGH THE BLOOD–BRAIN BARRIER AND INTO NEURONS

A hypoglycemic response is elicited by a decrease of blood glucose concentration to some point between 18 and 54 mg/dL (1 and 3 mM). The hypoglycemic response is a result of a decreased supply of glucose to the brain and starts with light-headedness and dizziness and may progress to coma. The slow rate of transport of glucose through the blood–brain barrier (from the blood into the cerebrospinal fluid) at low levels of glucose is thought to be responsible for this neuroglycopenic response. Glucose transport from the cerebrospinal fluid across the plasma membranes of neurons is rapid and is not rate limiting for ATP generation from glycolysis.

In the brain, the endothelial cells of the capillaries have extremely tight junctions, and glucose must pass from the blood into the extracellular cerebrospinal fluid by GLUT 1 transporters in the endothelial cell membranes (Fig. 27.14) and then through the basement membrane. Measurements of the overall process of glucose transport from the blood into the brain (mediated by GLUT 3 on neural cells) show a $K_{m,app}$ of 7 to 11 mM and a maximal velocity not much greater than the rate of glucose utilization by the brain. Thus, decreases of blood glucose below

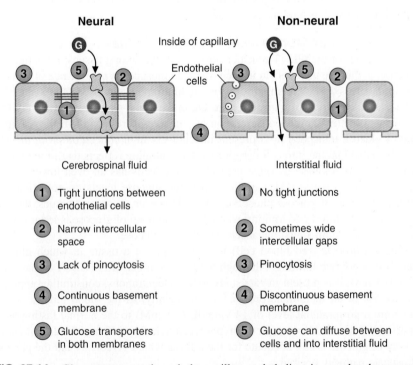

FIG. 27.14. Glucose transport through the capillary endothelium in neural and nonneural tissues. Characteristics of transport in each type of tissue are listed by numbers that refer to the numbers in the drawing. *G*, glucose.

the fasting level of 80 to 90 mg/dL (approximately 5 mM) are likely to significantly affect the rate of glucose metabolism in the brain because of reduced glucose transport into the brain.

CLINICAL COMMENTS

Deria Voider. One of five Americans experiences some form of gastrointestinal discomfort from 30 minutes to 12 hours after ingesting lactose-rich foods. Most become symptomatic when they consume more than 25 g lactose at one time (e.g., 1 pint of milk or its equivalent). **Deria Voider's** symptoms were caused by her "new" diet in this country, which included a glass of milk in addition to the milk she used on her cereal with breakfast each morning.

Management of lactose intolerance includes a reduction or avoidance of lactose-containing foods, depending on the severity of the deficiency of intestinal lactase. Hard cheeses (cheddar, swiss, Jarlsberg) are low in lactose and may be tolerated by patients with only moderate lactase deficiency. Yogurt with "live and active cultures" printed on the package contains bacteria that release free lactases when the bacteria are lysed by gastric acid and proteolytic enzymes. The free lactases then digest the lactose. Commercially available milk products that have been hydrolyzed with a lactase enzyme provide a 70% reduction in total lactose content, which may be adequate to prevent digestive symptoms in mildly affected patients. Tablets and capsules containing lactase are also available and should be taken half an hour before meals.

Many adults who have a lactase deficiency develop the ability to ingest small amounts of lactose in dairy products without experiencing symptoms. This adaptation probably involves an increase in the population of colonic bacteria that can cleave lactose and not a recovery or induction of human lactase synthesis. For many individuals, dairy products are the major dietary source of calcium, and their complete elimination from the diet can lead to osteoporosis. Lactose, however, is used as a "filler" or carrying agent in more than 1,000 prescription and over-the-counter drugs in this country. People with lactose intolerance often unwittingly ingest lactose with their medications.

Ann Sulin. Poorly controlled diabetic patients such as Ann Sulin frequently have elevations in serum glucose levels (hyperglycemia). This is often attributable to a lack of circulating, active insulin, which normally stimulates glucose uptake (through the recruitment of GLUT 4 transporters from the endoplasmic reticulum to the plasma membrane) by the peripheral tissues (heart, muscle, and adipose tissue). Without uptake by these tissues, glucose tends to accumulate within the bloodstream, leading to hyperglycemia.

Nona Melos. The large amount of H_2 produced on fructose ingestion suggested that **Nona Melos's** problem was one of a deficiency in fructose transport into the absorptive cells of the intestinal villi. If fructose were being absorbed properly, the fructose would not have traveled to the colonic bacteria, which metabolized the fructose to generate the hydrogen gas. To confirm the diagnosis, a jejunal biopsy was taken; lactase, sucrase, maltase, and trehalase activities were normal in the jejunal cells. The tissue was also tested for the enzymes of fructose metabolism; these were in the normal range as well. Although Nona had no sugar in her urine, malabsorption of disaccharides can result in their appearance in the urine if damage to the intestinal mucosal cells allows their passage into the interstitial fluid. When Nona was placed on a diet free of fruit juices and other foods containing fructose, she did well and could tolerate small amounts of pure sucrose.

More than 50% of the adult population is estimated to be unable to absorb fructose in high doses (50 g), and more than 10% cannot completely absorb 25 g fructose. These individuals, like those with other disorders of fructose metabolism, must avoid fruits and other foods that contain high concentrations of fructose.

BIOCHEMICAL COMMENTS

Cholera. *Cholera* is an acute watery diarrheal disorder caused by the water-borne, gram-negative bacterium *Vibrio cholerae*. It is a disease of antiquity; descriptions of epidemics of the disease date to before 500 BC. During epidemics, the infection is spread by large numbers of *Vibrio* that enter water sources from the voluminous liquid stools and contaminate the environment, particularly in areas of extreme poverty, where plumbing and modern waste-disposal systems are primitive or nonexistent. **Dennis Veere** experienced cholera after eating contaminated shellfish (see Chapter 10).

After being ingested, the *V. cholerae* organisms attach to the brush border of the intestinal epithelium and secrete an exotoxin that binds irreversibly to a specific chemical receptor (GM_1 ganglioside) on the cell surface. This exotoxin catalyzes an adenosine diphosphate (ADP)-ribosylation reaction that increases adenylate cyclase activity and thus cyclic adenosine monophosphate (cAMP) levels in the enterocyte. As a result, the normal absorption of sodium, anions, and water from the gut lumen into the intestinal cell is markedly diminished. The exotoxin also stimulates the crypt cells to secrete chloride, accompanied by cations and water, from the bloodstream into the lumen of the gut. The resulting loss of solute-rich diarrheal fluid may, in severe cases, exceed 1 L/hour, leading to rapid dehydration and even death.

The therapeutic approach to cholera takes advantage of the fact that the Na^+-dependent transporters for glucose and amino acids are not affected by the cholera exotoxin. As a result, coadministration of glucose and Na^+ by mouth results in the uptake of glucose and Na^+, accompanied by chloride and water, thereby partially correcting the ion deficits and fluid loss. Amino acids and small peptides are also absorbed by Na^+-dependent cotransport involving transport proteins distinct from the Na^+-dependent glucose transporters. Therefore, addition of protein to the glucose–sodium replacement solution enhances its effectiveness and markedly decreases the severity of the diarrhea. Adjunctive antibiotic therapy also shortens the diarrheal phase of cholera but does not decrease the need for the oral replacement therapy outlined earlier.

Key Concepts

- The major carbohydrates in the US diet are starch, lactose, and sucrose.
- Starch is a polysaccharide composed of many glucose units linked together through α-1,4- and α-1,6-glycosidic bonds.
- Lactose is a disaccharide composed of glucose and galactose.
- Sucrose is a disaccharide composed of glucose and fructose.
- Digestion converts all dietary carbohydrates to their respective monosaccharides.
- Amylase digests starch; it is found in the saliva and pancreas, which releases it into the lumen of the small intestine.
- Intestinal epithelial cells contain disaccharidases, which cleave lactose, sucrose, and digestion products of starch into monosaccharides.
- Dietary fiber is composed of polysaccharides that cannot be digested by human enzymes.
- Monosaccharides are transported into the absorptive intestinal epithelial cells via active transport systems.
- Monosaccharides released into the blood via the intestinal epithelial cells are recovered by tissues that use facilitative transporters.
- Diseases discussed in this chapter are summarized in Table 27.6.

Table 27.6   Diseases Discussed in Chapter 27

Disease or Disorder	Environmental or Genetic	Comments
Lactose intolerance	Both	Reduced levels of lactase on the intestinal epithelial cell surface lead to reduced lactose digestion in the intestinal lumen, providing substrate for flora in the large intestine. Metabolism of the lactose by these bacteria leads to the generation of organic acids and gases.
Type 2 diabetes	Both	Diets consisting of low glycemic index carbohydrates will be beneficial in controlling the rise in blood glucose levels after eating.
Fructose malabsorption	Genetic	Inability to absorb fructose in the small intestine, leading to colonic bacteria metabolism of fructose and the generation of organic acids and gases.
Cholera	Environmental	Increased cAMP levels in the intestinal epithelial cells lead to inhibition of ion transport and significant water extrusion from the affected cells, leading to severe diarrhea.

REVIEW QUESTIONS—CHAPTER 27

1. The facilitative transporter that is most responsible for transporting fructose from the blood into cells is which of the following?

    A. GLUT 1
    B. GLUT 2
    C. GLUT 3
    D. GLUT 4
    E. GLUT 5

2. An alcoholic patient developed pancreatitis that affected his exocrine pancreatic function. He exhibited discomfort after eating a high-carbohydrate meal. The patient most likely had a reduced ability to digest which of the following?

    A. Starch
    B. Lactose
    C. Fiber
    D. Sucrose
    E. Maltose

3. A type 1 diabetic neglects to take his insulin injections while on a weekend vacation. Cells of which tissue will be most greatly affected by this mistake?

    A. Brain
    B. Liver

    C. Muscle
    D. Red blood cells
    E. Pancreas

4. After digestion of a piece of cake that contains flour, milk, and sucrose as its primary ingredients, the major carbohydrate products that enter the blood are which of the following?

    A. Glucose
    B. Fructose and galactose
    C. Galactose and glucose
    D. Fructose and glucose
    E. Glucose, galactose, and fructose

5. A patient has a genetic defect that causes intestinal epithelial cells to produce disaccharidases of much lower activity than normal. Compared with a normal person, after eating a bowl of milk and oatmeal sweetened with table sugar, this patient will exhibit higher levels of which of the following?

    A. Maltose, sucrose, and lactose in the stool
    B. Starch in the stool
    C. Galactose and fructose in the blood
    D. Glycogen in the muscles
    E. Insulin in the blood

Glycogen is the storage form of glucose found in most types of cells. It is composed of glucosyl units linked by **α-1,4-glycosidic bonds**, with **α-1,6-branches** occurring roughly every 8 to 10 glucosyl units (Fig. 28.1). The liver and skeletal muscle contains the largest glycogen stores.

The formation of glycogen from glucose is an energy-requiring pathway that begins—like most of glucose metabolism—with the phosphorylation of glucose to **glucose 6-phosphate** (G6P). Glycogen synthesis from G6P involves the formation of uridine diphosphate glucose (**UDP-G**) and the transfer of glucosyl units from UDP-G to the ends of the glycogen chains by the enzyme **glycogen synthase**. Once the chains reach approximately 11 glucosyl units, a **branching enzyme** moves 6 to 8 units to form an α-1,6-branch.

Glycogenolysis, the pathway for glycogen degradation, is not the reverse of the biosynthetic pathway. The degradative enzyme **glycogen phosphorylase** removes glucosyl units one at a time from the ends of the glycogen chains, converting them to **glucose 1-phosphate** without resynthesizing UDP-G or UTP. A **debranching enzyme** removes the glucosyl residues near each branch point.

Liver glycogen serves as a source of **blood glucose**. To generate glucose, the glucose 1-phosphate produced from glycogen degradation is converted to G6P. **Glucose 6-phosphatase**, an enzyme found only in liver and kidney, converts G6P to free glucose, which then enters the blood.

Glycogen synthesis and degradation are regulated in liver by **hormonal-changes** that signal the need for blood glucose (see Chapter 26). The body maintains fasting blood glucose levels at approximately 80 mg/dL to ensure that the brain and other tissues that are dependent on glucose for the generation of adenosine triphosphate (ATP) have a continuous supply. The lack of dietary glucose, signaled by a decrease of the **insulin/glucagon ratio**, activates liver glycogenolysis and inhibits glycogen synthesis. **Epinephrine**, which signals an increased use of blood glucose and other fuels for exercise or emergency situations, also activates liver glycogenolysis. The hormones that regulate liver glycogen metabolism work principally through changes in the **phosphorylation** state of glycogen synthase in the biosynthetic pathway and glycogen phosphorylase in the degradative pathway.

In skeletal muscle, glycogen supplies G6P for ATP synthesis in the glycolytic pathway. Muscle glycogen phosphorylase is stimulated during exercise by the increase of adenosine monophosphate (**AMP**), an **allosteric activator** of the enzyme, and also by phosphorylation. The phosphorylation is stimulated by **calcium** released during contraction and by epinephrine—the fight-or-flight hormone. Glycogen synthesis is activated in resting muscles by the elevation of insulin after carbohydrate ingestion.

The neonate must rapidly adapt to an intermittent fuel supply after birth. Once the umbilical cord is clamped, the supply of glucose from the maternal circulation is interrupted. The combined effect of epinephrine and glucagon on the liver glycogen stores of the neonate rapidly restore glucose levels to normal.

FIG. 28.1. Glycogen structure. Glycogen is composed of glucosyl units linked by α-1,4-glycosidic bonds and α-1,6-glycosidic bonds. The branches occur more frequently in the center of the molecule, and less frequently in the periphery. The anomeric carbon that is not attached to another glucosyl residue (the reducing end) is attached to the protein glycogenin by a glycosidic bond. The hydrogen atoms have been omitted from this figure for clarity.

THE WAITING ROOM

A newborn baby girl, **Getta Carbo,** was born after a 38-week gestation. Her mother, a 36-year-old woman, developed a significant viral infection that resulted in a severe loss of appetite and recurrent vomiting in the month preceding delivery. Fetal bradycardia (slower than normal fetal heart rate) was detected with each uterine contraction of labor—a sign of possible fetal distress.

At birth, Getta was cyanotic (a bluish discoloration caused by a lack of adequate oxygenation of tissues) and limp. She responded to several minutes of assisted ventilation. Her Apgar score of 3 was low at 1 minute after birth, but improved to a score of 7 at 5 minutes. The Apgar score is an objective estimate of the overall condition of the newborn, determined at both 1 and 5 minutes after birth. The best score is 10 (normal in all respects).

Physical examination in the nursery at 10 minutes showed a thin, malnourished female newborn. Her body temperature was slightly low, her heart rate was rapid, and her respiratory rate of 35 breaths per minute was elevated. Getta's birth weight was only 2,100 g, compared with a normal value of 3,300 g. Her length was 47 cm, and her head circumference was 33 cm (low normal). The laboratory reported that Getta's serum glucose level when she was unresponsive was 14 mg/dL. A glucose value <40 mg/dL (2.5 mM) is considered to be abnormal in newborn infants.

At 5 hours of age, she was apneic (not breathing) and unresponsive. Ventilatory resuscitation was initiated and a cannula is placed in the umbilical vein. Blood for a glucose level was drawn through this cannula, and 5 mL of a 20% glucose solution was injected. Getta slowly responded to this therapy.

Jim Bodie's treadmill exercise and most other types of moderate exercise involving whole-body movement (running, skiing, dancing, tennis) increase the use of blood glucose and other fuels by skeletal muscles. The blood glucose is normally supplied by the stimulation of liver glycogenolysis and gluconeogenesis.

Jim Bodie, a 19-year-old body builder, was rushed to the hospital emergency room in a coma. One-half hour earlier, his mother had heard a loud crashing sound in the basement, where he had been lifting weights and completing his daily workout on the treadmill. She found her son on the floor having severe jerking movements of all muscles (a grand mal seizure).

In the emergency room, the doctors learned that despite the objections of his family and friends, Jim regularly used androgens and other anabolic steroids in an effort to bulk up his muscle mass.

On initial physical examination, he was comatose with occasional involuntary jerking movements of his extremities. Foamy saliva dripped from his mouth. He had bitten his tongue and had lost bowel and bladder control at the height of the seizure.

The laboratory reported a serum glucose level of 18 mg/dL (extremely low). The intravenous infusion of 5% glucose (5 g of glucose per 100 mL of solution), which had been started earlier, was increased to 10%. In addition, 50 g of glucose was given over 30 seconds through the intravenous tubing.

I.   STRUCTURE OF GLYCOGEN

Glycogen, the storage form of glucose, is a branched glucose polysaccharide composed of chains of glucosyl units linked by α-1,4-glycosidic bonds with α-1,6-branches, every 8 to 10 residues (see Fig. 28.1). In a molecule of this highly branched structure, only one glucosyl residue has an anomeric carbon that is not linked to another glucose residue. This anomeric carbon at the beginning of the chain is attached to the protein glycogenin. The other ends of the chains are called *nonreducing ends* (see Chapter 5). The branched structure permits rapid degradation and rapid synthesis of glycogen because enzymes can work on several chains simultaneously from the multiple nonreducing ends.

Glycogen is present in tissues as polymers of very high molecular weight (10^7 to 10^8 Da) collected together in glycogen particles. The enzymes involved in glycogen synthesis and degradation, and some of the regulatory enzymes are bound to the surface of the glycogen particles.

II.   FUNCTION OF GLYCOGEN IN SKELETAL MUSCLE AND LIVER

Glycogen is found in most cell types, where it serves as a reservoir of glucosyl units for adenosine triphosphate (ATP) generation from glycolysis.

Glycogen is degraded mainly to glucose 1-phosphate, which is converted to glucose 6-phosphate (G6P). In skeletal muscle and other cell types, the G6P enters the glycolytic pathway (Fig. 28.2). Glycogen is an extremely important fuel source for skeletal muscle when ATP demands are high and when G6P is used rapidly in anaerobic glycolysis. In many other cell types, the small glycogen reservoir serves a similar purpose; it is an emergency fuel source that supplies glucose for the generation of ATP in the absence of oxygen or during restricted blood flow. In general, glycogenolysis and glycolysis are activated together in these cells.

Glycogen serves a very different purpose in liver than in skeletal muscle and other tissues (see Fig. 28.2). *Liver glycogen* is the first and immediate source of glucose for the maintenance of blood glucose levels. In the liver, the G6P that is generated from glycogen degradation is hydrolyzed to glucose by *glucose 6-phosphatase*—an enzyme that is present only in the liver and kidneys. Glycogen degradation thus provides a readily mobilized source of blood glucose as dietary glucose decreases, or as exercise increases, the use of blood glucose by muscles.

FIG. 28.2. Glycogenolysis in skeletal muscle and liver. Glycogen stores serve different functions in muscle cells and liver. In the muscle and most other cell types, glycogen stores serve as a fuel source for the generation of ATP. In the liver, glycogen stores serve as a source of blood glucose.

The pathways of glycogenolysis and gluconeogenesis in the liver both supply blood glucose, and consequently, these two pathways are activated together by glucagon. *Gluconeogenesis*, the synthesis of glucose from amino acids and other gluconeogenic precursors (discussed in detail in Chapter 31), also forms G6P, so that glucose 6-phosphatase serves as a "gateway" to the blood for both pathways (see Fig. 28.2).

Regulation of glycogen synthesis serves to prevent futile cycling and waste of ATP. *Futile cycling* refers to a situation in which a substrate is converted to a product through one pathway, and the product is converted back to the substrate through another pathway. Because the biosynthetic pathway is energy-requiring, futile cycling results in a waste of high-energy phosphate bonds. Thus, glycogen synthesis is activated when glycogen degradation is inhibited and vice versa.

III. SYNTHESIS AND DEGRADATION OF GLYCOGEN

Glycogen synthesis, like almost all the pathways of glucose metabolism, begins with the phosphorylation of glucose to G6P by hexokinase or, in the liver, glucokinase (Fig. 28.3). G6P is the precursor of *glycolysis*, the pentose phosphate pathway, and pathways for the synthesis of other sugars. In the pathway for glycogen synthesis, G6P is converted to glucose 1-phosphate by *phosphoglucomutase*—a reversible reaction.

FIG. 28.3. Scheme of glycogen synthesis and degradation. *(S1)* G6P is formed from glucose by hexokinase in most cells, and glucokinase in the liver. It is a metabolic branch point for the pathways of glycolysis, the pentose phosphate pathway, and glycogen synthesis. *(S2)* UDP-glucose (UDP-G) is synthesized from glucose 1-phosphate. UDP-G is the branch point for glycogen synthesis and other pathways that require the addition of carbohydrate units. *(S3)* Glycogen synthesis is catalyzed by glycogen synthase and the branching enzyme. *(D1)* Glycogen degradation is catalyzed by glycogen phosphorylase and a debrancher enzyme. *(D2)* Glucose 6-phosphatase in the liver (and, to a small extent, the kidney) generates free glucose from G6P.

FIG. 28.4.   Formation of UDP-glucose. The high-energy phosphate bond of UTP provides the energy for the formation of a high-energy bond in UDP-glucose. Pyrophosphate (PP$_i$), released by the reaction, is cleaved to two inorganic phosphate (P$_i$).

FIG. 28.5.   Glycogen synthesis. See text for details.

Glycogen is both formed from and degraded to glucose 1-phosphate, but the biosynthetic and degradative pathways are separated and involve different enzymes (see Fig. 28.3). The *biosynthetic pathway* is an energy-requiring pathway; high-energy phosphate from UTP is used to activate the glucosyl residues to uridine diphosphate glucose (UDP-G) (Fig. 28.4). In the *degradative pathway*, the glycosidic bonds between the glucosyl residues in glycogen are simply cleaved by the addition of phosphate to produce glucose 1-phosphate (or water to produce free glucose), and UDP-G is not resynthesized. The existence of separate pathways for the formation and degradation of important compounds is a common theme in metabolism. Because the synthesis and degradation pathways use different enzymes, one can be activated while the other is inhibited.

A. Glycogen Synthesis

Glycogen synthesis requires the formation of α-1,4-glycosidic bonds to link glucosyl residues in long chains and the formation of an α-1,6-branch every 8 to 10 residues (Fig. 28.5). Most of glycogen synthesis occurs through the lengthening of the polysaccharide chains of a preexisting glycogen molecule (a glycogen primer) in which the reducing end of the glycogen is attached to the protein glycogenin. To lengthen the glycogen chains, glucosyl residues are added from UDP-G to the nonreducing ends of the chain by glycogen synthase. The anomeric carbon of each glucosyl residue is attached in an α-1,4-glycosidic bond to the hydroxyl on carbon 4 of the terminal glucosyl residue. When the chain reaches approximately 11 residues in length, a 6- to 8-residue piece is cleaved by amylo-4,6-transferase (also known as *branching enzyme*) and reattached to a glucosyl unit by an α-1,6-bond. Both chains continue to lengthen until they are long enough to produce two new branches. This process continues, producing highly branched molecules. Glycogen synthase, the enzyme that attaches the glucosyl residues in α-1,4-glycosidic bonds is the regulated step in the pathway. Branching of glycogen serves two major roles: increased sites for synthesis and degradation, and enhancing the solubility of the molecule.

The synthesis of new glycogen primer molecules also occurs. *Glycogenin*, the protein to which glycogen is attached, glycosylates itself (autoglycosylation) by attaching the glucosyl residue of UDP-G to the hydroxyl side chain of a serine residue in the protein. The protein then extends the carbohydrate chain (using UDP-G as the substrate) until the glucosyl chain is long enough to serve as a substrate for glycogen synthase.

To confirm a diagnosis of phosphory- lase deficiency (in either muscle or liver) a biopsy must be obtained, fol- lowed by a sensitive assay for phosphorylase activity within the biopsied tissue. There are several procedures to do this. The first is to incu- bate glycogen, inorganic phosphate, and a sample of the extracted biopsy tissue. If phosphorylase activity is present, glucose 1-phosphate will be produced. One can determine the amount of glu- cose 1-phosphate produced by converting it to G6P, using the enzyme phosphoglucomutase. The G6P levels are then measured by the conversion of G6P to 6-phosphogluconate using the enzyme G6P dehydrogenase. G6P dehydrogenase requires $NADP^+$, generating NADPH during the course of the reaction. The formation of NADPH can be fol- lowed spectrophotometrically as the absorbance at 340 nm will increase as NADPH is produced, and the increase in NADPH levels will be directly proportional to the amount of glucose 1-phosphate produced by phosphorylase. A second assay to measure phosphorylase activity uses radioactive glycogen as a substrate. The labeled glycogen is incubated with inorganic phosphate and sample extract, generating labeled glucose 1-phosphate. The radioactive glucose 1-phosphate is then separated from the glycogen and measured. A variation of this method is to use ^{32}P-labeled inorganic phosphate, and measure the radioactive glucose 1-phosphate produced. A third assay for phosphorylase activity is to measure the reverse reaction (glycogen synthesis). Under appropriate conditions, the phosphorylase reaction can go backward in which the glucose residue from glu- cose 1-phosphate is added to an existing glycogen chain, releasing P_i. The phosphate produced using this method is then measured in a sensitive spec- trophotometric assay.

FIG. 28.6. Glycogen degradation. See text for details.

B. Degradation of Glycogen

Glycogen is degraded by two enzymes: glycogen phosphorylase and the debrancher enzyme (Fig. 28.6). *Glycogen degradation* is a phosphorolysis reaction (breaking of a bond using a phosphate ion as a nucleophile). Enzymes that catalyze phospho- rolysis reactions are named *phosphorylase*. Because more than one type of phos- phorylase exists, the substrate usually is included in the name of the enzyme, such as glycogen phosphorylase or purine nucleoside phosphorylase.

The enzyme glycogen phosphorylase starts at the nonreducing end of a chain and successively cleaves glucosyl residues by adding phosphate to the anomeric carbon of the terminal glycosidic bond, thereby releasing glucose 1-phosphate and producing a free 4′-hydroxyl group on the glucose residue now at the end of the glycogen chain. However, glycogen phosphorylase cannot act on the glycosidic bonds of the four glucosyl residues closest to a branch point because the branch- ing chain sterically hinders a proper fit into the catalytic site of the enzyme. The *debrancher enzyme*, which catalyzes the removal of the four residues closest to the branch point, has two catalytic activities: it acts as a transferase and as an α-1,6- glucosidase. As a transferase, the debrancher first removes a unit containing three glucose residues and adds it to the end of a longer chain by an α-1,4-glycosidic bond. The one glucosyl residue remaining at the α-1,6-branch is hydrolyzed by the amylo-1,6-glucosidase activity of the debrancher, resulting in the release of free glucose. Thus, one glucose and approximately seven to nine glucose 1-phosphate residues are released for every branch point.

Some degradation of glycogen also occurs within lysosomes when glycogen particles become surrounded by membranes that then fuse with the lysosomal mem- branes. A lysosomal glucosidase hydrolyzes this glycogen to glucose.

IV. DISORDERS OF GLYCOGEN METABOLISM

A series of inborn errors of metabolism—the glycogen storage diseases—results from deficiencies in the enzymes of glycogenolysis (Table 28.1). The diseases are labeled I through X, and O. Several disorders have different subtypes as

A genetic defect of lysosomal glu- cosidase called *type II glycogen storage disease* or *Pompe disease*, leads to the accumulation of glycogen par- ticles in large, membrane-enclosed residual bodies, which disrupt the function of liver and muscle cells. Children with this disease usually die of heart failure at a few months of age.

Why do you think that a genetic defi- ciency in muscle glycogen phosphor- ylase (*McArdle disease*) is a mere inconvenience, whereas a deficiency of liver gly- cogen phosphorylase (*Hers disease*) can be lethal?

Table 28.1   Glycogen Storage Diseases

Type	Enzyme Affected	Primary Organ Involved	Manifestations[a]
O	Glycogen synthase	Liver	Hypoglycemia, hyperketonemia, failure to thrive, early death
I[b]	Glucose 6-phosphatase (Von Gierkes disease)	Liver	Enlarged liver and kidney, growth failure, severe fasting hypoglycemia, acidosis, lipemia, thrombocyte dysfunction
II	Lysosomal α-glucosidase (Pompe disease): may see clinical symptoms in childhood, juvenile, or adult life stages, depending on the nature of the mutation	All organs with lysosomes	Infantile form: early-onset progressive muscle hypotonia, cardiac failure, death before age 2 years Juvenile form: later-onset myopathy with variable cardiac involvement Adult form: limb-girdle muscular dystrophy-like features. Glycogen deposits accumulate in lysosomes
III	Amylo-1,6-glucosidase (debrancher): form IIIa is the liver and muscle enzymes; form IIIb is a liver-specific form; and form IIIc is a muscle-specific form	Liver, skeletal muscle, heart	Fasting hypoglycemia; hepatomegaly in infancy in some myopathic features. Glycogen deposits have short outer branches.
IV	Amylo-4,6-glucosidase (branching enzyme) (Andersen disease)	Liver	Hepatosplenomegaly; symptoms may arise from a hepatic reaction to the presence of a foreign body (glycogen with long outer branches). Usually fatal.
V	Muscle glycogen phosphorylase (McArdles disease) (expressed as either adult or infantile form)	Skeletal muscle	Exercise-induced muscular pain, cramps, and progressive weakness, sometimes with myoglobinuria
VI[c]	Liver glycogen phosphorylase (Hers disease) and its activating system (includes mutations in hepatic phosphorylase kinase and hepatic PKA)	Liver	Hepatomegaly, mild hypoglycemia; good prognosis
VII	Phosphofructokinase-1 (Tarui syndrome)	Muscle, red blood cells	As in type V; in addition, enzymopathic hemolysis
XI	GLUT 2 (glucose/galactose transporter); Fanconi-Bickel syndrome	Intestine, pancreas, kidney, liver	Glycogen accumulation in liver and kidney; rickets, growth retardation, glucosuria.

[a]All of these diseases except type O are characterized by increased glycogen deposits.
[b]Glucose 6-phosphatase is composed of several subunits that also transport glucose, glucose 6-phosphate, phosphate, and PPᵢ across the endoplasmic reticulum membranes. Therefore, there are several subtypes of this disease corresponding to defects in the different subunits. Type Ia is a lack of glucose 6-phosphatase activity; type Ib is a lack of glucose-6-phosphate translocase activity; type Ic is a lack of phosphotranslocase activity; type Id is a lack of glucose translocase activity.
[c]Glycogen storage diseases IX (hepatic phosphorylase kinase) and X (hepatic protein kinase A [PKA]) have been reclassified to VI, which now refers to the hepatic glycogen phosphorylase activating system.
Sources: Parker PH, Ballew M, Greene HL. Nutritional management of glycogen storage disease. *Annu Rev Nutr.* 1993;13:83–109. Copyright 1993 by Annual Reviews, Inc.; Shin YS. Glycogen storage disease: clinical, biochemical, and molecular heterogeneity. *Semin Pediatr Neurol.* 2006;13:115–120; Ozen H. Glycogen storage diseases: new perspectives. *World J Gastroenterol.* 2007;13:2541–2553.

indicated in the note of Table 28.1. *Muscle glycogen phosphorylase*, the key regulatory enzyme of glycogen degradation, is genetically different from liver glycogen phosphorylase, and thus a person may have a defect in one and not the other.

V. REGULATION OF GLYCOGEN SYNTHESIS AND DEGRADATION

The regulation of glycogen synthesis in different tissues matches the function of glycogen in each tissue. Liver glycogen serves principally for the support of blood glucose during fasting or during extreme need (e.g., exercise), and the degradative and biosynthetic pathways are regulated principally by changes in the insulin/glucagon ratio and by blood glucose levels, which reflect the availability of dietary glucose (Table 28.2). Degradation of liver glycogen is also activated by epinephrine, which is released in response to exercise, hypoglycemia, or other stress situations in which there is an immediate demand for blood glucose. In contrast, in skeletal muscles, *glycogen* is a reservoir of glucosyl units for the generation of ATP from glycolysis and glucose oxidation. As a consequence, muscle glycogenolysis is regulated principally by adenosine monophosphate (AMP), which signals a lack of ATP, and by Ca^{2+} released during contraction. Epinephrine, which is released in response to exercise and other stress situations, also activates skeletal muscle glycogenolysis. The glycogen stores of resting muscle decrease very little during fasting.

 Muscle glycogen is used within the muscle to support exercise. Thus, an individual with McArdle disease (type V glycogen storage disease) experiences no symptoms except unusual fatigue and muscle cramps during exercise. These symptoms may be accompanied by myoglobinuria and release of muscle creatine kinase into the blood.

Liver glycogen is the first reservoir for the support of blood glucose levels, and a deficiency in glycogen phosphorylase or any of the other enzymes of liver glycogen degradation can result in fasting hypoglycemia. The hypoglycemia is usually mild because patients can still synthesize glucose from gluconeogenesis (see Table 28.1).

Table 28.2   Regulation of Liver and Muscle Glycogen Stores[a]

State	Regulators	Response of Tissue
Liver		
Fasting	Blood: Glucagon ↑ Insulin ↓ Tissue: cAMP ↑	Glycogen degradation ↑ Glycogen synthesis ↓
Carbohydrate meal	Blood: Glucagon ↓ Insulin ↑ Glucose ↑ Tissue: cAMP ↓ Glucose ↑	Glycogen degradation ↓ Glycogen synthesis ↑
Exercise and stress	Blood: Epinephrine ↑ Tissue: cAMP ↑ Ca²⁺-calmodulin ↑	Glycogen degradation ↑ Glycogen synthesis ↓
Muscle		
Fasting (rest)	Blood: Insulin ↓	Glycogen synthesis ↓ Glucose transport ↓
Carbohydrate meal (rest)	Blood: Insulin ↑	Glycogen synthesis ↑ Glucose transport ↑
Exercise	Blood: Epinephrine ↑ Tissue: AMP ↓ Ca²⁺-calmodulin ↑ cAMP ↑	Glycogen synthesis ↓ Glycogen degradation ↓ Glycolysis ↑

[a]↑, increased compared with other physiologic states; ↓, decreased compared with other physiologic states.

A. Regulation of Glycogen Metabolism in Liver

Liver glycogen is synthesized after a carbohydrate meal when blood glucose levels are elevated and are degraded as blood glucose levels decrease. When an individual eats a carbohydrate-containing meal, blood glucose levels immediately increase, insulin levels increase, and glucagon levels decrease (see Fig. 26.8). The increase of blood glucose levels and the rise of the insulin/glucagon ratio inhibit glycogen degradation and stimulate glycogen synthesis. The immediate increased transport of glucose into peripheral tissues, and storage of blood glucose as glycogen, helps to bring circulating blood glucose levels back to the normal 80- to 100-mg/dL range of the fasted state. As the length of time after a carbohydrate-containing meal increases, insulin levels decrease, and glucagon levels increase. The fall of the insulin/glucagon ratio results in inhibition of the biosynthetic pathway and activation of the degradative pathway. As a result, liver glycogen is rapidly degraded to glucose, which is released into the blood.

Although glycogenolysis and gluconeogenesis are activated together by the same regulatory mechanisms, glycogenolysis responds more rapidly with a greater outpouring of glucose. A substantial proportion of liver glycogen is degraded within the first few hours after eating (Table 28.3). The rate of glycogenolysis is fairly constant for the first 22 hours, but in a prolonged fast, the rate decreases significantly as the liver glycogen supplies dwindle. Liver glycogen stores are therefore a rapidly rebuilt and degraded store of glucose, ever responsive to small and rapid changes of blood glucose levels.

Table 28.3   Effect of Fasting on Liver Glycogen Content in the Human

Length of Fast (h)	Glycogen Content (μmol/g)	Rate of Glycogenolysis (μmol/kg/min)
0	300	—
2	260	4.3
4	216	4.3
24	42	1.7
64	16	0.3

Maternal blood glucose readily crosses the placenta to enter the fetal circulation. During the last 9 or 10 weeks of gestation, glycogen formed from maternal glucose is deposited in the fetal liver under the influence of the insulin-dominated hormonal milieu of that period. At birth, maternal glucose supplies cease, causing a temporary physiologic drop in glucose levels in the newborn's blood, even in normal healthy infants. This drop serves as one of the signals for glucagon release from the newborn's pancreas, which in turn stimulates glycogenolysis. As a result, the glucose levels in the newborn return to normal.

Healthy full-term babies have adequate stores of liver glycogen to survive short periods (12 hours) of caloric deprivation provided other aspects of fuel metabolism are normal. Because **Getta Carbo's** mother was markedly anorexic during the critical period when the fetal liver is normally synthesizing glycogen from glucose supplied in the maternal blood, Getta's liver glycogen stores were lower than normal. Thus, because fetal glycogen is the major source of fuel for the newborn in the early hours of life, Getta became profoundly hypoglycemic within 5 hours of birth because of her low levels of stored carbohydrate.

Plasma glucose levels in the neonate. (From Mehta A. Prevention and management of neonatal hypoglycemia. *Arch Dis Child Fetal Neonatal Ed.* 1994;70:F54–F59.)

The normal range of blood glucose levels in the neonate lies between the two *purple lines*. The *dark blue area* represents the range of hypoglycemia in the neonate that should be treated. Treatment of neonates with blood glucose levels that fall within the *dashed red box*—the zone of clinical uncertainty—is controversial. The units of plasma glucose are given in mmol/L. Both mg/dL (mg/100 mL) and mmol/L are used clinically for the values of blood glucose; 80 mg/dL glucose is equivalent to 5 mmol/L (5 mM).

A patient was diagnosed as an infant with *type III glycogen storage disease*, a deficiency of debrancher enzyme (see Table 28.1). The patient had hepatomegaly (an enlarged liver) and experienced bouts of mild hypoglycemia. To diagnose the disease, glycogen was obtained from the patient's liver by biopsy after the patient had fasted overnight and compared with normal glycogen. The glycogen samples were treated with a preparation of commercial glycogen phosphorylase and commercial debrancher enzyme. The amounts of glucose 1-phosphate and glucose produced in the assay were then measured. The ratio of glucose 1-phosphate to glucose for the normal glycogen sample was 9:1, and the ratio for the patient was 3:1. Can you explain these results?

FIG. 28.7. The conversion of active and inactive forms of glycogen phosphorylase (**A**) and glycogen synthase (**B**). Note how the nomenclature changes depending on the phosphorylation and activity state of the enzyme.

1. NOMENCLATURE CONCERNS WITH ENZYMES THAT METABOLIZE GLYCOGEN

Both glycogen phosphorylase and glycogen synthase will be covalently modified to regulate their activity (Fig. 28.7). When it is activated by covalent modification, glycogen phosphorylase is referred to as *glycogen phosphorylase a* (remember *a* for active); when the covalent modification is removed and the enzyme is inactive, it is referred to as *glycogen phosphorylase b*. Glycogen synthase, when it is not covalently modified, is active and can be designated as glycogen synthase *a* or glycogen synthase *I* (the *I* stands for *independent* of modifiers for activity). When glycogen synthase is covalently modified, it is inactive in the form of glycogen synthase *b* or glycogen synthase *D* (for *dependent* on a modifier for activity).

2. REGULATION OF LIVER GLYCOGEN METABOLISM BY INSULIN AND GLUCAGON

Insulin and glucagon regulate liver glycogen metabolism by changing the phosphorylation state of glycogen phosphorylase in the degradative pathway and glycogen synthase in the biosynthetic pathway. An increase of glucagon and decrease of insulin during the fasting state initiates a cyclic adenosine monophosphate (cAMP)-directed phosphorylation cascade, which results in the phosphorylation of glycogen phosphorylase to an active enzyme and the phosphorylation of glycogen synthase to an inactive enzyme (Fig. 28.8). As a consequence, glycogen degradation is stimulated, and glycogen synthesis is inhibited.

3. GLUCAGON ACTIVATES A PHOSPHORYLATION CASCADE THAT CONVERTS GLYCOGEN PHOSPHORYLASE B TO GLYCOGEN PHOSPHORYLASE A

Glucagon regulates glycogen metabolism through its intracellular second messenger cAMP and protein kinase A (PKA) (see Chapter 26). Glucagon, by binding to its cell membrane receptor, transmits a signal through G proteins that activates adenylate cyclase, causing cAMP levels to increase (see Fig. 28.8). cAMP binds to the regulatory subunits of PKA, which dissociate from the catalytic subunits. The catalytic subunits of PKA are activated by the dissociation and phosphorylate the enzyme phosphorylase kinase—activating it. *Phosphorylase kinase* is the protein kinase that converts the inactive liver glycogen phosphorylase b conformer to the active glycogen phosphorylase a conformer by transferring a phosphate from ATP to a specific serine residue on the phosphorylase subunits. Because of the activation of glycogen phosphorylase, glycogenolysis is stimulated.

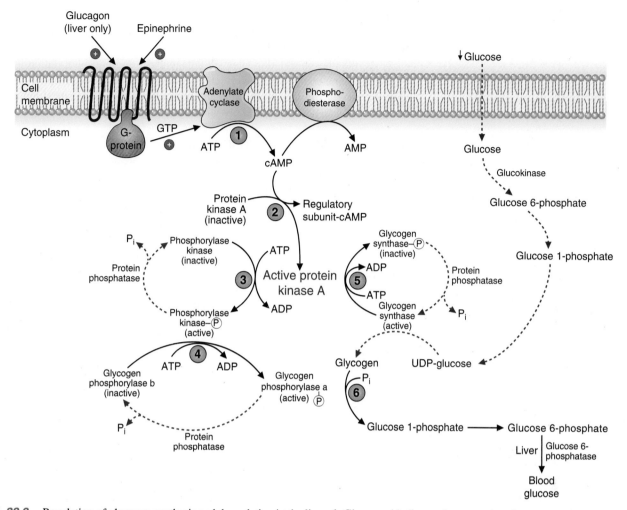

FIG. 28.8. Regulation of glycogen synthesis and degradation in the liver. **1.** Glucagon binding to the serpentine glucagon receptor or epinephrine binding to a serpentine β-receptor in the liver activates adenylate cyclase via G proteins, which synthesizes cAMP from ATP. **2.** cAMP binds to PKA (cAMP-dependent protein kinase), thereby activating the catalytic subunits. **3.** PKA activates phosphorylase kinase by phosphorylation. **4.** Phosphorylase kinase adds a phosphate to specific serine residues on glycogen phosphorylase b, thereby converting it to the active glycogen phosphorylase a. **5.** PKA also phosphorylates glycogen synthase thereby decreasing its activity. **6.** Because of the inhibition of glycogen synthase and the activation of glycogen phosphorylase, glycogen is degraded to glucose 1-phosphate. The *red dashed lines* denote reactions that are decreased in the livers of fasting individuals.

4. INHIBITION OF GLYCOGEN SYNTHASE BY GLUCAGON-DIRECTED PHOSPHORYLATION

When glycogen degradation is activated by the cAMP-stimulated phosphorylation cascade, glycogen synthesis is simultaneously inhibited. The enzyme glycogen synthase is also phosphorylated by PKA, but this phosphorylation results in a less active form, glycogen synthase b.

The phosphorylation of glycogen synthase is far more complex than glycogen phosphorylase. Glycogen synthase has multiple phosphorylation sites and is acted on by up to 10 different protein kinases. Phosphorylation by PKA does not, by itself, inactivate glycogen synthase. Instead, phosphorylation by PKA facilitates the subsequent addition of phosphate groups by other kinases, and these inactivate the enzyme. A term that has been applied to changes of activity resulting from multiple phosphorylations is hierarchical or synergistic phosphorylation—the phosphorylation of one site makes another site more reactive and easier to phosphorylate by a different protein kinase.

 With a deficiency of debrancher enzyme but normal levels of glycogen phosphorylase, the glycogen chains of the patient could be degraded in vivo only to within four residues of the branch point. When the glycogen samples were treated with the commercial preparation containing normal enzymes, one glucose residue was released for each α-1,6-branch. However, in the patient's glycogen sample, with the short outer branches, three glucose 1-phosphates and one glucose residue were obtained for each α-1,6-branch. Normal glycogen has 8 to 10 glucosyl residues per branch and thus gives a ratio of approximately 9 mmol glucose 1-phosphate to 1 mmol glucose.

Most of the enzymes that are regulated by phosphorylation have multiple phosphorylation sites. Glycogen phosphorylase, which has only one serine per subunit and can be phosphorylated only by phosphorylase kinase, is the exception. For some enzymes, the phosphorylation sites are antagonistic, and phosphorylation initiated by one hormone counteracts the effects of other hormones. For other enzymes, the phosphorylation sites are synergistic, and phosphorylation at one site stimulated by one hormone can act synergistically with phosphorylation at another site.

5. REGULATION BY PROTEIN PHOSPHATASES

At the same time that PKA and phosphorylase kinase are adding phosphate groups to enzymes, the protein phosphatases that remove this phosphate are inhibited. Protein phosphatases remove the phosphate groups, bound to serine or other residues of enzymes, by hydrolysis. *Hepatic protein-phosphatase-1* (PP-1), one of the major protein phosphatases involved in glycogen metabolism, removes phosphate groups from phosphorylase kinase, glycogen phosphorylase, and glycogen synthase. During fasting, hepatic PP-1 is inactivated by several mechanisms. One is dissociation from the glycogen particle, such that the substrates are no longer available to the phosphatase. The second is the binding of inhibitor proteins, such as the protein called *inhibitor-1*, which, when phosphorylated by a glucagon (or epinephrine)-directed mechanism, binds to and inhibits phosphatase action. Insulin indirectly activates hepatic PP-1 through its own signal transduction cascade initiated at the insulin receptor tyrosine kinase.

PP-1 will bind to proteins that target the phosphatase to glycogen particles. There are four such targeting proteins: G_M, G_L, R6, and R5/PTG (protein targeting to glycogen). G_M is found in the heart and skeletal muscle, G_L is found primarily in the liver, whereas R5/PTG and R6 are found in most tissues. The targeting subunits all bind to the same hydrophobic site on PP-1, leading to just one targeting subunit bound per PP-1 molecule. The targeting subunits allow for compartmentalized activation of PP-1 under the appropriate conditions, whereas other tissues or cellular compartments may still express an inhibited PP-1. Regulation of the phosphatase involves complex interactions between the target enzymes, the targeting subunits, the phosphatase, and protein inhibitor 1 and will not be considered further.

6. INSULIN IN LIVER GLYCOGEN METABOLISM

Insulin is antagonistic to glucagon in the degradation and synthesis of glycogen. The *glucose level in the blood* is the signal that controls the secretion of insulin and glucagon. Glucose stimulates insulin release and suppresses glucagon release; after a high-carbohydrate meal, one increases whereas the other decreases. However, insulin levels in the blood change to a greater degree with the fasting–feeding cycle than do the glucagon levels, and thus *insulin* is considered the principal regulator of glycogen synthesis and degradation. The role of insulin in glycogen metabolism is often overlooked because the mechanisms by which insulin reverses all of the effects of glucagon on individual metabolic enzymes is still under investigation. In addition to the activation of hepatic PP-1 through the insulin-receptor tyrosine kinase phosphorylation cascade, insulin may activate the phosphodiesterase that converts cAMP to AMP, thereby decreasing cAMP levels and inactivating PKA. Regardless of the mechanisms involved, insulin is able to reverse all of the effects of glucagon and is the most important hormonal regulator of blood glucose levels.

7. BLOOD GLUCOSE LEVELS AND GLYCOGEN SYNTHESIS
AND DEGRADATION

When an individual eats a high-carbohydrate meal, glycogen degradation immediately stops. Although the changes in insulin and glucagon levels are relatively rapid (10 to 15 minutes), the direct inhibitory effect of rising glucose levels on glycogen degradation is even more rapid. Glucose, as an allosteric effector, inhibits liver glycogen phosphorylase a by stimulating dephosphorylation of this enzyme. As insulin

Most of the enzymes that are regulated by phosphorylation also can be converted to the active conformation by allosteric effectors. *Glycogen synthase b*, the less active form of glycogen synthase, can be activated by the accumulation of G6P higher than physiologic levels. The activation of glycogen synthase by G6P may be important in individuals with glucose 6-phosphatase deficiency, a disorder known as *type I* or *von Gierke glycogen storage disease* (see Table 28.1). When G6P produced from gluconeogenesis accumulates in the liver, it activates glycogen synthesis even though the individual may be hypoglycemic and have low insulin levels. Glucose 1-phosphate is also elevated, resulting in the inhibition of glycogen phosphorylase. As a consequence, large glycogen deposits accumulate and hepatomegaly occurs.

An inability of liver and muscle to store glucose as glycogen contributes to the hyperglycemia in patients such as **Di Abietes**, with type 1 diabetes mellitus and in patients such as **Ann Sulin**, with type 2 diabetes mellitus. The absence of insulin in type 1 diabetes mellitus patients and the high levels of glucagon result in decreased activity of glycogen synthase. Glycogen synthesis in skeletal muscles of type 1 patients is also limited by the lack of insulin-stimulated glucose transport. Insulin resistance in type 2 patients has the same effect.

An injection of insulin suppresses glucagon release and alters the insulin/glucagon ratio. The result is rapid uptake of glucose into skeletal muscle and rapid conversion of glucose to glycogen in skeletal muscle and liver.

levels rise and glucagon levels fall, cAMP levels decrease and PKA reassociates with its inhibitory subunits and becomes inactive. The protein phosphatases are activated, and glycogen phosphorylase a and glycogen synthase b are dephosphorylated. The collective result of these effects is rapid inhibition of glycogen degradation and rapid activation of glycogen synthesis.

8. EPINEPHRINE AND CALCIUM IN THE REGULATION OF LIVER GLYCOGEN

Epinephrine, the fight-or-flight hormone, is released from the adrenal medulla in response to neural signals reflecting an increased demand for glucose. To flee from a dangerous situation, skeletal muscles use increased amounts of blood glucose to generate ATP. As a result, liver glycogenolysis must be stimulated. In the liver, epinephrine stimulates glycogenolysis through two different types of receptors: the α- and β-agonist receptors.

A. Epinephrine Acting at β-Receptors

Epinephrine, acting at the β-receptors, transmits a signal through G proteins to adenylate cyclase, which increases cAMP levels and activates PKA. Therefore, regulation of glycogen degradation and synthesis in liver by epinephrine and glucagon are similar (see Fig. 28.8).

B. Epinephrine Acting at α-Receptors

Epinephrine also binds to α-receptors in the hepatocyte. This binding activates glycogenolysis and inhibits glycogen synthesis principally by increasing the Ca^{2+} levels in the liver. The effects of epinephrine at the α-agonist receptor are mediated by the phosphatidylinositol bisphosphate (PIP_2)-Ca^{2+} signal transduction system, one of the principal intracellular second messenger systems employed by many hormones (Fig. 28.9) (see Chapter 11).

 In the neonate, the release of epinephrine during labor and birth normally contributes to restoring blood glucose levels. Unfortunately, **Getta Carbo** did not have adequate liver glycogen stores to support a rise in her blood glucose levels.

FIG. 28.9. Regulation of glycogen synthesis and degradation by epinephrine and Ca^{2+}. **1.** The effect of epinephrine binding to α-agonist receptors in the liver transmits a signal via G proteins to phospholipase C, which hydrolyzes PIP_2 to DAG and IP_3. **2.** IP_3 stimulates the release of Ca^{2+} from the endoplasmic reticulum. **3.** Ca^{2+} binds to the modifier protein calmodulin, which activates calmodulin-dependent protein kinase and phosphorylase kinase. Both Ca^{2+} and DAG activate protein kinase C. **4.** These three kinases phosphorylate glycogen synthase at different sites and decrease its activity. **5.** Phosphorylase kinase phosphorylates glycogen phosphorylase b to the active form. It therefore activates glycogenolysis as well as inhibiting glycogen synthesis.

In the PIP_2-Ca^{2+} signal transduction system, the signal is transferred from the epinephrine receptor to membrane-bound phospholipase C by G proteins. Phospholipase C hydrolyzes PIP_2 to form diacylglycerol (DAG) and inositol trisphosphate (IP_3). IP_3 stimulates the release of Ca^{2+} from the endoplasmic reticulum. Ca^{2+} and DAG activate protein kinase C. The amount of calcium bound to one of the calcium-binding proteins—*calmodulin*—is also increased.

Calcium/calmodulin associates as a subunit with several enzymes and modifies their activities. It binds to inactive phosphorylase kinase, thereby partially activating this enzyme. (The fully activated enzyme is both bound to the calcium/calmodulin subunit and phosphorylated.) Phosphorylase kinase then phosphorylates glycogen phosphorylase b, thereby activating glycogen degradation. *Calcium/calmodulin* is also a modifier protein that activates one of the glycogen synthase kinases (calcium/calmodulin synthase kinase). Protein kinase C, calcium/calmodulin synthase kinase, and phosphorylase kinase all phosphorylate glycogen synthase at different serine residues on the enzyme, thereby inhibiting glycogen synthase and thus glycogen synthesis.

The effect of epinephrine in the liver therefore enhances or is synergistic with the effects of glucagon. Epinephrine release during bouts of hypoglycemia or during exercise can stimulate hepatic glycogenolysis and inhibit glycogen synthesis very rapidly.

B. Regulation of Glycogen Synthesis and Degradation in Skeletal Muscle

The regulation of glycogenolysis in skeletal muscle is related to the availability of ATP for muscular contraction. Skeletal muscle glycogen produces glucose 1-phosphate and a small amount of free glucose. Glucose 1-phosphate is converted to G6P, which is committed to the glycolytic pathway; the absence of glucose 6-phosphatase in skeletal muscle prevents conversion of the glucosyl units from glycogen to blood glucose. Skeletal muscle glycogen is therefore degraded only when the demand for ATP generation from glycolysis is high. The highest demands occur during anaerobic glycolysis, which requires more moles of glucose for each ATP produced than oxidation of glucose to CO_2 (see Chapter 22). Anaerobic glycolysis occurs in tissues that have fewer *mitochondria*, a higher content of glycolytic enzymes, and higher levels of glycogen, or fast-twitch glycolytic fibers. It occurs most frequently at the onset of exercise—before vasodilation occurs to bring in blood-borne fuels. The regulation of skeletal muscle glycogen degradation therefore must respond very rapidly to the need for ATP—indicated by the increase in AMP.

The regulation of skeletal muscle glycogen synthesis and degradation differs from that in liver in several important respects: (1) glucagon has no effect on muscle, and thus glycogen levels in muscle do not vary with the fasting/feeding state; (2) AMP is an allosteric activator of the muscle isozyme of glycogen phosphorylase, but not liver glycogen phosphorylase (Fig. 28.10); (3) the effects of Ca^{2+} in muscle result principally from the release of Ca^{2+} from the sarcoplasmic reticulum after neural stimulation, and not from epinephrine-stimulated uptake; (4) glucose is not a physiologic inhibitor of glycogen phosphorylase a in muscle; (5) glycogen is a stronger feedback inhibitor of muscle glycogen synthase than of liver glycogen synthase, resulting in a smaller amount of stored glycogen per gram weight of muscle tissue. However, the effects of epinephrine-stimulated phosphorylation by PKA on skeletal muscle glycogen degradation and glycogen synthesis are similar to those occurring in liver (see Fig. 28.8).

Muscle glycogen phosphorylase is a genetically distinct isoenzyme of liver glycogen phosphorylase and contains an amino acid sequence that has a purine nucleotide-binding site. When AMP binds to this site, it changes the conformation at the catalytic site to a structure very similar to that in the phosphorylated enzyme (see Chapter 9, Fig. 9.9). Thus, hydrolysis of ATP to ADP and the consequent

Jim Bodie gradually regained consciousness with continued infusions of high-concentration glucose titrated to keep his serum glucose level between 120 and 160 mg/dL. Although he remained somnolent and moderately confused over the next 12 hours, he was eventually able to tell his physicians that he had self-injected approximately 80 U of regular (short-acting) insulin every 6 hours while eating a high-carbohydrate diet for the last 2 days preceding his seizure. Normal subjects under basal conditions secrete an average of 40 U of insulin daily. He had last injected insulin just before exercising. An article in a body-building magazine that he had read recently cited the anabolic effects of insulin on increasing muscle mass. He had purchased the insulin and necessary syringes from the same underground drug source from whom he regularly bought his anabolic steroids.

Normally, muscle glycogenolysis supplies the glucose required for the kinds of high-intensity exercise that require anaerobic glycolysis, such as weightlifting. Jim's treadmill exercise also uses blood glucose, which is supplied by liver glycogenolysis. The high serum insulin levels, resulting from the injection he gave himself just before his workout, activated both glucose transport into skeletal muscle and glycogen synthesis while inhibiting glycogen degradation. His exercise, which would continue to use blood glucose, could normally be supported by breakdown of liver glycogen. However, glycogen synthesis in his liver was activated and glycogen degradation was inhibited by the insulin injection.

FIG. 28.10. Activation of muscle glycogen phosphorylase during exercise. Glycogenolysis in skeletal muscle is initiated by muscle contraction, neural impulses, and epinephrine. **1.** AMP produced from the degradation of ATP during muscular contraction allosterically activates glycogen phosphorylase b. **2.** The neural impulses that initiate contraction release Ca^{2+} from the sarcoplasmic reticulum. The Ca^{2+} binds to calmodulin, which is a modifier protein that activates phosphorylase kinase. **3.** Phosphorylase kinase is also activated through phosphorylation by PKA. The formation of cAMP and the resultant activation of PKA are initiated by the binding of epinephrine to plasma membrane receptors.

increase of AMP generated by adenylate kinase during muscular contraction can directly stimulate glycogenolysis to provide fuel for the glycolytic pathway. AMP also stimulates glycolysis by activating phosphofructokinase-1, so this one effector activates both glycogenolysis and glycolysis. The activation of the calcium/calmodulin subunit of phosphorylase kinase by the Ca^{2+} released from the sarcoplasmic reticulum during muscle contraction also provides a direct and rapid means of stimulating glycogen degradation.

CLINICAL COMMENTS

Getta Carbo. Getta Carbo's hypoglycemia illustrates the importance of glycogen stores in the neonate. At birth, the fetus must make two major adjustments in the way fuels are used: It must adapt to using a greater variety of fuels than were available in utero, and it must adjust to intermittent feeding. In utero, the fetus receives a relatively constant supply of glucose from the maternal circulation through the placenta, producing a level of glucose in the fetus that approximates 75% of maternal blood levels. With regard to the hormonal regulation of fuel use in utero, fetal tissues function in an environment dominated by insulin, which promotes growth. During the last 10 weeks of gestation, this hormonal milieu leads to glycogen formation and storage. At birth, the infant's diet changes to one containing greater amounts of fat and lactose (galactose and glucose in equal ratio), presented at intervals rather than in a constant fashion. At the same time, the neonate's need for glucose is relatively larger than that of the adult because the newborn's ratio of brain to liver weight is greater. Thus, the infant has even greater difficulty maintaining glucose homeostasis than the adult.

At the moment that the umbilical cord is clamped, the normal neonate is faced with a metabolic problem: The high insulin levels of late fetal existence must be quickly reversed to prevent hypoglycemia. This reversal is accomplished through the secretion of the counterregulatory hormones: epinephrine and glucagon. Glucagon release is triggered by the normal decline of blood glucose after birth. The neural response that stimulates the release of both glucagon and epinephrine is activated by the anoxia, cord clamping, and tactile stimulation that are part of a normal delivery. These responses have been referred to as the "normal sensor function" of the neonate.

Within 3 to 4 hours of birth, these counterregulatory hormones reestablish normal serum glucose levels in the newborn's blood through their glycogenolytic and gluconeogenic actions. The failure of Getta's normal "sensor function" was partly caused by maternal malnutrition, which resulted in an inadequate deposition of glycogen in Getta's liver before birth. The consequence was a serious degree of postnatal hypoglycemia.

The ability to maintain glucose homeostasis during the first few days of life also depends on the activation of gluconeogenesis and the mobilization of fatty acids. Fatty acid oxidation in the liver not only promotes gluconeogenesis (see Chapter 31), but also generates ketone bodies. The neonatal brain has an enhanced capacity to use ketone bodies relative to that of infants (4-fold) and adults (40-fold). This ability is consistent with the relatively high fat content of breast milk.

Jim Bodie. Jim Bodie attempted to build up his muscle mass with androgens and with insulin. The anabolic (nitrogen-retaining) effects of androgens on skeletal muscle cells enhance muscle mass by increasing amino acid flux into muscle and by stimulating protein synthesis. Exogenous insulin has the potential to increase muscle mass by similar actions and also by increasing the content of muscle glycogen.

The most serious side effect of exogenous insulin administration is the development of severe hypoglycemia, such as what occurred in Jim's case. The immediate adverse effect relates to an inadequate flow of fuel (glucose) to the metabolizing brain. When hypoglycemia is extreme, the patient may suffer a seizure and, if the hypoglycemia worsens, irreversible brain damage may occur. If prolonged, the patient will lapse into a coma and die.

BIOCHEMICAL COMMENTS

Glycogen Synthase Kinase-3 (GSK-3). It should be clear that the regulation of glycogen metabolism is quite complex. Recent work has indicated that certain enzymes involved in regulating glycogen synthase activity also have far-reaching effects on other aspects of cell metabolism, such as cell structure, motility, growth, and survival.

The best example of this is GSK-3. The enzyme was first identified as being an inhibitor of glycogen synthase. GSK-3 refers to two isozymes: GSK3α and GSK3β. GSK-3 has been identified as a kinase that can phosphorylate >40 different proteins, including a large number of transcription factors. GSK-3 activity is also self-regulated by phosphorylation.

GSK-3 activity is reduced by phosphorylation of a serine residue near its amino terminal. Protein kinase A (PKA), Akt, and protein kinase C can all catalyze this inhibitory phosphorylation event. GSK-3 is most active on protein substrates that have already been phosphorylated by other kinases (the substrates are said to be primed for further phosphorylation events). For example, GSK-3 will add phosphates to glycogen synthase, but only after glycogen synthase had been phosphorylated by PKA.

GSK-3 binds to several proteins that sequester GSK-3 in certain pathways. This includes the wnt signaling pathway, disruption of which is a significant component of colon cancer, the patched–smoothened signal transduction pathway (see Chapter 18), and the phosphorylation of microtubule-associated proteins, which leads to altered cell motility. Activation of GSK-3 has also been linked to apoptosis, although GSK-3 activity is also required for cell survival.

One of the effects of insulin is to phosphorylate GSK-3 via activation of Akt, rendering the GSK-3 inactive. Loss of activity of GSK-3 will lead to activation of glycogen synthase activity and the pathways of energy storage. In animal models of type 2 diabetes, there is a loss of inhibitory control of GSK-3, leading to greater-than-normal GSK-3 activity, which antagonizes insulin action (promoting *insulin resistance*, a hallmark of type 2 diabetes). Studies in rats have shown that inhibitors of GSK-3 lowered blood glucose levels and stimulated glucose transport into muscles of insulin-resistant animals.

Inappropriate stimulation of GSK-3 has also been implicated in Alzheimer disease.

Current research concerning GSK-3 is geared toward understanding all of the roles of GSK-3 in cell growth and survival, and to decipher its actions in the multitude of multiprotein complexes with which it is associated. Inhibitors of GSK-3 are being examined as possible agents to treat diabetes, but interpretation of results is difficult due to the multitude of roles that GSK-3 plays within cells. It is possible that in the future, such drugs will be available to treat type 2 diabetes.

Key Concepts

- Glycogen is the storage form of glucose, composed of glucosyl units linked by α-1,4-glycosidic bonds with α-1,6-branches occurring about every 8 to 10 glucosyl units.
- Glycogen synthesis requires energy.
- Glycogen synthase transfers a glucosyl residue from the activated intermediate UDP-G to the non-reducing ends of existing glycogen chains during glycogen synthesis. The branching enzyme creates α-1,6-linkages in the glycogen chain.
- Glycogenolysis is the degradation of glycogen. Glycogen phosphorylase catalyzes a phosphorolysis reaction, using exogenous P_i to break α-1,4-linkages at the ends of glycogen chains, releasing glucose 1-phosphate. The debranching enzyme hydrolyzes the α-1,6-linkages in glycogen, releasing free glucose.
- Liver glycogen supplies blood glucose.
- Glycogen synthesis and degradation are regulated in the liver by hormonal changes that signify either a deficiency of or an excess of blood glucose.
- Lack of dietary glucose, signaled by a decrease of the insulin/glucagon ratio, activates liver glycogenolysis and inhibits glycogen synthesis. Epinephrine also activates liver glycogenolysis.
- Glucagon and epinephrine release lead to phosphorylation of glycogen synthase (inactivating it) and glycogen phosphorylase (activating it).
- Glycogenolysis in muscle supplies G6P for ATP synthesis in the glycolytic pathway.
- Muscle glycogen phosphorylase is allosterically activated by AMP, as well as by phosphorylation.
- Increases in sarcoplasmic Ca^{2+} stimulates phosphorylation of muscle glycogen phosphorylase.
- Diseases discussed in this chapter are summarized in Table 28.4.

Table 28.4.   Diseases Discussed in Chapter 28

Disease or Disorder	Environmental or Genetic	Comments
Newborn hypoglycemia	Environmental	Poor maternal nutrition may lead to inadequate glycogen levels in the newborn resulting in hypoglycemia during the early fasting period after birth.
Insulin overdose	Environmental	Insulin taken without carbohydrate ingestion will lead to severe hypoglycemia due to stimulation of glucose uptake by peripheral tissues, leading to insufficient glucose in the circulation for proper functioning of the nervous system.
Glycogen storage diseases	Genetic	These have been summarized in Table 28.1. Affect storage and use of glycogen with different levels of severity from mild to fatal.

1. The degradation of glycogen normally produces which of the following?
    A. More glucose than glucose 1-phosphate
    B. More glucose 1-phosphate than glucose
    C. Equal amounts of glucose and glucose 1-phosphate
    D. Neither glucose or glucose 1-phosphate
    E. Only glucose 1-phosphate

2. A patient has large deposits of liver glycogen, which after an overnight fast, had shorter-than-normal branches. This abnormality could be caused by a defective form of which one of the following proteins or activities?
    A. Glycogen phosphorylase
    B. Glucagon receptor
    C. Glycogenin
    D. Amylo-1,6-glucosidase
    E. Amylo-4,6-transferase

3. An adolescent patient with a deficiency of muscle phosphorylase was examined while exercising his or her forearm by squeezing a rubber ball. Compared with a normal person performing the same exercise, this patient would exhibit which of the following?
    A. Exercise for a longer time without fatigue.
    B. Have increased glucose levels in blood drawn from his or her forearm.
    C. Have decreased lactate levels in blood drawn from his or her forearm.

    D. Have lower levels of glycogen in biopsy specimens from his or her forearm muscle.
    E. Hyperglycemia

4. In a glucose tolerance test, an individual in the basal metabolic state ingests a large amount of glucose. If the individual is normal, this ingestion should result in which of the following?
    A. An enhanced glycogen synthase activity in the liver
    B. An increased ratio of glycogen phosphorylase a to glycogen phosphorylase b in the liver
    C. An increased rate of lactate formation by red blood cells
    D. An inhibition of PP-1 activity in the liver
    E. An increase of cAMP levels in the liver

5. Consider a person with type 1 diabetes who has neglected to take insulin for the past 72 hours and has not eaten much as well. Which of the following best describes the activity level of hepatic enzymes involved in glycogen metabolism under these conditions?

	Glycogen Synthase	Phosphorylase Kinase	Glycogen Phosphorylase
A.	Active	Active	Active
B.	Active	Active	Inactive
C.	Active	Inactive	Inactive
D.	Inactive	Inactive	Inactive
E.	Inactive	Active	Inactive
F.	Inactive	Active	Active

29 Pathways of Sugar Metabolism: Pentose Phosphate Pathway, Fructose, and Galactose Metabolism

Glucose is at the center of carbohydrate metabolism and is the major dietary sugar. Other sugars in the diet are converted to intermediates of glucose metabolism, and their fates parallel that of glucose. When carbohydrates other than glucose are required for the synthesis of diverse compounds such as lactose, glycoproteins, or glycolipids, they are synthesized from glucose.

Fructose, the second most common sugar in the adult diet, is ingested principally as the monosaccharide or as part of sucrose (Fig. 29.1). It is metabolized principally in the liver (and to a lesser extent in the small intestine and kidney) by phosphorylation at the 1-position to form fructose 1-phosphate (fructose 1-P), followed by conversion to intermediates of the glycolytic pathway. The major products of its metabolism in liver are, therefore, the same as for glucose (including lactate, blood glucose, and glycogen). Essential fructosuria (fructokinase deficiency) and hereditary fructose intolerance (HFI) (a deficiency of the fructose 1-P cleavage by aldolase B) are inherited disorders of fructose metabolism.

Fructose synthesis from glucose in the polyol pathway occurs in seminal vesicles and other tissues. Aldose reductase converts glucose to the sugar alcohol sorbitol (a polyol), which is then oxidized to fructose. In the lens of the eye, elevated levels of sorbitol in diabetes mellitus may contribute to formation of cataracts.

Galactose is ingested principally as lactose, which is converted to galactose and glucose in the intestine. Galactose is converted to glucose principally in the liver. It is phosphorylated to galactose 1-phosphate (galactose 1-P) by galactokinase and activated to a uridine diphosphate (UDP)-sugar by galactosyl uridylyltransferase. The metabolic pathway subsequently generates glucose 1-phosphate (glucose 1-P). Classical galactosemia, a deficiency of galactosyl uridylyltransferase, results in the accumulation of galactose 1-P in the liver and the inhibition of hepatic glycogen metabolism and other pathways that require UDP-sugars. Cataracts can occur from accumulation of galactose in the blood, which is converted to galactitol (the sugar alcohol of galactose) in the lens of the eye.

The pentose phosphate pathway (also known as the hexose monophosphate shunt [HMP shunt]) consists of both oxidative and nonoxidative components (Fig. 29.2). In the oxidative pathway, glucose 6-phosphate (glucose 6-P) is oxidized to ribulose 5-phosphate (ribulose 5-P), CO_2, and NADPH. Ribulose 5-P, a pentose, can be converted to ribose 5-phosphate (ribose 5-P) for nucleotide biosynthesis. The NADPH is used for reductive pathways, such as fatty acid biosynthesis, detoxification of drugs by monooxygenases, and the glutathione defense system against injury by reactive oxygen species (ROS).

In the nonoxidative phase of the pathway, ribulose 5-P is converted to ribose 5-P and to intermediates of the glycolytic pathway. This portion of the pathway is reversible; therefore, ribose 5-P can also be formed from

Dietary
sucrose

Glucose

Dietary
fructose

Polyol
pathway

$^1 CH_2OH$

$^2 C = O$

$HO - ^3C - H$

$H - ^4C - OH$

$H - ^5C - OH$

$^6 CH_2OH$

↓

Intermediates of glycolysis

FIG. 29.1. Fructose. The sugar fructose is found in the diet as the free sugar in foods such as honey or as a component of the disaccharide sucrose in fruits and sweets. It also can be synthesized from glucose via the polyol pathway. In the lens of the eye, the polyol pathway contributes to the formation of cataracts. Fructose is metabolized by conversion to intermediates of glycolysis.

FIG. 29.2. Overview of the pentose phosphate pathway. The pentose phosphate pathway generates NADPH for reactions that require reducing equivalents (electrons) or ribose 5-P for nucleotide biosynthesis. Glucose 6-P is a substrate for both the pentose phosphate pathway and glycolysis. The five-carbon sugar intermediates of the pentose phosphate pathway are reversibly interconverted to intermediates of glycolysis. The portion of glycolysis that is not part of the pentose phosphate pathway is shown in *red*.

*intermediates of glycolysis. One of the enzymes involved in these sugar interconversions, **transketolase**, uses **thiamine pyrophosphate** as a coenzyme.*

The sugars produced by the pentose phosphate pathway enter glycolysis as fructose 6-phosphate (fructose 6-P) and glyceraldehyde 3-phosphate (glyceraldehyde 3-P), and their further metabolism in the glycolytic pathway generates NADH, adenosine triphosphate (ATP), and pyruvate. The overall equation for the conversion of glucose 6-P to fructose 6-P and glyceraldehyde 3-P through both the oxidative and nonoxidative reactions of the pentose phosphate pathway is

$$3 \text{ Glucose 6-P} + 6 \text{ NADP}^+ \rightarrow 3 \text{ CO}_2 + 6 \text{ NADPH} + 6 \text{ H}^+ + 2 \text{ fructose 6-P} + \text{glyceraldehyde 3-P}$$

THE WAITING ROOM

Candice Sucher is an 18-year-old girl who presented to her physician for a precollege physical examination. While taking her medical history, the doctor learned that she carefully avoided eating all fruits and any foods that contained table sugar. She related that from a very early age, she had learned that these foods caused severe weakness and symptoms suggestive of low blood sugar, such as tremulousness and sweating. Her medical history also indicated that her mother had described her as having been a very irritable baby who often cried incessantly, especially after meals, and vomited frequently. At these times, Candice's abdomen had become distended, and she became drowsy and apathetic. Her mother had intuitively eliminated certain foods from Candice's diet after which the severity and frequency of these symptoms diminished.

Erin Galway is a 3-week-old female infant who began vomiting 3 days after birth, usually within 30 minutes after breastfeeding. Her abdomen became distended at these times, and she became irritable and cried frequently. When her mother noted that the whites of Erin's eyes were yellow, she took her to a pediatrician. The doctor agreed that Erin was slightly jaundiced. He also noted an enlargement of her liver and questioned the possibility of early cataract formation in the lenses of Erin's eyes. He ordered liver and kidney function tests and did two separate dipstick urine tests in his office, one designed to measure only glucose in the urine and the other capable of detecting any of the reducing sugars.

Al Martini developed a fever of 101.5° F on the second day of his hospitalization for acute alcoholism. One of his physicians noticed that one of the lacerations on Mr. Martini's arm was red and swollen with some pus drainage. The pus was cultured and gram-positive cocci were found and identified as *Staphylococcus aureus*. Because his landlady stated that he had an allergy to penicillin and the concern over methicillin-resistant *S. aureus*, Al was started on a course of the antibiotic combination of trimethoprim and sulfamethoxazole (TMP/sulfa). To his landlady's knowledge, he had never been treated with a sulfa drug previously.

On the third day of therapy with TMP/sulfa for his infection, Mr. Martini was slightly jaundiced. His hemoglobin level had fallen by 3.5 g/dL from its value at admission, and his urine was red-brown because of the presence of free hemoglobin. Mr. Martini had apparently suffered acute hemolysis (lysis or destruction of some of his red blood cells) induced by his infection and exposure to the sulfa drug.

I. FRUCTOSE

Fructose is found in the diet as a component of sucrose in fruit, as a free sugar in honey, and in high-fructose corn syrup (see Fig. 29.1). Fructose enters epithelial cells and other types of cells by facilitated diffusion on the GLUT 5 transporter. It is metabolized to intermediates of glycolysis. Problems with fructose absorption and metabolism are relatively more common than with other sugars.

A. Fructose Metabolism

Fructose is metabolized by conversion to glyceraldehyde 3-phosphate (glyceraldehyde 3-P) and dihydroxyacetone phosphate, which are intermediates of glycolysis (Fig. 29.3). The steps parallel those of glycolysis. The first step in the metabolism of fructose, as with glucose, is phosphorylation. Fructokinase, the major kinase involved, phosphorylates fructose in the 1-position. Fructokinase has a high V_{max} and rapidly phosphorylates fructose as it enters the cell. The fructose 1-phosphate (fructose 1-P) formed is not an intermediate of glycolysis but rather is cleaved by aldolase B to dihydroxyacetone phosphate (an intermediate of glycolysis) and glyceraldehyde. Glyceraldehyde is then phosphorylated to glyceraldehyde 3-P by triose kinase. Dihydroxyacetone phosphate and glyceraldehyde 3-P are intermediates of the glycolytic pathway and can proceed through it to pyruvate, the tricarboxylic acid (TCA) cycle, and fatty acid synthesis. Alternatively, these intermediates can also be converted to glucose by gluconeogenesis. In other words, the fate of fructose parallels that of glucose.

 When individuals with defects of aldolase B ingest fructose, the extremely high levels of fructose 1-phosphate (fructose 1-P) that accumulate in the liver and kidney cause several adverse effects. Hypoglycemia results from inhibition of glycogenolysis and gluconeogenesis. Glycogen phosphorylase (and possibly phosphoglucomutase and other enzymes of glycogen metabolism) are inhibited by the accumulated fructose 1-P. Aldolase B is required for glucose synthesis from glyceraldehyde 3-phosphate (glyceraldehyde 3-P) and dihydroxyacetone phosphate, and its low activity in aldolase B-deficient individuals is further decreased by the accumulated fructose 1-P. The inhibition of gluconeogenesis results in lactic acidosis.

The accumulation of fructose 1-P also substantially depletes the intracellular phosphate pools. The fructokinase reaction uses adenosine triphosphate (ATP) at a rapid rate such that the mitochondria regenerate ATP rapidly, which leads to a drop in free phosphate levels. The low levels of phosphate release inhibition of adenosine monophosphate (AMP) deaminase, which converts AMP to inosine monophosphate (IMP). The nitrogenous base of IMP (hypoxanthine) is degraded to uric acid. The lack of phosphate and depletion of adenine nucleotides lead to a loss of ATP, further contributing to the inhibition of biosynthetic pathways, including gluconeogenesis.

Essential fructosuria is a rare and benign genetic disorder caused by a deficiency of the enzyme fructokinase. Why is this disease benign, when a deficiency of aldolase B (hereditary fructose intolerance [HFI]) can be fatal?

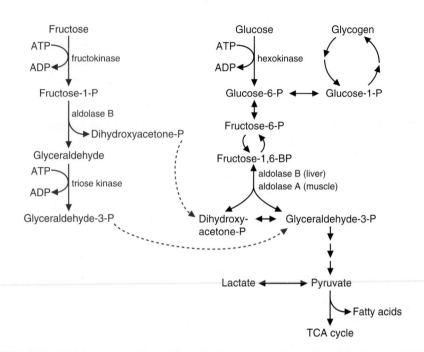

FIG. 29.3. Fructose metabolism. The pathway for the conversion of fructose to dihydroxyacetone phosphate and glyceraldehyde 3-phosphate (glyceraldehyde 3-P) is shown in *red*. These two compounds are intermediates of glycolysis and are converted in the liver principally to glucose, glycogen, or fatty acids. In the liver, aldolase B cleaves both fructose 1-phosphate (fructose 1-P) in the pathway for fructose metabolism and fructose 1,6-bisphosphate in the pathway for glycolysis.

The metabolism of fructose occurs principally in the liver and to a lesser extent in the small intestinal mucosa and proximal epithelium of the renal tubule because these tissues have both fructokinase and aldolase B. Aldolase exists as several isoforms: aldolases A, B, C, and fetal aldolase. Although all of these aldolase isoforms can cleave fructose 1,6-bisphosphate, the intermediate of glycolysis, only aldolase B can also cleave fructose 1-P. Aldolase A, present in muscle and most other tissues, and aldolase C, present in brain, have almost no ability to cleave fructose 1-P. Fetal aldolase, present in the liver before birth, is similar to aldolase C.

Aldolase B is the rate-limiting enzyme of fructose metabolism, although it is not a rate-limiting enzyme of glycolysis. It has a much lower affinity for fructose 1-P than fructose 1,6-bisphosphate and is very slow at physiologic levels of fructose 1-P. As a consequence, after ingesting a high dose of fructose, normal individuals accumulate fructose 1-P in the liver while it is slowly converted to glycolytic intermediates. Individuals with hereditary fructose intolerance (HFI) (a deficiency of aldolase B) accumulate much higher amounts of fructose 1-P in their livers.

Other tissues also have the capacity to metabolize fructose but do so much more slowly. The hexokinase isoforms present in muscle, adipose tissue, and other tissues can convert fructose to fructose 6-phosphate (fructose 6-P) but react so much more efficiently with glucose. As a result, fructose phosphorylation is very slow in the presence of physiologic levels of intracellular glucose and glucose 6-phosphate (glucose 6-P).

B. Synthesis of Fructose in the Polyol Pathway

Fructose can be synthesized from glucose in the polyol pathway. The polyol pathway is named for the first step of the pathway in which sugars are reduced to the sugar alcohol by the enzyme aldose reductase (Fig. 29.4). Glucose is reduced to the sugar alcohol sorbitol, and sorbitol is then oxidized to fructose. This pathway is present in seminal vesicles, which synthesize fructose for the seminal fluid. Spermatozoa use fructose as a major fuel source while in the seminal fluid and then

FIG. 29.4. The polyol pathway converts glucose to fructose.

switch to glucose once in the female reproductive tract. Use of fructose is thought to prevent acrosomal breakdown of the plasma membrane (and consequent activation) while the spermatozoa are still in the seminal fluid.

The polyol pathway is present in many tissues but its function in all tissues is not understood. Aldose reductase is relatively nonspecific, and its major function may be the metabolism of an aldehyde sugar other than glucose. The activity of this enzyme can lead to major problems in the lens of the eye where it is responsible for the production of sorbitol from glucose and galactitol from galactose. When the concentration of glucose or galactose is elevated in the blood, their respective sugar alcohols are synthesized in the lens more rapidly than they are removed, resulting in increased osmotic pressure within the lens.

II. GALACTOSE METABOLISM—METABOLISM TO GLUCOSE 1-PHOSPHATE

Dietary galactose is metabolized principally by phosphorylation to galactose 1-phosphate (galactose 1-P), and then conversion to uridine diphosphate (UDP)-galactose and glucose 1-phosphate (glucose 1-P) (Fig. 29.5). The phosphorylation of galactose, again an important first step in the pathway, is carried out by a specific kinase, galactokinase. The formation of UDP-galactose is accomplished by attack of the phosphate oxygen on galactose 1-P on the α-phosphate of UDP-glucose, releasing glucose 1-P while forming UDP-galactose. The enzyme that catalyzes this reaction is galactose 1-P uridylyltransferase. The UDP-galactose is then converted to UDP-glucose by the reversible UDP-glucose epimerase (the configuration of the hydroxyl group on carbon 4 is reversed in this reaction). The net result of this sequence of reactions is that galactose is converted to glucose 1-P at the expense of one high-energy bond of adenosine triphosphate (ATP). The sum of these reactions is indicated in the following equations:

(1) Galactose + ATP $\xrightarrow{\text{Galactokinase}}$ Galactose 1-P + ADP

(2) Galactose 1-P + UDP-glucose $\xrightarrow{\text{Galactose 1-P Uridylyltransferase}}$ UDP-galactose + glucose 1-P

(3) UDP-galactose $\xrightarrow{\text{UDP-glucose epimerase}}$ UDP-glucose

Net equation: Galactose + ATP → Glucose 1-P + ADP

FIG. 29.5. Metabolism of galactose. Galactose is phosphorylated to galactose 1-phosphate (galactose 1-P) by galactokinase. Galactose 1-P reacts with UDP-glucose to release glucose 1-P. Galactose, thus, can be converted to blood glucose, enter glycolysis, or enter any of the metabolic routes of glucose. In classical galactosemia, a deficiency of galactose 1-P uridylyltransferase (shown in *green*) results in the accumulation of galactose 1-P in tissues and the appearance of galactose in the blood and urine. In nonclassical galactosemia, a deficiency of galactokinase (shown in *red*) results in the accumulation of galactose.

 In essential fructosuria, fructose cannot be converted to fructose 1-phosphate (fructose 1-P). This condition is benign because no toxic metabolites of fructose accumulate in the liver, and the patient remains nearly asymptomatic. Some of the ingested fructose is slowly phosphorylated by hexokinase in nonhepatic tissues and metabolized by glycolysis, and some appears in the urine. There is no renal threshold for fructose; the appearance of fructose in the urine (fructosuria) does not require a high fructose concentration in the blood.

Hereditary fructose intolerance (HFI) conversely results in the accumulation of fructose 1-P and fructose. By inhibiting glycogenolysis and gluconeogenesis, the high levels of fructose 1-P caused the hypoglycemia that **Candice Sucher** experienced as an infant when she became apathetic and drowsy and as an adult when she experienced sweating and tremulousness.

 The accumulation of sorbitol in muscle and nerve tissues may contribute to the peripheral neuropathy characteristic of patients with poorly controlled diabetes mellitus. This is one of the reasons it is so important for **Di Abietes** (who has type 1 diabetes mellitus) and **Ann Sulin** (who has type 2 diabetes mellitus) to achieve good glycemic control.

 The accumulation of sugars and sugar alcohols in the lens of patients with hyperglycemia (e.g., diabetes mellitus) results in the formation of cataracts. Glucose levels are elevated and increase the synthesis of sorbitol and fructose. As a consequence, a high osmotic pressure is created in the lens. The high glucose and fructose levels also result in nonenzymatic glycosylation of lens proteins. The result of the increased osmotic pressure and the glycosylation of the lens protein is an opaque cloudiness of the lens known as a *cataract*. **Erin Galway** seemed to have an early cataract, probably caused by the accumulation of galactose and its sugar alcohol galactitol.

One of the most serious problems of classical galactosemia is irreversible mental retardation. Realizing this problem, **Erin Galway's** physician wanted to begin immediate dietary therapy. A test that measures galactose 1-phosphate (galactose 1-P) uridylyltransferase in erythrocytes was ordered. This test is an enzymatic assay that mixes the unknown sample (in this case, a lysate from red blood cells, which contain the enzyme) with galactose 1-P, uridine diphosphate (UDP)-glucose and $NADP^+$ in the presence of excess phosphoglucomutase and glucose-6-phosphate dehydrogenase. As the uridylyltransferase converts galactose 1-P to UDP-galactose and glucose 1-phosphate (glucose 1-P), the glucose 1-P is rapidly converted to glucose 6-phosphate (glucose 6-P) by phosphoglucomutase. The glucose 6-P is then converted to 6-phosphogluconate and NADPH by glucose-6-phosphate dehydrogenase. The resulting increase in absorbance at 340 nm allows a determination of the initial uridylyltransferase activity. The enzyme activity in **Erin Galway's** red blood cells was virtually absent, confirming the diagnosis of classical galactosemia.

The enzymes for galactose conversion to glucose 1-P are present in many tissues, including the adult erythrocyte, fibroblasts, and fetal tissues. The liver has high activity of these enzymes and can convert dietary galactose to blood glucose and glycogen. The fate of dietary galactose like that of fructose, therefore, parallels that of glucose. The ability to metabolize galactose is even greater in infants than in adults. Newborn infants ingest up to 1 g of galactose per kilogram per feeding (as lactose). Yet the rate of metabolism is so high that the blood level in the systemic circulation is less than 3 mg/dL, and none of the galactose is lost in the urine.

III. THE PENTOSE PHOSPHATE PATHWAY

The *pentose phosphate pathway* is essentially a scenic bypass route around the first stage of glycolysis that generates NADPH and ribose 5-phosphate (ribose 5-P) (as well as other pentose sugars). Glucose 6-P is the common precursor for both pathways. The oxidative first stage of the pentose phosphate pathway generates 2 moles of NADPH per mole of glucose 6-P oxidized. The second stage of the pentose phosphate pathway generates ribose 5-P and converts unused intermediates to fructose 6-P and glyceraldehyde 3-P in the glycolytic pathway (see Fig. 29.2). All cells require NADPH for reductive detoxification, and most cells require ribose 5-P for nucleotide synthesis. Consequently, the pathway is present in all cells. The enzymes reside in the cytosol as do the enzymes of glycolysis.

A. Oxidative Phase of the Pentose Phosphate Pathway

1. NADPH PRODUCTION

In the oxidative, first phase of the pentose phosphate pathway, glucose 6-P undergoes and oxidation and decarboxylation to a pentose sugar, ribulose 5-phosphate (ribulose 5-P) (Fig. 29.6). The first enzyme of this pathway, glucose-6-phosphate dehydrogenase, oxidizes the aldehyde at carbon 1 and reduces $NADP^+$ to NADPH. The gluconolactone that is formed is rapidly hydrolyzed to *6-phosphogluconate*, a sugar acid with a carboxylic acid group at carbon 1. The next oxidation step releases this carboxyl group as CO_2, with the electrons being transferred to $NADP^+$. This reaction is mechanistically very similar to the one catalyzed by isocitrate dehydrogenase in the TCA cycle. Thus, 2 moles of NADPH per mole of glucose 6-P are formed from this portion of the pathway.

NADPH, rather than NADH, is generally used in the cell in pathways that require the input of electrons for reductive reactions because the ratio of NADPH/$NADP^+$ is much greater than the NADH/NAD^+ ratio. The NADH generated from fuel oxidation is rapidly oxidized back to NAD^+ by NADH dehydrogenase in the electron-transport chain, so the level of NADH in the cell is very low.

NADPH can be generated from several reactions in the liver and other tissues but not in red blood cells. For example, in tissues with mitochondria, an energy-requiring transhydrogenase located near the complexes of the electron-transport chain can transfer reducing equivalents from NADH to $NADP^+$ to generate NADPH.

NADPH, however, cannot be oxidized directly by the electron-transport chain, and the ratio of NADPH to $NADP^+$ in cells is >1. The reduction potential of NADPH, therefore, can contribute to the energy needed for biosynthetic processes and provide a constant source of reducing power for detoxification reactions.

2. RIBOSE 5-PHOSPHATE FROM THE OXIDATIVE ARM OF THE PATHWAY

To generate ribose 5-P from the oxidative pathway, the ribulose 5-P formed from the action of the two oxidative steps is isomerized to produce ribose 5-P (a ketose-to-aldose conversion, similar to fructose 6-P being isomerized to glucose 6-P;

see Section III.B.1). The ribose 5-P can then enter the pathway for nucleotide synthesis if needed, or it can be converted to glycolytic intermediates, as described below (Section III.B) for the nonoxidative phase of the pentose phosphate pathway. The pathway through which the ribose 5-P travels is determined by the needs of the cell at the time of its synthesis.

B. The Nonoxidative Phase of the Pentose Phosphate Pathway

The nonoxidative reactions of this pathway are reversible reactions that allow intermediates of glycolysis (specifically, glyceraldehyde 3-P and fructose 6-P) to be converted to five-carbon sugars (such as ribose 5-P), and vice versa. The needs of the cell determine which direction this pathway proceeds. If the cell has produced ribose 5-P but does not need to synthesize nucleotides, then the ribose 5-P is converted to glycolytic intermediates. If the cell still requires NADPH, the ribose 5-P is converted back into glucose 6-P using nonoxidative reactions (see the following sections). And finally, if the cell already has a high level of NADPH but needs to produce nucleotides, the oxidative reactions of the pentose phosphate pathway are inhibited, and the glycolytic intermediates fructose 6-P and glyceraldehyde 3-P are used to produce the five-carbon sugars using exclusively the nonoxidative phase of the pentose phosphate pathway.

1. CONVERSION OF RIBOSE 5-PHOSPHATE TO GLYCOLYTIC INTERMEDIATES

The nonoxidative portion of the pentose phosphate pathway consists of a series of rearrangement and transfer reactions that first convert ribulose 5-P to ribose 5-P and xylulose 5-phosphate (xylulose 5-P), and then the ribose 5-P and xylulose 5-P

Erin Galway's urine was negative for glucose when measured with the glucose oxidase strip but was positive for the presence of a reducing sugar. The reducing sugar was identified as galactose. Her liver function tests showed an increase in serum bilirubin and in several liver enzymes. Albumin was present in her urine. These findings and the clinical history increased her physician's suspicion that Erin had classical galactosemia.

Classical galactosemia is caused by a deficiency of galactose 1-phosphate (galactose 1-P) uridylyltransferase. In this disease, galactose 1-P accumulates in tissues, and galactose is elevated in the blood and urine. This condition differs from the rarer deficiency of galactokinase (nonclassical galactosemia) in which galactosemia and galactosuria occur but galactose 1-P is not formed. Both enzyme defects result in cataracts from galactitol formation by aldose reductase in the polyol pathway. Aldose reductase has a relatively high K_m for galactose, approximately 12 to 20 mM, so galactitol is formed only in galactosemic patients who have eaten galactose. Galactitol is not further metabolized and diffuses out of the lens very slowly. Thus, hypergalactosemia is even more likely to cause cataracts than hyperglycemia. **Erin Galway**, although she is only 3 weeks old, appeared to have early cataracts forming in the lens of her eyes.

The transketolase activity of red blood cells is used to measure thiamine nutritional status and diagnose the presence of thiamine deficiency. The activity of transketolase is measured in the presence and absence of added thiamine pyrophosphate. If the thiamine intake of a patient is adequate, the addition of thiamine pyrophosphate does not increase the activity of transketolase because it already contains bound thiamine pyrophosphate. If the patient is thiamine-deficient, transketolase activity will be low, and adding thiamine pyrophosphate will greatly stimulate the reaction. **Al Martini** was diagnosed in Chapter 19 as having beriberi heart disease resulting from thiamine deficiency. The diagnosis was based on laboratory tests confirming the thiamine deficiency.

FIG. 29.6. Oxidative portion of the pentose phosphate pathway. Carbon 1 of glucose 6-P is oxidized to an acid and then released as CO_2 in an oxidation followed by a decarboxylation reaction. Each of the oxidation steps generates a NADPH.

How does the net energy yield from the metabolism of 3 mol of glucose 6-phosphate (glucose 6-P) through the pentose phosphate pathway to pyruvate compare with the yield of 3 mol of glucose 6-P through glycolysis?

FIG. 29.7. Ribulose 5-phosphate (ribulose 5-P) is epimerized (to xylulose 5-phosphate [xylulose 5-P], shown in *red*) and isomerized (to ribose 5-phosphate [ribose 5-P], shown in the *yellow* box).

Glyceraldehyde 3-phosphate

Sedoheptulose 7-phosphate

FIG. 29.8. Two-carbon unit transferred by transketolase. Transketolase cleaves the bond next to the keto group and transfers the two-carbon keto fragment to an aldehyde. Thiamine pyrophosphate carries the two-carbon fragment, forming a covalent bond with the carbon of the keto group.

are converted to intermediates of the glycolytic pathway. The enzymes involved are epimerase, isomerase, transketolase, and transaldolase.

The epimerase and isomerase convert ribulose 5-P to two other five-carbon sugars (Fig. 29.7). The isomerase converts ribulose 5-P to ribose 5-P. The epimerase changes the stereochemical position of one hydroxyl group (at carbon 3), converting ribulose 5-P to xylulose 5-P.

Transketolase transfers two-carbon fragments of keto sugars (sugars with a keto group at carbon 2) to other sugars. Transketolase picks up a two-carbon fragment from xylulose 5-P by cleaving the carbon–carbon bond between the keto group and the adjacent carbon, thereby releasing glyceraldehyde 3-P (Fig. 29.8). The two-carbon fragment is covalently bound to thiamine pyrophosphate, which transfers it to the aldehyde carbon of another sugar, forming a new ketose. The role of thiamine pyrophosphate here is, thus, very similar to its role in the oxidative decarboxylation of pyruvate and α-ketoglutarate (see Chapter 20, Section I.B). Two reactions in the pentose phosphate pathway use transketolase. In the first, the two-carbon keto fragment from xylulose 5-P is transferred to ribose 5-P to form sedoheptulose 7-phosphate (sedoheptulose 7-P); and in the other, a two-carbon keto fragment (usually derived from xylulose 5-P) is transferred to erythrose 4-phosphate (erythrose 4-P) to form fructose 6-P.

Transaldolase transfers a three-carbon keto fragment from sedoheptulose 7-P to glyceraldehyde 3-P to form erythrose 4-P and fructose 6-P (Fig. 29.9). The aldol cleavage occurs between the two hydroxyl carbons adjacent to the keto group (on carbons 3 and 4 of the sugar). This reaction is similar to the aldolase reaction in glycolysis, and the enzyme uses an active amino group from the side chain of lysine to catalyze the reaction.

The net result of the metabolism of 3 mol of ribulose 5-P in the pentose phosphate pathway is the formation of 2 mol of fructose 6-P and 1 mol of glyceraldehyde 3-P, which then continue through the glycolytic pathway with the production of NADH, ATP, and pyruvate. Because the pentose phosphate pathway begins with glucose 6-P and feeds back into the glycolytic pathway, it is sometimes called the *hexose monophosphate (HMP) shunt* (a shunt or a pathway for glucose 6-P). The reaction sequence starting from glucose 6-P, involving both the oxidative and nonoxidative phases of the pathway, is shown in Figure 29.10.

2. GENERATION OF RIBOSE 5-PHOSPHATE FROM INTERMEDIATES OF GLYCOLYSIS

The reactions catalyzed by the epimerase, isomerase, transketolase, and transaldolase are all reversible reactions under physiologic conditions. Thus, ribose 5-P required for purine and pyrimidine synthesis can be generated from intermediates of the glycolytic pathway, as well as from the oxidative phase of the pentose phosphate pathway. The sequence of reactions that generates ribose 5-P from intermediates of glycolysis is as follows:

(1) Fructose 6-P + glyceraldehyde 3-P $\xleftrightarrow{\text{Transketolase}}$ Erythrose 4-P + xylulose 5-P

(2) Erythrose 4-P + fructose 6-P $\xleftrightarrow{\text{Transaldolase}}$ Sedoheptulose 7-P + glyceraldehyde 3-P

(3) Sedoheptulose 7-P + glyceraldehyde 3-P $\xleftrightarrow{\text{Transketolase}}$ Ribose 5-P + xylulose 5-P

(4) 2 Xylulose 5-P $\xleftrightarrow{\text{Epimerase}}$ 2 Ribulose 5-P

(5) 2 Ribulose 5-P $\xleftrightarrow{\text{Isomerase}}$ 2 Ribose 5-P

Net equation: 2 Fructose 6-P + glyceraldehyde 3-P ↔ 3 Ribose 5-P

C. Role of the Pentose Phosphate Pathway in Generation of NADPH

In general, the oxidative phase of the pentose phosphate pathway is the major source of NADPH in cells. NADPH provides the reducing equivalents for biosynthetic reactions and for oxidation–reduction reactions involved in protection against the toxicity of reactive oxygen species (ROS) (see Chapter 24). The glutathione-mediated defense against oxidative stress is common to all cell types (including red blood cells), and the requirement for NADPH to maintain levels of reduced glutathione (GSH) probably accounts for the universal distribution of the pentose phosphate pathway among different types of cells. Figure 29.11 illustrates the importance of this pathway in maintaining the membrane integrity of the red blood

Doctors suspected that the underlying factor in the destruction of **Al Martini's** red blood cells was an X-linked defect in the gene that codes for glucose-6-phosphate dehydrogenase. The red blood cell is dependent on this enzyme for a source of NADPH to maintain reduced levels of glutathione, one of its major defenses against oxidative stress (see Chapter 24). Glucose-6-phosphate dehydrogenase deficiency is the most common known enzymopathy, affecting approximately 7% of the world's population and about 2% of the US population. Most glucose-6-phosphate dehydrogenase–deficient individuals are asymptomatic but can undergo an episode of hemolytic anemia if they are exposed to certain drugs, to certain types of infections, or if they ingest fava beans. When questioned, **Al Martini** replied that he did not know what a fava bean was and had no idea whether he was sensitive to them.

The net energy yield from 3 mol of glucose 6-P metabolized through the pentose phosphate pathway and then the last portion of the glycolytic pathway is 6 mol of NADPH, 3 mol of CO_2, 5 mol of NADH, 8 mol of ATP, and 5 mol of pyruvate. In contrast, the metabolism of 3 mol of glucose 6-P through glycolysis is 6 mol of NADH, 9 mol of ATP, and 6 mol of pyruvate.

Sedoheptulose 7-phosphate

+

Glyceraldehyde 3-phosphate

Transaldolase

Erythrose 4-phosphate

+

Fructose 6-phosphate

FIG. 29.9. Transaldolase transfers a three-carbon fragment that contains an alcohol group next to a keto group.

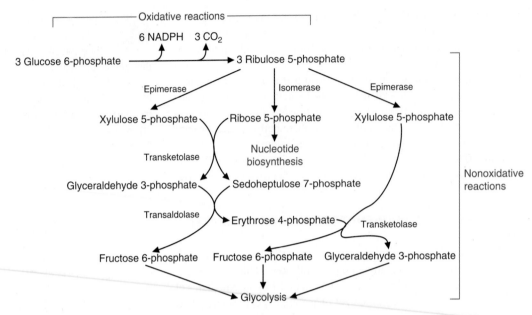

FIG. 29.10. A balanced sequence of reactions in the pentose phosphate pathway. The interconversion of sugars in the pentose phosphate pathway results in conversion of 3 glucose 6-P to 6 NADPH, 3 CO_2, 2 fructose 6-phosphate (fructose 6-P), and 1 glyceraldehyde 3-P.

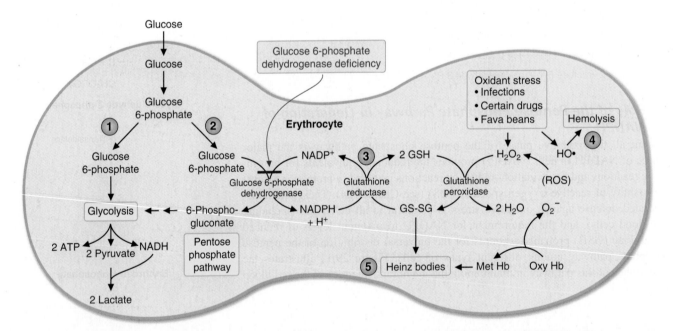

FIG. 29.11. Hemolysis caused by reactive oxygen species (ROS). *(1)* Maintenance of the integrity of the erythrocyte membrane depends on its ability to generate ATP and NADH from glycolysis. *(2)* NADPH is generated by the pentose phosphate pathway. *(3)* NADPH is used for the reduction of oxidized glutathione (GSSG) to reduced glutathione (GSH). Glutathione is necessary for the removal of H_2O_2 and lipid peroxides generated by ROS. *(4)* In the erythrocytes of healthy individuals, the continuous generation of superoxide ion from the nonenzymatic oxidation of hemoglobin provides a source of ROS. The glutathione defense system is compromised by glucose-6-phosphate dehydrogenase deficiency, infections, certain drugs, and the purine glycosides of fava beans. *(5)* As a consequence, Heinz bodies, aggregates of cross-linked hemoglobin, form on the cell membranes and subject the cell to mechanical stress as it tries to go through small capillaries. The action of the ROS on the cell membrane as well as mechanical stress from the lack of deformability result in hemolysis.

cells. NADPH is also used for anabolic pathways, such as fatty acid synthesis, cholesterol synthesis, and fatty acid chain elongation (Table 29.1). It is the source of reducing equivalents for cytochrome P450 hydroxylation of aromatic compounds, steroids, alcohols, and drugs. The highest concentrations of glucose-6-phosphate dehydrogenase are found in phagocytic cells where NADPH oxidase uses NADPH to form superoxide from molecular oxygen. The superoxide then generates hydrogen peroxide, which kills the microorganisms taken up by the phagocytic cells (see Chapter 24).

The entry of glucose 6-P into the pentose phosphate pathway is controlled by the cellular concentration of NADPH. NADPH is a strong product inhibitor of glucose-6-phosphate dehydrogenase, the first enzyme of the pathway. As NADPH is oxidized in other pathways, the product inhibition of glucose-6-phosphate dehydrogenase is relieved, and the rate of the enzyme is accelerated to produce more NADPH.

In the liver, the synthesis of fatty acids from glucose is a major route of NADPH reoxidation. The synthesis of liver glucose-6-phosphate dehydrogenase, like the key enzymes of glycolysis and fatty acid synthesis, is induced by the increased insulin:glucagon ratio after a high-carbohydrate meal. A summary of the possible routes that glucose 6-P may follow using the pentose phosphate pathway is presented in Table 29.2.

CLINICAL COMMENTS

Candice Sucher. Hereditary fructose intolerance (HFI) is caused by a low level of fructose 1-phosphate (fructose 1-P) aldolase activity in aldolase B, an isozyme of fructose 1,6-bisphosphate aldolase that is also capable of cleaving fructose 1-P. In persons of European descent, the most common defect is a single missense mutation in exon 5 (G → C), resulting in an amino acid substitution (Ala → Pro). As a result of this substitution, a catalytically impaired aldolase B is synthesized in abundance. The exact prevalence of HFI in the United States is not established but is approximately 1 per 15,000 to 25,000 population. The disease is transmitted by an autosomal recessive inheritance pattern.

When affected patients like **Candice Sucher** ingest fructose, fructose is converted to fructose 1-P. Because of the deficiency of aldolase B, fructose 1-P cannot be further metabolized to dihydroxyacetone phosphate and glyceraldehyde and accumulates in those tissues that have fructokinase (liver, kidney, and small intestine). Fructose is detected in the urine with the reducing sugar test (see the methods comment in Chapter 5). A DNA screening test (based on the generation of a new restriction site by the mutation) now provides a safe method to confirm a diagnosis of HFI.

Table 29.1   Pathways that Require NADPH

Detoxification
- Reduction of oxidized glutathione
- Cytochrome P450 monooxygenases

Reductive synthesis
- Fatty acid synthesis
- Fatty acid chain elongation
- Cholesterol synthesis
- Neurotransmitter synthesis
- Deoxynucleotide synthesis
- Superoxide synthesis

Table 29.2   Cellular Needs Dictate the Direction of the Pentose Phosphate Pathway Reactions

Cellular Need	Direction of Pathway
NADPH only	Oxidative reactions produce NADPH; nonoxidative reactions convert ribulose 5-P to glucose 6-P to produce more NADPH.
NADPH + ribose 5-P	Oxidative reactions produce NADPH and ribose 5-P; the isomerase converts ribulose 5-P to ribose 5-P.
Ribose 5-P only	Only the nonoxidative reactions. High NADPH inhibits glucose-6-phosphate dehydrogenase, so transketolase and transaldolase are used to convert fructose 6-P and glyceraldehyde 3-P to ribose 5-P.
NADPH and pyruvate	Both the oxidative and nonoxidative reactions are used. The oxidative reactions generate NADPH and ribulose 5-P. The nonoxidative reactions convert the ribulose 5-P to fructose 6-P and glyceraldehyde 3-P, and glycolysis converts these intermediates to pyruvate.

In infants and small children, the major symptoms include poor feeding, vomiting, intestinal discomfort, and failure to thrive. The greater the ingestion of dietary fructose, the more severe is the clinical reaction. The result of prolonged ingestion of fructose is ultrastructural changes in the liver and kidney that result in hepatic and renal failure. HFI is usually a disease of infancy because adults with fructose intolerance who have survived avoid the ingestion of fruits, table sugar, and other sweets.

Before the metabolic toxicity of fructose was appreciated, substitution of fructose for glucose in intravenous solutions and of fructose for sucrose in enteral tube feeding or diabetic diets was frequently recommended. (*Enteral tube feeding* refers to tubes placed into the gut; *parenteral tube feeding* refers to tubes placed into a vein, feeding intravenously.) Administration of intravenous fructose to patients with diabetes mellitus or other forms of insulin resistance avoided the hyperglycemia found with intravenous glucose, possibly because fructose metabolism in the liver bypasses the insulin-regulated step at phosphofructokinase-1 (PFK-1). However, because of the unregulated flow of fructose through glycolysis, intravenous fructose feeding frequently resulted in lactic acidosis (see Fig. 29.3). In addition, the fructokinase reaction is very rapid, and tissues became depleted of adenosine triphosphate (ATP) and phosphate when large quantities of fructose were metabolized over a short period. This led to cell death. Fructose is less toxic in the diet or in enteral feeding because of the relatively slow rate of fructose absorption.

 Erin Galway. **Erin Galway** has galactosemia, which is caused by a deficiency of galactose 1-phosphate (galactose 1-P) uridylyltransferase; it is one of the most common genetic diseases. *Galactosemia* is an autosomal recessive disorder of galactose metabolism that occurs in about 1 in 60,000 newborns. All of the states in the United States screen newborns for this disease because failure to begin immediate treatment results in mental retardation. Failure to thrive is the most common initial clinical symptom. Vomiting or diarrhea occurs in most patients, usually starting within a few days of beginning milk ingestion. Signs of deranged liver function, jaundice or hepatomegaly, are present almost as frequently after the first week of life. The jaundice of intrinsic liver disease may be accentuated by the severe hemolysis in some patients. Cataracts have been observed within a few days of birth.

Management of patients requires eliminating galactose from the diet. Failure to eliminate this sugar results in progressive liver failure and death. In infants, artificial milk made from casein or soybean hydrolysate is used.

 Al Martini. **Al Martini's** pus culture sent on the second day of his admission for acute alcoholism grew out *Staphylococcus aureus*. This organism has become resistant to a variety of antibiotics, so TMP/sulfa treatment was initiated. Unfortunately, it appeared that Mr. Martini had suffered an acute hemolysis (lysis or destruction of some of his red blood cells), probably induced by exposure to the sulfa drug and his infection to *S. aureus*. The hemoglobin that escaped from the lysed red blood cells was filtered by his kidneys and appeared in his urine.

By mechanisms that are not fully delineated, certain drugs (such as sulfa drugs and antimalarials), a variety of infectious agents, and exposure to fava beans can cause red blood cell destruction in individuals with a genetic deficiency of glucose-6-phosphate dehydrogenase. Presumably, these patients cannot generate enough reduced NADPH to defend against the reactive oxygen species (ROS). Although erythrocytes lack most of the other enzymatic sources of NADPH for the glutathione antioxidant system, they do have the defense mechanisms provided by the antioxidant vitamins E and C and catalase. Thus, individuals who are not totally deficient in glucose-6-phosphate dehydrogenase remain asymptomatic unless an additional oxidative stress such as an infection generates additional oxygen radicals.

Some drugs, such as the antimalarial primaquine and the sulfonamide that Mr. Martini is taking, affect the ability of red blood cells to defend against oxidative stress. *Fava beans*, which look like fat string beans and are sometimes called *broad beans*, contain the purine glycosides vicine and isouramil. These compounds react with glutathione. It has been suggested that cellular levels of reduced glutathione (GSH) decrease to such an extent that critical sulfhydryl groups in some key proteins cannot be maintained in reduced form.

The highest prevalence rates for glucose-6-phosphate dehydrogenase deficiency are found in tropical Africa and Asia, in some areas of the Middle East and the Mediterranean, and in Papua New Guinea. The geographic distribution of this deficiency is similar to that of sickle cell trait and is probably also related to the relative resistance it confers against the malaria parasite.

Because individuals with this deficiency are asymptomatic unless they are exposed to an "oxidant challenge," the clinical course of the hemolytic anemia is usually self-limited if the causative agent is removed. However, genetic polymorphism accounts for a substantial variability in the severity of the disease. Severely affected patients may have a chronic hemolytic anemia and other sequelae even without known exposure to drugs, infection, and other causative factors. In such patients, neonatal jaundice is also common and can be severe enough to cause death.

BIOCHEMICAL COMMENTS

Xylulose 5-phosphate (xylulose 5-P), in addition to its key role as an intermediate in the nonoxidative reactions of the hexose monophosphate (HMP) shunt pathway, also has an important role in regulating gene transcription. When excess carbohydrate is present in the diet, the liver has the responsibility for converting the excess carbohydrate into lipid (triacylglycerol; see Chapter 32) for storage. The large influx of glucose into the liver leads to an increase in xylulose 5-P levels. Xylulose 5-P activates protein phosphatase 2A (PP2A), which dephosphorylates, among several proteins, a cytoplasmic transcription factor, ChREBP (carbohydrate response element-binding protein). The dephosphorylation of ChREBP leads to its nuclear translocation where it binds to appropriate promoter elements and increases the transcription of its target genes. Such genes include, within the liver, the enzyme responsible for the terminal step of glycolysis, pyruvate kinase, and four enzymes involved in the synthesis of fatty acids (malic enzyme, citrate lyase, acetyl-CoA carboxylase, and fatty acid synthase). This promotes fatty acid biosynthesis, triglyceride synthesis, and the export of the triglycerides from the liver in the form of very low-density lipoproteins (VLDLs).

The transcription factor ChREBP is phosphorylated either by protein kinase A (which is activated by glucagon or epinephrine, signaling a need to oxidize fatty acids, and not to synthesize them) or an adenosine monophosphate (AMP)-activated protein kinase (indicating low energy levels, and a need for fatty acid oxidation). The AMP-activated protein kinase is discussed in greater detail in Section VI of this book. When it is phosphorylated, ChREBP leaves the nucleus and associates with scaffolding proteins in the cytoplasm where it waits to be activated via dephosphorylation.

Thus, regulation of ChREBP is related to the feeding and fasting cycles and results in alterations in enzyme levels that support the fed state. This cycle, of which xylulose 5-P is a key regulator, is just one of the many mechanisms established to coordinate carbohydrate and fatty acid metabolism. You will learn more of these mechanisms in the next section of this book.

Table 29.3   Diseases Discussed in Chapter 29

Disease or Disorder	Environmental or Genetic	Comments
Hereditary fructose intolerance	Genetic	Lack of aldolase B, leading to an accumulation of fructose 1-phosphate (fructose 1-P) after fructose ingestion. The increased levels of fructose 1-P interfere with glycogen metabolism and can lead to hypoglycemia.
Galactosemia	Genetic	Mutations in either galactokinase or galactose 1-phosphate (galactose 1-P) uridylyltransferase, leading to elevated galactose and/or galactose 1-P levels. This can lead to cataract formation (high galactose) and mental retardation (elevated galactose 1-P levels) if not treated early in life.
Glucose-6-phosphate dehydrogenase deficiency	Genetic, X-linked	Lack of glucose-6-phosphate dehydrogenase activity leads to hemolytic anemia in the presence of strong oxidizing agents.

Key Concepts

- Fructose is ingested principally as the monosaccharide or as part of sucrose. Fructose metabolism generates fructose 1-phosphate (fructose 1-P), which is then converted to intermediates of the glycolytic pathway.
- Galactose is ingested principally as lactose, which is converted to glucose and galactose in the intestine. Galactose metabolism generates, first, galactose 1-phosphate (galactose 1-P), which is converted to uridine diphosphate (UDP)-galactose. The end product is glucose 1-phosphate (glucose 1-P), which is isomerized to glucose 6-phosphate (glucose 6-P), which then enters glycolysis.
- The energy yield through glycolysis for both fructose and galactose is the same as for glucose metabolism.
- The pentose phosphate pathway consists of both oxidative and nonoxidative reactions.
- The oxidative steps of the pentose phosphate pathway generate NADPH and ribulose 5-phosphate (ribulose 5-P) from glucose 6-P.
  - Ribulose 5-P is converted to ribose 5-phosphate (ribose 5-P) for nucleotide biosynthesis.
  - NADPH is used as reducing power for biosynthetic pathways.
- The nonoxidative steps of the pentose phosphate pathway reversibly convert five-carbon sugars to fructose 6-phosphate (fructose 6-P) and glyceraldehyde 3-phosphate (glyceraldehyde 3-P).
- Table 29.3 summarizes diseases discussed in this chapter.

REVIEW QUESTIONS—CHAPTER 29

1. Hereditary fructose intolerance (HFI) is a rare recessive genetic disease that is most commonly caused by a mutation in exon 5 of the aldolase B gene. The mutation fortuitously creates a new ahaII recognition sequence. To test for the mutation, DNA was extracted from a wife, husband, and their two children, Jack and Jill. The DNA for exon 5 of the aldolase B gene was amplified by polymerase chain reaction (PCR), cleaved with ahaII, treated with alkali, subjected to electrophoresis on an agarose gel, and stained with a dye that binds to DNA.

   Which of the following conclusions can be made from the data presented?

   A. Both of the children have the disease.
   B. Neither of the children has the disease.
   C. Jill has the disease, Jack does not.
   D. Jack has the disease, Jill does not.
   E. There is not enough information to make a determination.

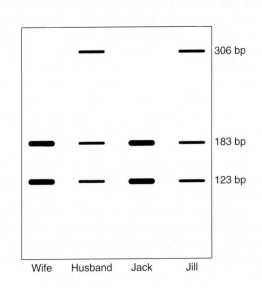

2. On examining the gel himself, the husband became concerned that he might not be the biologic father of one or both of the children. From the pattern on the gel, you can reasonably conclude which of the following?

    A. He is probably not Jill's father.
    B. He is probably not Jack's father.
    C. He could be the father of both children.
    D. He is probably not the father of either child.
    E. There is not enough information to make a determination.

3. An alcoholic is brought to the emergency room in a hypoglycemic coma. Because alcoholics are frequently malnourished, which of the following enzymes can be used to test for a thiamine deficiency?

    A. Aldolase
    B. Transaldolase
    C. Transketolase
    D. Glucose-6-phosphate dehydrogenase
    E. UDP-galactose epimerase

4. Intravenous fructose feeding can lead to lactic acidosis caused by which of the following?

    A. Bypassing the regulated pyruvate kinase step
    B. Bypassing the regulated phosphofructokinase-1 (PFK-1) step
    C. Allosterically activating aldolase B
    D. Allosterically activating lactate dehydrogenase
    E. Increasing the [ATP]:[ADP] ratio in liver

5. The polyol pathway of sorbitol production and the hexose monophosphate (HMP) shunt pathway are linked by which of the following?

    A. The HMP shunt produces 6-phosphogluconate, an intermediate in the polyol pathway.
    B. The HMP shunt produces NADPH, which is required for the polyol pathway.
    C. The HMP shunt produces ribitol, an intermediate of the polyol pathway.
    D. Both pathways use glucose as the starting material.
    E. Both pathways use fructose as the starting material.

30 Synthesis of Glycosides, Lactose, Glycoproteins, and Glycolipids

Many of the pathways for interconversion of sugars or the formation of sugar derivatives use activated sugars attached to nucleotides. Both uridine diphosphate **(UDP)-glucose** *and* **UDP-galactose** *are used for* **glycosyltransferase** *reactions in many systems. Lactose, for example, is synthesized from UDP-galactose and glucose in the mammary gland. UDP-glucose also can be oxidized to form UDP-glucuronate, which is used to form* **glucuronide derivatives** *of bilirubin and xenobiotic compounds. Glucuronide derivatives are generally more readily excreted in urine or bile than the parent compound.*

In addition to serving as fuel, carbohydrates are often found in **glycoproteins** *(carbohydrate chains attached to proteins) and* **glycolipids** *(carbohydrate chains attached to lipids).* **Nucleotide sugars** *are used to donate sugar residues for the formation of the glycosidic bonds in both glycoproteins and glycolipids. These carbohydrate groups have many different types of functions.*

Glycoproteins contain short chains of carbohydrates (oligosaccharides) that are usually branched. These oligosaccharides are generally composed of glucose, galactose, and their amino derivatives. In addition, mannose, L-fucose, and N-acetylneuraminic acid (NANA) are frequently present. The carbohydrate chains grow by the sequential addition of sugars to a **serine** *or* **threonine** *residue of the protein. Nucleotide sugars are the precursors. Branched carbohydrate chains also may be attached to the amide nitrogen of* **asparagine** *in the protein. In this case, the chains are synthesized on* **dolicholphosphate** *and subsequently transferred to the protein. Glycoproteins are found in mucus, in the blood, in compartments within the cell (such as lysosomes), in the extracellular matrix, and embedded in the cell membrane with the carbohydrate portion extending into the extracellular space.*

Glycolipids belong to the class of **sphingolipids.** *They are synthesized from nucleotide sugars that add monosaccharides sequentially to the hydroxymethyl group of the lipid ceramide (related to sphingosine). They often contain branches of NANA produced from cytidine monophosphate (CMP)-NANA. They are found in the cell membrane with the carbohydrate portion extruding from the cell surface. These carbohydrates, as well as some of the carbohydrates of glycoproteins, serve as* **cell recognition factors.**

THE WAITING ROOM

  To help support herself through medical school, **Erna Nemdy** works evenings in a hospital blood bank. She is responsible for ensuring that compatible donor blood is available to patients who need blood transfusions. As part of her training, Erna has learned that the external surfaces of all blood cells contain large numbers of antigenic determinants. These determinants are often glycoproteins or glycolipids that differ from one individual to another. As a result, all blood transfusions expose the recipient to many foreign immunogens. Most of these, fortunately, do not induce antibodies or they induce antibodies that elicit little or no immunologic response. For routine blood transfusions, therefore, tests are performed only for the presence of antigens that determine whether the patient's blood type is A, B, AB, or O, and Rh(D)-positive or -negative.

Jay Sakz's psychomotor development has become progressively more abnormal (see Chapter 15). At 2 years of age, he is obviously mentally retarded and nearly blind. His muscle weakness has progressed to the point that he cannot sit up or even crawl. As the result of a weak cough reflex, he is unable to clear his normal respiratory secretions and has had recurrent respiratory infections.

  Blood typing in a clinical lab uses antibodies that recognize either the A antigen, the B antigen, or the Rh(D) antigen. Each antigen is distinctive, in part, because of the different carbohydrate chains attached to the protein. The blood sample is mixed with each antibody individually. If cell clumping (agglutination) occurs, the red blood cells are expressing the carbohydrate that is recognized by the antibody (recall from Chapter 7 that antibodies are bivalent; the agglutination occurs because one arm of the antibody binds to antigen on one cell, while the other arm binds to antigen on a second cell, thereby bringing the cells together). If neither the A nor B antibodies causes agglutination, the blood type is O, indicating a lack of either antigen.

I. INTERCONVERSIONS INVOLVING NUCLEOTIDE SUGARS

Activated sugars attached to nucleotides are converted to other sugars, oxidized to sugar acids, and joined to proteins, lipids, or other sugars through glycosidic bonds.

A. Reactions of UDP-Glucose

Uridine diphosphate (UDP)-glucose is an activated sugar nucleotide that is a precursor of glycogen and lactose, UDP-glucuronate and glucuronides, and the carbohydrate chains in proteoglycans, glycoproteins, and glycolipids (Fig. 30.1). Both proteoglycans and glycosaminoglycans are discussed further in Chapter 49.

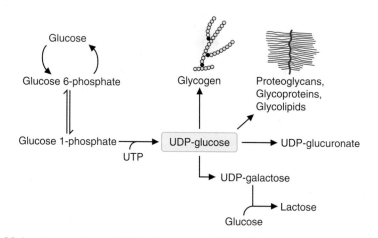

FIG. 30.1.   An overview of UDP-glucose metabolism. The activated glucose moiety of UDP-glucose can be attached by a glycosidic bond to other sugars, as in glycogen or the sugar oligosaccharide and polysaccharide side chains of proteoglycans, glycoproteins, and glycolipids. UDP-glucose also can be oxidized to UDP-glucuronate or epimerized to UDP-galactose, a precursor of lactose.

FIG. 30.2. Glycosyltransferases. These enzymes transfer sugars from nucleotide sugars to nucleophilic amino acid residues on proteins, such as the hydroxyl group of serine or the amide group of asparagine. Other transferases transfer specific sugars from a nucleotide sugar to a hydroxyl group of other sugars. The bond formed between the anomeric carbon of the sugar and the nucleophilic group of another compound is a glycosidic bond.

 What is the difference in structure between 6-phosphogluconate and glucuronic acid?

 A failure of the liver to transport, store, or conjugate bilirubin results in the accumulation of unconjugated bilirubin in the blood. Jaundice (or icterus), the yellowish tinge to the skin and the whites of the eyes (sclera) experienced by **Erin Galway**, occurs when plasma becomes supersaturated with bilirubin (>2 to 2.5 mg/dL) and the excess diffuses into tissues. When bilirubin levels are measured in the blood (see Chapter 6), one can measure either indirect bilirubin (this is the nonconjugated form of bilirubin, which is bound to albumin), direct bilirubin (the conjugated, water-soluble form), or total bilirubin (the sum of the direct and indirect levels). If total bilirubin levels are high, then a determination of direct and indirect bilirubin is needed to appropriately determine a cause for the elevation of total bilirubin.

In the synthesis of many of the carbohydrate portions of these compounds, a sugar is transferred from the nucleotide sugar to an alcohol or other nucleophilic group to form a glycosidic bond (Fig. 30.2). The use of UDP as a leaving group in this reaction provides the energy for formation of the new bond. The enzymes that form glycosidic bonds are sugar transferases (e.g., glycogen synthase is a glucosyltransferase). Transferases are also involved in the formation of the glycosidic bonds in bilirubin glucuronides, proteoglycans, and lactose.

B. UDP-Glucuronate: A Source of Negative Charges

One of the major routes of UDP-glucose metabolism is the formation of UDP-glucuronate, which serves as a precursor of other sugars and of glucuronides (Fig. 30.3). Glucuronate is formed by the oxidation of the alcohol on carbon 6 of glucose to an acid (through two oxidation states) by a NAD^+-dependent dehydrogenase (Fig. 30.4). Glucuronate is also present in the diet and can be formed from the degradation of inositol (the sugar alcohol that forms inositol trisphosphate[IP_3]), an intracellular second messenger for many hormones.

C. Formation of Glucuronides

The function of glucuronate in the excretion of bilirubin, drugs, xenobiotics, and other compounds containing a hydroxyl group is to add negative charges and increase their solubility. *Bilirubin* is a degradation product of heme that is formed in the reticuloendothelial system and is only slightly soluble in plasma. It is transported to the liver bound to albumin. In the liver, glucuronate residues are transferred from UDP-glucuronate to two carboxyl groups on bilirubin, sequentially forming bilirubin monoglucuronide and bilirubin diglucuronide, the "conjugated" forms of bilirubin (Fig. 30.5). The more soluble bilirubin diglucuronide (as compared with unconjugated bilirubin) is then actively transported into the bile for excretion.

Many xenobiotics, drugs, steroids, and other compounds with hydroxyl groups and low solubility in water are converted to glucuronides in a similar fashion by glucuronyltransferases present in the endoplasmic reticulum (ER) and cytoplasm of the liver and kidney (Table 30.1). This is one of the major conjugation pathways for excretion of these compounds.

FIG. 30.3. Metabolic routes of UDP-glucuronate. UDP-glucuronate is formed from UDP-glucose (shown in *black*). Glucuronate from UDP-glucuronate is incorporated into glycosaminoglycans (GAGs), where certain of the glucuronate residues are converted to iduronate (see Chapter 49). UDP-glucuronate is a precursor of UDP-xylose, another sugar residue incorporated into glycosaminoglycans. Glucuronate is also transferred to the carboxyl groups of bilirubin or the alcohol groups of steroids, drugs, and xenobiotics to form glucuronides. The "-ide" in the name glucuronide denotes that these compounds are glycosides. *Xenobiotics* are pharmacologically, endocrinologically, or toxicologically active substances that are not produced endogenously and, therefore, are foreign to an organism. Drugs are examples of xenobiotics.

Bilirubin diglucuronide

Glucuronates   Bilirubin

FIG. 30.5. Formation of bilirubin diglucuronide. A glycosidic bond is formed between the anomeric hydroxyl of glucuronate and the carboxylate groups of bilirubin. The addition of the hydrophilic carbohydrate group and the negatively charged carboxyl group of the glucuronide increases the water solubility of the conjugated bilirubin and allows the otherwise insoluble bilirubin to be excreted in the urine or bile. The hydrogen atoms on the sugars have been omitted from the figure for clarity.

Glucuronate, once formed, can reenter the pathways of glucose metabolism through reactions that eventually convert it to D-xylulose 5-phosphate, an intermediate of the pentose phosphate pathway. In most mammals other than humans, an intermediate of this pathway is the precursor of ascorbic acid (vitamin C). Humans, however, are deficient in this pathway and cannot synthesize vitamin C.

D. Synthesis of UDP-Galactose and Lactose from Glucose

Lactose is synthesized from UDP-galactose and glucose (Fig. 30.6). However, galactose is not required in the diet for lactose synthesis because galactose can be synthesized from glucose.

1. CONVERSION OF GLUCOSE TO GALACTOSE

Galactose and glucose are epimers; they differ only in the stereochemical position of one hydroxyl group, at carbon 4. Thus, the formation of UDP-galactose from UDP-glucose is an epimerization (Fig. 30.7). The epimerase does not actually transfer the hydroxyl group; it oxidizes the hydroxyl to a ketone by transferring electrons to NAD$^+$, and then donates electrons back to re-form the alcohol group on the other side of the carbon.

2. LACTOSE SYNTHESIS

Lactose is unique in that it is synthesized only in the mammary gland of the adult female for short periods during lactation. *Lactose synthase,* an enzyme

---

UDP-Glucose

2NAD$^+$ → UDP-glucose dehydrogenase → 2NADH + 2H$^+$

UDP-Glucuronate

UDP-glucuronate transferase (microsomal) / ROH (xenobiotics, drugs or other OH)

+ UDP

Glucuronide

Bile or urine

FIG. 30.4. Formation of glucuronate and glucuronides. A glycosidic bond is formed between the anomeric hydroxyl of glucuronate (at carbon 1) and the hydroxyl group of a nonpolar compound. The negatively charged carboxyl group of the glucuronate increases the water solubility and allows otherwise nonpolar compounds to be excreted in the urine or bile. The hydrogen atoms have been omitted from the figure for clarity.

 6-Phosphogluconate is produced by the first oxidative reaction in the pentose phosphate pathway, in which carbon 1 of glucose is oxidized to a carboxylate. In contrast, glucuronic acid is oxidized at carbon 6 to the carboxylate form.

 High concentrations of galactose 1-phosphate inhibit *phosphoglucomutase,* the enzyme that converts glucose 6-phosphate to glucose 1-phosphate. How can this inhibition account for the hypoglycemia and jaundice that accompany galactose-1-phosphate uridylyltransferase deficiency?

Table 30.1   Examples of Compounds Degraded and Excreted as Urinary Glucuronides

Estrogen (female sex hormone)
Progesterone (steroid hormone)
Triiodothyronine (thyroid hormone)
Acetylaminofluorene (xenobiotic carcinogen)
Meprobamate (drug for sleep)
Morphine (painkiller)

Many (60%) full-term newborns develop jaundice, termed *neonatal jaundice*. This is usually caused by an increased destruction of red blood cells after birth (the fetus has an unusually large number of red blood cells) and an immature bilirubin conjugating system in the liver. This leads to elevated levels of nonconjugated bilirubin, which is deposited in hydrophobic (fat) environments. If bilirubin levels reach a certain threshold at the age of 48 hours, the newborn is a candidate for phototherapy, in which the child is placed under lamps that emit light between the wavelengths of 425 and 475 nm. Bilirubin absorbs this light, undergoes chemical changes, and becomes more water-soluble. Usually, within a week of birth, the newborn's liver can handle the load generated from red blood cell turnover.

The inhibition of phosphoglucomutase by galactose 1-phosphate results in hypoglycemia by interfering with both the formation of uridine diphosphate (UDP)-glucose (the glycogen precursor) and the degradation of glycogen back to glucose 6-phosphate. Ninety percent of glycogen degradation leads to glucose 1-phosphate, which can only be converted to glucose 6-phosphate by phosphoglucomutase. When phosphoglucomutase activity is inhibited, less glucose 6-phosphate production occurs, and hence, less glucose is available for export. Thus, the stored glycogen is only approximately 10% efficient in raising blood glucose levels, and hypoglycemia results. UDP-glucose levels are reduced because glucose 1-phosphate is required to synthesize UDP-glucose, and in the absence of phosphoglucomutase activity, glucose 6-phosphate (derived from either the glucokinase reaction or gluconeogenesis) cannot be converted to glucose 1-phosphate. This prevents the formation of UDP-glucuronate, which is necessary to convert bilirubin to the diglucuronide form for transport into the bile. Bilirubin accumulates in tissues, giving them a yellow color (jaundice).

A pregnant woman who was extremely lactose-intolerant asked her physician if she would still be able to breastfeed her infant even though she could not drink milk or dairy products. What advice should she be given?

FIG. 30.6. Lactose synthesis. Lactose is a disaccharide composed of galactose and glucose. UDP-galactose for the synthesis of lactose in the mammary gland is usually formed from the epimerization of UDP-glucose. Lactose synthase catalyzes the attack of the C4 alcohol group of glucose on the anomeric carbon of the galactose, releasing UDP and forming a glycosidic bond. Lactose synthase is composed of a galactosyltransferase and α-lactalbumin, which is a regulatory subunit.

present in the ER of the lactating mammary gland, catalyzes the last step in lactose biosynthesis: the transfer of galactose from UDP-galactose to glucose (see Fig. 30.6). Lactose synthase has two protein subunits: a galactosyltransferase and α-lactalbumin. α-Lactalbumin is a modifier protein synthesized after parturition (childbirth) in response to the hormone prolactin. This enzyme subunit lowers the K_m of the galactosyltransferase for glucose from 1,200 to 1 mM, thereby increasing

FIG. 30.7. Epimerization of UDP-glucose to UDP-galactose. The epimerization of glucose to galactose occurs on UDP-sugars. The epimerase uses NAD^+ to oxidize the alcohol to a ketone, and then reduces the ketone back to an alcohol. The reaction is reversible; glucose being converted to galactose forms galactose for lactose synthesis, and galactose being converted to glucose is part of the pathway for the metabolism of dietary galactose. The hydrogen atoms have been omitted for clarity.

the rate of lactose synthesis. In the absence of α-lactalbumin, galactosyltransferase transfers galactosyl units to glycoproteins.

E. Formation of Sugars for Glycolipid and Glycoprotein Synthesis

The transferases that produce the oligosaccharide and polysaccharide side chains of glycolipids and attach sugar residues to proteins are specific for the sugar moiety and for the donating nucleotide (e.g., UDP, cytidine monophosphate [CMP], or guanosine diphosphate [GDP]). Some of the sugar nucleotides used for glycoprotein, proteoglycan (see Chapter 49), and glycolipid formation are listed in Table 30.2. They include the derivatives of glucose and galactose that we have already discussed, as well as acetylated amino sugars and derivatives of mannose. The reason for the large variety of sugars attached to proteins and lipids is that they have relatively specific and different functions, such as targeting a protein toward a membrane; providing recognition sites on the cell surface for other cells, hormones, or viruses or acting as lubricants or molecular sieves (see Chapter 49).

The pathways for use and formation of many of these sugars are summarized in Figure 30.8. Note that many of the steps are reversible, so that glucose and other dietary sugars enter a common pool from which the diverse sugars can be formed.

The amino sugars are all derived from glucosamine 6-phosphate. To synthesize glucosamine 6-phosphate, an amino group is transferred from the amide of glutamine to fructose 6-phosphate (Fig. 30.9). Amino sugars, such as glucosamine, can then be N-acetylated by an acetyltransferase. N-acetyltransferases are present in the ER and cytosol and provide another means of chemically modifying sugars, metabolites, drugs, and xenobiotic compounds. Individuals may vary greatly in their capacity for acetylation reactions.

Mannose is found in the diet in small amounts. Like galactose, it is an epimer of glucose, and mannose and glucose are interconverted by epimerization reactions at carbon 2. The interconversion can take place either at the level of fructose 6-phosphate to mannose 6-phosphate or at the level of the derivatized sugars (see Fig. 30.8). N-acetylmannosamine is the precursor of N-acetylneuraminic acid (NANA, a sialic acid) and GDP-mannose is the precursor of GDP-fucose (see Fig. 30.8). The negative charge on NANA is obtained by the addition of a three-carbon carboxyl moiety from phosphoenolpyruvate.

II. GLYCOPROTEINS

A. Structure and Function

Glycoproteins contain short carbohydrate chains covalently linked to either serine/threonine or asparagine residues in the protein. These oligosaccharide chains are often branched and they do not contain repeating disaccharides (Fig. 30.10). Most proteins in the blood are glycoproteins. They serve as hormones, antibodies, enzymes (including those of the blood clotting cascade), and as structural components of the extracellular matrix. Collagen contains galactosyl units and disaccharides composed of galactosyl-glucose attached to hydroxylysine residues (see Chapter 49). The secretions of mucus-producing cells, such as salivary mucin, are glycoproteins (Fig. 30.11).

Although most glycoproteins are secreted from cells, some are segregated in lysosomes, where they serve as the lysosomal enzymes that degrade various types of cellular and extracellular material. Other glycoproteins are produced like secretory proteins, but hydrophobic regions of the protein remain attached to the cell membrane, and the carbohydrate portion extends into the extracellular space (Fig. 30.12) (also see Chapter 15, Section I). These glycoproteins serve as receptors for compounds such as hormones, as transport proteins, and as cell attachment and cell–cell recognition sites. Bacteria and viruses also bind to these sites.

 Although the lactose in dairy products is a major source of galactose, the ingestion of lactose is not required for lactation. UDP-galactose in the mammary gland is derived principally from the epimerization of glucose. Dairy products are, however, a major dietary source of Ca^{2+}, so breastfeeding mothers need increased Ca^{2+} from another source.

Table 30.2   Examples of Sugar Nucleotides That Are Precursors for Transferase Reactions

UDP-glucose
UDP-galactose
UDP-glucuronic acid
UDP-xylose
UDP-N-acetylglucosamine
UDP-N-acetylgalactosamine
CMP-N-acetylneuraminic acid
GDP-fucose
GDP-mannose

UDP, uridine diphosphate; CMP, cytidine monophosphate; GDP, guanosine diphosphate.

 By identifying the nature of antigenic determinants on the surface of the donor's red blood cells, **Erna Nemdy** is able to classify the donor's blood as belonging to certain specific blood groups. These antigenic determinants are located in the oligosaccharides of the glycoproteins and glycolipids of the cell membranes. The most important blood group in humans is the ABO group, which comprises two antigens: A and B. Individuals with the A antigen on their cells belong to blood group A, those with B antigen belong to group B, and those with both A and B antigens belong to group AB. The absence of both the A and B antigens results in blood type O (see Fig. 30.17).

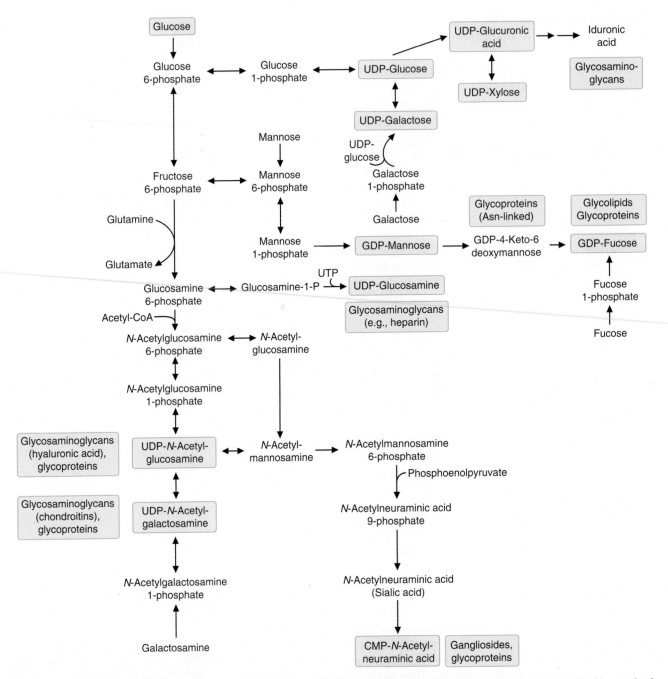

FIG. 30.8. Pathways for the interconversion of sugars. All of the different sugars found in glycosaminoglycans, gangliosides, and other compounds in the body can be synthesized from glucose. Dietary glucose, fructose, galactose, mannose, and other sugars enter a common pool from which other sugars are derived. The activated sugar is transferred from the nucleotide sugar, shown in *orange boxes*, to form a glycosidic bond with another sugar or amino acid residue. The *green box* next to each nucleotide sugar lists some of the compounds that contain the sugar. Iduronic acid, in the upper right corner of the diagram, is formed only after glucuronic acid is incorporated into a glycosaminoglycan (which is discussed in more detail in Chapter 49).

B. Synthesis

The protein portion of glycoproteins is synthesized on the ER. The carbohydrate chains are attached to the protein in the lumen of the ER and the Golgi complex. In some cases, the initial sugar is added to a serine or a threonine residue in the protein, and the carbohydrate chain is extended by the sequential addition of sugar residues to the nonreducing end. As seen in Table 30.2, UDP-sugars are the precursors for

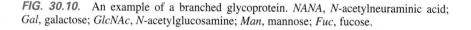

FIG. 30.10.   An example of a branched glycoprotein. *NANA*, *N*-acetylneuraminic acid; *Gal*, galactose; *GlcNAc*, *N*-acetylglucosamine; *Man*, mannose; *Fuc*, fucose.

N-Acetylglucosamine-6-P

FIG. 30.9.   The formation of *N*-acetyl-glucosamine 6-phosphate. The amino sugar is formed by a transfer of the amino group from the amide of glutamine to a carbon of the sugar. The amino group is acetylated by the transfer of an acetyl group from acetyl-CoA. The hydrogen atoms from the sugar have been omitted for clarity.

the addition of four of the seven sugars that are usually found in glycoproteins—glucose, galactose, *N*-acetylglucosamine, and *N*-acetylgalactosamine. GDP-sugars are the precursors for the addition of mannose and L-fucose, and CMP-NANA is the precursor for NANA. Dolichol phosphate (Fig. 30.13) (which is synthesized from isoprene units, as discussed in Chapter 34) is involved in transferring branched sugar chains to the amide nitrogen of asparagine residues. Sugars are removed and added as the glycoprotein moves from the ER through the Golgi complex (Fig. 30.14). As discussed in Chapter 10, the carbohydrate chain is used as a targeting marker for lysosomal enzymes.

I-cell (inclusion cell) disease is a rare condition in which lysosomal enzymes lack the mannose phosphate marker that targets them to lysosomes. The enzyme that is deficient in I-cell disease is a phosphotransferase located in the Golgi apparatus (Fig. 30.15). The phosphotransferase has the unique ability

Salivary mucin

-○- = Sialic acid

-●- = *N*-acetylglucosamine

FIG. 30.11.   Structure of salivary mucin. The sugars form hydrogen bonds with water. Sialic acid provides a negatively charged carboxylate group. The protein is extremely large, and the negatively charged sialic acids extend the carbohydrate chains (by charge repulsion) so the molecules occupy a large space. All of the salivary glycoproteins contain *O*-linked sugars. NANA is a sialic acid.

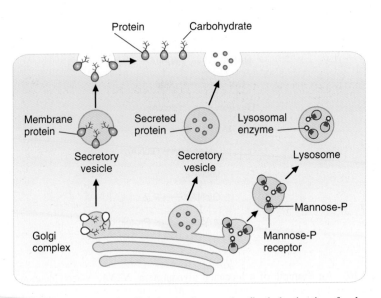

FIG. 30.12. Route from the Golgi complex to the final destination for lysosomal enzymes, cell membrane proteins, and secreted proteins, which include glycoproteins and proteoglycans.

to recognize lysosomal proteins because of their three-dimensional structure, such that they can all be appropriately tagged for transport to the lysosomes. Consequently, as a result of the lack of mannose phosphate, lysosomal enzymes are secreted from the cells. Because lysosomes lack their normal complement of enzymes, undegraded molecules accumulate within membranes inside these cells, forming inclusion bodies.

III. GLYCOLIPIDS

A. Function and Structure

Glycolipids are derivatives of the lipid sphingosine. These sphingolipids include the cerebrosides and the gangliosides (Fig. 30.16; see also Chapter 5, Fig. 5.22). They contain ceramide, with carbohydrate moieties attached to its hydroxymethyl group.

Glycolipids are involved in intercellular communication. Oligosaccharides of identical composition are present in both the glycolipids and glycoproteins associated with the cell membrane, where they serve as cell recognition factors. For example, carbohydrate residues in these oligosaccharides are the antigens of the ABO blood group substances (Fig. 30.17).

B. Synthesis

Cerebrosides are synthesized from ceramide and UDP-glucose or UDP-galactose. They contain a single sugar (a monosaccharide). Gangliosides contain oligosaccharides produced from UDP-sugars and CMP-NANA, which is the precursor for

FIG. 30.13. Structure of dolichol phosphate. In humans, the isoprene unit (*in brackets*) is repeated approximately 17 times (n = ~17).

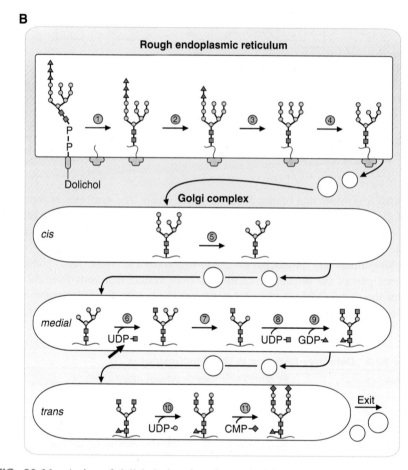

FIG. 30.14. Action of dolichol phosphate in synthesizing the high-mannose form of oligosaccharides (A) and the processing of these carbohydrate groups (B). Transfer of the branched oligosaccharide from dolichol phosphate to a protein in the lumen of the rough endoplasmic reticulum (RER) (step 1) and processing of the oligosaccharide (steps 2–11). Steps 1 through 4 occur in the RER. The glycoprotein is transferred in vesicles to the Golgi complex, where further modifications of the oligosaccharides occur (steps 5–11). (B modified with permission from Kornfeld R, Kornfeld S. Assembly of aspargine-linked oligosaccharides. Annu Rev Biochem. 1985;54:631–664. Copyright 1985 by Annual Reviews, Inc.)

FIG. 30.15. Synthesis of mannose 6-phosphate on the oligosaccharide of lysosomal proteins. The pathway for phosphorylating a mannose residue within the protein-attached oligosaccharide requires two steps. The first is a transfer of N-acetylglucosamine phosphate to the mannose residue, and the second is the release of N-acetylglucosamine from the intermediate product, leaving the phosphate behind on the mannose residue.

Ceramide ——— Galactose

Galactocerebroside

Ceramide ——— Glc – Gal – GalNAc
                              |
                            NANA

Ganglioside

Ceramide

FIG. 30.16. Structures of cerebrosides and gangliosides. In these glycolipids, sugars are attached to ceramide (shown below the glycolipids). The *boxed portion* of ceramide is sphingosine, from which the name "sphingolipids" is derived.

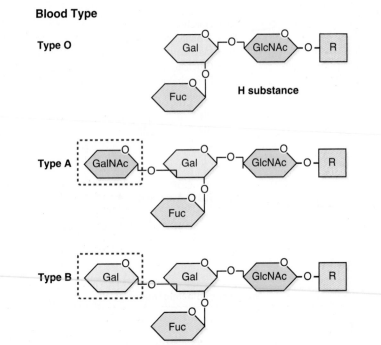

Blood Type

Type O

H substance

Type A

Type B

FIG. 30.17. Structures of the blood group substances. Note that these structures are the same except that type A has *N*-acetylgalactosamine (*GalNAc*) at the nonreducing end, type B has galactose (*Gal*), and type O has neither. *R* is either a protein or the lipid ceramide. Each antigenic determinant is boxed. *Fuc*, fucose; *GlcNAc*, *N*-acetylglucosamine; *Gal*, galactose.

the NANA residues that branch from the linear chain. The synthesis of the sphingolipids is described in more detail in Chapter 33. Defects in the degradation of sphingolipids lead to the sphingolipidoses (also known as the *gangliosidoses*), as outlined in Table 30.3.

Sphingolipids are produced in the Golgi complex. Their lipid component becomes part of the membrane of the secretory vesicle that buds from the *trans* face of the Golgi. After the vesicle membrane fuses with the cell membrane, the lipid component of the glycolipid remains in the outer layer of the cell membrane,

Table 30.3   Defective Enzymes in the Gangliosidoses

Disease	Enzyme Deficiency	Accumulated Lipid
Fucosidosis	α-Fucosidase	Cer–Glc–Gal–GalNAc–Gal:Fuc H-isoantigen
Generalized gangliosidosis	G_{M1}-β-galactosidase	Cer–Glc–Gal(NeuAc)–GalNAc:Gal G_{M1} ganglioside
Tay-Sachs disease	Hexosaminidase A	Cer–Glc–Gal(NeuAc):GalNAc G_{M2} ganglioside
Tay-Sachs variant or Sandhoff disease	Hexosaminidase A and B	Cer–Glc–Gal–Gal:GalNAc globoside plus G_{M2} ganglioside
Fabry disease	α-Galactosidase	Cer–Glc–Gal:Gal globotriaosylceramide
Ceramide lactoside lipidosis	Ceramide lactosidase (B-galactosidase)	Cer–Glc:Gal ceramide lactoside
Metachromatic leukodystrophy	Arylsulfatase A	Cer–Gal:OSO_3^{3-} sulfogalactosylceramide
Krabbe disease	β-Galactosidase	Cer:Gal galactosylceramide
Gaucher disease	β-Glucosidase	Cer:Glc glucosylceramide
Niemann-Pick disease	Sphingomyelinase	Cer:P–choline sphingomyelin
Farber disease	Ceramidase	Acyl:sphingosine ceramide

NeuAc, *N*-acetylneuraminic acid; Cer, ceramide; Glc, glucose; Gal, galactose; Fuc, fucose. The colon indicates the bond that cannot be broken due to the enzyme deficiency associated with the disease.

and the carbohydrate component extends into the extracellular space. Sometimes, the carbohydrate component is used as a recognition signal for foreign proteins; for example, cholera toxin (which affected **Dennis Veere**; see Chapter 10) binds to the carbohydrate portion of the G_{M1} ganglioside to allow its catalytic subunit to enter the cell.

CLINICAL COMMENTS

Erna Nemdy. During her stint in the hospital blood bank, **Erna Nemdy** learned that the importance of the ABO blood group system in transfusion therapy is based on two principles (Table 30.4): (1) Antibodies to A and to B antigens occur naturally in the blood serum of persons whose red blood cell surfaces lack the corresponding antigen (i.e., individuals with A antigens on their red blood cells have B antibodies in their serum and vice versa). These antibodies may arise as a result of previous exposure to cross-reacting antigens in bacteria and foods or to blood transfusions. (2) Antibodies to A and B are usually present in high titers and are capable of activating the entire complement system. As a result, these antibodies may cause intravascular destruction of a large number of incompatible red blood cells given inadvertently during a blood transfusion. Individuals with type AB blood have both A and B antigens and do not produce antibodies to either. Hence, they are "universal" recipients. They can safely receive red blood cells from individuals of A, B, AB, or O blood type. (However, they cannot safely receive serum from these individuals because it contains antibodies to A or B antigens.) Those with type O blood do not have either antigen. They are "universal" donors; that is, their red cells can safely be infused into type A, B, O, or AB individuals. (However, their serum contains antibodies to both A and B antigens and cannot be given safely to recipients with those antigens.)

The second important red blood cell group is the Rh group. It is important because one of its antigenic determinants, the D antigen, is a very potent immunogen, stimulating the production of a large number of antibodies. The unique carbohydrate composition of the glycoproteins that constitute the antigenic determinants on red blood cells in part contributes to the relative immunogenicity of the A, B, and Rh(D) red blood cell groups in human blood.

Jay Sakz. Tay-Sachs disease, the problem afflicting **Jay Sakz**, is an autosomal recessive disorder that is rare in the general population (1 in 300,000 births), but its prevalence in Jews of Eastern European extraction (who make up 90% of the Jewish population in the United States) is much higher (1 in 3,600 births). One in 28 Ashkenazi Jews carries this defective gene. Its presence can be discovered by measuring the tissue level of the protein produced by the gene (hexosaminidase A) or by recombinant DNA techniques. Skin fibroblasts of concerned couples planning a family are frequently used for these tests.

Carriers of the affected gene have a reduced but functional level of this enzyme that normally hydrolyzes a specific bond between an N-acetyl-D-galactosamine and a D-galactose residue in the polar head of the ganglioside.

No effective therapy is available. Enzyme replacement has met with little success because of the difficulties in getting the enzyme across the blood–brain barrier.

The blood group substances are oligosaccharide components of glycolipids and glycoproteins found in most cell membranes. Those located on red blood cells have been studied extensively. A single genetic locus with two alleles determines an individual's blood type. These genes encode glycosyltransferases involved in the synthesis of the oligosaccharides of the blood group substances.

Most individuals can synthesize the H substance, an oligosaccharide that contains a fucose linked to a galactose at the nonreducing end of the blood group substance (see Fig. 30.17). Type A individuals produce an N-acetylgalactosamine transferase (encoded by the *A* gene) that attaches N-acetylgalactosamine to the galactose residue of the H substance. Type B individuals produce a galactosyltransferase (encoded by the *B* gene) that links galactose to the galactose residue of the H substance. Type AB individuals have both alleles and produce both transferases. Thus, some of the oligosaccharides of their blood group substances contain N-acetylgalactosamine and some contain galactose. Type O individuals produce a defective transferase, and, therefore, they do not attach either N-acetylgalactosamine or galactose to the H substance. Thus, individuals of blood type O have only the H substance.

Erna Nemdy determined that a patient's blood type was AB. The new surgical resident was eager to give this patient a blood transfusion and, because AB blood is rare and an adequate amount was not available in the blood bank, he requested type A blood. Should Erna give him type A blood for his patient?

Table 30.4   Characteristics of the ABO Blood Groups

Red Cell Type	O	A	B	AB
Possible genotypes	OO	AA or AO	BB or BO	AB
Antibodies in serum	Anti-A and -B	Anti-B	Anti-A	None
Frequency (in Caucasians)	45%	40%	10%	5%
Can accept blood types	O	A, O	B, O	A, B, AB, O

A: The patient could safely receive type A blood **cells** from another person because he has both A and B antigens on his own cells and does not have antibodies in his serum to either type A or B cells. However, he should not be given type A serum (or type A whole blood) because type A serum contains antibodies to type B antigens, which are present on his cells.

Tay-Sachs disease, which is one of the gangliosidoses, is a multifaceted disorder. The sphingolipidoses, which include Fabry and Gaucher diseases, affect mainly the brain, the skin, and the reticuloendothelial system (e.g., liver and spleen). In these diseases, complex lipids accumulate. Each of these lipids contains a ceramide as part of its structure (see Table 30.3). The rate at which the lipid is synthesized is normal. However, the lysosomal enzyme required to degrade it is not very active, either because it is made in deficient quantities as a result of a mutation in a gene that specifically codes for the enzyme or because a critical protein required to activate the enzyme is deficient. Because the lipid cannot be degraded, it accumulates and causes degeneration of the affected tissues, with progressive malfunction such as the psychomotor deficits that occur as a result of the central nervous system involvement seen in most of these storage diseases.

BIOCHEMICAL COMMENTS

Biochemistry of Tay-Sachs Disease. Hexosaminidase A, the defective enzyme in Tay-Sachs disease, is actually composed of two subunits, an α- and a β-chain. The exact stoichiometry of the active enzyme is unknown, but it may be $\alpha_2\beta_2$. The α-subunit is coded for by the *HexA* gene, whereas the β-subunit is coded for by the *HexB* gene. In Tay-Sachs disease, the α-subunit is defective, and hexosaminidase A activity is lost. However, the β-subunit can form active tetramers in the absence of the α-subunit, and this activity, named *hexosaminidase B*, which cleaves the glycolipid globoside, retains activity in children with Tay-Sachs disease. Thus, children with Tay-Sachs disease accumulate the ganglioside G_{M2} but not globoside (Fig. 30.18).

Mutation of the *HexB* gene, and production of a defective β-subunit, leads to inactivation of both hexosaminidase A and B activity. Such a mutation leads to Sandhoff disease. Both activities are lost because both activities require a functional β-subunit. The clinical course of this disease is similar to Tay-Sachs but with an accelerated timetable because of the initial accumulation of both G_{M2} and globoside in the lysosomes.

A third type of mutation also can lead to disease symptoms similar to those of Tay-Sachs disease. Children were identified with Tay-Sachs symptoms, but when both hexosaminidase A and B activities were measured in a test tube, they were normal. This disease, ultimately named *Sandhoff activator disease*, is caused by a mutation in a protein that is needed to activate hexosaminidase A activity. In the absence of

FIG. 30.18. Substrate specificities of hexosaminidase A, B, and the function of the activator protein. Defects in the β-subunit inactivate both HexA and HexB activities, leading to G_{M2} and globoside accumulation. A defect in Sandhoff activator protein also leads to G_{M2} accumulation, as HexA activity is reduced. Defects in the α-subunit inactivate only HexA activity, such that HexB activity toward globoside is unaffected. *Glc*, glucose; *Gal*, galactose; *NAcGal*, N-acetylgalactosamine.

the activator, hexosaminidase A activity is minimal, and G_{M2} initially accumulates in lysosomes. This mutation has no effect on hexosaminidase B activity.

When a glycolipid cannot be degraded because of an enzymatic mutation, it accumulates in residual bodies (vacuoles that contain material that lysosomal enzymes cannot digest). Normal cells contain a small number of residual bodies, but in diseases of lysosomal enzymes, large numbers of residual bodies accumulate within the cell, eventually interfering with normal cell function.

In 70% of the cases of Tay-Sachs disease in persons of Ashkenazi Jewish background, exon 11 of the gene for the α-chain of hexosaminidase A contains a mutation. The normal gene sequence encodes a protein with the amino acids Arg–Ile–Ser–Tyr–Gly–Pro–Asp in this region, as shown in the following:

$$
\begin{array}{c}
\quad\quad\quad 10 \quad\quad\quad\quad 20 \\
5'-\text{CGTATATCCTATGGCCCTGAC} \\
\text{Arg}-\text{Ile}-\text{Ser}-\text{Tyr}-\text{Gly}-\text{Pro}-\text{Asp}
\end{array}
$$

The mutant DNA sequence for this area is

$$
\begin{array}{c}
\quad\quad\quad 10 \quad\quad\quad\quad 20 \\
5'-\text{CGTATATC}\underline{\text{TATC}}\text{CTATGGCCCTGAC} \\
\text{Arg}-\text{Ile}-\text{Ser}-\text{Ile}-\text{Leu}-\text{Trp}-\text{Pro}-\text{Stop}
\end{array}
$$

A four-base insertion (underlined) occurs in the mutated gene, which alters the reading frame of the protein and also introduces a premature stop codon farther down the protein, so no functional α-subunit can be produced.

Key Concepts

- Reactions between sugars or the formation of sugar derivatives use sugars activated by attachment to nucleotides (a nucleotide sugar).
- UDP-glucose and UDP-galactose are substrates for many glycosyltransferase reactions.
- Lactose is formed from UDP-galactose and glucose.
- UDP-glucose is oxidized to UDP-glucuronate, which forms glucuronide derivatives of various hydrophobic compounds, making them more readily excreted in urine or bile than the parent compound.
- Glycoproteins and glycolipids contain various types of carbohydrate residues.
- The carbohydrates in glycoproteins can be either O-linked or N-linked and are synthesized in the endoplasmic reticulum and the Golgi apparatus.
- For O-linked carbohydrates, the carbohydrates are added sequentially (via nucleotide sugar precursors), beginning with a sugar linked to the hydroxyl group of the amino acid side chains of serine or threonine.
- For N-linked carbohydrates, the branched carbohydrate chain is first synthesized on dolichol phosphate and then transferred to the amide nitrogen of an asparagine residue of the protein.
- Glycolipids belong to the class of sphingolipids that add carbohydrate groups to the base ceramide one at a time from nucleotide sugars.
- Defects in the degradation of glycosphingolipids lead to a class of lysosomal diseases known as the *sphingolipidoses*.
- Table 30.5 summarizes the diseases discussed in this chapter.

Table 30.5   Diseases Discussed in Chapter 30

Disease or Disorder	Environmental or Genetic	Comments
Blood transfusions	Both	Blood typing is dependent on antigens on the cell surface, particularly the carbohydrate content of the antigen
Tay-Sachs disease	Genetic	Lack of hexosaminidase A activity, leading to an accumulation of G_{M2} in the lysosomes
Jaundice	Both	Lack of ability to conjugate bilirubin with glucuronic acid in the liver
Sphingolipidoses	Genetic	Defects in ganglioside and sphingolipid degradation, as summarized in Table 30.3

1. Which of the following best describes a mother with galactosemia caused by a deficiency of galactose-1-phosphate uridylyltransferase?

    A. She can convert galactose to UDP-galactose for lactose synthesis during lactation.
    B. She can form galactose 1-phosphate from galactose.
    C. She can use galactose as a precursor to glucose production.
    D. She can use galactose to produce glycogen.
    E. She will have lower than normal levels of serum galactose after drinking milk.

2. The immediate carbohydrate precursors for glycolipid and glycoprotein synthesis are which of the following?

    A. Sugar phosphates
    B. Sugar acids
    C. Sugar alcohols
    D. Nucleotide sugars
    E. Acylsugars

3. A newborn is diagnosed with neonatal jaundice. In this patient, the bilirubin produced lacks which of the following carbohydrates?

    A. Glucose
    B. Gluconate

C. Glucuronate
D. Galactose
E. Galactitol

4. The nitrogen donor for the formation of amino sugars is which of the following?

    A. Ammonia
    B. Asparagine
    C. Glutamine
    D. Adenine
    E. Dolichol

5. Which of the following glycolipids would accumulate in a patient with Sandhoff disease?

    A. G_{M1}
    B. Lactosylceramide
    C. Globoside
    D. Glucocerebroside
    E. G_{M3}

Gluconeogenesis and Maintenance of Blood Glucose Levels

*During fasting, many of the reactions of glycolysis are reversed as the liver produces glucose to maintain blood glucose levels. This process of **glucose production** is called **gluconeogenesis**.*

*Gluconeogenesis, which occurs primarily in the liver, is the pathway for the synthesis of glucose from compounds other than carbohydrates. In humans, the major precursors of glucose are **lactate**, **glycerol**, and **amino acids**, particularly **alanine**. Except for three key sequences, the reactions of gluconeogenesis are reversals of the steps of glycolysis (Fig. 31.1). The sequences of gluconeogenesis that do not use enzymes of glycolysis involve the irreversible, regulated steps of glycolysis. These three sequences are the conversion of (1) pyruvate to phosphoenolpyruvate (PEP), (2) fructose 1,6-bisphosphate to fructose 6-phosphate, and (3) glucose 6-phosphate to glucose.*

Some tissues of the body such as the brain and red blood cells cannot synthesize glucose on their own but depend on glucose for energy. On a long-term basis, most tissues also require glucose for other functions, such as synthesis of the ribose moiety of nucleotides or the carbohydrate portion of glycoproteins and glycolipids. Therefore, to survive, humans must have mechanisms for maintaining blood glucose levels.

*After a meal containing carbohydrates, blood glucose levels rise (Fig. 31.2). Some of the glucose from the diet is stored in the liver as **glycogen**. After 2 or 3 hours of fasting, this glycogen begins to be degraded by the process of **glycogenolysis**, and glucose is released into the blood. As glycogen stores decrease, **adipose triacylglycerols** are also degraded, providing **fatty acids** as an alternative fuel and glycerol for the synthesis of glucose by gluconeogenesis. Amino acids are also released from the muscle to serve as gluconeogenic precursors.*

During an overnight fast, blood glucose levels are maintained by both glycogenolysis and gluconeogenesis. However, after approximately 30 hours of fasting, liver glycogen stores are mostly depleted. Subsequently, gluconeogenesis is the only source of blood glucose.

*Changes in the metabolism of glucose that occur during the switch from the fed to the fasting state are regulated by the hormones **insulin** and **glucagon**. Insulin is elevated in the fed state, and glucagon is elevated during fasting. Insulin stimulates the **transport** of glucose into certain cells such as those in muscle and adipose tissue. Insulin also alters the activity of key enzymes that regulate metabolism, stimulating the storage of fuels. Glucagon counters the effects of insulin, stimulating the release of stored fuels and the conversion of lactate, amino acids, and glycerol to glucose.*

Blood glucose levels are maintained not only during fasting but also during exercise when muscle cells take up glucose from the blood and oxidize it for energy. During exercise, the liver supplies glucose to the blood by the processes of glycogenolysis and gluconeogenesis.

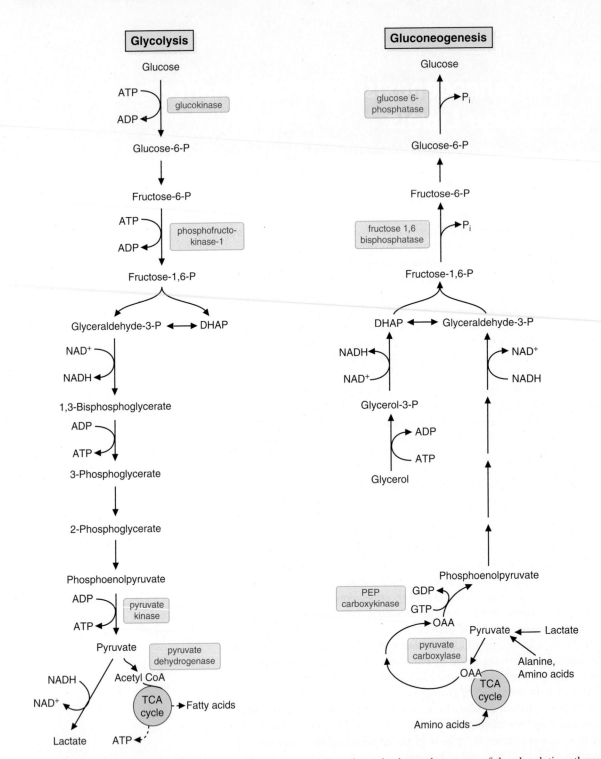

FIG. 31.1. Glycolysis and gluconeogenesis in the liver. The gluconeogenic pathway is almost the reverse of the glycolytic pathway, except for three reaction sequences. At these three steps, the reactions are catalyzed by different enzymes. The energy requirements of these reactions differ, and one pathway can be activated while the other is inhibited. The steps for which enzyme names are indicated are the irreversible steps of those pathways. All other steps are reversible, although for clarity, this is not indicated in the figure.

THE WAITING ROOM

Al Martini, a known alcoholic, was brought to the emergency room by his landlady, who stated that he had been drinking heavily for the past week. During this time, his appetite had gradually diminished, and he had not eaten any food for the past 3 days. He was confused, combative, tremulous, and sweating profusely. His speech was slurred. His heart rate was rapid (110 beats/ minute). As his blood pressure was being determined, he had a grand mal seizure. His blood glucose drawn just before the onset of the seizure was 28 mg/dL or 1.6 mM (reference range for overnight fasting blood glucose, 80 to 100 mg/dL or 4.4 to 5.6 mM). His blood ethanol level drawn at the same time was 295 mg/dL (intoxication level, i.e., "confused" stage, 150 to 300 mg/dL).

Emma Wheezer presented to the emergency room 3 days after being discharged from the hospital following a 10-day admission for severe refractory bronchial asthma. She required high-dose intravenous *methylprednisolone* (a synthetic anti-inflammatory glucocorticoid) for the first 8 days of her stay. After 2 additional days on oral prednisone, she was discharged on substantial pharmacologic doses of this steroid and instructed to return to her physician's office in 5 days. She presented now with marked *polyuria* (increased urination), *polydipsia* (increased thirst), and muscle weakness. Her blood glucose was 275 mg/dL or 15 mM (reference range, 80 to 100 mg/dL or 4.4 to 5.6 mM).

Di Abietes could not remember whether she had taken her 6:00 PM insulin dose, when, in fact, she had done so. Unfortunately, she decided to give herself her evening dose (for the second time). When she did not respond to her alarm clock at 6:00 AM the following morning, her roommate tried unsuccessfully to awaken her. The roommate called an ambulance, and Di was rushed to the hospital emergency room in a coma. Her pulse and blood pressure at admission were normal. Her skin was flushed and slightly moist. Her respirations were slightly slow.

Ann O'Rexia continues to resist efforts on the part of her psychiatrist and family physician to convince her to increase her caloric intake. Her body weight varies between 97 and 99 lb, far below the desirable weight for a woman who is 5 ft 7 in tall. In spite of her severe diet, her fasting blood glucose levels range from 55 to 70 mg/dL. She denies having any hypoglycemic symptoms.

Otto Shape has complied with his calorie-restricted diet and aerobic exercise program. He has lost another 7 lb and is closing in on his goal of weighing 154 lb. He notes increasing energy during the day and remains alert during lectures and assimilates the lecture material noticeably better than he did before starting his weight loss and exercise program. He jogs for 45 minutes each morning before breakfast.

I. GLUCOSE METABOLISM IN THE LIVER

Glucose serves as a fuel for most tissues of the body. It is the major fuel for certain tissues such as the brain and red blood cells. After a meal, food is the source of blood glucose. The liver oxidizes glucose and stores the excess as glycogen. The liver also uses the pathway of glycolysis to convert glucose to pyruvate, which provides carbon for the synthesis of fatty acids. Glycerol 3-phosphate, produced from glycolytic intermediates, combines with fatty acids to form triacylglycerols, which

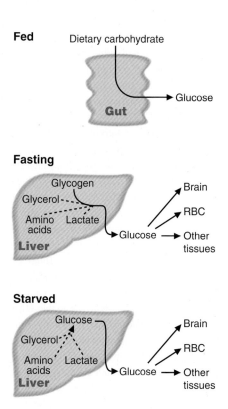

FIG. 31.2. Sources of blood glucose in the fed, fasting, and starved states. *RBC*, red blood cells.

The measurement of ketones in the blood and urine can indicate the level of starvation or the presence of diabetic ketoacidosis (DKA). There are several methods to detect ketones. One is the use of reagent strips for urine (based on the reaction of sodium nitroprusside with acetoacetate), but this method does not detect the major blood ketone (β-hydroxybutyrate). A cyclic enzymatic method has been developed to overcome this, in which blood or plasma samples are incubated with acetoacetate decarboxylase, which removes all acetoacetate from the sample (converting it to acetone and carbon dioxide). Once this has been accomplished, β-hydroxybutyrate dehydrogenase is then incubated with the sample, along with thio-NAD$^+$. The thio-NAD$^+$ is converted to thio-NADH, generating a colored product and acetoacetate. Thio-NADH absorbs light at 405 nm, in the visible range, as compared to NADH, which absorbs at 340 nm, in the UV range. The use of thio-NAD$^+$ allows clinical laboratory instrumentation to be used. The acetoacetate is then recycled back to β-hydroxybutyrate, in which NADH is converted to NAD$^+$. The β-hydroxybutyrate produced is then cycled back to acetoacetate, generating more thio-NADH. The cycling enhances the sensitivity of the assay. Once equilibrium is reached, one can calculate from the change in absorbance per minute the concentration of the β-hydroxybutyrate in the sample.

are secreted into the blood in very low-density lipoproteins (VLDLs; explained further in Chapter 32). During fasting, the liver releases glucose into the blood so that glucose-dependent tissues do not suffer from a lack of energy. Two mechanisms are involved in this process: glycogenolysis and gluconeogenesis. Hormones, particularly insulin and glucagon, dictate whether glucose flows through glycolysis or whether the reactions are reversed and glucose is produced via gluconeogenesis.

II. GLUCONEOGENESIS

Gluconeogenesis, the process by which glucose is synthesized from noncarbohydrate precursors, occurs mainly in the liver under fasting conditions. Under the more extreme conditions of starvation, the kidney cortex also may produce glucose. For the most part, the glucose produced by the kidney cortex is used by the kidney medulla, but some may enter the bloodstream.

Starting with pyruvate, most of the steps of gluconeogenesis are simply reversals of those of glycolysis (Fig. 31.3). In fact, these pathways differ at only three points. Enzymes involved in catalyzing these steps are regulated so that either glycolysis or gluconeogenesis predominates, depending on physiologic conditions.

Most of the steps of gluconeogenesis use the same enzymes that catalyze the process of glycolysis. The flow of carbon, of course, is in the reverse direction.

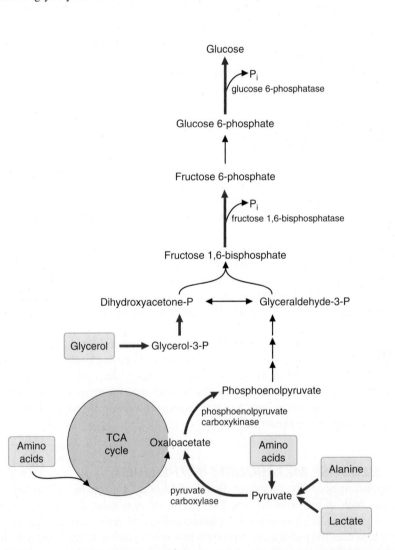

FIG. 31.3. Key reactions of gluconeogenesis. The precursors are amino acids (particularly alanine), lactate, and glycerol. *Heavy red arrows* indicate steps that differ from those of glycolysis.

Three reaction sequences of gluconeogenesis differ from the corresponding steps of glycolysis. They involve the conversion of pyruvate to phosphoenolpyruvate (PEP) and the reactions that remove phosphate from fructose 1,6-bisphosphate to form fructose 6-phosphate and from glucose 6-phosphate to form glucose (see Fig. 31.3). The conversion of pyruvate to PEP is catalyzed during gluconeogenesis by a series of enzymes instead of the single enzyme used for glycolysis. The reactions that remove phosphate from fructose 1,6-bisphosphate and from glucose 6-phosphate each use single enzymes that differ from the corresponding enzymes of glycolysis. Although phosphate is added during glycolysis by kinases, which use adenosine triphosphate (ATP), it is removed during gluconeogenesis by phosphatases that release inorganic phosphate (P_i) via hydrolysis reactions.

A. Precursors for Gluconeogenesis

The three major carbon sources for gluconeogenesis in humans are lactate, glycerol, and amino acids, particularly alanine. Lactate is produced by anaerobic glycolysis in tissues such as exercising muscle or red blood cells, as well as by adipocytes during the fed state. Glycerol is released from adipose stores of triacylglycerol, and amino acids come mainly from amino acid pools in muscle where they may be obtained by degradation of muscle protein. Alanine, the major gluconeogenic amino acid, is produced in the muscle from other amino acids and from glucose (see Chapter 38). Because ethanol metabolism only gives rise to acetyl coenzyme A (acetyl-CoA), the carbons of ethanol cannot be used for gluconeogenesis.

B. Formation of Gluconeogenic Intermediates from Carbon Sources

The carbon sources for gluconeogenesis form pyruvate, intermediates of the tricarboxylic acid (TCA) cycle or intermediates that are common to both glycolysis and gluconeogenesis.

1.   LACTATE, AMINO ACIDS, AND GLYCEROL

Pyruvate is produced in the liver from the gluconeogenic precursors lactate and alanine. Lactate dehydrogenase oxidizes lactate to pyruvate, generating NADH (see Fig. 31.4A), and alanine aminotransferase converts alanine to pyruvate (see Fig. 31.4B).

Although alanine is the major gluconeogenic amino acid, other amino acids such as serine serve as carbon sources for the synthesis of glucose because they also form pyruvate, the substrate for the initial step in the process. Some amino acids form intermediates of the TCA cycle (see Chapter 20), which can enter the gluconeogenic pathway.

 Comatose patients in DKA have the smell of acetone (a derivative of the ketone body acetoacetate) on their breath. In addition, patients with DKA have deep, relatively rapid respirations typical of acidotic patients (Kussmaul respirations). These respirations result from an acidosis-induced stimulation of the respiratory center in the brain. More CO_2 is exhaled in an attempt to reduce the amount of acid in the body: $H^+ + HCO_3 \rightarrow H_2CO_3 \rightarrow H_2O + CO_2$ (exhaled).

The severe hyperglycemia of DKA also causes osmotic diuresis (i.e., glucose entering the urine carries an iso-osmotic amount of water with it), which, in turn, causes a contraction of blood volume. Volume depletion may be aggravated by vomiting, which is common in patients with DKA. DKA may cause dehydration (dry mucous membranes and loss of skin turgor), low blood pressure, and a rapid heartbeat. These respiratory and hemodynamic alterations are not seen in patients with hypoglycemic coma. The flushed, wet skin of hypoglycemic coma is in contrast to the dry skin observed in DKA.

 Diabetes mellitus (DM) should be suspected if a venous plasma glucose level drawn regardless of when food was last eaten (a "random" sample of blood glucose) is "unequivocally elevated" (i.e., >200 mg/dL), particularly in a patient who manifests the classic signs and symptoms of chronic hyperglycemia (polydipsia, polyuria, blurred vision, headaches, rapid weight loss, sometimes accompanied by nausea and vomiting). To confirm the diagnosis, the patient should fast overnight (10 to 16 hours), and the blood glucose measurement should be repeated. Values of <100 mg/dL are considered normal. Values greater than or equal to 126 mg/dL are indicative of DM. The level of glycosylated hemoglobin (HbA1c) can also be measured to make the diagnosis, and if greater than 6.5% is diagnostic for DM. The levels of HbA1c can also gauge the extent of hyperglycemia over the past 4 to 8 weeks and is used to guide treatment. Values of fasting blood glucose between 100 and 125 mg/dL are designated impaired fasting glucose (IFG) (or prediabetes), and further testing should be performed to determine whether these individuals will eventually develop overt DM. Individuals with blood glucose levels in this range have been defined as "prediabetes." The determination that fasting blood glucose levels of 126 mg/ L or a percentage of glycosylated hemoglobin of greater than 6.5% diagnostic for DM is based on data indicating that at these levels of glucose or glycosylated hemoglobin, patients begin to develop complications of DM, specifically retinopathy.

The renal tubular transport maximum in the average healthy subject is such that glucose will not appear in the urine until the blood glucose level is >180 mg/dL. As a result, reagent tapes (Tes-Tape or Dextrostix) designed to detect the presence of glucose in the urine are not sensitive enough to establish a diagnosis of early DM.

FIG. 31.4. Metabolism of gluconeogenic precursors. **A.** Conversion of lactate to pyruvate. **B.** Conversion of alanine to pyruvate. In this reaction, alanine aminotransferase transfers the amino group of alanine to α-ketoglutarate (α-kg) to form glutamate. The coenzyme for this reaction, pyridoxal phosphate, accepts and donates the amino group. **C.** Conversion of glycerol to dihydroxyacetone phosphate (DHAP).

 Glucocorticoids are naturally occurring steroid hormones. In humans, the major glucocorticoid is cortisol. Glucocorticoids are produced in the adrenal cortex in response to various types of stress (see Chapter 43). One of their actions is to stimulate the degradation of muscle protein. Thus, increased amounts of amino acids become available as substrates for gluconeogenesis. **Emma Wheezer** noted muscle weakness, a result of the muscle-degrading action of the synthetic glucocorticoid prednisone, which she was taking for its anti-inflammatory effects.

 In a fatty acid with 19 carbons, how many carbons (and which ones) have the capability to form glucose?

The carbons of glycerol are gluconeogenic because they form *dihydroxyacetone phosphate* (DHAP), a glycolytic intermediate (see Fig. 31.4C).

2. PROPIONATE

Fatty acids with an odd number of carbon atoms, which are obtained mainly from vegetables in the diet, produce propionyl-CoA from the three carbons at the ω-end of the chain (see Chapter 23). These carbons are relatively minor precursors of glucose in humans. Propionyl-CoA is converted to methylmalonyl-CoA, which is rearranged to form succinyl-CoA, a four-carbon intermediate of the TCA cycle that can be used for gluconeogenesis. The remaining carbons of an odd-chain fatty acid form acetyl-CoA, from which no net synthesis of glucose occurs. In some species, propionate is a major source of carbon for gluconeogenesis. Ruminants can produce massive amounts of glucose from propionate. In cows, the cellulose in grass is converted to propionate by bacteria in the rumen. This substrate is then used to generate more than 5 lb of glucose each day by the process of gluconeogenesis.

β-Oxidation of fatty acids produces acetyl-CoA. Because the pyruvate dehydrogenase reaction is thermodynamically and kinetically irreversible, acetyl-CoA does not form pyruvate for gluconeogenesis. Therefore, if acetyl-CoA is to produce glucose, it must enter the TCA cycle and be converted to malate. For every two carbons of acetyl-CoA that are converted to malate, two carbons are released as CO_2: one in the reaction catalyzed by isocitrate dehydrogenase and the other in the reaction catalyzed by α-ketoglutarate dehydrogenase. Therefore, there is no *net* synthesis of glucose from acetyl-CoA.

C. Pathway of Gluconeogenesis

Gluconeogenesis occurs by a pathway that reverses many, but not all, of the steps of glycolysis.

1. CONVERSION OF PYRUVATE TO PHOSPHOENOLPYRUVATE

In glycolysis, PEP is converted to pyruvate by pyruvate kinase. In gluconeogenesis, a series of steps is required to accomplish the reversal of this reaction (Fig. 31.5).

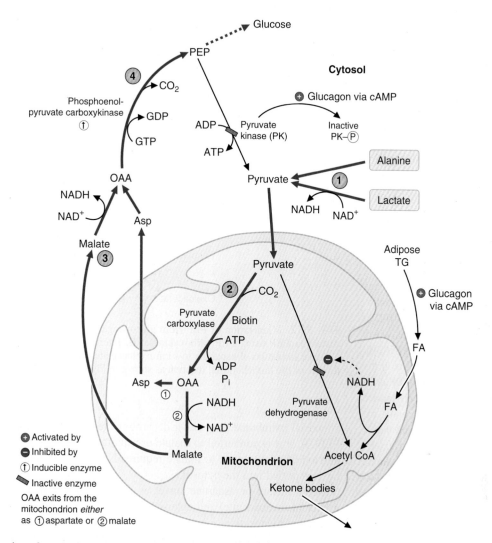

FIG. 31.5. Conversion of pyruvate to PEP in the liver. Follow the shaded circled numbers on the diagram, starting with the precursors alanine and lactate. The first step is the conversion of alanine and lactate to pyruvate. Pyruvate then enters the mitochondria and is converted to OAA (*circle* 2) by pyruvate carboxylase. Pyruvate dehydrogenase has been inactivated by both the NADH and acetyl-CoA generated from fatty acid oxidation, which allows oxaloacetate production for gluconeogenesis. The oxaloacetate formed in the mitochondria is converted to either malate or aspartate to enter the cytoplasm via the malate/aspartate shuttle. In the cytoplasm, the malate or aspartate is converted back into oxaloacetate (*circle* 3), and phosphoenolpyruvate carboxykinase converts it to PEP (*circle* 4). The PEP formed is not converted to pyruvate because pyruvate kinase has been inactivated by phosphorylation by the cAMP-dependent protein kinase under these conditions. The white circled numbers are alternative routes for exit of carbon from the mitochondrion using the malate/aspartate shuttle. *OAA*, oxaloacetate; *FA*, fatty acid; *TG*, triacylglycerol.

Pyruvate is carboxylated by pyruvate carboxylase to form oxaloacetate. This enzyme, which requires biotin, is the catalyst of an anaplerotic (refilling) reaction of the TCA cycle (see Chapter 20). In gluconeogenesis, this reaction replenishes the oxaloacetate that is used for the synthesis of glucose (Fig. 31.6).

The CO_2 that was added to pyruvate to form oxaloacetate is released in the reaction catalyzed by phosphoenolpyruvate carboxykinase (PEPCK), which generates PEP (Fig. 31.7A). For this reaction, guanosine triphosphate (GTP) provides a source of energy as well as the phosphate group of PEP. Pyruvate carboxylase is found in mitochondria. In various species, PEPCK is located either in the cytosol or in mitochondria, or it is distributed between these two compartments. In humans, the enzyme is distributed about equally in each compartment.

Oxaloacetate, generated from pyruvate by pyruvate carboxylase or from amino acids that form intermediates of the TCA cycle, does not readily cross the mito-

 Only the three carbons at the ω-end of an odd-chain fatty acid that form propionyl-CoA are converted to glucose. The remaining 16 carbons of a fatty acid with 19 carbons form acetyl-CoA, which does not form any net glucose.

FIG. 31.6. Conversion of pyruvate to oxaloacetate.

FIG. 31.7. Generation of PEP from gluconeogenic precursors. **A.** Conversion of oxalo-acetate to PEP using PEP carboxykinase. **B.** Interconversion of oxaloacetate and malate. **C.** Transamination of aspartate to form oxaloacetate. Note that the cytosolic reaction is the reverse of the mitochondrial reaction as shown in Figure 31.5.

 Excessive ethanol metabolism blocks the production of gluconeo-genic precursors. Cells have limited amounts of NAD, which exist either as NAD^+ or as NADH. As the levels of NADH rise, those of NAD^+ fall, and the ratio of the concentrations of NADH and NAD^+ ([NADH]/[NAD^+]) increases. In the presence of ethanol, which is very rapidly oxidized in the liver, the [NADH]/[NAD^+] ratio is much higher than it is in the normal fasting liver. High levels of NADH drive the lactate dehydrogenase reaction toward lactate. Therefore, lactate cannot enter the gluconeogenic pathway, and pyruvate that is generated from alanine is converted to lactate. Because glycerol is oxidized by NAD^+ during its conversion to DHAP, the conversion of glyc-erol to glucose is also inhibited when NADH levels are elevated. Consequently, the major precursors lactate, alanine, and glycerol are not used for gluconeogenesis under conditions in which alcohol metabolism is high.

chondrial membrane. It is either decarboxylated to form PEP by the mitochondrial PEPCK or it is converted to malate or aspartate (see Figs. 31.7B and C). The conversion of oxaloacetate to malate requires NADH. PEP, malate, and aspartate can be transported into the cytosol.

After malate or aspartate traverses the mitochondrial membrane (acting as a carrier of oxaloacetate) and enters the cytosol, it is reconverted to oxaloacetate by reversal of the reactions given previously (see Figs. 31.7B and C). The conversion of malate to oxaloacetate generates NADH. Whether oxaloacetate is transported across the mitochondrial membrane as malate or aspartate depends on the need for reducing equivalents in the cytosol. NADH is required to reduce 1,3-bisphosphoglycerate to glyceraldehyde 3-phosphate during gluconeogenesis.

Oxaloacetate, produced from malate or aspartate in the cytosol, is converted to PEP by the cytosolic PEPCK (see Fig. 31.7A).

2. CONVERSION OF PHOSPHOENOLPYRUVATE TO FRUCTOSE 1,6-BISPHOSPHATE

The remaining steps of gluconeogenesis occur in the cytosol (Fig. 31.8). Starting with PEP as a substrate, the steps of glycolysis are reversed to form glyceraldehyde 3-phosphate. For every two molecules of glyceraldehyde 3-phosphate that are formed, one is converted to DHAP. These two triose phosphates, DHAP and glyc-eraldehyde 3-phosphate, condense to form fructose 1,6-bisphosphate by a reversal of the aldolase reaction. Because glycerol forms DHAP, it enters the gluconeogenic pathway at this level.

3. CONVERSION OF FRUCTOSE 1,6-BISPHOSPHATE TO FRUCTOSE 6-PHOSPHATE

The enzyme fructose 1,6-bisphosphatase releases P_i from fructose 1,6-bisphosphate to form fructose 6-phosphate. This is not a reversal of the phosphofructokinase-1 (PFK-1) reaction; ATP is not produced when the phosphate is removed from the 1-position of fructose 1,6-bisphosphate because that is a low-energy phosphate bond. Rather, P_i is released in this hydrolysis reaction. In the next reaction of

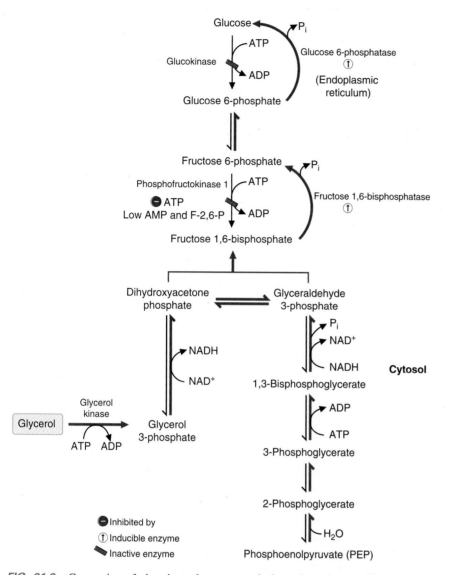

FIG. 31.8. Conversion of phosphoenolpyruvate and glycerol to glucose. Gluconeogenic reactions are indicated by the *red arrows*. Glucokinase is inactive because of the low levels of glucose in the cell (below the K_m for glucokinase), whereas PFK-1 is inactive because of the low concentration of the allosteric activators AMP and fructose 2,6-bisphosphate, coupled to high concentrations of ATP, an allosteric inhibitor.

gluconeogenesis, fructose 6-phosphate is converted to glucose 6-phosphate by the same isomerase used in glycolysis (phosphoglucoisomerase).

4. CONVERSION OF GLUCOSE 6-PHOSPHATE TO GLUCOSE

Glucose 6-phosphatase hydrolyzes P_i from glucose 6-phosphate, and free glucose is released into the blood. As with fructose 1,6-bisphosphatase, this is not a reversal of the glucokinase reaction because the phosphate bond in glucose 6-phosphate is a low-energy bond, and ATP is not generated at this step.

Glucose 6-phosphatase is located in the membrane of the endoplasmic reticulum. It is used not only in gluconeogenesis but also to produce blood glucose from the breakdown of liver glycogen.

D. Regulation of Gluconeogenesis

Although gluconeogenesis occurs during fasting, it is also stimulated during prolonged exercise, by a high-protein diet, and under conditions of stress. The factors

Al Martini had not eaten for 3 days, so he had no dietary source of glucose, and his liver glycogen stores were essentially depleted. He was solely dependent on gluconeogenesis to maintain his blood glucose levels. One of the consequences of ethanol ingestion and the subsequent rise in NADH levels is that the major carbon sources for gluconeogenesis cannot readily be converted to glucose. For example, amino acids that form intermediates of the tricarboxylic acid (TCA) cycle are converted to malate, which enters the cytosol and is converted to oxaloacetate, which proceeds through gluconeogenesis to form glucose. When excessive amounts of ethanol are ingested, elevated NADH levels inhibit the conversion of malate to oxaloacetate in the cytosol. Therefore, carbons from amino acids that form intermediates of the TCA cycle cannot be converted to glucose as readily. As a result of the excessive NADH formed during his alcoholic binges, Mr. Martini became hypoglycemic. His blood glucose level was 28 mg/dL.

that promote the overall flow of carbon from pyruvate to glucose include the availability of substrate and changes in the activity or amount of certain key enzymes of glycolysis and gluconeogenesis.

1. AVAILABILITY OF SUBSTRATE

Gluconeogenesis is stimulated by the flow of its major substrates from peripheral tissues to the liver. Glycerol is released from adipose tissue whenever the levels of insulin are low and the levels of glucagon or the "stress" hormones, epinephrine and cortisol (a glucocorticoid), are elevated in the blood (see Chapter 26). Lactate is produced by muscle during exercise and by red blood cells. Amino acids are released from muscle whenever insulin is low or when cortisol is elevated. Amino acids are also available for gluconeogenesis when the dietary intake of protein is high and intake of carbohydrate is low.

2. ACTIVITY OR AMOUNT OF KEY ENZYMES

Three sequences in the pathway of gluconeogenesis are regulated:

1. Pyruvate → PEP
2. Fructose 1,6-bisphosphate → fructose 6-phosphate
3. Glucose 6-phosphate → glucose

These steps correspond to those in glycolysis that are catalyzed by regulatory enzymes. The enzymes involved in these steps of gluconeogenesis differ from those that catalyze the reverse reactions in glycolysis. The net flow of carbon whether from glucose to pyruvate (glycolysis) or from pyruvate to glucose (gluconeogenesis) depends on the relative activity or amount of these glycolytic or gluconeogenic enzymes (Fig. 31.9 and Table 31.1).

3. CONVERSION OF PYRUVATE TO PHOSPHOENOLPYRUVATE

Pyruvate, a key substrate for gluconeogenesis, is derived from lactate and amino acids, particularly alanine. Pyruvate is not converted to acetyl-CoA under conditions that favor gluconeogenesis because pyruvate dehydrogenase is relatively inactive. Instead, pyruvate is converted to oxaloacetate by pyruvate carboxylase. Subsequently, oxaloacetate is converted to PEP by PEPCK. Because of the activity state of the enzymes discussed in subsequent sections, PEP reverses the steps of glycolysis, ultimately forming glucose.

Pyruvate dehydrogenase is inactive. Under conditions of fasting, insulin levels are low, and glucagon levels are elevated. Consequently, fatty acids and glycerol are released from the triacylglycerol stores of adipose tissue. Fatty acids travel to the liver where they undergo β-oxidation producing acetyl-CoA, NADH, and ATP. As a consequence, the concentration of adenosine diphosphate (ADP) decreases. These changes result in the phosphorylation of pyruvate dehydrogenase to the inactive form. Therefore, pyruvate is not converted to acetyl-CoA (see Chapter 20).

Pyruvate carboxylase is active. Acetyl-CoA, which is produced by oxidation of fatty acids, activates pyruvate carboxylase. Therefore, pyruvate, derived from lactate or alanine, is converted to oxaloacetate. Acetyl-CoA levels, then, reciprocally regulate pyruvate dehydrogenase and pyruvate carboxylase. High levels of acetyl-CoA inhibit pyruvate dehydrogenase while activating pyruvate carboxylase.

Phosphoenolpyruvate carboxykinase is induced. Oxaloacetate produces PEP in a reaction catalyzed by PEPCK. Cytosolic PEPCK is an inducible enzyme, which means that the quantity of the enzyme in the cell increases because of increased transcription of its gene and increased translation of its mRNA. The major inducer is cyclic adenosine monophosphate (cAMP), which is increased by hormones that activate adenylate cyclase. Adenylate cyclase produces cAMP from ATP. Glucagon

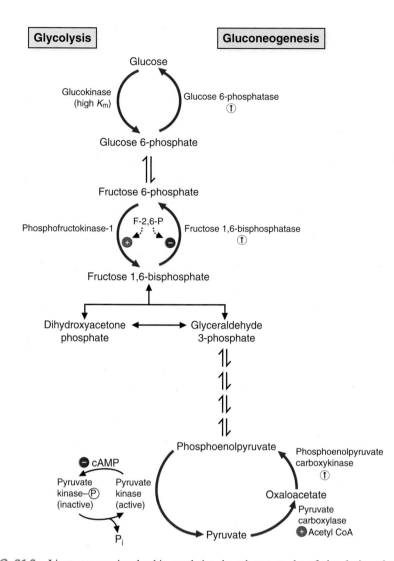

FIG. 31.9. Liver enzymes involved in regulating the substrate cycles of glycolysis and gluco-neogenesis. *Heavy arrows* indicate the three substrate cycles. F-2,6-P, fructose 2,6-bisphosphate; ⊕, activated by; ⊖, inhibited by; ⬆, inducible enzyme.

Table 31.1   Regulation of Enzymes of Glycolysis and Gluconeogenesis in Liver

Enzyme	Mechanism
A. Glycolytic enzymes	
Pyruvate kinase	Activated by F 1,6-BP
	Inhibited by ATP, alanine
	Inhibited by phosphorylation (glucagon and epinephrine lead to an increase in cAMP levels, which activates protein kinase A)
Phosphofructokinase-1	Activated by F 2,6-BP, AMP Inhibited by ATP, citrate
Glucokinase	High K_m for glucose
	Induced by insulin
B. Gluconeogenic enzymes	
Pyruvate carboxylase	Activated by acetyl-CoA
Phosphoenolpyruvate carboxykinase	Induced (increase in gene transcription) by glucagon, epinephrine, glucocorticoids
	Repressed by insulin
Glucose 6-phosphatase	Induced (increase in gene transcription) during fasting
Fructose 1,6-bisphosphatase	Inhibited by F 2,6-BP, AMP
	Induced (increase in gene transcription) during fasting

F 1,6-BP, fructose 1,6-bisphosphate; F 2,6-BP, fructose 2,6-bisphosphate; ATP, adenosine triphosphate; cAMP, cyclic adenosine monophosphate; AMP, adenosine monophosphate.

The mechanism of action of steroid hormones on glucose homeostasis differs from that of glucagon or epinephrine (see Chapters 16 and 26). Glucocorticoids are steroid hormones that stimulate gluconeogenesis, in part, because they induce the synthesis of PEPCK. **Emma Wheezer** had elevated levels of blood glucose because she was being treated with large pharmacologic doses of *dexamethasone*, a potent synthetic glucocorticoid.

is the hormone that causes cAMP to rise during fasting, whereas epinephrine acts during exercise or stress. cAMP activates protein kinase A, which phosphorylates a set of specific transcription factors (cAMP-response element binding protein, CREB) that stimulate transcription of the PEPCK gene (see Chapter 16 and Fig. 16.17). Increased synthesis of mRNA for PEPCK results in increased synthesis of the enzyme. Cortisol, the major human glucocorticoid, also induces PEPCK but through a different regulatory site on the PEPCK promoter.

Pyruvate kinase is inactive. When glucagon is elevated, liver pyruvate kinase is phosphorylated and inactivated by a mechanism that involves cAMP and protein kinase A. Therefore, PEP is not reconverted to pyruvate. Rather, it continues along the pathway of gluconeogenesis. If PEP were reconverted to pyruvate, these substrates would simply cycle, causing a net loss of energy with no net generation of useful products. The inactivation of pyruvate kinase prevents such futile cycling and promotes the net synthesis of glucose.

4. CONVERSION OF FRUCTOSE 1,6-BISPHOSPHATE TO FRUCTOSE 6-PHOSPHATE

The carbons of PEP reverse the steps of glycolysis, forming fructose 1,6-bisphosphate. Fructose 1,6-bisphosphatase acts on this bisphosphate to release P_i and produce fructose 6-phosphate. A futile substrate cycle is prevented at this step because, under conditions that favor gluconeogenesis, the concentrations of the compounds that activate the glycolytic enzyme PFK-1 are low. These same compounds, fructose 2,6-bisphosphate (whose levels are regulated by insulin and glucagon) and AMP, are allosteric inhibitors of fructose 1,6-bisphosphatase. When the concentrations of these allosteric effectors are low, PFK-1 is less active, fructose 1,6-bisphosphatase is more active, and the net flow of carbon is toward fructose 6-phosphate and, thus, toward glucose. The synthesis of fructose 1,6-bisphosphatase is also induced during fasting.

5. CONVERSION OF GLUCOSE 6-PHOSPHATE TO GLUCOSE

Glucose 6-phosphatase catalyzes the conversion of glucose 6-phosphate to glucose, which is released from the liver cell (Fig. 31.10). The glycolytic enzyme glucokinase, which catalyzes the reverse reaction, is relatively inactive during gluconeogenesis. Glucokinase, which has a high $S_{0.5}$ (K_m) for glucose (see Chapter 9, Fig. 9.3), is not very active during fasting because the blood glucose level is lower (approximately 5 mM) than the $S_{0.5}$ of the enzyme.

Glucokinase is also an inducible enzyme. The concentration of the enzyme increases in the fed state, when blood glucose and insulin levels are elevated, and decreases in the fasting state, when glucose and insulin are low.

E. Energy Is Required for the Synthesis of Glucose

During the gluconeogenic reactions, 6 mol of high-energy phosphate bonds are cleaved. Two mol of pyruvate are required for the synthesis of 1 mol of glucose. As 2 mol of pyruvate are carboxylated by pyruvate carboxylase, 2 mol of ATP are hydrolyzed. PEPCK requires 2 mol of GTP (the equivalent of 2 mol of ATP) to convert 2 mol of oxaloacetate to 2 mol of PEP. An additional 2 mol of ATP are used when 2 mol of 3-phosphoglycerate are phosphorylated, forming 2 mol of 1,3-bisphosphoglycerate. Energy in the form of reducing equivalents (NADH) is also required for the conversion of 1,3-bisphosphoglycerate to glyceraldehyde 3-phosphate. Under fasting conditions, the energy required for gluconeogenesis is obtained from β-oxidation of fatty acids. Defects in fatty acid oxidation can lead to hypoglycemia because of reduced fatty acid–derived energy production within the liver.

Glucose 6-phosphatase is used in both glycogenolysis and gluconeogenesis to produce free glucose from glucose 6-phosphate.

FIG. 31.10. Location and function of glucose 6-phosphatase. Glucose 6-phosphate travels on a transporter into the endoplasmic reticulum (ER), where it is hydrolyzed by glucose 6-phosphatase to glucose and inorganic phosphate (P_i). These products travel back to the cytosol on transporters.

III. CHANGES IN BLOOD GLUCOSE LEVELS AFTER A MEAL

The metabolic transitions that occur as a person eats a meal and progresses through the various stages of fasting have been described in detail in previous chapters. This chapter summarizes the concepts presented in these previous chapters. Because a thorough understanding of these concepts is so critical to medicine, a summary is not only warranted but is also essential.

After a high-carbohydrate meal, blood glucose rises from a fasting level of approximately 80 to 100 mg/dL (~5 mM) to a level of approximately 120 to 140 mg/dL (8 mM) within a period of 30 minutes to 1 hour (Fig. 31.11). The concentration of glucose in the blood then begins to decrease, returning to the fasting range by approximately 2 hours after the meal (see also Chapter 26).

Blood glucose levels increase as dietary glucose is digested and absorbed. The values go no higher than approximately 140 mg/dL in a normal, healthy person because tissues take up glucose from the blood, storing it for subsequent use and oxidizing it for energy. After the meal is digested and absorbed, blood glucose levels decline because cells continue to metabolize glucose.

If blood glucose levels continued to rise after a meal, the high concentration of glucose would cause the release of water from tissues as a result of the osmotic effect of glucose. Tissues would become dehydrated, and their function would be affected. If hyperglycemia becomes severe, a hyperosmolar coma could result from dehydration of the brain.

Conversely, if blood glucose levels continued to drop after a meal, tissues that depend on glucose would suffer from a lack of energy. If blood glucose levels dropped abruptly, the brain would not be able to produce an adequate amount of ATP. Light-headedness and dizziness would result, followed by drowsiness and, eventually, coma. Red blood cells would not be able to produce enough ATP to maintain the integrity of their membranes. Hemolysis of these cells would decrease the transport of oxygen to the tissues of the body. Eventually, all tissues that rely on oxygen for energy production would fail to perform their normal functions. If the problem were severe enough, death could result.

Devastating consequences of glucose excess or insufficiency are normally avoided because the body is able to regulate its blood glucose levels. As the concentration of blood glucose approaches the normal fasting range of 80 to 100 mg/dL roughly 2 hours after a meal, the process of glycogenolysis is activated in the liver. Liver glycogen is the primary source of blood glucose during the first few hours of fasting. Subsequently, gluconeogenesis begins to play a role as an additional source of blood glucose. The carbon for gluconeogenesis, a process that occurs in the liver, is supplied by other tissues. Exercising muscle and red blood cells provide lactate through glycolysis; muscle also provides amino acids by degradation of protein; and glycerol is released from adipose tissue as triacylglycerol stores are mobilized.

Even during a prolonged fast, blood glucose levels do not decrease dramatically. After 5 to 6 weeks of starvation, blood glucose levels decrease to only approximately 65 mg/dL (Table 31.2).

FIG. 31.11.   Blood glucose concentrations at various times after a meal.

Table 31.2   Blood Glucose Levels at Various Stages of Fasting

Stage of Fasting	Glucose (mg/dL)
Glucose, 700 g/d IV	100
Fasting, 12 h	80
Starvation, 3 d	70
Starvation, 5–6 wk	65

IV, intravenous.
Source: Ruderman NB, Aoki TT, Cahill GF Jr. Gluconeogenesis and its disorders in man. In: Hanson RW, Mehlman MA, eds. *Gluconeogenesis: Its Regulation in Mammalian Species.* New York, NY: John Wiley & Sons; 1976:517.

When **Di Abietes** inadvertently injected an excessive amount of insulin, she caused an acute reduction in her blood glucose levels, which dropped acutely 4 to 5 hours later while she was asleep. Had she been awake, she would have first experienced symptoms caused by hypoglycemia-induced hyperactivity of her sympathetic nervous system (e.g., sweating, tremulousness, palpitations). Eventually, as her hypoglycemia became more profound, she would have experienced symptoms of "neuroglycopenia" (inadequate glucose supply to the brain), such as confusion, speech disturbances, emotional instability, possible seizure activity, and, finally, coma. She reached this neuroglycopenic stage of hypoglycemia while sleeping and thus could not be aroused at 6:00 AM.

Ann O' Rexia, whose intake of glucose and of glucose precursors has been severely restricted, has not developed any of these manifestations. Her lack of hypoglycemic symptoms can be explained by the very gradual reduction of her blood glucose levels as a consequence of near starvation and her ability to maintain blood glucose levels within an acceptable fasting range through hepatic gluconeogenesis. In addition, lipolysis of adipose triacylglycerols produces fatty acids, which are used as fuel and converted to ketone bodies by the liver. The oxidation of fatty acids and ketone bodies by the brain and muscle reduces the need for blood glucose.

In **Di Abietes'** case, the excessive dose of insulin inhibited lipolysis and ketone body synthesis, so these alternative fuels were not available to spare blood glucose. The rapidity with which hypoglycemia was induced could not be compensated for quickly enough by hepatic gluconeogenesis, which was inhibited by the insulin, and hypoglycemia ensued.

An immediate fingerstick revealed that Di's capillary blood glucose level was <20 mg/dL. An intravenous infusion of a 50% solution of glucose was started, and her blood glucose level was determined frequently. When Di regained consciousness, the intravenous solution was eventually changed to 10% glucose. After 6 hours, her blood glucose levels stayed in the upper normal range, and she was able to tolerate oral feedings. She was transferred to the metabolic unit for overnight monitoring. By the next morning, her previous diabetes treatment regimen could be reestablished. The reasons that she had developed hypoglycemic coma were explained to Di, and she was discharged to the care of her family doctor.

A. Blood Glucose Levels in the Fed State

The major factors involved in regulating blood glucose levels are the blood glucose concentration itself and hormones, particularly insulin and glucagon.

As blood glucose levels rise after a meal, the increased glucose concentration stimulates the β-cells of the pancreas to release insulin (Fig. 31.12). Certain amino acids, particularly arginine and leucine, also stimulate insulin release from the pancreas.

Blood levels of glucagon, which is secreted by the α-cells of the pancreas, may increase or decrease, depending on the content of the meal. Glucagon levels decrease in response to a high-carbohydrate meal, but they increase in response to a high-protein meal. After a typical mixed meal containing carbohydrate, protein, and fat, glucagon levels remain relatively constant, whereas insulin levels increase.

1. FATE OF DIETARY GLUCOSE IN THE LIVER

After a meal, the liver oxidizes glucose to meet its immediate energy needs. Any excess glucose is converted to stored fuels. Glycogen is synthesized and stored in the liver, and glucose is converted to fatty acids and to the glycerol moiety that reacts with the fatty acids to produce triacylglycerols. These triacylglycerols are packaged in VLDL and transported to adipose tissue where the fatty acids are stored in adipose triacylglycerols. The VLDL can also deliver triglycerides (fatty acids) to the muscle for immediate oxidation, if required.

Regulatory mechanisms control the conversion of glucose to stored fuels. As the concentration of glucose increases in the hepatic portal vein, the concentration of glucose in the liver may increase from the fasting level of 80 to 100 mg/dL (~5 mM) to a concentration of 180 to 360 mg/dL (10 to 20 mM). Consequently, the velocity of the glucokinase reaction increases because this enzyme has a high $S_{0.5}$ (K_m) for glucose (Fig. 31.13). Glucokinase is also induced by a high-carbohydrate diet; the quantity of the enzyme increases in response to elevated insulin levels.

Insulin promotes the storage of glucose as glycogen by countering the effects of glucagon-stimulated phosphorylation. The response to insulin activates the phosphatases that dephosphorylate glycogen synthase (which leads to glycogen synthase activation) and glycogen phosphorylase (which leads to inhibition of the enzyme)

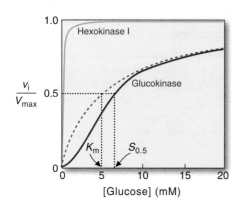

FIG. 31.13. Velocity of the glucokinase reaction.

FIG. 31.12. Blood glucose, insulin, and glucagon levels after a high-carbohydrate meal and after a high-protein meal.

(Fig. 31.14A). Insulin also promotes the synthesis of the triacylglycerols that are released from the liver into the blood as VLDL. The regulatory mechanisms for this process are described in Chapter 33.

2. FATE OF DIETARY GLUCOSE IN PERIPHERAL TISSUES

Almost every cell in the body oxidizes glucose for energy. Certain critical tissues, particularly the brain, other nervous system tissues, and red blood cells depend especially on glucose for their energy supply. The brain requires approximately 150 g of glucose per day. In addition, approximately 40 g of glucose per day is required by other glucose-dependent tissues. Furthermore, all tissues require glucose for the pentose phosphate pathway, and many tissues use glucose for synthesis of glycoproteins and other carbohydrate-containing compounds.

Insulin stimulates the transport of glucose into adipose and muscle cells by promoting the recruitment of glucose transporters to the cell membrane (see Fig. 31.14C). Other tissues such as the liver, brain, and red blood cells have a different type of glucose transporter that is not significantly affected by insulin.

In muscle, glycogen is synthesized after a meal by a mechanism similar to that in the liver (see Fig. 31.14B). Metabolic differences exist between these tissues (see Chapter 28), but, in essence, insulin stimulates glycogen synthesis in resting muscle as it does in the liver. A key difference between muscle and liver is that insulin greatly stimulates the transport of glucose into muscle cells but only slightly stimulates its transport into liver cells.

3. RETURN OF BLOOD GLUCOSE TO FASTING LEVELS

After a meal has been digested and absorbed, blood glucose levels reach a peak and then begin to decline. The uptake of dietary glucose by cells particularly those in the liver, muscle, and adipose tissue lowers blood glucose levels. By 2 hours after a meal, blood glucose levels return to the normal fasting level of <100 mg/dL.

B. Blood Glucose Levels in the Fasting State

1. CHANGES IN INSULIN AND GLUCAGON LEVELS

During fasting, as blood glucose levels decrease, insulin levels decrease and glucagon levels rise. These hormonal changes cause the liver to degrade glycogen by the process of glycogenolysis and to produce glucose by the process of gluconeogenesis so that blood glucose levels are maintained.

2. STIMULATION OF GLYCOGENOLYSIS

Within a few hours after a high-carbohydrate meal, glucagon levels begin to rise. Glucagon binds to cell surface receptors and activates adenylate cyclase, causing cAMP levels in liver cells to rise (Fig. 31.15). cAMP activates protein kinase A,

FIG. 31.15. Regulation of glycogenolysis in the liver by glucagon. (*1*) Glucagon binding to its receptor leads to activation of adenylate cyclase, which leads to an increase in cAMP levels. (*2*) cAMP binds to the regulatory subunits of protein kinase A, thereby activating the catalytic subunit. (*3*) Active protein kinase A phosphorylates and activates phosphorylase kinase, while simultaneously inactivating glycogen synthase (*4*). (*5*) Active phosphorylase kinase converts glycogen phosphorylase b to glycogen phosphorylase a. (*6*) Phosphorylase a degrades glycogen, producing glucose 1-phosphate, which is converted to glucose 6-phosphate, then glucose, for export into the blood.

FIG. 31.14. Glucose metabolism in various tissues. **A.** Effect of insulin on glycogen synthesis and degradation and on very low-density lipoprotein (VLDL) synthesis in the liver. **B.** Glucose metabolism in resting muscle in the fed state. Transport of glucose into cells and synthesis of glycogen are stimulated by insulin. **C.** Glucose metabolism in adipose tissue in the fed state. *FA*, fatty acids; *DHAP*, dihydroxyacetone phosphate; *TG*, triacylglycerol; ⊕, stimulated by insulin; ⊖, inhibited by insulin.

which phosphorylates and inactivates glycogen synthase. Therefore, glycogen synthesis decreases.

At the same time, protein kinase A stimulates glycogen degradation by a two-step mechanism. Protein kinase A phosphorylates and activates phosphorylase kinase. This enzyme, in turn, phosphorylates and activates glycogen phosphorylase.

Glycogen phosphorylase catalyzes the phosphorolysis of glycogen, producing glucose 1-phosphate, which is converted to glucose 6-phosphate. Dephosphorylation of glucose 6-phosphate by glucose 6-phosphatase produces free glucose, which then enters the blood.

3. STIMULATION OF GLUCONEOGENESIS

By 4 hours after a meal, the liver is supplying glucose to the blood not only by the process of glycogenolysis but also by the process of gluconeogenesis. Hormonal changes cause peripheral tissues to release precursors that provide carbon for gluconeogenesis, specifically lactate, amino acids, and glycerol.

Regulatory mechanisms promote the conversion of gluconeogenic precursors to glucose (Fig. 31.16). These mechanisms prevent the occurrence of potential futile cycles, which would continuously convert substrates to products while consuming energy but producing no useful result.

These regulatory mechanisms inactivate the glycolytic enzymes pyruvate kinase, PFK-1, and glucokinase during fasting and promote the flow of carbon to glucose via gluconeogenesis. These mechanisms operate at the three steps where glycolysis and gluconeogenesis differ.

1. Pyruvate (derived from lactate and alanine) is converted by the gluconeogenic pathway to PEP. PEP is not reconverted to pyruvate (a potentially futile cycle) because glucagon-stimulated phosphorylation inactivates pyruvate kinase. Therefore, PEP reverses the steps of glycolysis and forms fructose 1,6-bisphosphate.
2. Fructose 1,6-bisphosphate is converted to fructose 6-phosphate by a bisphosphatase. Because the glycolytic enzyme PFK-1 is relatively inactive mainly as a result of low fructose 2,6-bisphosphate levels, fructose 6-phosphate is not converted back to fructose 1,6-bisphosphate, and a second potential futile cycle is avoided. The low fructose 2,6-bisphosphate levels are attributable in part to the phosphorylation of phosphofructokinase-2 by protein kinase A, which has been activated in response to glucagon. Fructose 6-phosphate is converted to glucose 6-phosphate.
3. Glucose 6-phosphate is dephosphorylated by glucose 6-phosphatase, forming free glucose. Because glucokinase has a high $S_{0.5}$ (K_m) for glucose and glucose concentrations are relatively low in liver cells during fasting, glucose is released into the blood. Therefore, the third potential futile cycle does not occur.
4. Enzymes that participate in gluconeogenesis, but not in glycolysis, are active under fasting conditions. Pyruvate carboxylase is activated by acetyl-CoA, derived from oxidation of fatty acids. PEPCK, fructose 1,6-bisphosphatase, and glucose 6-phosphatase are induced; that is, the quantity of the enzymes increases. Fructose 1,6-bisphosphatase is also active because levels of fructose 2,6-bisphosphate, an inhibitor of the enzyme, are low.

4. STIMULATION OF LIPOLYSIS

The hormonal changes that occur during fasting stimulate the breakdown of adipose triacylglycerols (see Chapters 3, 33, and 43). Consequently, fatty acids and glycerol are released into the blood (Fig. 31.17). Glycerol serves as a source of carbon for gluconeogenesis. Fatty acids become the major fuel of the body and are oxidized to CO_2 and H_2O by various tissues, which enable these tissues to decrease their use of glucose. Fatty acids are also oxidized to acetyl-CoA in the liver to provide energy for gluconeogenesis. In a prolonged fast, acetyl-CoA is converted to ketone bodies, which enter the blood and serve as an additional fuel source for the muscle and the brain.

C. Blood Glucose Levels during Prolonged Fasting (Starvation)

During prolonged fasting, several changes occur in fuel use. These changes cause tissues to use less glucose than they use during a brief fast and to use predominantly fuels derived from adipose triacylglycerols (i.e., fatty acids and their derivatives, the ketone bodies). Therefore, blood glucose levels do not decrease drastically. In fact, even after 5 to 6 weeks of starvation, blood glucose levels are still in the range of 65 mg/dL (Fig. 31.18; see Table 31.2).

The major change that occurs in starvation is a dramatic elevation of blood ketone body levels after 3 to 5 days of fasting (see Fig. 31.18). At these levels, the brain and other nervous tissues begin to use ketone bodies and, consequently, they oxidize less glucose, requiring roughly one-third as much glucose (approximately 40 g/day) as under normal dietary conditions. As a result of reduced glucose use, the rate of gluconeogenesis in the liver decreases, as does the production of urea (see Fig. 31.18). Because in this stage of starvation, amino acids obtained from the

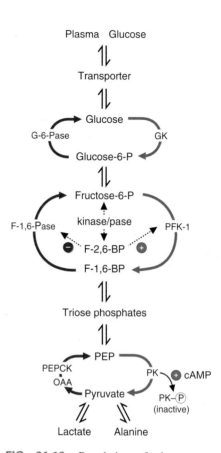

FIG. 31.16. Regulation of gluconeogenesis (*red arrows*) in the liver. *GK*, glucokinase; *G-6-Pase*, glucose 6-phosphatase; *PK*, pyruvate kinase; *OAA*, oxaloacetate; *PEPCK*, phosphoenolpyruvate carboxykinase; *F-1,6-Pase*, fructose 1,6-bisphosphatase; *F-2,6-BP*, fructose 2,6-bisphosphate; *PFK-1*, phosphofructokinase-1.

 The pathophysiology leading to an elevation of blood glucose after a meal differs between patients with type 1 diabetes mellitus and those with type 2 diabetes mellitus. **Di Abietes**, who has type 1 disease, cannot secrete insulin adequately in response to a meal because of a defect in the β-cells of her pancreas. **Ann Sulin**, however, has type 2 disease. In this form of the disorder, the cause of glucose intolerance is more complex, involving at least a delay in the release of relatively appropriate amounts of insulin after a meal combined with a degree of resistance to the actions of insulin in skeletal muscle and adipocytes. Excessive hepatic gluconeogenesis occurs even though blood glucose levels are elevated.

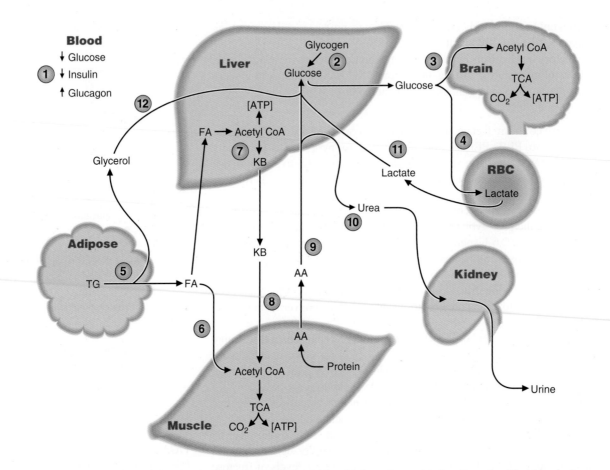

FIG. 31.17. Tissue interrelationships during fasting. *(1)* Blood glucose levels drop, decreasing insulin and raising blood glucagon levels. *(2)* Glycogenolysis is induced in the liver to raise blood glucose levels. *(3)* The brain uses the glucose released by the liver, as do the red blood cells *(4)*. *(5)* Adipose tissues are induced to release free fatty acids and glycerol from stored triglycerides. *(6)* The muscle and liver use fatty acids for energy. *(7)* The liver converts fatty acid–derived acetyl-CoA to ketone bodies for export, which the muscles *(8)* and brain can use for energy. *(9)* Protein turnover is induced in muscle, and amino acids leave the muscle and travel to the liver for use as gluconeogenic precursors. *(10)* The high rate of amino acid metabolism in the liver generates urea, which travels to the kidney for excretion. *(11)* Red blood cells produce lactate, which returns to the liver as a substrate for gluconeogenesis. *(12)* The glycerol released from adipose tissue is used by the liver for gluconeogenesis. *KB*, ketone bodies; *FA*, fatty acids; *AA*, amino acids; *TG*, triacylglycerols.

degradation of existing proteins are the major gluconeogenic precursor; reducing glucose requirements in tissues reduces the rate of protein degradation and hence the rate of urea formation. Protein from muscle and other tissues is, therefore, spared because there is less need for amino acids for gluconeogenesis.

Body protein, particularly muscle protein, is not primarily a storage form of fuel in the same sense as glycogen or triacylglycerol; proteins have many functions besides fuel storage. For example, proteins function as enzymes, as structural proteins, and in muscle contraction. If tissue protein is degraded to too great an extent, body function can be severely compromised. If starvation continues and no other problems such as infections occur, a starving individual usually dies because of severe protein loss that causes malfunction of major organs, such as the heart. Therefore, the increase in ketone body levels that results in the sparing of body protein allows individuals to survive for extended periods without ingesting food.

D. Summary of Sources of Blood Glucose

Immediately after a meal, dietary carbohydrates serve as the major source of blood glucose (Fig. 31.19). As blood glucose levels return to the fasting range within

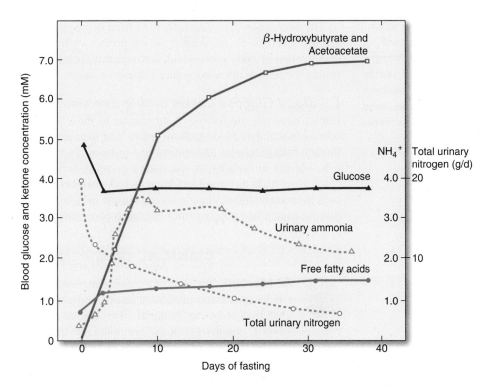

FIG. 31.18. Changes in blood fuels during fasting. The units for fatty acids, glucose, and ketone bodies are millimolar (*on left*) and for urinary nitrogen and ammonia are grams per day (*on right*). (Modified from Linder MC, ed. *Nutritional Biochemistry and Metabolism with Clinical Applications.* 2nd ed. Norwalk, CT: Appleton & Lange; 1991:103. Copyright 1991 Appleton & Lange.)

2 hours after a meal, glycogenolysis is stimulated and begins to supply glucose to the blood. Subsequently, glucose is also produced by gluconeogenesis.

During a 12-hour fast, glycogenolysis is the major source of blood glucose. Thus, it is the major pathway by which glucose is produced in the basal state (after a 12-hour fast). However, by approximately 16 hours of fasting, glycogenolysis and gluconeogenesis contribute equally to the maintenance of blood glucose.

By 30 hours after a meal, liver glycogen stores are substantially depleted. Subsequently, gluconeogenesis is the primary source of blood glucose.

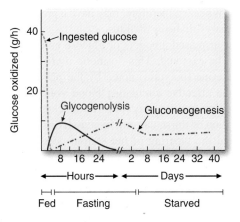

FIG. 31.19. Sources of blood glucose in fed, fasting, and starved states. Note that the scale changes from hours to days. (From Ruderman NB, Aoki TT, Cahill GF Jr. In: Hanson RW, Mehlman MA, eds. *Gluconeogenesis: Its Regulation in Mammalian Species.* New York, NY: John Wiley & Sons; 1976:518. Copyright 1976 John Wiley & Sons.)

Otto Shape is able to jog for 45 minutes before eating breakfast without developing symptoms of hypoglycemia in spite of enhanced glucose use by skeletal muscle during exercise. He maintains his blood glucose level in an adequate range through hepatic glycogenolysis and gluconeogenesis.

The mechanisms that cause fats to be used as the major fuel and that allow blood glucose levels to be maintained during periods of food deprivation result in the conservation of body protein and, consequently, permit survival during prolonged fasting for periods often exceeding 1 month or more.

E. Blood Glucose Levels during Exercise

During exercise, mechanisms very similar to those that are used during fasting operate to maintain blood glucose levels. The liver maintains blood glucose levels through both glucagon- and epinephrine-induced glycogenolysis and gluconeogenesis. The use of fuels by muscle during exercise, including the uptake and use of blood glucose, is discussed in Chapter 47. Remember that muscle glycogen is not used to maintain blood glucose levels; muscle cells lack glucose 6-phosphatase, so glucose cannot be produced from glucose 6-phosphate for export.

CLINICAL COMMENTS

Al Martini. The chronic excessive ingestion of ethanol concurrent with a recent reduction in nutrient intake caused **Al Martini's** blood glucose level to decrease to 28 mg/dL. This degree of hypoglycemia caused the release of several "counterregulatory" hormones into the blood, including glucagon, growth hormone, cortisol, and epinephrine (adrenaline).

Some of the patient's signs and symptoms are primarily the result of an increase in adrenergic nervous system activity after a rapid decrease in blood glucose. The subsequent increase in epinephrine levels in the blood leads to tremulousness, excessive sweating, and rapid heart rate. Other manifestations arise when the brain has insufficient glucose, hence the term "neuroglycopenic symptoms." Mr. Martini was confused, combative, had slurred speech, and eventually had a grand mal seizure. If he was not treated quickly by intravenous glucose administration, Mr. Martini might have lapsed into a coma. Permanent neurologic deficits and even death may result if severe hypoglycemia is not corrected within 6 to 10 hours.

Emma Wheezer. The elevation in blood glucose that occurred in **Emma Wheezer's** case was primarily a consequence of the large pharmacologic doses of glucocorticoid that she received in an effort to reduce the intrabronchial inflammatory reaction characteristic of asthmatic bronchospasm. Although the development of hyperglycemia in this case could be classified as a "secondary" form of diabetes mellitus (caused by the activation of liver glucose export by the drug), most patients treated with glucocorticoids do not develop glucose intolerance. Ms. Wheezer, therefore, may have a predisposition to the eventual development of "primary" diabetes mellitus.

In hyperglycemia, increased amounts of glucose enter the urine, causing large amounts of water to be excreted. This "osmotic diuresis" is responsible for the increased volume of urine (polyuria) noted by the patient. Because of increased urinary water loss, the effective circulating blood volume is reduced. Therefore, less blood reaches volume-sensitive receptors in the central nervous system, which then trigger the sensation of thirst, causing increased drinking activity (polydipsia).

A diabetic diet and the tapering of her steroid dose over a period of several weeks gradually returned Ms. Wheezer's blood glucose level to the normal range.

Di Abietes and Ann Sulin. Chronically elevated levels of glucose in the blood may contribute to the development of the microvascular complications of diabetes mellitus, such as diabetic retinal damage, kidney damage, and nerve damage, as well as macrovascular complications such as cerebrovascular, peripheral vascular, and coronary vascular insufficiency. The precise mechanism by which long-term hyperglycemia induces these vascular changes is not fully established.

One postulated mechanism proposes that nonenzymatic glycation (glycosylation) of proteins in vascular tissue alters the structure and functions of these proteins. A protein that is exposed to chronically increased levels of glucose will covalently bind glucose, a process called *glycation* or *glycosylation*. This process is not regulated by enzymes (see Chapter 9). These nonenzymatically glycated proteins slowly form cross-linked protein adducts (often called *advanced glycosylation end products*) within the microvasculature and macrovasculature.

By cross-linking vascular matrix proteins and plasma proteins, chronic hyperglycemia may cause narrowing of the luminal diameter of the microvessels in the retina (causing diabetic retinopathy), the renal glomeruli (causing diabetic nephropathy), and the microvessels supplying peripheral and autonomic nerve fibers (causing diabetic neuropathy). The same process has been postulated to accelerate atherosclerotic change in the macrovasculature, particularly in the brain (causing strokes), the coronary arteries (causing heart attacks), and the peripheral arteries (causing peripheral arterial insufficiency and possibly gangrene). The abnormal lipid metabolism associated with poorly controlled diabetes mellitus also may contribute to the accelerated atherosclerosis associated with this metabolic disorder (see Chapters 33 and 34).

Until recently, it was argued that meticulous control of blood glucose levels in a patient with diabetes would not necessarily prevent or even slow these complications of chronic hyperglycemia. The results of the Diabetes Control and Complications Trial, followed by the United Kingdom Prospective Diabetes study, however, suggest that maintaining long-term tightly controlled blood glucose levels in patients with diabetes slows the progress of unregulated glycation of proteins as well as corrects their dyslipidemia. In this way, careful control may favorably affect the course of the microvascular complications of diabetes mellitus in patients such as **Di Abietes** and **Ann Sulin**.

BIOCHEMICAL COMMENTS

Glucose Production. Plants are the ultimate source of the earth's supply of glucose. Plants produce glucose from atmospheric CO_2 by the process of photosynthesis (Fig. 31.20A). In contrast to plants, humans cannot synthesize glucose by the fixation of CO_2. Although we have a process called *gluconeogenesis*, the term may really be a misnomer. Glucose is not generated anew by gluconeogenesis; compounds produced from glucose are simply recycled to glucose. We obtain glucose from the plants, including bacteria, that we eat and, to some extent, from animals in our food supply. We use this glucose both as a fuel and as a source of carbon for the synthesis of fatty acids, amino acids, and other sugars (see Fig. 31.20B). We store glucose as glycogen, which, along with gluconeogenesis, provides glucose when needed for energy (see Fig. 31.20C).

Lactate, one of the carbon sources for gluconeogenesis, is actually produced from glucose by tissues that obtain energy by oxidizing glucose to pyruvate through glycolysis. The pyruvate is then reduced to lactate, released into the bloodstream, and reconverted to glucose by the process of gluconeogenesis in the liver. This process is known as the *Cori cycle* (Fig. 31.20D).

Carbons of alanine, another carbon source for gluconeogenesis, may be produced from glucose. In muscle, glucose is converted via glycolysis to pyruvate and transaminated to alanine. Alanine from muscle is recycled to glucose in the liver. This process is known as the *glucose–alanine cycle* (Fig. 31.20E). Glucose also may be used to produce nonessential amino acids other than alanine, which are subsequently reconverted to glucose in the liver by gluconeogenesis. Even the essential amino acids that we obtain from dietary proteins are synthesized in plants and bacteria using glucose as the major source of carbon. Therefore, all amino acids

FIG. 31.20. **A–F.** Recycling of glucose.

Table 31.3   Diseases Discussed in Chapter 31

Disease or Disorder	Environmental or Genetic	Comments
Ethanol-induced hypoglycemia	Environmental	Ethanol, combined with poor nutrition, leads to hypoglycemia caused by excessive ethanol metabolism altering the NADH/NAD⁺ ratio in the liver.
Asthma	Environmental	A treatment to reduce bronchoconstriction is inhalation/administration of glucocorticoids. Such treatments stimulate gluconeogenesis and can lead to hyperglycemia.
Insulin overdose	Environmental	Hypoglycemia as a result of insulin overdose caused by insulin stimulation of glucose transport into muscle and fat cells.
Anorexia	Both	The use of ketone bodies as an alternative energy source during prolonged fasting preserves muscle protein as reduced levels of glucose are now required by the nervous system.
Weight loss	Environmental	Maintenance of blood glucose levels during dieting occurs caused by glycogen release.
Diabetic ketoacidosis	Environmental	Excessive production of ketone bodies in a patient with type 1 diabetes whose insulin levels are too low, coupled with hyperglycemia; rarely observed in type 2 diabetes.

that are converted to glucose in humans, including the essential amino acids, were originally synthesized from glucose.

The production of glucose from *glycerol*, the third major source of carbon for gluconeogenesis, is also a recycling process. Glycerol is derived from glucose via the DHAP intermediate of glycolysis. Fatty acids are then esterified to the glycerol and stored as triacylglycerol. When these fatty acids are released from the triacylglycerol, the glycerol moiety can travel to the liver and be reconverted to glucose (see Fig. 31.20F).

Key Concepts

- The process of glucose production is termed *gluconeogenesis*. Gluconeogenesis occurs primarily in the liver.
- The major precursors for glucose production are lactate, glycerol, and amino acids.
- The gluconeogenic pathway uses the reversible reactions of glycolysis, plus additional reactions to bypass the irreversible steps.
  - Pyruvate carboxylase (pyruvate to oxaloacetate) and phosphoenolpyruvate carboxykinase (PEPCK, oxaloacetate to phosphoenolpyruvate [PEP]) bypass the pyruvate kinase step.
  - Fructose 1,6-bisphosphatase (fructose 1,6-bisphosphate to fructose 6-phosphate) bypasses the phosphofructokinase-1 (PFK-1) step.
  - Glucose 6-phosphatase (glucose 6-phosphate to glucose) bypasses the glucokinase step.
- Gluconeogenesis and glycogenolysis are carefully regulated so that blood glucose levels can be maintained at a constant level during fasting. The regulation of triglyceride metabolism is also linked to the regulation of blood glucose levels.
- Table 31.3 summarizes the diseases discussed in this chapter.

REVIEW QUESTIONS—CHAPTER 31

1. A common intermediate in the conversion of glycerol and lactate to glucose is which of the following?

    A. Pyruvate
    B. Oxaloacetate
    C. Malate
    D. Glucose 6-phosphate
    E. Phosphoenolpyruvate

2. A patient presented with a bacterial infection that produced an endotoxin that inhibits phosphoenolpyruvate carboxykinase (PEPCK). In this patient, then, under these conditions, glucose production from which of the following precursors would be inhibited?

    A. Alanine
    B. Glycerol

C. Even-chain-number fatty acids
D. Phosphoenolpyruvate
E. Galactose

3. Which of the following statements best describes glucagon?

    A. It acts as an anabolic hormone.
    B. It acts on skeletal muscle, liver, and adipose tissue.
    C. It acts primarily on the liver and adipose tissue.
    D. Its concentration in the blood increases after a high-carbohydrate meal.
    E. Its concentration increases in the blood when insulin levels increase.

4. Which of the following is most likely to occur in a normal individual after ingesting a high-carbohydrate meal?

    A. Only insulin levels decrease.
    B. Only insulin levels increase.

C. Only glucagon levels increase.
D. Both insulin and glucagon levels decrease.
E. Both insulin and glucagon levels increase.

5. A patient arrives at the hospital in an ambulance. He or she is currently in a coma. Before lapsing into the coma, his or her symptoms included vomiting, dehydration, low blood pressure, and a rapid heartbeat. He or she also had relatively rapid respirations, resulting in more carbon dioxide being exhaled. These symptoms are consistent with which of the following conditions?

    A. The patient lacks a pancreas.
    B. Ketoalkalosis
    C. Hypoglycemic coma
    D. Diabetic ketoacidosis
    E. Insulin shock in a patient with diabetes

Lipid Metabolism

Most of the lipids found in the body fall into the categories of fatty acids and triacylglycerols; glycerophospholipids and sphingolipids; eicosanoids; cholesterol, bile salts, and steroid hormones; and fat-soluble vitamins. These lipids have very diverse chemical structures and functions. However, they are related by a common property—their relative insolubility in water.

Fatty acids, which are stored as triacylglycerols, serve as fuels, providing the body with its major source of energy (Fig. VI.1). Glycerophospholipids and sphingolipids, which contain esterified fatty acids, are found in membranes and in blood lipoproteins at the interfaces between the lipid components of these structures and the surrounding water. These membrane lipids form hydrophobic barriers between subcellular compartments and between cellular constituents and the extracellular milieu. Polyunsaturated fatty acids containing 20 carbons form the eicosanoids, which regulate many cellular processes (Fig. VI.2).

Cholesterol adds stability to the phospholipid bilayer of membranes. It serves as the precursor of the bile salts, detergentlike compounds that function in the process of lipid digestion and absorption (Fig. VI.3). Cholesterol also serves as the precursor of the steroid hormones, which have many actions, including the regulation of metabolism, growth, and reproduction.

The fat-soluble vitamins are lipids that are involved in such varied functions as vision, growth, and differentiation (vitamin A), blood clotting (vitamin K), prevention of oxidative damage to cells (vitamin E), and calcium metabolism (vitamin D).

Triacylglycerols, the major dietary lipids, are digested in the lumen of the intestine (Fig. VI.4). The initial digestive products, free fatty acids and 2-monoacylglycerol, are reconverted to triacylglycerols in intestinal epithelial cells, packaged in lipoproteins known as chylomicrons (so they can safely enter the circulation) and secreted into the lymph. Ultimately, chylomicrons enter the blood, serving as one of the major blood lipoproteins.

Very low-density lipoprotein (VLDL) is produced in the liver, mainly from dietary carbohydrate. Lipogenesis is an insulin-stimulated process through which glucose is converted to fatty acids, which are subsequently esterified to glycerol to form the triacylglycerols that are packaged in VLDL and secreted from the liver. Thus, chylomicrons primarily transport dietary lipids, and VLDL transports endogenously synthesized lipids.

The triacylglycerols of chylomicrons and VLDL are digested by lipoprotein lipase (LPL), an enzyme found attached to capillary endothelial cells (see Fig. VI.4). The fatty acids that are released are taken up by muscle and many other tissues and oxidized to CO_2 and water to produce energy (see Chapter 23). After a meal, these fatty acids are taken up by adipose tissue and stored as triacylglycerols.

LPL converts chylomicrons to chylomicron remnants and VLDL to intermediate-density lipoprotein (IDL). These products, which have relatively low triacylglycerol content, are taken up by the liver by the process of endocytosis and degraded by lysosomal action. IDL may also be converted to low-density lipoprotein (LDL) by further digestion of triacylglycerol. Endocytosis of LDL occurs in peripheral tissues as well as the liver (Table VI.1) and is the major means of cholesterol transport and delivery to peripheral tissues.

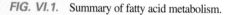

FIG. VI.1. Summary of fatty acid metabolism.

FIG. VI.2. Summary of eicosanoid synthesis. *EPA*, eicosapentaenoic acid.

FIG. VI.3. Summary of cholesterol metabolism.

Table VI.1 Blood Lipoproteins

Chylomicrons
- Produced in intestinal epithelial cells from dietary fat
- Carries triacylglycerol in blood

VLDL (very low-density lipoprotein)
- Produced in liver mainly from dietary carbohydrate
- Carries triacylglycerol in blood

IDL (intermediate-density lipoprotein)
- Produced in blood (remnant of VLDL after triacylglycerol digestion)
- Endocytosed by liver or converted to LDL

LDL (low-density lipoprotein)
- Produced in blood (remnant of IDL after triacylglycerol digestion; end product of VLDL)
- Contains high concentration of cholesterol and cholesterol esters
- Endocytosed by liver and peripheral tissues

HDL (high-density lipoprotein)
- Produced in liver and intestine
- Exchanges proteins and lipids with other lipoproteins
- Functions in the return of cholesterol from peripheral tissues to the liver

FIG. VI.4. Overview of triacylglycerol metabolism in the fed state. *TG*, triacylglycerol; *2-MG*, 2-monoacylglycerol; *FA*, fatty acid; *circled TG*, triacylglycerols of VLDL and chylomicrons; *LPL*, lipoprotein lipase.

The principal function of high-density lipoprotein (HDL) is to transport excess cholesterol obtained from peripheral tissues to the liver and to exchange proteins and lipids with chylomicrons and VLDL. The protein exchange converts "nascent" particles to "mature" particles.

During fasting, fatty acids and glycerol are released from adipose triacylglycerol stores (Fig. VI.5). The glycerol travels to the liver and is used for gluconeogenesis. Only the liver contains glycerol kinase, which is required for glycerol metabolism. The fatty acids form complexes with albumin in the blood and are taken up by muscle, kidney, and other tissues, where adenosine triphosphate (ATP) is generated by their oxidation to CO_2 and water. Liver also converts some of the carbon to ketone bodies, which are released into the blood. Ketone bodies are oxidized for energy in muscle, kidney, and other tissues during fasting, and in the brain during prolonged starvation (see Chapter 23).

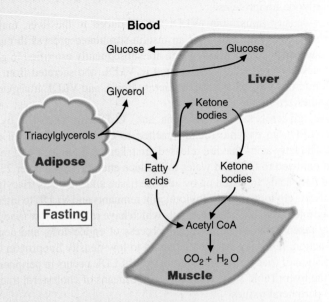

FIG. VI.5. Overview of triacylglycerol metabolism during fasting.

584

Triacylglycerols are the major fat in the human diet, consisting of three **fatty acids** esterified to a **glycerol** backbone. Limited digestion of these lipids occurs in the mouth (**lingual lipase**) and stomach (**gastric lipase**) because of the low solubility of the substrate. In the intestine, however, the fats are emulsified by **bile salts** that are released from the gallbladder. This increases the available surface area of the lipids for **pancreatic lipase** and **colipase** to bind and to digest the triglycerides. Degradation products are **free fatty acids** and **2-monoacylglycerol**. When partially digested food enters the intestine, the hormone **cholecystokinin** is secreted by the intestine, which signals the gallbladder to contract and release bile acids, and the pancreas to release digestive enzymes.

In addition to triacylglycerols, phospholipids, cholesterol, and cholesterol esters (cholesterol esterified to fatty acids) are present in the foods we eat. Phospholipids are hydrolyzed in the intestinal lumen by **phospholipase A2**, and cholesterol esters are hydrolyzed by **cholesterol esterase**. Both of these enzymes are secreted from the pancreas.

The products of enzymatic digestion (free fatty acids, glycerol, **lysophospholipids**, cholesterol) form **micelles** with bile acids in the intestinal lumen. The micelles interact with the enterocyte membrane and allow diffusion of the lipid-soluble components across the enterocyte membrane into the cell. The bile acids, however, do not enter the enterocyte at this time. They remain in the intestinal lumen, travel farther down, and are then reabsorbed and sent back to the liver by the **enterohepatic circulation**. This allows the bile salts to be used multiple times in fat digestion.

The intestinal epithelial cells resynthesize triacylglycerol from free fatty acids and 2-monoacylglycerol and package them with a protein, **apolipoprotein B-48**, phospholipids, and cholesterol esters into a soluble **lipoprotein particle** known as a **chylomicron**. The chylomicrons are secreted into the **lymph** and eventually end up in the circulation where they can distribute dietary lipids to all tissues of the body.

Once they are in the circulation, the newly released ("nascent") chylomicrons interact with another lipoprotein particle, **high-density lipoprotein (HDL)** and acquire two **apoproteins** from HDL, **apoprotein CII (apoCII)** and **apoprotein E (apoE)**. This converts the nascent chylomicron to a "mature" chylomicron. The apoCII on the mature chylomicron activates the enzyme **lipoprotein lipase (LPL)**, which is located on the inner surface of the capillary endothelial cells of muscle and adipose tissue. The LPL digests the triglyceride in the chylomicron, producing free fatty acids and glycerol. The fatty acids enter the adjacent organs either for energy production (muscle) or fat storage (adipocyte). The glycerol that is released is metabolized in the liver.

As the chylomicron loses triglyceride, its density increases and it becomes a **chylomicron remnant**, which is taken up by the liver by receptors that recognize apoE. In the liver, the chylomicron remnant is degraded into its component parts for further disposition by the liver.

 The lymph system is a network of vessels that surround interstitial cavities in the body. Cells secrete various compounds into the lymph, and the lymph vessels transport these fluids away from the interstitial spaces in the body tissues and into the bloodstream. In the case of the intestinal lymph system, the lymph enters the bloodstream through the thoracic duct. These vessels are designed so that under normal conditions the contents of the blood cannot enter the lymphatic system. The lymph fluid is similar in composition to that of the blood but lacks the cells found in blood.

Amylase is produced only in the salivary glands and the acinar cells of the pancreas. Thus, elevated serum amylase can be a sign of pancreatitis. Salivary gland lesions, such as mumps, can also increase serum amylase levels. Amylase is the enzyme that digests starch, and several automated assays can detect its activity in the serum or urine. A recent method uses an enzyme-coupled system linked to an increase in ultraviolet light absorption at 340 nm. Maltopentose (five glucose residues linked by α-[1,4]-bonds) is the artificial substrate, and amylase cleaves this substrate to maltose and maltotriose (two and three linked sugars, respectively). α-Glucosidase, which is added to the reaction mixture, cleaves the products of amylase digestion to free glucose. Once free glucose is formed, hexokinase, which has also been added to the assay mixture, converts the glucose-to-glucose 6-phosphate, and then glucose-6-phosphate dehydrogenase (another component of the assay mixture) converts glucose 6-phosphate to 6-phosphogluconate, with the production of NADPH from NADP$^+$. By measuring the change in absorbance at 340 nm, it can be determined how much NADPH is produced, which can then be converted into units of amylase activity for the production of glucose.

As an alternative, chromogenic assays have also been developed. One of these assays uses a starch substrate to which a chromogenic dye has been attached, which renders the starch–dye complex insoluble. As amylase cleaves the starch substrate, the smaller particles produced are soluble, which leads to the chromogen being solubilized, and a change in the color of the solution.

Currently, 38% of the calories (kcal) in the typical US diet come from fat. The content of fat in the diet increased from the early 1900s until the 1960s, and then decreased as we became aware of the unhealthy effects of a high-fat diet. According to current recommendations, fat should provide no more than 30% of the total calories of a healthy diet.

THE WAITING ROOM

Will Sichel has had several episodes of mild back and lower extremity pain over the last year, probably caused by minor sickle cell crises. He then developed severe right upper abdominal pain radiating to his lower right chest and his right flank 36 hours before being admitted to the emergency room. He states that the pain is not like his usual crisis pain. Intractable vomiting began 12 hours after the onset of these new symptoms. He reports that his urine is the color of iced tea and his stool now has a light clay color.

On physical examination, his body temperature is slightly elevated, and his heart rate is rapid. The whites of his eyes (the sclerae) are obviously jaundiced (or icteric, a yellow discoloration caused by the accumulation of bilirubin pigment). He is exquisitely tender to pressure over his right upper abdomen.

The emergency room physician suspects that Will is not in sickle cell crisis but instead has either acute cholecystitis (gallbladder inflammation) or a gallstone lodged in his common bile duct, causing cholestasis (the inability of the bile from the liver to reach his small intestine). His hemoglobin level is low at 7.6 mg/dL (reference range, 12 to 16 mg/dL) but unchanged from his baseline 3 months earlier. His serum total bilirubin level is 3.2 mg/dL (reference range, 0.2 to 1.0 mg/dL), and his direct (conjugated) bilirubin level is 0.9 mg/dL (reference range, 0 to 0.2 mg/dL).

Intravenous fluids were started; he was not allowed to take anything by mouth; a nasogastric tube was passed and placed on constant suction; and symptomatic therapy was started for pain and nausea. He was sent for an ultrasonographic (ultrasound) study of his upper abdomen.

Al Martini has continued to abuse alcohol and to eat poorly. After a particularly heavy intake of vodka, a steady severe pain began in his upper mid abdomen. This pain spread to the left upper quadrant and eventually radiated to his mid back. He began vomiting nonbloody material and was brought to the hospital emergency room with fever, a rapid heartbeat, and a mild reduction in blood pressure. On physical examination, he was dehydrated and tender to pressure over the upper abdomen. His vomitus and stool were both negative for occult blood.

Blood samples were sent to the laboratory for a variety of hematologic and chemical tests, including a measurement of serum amylase and lipase, digestive enzymes that are normally secreted from the exocrine pancreas through the pancreatic ducts into the lumen of the small intestine.

I. DIGESTION OF TRIACYLGLYCEROLS

Triacylglycerols are the major fat in the human diet because they are the major storage lipid in the plants and animals that constitute our food supply. Triacylglycerols contain a glycerol backbone to which three fatty acids are esterified (Fig. 32.1). The main route for digestion of triacylglycerols involves hydrolysis to fatty acids and 2-monoacylglycerol in the lumen of the intestine. However, the route depends to some extent on the chain length of the fatty acids. Lingual and gastric lipases are produced by cells at the back of the tongue and in the stomach, respectively. These lipases preferentially hydrolyze short- and medium-chain fatty acids (containing 12 or fewer carbon atoms) from dietary triacylglycerols. Therefore, they are most active in infants and young children who drink relatively large quantities of cow's milk, which contains triacylglycerols with a high percentage of short- and medium-chain fatty acids.

FIG. 32.1. Structure of a triacylglycerol. The glycerol moiety is highlighted, and its carbons are numbered.

A. Action of Bile Salts

Dietary fat leaves the stomach and enters the small intestine where it is emulsified (suspended in small particles in the aqueous environment) by bile salts (Fig. 32.2). The bile salts are amphipathic compounds (containing both hydrophobic and hydrophilic components), synthesized in the liver (see Chapter 34 for the pathway) and secreted via the gallbladder into the intestinal lumen. The contraction of the gallbladder and secretion of pancreatic enzymes are stimulated by the gut hormone cholecystokinin, which is secreted by the intestinal cells when stomach contents enter the intestine. Bile salts act as detergents, binding to the globules of dietary fat as they are broken up by the peristaltic action of the intestinal muscle. This emulsified fat, which has an increased surface area compared with unemulsified fat, is attacked by digestive enzymes from the pancreas (Fig. 32.3).

B. Action of Pancreatic Lipase

The major enzyme that digests dietary triacylglycerols is a lipase produced in the pancreas. Pancreatic lipase is secreted along with another protein, colipase, in response to the release of cholecystokinin from the intestine. The peptide hormone secretin is also released by the small intestine in response to acidic materials (such as the partially digested materials from the stomach, which contains HCl) entering the duodenum. Secretin signals the liver, pancreas, and certain intestinal cells to secrete bicarbonate. Bicarbonate raises the pH of the contents of the intestinal lumen into a range (pH ~6) that is optimal for the action of all of the digestive enzymes of the intestine.

Bile salts inhibit pancreatic lipase activity by coating the substrate and not allowing the enzyme access to the substrate. The colipase binds to the dietary fat and to the lipase, relieving the bile salt inhibition and allowing triglyceride to enter the active site of the lipase. This enhances lipase activity. Pancreatic lipase hydrolyzes fatty acids of all chain lengths from positions 1 and 3 of the glycerol moiety of the triacylglycerol, producing free fatty acids and 2-monoacylglycerol—that is,

 The mammary gland produces milk, which is the major source of nutrients for the breastfed human infant. The fatty acid composition of human milk varies, depending on the diet of the mother. However, long-chain fatty acids predominate, particularly palmitic, oleic, and linoleic acids. Although the amount of fat contained in human milk and cow's milk is similar, cow's milk contains more short- and medium-chain fatty acids and does not contain the long-chain, polyunsaturated fatty acids found in human milk that are important in brain development.

Although the concentrations of pancreatic lipase and bile salts are low in the intestinal lumen of the newborn infant, the fat of human milk is still readily absorbed. This is true because lingual and gastric lipases produced by the infant partially compensate for the lower levels of pancreatic lipase. The human mammary gland also produces lipases that enter the milk. One of these lipases, which require lower levels of bile salts than pancreatic lipase, is not inactivated by stomach acid and functions in the intestine for several hours.

 Al Martini's serum levels of pancreatic amylase (which digests dietary starch) and pancreatic lipase were elevated, a finding consistent with a diagnosis of acute pancreatitis. The elevated levels of these enzymes in the blood are the result of their escape from the inflamed exocrine cells of the pancreas into the surrounding pancreatic veins. The cause of this inflammatory pancreatic process in this case was related to the toxic effect of acute and chronic excessive alcohol ingestion.

FIG. 32.2. Structure of a bile salt. The bile salts are derived from cholesterol and retain the cholesterol ring structure. They differ from cholesterol in that the rings in bile salts contain more hydroxyl groups and a polar side chain and lack a C5–C6 double bond.

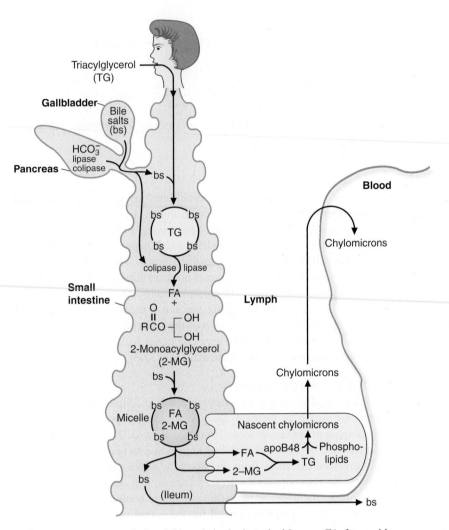

FIG. 32.3. Digestion of triacylglycerols in the intestinal lumen. *FA*, fatty acid.

Triacylglycerol

Diacylglycerol

2-Monoacylglycerol

FIG. 32.4. Action of pancreatic lipase. Fatty acids (FAs) are cleaved from positions 1 and 3 of the triacylglycerol, and a monoacylglycerol with a fatty acid at position 2 is produced.

glycerol with a fatty acid esterified at position 2 (Fig. 32.4). The pancreas also produces esterases that remove fatty acids from compounds (such as cholesterol esters) and phospholipase A2 (which is released in its zymogen form and is activated by trypsin) that digests phospholipids to a free fatty acid and a lysophospholipid (Fig. 32.5).

II. ABSORPTION OF DIETARY LIPIDS

The fatty acids and 2-monoacylglycerols produced by digestion are packaged into micelles, tiny microdroplets that are emulsified by bile salts (see Fig. 32.3). For bile salt micelles to form, the concentration of bile salts in the intestinal lumen must reach 5 to 15 mM (the critical micelle concentration, CMC). Below this concentration, the bile salts are soluble; above it, micelles will form. Other dietary lipids, such as cholesterol, lysophospholipids, and fat-soluble vitamins, are also packaged in these micelles. The micelles travel through a layer of water (the unstirred water layer) to the microvilli on the surface of the intestinal epithelial cells, where the fatty acids, 2-monoacylglycerols, and other dietary lipids are absorbed, but the bile salts are left behind in the lumen of the gut.

The bile salts are extensively resorbed when they reach the ileum. Greater than 95% of the bile salts are recirculated, traveling through the enterohepatic

A

Cholesterol ester

Cholesterol esterase

Cholesterol

B

Phospholipid

Phospholipase A2

Lysophospholipid

FIG. 32.5. Action of pancreatic esterases (**A**) and phospholipase A2 (**B**).

In patients such as **Will Sichel** who have severe and recurrent episodes of increased red blood cell destruction (hemolytic anemia), greater than normal amounts of the red cell pigment heme must be processed by the liver and spleen. In these organs, heme (derived from hemoglobin) is degraded to bilirubin, which is excreted by the liver in the bile.

If large quantities of bilirubin are presented to the liver as a consequence of acute hemolysis, the capacity of the liver to conjugate it, that is, convert it to the water-soluble bilirubin diglucuronide, can be overwhelmed. As a result, a greater percentage of the bilirubin entering the hepatic biliary ducts in patients with hemolysis is in the less water-soluble forms. In the gallbladder, these relatively insoluble particles tend to precipitate as gallstones that are rich in calcium bilirubinate. In some patients, one or more stones may leave the gallbladder through the cystic duct and enter the common bile duct. Most pass harmlessly into the small intestine and are later excreted in the stool. Larger stones, however, may become entrapped in the lumen of the common bile duct, where they cause varying degrees of obstruction to bile flow (cholestasis) with associated ductal spasm, producing pain. If adequate amounts of bile salts do not enter the intestinal lumen, dietary fats cannot readily be emulsified and digested.

circulation to the liver, which secretes them into the bile for storage in the gallbladder and ejection into the intestinal lumen during another digestive cycle (Fig. 32.6).

Short- and medium-chain fatty acids (C4 to C12) do not require bile salts for their absorption. They are absorbed directly into intestinal epithelial cells. Because they do not need to be packaged to increase their solubility, they enter the portal blood (rather than the lymph) and are transported to the liver bound to serum albumin.

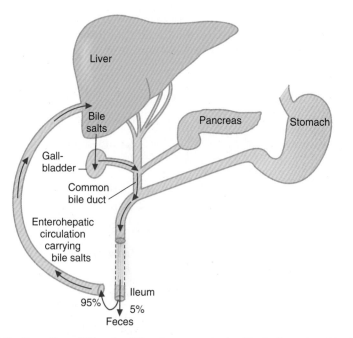

FIG. 32.6. Recycling of bile salts. Bile salts are synthesized in the liver, stored in the gallbladder, secreted into the small intestine, resorbed in the ileum, and returned to the liver via the enterohepatic circulation. Under normal circumstances, 5% or less of luminal bile acids are excreted in the stool.

When he was finally able to tolerate a full diet, **Al Martini's** stools became bulky, glistening, yellow-brown, and foul smelling. They floated on the surface of the toilet water. What caused this problem?

FIG. 32.7. Resynthesis of triacylglycerols in intestinal epithelial cells. Fatty acids (FA), produced by digestion, are activated in intestinal epithelial cells and then esterified to the 2-monoacylglycerol produced by digestion. The triacylglycerols are packaged in nascent chylomicrons and secreted into the lymph.

Al Martini's stool changes are characteristic of steatorrhea (fat-laden stools caused by malabsorption of dietary fats), in this case caused by a lack of pancreatic secretions, particularly pancreatic lipase, which normally digests dietary fat. Steatorrhea also may be caused by insufficient production or secretion of bile salts. Therefore, **Will Sichel** might also develop this condition.

Because the fat-soluble vitamins (A, D, E, and K) are absorbed from micelles along with the long-chain fatty acids and 2-monoacylglycerols, prolonged obstruction of the duct that carries exocrine secretions from the pancreas and the gallbladder into the intestine (via the common duct) could lead to a deficiency of these metabolically important substances. If the obstruction of **Will Sichel's** common duct continues, he will eventually suffer from a fat-soluble vitamin deficiency.

III. SYNTHESIS OF CHYLOMICRONS

Within the intestinal epithelial cells, the fatty acids and 2-monoacylglycerols are condensed by enzymatic reactions in the smooth endoplasmic reticulum to form triacylglycerols. The fatty acids are activated to fatty acyl-coenzyme A (fatty acyl-CoA) by the same process used for activation of fatty acids before β-oxidation (see Chapter 23). A fatty acyl-CoA then reacts with a 2-monoacylglycerol to form a diacylglycerol, which reacts with another fatty acyl-CoA to form a triacylglycerol (Fig. 32.7). The reactions for triacylglycerol synthesis in intestinal cells differ from those in liver and adipose cells in that 2-monoacylglycerol is an intermediate in triacylglycerol synthesis in intestinal cells, whereas phosphatidic acid is the necessary intermediate in other tissues.

Triacylglycerols are transported in lipoprotein particles because they are insoluble in water. If triacylglycerols entered the blood directly, they would coalesce, impeding blood flow. Intestinal cells package triacylglycerols together with proteins and phospholipids in chylomicrons, which are lipoprotein particles that do not readily coalesce in aqueous solutions (Fig. 32.8). Chylomicrons also contain

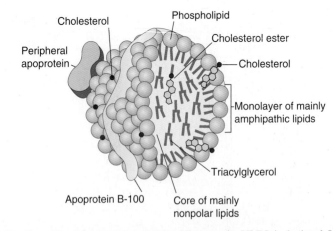

FIG. 32.8. Example of the structure of a blood lipoprotein. VLDL is depicted. Lipoproteins contain phospholipids and proteins on the surface, with their hydrophilic regions interacting with water. Hydrophobic molecules are in the interior of the lipoprotein. The hydroxyl group of cholesterol is near the surface. In cholesterol esters, the hydroxyl group is esterified to a fatty acid. Cholesterol esters are found in the interior of lipoproteins and are synthesized by reaction of cholesterol with an activated fatty acid (see Chapter 33).

FIG. 32.9. Composition of a typical chylomicron. Although the composition varies to some extent, the major component is triacylglycerol (TG). *C*, cholesterol; *CE*, cholesterol ester; *PL*, phospholipid.

FIG. 32.10. Formation and secretion of nascent chylomicrons. The triacylglycerol is produced in the smooth endoplasmic reticulum (SER) of intestinal epithelial cells from the digestive products, fatty acids, and 2-monoacylglycerols. The protein is synthesized in the rough endoplasmic reticulum (RER). The major apoprotein in chylomicrons is B-48. Assembly of the lipoproteins occurs in both the ER and the Golgi complex.

cholesterol and fat-soluble vitamins, but their major component is triglyceride derived from the diet (Fig. 32.9). The protein constituents of the lipoproteins are known as apoproteins.

The major apoprotein associated with chylomicrons as they leave the intestinal cells is B-48 (Fig. 32.10). The B-48 apoprotein is structurally and genetically related to the B-100 apoprotein synthesized in the liver that serves as a major protein of another lipid carrier, very low-density lipoprotein (VLDL). These two apoproteins are encoded by the same gene. In the intestine, the primary transcript of this gene undergoes RNA editing (Fig. 32.11, and see Chapter 16). A stop codon is generated that causes a protein to be produced in the intestine that is 48% of the size of the protein produced in the liver—hence, the designations B-48 and B-100.

The protein component of the lipoproteins is synthesized on the rough endoplasmic reticulum (RER). Lipids, which are synthesized in the smooth endoplasmic reticulum, are complexed with the proteins to form the chylomicrons (see Fig. 32.10).

IV. TRANSPORT OF DIETARY LIPIDS IN THE BLOOD

By the process of exocytosis, nascent chylomicrons are secreted by the intestinal epithelial cells into the chyle of the lymphatic system and enter the blood through the thoracic duct. Nascent chylomicrons begin to enter the blood within 1 to 2 hours after the start of a meal; as the meal is digested and absorbed, they continue to enter the blood for many hours. Initially, the particles are called nascent (newborn) chylomicrons. As they accept proteins from high-density lipoprotein (HDL) within the lymph and the blood, they become "mature" chylomicrons.

Olestra is an artificial fat substitute designed to allow individuals to obtain the taste and food consistency of fat without the calories from fat. The structure of olestra is shown and consists of a sucrose molecule to which fatty acids are esterified to the hydroxyl groups.

Olestra = octa-acyl sucrose
R = fatty acyl group

The fatty acids attached to sucrose are resistant to hydrolysis by pancreatic lipase, so olestra passes through the intestine intact and is eliminated in the feces. As a result, no useful calories can be obtained through the metabolism of olestra, although in the mouth, the sucrose portion of the molecule imparts a sweet taste. Because olestra can pass through the digestive system unimpeded, it can also carry with it essential fat-soluble vitamins. Therefore, foods prepared with olestra are supplemented with these vitamins.

Because of their high triacylglycerol content, chylomicrons are the least dense of the blood lipoproteins. When blood is collected from patients with certain types of hyperlipoproteinemias (high concentrations of lipoproteins in the blood) in which chylomicron levels are elevated, and the blood is allowed to stand in the refrigerator overnight, the chylomicrons float to the top of the liquid and coalesce, forming a creamy layer.

 One manner in which individuals can lose weight is to inhibit the activity of pancreatic lipase. This results in reduced fat digestion and absorption and a reduced caloric yield from the diet. The drug orlistat is a chemically synthesized derivative of lipstatin, a natural lipase inhibitor found in certain bacteria. The drug works in the intestinal lumen and forms a covalent bond with the active-site serine residues of both gastric and pancreatic lipase, thereby inhibiting their activities. Nondigested triglycerides are not absorbed by the intestine and are eliminated in the feces. Under normal use of the drug, approximately 30% of dietary fat absorption is inhibited. Because excessive nondigested fat in the intestines can lead to gastrointestinal distress related to excessive intestinal gas formation, individuals who take this drug need to follow a diet with reduced daily intake of fat, which should be evenly distributed among the meals of the day.

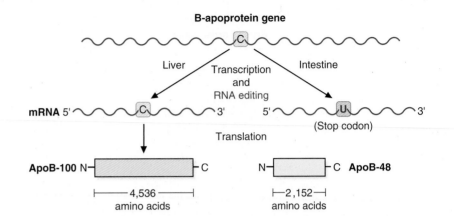

FIG. 32.11. B apoprotein gene. The gene, located on chromosome 2, is transcribed and translated in liver to produce apoB-100, which is 4,536 amino acids in length (one of the longest single-polypeptide chains). In intestinal cells, RNA editing converts a cytosine (C) to a uracil (U) via deamination, producing a stop codon. Consequently, the B apoprotein of intestinal cells (apoB-48) contains only 2,152 amino acids. ApoB-48 is 48% of the size of apoB-100.

HDL transfers proteins to the nascent chylomicrons, particularly apoE and apoCII (Fig. 32.12). ApoE is recognized by membrane receptors, particularly those on the surface of liver cells, allowing apoE-bearing lipoproteins to enter these cells by endocytosis for subsequent digestion by lysosomes. ApoCII acts as an activator of lipoprotein lipase (LPL), the enzyme on capillary endothelial cells, primarily within muscle and adipose tissue, which digests the triacylglycerols of the chylomicrons and VLDL in the blood.

V. FATE OF CHYLOMICRONS

The triacylglycerols of the chylomicrons are digested by LPL attached to the proteoglycans in the basement membranes of endothelial cells that line the capillary

FIG. 32.12. Transfer of proteins from HDL to chylomicrons. Newly synthesized chylomicrons (nascent chylomicrons) mature as they receive apoproteins CII and E from HDL. HDL functions in the transfer of these apoproteins and also in transfer of cholesterol from peripheral tissues to the liver (see Table VI.1 in the introduction to Section Six).

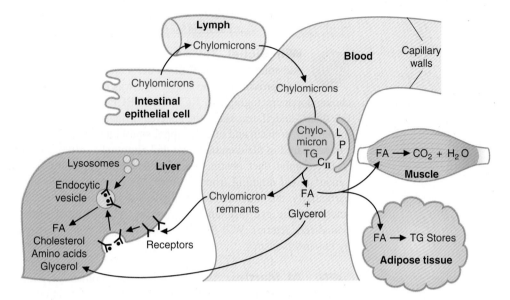

FIG. 32.13. Fate of chylomicrons. Nascent chylomicrons are synthesized in intestinal epithelial cells, secreted into the lymph, pass into the blood, and become mature chylomicrons (see Fig. 32.10). On capillary walls in adipose tissue and muscle, lipoprotein lipase (LPL) activated by apoCII digests the triacylglycerols (TGs) of chylomicrons to fatty acids and glycerol. Fatty acids (FAs) are oxidized in muscle or stored in adipose cells as triacylglycerols. The remnants of the chylomicrons are taken up by the liver by receptor-mediated endocytosis (through recognition of apoE on the remnant). Lysosomal enzymes within the hepatocyte digest the remnants, releasing the products into the cytosol.

walls (Fig. 32.13). LPL is produced by adipose cells, muscle cells (particularly cardiac muscle), and cells of the lactating mammary gland. The isozyme synthesized in adipose cells has a higher K_m than the isozyme synthesized in muscle cells. Therefore, adipose LPL is more active after a meal, when chylomicrons levels are elevated in the blood. Insulin stimulates the synthesis and secretion of adipose LPL so that after a meal, when triglyceride levels increase in circulation, LPL has been upregulated (through insulin release) to facilitate the hydrolysis of fatty acids from the triglyceride.

The fatty acids released from triacylglycerols by LPL are not very soluble in water. They become soluble in blood by forming complexes with the protein albumin. The major fate of the fatty acids is storage as triacylglycerol in adipose tissue. However, these fatty acids also may be oxidized for energy in muscle and other tissues (see Fig. 32.13). The LPL in the capillaries of muscle cells has a lower K_m than adipose LPL. Thus, muscle cells can obtain fatty acids from blood lipoproteins whenever they are needed for energy, even if the concentration of the lipoproteins is low.

The glycerol released from chylomicron triacylglycerols by LPL may be used for triacylglycerol synthesis in the liver in the fed state.

The portion of a chylomicron that remains in the blood after LPL action is known as a chylomicron remnant. The remnant has lost many of the apoC molecules bound to the mature chylomicron, which exposes apoE. This remnant binds to receptors on hepatocytes (the major cells of the liver), which recognize apoE, and is taken up by the process of endocytosis. Lysosomes fuse with the endocytic vesicles, and the chylomicron remnants are degraded by lysosomal enzymes. The products of lysosomal digestion (e.g., fatty acids, amino acids, glycerol, cholesterol, phosphate) can be reused by the cell.

 Heparin is a complex polysaccharide that is a component of proteoglycans (see Chapter 49). Isolated heparin is frequently used as an anticoagulant because it binds to antithrombin III (ATIII), and the activated ATIII then binds factors necessary for clotting and inhibits them from working. As LPL is bound to the capillary endothelium through binding to proteoglycans, heparin also can bind to LPL and dislodge it from the capillary wall. This leads to loss of LPL activity and an increase of triglyceride content in the blood.

CLINICAL COMMENTS

Will Sichel. The upper abdominal ultrasound study showed a large gallstone lodged in **Will Sichel's** common bile duct with dilation of this duct proximal to the stone. Will was scheduled for endoscopic retrograde cholangiopancreatography (ERCP). (An ERCP involves cannulation of the common bile duct—and, if necessary, the pancreatic duct—through a tube placed through the mouth and stomach and into the upper small intestine.) With this technique, a stone can be snared in the common duct and removed to relieve an obstruction.

If common duct obstruction is severe enough, bilirubin flows back into the venous blood draining from the liver. As a consequence, serum bilirubin levels, particularly the indirect (unconjugated) fraction, increase. Tissues such as the sclerae of the eye take up this pigment, which causes them to become yellow (jaundiced, icteric). Will Sichel's condition was severe enough to cause jaundice by this mechanism.

Al Martini. Alcohol excess may produce proteinaceous plugs in the small pancreatic ducts, causing back pressure injury and autodigestion of the pancreatic acini drained by these obstructed channels. This process causes one form of acute pancreatitis. Al Martini had an episode of acute alcohol-induced pancreatitis superimposed on a more chronic alcohol-related inflammatory process in the pancreas—in other words, chronic pancreatitis. As a result of decreased secretion of pancreatic lipase through the pancreatic ducts and into the lumen of the small intestine, dietary fat was not absorbed at a normal rate, and steatorrhea (fat-rich stools) occurred. If abstinence from alcohol does not allow adequate recovery of the enzymatic secretory function of the pancreas, Mr. Martini will have to take a commercial preparation of pancreatic enzymes with meals that contain even minimal amounts of fat.

BIOCHEMICAL COMMENTS

Microsomal Triglyceride Transfer Protein. The assembly of chylomicrons within the endoplasmic reticulum (ER) of the enterocyte requires the activity of microsomal triglyceride transfer protein (MTP). The protein is a dimer of two nonidentical subunits. The smaller subunit (57 kDa) is protein disulfide isomerase (PDI; see Chapter 7, Section IX.A), whereas the larger subunit (97 kDa) contains the triglyceride transfer activity. MTP accelerates the transport of triglycerides, cholesterol esters, and phospholipids across membranes of subcellular organelles. The role of PDI in this complex is not known; the disulfide isomerase activity of this subunit is not needed for triglyceride transport to occur. The lack of triglyceride transfer activity leads to the disease **abetalipoproteinemia**. This disease affects both chylomicron assembly in the intestine and very low-density lipoprotein (VLDL) assembly in the liver. Both particles require a B apoprotein for their assembly (apoB-48 for chylomicrons, apoB-100 for VLDL), and MTP binds to the B apoproteins. For both chylomicron and VLDL assembly, a small apoB-containing particle is first produced within the lumen of the ER. The appropriate apoB is made on the rough endoplasmic reticulum (RER) and is inserted into the ER lumen during its synthesis (see Chapter 15, Section IX). As the protein is being translated, lipid (a small amount of triglyceride) begins to associate with the protein, and the lipid association is catalyzed by MTP. This leads to the generation of small apoB-containing particles; these particles are not formed in patients with abetalipoproteinemia. Thus, it appears that MTP activity is necessary to transfer triacylglycerol formed within the ER to the apoB protein. The second stage of particle assembly is the fusion of the initial apoB particle

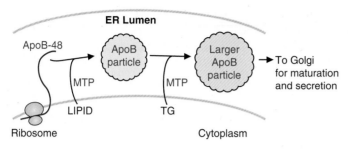

FIG. 32.14. A model of microsomal triglyceride transfer protein (MTP) action. MTP is required to transfer lipid to apoB-48 as it is synthesized and to transfer lipid from the cytoplasm to the lumen of the endoplasmic reticulum.

with triacylglycerol droplets within the ER. The role of MTP in this second step is still under investigation; it may be required for the transfer of triacylglycerol from the cytoplasm to the lumen of the ER to form this lipid droplet. These steps are illustrated in Figure 32.14.

The symptoms of abetalipoproteinemia include lipid malabsorption (and its accompanying symptoms such as steatorrhea and vomiting), which can result in caloric deficiencies and weight loss. Because lipid-soluble vitamin distribution occurs through chylomicron circulation, signs and symptoms of deficiencies in the lipid-soluble vitamins may be seen in these patients.

MTP inhibitors have been investigated and studied for their effect on circulating lipid and cholesterol levels. Although the inhibitors discovered to date are effective in lowering circulating lipid levels, they also initiate severe hepatic steatosis (fatty liver), an unacceptable complication that could lead to liver failure. The steatosis comes about by an accumulation of triglyceride in the liver because of the inability to form VLDL and export the triglyceride from the liver. The accumulation of triglyceride within hepatocytes will eventually interfere with hepatic function and structure. Current research for MTP inhibitors is aimed toward reducing the severity of fat accumulation in the liver (e.g., by specifically targeting the intestinal MTP without affecting the hepatic MTP).

Key Concepts

- Triacylglycerols are the major fat source in the human diet.
- Lipases (lingual lipase in the saliva and gastric lipase in the stomach) perform limited digestion of triacylglycerol before food enters the intestine.
- As food enters the intestine, cholecystokinin is released, which signals the gallbladder to release bile acids and the exocrine pancreas to release digestive enzymes.
- Within the intestine, bile salts emulsify fats, which increase their accessibility to pancreatic lipase and colipase.
- Triacylglycerols are degraded to form free fatty acids and 2-monoacylgylcerol by pancreatic lipase and colipase.
- Dietary phospholipids are hydrolyzed by pancreatic phospholipase A2 in the intestine.
- Dietary cholesterol esters (cholesterol esterified to a fatty acid) are hydrolyzed by pancreatic cholesterol esterase in the intestine.
- Micelles, consisting of bile acids and the products of fat digestion, form within the intestinal lumen and interact with the enterocyte membrane. Lipid-soluble components diffuse from the micelle into the cell.
- Bile salts are resorbed farther down the intestinal tract and returned to the liver by the enterohepatic circulation.
- The intestinal epithelial cells resynthesize triacylglycerol and package them into nascent chylomicrons for release into the circulation.
- Once they are in the circulation, the nascent chylomicrons interact with HDL particles and acquire two additional protein components: apoCII and apoE.

Table 32.1   Diseases Discussed in Chapter 32

Disease or Disorder	Environmental or Genetic	Comments
Sickle cell disease	Genetic	Cholecystitis may result as a consequence of sickle cell disease because of increased red cell destruction in the spleen, and an inability of the liver to conjugate all of the bilirubin resulting from heme degradation.
Alcoholism	Both	Pancreatitis may result from chronic alcohol abuse, leading to malabsorption problems within the intestine.

- ApoCII activates lipoprotein lipase on capillary endothelium of muscle and adipose tissue, which digests the triglycerides in the chylomicron. The fatty acids released from the chylomicron enter the muscle for energy production or the fat cell for storage. The glycerol released is metabolized only in the liver.
- As the chylomicron loses triglyceride, its density increases, and it becomes a chylomicron remnant. Chylomicron remnants are removed from circulation by the liver through specific binding of the remnant to apoE receptors on the liver membrane.
- Once it is in the liver, the remnant is degraded, and the lipids are recycled.
- Table 32.1 summarizes the diseases discussed in this chapter.

REVIEW QUESTIONS—CHAPTER 32

1. The most abundant component of chylomicrons is which of the following?

    A. apoB-48
    B. Triglyceride
    C. Phospholipid
    D. Cholesterol
    E. Cholesterol ester

2. The conversion of nascent chylomicrons to mature chylomicrons requires which of the following?

    A. Bile salts
    B. 2-Monoacylglycerol
    C. Lipoprotein lipase
    D. High-density lipoprotein
    E. Lymphatic system

3. The apoproteins B-48 and B-100 are similar with respect to which of the following?

    A. They are synthesized from the same gene.
    B. They are derived by alternative spicing of the same hnRNA.
    C. apoB-48 is a proteolytic product of apoB-100.
    D. Both are found in mature chylomicrons.
    E. Both are found in very low-density lipoproteins.

4. Bile salts must reach a particular concentration within the intestinal lumen before they are effective agents for lipid digestion. This is because of which of the following?

    A. The bile salt concentration must be equal to the triglyceride concentration.
    B. The bile salt solubility in the lumen is a critical factor.
    C. The ability of bile salts to bind lipase is concentration dependent.
    D. The bile salts cannot be reabsorbed in the ileum until they reach a certain concentration.
    E. The bile salts do not activate lipase until they reach a particular concentration.

5. Type III hyperlipidemia is caused by a deficiency of apoprotein E. Analysis of the serum of patients with this disorder would exhibit which of the following?

    A. An absence of chylomicrons after eating
    B. Higher than normal levels of VLDL after eating
    C. Normal triglyceride levels
    D. Elevated triglyceride levels
    E. Lower than normal triglyceride levels

33 Synthesis of Fatty Acids, Triacylglycerols, and the Major Membrane Lipids

Fatty acids are synthesized mainly in the liver in humans, with dietary glucose serving as the major source of carbon. Glucose is converted through glycolysis to pyruvate, which enters the mitochondrion and forms both acetyl coenzyme A (acetyl-CoA) and oxaloacetate (Fig. 33.1). These two compounds condense, forming citrate. Citrate is transported to the **cytosol**, where it is cleaved to form acetyl-CoA, the source of carbon for the reactions that occur on the **fatty acid synthase complex**. The key regulatory enzyme for the process, **acetyl-CoA carboxylase**, produces **malonyl-CoA** from acetyl-CoA.

The growing fatty acid chain, attached to the fatty acid synthase complex in the cytosol, is elongated by the sequential addition of two-carbon units provided by malonyl-CoA. **NADPH**, produced by the **pentose phosphate pathway** and the **malic enzyme**, provides **reducing equivalents**. When the growing fatty acid chain is 16 carbons in length, it is released as **palmitate**. After activation to a CoA derivative, palmitate can be elongated and desaturated to produce a series of fatty acids.

Fatty acids, produced in cells or obtained from the diet, are used by various tissues for the synthesis of **triacylglycerols** (the major storage form of fuel) and the **glycerophospholipids** and **sphingolipids** (the major components of cell membranes).

In the liver, triacylglycerols are produced from fatty acyl-CoA and glycerol 3-phosphate. **Phosphatidic acid** serves as an intermediate in this pathway. The triacylglycerols are not stored in the liver but rather packaged with apoproteins and other lipids in **very low-density lipoprotein (VLDL)** and secreted into the blood (see Fig. 33.1).

In the capillaries of various tissues (particularly adipose tissue, muscle, and the lactating mammary gland), **lipoprotein lipase (LPL)** digests the triacylglycerols of VLDL, forming **fatty acids** and **glycerol** (Fig. 33.2). The glycerol travels to the liver where it is used. Some of the fatty acids are oxidized by muscle and other tissues. After a meal, however, most of the fatty acids are converted to triacylglycerols in **adipose cells**, where they are **stored**. These fatty acids are released during fasting and serve as the predominant fuel for the body.

Glycerophospholipids are also synthesized from fatty acyl-CoA, which forms esters with glycerol 3-phosphate, producing phosphatidic acid. Various head groups are added to carbon 3 of the glycerol-3-phosphate moiety of phosphatidic acid, generating amphipathic compounds such as **phosphatidylcholine, phosphatidylinositol,** and **cardiolipin** (Fig. 33.3A). In the formation of **plasmalogens** and **platelet-activating factor (PAF)**, a long-chain fatty alcohol forms an **ether** with carbon 1, replacing the fatty acyl ester (see Fig. 33.3B). Cleavage of phospholipids is catalyzed by **phospholipases** found in cell membranes, lysosomes, and pancreatic juice.

Sphingolipids, which are prevalent in membranes and the myelin sheath of the central nervous system, are built on **serine** rather than glycerol. In the synthesis of sphingolipids, serine and palmitoyl-CoA condense, forming a

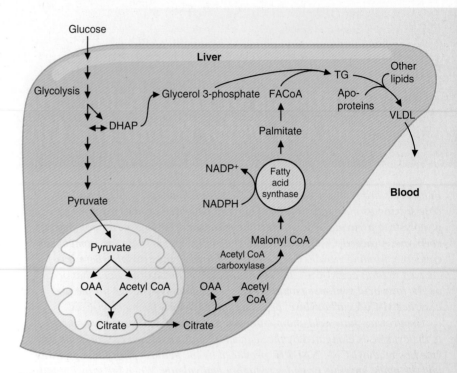

FIG. 33.1. Lipogenesis, the synthesis of triacylglycerols (TGs) from glucose. In humans, the synthesis of fatty acids from glucose occurs mainly in the liver. Fatty acids (*FAs*) are converted to *TG*, packaged in *VLDL*, and secreted into the blood. *OAA*, oxaloacetate.

*compound that is related to **sphingosine**. Reduction of this compound, followed by addition of a second fatty acid in amide linkage, produces **ceramide**. Carbohydrate groups attach to ceramide, forming **glycolipids** such as the **cerebrosides**, **globosides**, and **gangliosides** (see Fig. 33.3C). The addition of **phosphocholine** to ceramide produces **sphingomyelin**. These sphingolipids are degraded by lysosomal enzymes.*

FIG. 33.2. Fate of VLDL triacylglycerol (TG). The *TG* of *VLDL*, produced in the liver, is digested by lipoprotein lipase (*LPL*), present on the endothelial cells lining the capillaries in adipose and skeletal muscle tissue. Fatty acids are released and either oxidized or stored in tissues as *TG*. Glycerol is used by the liver because hepatocytes contain glycerol kinase. *FA*, fatty acid (or fatty acyl group).

FIG. 33.3.   **A.** General structure of a glycerophospholipid. The fatty acids are joined by ester bonds to the glycerol moiety. Various combinations of fatty acids may be present. The fatty acid at carbon 2 of the glycerol is usually unsaturated. The head group is the group attached to the phosphate on position 3 of the glycerol moiety. Choline is the most common head group, but ethanolamine, serine, inositol, or phosphatidylglycerol also may be present. The phosphate group is negatively charged, and the head group may carry a positive charge (choline and ethanolamine), or both a positive and a negative charge (serine). The inositol may be phosphorylated and thus negatively charged. **B.** General structure of a plasmalogen. Carbon 1 of glycerol is joined to a long-chain fatty alcohol by an ether linkage. The fatty alcohol group has a double bond between carbons 1 and 2. The head group is usually ethanolamine or choline. **C.** General structures of the sphingolipids. The "backbone" is sphingosine rather than glycerol. Ceramide is sphingosine with a fatty acid joined to its amino group by an amide linkage. Sphingomyelin contains phosphocholine, whereas glycolipids contain carbohydrate groups.

THE WAITING ROOM

The dietician did a careful analysis of **Percy Veere's** diet, which was indeed low in fat, adequate in protein, but excessive in carbohydrates, especially refined sugars. Percy's total caloric intake averaged about 430 kilocalories (kcal) a day in excess of his isocaloric requirements. This excess carbohydrate was being converted to fats, accounting for Percy's weight gain. A new diet with a total caloric content that would prevent further gain in weight was prescribed.

Cholesterol determinations in serum use a sequence of enzyme-coupled reactions. Cholesteryl esterase is used to release the fatty acids esterified to circulating cholesterol, producing free cholesterol. The second enzyme in the sequence, cholesterol oxidase, oxidizes cholesterol and reduces oxygen to form hydrogen peroxide. Horseradish peroxidase is then used to catalyze the conversion of a colorless dye to a colored dye via an oxidation–reduction reaction using the electrons from hydrogen peroxide. The intensity of the color obtained is directly proportional to the level of cholesterol in the sample.

Serum triglycerides can also be determined by enzymatic means. The serum sample is treated with a bacterial lipase, which cleaves triglyceride into three fatty acids plus glycerol. The glycerol is converted to glycerol 3-phosphate by glycerol kinase, and glycerophosphate oxidase will generate dihydroxyacetone phosphate and hydrogen peroxide. As with the cholesterol determination, the hydrogen peroxide is used as a reducing agent to convert a colorless dye to a colored dye, and the intensity of color produced is directly proportional to the amount of triglyceride in the sample. Because there is always free glycerol in serum samples, a blank is also run in which the lipase step is omitted. The blank value obtained is subtracted from the sample run in the presence of lipase.

Percy Veere's mental depression slowly responded to antidepressant medication, to the therapy sessions with his psychiatrist, and to frequent visits from an old high school sweetheart whose husband had died several years earlier. While he was hospitalized for malnutrition, Mr. Veere's appetite returned. By the time of discharge, he had gained back 8 of the 22 lb he had lost and weighed 133 lb.

During the next few months, Mr. Veere developed a craving for "sweet foods" such as the candy he bought and shared with his new friend. After 6 months of this high-carbohydrate courtship, Percy had gained another 22 lb and now weighed 155 lb, 8 lb more than he weighed when his depression began. He became concerned about the possibility that he would soon be overweight and consulted his dietitian, explaining that he had faithfully followed his low-fat diet but had "gone overboard" with carbohydrates. He asked whether it was possible to become fat without eating fat.

Cora Nari's hypertension and heart failure have been well controlled on medication, and she has lost 10 lb since she had her recent heart attack. Her fasting serum lipid profile before discharge from the hospital indicated a significantly elevated serum low-density lipoprotein (LDL) cholesterol level of 175 mg/dL (recommended level for a patient with known coronary artery disease is 100 mg/dL or less), a serum triacylglycerol level of 280 mg/dL (reference range, 60 to 150 mg/dL), and a serum high-density lipoprotein (HDL) cholesterol level of 34 mg/dL (reference range, >50 mg/dL for healthy women). While she was still in the hospital, she was asked to obtain the most recent serum lipid profiles of her older brother and her younger sister, both of whom were experiencing chest pain. Her brother's profile showed normal triacylglycerols, moderately elevated LDL cholesterol, and significantly suppressed HDL cholesterol levels. Her sister's profile showed only hypertriglyceridemia (high blood triacylglycerols).

Colleen Lakker was born 6 weeks prematurely. She appeared normal until about 30 minutes after delivery, when her respirations became rapid at 64 breaths per minute with audible respiratory grunting. The spaces between her ribs (intercostal spaces) retracted inward with each inspiration, and her lips and fingers became cyanotic from a lack of oxygen in her arterial blood. An arterial blood sample indicated a low partial pressure of oxygen (Po_2) and a slightly elevated partial pressure of carbon dioxide (Pco_2). The arterial pH was somewhat suppressed, in part, from an accumulation of lactic acid secondary to the hypoxemia (a low level of oxygen in her blood). A chest radiograph showed a fine reticular granularity of the lung tissue, especially in the left lower lobe area. From these clinical data, a diagnosis of respiratory distress syndrome (RDS), also known as hyaline membrane disease, was made.

Colleen was immediately transferred to the neonatal intensive care unit, where, with intensive respiration therapy, she slowly improved.

I. FATTY ACID SYNTHESIS

Fatty acids are synthesized whenever an excess of calories is ingested. The major source of carbon for the synthesis of fatty acids is dietary carbohydrate. An excess of dietary protein also can result in an increase in fatty acid synthesis. In this case, the carbon source is amino acids that can be converted to acetyl-CoA or tricarboxylic acid (TCA) cycle intermediates (see Chapter 39). Fatty acid synthesis occurs primarily in the liver in humans, although it can also occur, to a lesser extent, in adipose tissue.

When an excess of dietary carbohydrate is consumed, glucose is converted to acetyl-CoA, which provides the two-carbon units that condense in a series of reactions on the fatty acid synthase complex, producing palmitate (see Fig. 33.1). Palmitate is then converted to other fatty acids. The fatty acid synthase complex is located in the cytosol and, therefore, it uses cytosolic acetyl-CoA.

A. Conversion of Glucose to Cytosolic Acetyl-CoA

The pathway for the synthesis of cytosolic acetyl-CoA from glucose begins with glycolysis, which converts glucose to pyruvate in the cytosol (Fig. 33.4). Pyruvate enters mitochondria, where it is converted to acetyl-CoA by pyruvate dehydrogenase and to oxaloacetate by pyruvate carboxylase. The pathway that pyruvate follows is dictated by the acetyl-CoA levels in the mitochondria. When acetyl-CoA levels are high, pyruvate dehydrogenase is inhibited and pyruvate carboxylase activity is stimulated. As oxaloacetate levels increase because of the activity of pyruvate carboxylase, oxaloacetate condenses with acetyl-CoA to form citrate. This condensation reduces the acetyl-CoA levels, which leads to the activation of pyruvate dehydrogenase and inhibition of pyruvate carboxylase. Through such reciprocal regulation, citrate can be continuously synthesized and transported across the inner mitochondrial membrane. In the cytosol, citrate is cleaved by citrate lyase to re-form acetyl-CoA and oxaloacetate. This circuitous route is required because pyruvate dehydrogenase, the enzyme that converts pyruvate to acetyl-CoA, is found only in mitochondria and because acetyl-CoA cannot directly cross the mitochondrial membrane.

The NADPH required for fatty acid synthesis is generated by the pentose phosphate pathway (see Chapter 29) and from recycling of the oxaloacetate produced by citrate lyase (Fig. 33.5). Oxaloacetate is converted back to pyruvate in two steps: the reduction of oxaloacetate to malate by NAD^+-dependent malate dehydrogenase and the oxidation and decarboxylation of malate to pyruvate by an $NADP^+$-dependent malate dehydrogenase (malic enzyme) (Fig. 33.6). The pyruvate formed by malic enzyme is reconverted to citrate. The NADPH that is generated by malic enzyme, along with the NADPH generated by glucose-6-phosphate and gluconate-6-phosphate dehydrogenases in the pentose phosphate pathway, is used for the reduction reactions that occur on the fatty acid synthase complex (Fig. 33.7).

FIG. 33.4.   Conversion of glucose to cytosolic acetyl-CoA. *OAA*, oxaloacetate.

FIG. 33.5.   Fate of citrate in the cytosol. Citrate lyase is also called citrate cleavage enzyme. *OAA*, oxaloacetate; ↑, inducible enzyme.

FIG. 33.6.   Reaction catalyzed by malic enzyme. This enzyme is also called the decarboxylating or NADP-dependent malate dehydrogenase.

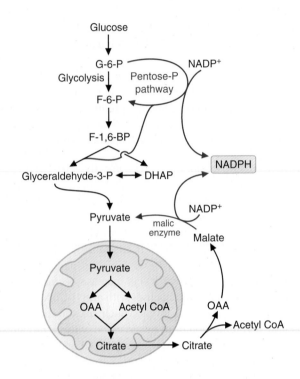

FIG. 33.7. Sources of NADPH for fatty acid synthesis. NADPH is produced by the pentose phosphate pathway and by malic enzyme. *F-1,6-BP*, fructose 1,6-bisphosphate; *F-6-P*, fructose 6-phosphate; *G-6-P*, glucose 6-phosphate; *OAA*, oxaloacetate.

The generation of cytosolic acetyl-CoA from pyruvate is stimulated by elevation of the insulin/glucagon ratio after a carbohydrate meal. Insulin activates pyruvate dehydrogenase by stimulating the phosphatase that dephosphorylates the enzyme to an active form (see Chapter 20). The synthesis of malic enzyme, glucose-6-phosphate dehydrogenase, and citrate lyase is induced by the high insulin/glucagon ratio. The ability of citrate to accumulate, and to leave the mitochondrial matrix for the synthesis of fatty acids, is attributable to the allosteric inhibition of isocitrate dehydrogenase by high energy levels within the matrix under these conditions. The concerted regulation of glycolysis and fatty acid synthesis is described in Chapter 36.

B. Conversion of Acetyl-CoA to Malonyl-CoA

Cytosolic acetyl-CoA is converted to malonyl-CoA, which serves as the immediate donor of the two-carbon units that are added to the growing fatty acid chain on the fatty acid synthase complex. To synthesize malonyl-CoA, acetyl-CoA carboxylase adds a carboxyl group to acetyl-CoA in a reaction that requires biotin and adenosine triphosphate (ATP) (Fig. 33.8).

Acetyl-CoA carboxylase is the rate-limiting enzyme of fatty acid synthesis. Its activity is regulated by phosphorylation, allosteric modification, and induction/repression of its synthesis (Fig. 33.9). Citrate allosterically activates acetyl-CoA carboxylase by causing the individual enzyme molecules (each composed of four subunits) to polymerize. Palmitoyl-CoA, produced from palmitate (the end product of fatty acid synthase activity), inhibits acetyl-CoA carboxylase. Phosphorylation by an adenosine monophosphate (AMP)-activated protein kinase inhibits the enzyme in the fasting state when energy levels are low. AMP is a much more sensitive indicator of low energy levels because of the adenylate kinase reaction. The [AMP]/[ATP] ratio is proportional to the square of the [ADP]/[ATP] ratio, so a fivefold change in adenosine diphosphate (ADP) levels corresponds to a 25-fold

FIG. 33.8. Reaction catalyzed by acetyl-CoA carboxylase. CO_2 is covalently attached to biotin, which is linked by an amide bond to the ϵ-amino group of a lysine residue of the enzyme. Hydrolysis of ATP is required for the attachment of CO_2 to biotin.

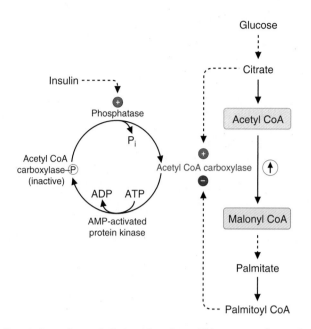

FIG. 33.9. Regulation of acetyl-CoA carboxylase. This enzyme is regulated allosteri-cally, both positively and negatively, by phosphorylation (Ⓟ) and dephosphorylation, and by diet-induced induction (⬆). It is active in the dephosphorylated state when citrate causes it to polymerize. Dephosphorylation is catalyzed by an insulin-stimulated phosphatase. Low energy levels, via activation of the AMP-activated protein kinase, cause the enzyme to be phosphorylated and inactivated. The ultimate product of fatty acid synthesis, palmitate, is converted to its CoA derivative, palmitoyl-CoA, which inhibits the enzyme. A high-calorie diet increases the rate of transcription of the gene for acetyl-CoA carboxylase, whereas a low-calorie diet reduces transcription of this gene.

change in AMP levels. Acetyl-CoA carboxylase is activated by dephosphorylation in the fed state when energy and insulin levels are high. A high insulin/glucagon ratio also results in induction of the synthesis of both acetyl-CoA carboxylase and the next enzyme in the pathway, fatty acid synthase.

C. Fatty Acid Synthase Complex

As an overview, fatty acid synthase sequentially adds two-carbon units from malonyl-CoA to the growing fatty acyl chain to form palmitate. After the addition of each two-carbon unit, the growing chain undergoes two reduction reactions that require NADPH.

Fatty acid synthase is a large enzyme composed of two identical subunits, which each have seven catalytic activities and an acyl carrier protein (ACP) segment in a continuous polypeptide chain. The ACP segment contains a phosphopantetheine residue that is derived from the cleavage of coenzyme A (Fig. 33.10). The two dimers associate in a head-to-tail arrangement, so that the phosphopantetheinyl sulfhydryl group on one subunit and a cysteinyl sulfhydryl group on another subunit are closely aligned.

In the *initial step* of fatty acid synthesis, an acetyl moiety is transferred from acetyl-CoA to the ACP phosphopantetheinyl sulfhydryl group of one subunit and then to the cysteinyl sulfhydryl group of the other subunit. The malonyl moiety from malonyl-CoA then attaches to the ACP phosphopantetheinyl sulf-hydryl group of the first subunit. The acetyl and malonyl moieties condense, with the release of the malonyl carboxyl group as CO_2. A four-carbon β-keto acyl chain is now attached to the ACP phosphopantetheinyl sulfhydryl group (Fig. 33.11).

FIG. 33.10. Phosphopantetheinyl residue of the fatty acid synthase complex. The portion derived from the vitamin, pantothenic acid, is indicated. Phosphopantetheine is covalently linked to a serine residue of the acyl carrier protein (ACP) segment of the enzyme. The sulf-hydryl group reacts with malonyl-CoA to form a thioester during the synthesis of fatty acids.

FIG. 33.11. Addition of a two-carbon unit to an acetyl group on fatty acid synthase. The malonyl group attaches to the phosphopantetheinyl residue (*P*) of the ACP of the fatty acid synthase. The acetyl group, which is attached to a cysteinyl sulfhydryl group, condenses with the malonyl group. CO_2 is released, and a 3-ketoacyl group is formed. The carbon that eventually forms the ω-methyl group of palmitate is labeled ω.

A series of three reactions first reduces the four-carbon keto group to an alcohol, then removes water to form a double bond, and lastly reduces the double bond (Fig. 33.12). NADPH provides the reducing equivalents for these reactions. The net result is that the original acetyl group is elongated by two carbons.

The four-carbon fatty acyl chain is then transferred to the cysteinyl sulfhydryl group and subsequently condenses with a malonyl group. This sequence of reactions is repeated until the chain is 16 carbons in length. At this point, hydrolysis occurs, and palmitate is released (Fig. 33.13).

Palmitate is elongated and desaturated to produce a series of fatty acids. In the liver, palmitate and other newly synthesized fatty acids are converted to triacylglycerols that are packaged into very low-density lipoprotein (VLDL) for secretion.

FIG. 33.12. Reduction of a β-ketoacyl group on the fatty acid synthase complex. NADPH is the reducing agent.

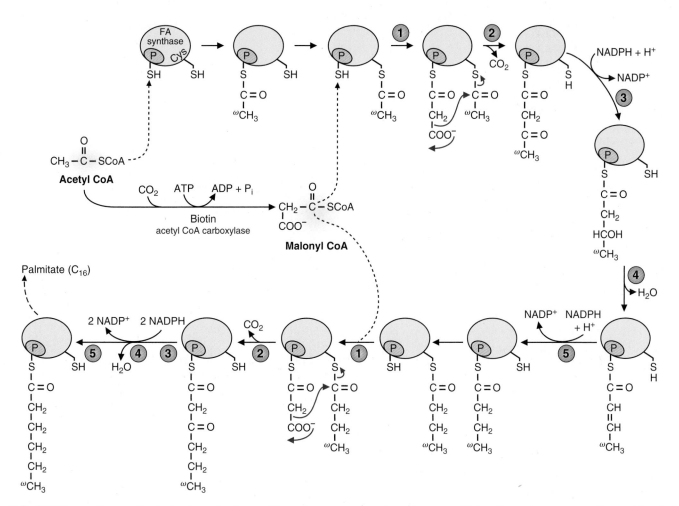

FIG. 33.13. Synthesis of palmitate on the fatty acid synthase complex. Initially, acetyl-CoA adds to the synthase. It provides the ω-methyl group of palmitate. Malonyl-CoA provides the two-carbon units that are added to the growing fatty acyl chain. The addition and reduction steps are repeated until palmitate is produced. *(1)* Transfer of the malonyl group to the phosphopantetheinyl residue. *(2)* Condensation of the malonyl and fatty acyl groups. *(3)* Reduction of the β-ketoacyl group. *(4)* Dehydration. *(5)* Reduction of the double bond. *P*, a phosphopantetheinyl group attached to the fatty acid synthase complex; *Cys-SH*, a cysteinyl residue on a different subunit of the fatty acid synthase.

In the liver, the oxidation of newly synthesized fatty acids back to acetyl-CoA via the mitochondrial β-oxidation pathway is prevented by malonyl-CoA. Carnitine: palmitoyl transferase I, the enzyme involved in the transport of long-chain fatty acids into mitochondria (see Chapter 23), is inhibited by malony-CoA (Fig. 33.14). Malonyl-CoA levels are elevated when acetyl-CoA carboxylase is activated, and thus fatty acid oxidation is inhibited while fatty acid synthesis is proceeding. This inhibition prevents the occurrence of a futile cycle.

Q: Where does the methyl group of the first acetyl-CoA that binds to fatty acid synthase appear in palmitate, the final product?

D. Elongation of Fatty Acids

After synthesis on the fatty acid synthase complex, palmitate is activated, forming palmitoyl-CoA. Palmitoyl-CoA and other activated long-chain fatty acids can be elongated, two carbons at a time, by a series of reactions that occur in the endoplasmic reticulum (Fig. 33.15). Malonyl-CoA serves as the donor of the two-carbon units, and NADPH provides the reducing equivalents. The series of elongation reactions resemble those of fatty acid synthesis except that the fatty acyl chain is attached to coenzyme A rather than to the phosphopantetheinyl residue of an ACP. The major elongation reaction that occurs in the body involves the conversion of

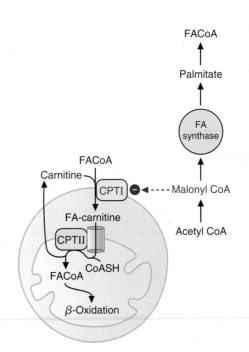

FIG. 33.14. Inhibition of carnitine: palmitoyl transferase (*CPTI*, also called carnitine: acyl transferase I) by malonyl-CoA. During fatty acid synthesis, malonyl-CoA levels are high. This compound inhibits *CPTI*, which is involved in the transport of long-chain fatty acids into mitochondria for β-oxidation. This mechanism prevents newly synthesized fatty acids from undergoing immediate oxidation.

palmitoyl-CoA (C16) to stearyl-CoA (C18). Very long-chain fatty acids (C22 to C24) are also produced, particularly in the brain.

E. Desaturation of Fatty Acids

Desaturation of fatty acids involves a process that requires molecular oxygen (O_2), NADH, and cytochrome b_5. The reaction, which occurs in the endoplasmic reticulum, results in the oxidation of both the fatty acid and NADH (Fig. 33.16). The most common desaturation reactions involve the placement of a double bond between carbons 9 and 10 in the conversion of palmitic acid to palmitoleic acid (16:1, Δ^9) and the conversion of stearic acid to oleic acid (18:1, Δ^9). Other positions that can be desaturated in humans include carbons 5 and 6.

Polyunsaturated fatty acids with double bonds, three carbons from the methyl end (ω3 fatty acids) and six carbons from the methyl end (ω6 fatty acids), are required for the synthesis of eicosanoids (see Chapter 35). Because humans cannot synthesize these fatty acids de novo (i.e., from glucose via palmitate), they must be present in the diet or the diet must contain other fatty acids that can be converted to these fatty acids. We obtain ω6 and ω3 polyunsaturated fatty acids mainly from dietary plant oils that contain the ω6 fatty acid linoleic acid (18:2, $\Delta^{9,12}$) and the ω3 fatty acid α-linolenic acid (18:3, $\Delta^{9,12,15}$). Linoleic and linolenic acids are thus considered essential fatty acids for the human diet. In the body, linoleic acid can be converted by elongation and desaturation reactions to arachidonic acid (20:4, $\Delta^{5,8,11,14}$), which is used for the synthesis of the major class of human prostaglandins and other eicosanoids (Fig. 33.17). Elongation and desaturation of α-linolenic acid produces eicosapentaenoic acid (EPA; 20:5, $\Delta^{5,8,11,14,17}$), which is the precursor of a different class of eicosanoids (see Chapter 35).

Plants are able to introduce double bonds into fatty acids in the region between C10 and the ω-end and, therefore, can synthesize ω3 and ω6 polyunsaturated fatty acids. Fish oils also contain ω3 and ω6 fatty acids, particularly EPA

FIG. 33.15. Elongation of long-chain fatty acids in the endoplasmic reticulum. The example shown is palmitoyl-CoA being extended to stearoyl-CoA.

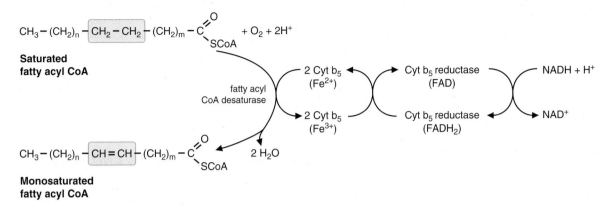

FIG. 33.16.   Desaturation of fatty acids. The process occurs in the endoplasmic reticulum and uses molecular oxygen. Both the fatty acid and NADH are oxidized. Human desaturases cannot introduce double bonds between carbon 9 and the methyl end. Therefore, m is equal to or less than 7.

(ω3, 20:5, $\Delta^{5,8,11,14,17}$) and docosahexaenoic acid (DHA; ω3, 22:6, $\Delta^{4,7,10,13,16,19}$). Fish obtain these fatty acids by eating phytoplankton (plants that float in water).

Arachidonic acid is listed in some textbooks as an essential fatty acid. Although it is an ω6 fatty acid, it is not essential in the diet if linoleic acid is present because arachidonic acid can be synthesized from dietary linoleic acid (see Fig. 33.17).

 The methyl group of acetyl-CoA becomes the ω-carbon (the terminal methyl group) of palmitate. Each new two-carbon unit is added to the carboxyl end of the growing fatty acyl chain (see Fig. 33.11).

FIG. 33.17.   Conversion of linoleic acid to arachidonic acid. Dietary linoleic acid (as linoleoyl-CoA) is desaturated at carbon 6, elongated by two carbons, and then desaturated at carbon 5 to produce arachidonyl-CoA.

The gene for glycerol kinase is located on the X chromosome close to the *DMD* gene (which codes for dystrophin) and the *NROB1* gene (which codes for a protein designated as *DAX1*). *DAX1* is critical for the development of the adrenal glands, pituitary, hypothalamus, and gonads. Complex glycerol kinase deficiency results from a contiguous deletion of the X chromosome, which deletes all or part of the glycerol kinase gene along with the *NROB1* gene and/or the *DMD* gene. The patient exhibits adrenal insufficiency, hyperglycerolemia, and, if the *DMD* gene is deleted, Duchenne muscular dystrophy.

Abetalipoproteinemia, which is caused by a lack of microsomal triglyceride transfer protein (MTP; see Chapter 32) activity, results in an inability to assemble both chylomicrons in the intestine and VLDL particles in the liver.

Why do some alcoholics have high VLDL levels?

The fact that several different abnormal lipoprotein profiles were found in **Cora Nari** and her siblings, and that each had evidence of coronary artery disease, suggests that Cora has familial combined hyperlipidemia (FCH). This diagnostic impression is further supported by the finding that Cora's profile of lipid abnormalities appeared to change somewhat from one determination to the next, a characteristic of FCH. This hereditary disorder of lipid metabolism is believed to be quite common, with an estimated prevalence of about 1 per 100 population.

The mechanisms for FCH are incompletely understood but may involve, in part, a genetically determined increase in the production of apoprotein B-100. As a result, packaging of VLDL is increased and blood VLDL levels may be elevated. Depending on the efficiency of lipolysis of VLDL by LPL, VLDL levels may be normal and LDL levels may be elevated, or both VLDL and LDL levels may be high. In addition, the phenotypic expression of FCH in any given family member may be determined by the degree of associated obesity, the diet, the use of specific drugs, or other factors that change over time. Additionally, FCH may be a multigenic trait, and even though the disease appears as an autosomal dominant trait in pedigree analysis, no genes have yet been definitively linked to this condition.

The essential fatty acid linoleic acid is required in the diet for at least two reasons: (1) It serves as a precursor of arachidonic acid from which eicosanoids are produced. (2) It covalently binds another fatty acid attached to cerebrosides in the skin, forming an unusual lipid (acylglucosylceramide) that helps to make the skin impermeable to water. This function of linoleic acid may help to explain the red, scaly dermatitis and other skin problems associated with a dietary deficiency of essential fatty acids.

II. SYNTHESIS OF TRIACYLGLYCEROLS AND VERY LOW-DENSITY LIPOPROTEIN PARTICLES

In liver and adipose tissue, triacylglycerols are produced by a pathway that contains a phosphatidic acid intermediate (Fig. 33.18). Phosphatidic acid is also the precursor of the glycerolipids found in cell membranes and the blood lipoproteins.

The sources of glycerol 3-phosphate, which provides the glycerol moiety for triacylglycerol synthesis, differ in liver and adipose tissue. In liver, glycerol 3-phosphate is produced from the phosphorylation of glycerol by glycerol kinase or from the reduction of dihydroxyacetone phosphate (DHAP) derived from glycolysis. White adipose tissue lacks glycerol kinase and can produce glycerol 3-phosphate only from glucose via DHAP. Thus, adipose tissue can store fatty acids only when glycolysis is activated, that is, in the fed state.

In both adipose tissue and liver, triacylglycerols are produced by a pathway in which glycerol 3-phosphate reacts with fatty acyl-CoA to form phosphatidic acid. Dephosphorylation of phosphatidic acid produces diacylglycerol. Another fatty acyl-CoA reacts with the diacylglycerol to form a triacylglycerol (see Fig. 33.18).

The triacylglycerol, which is produced in the smooth endoplasmic reticulum of the liver, is packaged with cholesterol, phospholipids, and proteins (synthesized in the rough endoplasmic reticulum) to form VLDL (Fig. 33.19, see Fig. 32.8). The microsomal triglyceride transfer protein (MTP), which is required for chylomicron assembly, is also required for VLDL assembly. The major protein of VLDL is apoB-100. There is one long apoB-100 molecule wound through the surface of each VLDL particle. ApoB-100 is encoded by the same gene as the apoB-48 of chylomicrons, but it is a longer protein (see Fig. 32.11). In intestinal cells, RNA editing produces a smaller messenger RNA (mRNA) and thus a shorter protein, apoB-48.

VLDL is processed in the Golgi complex and secreted into the blood by the liver (Figs. 33.20 and 33.21). The fatty acid residues of the triacylglycerols ultimately are stored in the triacylglycerols of adipose cells. Note that, in comparison to chylomicrons (see Chapter 32), VLDL particles are denser because they contain a lower percentage of triglyceride than do the chylomicrons. Similar to chylomicrons, VLDL particles are first synthesized in a nascent form, and on entering the circulation, they acquire apoproteins CII and E from HDL particles to become mature VLDL particles.

III. FATE OF THE VERY LOW-DENSITY LIPOPROTEIN TRIGLYCERIDE

Lipoprotein lipase (LPL), which is attached to the basement membrane proteoglycans of capillary endothelial cells, cleaves the triacylglycerols in both VLDL and chylomicrons, forming fatty acids and glycerol. Apoprotein CII, which these lipoproteins obtain from HDL, activates LPL. The low K_m of the muscle LPL isozyme permits muscle to use the fatty acids of chylomicrons and VLDL as a source of fuel even when the blood concentration of these lipoproteins is very low. The LPL isozyme in adipose tissue has a high K_m and is most active after

In alcoholism, NADH levels in the liver are elevated (see Chapter 25). High levels of NADH inhibit the oxidation of fatty acids. Therefore, fatty acids, mobilized from adipose tissue, are reesterified to glycerol 3-phosphate in the liver, forming triacylglycerols, which are packaged into VLDL and secreted into the blood. Elevated VLDL is frequently associated with chronic alcoholism. As alcohol-induced liver disease progresses, the ability to secrete the triacylglycerols is diminished, resulting in a fatty liver.

FIG. 33.18. Synthesis of triacylglycerol in liver and adipose tissue. Glycerol 3-phosphate is produced from glucose in both tissues. It is also produced from glycerol in liver but not in adipose tissue, which lacks glycerol kinase. The steps from glycerol 3-phosphate are the same in the two tissues. *FA*, fatty acyl group.

a meal, when blood levels of chylomicrons and VLDL are elevated. The fate of the VLDL particle after triglyceride has been removed by LPL is the generation of an IDL (intermediate-density lipoprotein) particle, which can further lose triglyceride to become an LDL particle. The fate of the IDL and LDL particles is discussed in Chapter 34.

FIG. 33.19. Composition of a typical VLDL particle. The major component is triacylglycerol (*TG*). *C*, cholesterol; *CE*, cholesterol ester; *PL*, phospholipid.

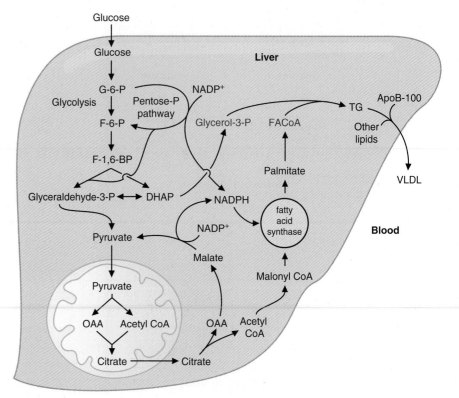

FIG. 33.20. Synthesis of VLDL from glucose in the liver. *G-6-P*, glucose 6-phosphate; *F-6-P*, fructose 6-phosphate; *F-1,6-BP*, fructose 1,6-bisphosphate; *FA*, fatty acyl group; *TG*, triacylglycerol.

IV. STORAGE OF TRIACYLGLYCEROLS IN ADIPOSE TISSUE

After a meal, the triacylglycerol stores of adipose tissue increase (Fig. 33.22). Adipose cells synthesize LPL and secrete it into the capillaries of adipose tissue when the insulin/glucagon ratio is elevated. This enzyme digests the triacylglycerols of both chylomicrons and VLDL. The fatty acids enter adipose cells and are

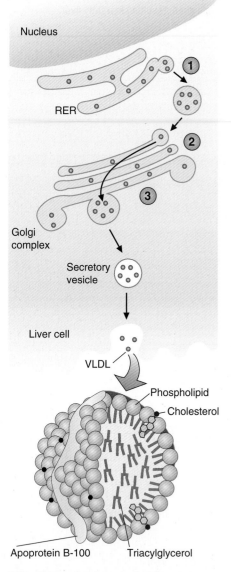

FIG. 33.21. Synthesis, processing, and secretion of VLDL. Proteins synthesized on the rough endoplasmic reticulum (*RER*) (*circle 1*) are packaged with triacylglycerols in the ER and Golgi complex to form VLDL (*circle 2*). VLDL are transported to the cell membrane in secretory vesicles (*circle 3*) and secreted by exocytosis. *Red circles* represent VLDL particles. An enlarged VLDL particle is depicted at the bottom of the figure.

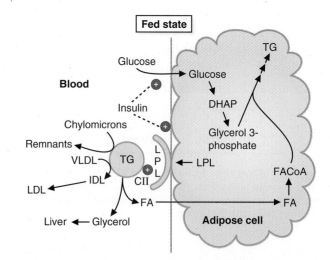

FIG. 33.22. Conversion of the fatty acid (*FA*) from the triacylglycerols (*TG*) of chylomicrons and VLDL to the *TG* stored in adipose cells. Note that insulin stimulates both the transport of glucose into adipose cells and the synthesis and secretion of lipoprotein lipase (*LPL*) from the cells. Glucose provides the glycerol 3-phosphate for *TG* synthesis. Apoprotein CII activates *LPL*.

activated, forming fatty acyl-CoA, which reacts with glycerol 3-phosphate to form triacylglycerol by the same pathway used in the liver (see Fig. 33.18). Because adipose tissue lacks glycerol kinase and cannot use the glycerol produced by LPL, the glycerol travels through the blood to the liver, which uses it for the synthesis of triacylglycerol. In adipose cells, under fed conditions, glycerol 3-phosphate is derived from glucose.

In addition to stimulating the synthesis and release of LPL, insulin stimulates glucose metabolism in adipose cells. Insulin leads to the activation of the glycolytic enzyme phosphofructokinase-1 by the activation of the kinase activity of phosphofructokinase-2, which increases fructose 2,6-bisphosphate levels. Insulin also stimulates the dephosphorylation of pyruvate dehydrogenase, so that the pyruvate produced by glycolysis can be oxidized in the TCA cycle. Furthermore, insulin stimulates the conversion of glucose to fatty acids in adipose cells, although the liver is the major site of fatty acid synthesis in humans.

V. RELEASE OF FATTY ACIDS FROM ADIPOSE TRIACYLGLYCEROLS

During fasting, the decrease of insulin and the increase of glucagon cause cyclic adenosine monophosphate (cAMP) levels to rise in adipose cells, stimulating lipolysis (Fig. 33.23). Protein kinase A phosphorylates hormone-sensitive lipase to produce a more active form of the enzyme. Hormone-sensitive lipase, also known as adipose triacylglycerol lipase, cleaves a fatty acid from a triacylglycerol. Subsequently, other lipases complete the process of lipolysis, and fatty acids and glycerol are released into the blood. Simultaneously, to regulate the amount of fatty acids released into circulation, triglyceride synthesis occurs along with glyceroneogenesis (see Section VI).

The fatty acids, which travel in the blood complexed with albumin, enter cells of muscle and other tissues, where they are oxidized to CO_2 and water to produce energy. During prolonged fasting, acetyl-CoA produced by β-oxidation of fatty

 Fatty acids for VLDL synthesis in the liver may be obtained from the blood or they may be synthesized from glucose. In a healthy individual, the major source of the fatty acids of VLDL triacylglycerol is excess dietary glucose. In individuals with diabetes mellitus, fatty acids mobilized from adipose triacylglycerols in excess of the oxidative capacity of tissues are a major source of the fatty acids reesterified in liver to VLDL triacylglycerol. These individuals frequently have elevated levels of blood triacylglycerols.

 Because the fatty acids of adipose triacylglycerols come both from chylomicrons and VLDL, we produce our major fat stores both from dietary fat (which produces chylomicrons) and dietary sugar (which produces VLDL). An excess of dietary protein also can be used to produce the fatty acids for VLDL synthesis. The dietician carefully explained to **Percy Veere** that we can become fat from eating excess fat, excess sugar, or excess protein.

 In some cases of hyperlipidemia, LPL is defective. If a blood lipid profile is performed on patients with an LPL deficiency, which lipids will be elevated?

FIG. 33.23. Mobilization of adipose triacylglycerol (*TG*). In the fasted state, when insulin levels are low and glucagon is elevated, intracellular cyclic adenosine monophosphate (cAMP) increases and activates protein kinase A, which phosphorylates hormone-sensitive lipase (HSL). Phosphorylated HSL is active and initiates the breakdown of adipose *TG*. Reesterification of fatty acids does occur, along with glyceroneogenesis, in the fasted state to regulate the release of fatty acids from the adipocyte. HSL is also called triacylglycerol lipase. *FA*, fatty acid.

Individuals with a defective LPL have high blood triacylglycerol levels. Their levels of chylomicrons and VLDL, which contain large amounts of triacylglycerols, are elevated because they are not digested at the normal rate by LPL.

acids in the liver is converted to ketone bodies, which are released into the blood. The glycerol derived from lipolysis in adipose cells is used by the liver during fasting as a source of carbon for gluconeogenesis.

VI. REGULATION OF FATTY ACID RELEASE BY GLYCERONEOGENESIS

Recently, another important mechanism that regulates free fatty acid release from the adipocyte has been described. Fatty acids within the adipocyte are also used to resynthesize triglyceride as a mechanism to limit fatty acid release into the circulation. Resynthesis of triglycerides (which is occurring at the same time that hormone-sensitive lipase is active) depends on an adequate supply of glycerol 3-phosphate, which is in turn dependent on adipose glyceroneogenesis (synthesis of new glycerol). Thus, within the adipocyte, hormone-sensitive lipase initiates the conversion of triglyceride to glycerol and three free fatty acids. The glycerol is sent to the liver for gluconeogenesis; however, within the adipocyte, glycerol 3-phosphate is synthesized from the carbons of amino acids, lactate, or pyruvate (Fig. 33.24). The key enzyme that allows this to occur is phosphoenolpyruvate carboxykinase (PEPCK), which is induced in the adipocyte by elevated cAMP levels (through the cAMP response element binding protein [CREB] family of transcription factors). Elevated adipocyte cAMP levels occur in response to glucagon or epinephrine, two signals that indicate the adipocyte should release fatty acids into the circulation. The pyruvate formed in the adipocyte from lactate is converted to oxaloacetate by pyruvate carboxylase. Amino acid carbons that are metabolized to TCA cycle intermediates are also converted to oxaloacetate. The oxaloacetate is converted to phosphoenolpyruvate (PEP) via the induced PEPCK, and the PEP follows the gluconeogenic pathway to DHAP, which is then reduced to glycerol 3-phosphate. The glycerol 3-phosphate is used to reesterify free fatty acids before they leave the adipocyte, thus modulating free fatty acid release by the fat cells. It has been demonstrated that as much as 30% to 40% of the released fatty acids are reesterified to triglyceride without ever leaving the adipocyte.

FIG. 33.24. Recycling of free fatty acids and the regeneration of glycerol 3-phosphate within the adipocyte under fasting conditions. *OAA*, oxaloacetate; *2PG*, 2-phosphoglycerate; *3PG*, 3-phosphoglycerate; *G3P*, glyceraldehyde 3-phosphate; *DHAP*, dihydroxyacetone phosphate; *TG*, triglyceride; *HSL*, hormone-sensitive lipase; *FFA*, free fatty acids; *PEPCK*, phosphoenolpyruvate carboxykinase.

Data to support the important role of glyceroneogenesis in modulating fatty acid release from the adipocyte have been obtained in mice. Mice that have been engineered so that they no longer express adipocyte PEPCK have reduced triglyceride levels and increased levels of serum free fatty acids (if PEPCK is not expressed, glyceroneogenesis will not occur, the levels of reesterification will be low, so increased levels of fatty acids will be released into the circulation). Mice that have been engineered to overproduce PEPCK have dysregulated glyceroneogenesis (too much reesterification) and are obese, with reduced free fatty acid release upon hormone-sensitive lipase activation. The role of glyceroneogenesis in overall lipid metabolism, and type 2 diabetes, is currently a subject of intense investigation.

VII. METABOLISM OF GLYCEROPHOSPHOLIPIDS AND SPHINGOLIPIDS

Fatty acids, obtained from the diet or synthesized from glucose, are the precursors of glycerophospholipids and of sphingolipids (Fig. 33.25). These lipids are major components of cellular membranes. Glycerophospholipids are also components of blood lipoproteins, bile, and lung surfactant. They are the source of the polyunsaturated fatty acids, particularly arachidonic acid, that serve as precursors of the eicosanoids (e.g., prostaglandins, thromboxanes, leukotrienes; see Chapter 35). Ether glycerophospholipids differ from other glycerophospholipids in that the alkyl or alkenyl chain (an alkyl chain with a double bond) is joined to carbon 1 of the glycerol moiety by an ether rather than an ester bond. Examples of ether lipids are the plasmalogens and platelet-activating factor (PAF). Sphingolipids are particularly important in signal transduction and in forming the myelin sheath surrounding nerves in the central nervous system.

In glycerolipids and ether glycerolipids, glycerol serves as the backbone to which fatty acids and other substituents are attached. Sphingosine, derived from serine, provides the backbone for sphingolipids.

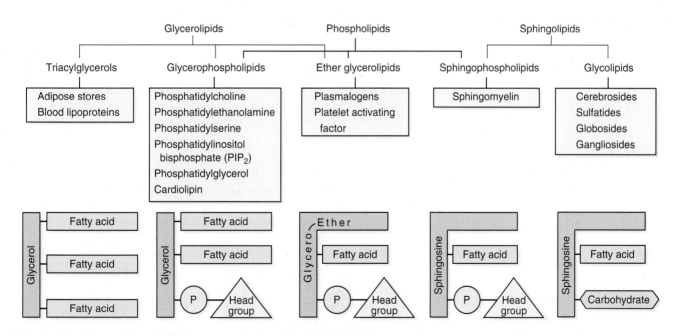

FIG. 33.25.   Types of glycerolipids and sphingolipids. Glycerolipids contain glycerol, and sphingolipids contain sphingosine. The category of phospholipids overlaps both glycerolipids and sphingolipids. The head groups include choline, ethanolamine, serine, inositol, glycerol, and phosphatidylglycerol. The carbohydrates are monosaccharides (which may be sulfated), oligosaccharides, and oligosaccharides with branches of *N*-acetylneuraminic acid. *P*, phosphate.

A. *Synthesis of Phospholipids Containing Glycerol*

1. GLYCEROPHOSPHOLIPIDS

The initial steps in the synthesis of glycerophospholipids are similar to those of triacylglycerol synthesis. Glycerol 3-phosphate reacts with two activated fatty acids to form phosphatidic acid. Two different mechanisms are then used to add a head group to the molecule (Fig. 33.26). A head group is a chemical group, such as choline or serine, attached to carbon 3 of a glycerol moiety that contains hydrophobic groups, usually fatty acids, at positions 1 and 2. Head groups are hydrophilic, either charged or polar. The head groups all contain a free hydroxyl group, which is used to link to the phosphate on carbon 3 of the glycerol backbone.

In the first mechanism, phosphatidic acid is cleaved by a phosphatase to form diacylglycerol (DAG). DAG then reacts with an activated head group. In the synthesis of phosphatidylcholine, the head group choline is activated by combining with cytidine triphosphate (CTP) to form cytidine diphosphate (CDP)-choline (Fig. 33.27). Phosphocholine is then transferred to carbon 3 of DAG, and cytidine monophosphate (CMP) is released. Phosphatidylethanolamine is produced by a similar reaction involving CDP-ethanolamine.

Various types of interconversions occur among these phospholipids (see Fig. 33.27). Phosphatidylserine is produced by a reaction in which the ethanolamine moiety of phosphatidylethanolamine is exchanged for serine. Phosphatidylserine can be converted back to phosphatidylethanolamine by a decarboxylation reaction. Phosphatidylethanolamine can be methylated to form phosphatidylcholine (see Chapter 40).

In the second mechanism for the synthesis of glycerolipids, phosphatidic acid reacts with CTP to form CDP-DAG (Fig. 33.28). This compound can react with phosphatidylglycerol (which itself is formed from the condensation of CDP-DAG and glycerol 3-phosphate) to produce cardiolipin or with inositol to produce phosphatidylinositol. Cardiolipin is a component of the inner mitochondrial membrane. Phosphatidylinositol can be phosphorylated to form phosphatidylinositol 4,5-bisphosphate (PIP_2), which is a component of cell membranes. In response to signals such as the binding of hormones to membrane receptors, PIP_2 can be cleaved to form the second messengers DAG and inositol triphosphate (IP_3) (see Chapter 11).

2. ETHER GLYCEROLIPIDS

The ether glycerolipids are synthesized from the glycolytic intermediate DHAP. A fatty acyl-CoA reacts with carbon 1 of DHAP, forming an ester (Fig. 33.29). This

Phosphatidylcholine (lecithin) is not required in the diet because it can be synthesized in the body. The components of phosphatidylcholine (including choline) all can be produced, as shown in Figure 33.27. A pathway for de novo choline synthesis from glucose exists, but the rate of synthesis is inadequate to provide for the necessary amounts of choline. Thus, choline has been classified as an essential nutrient, with an adequate intake (AI) of 425 mg/day in women and 550 mg/day in men.

Because choline is widely distributed in the food supply, primarily in phosphatidylcholine (lecithin), deficiencies have not been observed in humans on a normal diet. Deficiencies may occur, however, in patients on total parenteral nutrition (TPN), that is, supported solely by intravenous feeding. The fatty livers that have been observed in these patients probably result from a decreased ability to synthesize phospholipids for VLDL formation.

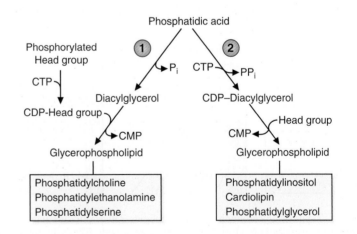

FIG. 33.26. Strategies for addition of the head group to form glycerophospholipids. In both cases, cytidine triphosphate (CTP) is used to drive the reaction.

FIG. 33.27. Synthesis of phosphatidylcholine, phosphatidylethanolamine, and phosphatidylserine. The multiple pathways reflect the importance of phospholipids in membrane structure. For example, phosphatidylcholine (PC) can be synthesized from dietary choline when it is available. If choline is not available, PC can be made from dietary carbohydrate, although the amount synthesized is inadequate to prevent choline deficiency. SAM is S-adenosylmethionine, a methyl group donor for many biochemical reactions (see Chapter 40).

FIG. 33.28. Synthesis of cardiolipin and phosphatidylinositol.

FIG. 33.29. Synthesis of a plasmalogen.

fatty acyl group is exchanged for a fatty alcohol, produced by reduction of a fatty acid. Thus, the ether linkage is formed. Then the keto group on carbon 2 of the DHAP moiety is reduced and esterified to a fatty acid. Addition of the head group proceeds by a series of reactions analogous to those for synthesis of phosphatidyl-choline. Formation of a double bond between carbons 1 and 2 of the alkyl group produces a plasmalogen. Ethanolamine plasmalogen is found in myelin and choline plasmalogen in heart muscle. PAF is similar to choline plasmalogen except that an acetyl group replaces the fatty acyl group at carbon 2 of the glycerol moiety, and the alkyl group on carbon 1 is saturated. PAF is released from phagocytic blood cells in response to various stimuli. It causes platelet aggregation, edema, and hypotension, and it is involved in the allergic response. Plasmalogen synthesis occurs within peroxisomes, and in individuals with Zellweger syndrome (a defect in peroxisome biogenesis), plasmalogen synthesis is compromised. If it is severe enough, this syndrome leads to death at an early age.

The respiratory distress syndrome (RDS) of a premature infant such as **Colleen Lakker** is, in part, related to a deficiency in the synthesis of a substance known as lung surfactant. The major constituents of surfactant are dipalmitoylphosphatidylcholine, phosphatidylglycerol, apoproteins (surfactant proteins: Sp-A, Sp-B, and Sp-C), and cholesterol.

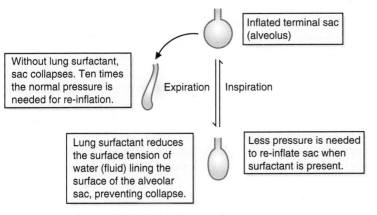

**Dipalmitoylphosphatidylcholine,
the major component of lung surfactant**

These components of lung surfactant normally contribute to a reduction in the surface tension within the air spaces (alveoli) of the lung, preventing their collapse. The premature infant has not yet begun to produce adequate amounts of lung surfactant.

The effect of lung surfactant

B. Degradation of Glycerophospholipids

Phospholipases located in cell membranes or in lysosomes degrade glycerophospholipids. Phospholipase A1 removes the fatty acyl group on carbon 1 of the glycerol moiety, and phospholipase A2 removes the fatty acid on carbon 2 (Fig. 33.30). The C2 fatty acid in cell membrane phospholipids is usually an unsaturated fatty acid, which is frequently arachidonic acid. It is removed in response to signals for the synthesis of eicosanoids. The bond joining carbon 3

FIG. 33.30. Bonds cleaved by phospholipases.

FIG. 33.31. Synthesis of ceramide. The changes that occur in each reaction are highlighted. *PLP,* pyridoxal phosphate.

of the glycerol moiety to phosphate is cleaved by phospholipase C. Hormonal stimuli activate phospholipase C, which hydrolyzes PIP_2 to produce the second messengers DAG and IP_3. The bond between the phosphate and the head group is cleaved by phospholipase D, producing phosphatidic acid and the free alcohol of the head group.

Phospholipase A2 provides the major repair mechanism for membrane lipids damaged by oxidative free radical reactions. Arachidonic acid, which is a polyunsaturated fatty acid, can be peroxidatively cleaved in free radical reactions to malondialdehyde and other products. Phospholipase A2 recognizes the distortion of membrane structure caused by the partially degraded fatty acid and removes it. Acyltransferases then add back a new arachidonic acid molecule.

C. Sphingolipids

Sphingolipids serve in intercellular communication and as the antigenic determinants of the ABO blood groups. Some are used as receptors by viruses and bacterial toxins, although it is unlikely that this was the purpose for which they originally evolved. Before the functions of the sphingolipids were elucidated, these compounds appeared to be inscrutable riddles. They were, therefore, named for the Sphinx of Thebes, who killed passersby who could not solve her riddle.

The synthesis of sphingolipids begins with the formation of ceramide (Fig. 33.31). Serine and palmitoyl-CoA condense to form a product that is reduced. A very long-chain fatty acid (usually containing 22 carbons) forms an amide with the amino group, a double bond is generated, and ceramide is formed.

Ceramide reacts with phosphatidylcholine to form sphingomyelin, a component of the myelin sheath (Fig. 33.32) and the only sphingosine-based phospholipid. Ceramide also reacts with uridine diphosphate (UDP)-sugars to form cerebrosides, which contain a single monosaccharide, usually galactose or glucose. Galactocerebroside may react with 3′-phosphoadenosine 5′-phosphosulfate (PAPS, an active sulfate donor; Fig. 33.33) to form sulfatides, the major sulfolipids of the brain.

Additional sugars may be added to ceramide to form globosides, and gangliosides are produced by the addition of *N*-acetylneuraminic acid (NANA) as branches from the oligosaccharide chains (see Fig. 33.32 and Chapter 30).

Sphingolipids are degraded by lysosomal enzymes (see Chapter 30). Deficiencies of these enzymes result in a group of lysosomal storage diseases known as the *sphingolipidoses.*

VIII. THE ADIPOCYTE AS AN ENDOCRINE ORGAN

It has become increasingly apparent in recent years that adipose tissue does more than just store triglyceride; it is also an active endocrine organ that secretes a variety of factors to regulate both glucose and fat metabolism. Two of the best characterized factors are leptin and adiponectin.

A. Leptin

Leptin was initially discovered in an obese mouse model as a circulating factor that, when added to a genetically obese mouse (ob/ob), resulted in a loss of weight. Leptin binds to a receptor that is linked to janus kinase (JAK) (see Chapter 11), so leptin's signal is transmitted by variations in the activity of the signal transducer and activator transcription (STAT) factors. Leptin is released from adipocytes as their triglyceride levels increase and binds to receptors in the hypothalamus, which leads to the release of neuropeptides that signal a cessation of eating (anorexigenic factors). Giving leptin to leptin-deficient patients will result in a weight loss, but administering leptin to obese patients does not have the same effect. It is believed that the lack of a leptin effect is caused by the development of leptin resistance in many obese patients. Leptin resistance could result from the constant stimulation

FIG. 33.32. Synthesis of sphingolipids from ceramide. Phosphocholine or sugars add to the hydroxymethyl group of ceramide (*in yellow box*) to form sphingomyelins, cerebrosides, sulfatides, globosides, and gangliosides. The ganglioside shown in the figure is GM2. *Gal*, galactose; *Glc*, glucose; *GalNAc*, N-acetylgalactosamine; *NANA*, N-acetylneuraminic acid.

of the leptin receptors in obese individuals, leading to receptor desensitization. Another possibility is leptin-induced synthesis of factors that block leptin-induced signal transduction. As an example, leptin induces the synthesis of SOCS3 (suppressor of cytokine signaling-3), a factor that antagonizes STAT activation. Long-term leptin stimulation may lead to constant expression of SOCS3, which would result in a diminished cellular response to leptin.

FIG. 33.33. The synthesis of 3′-phosphoadenosine 5′-phosphosulfate (PAPS), an active sulfate donor. PAPS donates sulfate groups to cerebrosides to form sulfatides and is also involved in glycosaminoglycan biosynthesis (see Chapter 49). *Ad*, adenine.

B. Adiponectin

Adiponectin is the most abundantly secreted hormone from the adipocyte. Unlike leptin, adiponectin secretion is reduced as the adipocyte gets larger. The reduced secretion of adiponectin may be linked to the development of insulin resistance in obesity (reduced cellular responses to insulin; see the Biochemical Comments for a further discussion of insulin resistance). Adiponectin will bind to either of two receptors (AdipoR1 and AdipoR2), which initiate a signal transduction cascade resulting in the activation of the AMP-activated protein kinase (AMPK) and activation of the nuclear transcription factor PPAR-α (peroxisome proliferator-activated receptor-α).

Within the muscle, activation of AMPK leads to enhanced fatty acid oxidation and glucose uptake. Within the liver, activation of AMPK also leads to enhanced fatty acid oxidation, as opposed to synthesis. AMPK activation in liver and muscle, then, leads to a reduction of blood glucose levels and free fatty acids. Recall that as the adipocytes increase in size, less adiponectin is released; therefore, as obesity occurs, it is more difficult for circulating fatty acids and glucose to be used by the tissues. This contributes, in part, to the elevated glucose and fat levels seen in the circulation of obese patients (the insulin resistance syndrome).

Activation of PPAR-α (see Chapter 46 for more details) leads to enhanced fatty acid oxidation by the liver and muscle. PPAR-α is the target of the fibrate group of lipid-lowering drugs. PPAR-α activation leads to increased transcription of genes involved in fatty acid transport, energy uncoupling, and fatty acid oxidation (for further information on the action of fibrates, see the Biochemical Comments in Chapter 34).

The thiazolidinedione group of antidiabetic drugs (such as pioglitazone) is used to control type 2 diabetes. These drugs bind to and activate PPAR-γ in adipose tissues and lead, in part, to increased adiponectin synthesis and release, which aids in reducing circulating fat and glucose levels.

CLINICAL COMMENTS

Percy Veere. If Percy Veere had continued to eat a hypercaloric diet rich in carbohydrates, he would have become obese. In an effort to define obesity, it has been agreed internationally that the ratio of the patient's body weight in kilograms to his or her height in meters squared (W/H^2) is the most useful and reproducible measure. This ratio is referred to as the *body mass index* (BMI). Normal men and women fall into the range of 18.5 to 25. Percy's current value is 21.3 and rising.

It is estimated that more than 30% of adults in the United States have a BMI of >30, with more than 60% exhibiting a BMI of >25. For individuals with a BMI of >27, which is quite close to a weight 20% above the "ideal" or desirable weight, an attempt at weight loss should be strongly advised. The idea that obesity is a benign condition unless it is accompanied by other risk factors for cardiovascular disease is disputed by several long-term, properly controlled prospective studies. These studies show that obesity is an independent risk factor not only for heart attacks and strokes, but also for the development of insulin resistance, type 2 diabetes mellitus, hypertension, and gallbladder disease.

Percy did not want to become overweight and decided to follow his new diet faithfully.

Cora Nari. Because Cora Nari's lipid profile indicated an elevation in both serum triacylglycerols and LDL cholesterol, she was classified as having a combined hyperlipidemia. The dissimilarities in the lipid profiles of Cora and her two siblings, both of whom were experiencing anginal chest pain, are characteristic of the multigenic syndrome referred to as *familial combined hyperlipidemia* (FCH).

Approximately 1% of the North American population has FCH. It is the most common cause of coronary artery disease in the United States. In contrast to patients with familial hypercholesterolemia (FH), patients with FCH do not have fatty deposits within the skin or tendons (xanthomas) (see Chapter 34). In FCH, coronary artery disease usually appears by the fifth decade of life.

Treatment of FCH includes restriction of dietary fat. Patients who do not respond adequately to dietary therapy are treated with antilipidemic drugs. Selection of the appropriate antilipidemic drugs depends on the specific phenotypic expression of the patients' multigenic disease as manifested by their particular serum lipid profile. In Cora's case, a decrease in both serum triacylglycerols and LDL cholesterol must be achieved. If possible, her serum HDL cholesterol level should also be raised to a level >50 mg/dL.

To accomplish these therapeutic goals, her physician initially prescribed a statin (pravastatin) and fast-release nicotinic acid (niacin) because these agents have the potential to lower serum triacylglycerol levels and cause a reciprocal rise in serum HDL cholesterol levels, as well as complementing the statin in lowering serum total and LDL cholesterol levels. The mechanisms suggested for niacin's triacylglycerol-lowering action include enhancement of the action of LPL, inhibition of lipolysis in adipose tissue, and a decrease in esterification of triacylglycerols in the liver (see Chapter 34, Table 34.5). The mechanism by which niacin lowers the serum total and LDL cholesterol levels is related to the decrease in hepatic production of VLDL. When the level of VLDL in the circulation decreases, the production of its daughter particles, IDL and LDL, also decreases. Cora found niacin's side effects of flushing and itching to be intolerable so the drug was discontinued.

Statins, such as pravastatin, inhibit cholesterol synthesis by inhibiting the activity of hydroxymethylglutaryl-CoA (HMG-CoA) reductase, the rate-limiting enzyme in the pathway (see Chapter 34). After 3 months of therapy, pravastatin decreased Cora's LDL cholesterol from a pretreatment level of 175 mg/dL to 122 mg/dL (still higher than the recommended treatment goal of 100 mg/dL or less in a patient with established coronary artery disease). Her fasting serum triacylglycerol concentration was decreased from a pretreatment level of 280 mg/dL to 178 mg/dL (a treatment goal for serum triacylglycerol when the pretreatment level is <500 mg/dL has not been established). In patients with diabetes, the goal is to bring the triacylglycerol level to 150 mg/dL or less.

 Colleen Lakker. Colleen Lakker suffered from respiratory distress syndrome (RDS), which is a major cause of death in the newborn. RDS is preventable if prematurity can be avoided by appropriate management of high-risk pregnancy and labor. Before delivery, the obstetrician must attempt to predict and possibly treat pulmonary prematurity in utero. For example, estimation of fetal head circumference by ultrasonography, monitoring for fetal arterial oxygen saturation, and determination of the ratio of the concentrations of phosphatidylcholine (lecithin) and that of sphingomyelin in the amniotic fluid may help to identify premature infants who are predisposed to RDS (Fig. 33.34).

The administration of synthetic corticosteroids 48 to 72 hours before delivery of a fetus of <33 weeks of gestation in women who have toxemia of pregnancy, diabetes mellitus, or chronic renal disease may reduce the incidence or mortality of RDS by stimulating fetal synthesis of lung surfactant.

The administration of one dose of surfactant into the trachea of the premature infant immediately after birth may transiently improve respiratory function but does not improve overall mortality. In Colleen's case, intensive therapy allowed her to survive this acute respiratory complication of prematurity.

FIG. 33.34. Comparison of phosphatidylcholine and sphingomyelin in amniotic fluid. Phosphatidylcholine is the major lipid in lung surfactant. The concentration of phosphatidylcholine relative to sphingomyelin rises at 35 weeks of gestation, indicating pulmonary maturity.

BIOCHEMICAL COMMENTS

Metabolic Syndrome. Obesity is a relatively modern problem brought about by an excess of nutrients and reduced physical activity. As individuals become obese, adipocyte function, in terms of its biochemical and endocrine roles, is altered. Adiponectin levels fall, and with it, reduced fatty acid oxidation occurs in tissues. The release of free fatty acids is also increased in large adipocytes, presumably because of the high concentration of substrate (triglyceride), even if hormone-sensitive lipase is not activated. This is coupled with a deficiency of perilipins in obese individuals. Perilipins are adipocyte phosphoproteins that bind to triacylglycerol droplets and regulate the accessibility of the triglyceride to the lipases. A decrease in perilipin synthesis leads to an enhanced basal rate of lipolysis.

Fat cells begin to proliferate early in life, starting in the third trimester of gestation. Proliferation essentially ceases before puberty, and thereafter fat cells change mainly in size. However, some increase in the number of fat cells can occur in adulthood if preadipocytes are induced to proliferate by growth factors and changes in the nutritional state. Weight reduction results in a decrease in the size of fat cells rather than a decrease in number. After weight loss, the amount of LPL, an enzyme involved in the transfer of fatty acids from blood triacylglycerols to the triacylglycerol stores of adipocytes, increases. In addition, the amount of mRNA for LPL also increases. All of these factors suggest that individuals who become obese, particularly those who do so early in life, will have difficulty losing weight and maintaining a lower body adipose mass.

Signals that initiate or inhibit feeding are extremely complex and include psychologic and hormonal factors as well as neurotransmitter activity. These signals are integrated and relayed through the hypothalamus. Destruction of specific regions of the hypothalamus can lead to overeating and obesity or to anorexia and weight loss. Overeating and obesity are associated with damage to the ventromedial or the paraventricular nucleus, whereas weight loss and anorexia are related to damage to more lateral hypothalamic regions. Compounds that act as satiety signals have been identified in brain tissue and include leptin and glucagonlike peptide-1 (GLP-1). Appetite suppressors developed from compounds such as these may be used in the future for the treatment of obesity.

Increased circulating levels of nonesterified (or free) fatty acids (NEFAs) are observed in obesity and is associated with insulin resistance. Insulin resistance is also a hallmark of type 2 diabetes. There are several theories about why increased NEFA promote insulin resistance. One will be presented here, along with the effects of NEFA on insulin release from the pancreas. As NEFA levels in the circulation rise, muscle begins to use predominantly NEFA as an energy source. This reduces muscle glucose metabolism, as a result of the buildup of acetyl-CoA in the mitochondria, export of citrate to the cytoplasm, and inhibition of PFK-1. Because glucose is not being metabolized, its uptake by muscle is reduced. As muscle is the predominant tissue that takes up glucose in response to insulin, impaired glucose uptake (resulting from fat oxidation) is manifested as a sign of insulin resistance. NEFA are also postulated to interfere with pancreatic β-cell secretion of insulin, further contributing to insulin resistance (see the following text for more on this topic).

Obesity, insulin resistance, and altered blood lipid levels are the start of a syndrome known as *metabolic syndrome*. Metabolic syndrome is diagnosed based on the recommendations of the National Cholesterol Education Program (NCEP) Adult Treatment Panel III (ATP III), with minor modifications. For a diagnosis of metabolic syndrome, at least three of the following components should be evident:

- Increased waist circumference (40 in or more for men, 35 in or more for women)
- Elevated triglycerides ($\geq$150 mg/dL)
- Reduced HDL (<40 mg/dL for men, <50 mg/dL for women)
- Elevated blood pressure ($\geq$130/85 mm Hg)
- Elevated fasting glucose ($\geq$100 mg/dL)

Individuals with metabolic syndrome are at increased risk for type 2 diabetes and cardiovascular disease. Treatment, in addition to lifestyle changes to reduce weight, increase exercise, and change diet, will be discussed further in Chapter 34.

A characteristic of the metabolic syndrome is insulin resistance. Part of this resistance is caused by altered insulin release from the β-cells of the pancreas under hyperlipidemic conditions. To understand how this occurs, it is necessary to revisit normal glucose-stimulated insulin secretion (see Fig. 26.11).

Glucose is metabolized in the pancreatic β-cell to generate ATP, which closes ATP-sensitive K^+ channels, which leads to a membrane depolarization, which activates voltage-gated Ca^{2+} channels in the membrane. The corresponding increase in intracellular calcium levels leads to stimulation of the exocytosis of insulin-containing vesicles. However, the process is more complicated than this and is coupled to pyruvate cycling within the β-cell and the generation of NADPH. The exact role of NADPH in stimulating insulin release has not yet been elucidated.

Islet cells express pyruvate carboxylase, but very low levels of PEPCK. As can be seen in Figure 33.35, NADPH is generated in the cytosol of the islets cells by malic enzyme and the cytosolic isozyme of isocitrate dehydrogenase, which uses $NADP^+$ instead of NAD^+, as the mitochondrial enzyme does.

Thus, under normal conditions, glucose is metabolized to pyruvate, and the pyruvate enters the mitochondrion. Some of the pyruvate is converted to acetyl-CoA to generate energy; some of the pyruvate is converted to oxaloacetate. The oxaloacetate generated can be converted to malate and exported to the cytoplasm, where it is recycled to pyruvate by malic enzyme, generating NADPH. Alternatively, the oxaloacetate and acetyl-CoA generated within the mitochondria can condense and form citrate, isocitrate, and α-ketoglutarate, all of which can leave the mitochondria and enter the cytosol. Cytosolic isocitrate is oxidized to α-ketoglutarate, generating NADPH. Cytosolic citrate is split by citrate lyase to acetyl-CoA and oxaloacetate, and the oxaloacetate is reduced to malate and cycled to pyruvate, generating more NADPH. The cytosolic acetyl-CoA is used for limited fatty acid production in the islet cell. The elevated cytosolic NADPH then aids, in an unknown manner, in the release of insulin from the β-cell.

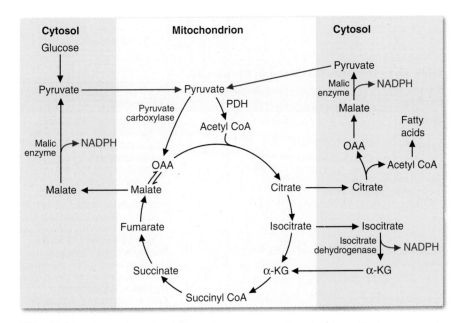

FIG. 33.35. Generation of NADPH via pyruvate cycling in islet cells in response to glucose. Details are provided in the text. (Adapted from Muoio DM, Newgard CB. Obesity-related derangements in metabolic regulation. *Annu Rev Biochem.* 2006;75:367–401.)

So what goes wrong when β-cells are chronically exposed to high levels of NEFA in the circulation? The β-cell begins to oxidize the fatty acids, which dramatically raises the acetyl-CoA levels in the β-cell mitochondria. This leads to the activation of pyruvate carboxylase and enhanced pyruvate cycling, with significant increases in resting NADPH levels. This then leads to blunted increases in NADPH levels when glucose levels increase, as pyruvate cycling is already maximal because of the activation of pyruvate carboxylase. Thus, the β-cell releases less insulin in response to the increase in blood glucose levels, thereby contributing further to hyperglycemia that was initiated by the resistance to insulin's action in peripheral tissues.

Key Concepts

- Fatty acids are synthesized mainly in the liver, primarily from glucose.
- Glucose is converted to pyruvate via glycolysis, which enters the mitochondrion and forms both acetyl-CoA and oxaloacetate, which then forms citrate.
- The newly synthesized citrate is transported to the cytosol, where it is cleaved to form acetyl-CoA, which is the source of carbons for fatty acid biosynthesis.
- Two enzymes, acetyl-CoA carboxylase (the key regulatory step) and fatty acid synthase, produce palmitic acid (16 carbons, no double bonds) from acetyl-CoA. After activation to palmitoyl-CoA, the fatty acid can be elongated or desaturated (adding double bonds) by enzymes in the endoplasmic reticulum.
- Fatty acids are used to produce triacylglycerols (for energy storage) and glycerophospholipids and sphingolipids (for structural components of cell membranes).
- Liver-derived triacylglycerol is packaged with various apoproteins and secreted into the circulation as VLDL.
- As with dietary chylomicrons, LPL in the capillaries of adipose tissue, muscle, and the lactating mammary gland digests the triacylglycerol of VLDL, forming fatty acids and glycerol.
- Glycerophospholipids, synthesized from fatty acyl-CoA and glycerol 3-phosphate, are all derived from phosphatidic acid. Various head groups are added to phosphatidic acid to form the mature glycerophospholipids.
- Phospholipid degradation is catalyzed by phospholipases.
- Sphingolipids are synthesized from sphingosine, which is derived from palmitoyl-CoA and serine. Glycolipids, such as cerebrosides, globosides, and gangliosides, are sphingolipids.
- The sole sphingosine-based phospholipid is sphingomyelin.
- The adipocyte is an active endocrine organ, producing adipokines that help to regulate appetite and adipocyte size.
- Metabolic syndrome refers to a clustering of a variety of metabolic abnormalities that together dramatically increase the risk of type 2 diabetes and cardiovascular disease.
- Diseases discussed in this chapter are summarized in Table 33.1.

Table 33.1   Diseases Discussed in Chapter 33

Disease or Disorder	Environmental or Genetic	Comments
Obesity	Both	Weight gain will occur from excessive calorie consumption: fat can be derived from carbohydrates, protein, and triglyceride in the diet
Heart disease, familial combined hyperlipidemia (FCH)	Both	FCH, leading to elevated cholesterol and triglyceride levels in the serum. Levels of lipid in the blood, and symptoms displayed by patients, will vary from patient to patient.
Respiratory distress syndrome	Both	Inability of lungs to properly expand and contract due to lack of surfactant, a complex mixture of lipids and apoproteins
Abetalipoproteinemia	Genetic	Lack of microsomal triglyceride transport protein, leading to reduced production of VLDL and chylomicrons within the liver and intestine, respectively

1. Which of the following is involved in the synthesis of triacylglycerols in adipose tissue?

    A. Fatty acids obtained from chylomicrons and VLDL
    B. Glycerol 3-phosphate derived from blood glycerol
    C. 2-Monoacylglycerol as an obligatory intermediate
    D. LPL to catalyze the formation of ester bonds
    E. Acetoacetyl-CoA as an obligatory intermediate

2. A molecule of palmitic acid, attached to carbon 1 of the glycerol moiety of a triacylglycerol, is ingested and digested. The fatty acid is stored in a fat cell and ultimately is oxidized to carbon dioxide and water in a muscle cell. Choose the molecular complex in the blood in which the palmitate residue is carried from the lumen of the gut to the surface of the gut epithelial cell.

    A. VLDL
    B. Chylomicron
    C. Fatty acid–albumin complex
    D. Bile salt micelle
    E. LDL

3. A patient with hyperlipoproteinemia would be most likely to benefit from a low-carbohydrate diet if the lipoproteins that are elevated in blood are which of the following?

    A. Chylomicrons
    B. VLDL
    C. HDL
    D. LDL
    E. IDL

4. Which of the following is a characteristic of sphingosine?

    A. It is converted to ceramide by reacting with a UDP-sugar.
    B. It contains a glycerol moiety.
    C. It is synthesized from palmitoyl-CoA and serine.
    D. It is a precursor of cardiolipin.
    E. It is only synthesized in neuronal cells.

5. Newly synthesized fatty acids are not immediately degraded because of which of the following?

    A. Tissues that synthesize fatty acids do not contain the enzymes that degrade fatty acids.
    B. High NADPH levels inhibit β-oxidation.
    C. In the presence of insulin, the key fatty acid degrading enzyme is not induced.
    D. Newly synthesized fatty acids cannot be converted to their CoA derivatives.
    E. Transport of fatty acids into mitochondria is inhibited under conditions in which fatty acids are being synthesized.

34 Cholesterol Absorption, Synthesis, Metabolism, and Fate

*Cholesterol is one of the most well-recognized molecules in human biology, in part because of the direct relationship between its concentrations in blood and tissues and the development of **atherosclerotic vascular disease**. Cholesterol, which is transported in the blood in **lipoproteins** because of its absolute insolubility in water, serves as a **stabilizing component of cell membranes** and as a precursor of the **bile salts** and **steroid hormones**. Precursors of cholesterol are converted to **ubiquinone, dolichol**, and, in the skin, to **cholecalciferol, the active form of vitamin D**. As a **major component of blood lipoproteins**, cholesterol can appear in its free, unesterified form in the outer shell of these macromolecules and as cholesterol esters in the lipoprotein core.*

*Cholesterol is obtained from the diet or synthesized by a pathway that occurs in most cells of the body, but to a greater extent in cells of the liver and intestine. The precursor for cholesterol synthesis is **acetyl coenzyme A (acetyl-CoA)**, which can be produced from glucose, fatty acids, or amino acids. Two molecules of acetyl-CoA form **acetoacetyl-CoA**, which condenses with another molecule of acetyl-CoA to form **hydroxymethylglutaryl-CoA (HMG-CoA)**. Reduction of HMG-CoA produces **mevalonate**. This reaction, catalyzed by **HMG-CoA reductase**, is the major rate-limiting step of cholesterol synthesis. Mevalonate produces isoprene units that condense, eventually forming **squalene**. Cyclization of squalene produces the steroid ring system, and several subsequent reactions generate cholesterol. The adrenal cortex and the gonads also synthesize cholesterol in significant amounts and use it as a precursor for steroid hormone synthesis.*

*Cholesterol is packaged in **chylomicrons** in the intestine and in **very low-density lipoprotein (VLDL)** in the liver. It is transported in the blood in these lipoprotein particles, which also transport triacylglycerols. As the triacylglycerols of the blood lipoproteins are digested by lipoprotein lipase, chylomicrons are converted to **chylomicron remnants**, and VLDL is converted to **intermediate-density lipoprotein (IDL)** and subsequently to **low-density lipoprotein (LDL)**. These products return to the liver, where they bind to receptors in cell membranes and are taken up by endocytosis and digested by lysosomal enzymes. LDL is also endocytosed by nonhepatic (peripheral) tissues. Cholesterol and other products of lysosomal digestion are released into the cellular pools. The liver uses this recycled cholesterol, and the cholesterol that is synthesized from acetyl-CoA, to produce VLDL and to synthesize bile salts.*

*Intracellular cholesterol obtained from blood lipoproteins decreases the synthesis of cholesterol within cells, stimulates the storage of cholesterol as cholesterol esters, and decreases the synthesis of **LDL receptors**. LDL receptors are found on the surface of the cells and bind various classes of lipoproteins before endocytosis.*

*Although **high-density lipoprotein (HDL)** contains triacylglycerols and cholesterol, its function is very different from that of the chylomicrons and VLDL, which transport triacylglycerols. HDL exchanges proteins and lipids with the other lipoproteins in the blood. HDL transfers **apolipoprotein E (apo E) and*** *apolipoprotein CII (apo CII)* to chylomicrons and VLDL. After digestion of the VLDL triacylglycerols, apo E and apo CII are transferred back to HDL. In addition, HDL obtains cholesterol from other lipoproteins and from cell membranes and converts it to **cholesterol esters** by the **lecithin-cholesterol acyltransferase (LCAT)** reaction. Then HDL either directly transports cholesterol and cholesterol esters to the liver or transfers cholesterol esters to other lipoproteins via the **cholesterol ester transfer protein (CETP)**. Ultimately, lipoprotein particles carry the cholesterol and cholesterol esters to the liver, where endocytosis and lysosomal digestion occur. Thus, **reverse cholesterol transport** (i.e., the return of cholesterol to the liver) is a major function of HDL.

Elevated levels of cholesterol in the blood are associated with the formation of **atherosclerotic plaques** that can occlude blood vessels, causing heart attacks and strokes. Although high levels of LDL cholesterol are especially atherogenic, high levels of HDL cholesterol are protective because HDL particles are involved in the process of removing cholesterol from tissues, such as the lining cells of vessels, and returning it to the liver.

Bile salts, which are produced in the liver from cholesterol obtained from the blood lipoproteins or synthesized from acetyl-CoA, are secreted into the bile. They are stored in the gallbladder and released into the intestine during a meal. The bile salts emulsify dietary triacylglycerols, thus aiding in digestion. The digestive products are absorbed by intestinal epithelial cells from bile salt micelles, tiny microdroplets that contain bile salts at their water interface. After the contents of the micelles are absorbed, most of the bile salts travel to the ileum, where they are resorbed and recycled by the liver. Less than 5% of the bile salts that enter the lumen of the small intestine are eventually excreted in the feces.

Although the fecal excretion of bile salts is relatively low, it is a major means by which the body disposes of the steroid nucleus of cholesterol. Because the ring structure of cholesterol cannot be degraded in the body, it is excreted mainly in the bile as free cholesterol and bile salts.

The steroid hormones, derived from cholesterol, include the adrenal cortical hormones (e.g., cortisol, aldosterone, and the adrenal sex steroids dehydroepiandrosterone [DHEA] and androstenedione) and the gonadal hormones (e.g., the ovarian and testicular sex steroids, such as testosterone and estrogen).

THE WAITING ROOM

At his next office visit, **Ivan Applebod's** case was reviewed by his physician. Mr. Applebod has several of the major risk factors for coronary heart disease (CHD). These include a sedentary lifestyle, marked obesity, hypertension, hyperlipidemia, and early type 2 diabetes. Unfortunately, he has not followed his doctor's advice with regard to a diabetic diet designed to effect a significant loss of weight, nor has he followed an aerobic exercise program. As a consequence, his weight has gone from 270 to 281 lb. After a 14-hour fast, his serum glucose is now 214 mg/dL (normal, <100 mg/dL), and his serum total cholesterol level is 314 mg/dL (desired level is ≤200 mg/dL). His serum triacylglycerol level is 295 mg/dL (desired level is ≤150 mg/dL), and his serum high-density lipoprotein (HDL) cholesterol is 24 mg/dL (desired level is ≥40 mg/dL for a man). His calculated serum low-density lipoprotein (LDL) cholesterol level is 231 mg/dL (desired level for a person with two or more risk factors for CHD is ≤130 mg/dL, unless

Until recently, the concentration of low-density lipoprotein (LDL) cholesterol could only be directly determined by sophisticated laboratory techniques not available for routine clinical use. As a consequence, the LDL cholesterol concentration in the blood was derived indirectly by using the Friedewald formula: the sum of the high-density lipoprotein (HDL) cholesterol level and the triacylglycerol (TG) level divided by 5 (which gives an estimate of the VLDL cholesterol level) subtracted from the total cholesterol level:

$$LDL\ cholesterol = total\ cholesterol$$
$$- [HDL\ cholesterol$$
$$+ (TG/5)]$$

This equation yields inaccurate LDL cholesterol levels 15% to 20% of the time and fails completely when serum triacylglycerol levels are >400 mg/dL.

A recently developed test called *LDL direct* isolates LDL cholesterol by using a special immunoseparation reagent. Not only is this direct assay for LDL cholesterol more accurate than the indirect Friedewald calculation, it also is not affected by mildly to moderately elevated serum triacylglycerol levels and can be used for a patient who has not fasted. It does not require the expense of determining serum total cholesterol, HDL cholesterol, and triacylglycerol levels.

Table 34.1   ATP III: LDL-C Goals and Cut Points for Therapy in Different Risk Categories

Risk Category	LDL Goal (mg/dL)	LDL Level at Which to Initiate Therapeutic Lifestyle Changes (mg/dL)	LDL Level at Which to Consider Drug Therapy (mg/dL)
CHD or CHD risk equivalents (10-year risk >20%)	<100	≥100	≥130 (100–129: drug optional)
2+ risk factors (10-year risk ≤20%)	<130	≥130	10-year risk 10%–20%: ≥130 10-year risk <10%: ≥160
0–1 risk factor	<160	≥160	≥190 (160–189: LDL-lowering drug optional)

LDL-C, low-density lipoprotein cholesterol; CHD, coronary heart disease. These values are expected to be updated in the fall of 2011. See http://www.nhlbi.nih.gov/guidelines/cholesterol/atp4/index.htm
Source: Executive summary of the National Cholesterol Education Program. Third report of the National Cholesterol Education Programs (NCEP) Expert Panel on Detection, Evaluation, and Treatment of High Blood Cholesterol in Adults (Adult Treatment Panel III). Final report. *Circulation.* 2002;106:3145–3457.

one of the risk factors is diabetes mellitus, in which case the LDL cholesterol level should be <100 mg/dL). Mr. Applebod exhibits sufficient criteria to be classified as having metabolic syndrome.

Ann Jeina was carefully followed by her physician after she survived her heart attack. Before she was discharged from the hospital, after a 14-hour fast, her serum triacylglycerol level was 158 mg/dL (slightly above the upper range of normal), and her HDL cholesterol level was low at 32 mg/dL (normal for women is ≥50 mg/dL). Her serum total cholesterol level was elevated at 420 mg/dL (reference range is ≤200 mg/dL for a woman with known CHD). From these values, her LDL cholesterol level was calculated to be 356 mg/dL (desirable level for a person with established heart disease is <100 mg/dL).

Both of Ms. Jeina's younger brothers had "very high" serum cholesterol levels, and both had suffered heart attacks in their midforties. With this information, a tentative diagnosis of familial hypercholesterolemia, type IIA, was made, and the patient was started on a step I diet as recommended by the National Cholesterol Education Program (NCEP) Adult Treatment Panel III. This panel recommends that decisions with regard to when dietary and drug therapy should be initiated based on the serum LDL cholesterol level, as detailed in Table 34.1.

Because a step I diet (Table 34.2) usually lowers serum total and LDL cholesterol levels by no more than 15%, Ms. Jeina was also started on a potent statin, atorvastatin, as she had already experienced a myocardial infarction, and her LDL is greater than 30 points above the recommended level.

Table 34.2   Dietary Therapy for Elevated Blood Cholesterol

Nutrient	Step I Diet	Step II Diet[a]
Cholesterol[b]	<300 mg/d	<200 mg/d
Total fat	≤30%[b]	30%
Saturated fat	8%–10%	<7%
Polyunsaturated fat	≤10%	≤10%
Monounsaturated fat	≤15%	≤15%
Carbohydrates	≥55%	≥55%
Protein	~15%	~15%
Calories	To achieve and maintain desirable body weight	

[a]The step II diet is applied if 3 months on the step I diet has failed to reduce blood cholesterol to the desired level (see Table 34.1).
[b]Except for the values given in milligram per day, all values are percentage of total calories eaten daily.
Source: Based on National Cholesterol Education Program. Summary of the second report of the National Cholesterol Education Program (NCEP) Expert Panel on Detection, Evaluation, and Treatment of High Blood Cholesterol in Adults (Adult Treatment Panel II). *JAMA.* 1993;269(23):3015–3023.

Vera Leizd is a 34-year-old woman in whom pubertal changes began at age 12, leading to the development of normal secondary sexual characteristics and the onset of menses at age 13. Her menstrual periods occurred on a monthly basis over the next 7 years, but the flow was scant. At age 20, she noted a gradual increase in her intermenstrual interval from her normal of 28 days to 32 to 38 days. The volume of her menstrual flow also gradually diminished. After 7 months, her menstrual periods ceased. She complained of increasing oiliness of her skin, the appearance of acnelike lesions on her face and upper back, and the appearance of short, dark terminal hairs on the mustache and sideburn areas of her face. The amount of extremity hair also increased, and she noticed a disturbing loss of hair from her scalp.

I. INTESTINAL ABSORPTION OF CHOLESTEROL

Cholesterol absorption by intestinal cells is a key regulatory point in human sterol metabolism because it ultimately determines what percentage of the 1,000 mg of biliary cholesterol produced by the liver each day, and what percentage of the 300 mg of dietary cholesterol entering the gut per day is eventually absorbed into the blood. In normal subjects, approximately 55% of this intestinal pool enters the blood through the enterocyte each day. The details of cholesterol absorption from dietary sources were outlined in Chapter 32.

Although the absorption of cholesterol from the intestinal lumen is a diffusion-controlled process, there is also a mechanism to remove unwanted or excessive cholesterol and plant sterols from the enterocyte. The transport of sterols out of the enterocyte and into the gut lumen is related to the products of genes that code for the adenosine triphosphate (ATP)-binding cassette (*ABC*) protein family, specifically *ABCG5* and *ABCG8*. These proteins couple ATP hydrolysis to the transport of unwanted or excessive cholesterol and plant sterols (phytosterols) from the enterocyte back into the gut lumen. Another member of the *ABC* family, *ABCA1*, is required for reverse cholesterol transport and the biogenesis of HDL. Cholesterol cannot be metabolized to carbon dioxide and water and is, therefore, eliminated from the body principally in the feces as unreabsorbed sterols and bile acids. *ABC* protein expression increases the amount of sterols present in the gut lumen, with the potential to increase elimination of the sterols into the feces. Patients with a condition known as phytosterolemia (a rare autosomal recessive disease, also known as *sitosterolemia*) have a defect in the function of either *ABCG5* or *ABCG8* in the enterocytes, which leads to accumulation of cholesterol and phytosterols within these cells. These eventually reach the bloodstream, markedly elevating the level of cholesterol and phytosterol in the blood. This accounts for the increased cardiovascular morbidity in individuals with this disorder. From these experiments of nature, it is clear that agents that either amplify the expression of the *ABC* proteins within enterocytes or that block cholesterol absorption from the lumen have therapeutic potential in the treatment of patients with hypercholesterolemia. *Ezetimibe* is a compound that is structurally different from the sterols. Its primary action in lowering serum cholesterol levels is to block cholesterol absorption through a specific but as yet poorly characterized cholesterol absorption mechanism in the brush border of enterocytes. The target of ezetimibe is the Niemann–Pick C1-like 1 protein (NPC1L1), which is believed to transport cholesterol into cells via an absorptive endocytotic mechanism, involving the protein clathrin. The reduction of cholesterol absorption from the intestinal lumen has been shown to reduce blood levels of LDL cholesterol, particularly when used with a drug that also blocks endogenous cholesterol synthesis.

II. CHOLESTEROL SYNTHESIS

Cholesterol is an alicyclic compound whose basic structure includes the perhydro-cyclopentanophenanthrene nucleus containing four fused rings (Fig. 34.1). In its "free" form, the cholesterol molecule contains 27 carbon atoms, a simple hydroxyl

Q: What effect would be predicted for ezetimibe on endogenous cholesterol synthesis?

FIG. 34.1. The basic ring structure of sterols; the perhydrocyclopentanophenanthrene nucleus. Each ring is labeled *A*, *B*, *C*, or *D*.

If less cholesterol is obtained from diet, then cellular cholesterol synthesis would be upregulated. Thus, ezetimibe has a better chance of reducing whole body cholesterol levels when endogenous cholesterol synthesis is also inhibited, than in the absence of such inhibition.

FIG. 34.2. The structure of cholesterol.

group at C3, a double bond between C5 and C6, an eight-membered hydrocarbon chain attached to carbon 17 in the D-ring, a methyl group (carbon 19) attached to carbon 10, and a second methyl group (carbon 18) attached to carbon 13 (Fig. 34.2).

Approximately one-third of plasma cholesterol exists in the free (or unesterified) form. The remaining two-thirds exist as cholesterol esters in which a long-chain fatty acid (usually linoleic acid) is attached by ester linkage to the hydroxyl group at C3 of the A-ring. The proportions of free and esterified cholesterol in the blood can be measured using methods such as high-performance liquid chromatography (HPLC).

The structure of cholesterol suggests that its synthesis involves multimolecular interactions and significant reducing power. All 27 carbons are derived from one precursor, acetyl-CoA. Acetyl-CoA can be obtained from several sources, including the β-oxidation of fatty acids, the oxidation of ketogenic amino acids such as leucine and lysine, and the pyruvate dehydrogenase reaction. The reducing power for cholesterol synthesis is supplied in the form of NADPH. The latter is provided by glucose-6-phosphate dehydrogenase and 6-phosphogluconate dehydrogenase of the hexose monophosphate shunt pathway (see Chapter 29). Cholesterol synthesis occurs in the cytosol, requiring hydrolysis of high-energy thioester bonds of acetyl-CoA and phosphoanhydride bonds of ATP. Its synthesis occurs in four stages.

FIG. 34.3. The conversion of three molecules of acetyl-CoA to mevalonic acid.

A. Stage 1: Synthesis of Mevalonate from Acetyl-CoA

The first stage of cholesterol synthesis leads to the production of the intermediate mevalonate (Fig. 34.3). The synthesis of mevalonate is the committed, rate-limiting step in cholesterol formation. In this cytoplasmic pathway, two molecules of acetyl-CoA condense, forming acetoacetyl-CoA, which then condenses with a third molecule of acetyl-CoA to yield the six-carbon compound β-hydroxy-β-methylglutaryl-CoA (HMG-CoA). The HMG-CoA synthase in this reaction is present in the cytosol and is distinct from the mitochondrial HMG-CoA synthase that catalyses HMG-CoA synthesis involved in production of ketone bodies. The committed step and major point of regulation of cholesterol synthesis in stage 1 involves reduction of HMG-CoA to mevalonate, a reaction that is catalyzed by HMG-CoA reductase, an enzyme embedded in the membrane of the endoplasmic reticulum. HMG-CoA reductase contains eight membrane-spanning domains, and the amino-terminal domain, which faces the cytoplasm, contains the enzymatic activity. The reducing equivalents for this reaction are donated by two molecules of NADPH. The regulation of the activity of HMG-CoA reductase is controlled in multiple ways.

Ann Jeina's serum total and LDL cholesterol levels improved only modestly after 3 months on a step I diet and the statin. Three additional months on a more severe low-fat diet (step II diet) brought little further improvement.

1. TRANSCRIPTIONAL CONTROL

The rate of synthesis of HMG-CoA reductase messenger RNA (mRNA) is controlled by one of the family of sterol-regulatory element-binding proteins (SREBPs)

FIG. 34.4. Regulation of HMG-CoA reductase activity. See text for details and abbreviations. **A.** Transcriptional control. **B.** Regulation by proteolysis. **C.** Regulation by phosphorylation.

(Fig. 34.4A). These transcription factors belong to the basic helix–loop–helix leucine zipper (bHLH-Zip) family of transcription factors that directly activate the expression of more than 30 genes dedicated to the synthesis and uptake of cholesterol, fatty acids, triacylglycerols, and phospholipids as well as the production of the NADPH cofactors required to synthesize these molecules.

SREBPs specifically enhance transcription of the HMG-CoA reductase gene by binding to the sterol-regulatory element (SRE) upstream of the gene. When bound, the rate of transcription is increased. SREBPs, after synthesis, are integral proteins of the endoplasmic reticulum (ER). The SREBP is bound to SCAP (*S*REBP *c*leavage-*a*ctivating *p*rotein) in the ER membrane when cholesterol levels are high. When cholesterol levels drop, the sterol leaves its SCAP-binding site, and the SREBP:SCAP complex is transported to the Golgi apparatus. Within the Golgi, two proteolytic cleavages occur (via the site 1 [S1P] and site 2 [S2P] proteases), which release the N-terminal transcription factor domain from the Golgi membrane. Once released, the active amino terminal component travels to the nucleus to bind to SREs. The soluble SREBPs are rapidly turned over and need to be continuously produced to stimulate reductase mRNA transcription effectively. When cytoplasmic sterol levels rise, the sterols bind to SCAP and prevent translocation of the complex to the Golgi, leading to a decrease in transcription of the reductase gene and thus less reductase protein being produced.

2. PROTEOLYTIC DEGRADATION OF HMG-COA REDUCTASE

Rising levels of cholesterol and bile salts in cells that synthesize these molecules also may cause a change in the oligomerization state of the membrane domain of HMG-CoA reductase, rendering the enzyme more susceptible to proteolysis (see Fig. 34.4B). This, in turn, decreases its activity. The membrane domains of HMG-CoA reductase contain sterol-sensing regions, which are similar to those in SCAP.

3. REGULATION BY COVALENT MODIFICATION

In addition to the inductive and repressive influences we have mentioned, the activity of the reductase is also regulated by phosphorylation and dephosphorylation (see Fig. 34.4C). Elevated glucagon levels increase phosphorylation of the enzyme, thereby inactivating it, whereas hyperinsulinemia increases the activity of the reductase by activating phosphatases, which dephosphorylate the reductase. Increased levels of intracellular sterols also may increase phosphorylation of HMG-CoA reductase, thereby reducing its activity as well (feedback suppression). Thyroid hormone also increases enzyme activity, whereas glucocorticoids decrease its activity. The enzyme that phosphorylates HMG-CoA reductase is the adenosine monophosphate (AMP)-activated protein kinase, which itself is regulated by phosphorylation by one of several AMP-activated protein kinase kinases (one of which is LKB1, described further in the following text). Thus, cholesterol synthesis decreases when ATP levels are low and increases when ATP levels are high, similar to what occurs with fatty acid synthesis (recall that acetyl-CoA carboxylase is also phosphorylated and inhibited by the AMP-activated protein kinase). The need for ATP in cholesterol biosynthesis will be evident as the further reactions of the pathway are discussed.

B. Stage 2: Conversion of Mevalonate to Two Activated Isoprenes

In the second stage of cholesterol synthesis, three phosphate groups are transferred from three molecules of ATP to mevalonate (Fig. 34.5). The purpose of these phosphate transfers is to activate both carbon 5 and the hydroxyl group on carbon 3 for further reactions in which these groups will participate. The phosphate group attached to the C3 hydroxyl group of mevalonate in the 3-phospho-5-pyrophosphomevalonate intermediate is removed along with the carboxyl group on C1. This produces a double bond in the five-carbon product, Δ^3-isopentenyl pyrophosphate, the first of two activated isoprenes that are necessary for the synthesis of cholesterol. The second activated isoprene is formed when Δ^3-isopentenyl pyrophosphate is isomerized to dimethylallyl pyrophosphate (see Fig. 34.5). Isoprenes, in addition to being used for cholesterol biosynthesis, are also used in the synthesis of coenzyme Q and dolichol.

C. Stage 3: Condensation of Six Activated Five-Carbon Isoprenes to Form the 30-Carbon Squalene

The next stage in the biosynthesis of cholesterol involves the head-to-tail condensation of isopentenyl pyrophosphate and dimethylallyl pyrophosphate. The "head" in this case refers to the end of the molecule to which pyrophosphate is linked. In this reaction, the pyrophosphate group of dimethylallyl pyrophosphate is displaced, and a 10-carbon chain, known as *geranyl pyrophosphate*, is generated (Fig. 34.6). Geranyl pyrophosphate then undergoes another head-to-tail condensation with isopentenyl pyrophosphate, resulting in the formation of the 15-carbon intermediate, farnesyl pyrophosphate. After this, two molecules of farnesyl pyrophosphate undergo a head-to-head fusion, and both pyrophosphate groups are removed to form squalene, a compound that was first isolated from the liver of sharks (genus *Squalus*). Squalene contains 30 carbons (24 in the main chain and 6 in the methyl group branches; see Fig. 34.6).

Geranyl pyrophosphate and farnesyl pyrophosphate are key components in cholesterol biosynthesis, and both farnesyl and geranyl groups can form covalent bonds with proteins, particularly the G proteins and certain proto-oncogene products involved in signal transduction. These hydrophobic groups anchor the proteins in the cell membrane.

FIG. 34.5. The formation of activated isoprene units (Δ^3-isopentenyl pyrophosphate and dimethylallyl pyrophosphate) from mevalonic acid. Note the large ATP requirement for these steps.

D. Stage 4: Conversion of Squalene to the Four-Ring Steroid Nucleus

The enzyme squalene monooxygenase adds a single oxygen atom from O_2 to the end of the squalene molecule, forming an epoxide. NADPH then reduces the other oxygen atom of O_2 to H_2O. The unsaturated carbons of the squalene 2,3-epoxide are aligned in a way that allows conversion of the linear squalene epoxide into a cyclic structure. The cyclization leads to the formation of lanosterol, a sterol with the four-ring structure characteristic of the steroid nucleus. A series of complex reactions,

FIG. 34.6. The formation of squalene from six isoprene units. The activation of the isoprene units drives their condensation to form geranyl pyrophosphate, farnesyl pyrophosphate, and squalene.

FIG. 34.7. The conversion of squalene to cholesterol. Squalene is shown in a different conformation than in Figure 34.6 to indicate better how the cyclization reaction occurs.

containing many steps and elucidated in the late 1950s, leads to the formation of cholesterol (Fig. 34.7).

III. SEVERAL FATES OF CHOLESTEROL

Almost all mammalian cells are capable of producing cholesterol. Most of the biosynthesis of cholesterol occurs within liver cells, although the gut, the adrenal cortex, and the gonads (as well as the placenta in pregnant women) also produce significant quantities of the sterol. A fraction of hepatic cholesterol is used for the synthesis of hepatic membranes, but the bulk of synthesized cholesterol is secreted from the hepatocyte as one of three moieties: cholesterol esters, biliary cholesterol (cholesterol found in the bile), or bile acids. Cholesterol ester production in the liver is catalyzed by acyl-CoA–cholesterol acyl transferase (ACAT). ACAT catalyzes the transfer of a fatty acid from coenzyme A to the hydroxyl group on carbon 3 of cholesterol (Fig. 34.8). Cholesterol esters are more hydrophobic than is free cholesterol. The liver packages some of the esterified cholesterol into the hollow core of lipoproteins, primarily VLDL. VLDL is secreted from the hepatocyte into the blood and transports the cholesterol esters (triacylglycerols, phospholipids, apoproteins, etc.) to the tissues that require greater amounts of cholesterol than they can synthesize de novo. These tissues then use the cholesterol for the synthesis of membranes, for the formation of steroid hormones, and for the biosynthesis of vitamin D. The residual cholesterol esters not used in these ways are stored in the liver for later use.

The hepatic cholesterol pool serves as a source of cholesterol for the synthesis of the relatively hydrophilic bile acids and their salts (see Chapter 32). These derivatives of cholesterol are very effective detergents because they contain both polar and nonpolar regions. They are introduced into the biliary ducts of the liver. They are stored and concentrated in the gallbladder and later discharged into the gut in response to the ingestion of food. They aid in the digestion of intraluminal lipids by forming micelles with them, which increases the surface area of lipids exposed to the digestive action of intraluminal lipases. Free cholesterol also enters the gut lumen via the biliary tract (approximately 1,000 mg daily, which mixes with 300 mg of dietary cholesterol to form an intestinal pool, roughly 55% of which is resorbed by the enterocytes and enters the bloodstream daily). On a low-cholesterol diet, the liver synthesizes approximately 800 mg of cholesterol per day to replace bile salts and cholesterol lost from the enterohepatic circulation into the feces. Conversely, a greater intake of dietary cholesterol suppresses the rate of hepatic cholesterol synthesis (feedback repression).

IV. SYNTHESIS OF BILE SALTS

A. Conversion of Cholesterol to Cholic Acid and Chenocholic Acid

Bile salts are synthesized in the liver from cholesterol by reactions that hydroxylate the steroid nucleus and cleave the side chain. In the first and rate-limiting reaction, an α-hydroxyl group is added to carbon 7 (on the α side of the B-ring). The activity of the 7-α-hydroxylase that catalyzes this step is decreased by an increase in bile salt concentration (Fig. 34.9).

In subsequent steps, the double bond in the B-ring is reduced, and an additional hydroxylation may occur. Two different sets of compounds are produced. One set has α-hydroxyl groups at positions 3, 7, and 12 and produces the cholic acid series

FIG. 34.8. The ACAT reaction, producing cholesterol esters. *ACAT*, acyl-CoA–cholesterol acyl transferase.

FIG. 34.9. The reaction catalyzed by 7-α-hydroxylase. An α-hydroxyl group is formed at position 7 of cholesterol. This reaction, which is inhibited by bile salts, is the rate-limiting step in bile salt synthesis.

FIG. 34.10. Synthesis of bile salts. Two sets of bile salts are generated: one with α-hydroxyl groups at positions 3 and 7 (the chenocholate series) and the other with α-hydroxyls at positions 3, 7, and 12 (the cholate series). Note how bile salt accumulation will inhibit the initial step of the pathway, catalyzed by 7-α-hydroxylase.

of bile salts. The other set has α-hydroxyl groups only at positions 3 and 7 and produces the chenodeoxycholic acid series (also known as the *chenocholic acid series*, Fig. 34.10). Three carbons are removed from the side chain by an oxidation reaction. The remaining five-carbon fragment attached to the ring structure contains a carboxyl group (see Fig. 34.10).

The pK_a of the bile acids is approximately 6. Therefore, in the contents of the intestinal lumen, which normally have a pH of 6, approximately 50% of the molecules are present in the protonated form and 50% are ionized, which form bile salts. (The terms *bile acids* and *bile salts* are often used interchangeably, but bile salts actually refers to the ionized form of the molecules.)

B. Conjugation of Bile Salts

The carboxyl group at the end of the side chain of the bile salts is activated by a reaction that requires ATP and coenzyme A. The CoA derivatives can react with either glycine or taurine (which is derived from cysteine), forming amides that are known as conjugated bile salts (Fig. 34.11). In glycocholic acid and glycochenodeoxycholic acid, the bile acids are conjugated with glycine. These compounds have a pK_a of approximately 4, so compared to their unconjugated forms, a higher percentage of the molecules is present in the ionized form at the pH of the intestine. The taurine conjugates, taurocholic and taurochenodeoxycholic acid, all have a pK_a of approximately 2. Therefore, compared with the glycoconjugates, an even greater percentage of the molecules of these conjugates are ionized in the lumen of the gut.

V. FATE OF THE BILE SALTS

The bile salts are produced in the liver and secreted into the bile (Fig. 34.12). They are stored in the gallbladder and released into the intestine during a meal, where they serve as detergents that aid in the digestion of dietary lipids (see Chapter 32).

Intestinal bacteria deconjugate and dehydroxylate the bile salts, removing the glycine and taurine residues and the hydroxyl group at position 7. The bile salts that lack a hydroxyl group at position 7 are called *secondary bile salts*. The deconjugated and dehydroxylated bile salts are less soluble and, therefore, are less readily resorbed

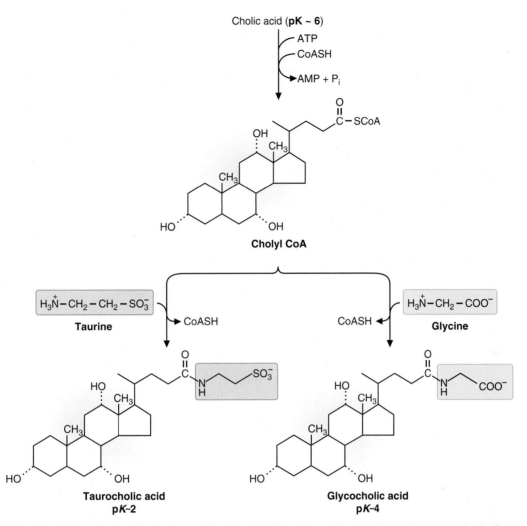

FIG. 34.11. Conjugation of bile salts. Conjugation lowers the pK_a of the bile salts, making them better detergents; that is, they are more ionized in the contents of the intestinal lumen (pH $\approx$ 6) than are the unconjugated bile salts ($pK_a \approx$ 6). The reactions are the same for the chenocholic acid series of bile salts.

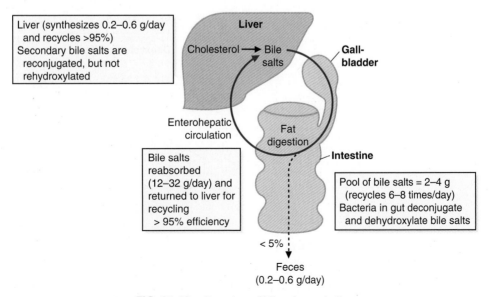

FIG. 34.12.   Overview of bile salt metabolism.

from the intestinal lumen than the bile salts that have not been subjected to bacterial action (Fig. 34.13). Lithocholic acid, a secondary bile salt that has a hydroxyl group only at position 3, is the least soluble bile salt. Its major fate is excretion.

Greater than 95% of the bile salts are resorbed in the ileum and return to the liver via the enterohepatic circulation (via the portal vein; see Fig. 34.12). The secondary

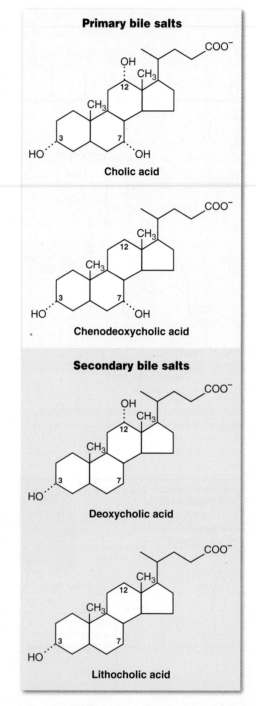

FIG. 34.13. Structures of the primary and secondary bile salts. Primary bile salts form conjugates with taurine or glycine in the liver. After secretion into the intestine, they may be deconjugated and dehydroxylated by the bacterial flora, forming secondary bile salts. Note that dehydroxylation occurs at position 7, forming the deoxy family of bile salts. Dehydroxylation at position 12 also leads to excretion of the bile salt.

bile salts may be reconjugated in the liver, but they are not rehydroxylated. The bile salts are recycled by the liver, which secretes them into the bile. This enterohepatic recirculation of bile salts is extremely efficient. Less than 5% of the bile salts entering the gut are excreted in the feces each day. Because the steroid nucleus cannot be degraded in the body, the excretion of bile salts serves as a major route for removal of the steroid nucleus and thus of cholesterol from the body.

VI. TRANSPORT OF CHOLESTEROL BY THE BLOOD LIPOPROTEINS

Because they are hydrophobic and essentially insoluble in the water of the blood, cholesterol and cholesterol esters, like triacylglycerols and phospholipids, must be transported through the bloodstream packaged as lipoproteins. These macromolecules are water-soluble. Each lipoprotein particle is composed of a core of hydrophobic lipids such as cholesterol esters and triacylglycerols surrounded by a shell of polar lipids (the phospholipids), which allows a hydration shell to form around the lipoprotein (see Fig. 32.8). This occurs when the positive charge of the nitrogen atom of the phospholipid (phosphatidylcholine, phosphatidylethanolamine, or phosphatidylserine) forms an ionic bond with the negatively charged hydroxyl ion of the environment. In addition, the shell contains a variety of apoproteins that also increase the water solubility of the lipoprotein. Free cholesterol molecules are dispersed throughout the lipoprotein shell to stabilize it in a way that allows it to maintain its spherical shape. The major carriers of lipids are chylomicrons (see Chapter 32), VLDL, and HDL. Metabolism of VLDL leads to IDL and LDL. Metabolism of chylomicrons leads to formation of chylomicron remnants.

Through this carrier mechanism, lipids leave their tissue of origin, enter the bloodstream, and are transported to the tissues, where their components are either used in synthetic or oxidative process or stored for later use. The apoproteins ("apo" describes the protein within the shell of the particle in its lipid-free form) not only add to the hydrophilicity and structural stability of the particle, they have other functions as well: (1) They activate certain enzymes required for normal lipoprotein metabolism and (2) they act as ligands on the surface of the lipoprotein that target specific receptors on peripheral tissues that require lipoprotein delivery for their innate cellular functions.

Ten principal apoproteins have been characterized. Their tissue sources, molecular mass, distribution within lipoproteins, and metabolic functions are shown in Table 34.3.

The lipoproteins themselves are distributed among eight major classes. Some of their characteristics are shown in Table 34.4. Each class of lipoprotein has a specific function determined by its apolipoprotein content, its tissue of origin, and the proportion of the macromolecule made up of triacylglycerols, cholesterol esters, free cholesterol, and phospholipids (see Tables 34.3 and 34.4).

A. The Chylomicrons

Chylomicrons are the largest of the lipoproteins and the least dense because of their rich triacylglycerol content. They are synthesized from dietary lipids (the "exogenous" lipoprotein pathway) within the epithelial cells of the small intestine and then secreted into the lymphatic vessels draining the gut (see Fig. 32.13). They enter the bloodstream via the left subclavian vein. The major apolipoproteins of chylomicrons are apolipoprotein B_{48} (apoB_{48}), apoCII, and apoE (see Table 34.3). The apoCII activates lipoprotein lipase (LPL), an enzyme that projects into the lumen of capillaries in adipose tissue, cardiac muscle, skeletal muscle, and the acinar cells of mammary tissue. This activation allows LPL to hydrolyze the chylomicrons, leading to the release of free fatty acids derived from core triacylglycerides of the lipoprotein into these target cells. The muscle cells then oxidize the fatty acids as fuel, whereas the adipocytes and mammary cells store them as triacylglycerols (fat) or, in the case

Table 34.3   Characteristics of the Major Apoproteins

Apoprotein	Primary Tissue Source	Molecular Mass (Daltons)	Lipoprotein Distribution	Metabolic Function
ApoAI	Intestine, liver	28,016	HDL (chylomicrons)	Activates LCAT; structural component of HDL
ApoAII	Liver	17,414	HDL (chylomicrons)	Uncertain; may regulate transfer of apoproteins from HDL to other lipoprotein particles
ApoAIV	Intestine	46,465	HDL (chylomicrons)	Uncertain; may be involved in assembly of HDL and chylomicrons
ApoB$_{48}$	Intestine	264,000	Chylomicrons	Assembly and secretion of chylomicrons from small bowel
ApoB$_{100}$	Liver	540,000	VLDL, IDL, LDL	VLDL assembly and secretion; structural protein of VLDL, IDL, and LDL; ligand for LDL receptor
ApoCI	Liver	6,630	Chylomicrons, VLDL, IDL, HDL	Unknown; may inhibit hepatic uptake of chylomicron and VLDL remnants
ApoCII	Liver	8,900	Chylomicrons, VLDL, IDL, HDL	Cofactor activator of lipoprotein lipase (LPL)
ApoCIII	Liver	8,800	Chylomicrons, VLDL, IDL, HDL	Inhibitor of LPL; may inhibit hepatic uptake of chylomicrons and VLDL remnants
ApoE	Liver	34,145	Chylomicron remnants, VLDL, IDL, HDL	Ligand for binding of several lipoproteins to the LDL receptor, to the LDL receptor-related protein (LRP), and possibly to a separate apoE receptor
Apo(a)	Liver		Lipoprotein "little" a (Lp[a])	Unknown; consists of apoB$_{100}$ linked by a disulfide bond to apoprotein(a)

HDL, high-density lipoprotein; LCAT, lecithin-cholesterol acyltransferase; VLDL, very low-density lipoprotein; IDL, intermediate-density lipoprotein; LDL, low-density lipoprotein.

Table 34.4   Characteristics of the Major Lipoproteins

Lipoprotein	Density Range (g/mL)	Particle Diameter (mm) Range	Electrophoretic Mobility	Lipid (%)[a]			Function
				TG	Chol	PL	
Chylomicrons	0.930	75–1200	Origin	80–95	2–7	3–9	Deliver dietary lipids
Chylomicron remnants	0.930–1.006	30–80	Slow pre-β				Return dietary lipids to the liver
VLDL	0.930–1.006	30–80	Pre-β	55–80	5–15	10–20	Deliver endogenous lipids
IDL	1.006–1.019	25–35	Slow pre-β	20–50	20–40	15–25	Return endogenous lipids to the liver; precursor of LDL
LDL	1.019–1.063	18–25	β	5–15	40–50	20–25	Deliver cholesterol to cells
HDL$_2$	1.063–1.125	9–12	α	5–10	15–25	20–30	Reverse cholesterol transport
HDL$_3$	1.125–1.210	5–9	α				Reverse cholesterol transport
Lip(a)	1.050–1.120	25	Pre-β				

TG, triacylglycerol; Chol, the sum of free and esterified cholesterol; PL, phospholipid; VLDL, very low-density lipoprotein; IDL, intermediate-density lipoprotein; LDL, low-density lipoprotein; HDL, high-density lipoprotein.
[a]The remaining percentage composition is composed of apoproteins.

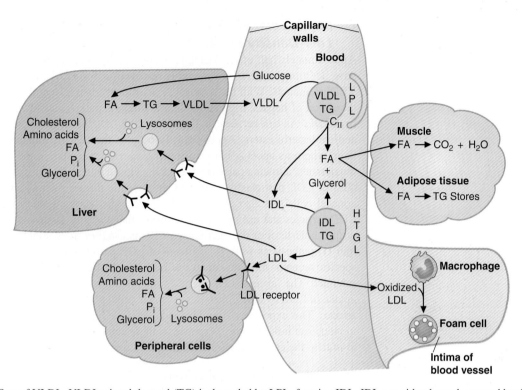

FIG. 34.14. Fate of VLDL. VLDL triacylglycerol (TG) is degraded by LPL, forming IDL. IDL can either be endocytosed by the liver through a receptor-mediated process or further digested, mainly by hepatic triacylglycerol lipase (HTGL), to form LDL. LDL may be endocytosed by receptor-mediated processes in the liver or in peripheral cells. LDL also may be oxidized and taken up by "scavenger" receptors on macrophages. The scavenger pathway plays a role in atherosclerosis. *FA*, fatty acids; P_i, inorganic phosphate.

of the lactating breast, use them for milk formation. The partially hydrolyzed chylomicrons remaining in the bloodstream (the chylomicron remnants), now partly depleted of their core triacylglycerols, have lost their apoCII but still retain their apoE and apoB$_{48}$ proteins. Receptors in the plasma membranes of the liver cells bind to apoE on the surface of these remnants, allowing them to be taken up by the liver through a process of receptor-mediated endocytosis (see the following text).

B. Very Low-Density Lipoprotein

If dietary intake of carbohydrates exceeds the immediate fuel requirements of the liver, the excess carbohydrates are converted to triacylglycerols, which, along with free and esterified cholesterol, phospholipids, and the major apoprotein apoB$_{100}$ (see Table 34.3), are packaged to form nascent VLDL. These particles are then secreted from the liver (the "endogenous" pathway of lipoprotein metabolism) into the bloodstream (Fig. 34.14), where they accept apoCII and apoE from circulating HDL particles. This then forms the mature VLDL particle. The density, particle size, and lipid content of VLDL particles are given in Table 34.3. These particles are then transported from the hepatic veins to capillaries in skeletal and cardiac muscle and adipose tissue, as well as lactating mammary tissues, where LPL is activated by apoCII in the VLDL particles. The activated enzyme facilitates the hydrolysis of the triacylglycerol in VLDL, causing the release of fatty acids and glycerol from a portion of core triacylglycerols. These fatty acids are oxidized as fuel by muscle cells, used in the resynthesis of triacylglycerols in fat cells, and used for milk production in the lactating breast. The residual particles remaining in the bloodstream are called *VLDL remnants*. Approximately 50% of these remnants are taken up from the blood by liver cells through the binding of VLDL apoE to the hepatocyte plasma membrane apoE receptor, followed by endocytic internalization of the VLDL remnant.

C. Intermediate-Density Lipoprotein and Low-Density Lipoprotein

Approximately half of the VLDL remnants are not taken up by the liver but, instead, have additional core triacylglycerols removed to form IDL, a specialized class of VLDL remnants. With the removal of additional triacylglycerols from IDL through the action of hepatic triglyceride lipase within hepatic sinusoids, LDL is generated from IDL. As can be seen in Table 34.4, the LDL particles are rich in cholesterol and cholesterol esters. Approximately 60% of the LDL is transported back to the liver, where its apoB$_{100}$ binds to specific apoB$_{100}$ receptors in the liver cell plasma membranes, allowing particles to be endocytosed into the hepatocyte. The remaining 40% of LDL particles is carried to extrahepatic tissues such as adrenocortical and gonadal cells that also contain apoB$_{100}$ receptors, allowing them to internalize the LDL particles and use their cholesterol for the synthesis of steroid hormones. Some of the cholesterol of the internalized LDL is used for membrane synthesis and vitamin D synthesis as well. If an excess of LDL particles is present in the blood, this specific receptor-mediated uptake of LDL by hepatic and nonhepatic tissue becomes saturated. The "excess" LDL particles are now more readily available for nonspecific uptake of LDL by macrophages (scavenger cells) present near the endothelial cells of arteries. This exposure of vascular endothelial cells to high levels of LDL is believed to induce an inflammatory response by these cells, a process that has been suggested to initiate the complex cascade of atherosclerosis discussed in following sections.

D. High-Density Lipoprotein

The fourth class of lipoproteins is HDL, which plays several roles in whole-body lipid metabolism.

1. SYNTHESIS OF HIGH-DENSITY LIPOPROTEIN

HDL particles can be created by several mechanisms. The first is synthesis of nascent HDL by the liver and intestine as a relatively small molecule whose shell, like that of other lipoproteins, contains phospholipids, free cholesterol, and a variety of apoproteins, predominant among which are apoAI, apoAII, apoCI, and apoCII (see Table 34.3). Very low levels of triacylglycerols or cholesterol esters are found in the hollow core of this early, or nascent, version of HDL.

A second method for HDL generation is the budding of apoproteins from chylomicrons and VLDL particles as they are digested by LPL. The apoproteins (particularly apoAI) and shells can then accumulate more lipid, as described in the following text.

A third method for HDL generation is free apoAI, which may be shed from other circulating lipoproteins. The apoAI acquires cholesterol and phospholipids from other lipoproteins and cell membranes, forming a nascentlike HDL particle within the circulation.

2. MATURATION OF NASCENT HIGH-DENSITY LIPOPROTEIN

In the process of maturation, the nascent HDL particles accumulate phospholipids and cholesterol from cells lining the blood vessels. As the central hollow core of nascent HDL progressively fills with cholesterol esters, HDL takes on a more globular shape to eventually form the mature HDL particle. The transfer of lipids to nascent HDL does not require enzymatic activity.

3. REVERSE CHOLESTEROL TRANSPORT

A major benefit of HDL particles derives from their ability to remove cholesterol from cholesterol-laden cells and to return the cholesterol to the liver, a process known as *reverse cholesterol transport*. This is particularly beneficial in vascular tissue; by reducing cellular cholesterol levels in the subintimal space, the likelihood that foam cells (lipid-laden macrophages that engulf oxidized LDL-cholesterol and represent an early stage in the development of atherosclerotic plaque) will form within the blood vessel wall is reduced.

Reverse cholesterol transport requires a directional movement of cholesterol from the cell to the lipoprotein particle. Cells contain the protein *ABCA1* (ATP-binding cassette protein 1) that uses ATP hydrolysis to move cholesterol from the inner leaflet of the membrane to the outer leaflet (similar to the efflux of phytosterols by *ABCG5* and *ABCG8*, see Section I of this chapter). Once the cholesterol has reached the outer membrane leaflet, the HDL particle can accept it; but if the cholesterol is not modified within the HDL particle, the cholesterol can leave the particle by the same route that it entered. To trap the cholesterol within the HDL core, the HDL particle acquires the enzyme lecithin-cholesterol acyltransferase (LCAT) from the circulation (LCAT is synthesized and secreted by the liver). LCAT catalyzes the transfer of a fatty acid from the 2-position of lecithin (phosphatidylcholine) in the phospholipid shell of the particle to the 3-hydroxyl group of cholesterol, forming a cholesterol ester (Fig. 34.15). The cholesterol ester migrates to the core of the HDL particle and is no longer free to return to the cell.

Elevated levels of lipoprotein-associated cholesterol in the blood, particularly that associated with LDL but also that in the more triacylglycerol-rich lipoproteins, are associated with the formation of cholesterol-rich atheromatous plaque in the vessel wall, leading eventually to diffuse atherosclerotic vascular disease

Two genetically determined disorders, familial HDL deficiency and Tangier disease, result from mutations in the adenosine triphosphate (ATP)-binding cassette 1 (*ABCA1*) protein. Cholesterol-depleted HDL cannot transport free cholesterol from cells that lack the ability to express this protein. As a consequence, HDL is rapidly degraded. These disorders have established a role for *ABCA1* protein in the regulation of HDL levels in the blood.

FIG. 34.15. The reaction catalyzed by LCAT. R_1, saturated fatty acid; R_2, unsaturated fatty acid.

Because **Ann Jeina** continued to experience intermittent chest pain in spite of good control of her hypertension and a 20-lb weight loss, her physician decided that in addition to seeing a cardiologist to further evaluate the chest pain, a second drug is needed to be added to her regimen to further lower her blood LDL cholesterol level. Consequently, treatment with ezetimibe, a drug that blocks cholesterol absorption from the intestine, was added to complement the atorvastatin Ann was already taking.

that may result in acute cardiovascular events, such as myocardial infarction, stroke, or symptomatic peripheral vascular insufficiency. High levels of HDL in the blood, therefore, are believed to be vasculoprotective because these high levels increase the rate of reverse cholesterol transport "away" from the blood vessels and "toward" the liver ("out of harm's way").

4. FATE OF HIGH-DENSITY LIPOPROTEIN CHOLESTEROL

Mature HDL particles can bind to specific receptors on hepatocytes (such as the apoE receptor), but the primary means of clearance of HDL from the blood is through its uptake by the scavenger receptor SR-B1. This receptor is present on many cell types. It does not carry out endocytosis per se, but once the HDL particle is bound to the receptor, its cholesterol and cholesterol esters are transferred into the cells. When depleted of cholesterol and its esters, the HDL particle dissociates from the SR-B1 receptor and reenters the circulation. SR-B1 receptors can be upregulated in certain cell types that require cholesterol for biosynthetic purposes, such as the cells that produce the steroid hormones. The SR-B1 receptors are not downregulated when cholesterol levels are high.

5. HIGH-DENSITY LIPOPROTEIN INTERACTIONS WITH OTHER PARTICLES

In addition to its ability to pick up cholesterol from cell membranes, HDL also exchanges apoproteins and lipids with other lipoproteins in the blood. For example, HDL transfers apoE and apoCII to chylomicrons and to VLDL. The apoCII stimulates the degradation of the triacylglycerols of chylomicrons and VLDL by activating LPL (Fig. 34.16). After digestion of the chylomicrons and the VLDL triacylglycerols, apoE and apoCII are transferred back to HDL. When HDL obtains free cholesterol from cell membranes, the free cholesterol is esterified at the third carbon of the A-ring via the LCAT reaction (see Fig. 34.14). From this point, HDL either transports the free cholesterol and cholesterol esters directly to the liver,

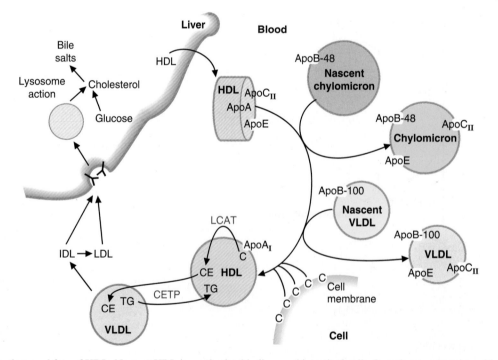

FIG. 34.16. Functions and fate of HDL. Nascent HDL is synthesized in liver and intestinal cells. It exchanges proteins with chylomicrons and VLDL. HDL picks up cholesterol (C) from cell membranes. This cholesterol is converted to cholesterol ester (CE) by the LCAT reaction. HDL transfers CE to VLDL in exchange for triacylglycerol (TG). The cholesterol ester transfer protein (CETP) mediates this exchange.

as described earlier, or by CETP to circulating triacylglycerol-rich lipoproteins such as VLDL and VLDL remnants (see Fig. 34.16). In exchange, triacylglycerols from the latter lipoproteins are transferred to HDL (Fig. 34.17). The greater the concentration of triacylglycerol-rich lipoproteins in the blood, the greater will be the rate of these exchanges. Thus, the CETP exchange pathway may explain the observation that whenever triacylglycerol-rich lipoproteins are present in the blood in high concentrations, the amount of cholesterol reaching the liver via cholesterol-enriched VLDL and VLDL remnants increases, and a proportional reduction in the total amount of cholesterol and cholesterol esters that are transferred directly to the liver via HDL occurs. Mature HDL particles are designated as HDL_3; after reverse cholesterol transport and the accumulation of cholesterol esters, they become the atherogenic protective form, HDL_2. The CETP reaction then leads to the loss of cholesterol and gain of triacylglycerol, such that the particles become larger and eventually regenerate HDL_3 particles (see Table 34.4). Hepatic lipase can then remove triacylglycerol from HDL_3 particles to regenerate HDL_2 particles.

VII. LIPOPROTEINS ENTER CELLS BY RECEPTOR-MEDIATED ENDOCYTOSIS

As stated earlier, each lipoprotein particle contains specific apoproteins on its surface that act as ligands for specific plasma membrane receptors on target tissues such as the liver, the adrenal cortex, the gonads, and other cells that require one or more of the components of the lipoproteins. With the exception of the scavenger receptor SR-B1, the interaction of ligand and receptor initiates the process of endocytosis shown for LDL in Figure 34.18. The receptors for LDL, for example, are found in specific areas of the plasma membrane of the target cell for circulating lipoproteins. These are known as coated pits, and they contain a unique protein

FIG. 34.17. Function of cholesterol ester transfer protein (CETP). CETP transfers cholesterol esters (CEs) from HDL to VLDL in exchange for triacylglycerol (TG).

 The cholesterol ester transfer protein (CETP) reaction, under conditions of high levels of triglyceride-rich lipoproteins, generates elevated levels of HDL_3, which are less atheroprotective than HDL_2. CETP inhibitors are currently being evaluated as a means of increasing HDL_2 levels, with limited success. Initial clinical trials of a promising drug were terminated early because of an increased incidence of cardiovascular events when the drug was given in combination with an inhibitor of hydroxymethylglutaryl-CoA (HMG-CoA) reductase. Different CETP inhibitors, however, are currently being examined as potential HDL_2 elevating agents.

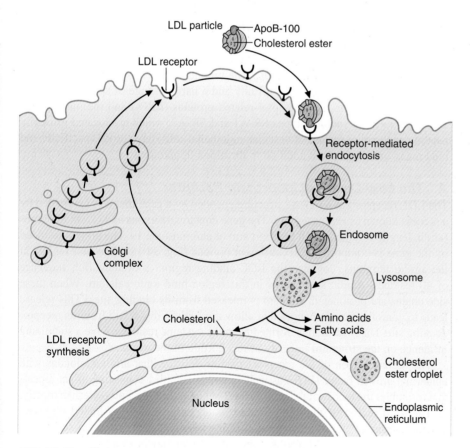

FIG. 34.18. Cholesterol uptake by receptor-mediated endocytosis.

called *clathrin*. The plasma membrane in the vicinity of the receptor–LDL complex invaginates and fuses to form an endocytic vesicle. These vesicles then fuse with lysosomes, acidic subcellular vesicles that contain several degradative enzymes. The cholesterol esters of LDL are hydrolyzed to form free cholesterol, which is rapidly reesterified through the action of ACAT. This rapid reesterification is necessary to avoid the damaging effect of high levels of free cholesterol on cellular membranes. The newly esterified cholesterol contains primarily oleate or palmitoleate (monounsaturated fatty acids), unlike those of the cholesterol esters in LDL, which are rich in linoleate, a polyunsaturated fatty acid.

As is true for the synthesis and activity of HMG-CoA reductase, the synthesis of the LDL receptor itself is subject to feedback inhibition by increasing levels of cholesterol within the cell. One probable mechanism for this feedback regulation involves one or more of the SREBPs described earlier. These proteins or the cofactors that are required for the full expression of genes that code for the LDL receptor are also capable of sensing the concentration of sterols within the cell. When sterol levels are high, the process that leads to the binding of the SREBP to the SRE of these genes is suppressed (see Fig. 34.4A). The rate of synthesis from mRNA for the LDL receptor is diminished under these circumstances. This, in turn, appropriately reduces the amount of cholesterol that can enter these cholesterol-rich cells by receptor-mediated endocytosis (downregulation of receptor synthesis). When the intracellular levels of cholesterol decrease, these processes are reversed, and cells act to increase their cholesterol levels. Both synthesis of cholesterol from acetyl-CoA and synthesis of LDL receptors are stimulated. An increased number of receptors (upregulation of receptor synthesis) results in an increased uptake of LDL cholesterol from the blood, with a subsequent reduction of LDL-cholesterol levels. At the same time, the cellular cholesterol pool is replenished.

VIII. LIPOPROTEIN RECEPTORS

The best characterized lipoprotein receptor, the LDL receptor, specifically recognizes apoB$_{100}$ and apoE. Therefore, this receptor binds VLDL, IDL, and chylomicron remnants in addition to LDL. The binding reaction is characterized by its saturability and occurs with high affinity and a narrow range of specificity. Other receptors, such as the LDL receptor-related proteins (LRPs) and the macrophage scavenger receptor (notably types SR-A1 and SR-A2, which are located primarily near the endothelial surface of vascular endothelial cells) have broad specificity and bind many other ligands in addition to the blood lipoproteins.

A. The Low-Density Lipoprotein Receptor

The LDL receptor has a mosaic structure encoded by a gene that was assembled by a process known as *exon shuffling*. The gene contains 18 exons and is >45 kilobases (kb) in length; it is located on the short arm of chromosome 19. The protein encoded by the gene is composed of six different regions (Fig. 34.19). The first region, at the amino terminus, contains the LDL-binding region, a cysteine-rich sequence of 40 residues. Acidic side chains in this region bind ionic calcium. When these side chains are protonated, calcium is released from its binding sites. This release leads to conformational changes that allow the LDL to dissociate from its receptor docking site. Disulfide bonds, formed from the cysteine residues, have a stabilizing influence on the structural integrity of this portion of the receptor.

The second region of the receptor contains domains that are homologous with epidermal growth factor (EGF) as well as with a complex consisting of six repeats that resembles the blades of the transducin β-subunit, forming a propellerlike moiety.

The third region of the LDL receptor contains a chain of *N*-linked oligosaccharides, whereas the fourth region contains a domain that is rich in serine and threonine and contains *O*-linked sugars. This region may have a role in physically

FIG. 34.19.   Structure of the LDL receptor. The protein has six major regions, which are described in this text.

extending the receptor away from the membrane so that the LDL-binding region is accessible to the LDL molecule.

The fifth region contains 22 hydrophobic residues that constitute the membrane-spanning unit of the receptor, whereas the sixth region extends into the cytosol, where it regulates the interaction between the C-terminal domain of the LDL receptor and the clathrin-containing coated pit where the process of receptor-mediated endocytosis is initiated.

The number of LDL receptors, the binding of LDL to its receptors, and the post-receptor binding process can be diminished for a variety of reasons, all of which may lead to an accumulation of LDL cholesterol in the blood and premature atherosclerosis. These abnormalities can result from mutations in one (heterozygous—seen in approximately 1 in 500 people) or both (homozygous—seen in about 1 in 1 million people) of the alleles for the LDL receptor (familial hypercholesterolemia). Heterozygotes produce approximately half of the normal complement of LDL receptors, whereas the homozygotes produce almost no LDL receptor protein (receptor-negative familial hypercholesterolemia). The latter have serum total cholesterol levels in the range of 500 to 800 mg/dL.

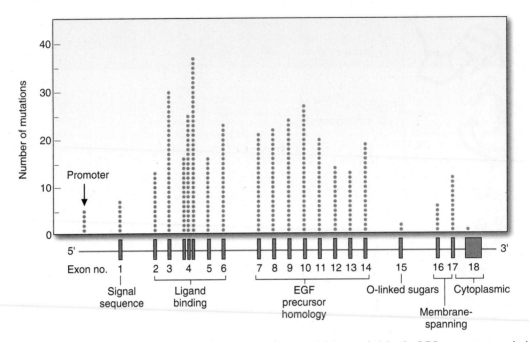

FIG. 34.20. Location of 353 point mutations and small deletions/insertions (<25 base pairs) in the LDL receptor gene in individuals with familial hypercholesterolemia (FH). Exons are shown as vertical boxes and introns as the lines connecting them. (From Goldstein JL, Hobbs HH, Brown MS. Familial hypercholesterolaemia. In: Scriver CR, Beaudet AL, Sly WS, et al., eds. *The Metabolic and Molecular Bases of Inherited Disease.* Vol 3. 8th ed. New York, NY: McGraw-Hill; 2001:2863–2913.)

Ann Jeina's blood lipid levels (in mg/dL) were

Triacylglycerol	158
Total cholesterol	420
HDL cholesterol	32
LDL cholesterol	356

She was diagnosed as having familial hypercholesterolemia (FH), type IIA, which is caused by genetic defects in the gene that encodes the LDL receptor (see Fig. 34.20). As a result of the receptor defect, LDL cannot readily be taken up by cells, and its concentration in the blood is elevated.

LDL particles contain a high percentage, by weight, of cholesterol and cholesterol esters, more than other blood lipoproteins. However, LDL triacylglycerol levels are low because LDL is produced by digestion of the triacylglycerols of very low-density lipoprotein (VLDL) and intermediate-density lipoprotein (IDL). Therefore, individuals with type IIA hyperlipoproteinemia have very high blood cholesterol levels, but their levels of triacylglycerols may be in or near the normal range (see Table 34.4).

The genetic mutations are mainly deletions, but insertions or duplications also occur, as well as missense and nonsense point mutations (Fig. 34.20). Four classes of mutations have been identified. The first class involves "null" alleles that either direct the synthesis of no protein at all or a protein that cannot be precipitated by antibodies to the LDL receptor. In the second class, the alleles encode proteins, but they cannot be transported to the cell surface. The third class of mutant alleles encodes proteins that reach the cell surface but cannot bind LDL normally. Finally, the fourth class encodes proteins that reach the surface and bind LDL but fail to cluster and internalize the LDL particles. The result of each of these mutations is that blood levels of LDL are elevated because cells cannot take up these particles at a normal rate.

B. Low-Density Lipoprotein Receptor-Related Protein

The LRP is structurally related to the LDL receptor but recognizes a broader spectrum of ligands. In addition to lipoproteins, it binds the blood proteins α_2-macroglobulin (a protein that inhibits blood proteases) and tissue plasminogen activator (TPA) and its inhibitors. The LRP receptor recognizes the apoE of lipoproteins and binds remnants produced by the digestion of the triacylglycerols of chylomicrons and VLDL by LPL. Thus, one of its functions is believed to be clearing these remnants from the blood. The LRP receptor is abundant in the cell membranes of the liver, brain, and placenta. In contrast to the LDL receptor, synthesis of the LRP receptor is not significantly affected by an increase in the intracellular concentration of cholesterol. However, insulin causes the number of these receptors on the cell surface to increase, consistent with the need to remove chylomicron remnants that otherwise would accumulate after eating a meal.

C. Macrophage Scavenger Receptor

Some cells, particularly the phagocytic macrophages, have nonspecific receptors known as *scavenger* receptors that bind various types of molecules, including oxidatively modified LDL particles. There are several different types of scavenger receptors. SR-B1 is used primarily for HDL binding, whereas the scavenger receptors expressed on macrophages are SR-A1 and SR-A2. Modification of LDL frequently involves oxidative damage, particularly of polyunsaturated fatty acyl groups (see Chapter 24). In contrast to the LDL receptors, the scavenger receptors are not subject to downregulation. The continued presence of scavenger receptors in the cell membrane allows the cells to take up oxidatively modified LDL long after intracellular cholesterol levels are elevated. When the macrophages become engorged with lipid, they are called *foam cells*. An accumulation of these foam cells in the subendothelial space of blood vessels form the earliest gross evidence of a developing atherosclerotic plaque known as a *fatty streak*.

The processes that cause oxidation of LDL involve superoxide radicals, nitric oxide, hydrogen peroxide, and other oxidants (see Chapter 24). Antioxidants such as vitamin E, ascorbic acid (vitamin C), and carotenoids may be involved in protecting LDL from oxidation.

IX. ANATOMIC AND BIOCHEMICAL ASPECTS OF ATHEROSCLEROSIS

The normal artery is composed of three distinct layers (Fig. 34.21). That which is closest to the lumen of the vessel, the intima, is lined by a monolayer of endothelial cells that are bathed by the circulating blood. Just beneath these specialized cells lies the subintimal extracellular matrix, in which some vascular smooth muscle cells are embedded (the subintimal space). The middle layer, known as the *tunica media*, is separated from the intima by the internal elastic lamina. The tunica media contains lamellae of smooth muscle cells surrounded by an elastin- and collagen-rich matrix. The external elastic lamina forms the border between the tunica media and the outermost layer, the adventitia. This layer contains nerve fibers and mast cells. It is the origin of the vasa vasorum, which supplies blood to the outer two-thirds of the tunica media.

The initial step in the development of an atherosclerotic lesion within the wall of an artery is the formation of a fatty streak. The fatty streak represents an accumulation of lipid-laden macrophages or foam cells in the subintimal space. These fatty streaks are visible as a yellow-white linear streak that bulges slightly into the lumen of the vessel. These streaks are initiated when one or more known vascular risk factors for atherosclerosis, all of which have the potential to injure the vascular endothelial cells, reach a critical threshold at the site of future lesions. Examples of such risk factors include elevated intra-arterial pressure (arterial hypertension); elevated circulating levels of various lipids such as LDL, chylomicron remnants, and VLDL remnants; or low levels of circulating HDL, cigarette smoking, chronic elevations

Ivan Applebod's blood lipid levels were:

Triacylglycerol	295
Total cholesterol	314
HDL cholesterol	24
LDL cholesterol	231

The elevated serum levels of LDL cholesterol found in patients such as **Ivan Applebod** who have type 2 diabetes mellitus is multifactorial. One of the mechanisms responsible for this increase involves the presence of chronically elevated levels of glucose in the blood of poorly controlled diabetics. This prolonged hyperglycemia increases the rate of nonenzymatic attachment of glucose to various proteins in the body, a process referred to as glycation or glycosylation of proteins.

Glycation may adversely affect the structure or the function of the protein involved. For example, glycation of the LDL receptor and of proteins in the LDL particle may interfere with the normal "fit" of LDL particles with their specific receptors. As a result, less circulating LDL is internalized into cells by receptor-mediated endocytosis, and the serum LDL cholesterol level rises. Additionally, because Mr. Applebod is obese, he exhibits higher than normal levels of circulating free fatty acids, which the liver uses to increase the synthesis of VLDL, leading to hypertriglyceridemia.

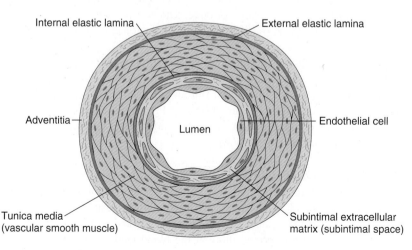

FIG. 34.21. The different layers of the arterial wall.

In addition to dietary therapy, aimed at reducing her blood cholesterol levels, **Ann Jeina** was treated with atorvastatin, a hydroxymethylglutaryl-CoA (HMG-CoA) reductase inhibitor. The HMG-CoA reductase inhibitors decrease the rate of synthesis of cholesterol in cells. As cellular cholesterol levels decrease, the synthesis of LDL receptors increases. As the number of receptors increase on the cell surface, the uptake of LDL is accelerated. Consequently, the blood level of LDL cholesterol decreases. Ann was also treated with ezetimibe, which blocks cholesterol absorption from the intestinal lumen.

High-density lipoprotein (HDL) is considered to be the "good cholesterol" because it accepts free cholesterol from peripheral tissues, such as cells in the walls of blood vessels. This cholesterol is converted to cholesterol ester, part of which is transferred to VLDL by cholesterol ester transfer protein (CETP) and returned to the liver by IDL and LDL. The remainder of the cholesterol is transferred directly as part of the HDL molecule to the liver. The liver reuses the cholesterol in the synthesis of VLDL, converts it to bile salts, or excretes it directly into the bile. HDL, therefore, tends to lower blood cholesterol levels. Lower blood cholesterol levels correlate with lower rates of death caused by atherosclerosis.

in blood glucose levels, high circulating levels of the vasoconstricting octapeptide angiotensin II, and others. The resulting insult to endothelial cells may trigger these cells to secrete adhesion molecules that bind to circulating monocytes and markedly slow their rate of movement past the endothelium. When these monocytic cells are slowed enough, they accumulate and have access to the physical spaces that exist between endothelial cells. This accumulation of monocytic cells resembles the classical inflammatory response to injury. These changes have led to the suggestion that atherosclerosis is, in fact, an inflammatory disorder and, therefore, is one that might be prevented or attenuated through the use of anti-inflammatory agents such as acetylsalicylic acid (aspirin) and HMG-CoA reductase inhibitors (statins), which have been shown to suppress the inflammatory cascade as well as to inhibit the action of HMG-CoA reductase.

The monocytic cells are transformed into macrophages that migrate through the spaces between endothelial cells. They enter the subintimal space under the influence of chemoattractant cytokines (e.g., chemokine macrophage chemoattractant protein I) secreted by vascular cells in response to exposure to oxidatively modified fatty acids within the lipoproteins.

The macrophages can replicate and exhibit augmented expression of receptors that recognize oxidatively modified lipoproteins. Unlike the classic LDL receptors on liver and many nonhepatic cells, these macrophage-bound receptors are high-capacity, low-specificity receptors (scavenger receptors). They bind to and internalize oxidatively modified fatty acids within LDLs to become subintimal foam cells as described previously. As these foam cells accumulate, they deform the overlying endothelium, causing microscopic separations between endothelial cells, exposing these foam cells and the underlying extracellular matrix to the blood. These exposed areas serve as sites for platelet adhesion and aggregation. Activated platelets secrete cytokines that perpetuate this process and increase the potential for thrombus (clot) formation locally. As the evolving plaque matures, a fibrous cap forms over its expanding "roof," which now bulges into the vascular lumen, thereby partially occluding it. Vascular smooth muscle cells now migrate from the tunica media to the subintimal space and secrete additional plaque matrix material. The smooth muscle cells also secrete metalloproteinases that thin the fibrous cap near its "elbow" at the periphery of the plaque. This thinning progresses until the fibrous cap ruptures, allowing the plaque contents to physically contact the procoagulant elements present within the circulation. This leads to acute thrombus formation. If this thrombus completely occludes the remaining lumen of the vessel, an infarction of tissues distal to the occlusion (i.e., an acute myocardial infarction) may occur (Fig. 34.22). Most plaques that rupture also contain focal areas of calcification, which appears to result from the induction of the same cluster of genes as those that promote the formation of bone. The inducers for this process include oxidized sterols as well as transforming growth factor β (TGF-β) derived from certain vascular cells.

Finally, high intraluminal shear forces develop in these thinning or eroded areas of the plaque's fibrous cap, inducing macrophages to secrete additional metalloproteinases that further degrade the arterial-fibrous cap matrix. This contributes further to plaque rupture and thrombus formation (see Fig. 34.22). The consequence is a macrovascular ischemic event such as an acute myocardial infarction (AMI) or an acute cerebrovascular accident (CVA).

X. STEROID HORMONES

Cholesterol is the precursor of all five classes of steroid hormones: glucocorticoids, mineralocorticoids, androgens, estrogens, and progestins. These hormones are synthesized in the adrenal cortex, ovaries, testes, and ovarian corpus luteum. Steroid hormones are transported through the blood from their sites of synthesis to their target organs, where, because of their hydrophobicity, they cross the cell

In patients such as **Ann Jeina** and **Ivan Applebod**, who have elevated levels of VLDL or LDL, HDL levels are often low. These patients are predisposed to atherosclerosis and suffer from a high incidence of heart attacks and strokes.

Exercise and estrogen administration both increase HDL levels. This is one of the reasons exercise is often recommended to aid in the prevention or treatment of heart disease. Prior to menopause, the incidence of heart attacks is relatively low in women, but it rises after menopause and increases to the level found in men by the age of 65 or 70 years. Moderate consumption of ethanol (alcohol) has also been correlated with increased HDL levels. Recent studies suggest that the beneficial amount of ethanol may be quite low, about two small glasses of wine a day, and that beneficial effects ascribed to ethanol may result from other components of wine and alcoholic beverages. In spite of the evidence that postmenopausal hormone replacement therapy (HRT) decreases circulating levels of LDL and increases HDL levels, recent data suggest that HRT may actually increase the rate of atherosclerotic vascular disease in these women. As a result, the accepted indications for estrogen administration are now limited to intolerable "hot flashes" or vaginal dryness.

FIG. 34.22. Evolution of an atherosclerotic plaque. Plaque capsule eroded near the "elbow" of plaque creating an early plaque fissure (**A**), which may heal as plaque increases in size (**B**) or may grow as thrombus expands, having an intraluminal portion and an intraintimal portion (**C**). If the fissure is not properly sealed, the thrombus may grow and completely occlude the vessel lumen (**D**), causing an acute infarction of tissues downstream of the vessel occlusion.

membrane and bind to specific receptors in either the cytoplasm or the nucleus. The bound receptors then bind to DNA to regulate gene transcription (see Chapter 16, Section III.C.2, and Fig. 16.12). Because of their hydrophobicity, steroid hormones must be complexed with a serum protein. Serum albumin can act as a nonspecific carrier for the steroid hormones, but there are specific carriers as well. The cholesterol used for steroid hormone synthesis is synthesized in the tissues from acetyl-CoA, extracted from intracellular cholesterol ester pools, or taken up by the cell in the form of cholesterol-containing lipoproteins (either internalized by the LDL receptor or absorbed by the SR-B1 receptor). In general, glucocorticoids and progestins contain 21 carbons, androgens contain 19 carbons, and estrogens contain 18 carbons. The specific complement of enzymes present in the cells of an organ determines which hormones the organ can synthesize.

The oxidative reactions that lead to the synthesis and secretion of glucocorticoids such as cortisol are stimulated by adrenocorticotropic hormone (ACTH) from the anterior pituitary gland. The role of cortisol as a stress-released hormone is discussed in Chapter 43.

Mineralocorticoids such as aldosterone are also synthesized in the adrenal cortex and are secreted in response to angiotensin II or III, rising potassium levels in the blood, or hyponatremia (low levels of sodium ions in the blood). Aldosterone stimulates sodium reuptake in the kidney, sweat glands, salivary glands, and other tissues, with a resulting increase in extracellular fluid volume and eventually in blood pressure. The angiotensins are produced in response to a reduction in extracellular fluid volume, which may occur as a result of such things as excessive sweating, persistent vomiting without sufficient rehydration, or bleeding without adequate replacement of blood.

Lipoprotein(a) is essentially an LDL particle that is covalently bound to apoprotein(a). It is called "lipoprotein little a" to avoid confusion with the apoprotein A found in LDL. The structure of apoprotein(a) is very similar to that of plasminogen, a precursor of the protease plasmin that degrades fibrin, a major component of blood clots. Lipoprotein(a), however, cannot be converted to active plasmin. There are reports that high concentrations of lipoprotein(a) correlate with an increased risk of coronary artery disease, even in patients in whom the lipid profile is otherwise normal. The physiologic function of lipoprotein(a) remains elusive.

Vera Leizd consulted her gynecologist, who confirmed that her problems were probably the result of an excess production of androgens (virilization) and ordered blood and urine studies to determine whether Vera's adrenal cortices or her ovaries were causing her virilizing syndrome.

Androgens such as testosterone are synthesized in the Leydig cells of the testes and to a lesser extent in the ovary and are secreted in response to luteinizing hormone (LH) produced in the anterior pituitary gland. In men, testosterone is commonly converted to dihydrotestosterone (DHT), a higher affinity form of the hormone, within specific target tissues. This active form of the hormone stimulates the production of sperm proteins in Sertoli cells and the development of secondary sex characteristics.

Estrogens such as 17-β-estradiol are synthesized in the ovarian follicle and the corpus luteum, from which their secretion is stimulated by follicle-stimulating hormone (FSH) produced in the anterior pituitary gland. In women, 17-β-estradiol feeds back negatively on the synthesis and secretion of the pituitary gonadotropins, such as FSH. Estrogen and progesterone prepare the uterine endometrium for implantation of the fertilized ovum, and among other actions promote differentiation of the mammary gland.

Progestogens such as progesterone are synthesized in the corpus luteum, and their secretion is stimulated by LH. As mentioned, in concert with estradiol, progesterone prepares the uterine endometrium for implantation of the fertilized ovum and acts as a differentiation factor in mammary gland development.

The biosynthesis of glucocorticoids and mineralocorticoids (in the adrenal cortex), and that of sex steroids (in the adrenal cortex and gonads), requires several distinct cytochrome P450 enzymes (see Chapter 24). These monooxygenases are involved in the transfer of electrons from NADPH through electron-transfer protein intermediates to molecular oxygen, which then oxidizes a variety of the ring carbons of cholesterol.

Cholesterol is converted to progesterone in the first two steps of the synthesis of all steroid hormones. Cytochrome P450$_{SCC}$ side-chain cleavage enzyme (previously referred to as *cholesterol desmolase* and classified as CYP11A) is located in the mitochondrial inner membrane and removes six carbons from the side chain of cholesterol, forming pregnenolone, which has 21 carbons (Fig. 34.23). The next step, the conversion of pregnenolone to progesterone, is catalyzed by 3-β-hydroxysteroid dehydrogenase, an enzyme that is not a member of the cytochrome P450 family. Other steroid hormones are produced from progesterone by reactions that involve the other members of the P450 family. These include the mitochondrial enzyme cytochrome P450$_{C11}$ (CYP11B1), which catalyzes β-hydroxylation at carbon 11 and two ER enzymes: P450$_{C17}$ (17-α-hydroxylation, CYP17) and P450$_{C21}$ (hydroxylation at carbon 21, CYP21). As the synthesis of the steroid hormones is discussed, notice how certain enzymes are used in more than one pathway. Defects in these enzymes lead to multiple abnormalities in steroid synthesis, which, in turn, results in a variety of abnormal phenotypes.

A. Synthesis of Cortisol

The adrenocortical biosynthetic pathway that leads to cortisol synthesis occurs in the middle layer of the adrenal cortex, known as the zona fasciculata. Free cholesterol is transported by an intracellular carrier protein to the inner mitochondrial membrane of cells (Fig. 34.24), where the side chain is cleaved to form pregnenolone. Pregnenolone returns to the cytosol, where it forms progesterone.

In the membranes of the endoplasmic reticulum, the enzyme P450$_{C17}$ (CYP17) catalyzes the hydroxylation of C17 of progesterone or pregnenolone and can also catalyze the cleavage of the two-carbon side chain of these compounds at C17 (a C17–C20 lyase activity), which forms androstenedione from 17-α-hydroxyprogesterone. These two separate functions of the same enzyme allow further steroid synthesis to proceed along two separate pathways: The 17-hydroxylated steroids that retain their side chains are precursors of cortisol (C21), whereas those from which the side chain was cleaved (C19 steroids)

FIG. 34.23. Synthesis of the steroid hormones. The rings of the precursor, cholesterol, are lettered. Dihydrotestosterone is produced from testosterone by reduction of the carbon–carbon double bond in ring A. *DHEA*, dehydroepiandrosterone. The *dashed lines* indicate alternative pathways to the major pathways indicated. The starred enzymes are those that may be defective in congenital adrenal hyperplasia.

FIG. 34.24. Cellular route for cortisol synthesis. Cholesterol is synthesized from acetyl-CoA or derived from low-density lipoprotein (LDL), which is endocytosed and digested by lysosomal enzymes. Cholesterol is stored in cells of the adrenal cortex as cholesterol esters. ACTH signals the cell to convert cholesterol to cortisol and transmits its signal through a G protein–coupled receptor that results in the activation of adenylate cyclase, and, ultimately, PKA. *(1)* Cholesterol desmolase (P450$_{SCC}$, involved in side-chain cleavage); *(2)* 3-β-hydroxysteroid dehydrogenase; *(3)* 17-α-hydroxylase (P450$_{C17}$); *(4)* 21-hydroxylase (P450$_{C21}$); *(5)* 11-β-hydroxylase (P450$_{C11}$).

are precursors of androgens (male sex hormones) and estrogens (female sex hormones).

In the pathway of cortisol synthesis, the 17-hydroxylation of progesterone yields 17-α-hydroxyprogesterone, which is then hydroxylated by the P450$_{C21}$ (CYP21) complex at carbon 21 to form 11-deoxycortisol. Progesterone can also be hydroxylated directly by P450$_{C21}$ within the ER to form deoxycorticosterone (DOC), which is a precursor of the mineralocorticoid, aldosterone (see Fig. 34.23).

The final step in cortisol synthesis requires transport of 11-deoxycortisol back to the inner membrane of the mitochondria, where P450$_{C11}$ (11-β-hydroxylase, CYP11B1) catalyzes the β-hydroxylation of the substrate at carbon 21, in a reaction that requires molecular oxygen and electrons derived from NADPH, to form cortisol. The rate of biosynthesis of cortisol and other adrenal steroids depends on stimulation of the adrenal cortical cells by ACTH.

B. Synthesis of Aldosterone

The synthesis of the potent mineralocorticoid aldosterone in the zona glomerulosa of the adrenal cortex also begins with the conversion of cholesterol to progesterone (see Figs. 34.23 and 34.24). Progesterone is then hydroxylated at C21, a reaction catalyzed by P450$_{C21}$ (CYP21), to yield DOC. The P450$_{C11}$ (CYP11B1) enzyme system then catalyzes the reactions that convert DOC to corticosterone. The terminal steps in aldosterone synthesis, catalyzed by the P450 aldosterone system (CYP11B2), involve the oxidation of corticosterone to 18-hydroxycorticosterone, which is oxidized to aldosterone.

The primary stimulus for aldosterone production is the octapeptide angiotensin II, although hyperkalemia (greater than normal levels of potassium in the blood) or hyponatremia (less than normal levels of sodium in the blood) may stimulate aldosterone synthesis directly as well. ACTH has a permissive action in aldosterone production. It allows cells to respond optimally to their primary stimulus, angiotensin II.

C. Synthesis of the Adrenal Androgens

Adrenal androgen biosynthesis proceeds from cleavage of the 2-carbon side chain of 17-hydroxypregnenolone at C17 to form the 19-carbon adrenal androgen dehydroepiandrosterone (DHEA) and its sulfate derivative (DHEAS) in the zona reticulosum of the adrenal cortex (see Fig. 34.23). These compounds, which are weak androgens, represent a significant percentage of the total steroid production by the normal adrenal cortex and are the major androgens synthesized in the adrenal gland.

Androstenedione, another weak adrenal androgen, is produced by oxidation of the β-hydroxy group to a carbonyl group by 3-β-hydroxysteroid dehydrogenase. This androgen is converted to testosterone primarily in extra-adrenal tissues. Although the adrenal cortex makes very little estrogen, the weak adrenal androgens may be converted to estrogens in the peripheral tissues, particularly in adipose tissue (Fig. 34.25).

D. Synthesis of Testosterone

Luteinizing hormone (LH) from the anterior pituitary stimulates the synthesis of testosterone and other androgens by the Leydig cells of the human testicle. In many ways, the pathways leading to androgen synthesis in the testicle are similar to those described for the adrenal cortex. In the human testicle, the predominant pathway leading to testosterone synthesis is through pregnenolone to 17-α-hydroxypregnenolone to DHEA (the Δ^5 pathway), and then from DHEA to androstenedione, and from androstenedione to testosterone (see Fig. 34.23). As for all steroids, the rate-limiting step in testosterone production is the conversion of cholesterol to pregnenolone. LH controls the rate of side-chain cleavage from cholesterol at carbon 21 to form pregnenolone and thus regulates the rate of testosterone synthesis. In its target cells, the double bond in ring A of testosterone is reduced through the action of 5-α-reductase, forming the active hormone DHT.

 Hyperplasia or tumors of the adrenal cortex that produce excess aldosterone result in a condition known as primary aldosteronism, which is characterized by enhanced sodium and water retention, resulting in hypertension.

 Although aldosterone is the major mineralocorticoid in humans, excessive production of a weaker mineralocorticoid, DOC, which occurs in patients with a deficiency of the 11-hydroxylase (the P450$_{C11}$ enzyme, CYP11B1), may lead to clinical signs and symptoms of mineralocorticoid excess even though aldosterone secretion is suppressed in these patients.

Adrenal

Dehydroepiandrosterone   Androstenedione

Adipose tissue   Extra-adrenal tissues

Estrogens   Testosterone

FIG. 34.25. Adrenal androgens. These weak androgens are converted to testosterone or estrogens in other tissues.

 Congenital adrenal hyperplasia (CAH) is a group of diseases caused by a genetically determined deficiency in a variety of enzymes required for cortisol synthesis. The most common deficiency is that of 21-α-hydroxylase (CYP21), the activity of which is necessary to convert progesterone to 11-deoxycorticosterone and 17-α-hydroxyprogesterone to 11-deoxycortisol. Thus, this deficiency reduces both aldosterone and cortisol production without affecting androgen production. If the enzyme deficiency is severe, the precursors for aldosterone and cortisol production are shunted to androgen synthesis, producing an overabundance of androgens, which leads to prenatal masculinization in females and postnatal virilization in males. Another enzyme deficiency in this group of diseases is that of 11-β-hydroxylase (CYP11B1), which results in the accumulation of 11-deoxycorticosterone. An excess of this mineralocorticoid leads to hypertension (through binding of 11-deoxycorticosterone to the aldosterone receptor). In this form of CAH, 11-deoxycortisol also accumulates, but its biologic activity is minimal and no specific clinical signs and symptoms result. The androgen pathway is unaffected, and the increased adrenocorticotropic hormone (ACTH) levels may increase the levels of adrenal androgens in the blood. A third possible enzyme deficiency is that of 17-α-hydroxylase (CYP17). A defect in 17-α-hydroxylase leads to aldosterone excess and hypertension; however, because adrenal androgen synthesis requires this enzyme, no virilization occurs in these patients.

Biologically, the most potent circulating androgen is testosterone. Approximately 50% of the testosterone in the blood in a normal woman is produced equally in the ovaries and in the adrenal cortices. The remaining half is derived from ovarian and adrenal androstenedione, which, after secretion into the blood, is converted to testosterone in adipose tissue, muscle, liver, and skin. The adrenal cortex, however, is the major source of the relatively weak androgen dehydroepiandrosterone (DHEA). The serum concentration of its stable metabolite, DHEAS, is used as a measure of adrenal androgen production in hyperandrogenic patients with diffuse excessive growth of secondary sexual hair (e.g., facial hair as well as that in the axillae, the suprapubic area, the chest, and the upper extremities).

The results of the blood tests on **Vera Leizd** showed that her level of testosterone was normal but that her serum DHEAS level was significantly elevated. Which tissue was the most likely source of the androgens that caused Vera's hirsutism (a male pattern of secondary sexual hair growth)?

Rickets is a disorder of young children caused by a deficiency of vitamin D. Low levels of calcium and phosphorus in the blood are associated with skeletal deformities in these children.

E. Synthesis of Estrogens and Progesterone

Ovarian production of estrogens, progestins (compounds related to progesterone), and androgens requires the activity of the cytochrome P450 family of oxidative enzymes used for the synthesis of other steroid hormones. Ovarian estrogens are C18 steroids with a phenolic hydroxyl group at C3 and either a hydroxyl group (estradiol) or a ketone group (estrone) at C17. Although the major steroid-producing compartments of the ovary (the granulosa cell, the theca cell, the stromal cell, and the cells of the corpus luteum) have all of the enzyme systems required for the synthesis of multiple steroids, the granulosa cells secrete primarily estrogens, the theca and stromal cells secrete primarily androgens, and the cells of the corpus luteum secrete primarily progesterone.

The ovarian granulosa cell, in response to stimulation by FSH from the anterior pituitary gland and through the catalytic activity of P450 aromatase (CYP19), converts testosterone to estradiol, the predominant and most potent of the ovarian estrogens (see Fig. 34.23). Similarly, androstenedione is converted to estrone in the ovary, although the major site of estrone production from androstenedione occurs in extraovarian tissues, principally skeletal muscle and adipose tissue.

XI. VITAMIN D SYNTHESIS

Vitamin D is unique in that it can be either obtained from the diet (as vitamin D_2 or D_3) or synthesized from a cholesterol precursor, a process that requires reactions in the skin, liver, and kidney. The calciferols, including several forms of vitamin D, are a family of steroids that affect calcium homeostasis (Fig. 34.26). Cholecalciferol (vitamin D_3) requires ultraviolet light for its production from 7-dehydrocholesterol, which is present in cutaneous tissues (skin) in animals and available from ergosterol in plants. This irradiation cleaves the carbon–carbon bond at C9–C10, opening the B-ring to form cholecalciferol, an inactive precursor of $1,25\text{-}(OH)_2$-cholecalciferol (calcitriol). Calcitriol is the most potent biologically active form of vitamin D (see Fig. 34.26).

The formation of calcitriol from cholecalciferol begins in the liver and ends in the kidney, where the pathway is regulated. In this activation process, carbon 25 of vitamin D_2 or D_3 is hydroxylated in the microsomes of the liver to form 25-hydroxycholecalciferol (calcidiol). Calcidiol circulates to the kidney bound to vitamin D–binding globulin (transcalciferin). In the proximal convoluted tubule of the kidney, a mixed-function oxidase, which requires molecular O_2 and NADPH as cofactors, hydroxylates carbon 1 on the A-ring to form calcitriol. This step is tightly regulated and is the rate-limiting step in the production of the active hormone. The release of parathyroid hormone from the parathyroid gland results in activation of this last step of active hormone formation.

$1,25\text{-}(OH)_2D_3$ (calcitriol) is approximately 100 times more potent than $25\text{-}(OH)D_3$ in its actions, yet $25\text{-}(OH)D_3$ is present in the blood in a concentration that may be 100 times greater, which suggests that it may play some role in calcium and phosphorus homeostasis.

The biologically active forms of vitamin D are sterol hormones and, like other steroids, diffuse passively through the plasma membrane. In the intestine, bone, and kidney, the sterol then moves into the nucleus and binds to specific vitamin D_3 receptors. This complex activates genes that encode proteins mediating the action of active vitamin D_3. In the intestinal mucosal cell, for example, transcription of genes that encode calcium-transporting proteins are activated. These proteins are capable of carrying Ca^{2+} (and phosphorus) absorbed from the gut lumen across the cell, making it available for eventual passage into the circulation.

CLINICAL COMMENTS

Ann Jeina. Ann Jeina is typical of patients with essentially normal serum triacylglycerol levels and elevated serum total cholesterol levels that are repeatedly in the upper 1% of the general population (e.g., 325 to 500 mg/dL). When similar lipid abnormalities are present in other family members in a pattern of autosomal dominant inheritance and no secondary causes for these lipid alterations (e.g., hypothyroidism) are present, the entity referred to as *familial hypercholesterolemia (FH)*, type IIA, is the most likely cause of this hereditary dyslipidemia.

FH is a genetic disorder caused by an abnormality in one or more alleles responsible for the formation or the functional integrity of high-affinity low-density lipoprotein (LDL) receptors on the plasma membrane of cells that normally initiate the internalization of circulating LDL and other blood lipoproteins. Heterozygotes for FH (1 in 500 of the population) have roughly one-half of the normal complement or functional capacity of such receptors, whereas homozygotes (1 in 1 million of the population) have essentially no functional LDL receptors. The rare patient with the homozygous form of FH has a more extreme elevation of serum total and LDL cholesterol than does the heterozygote and, as a result, has a more profound predisposition to premature coronary artery disease.

Chronic hypercholesterolemia not only may cause the deposition of lipid within vascular tissues leading to atherosclerosis but also may cause the deposition of lipid within the skin and eye. When this occurs in the medial aspect of the upper and lower eyelids, it is referred to as *xanthelasma.* Similar deposits known as *xanthomas* may occur in the iris of the eye (arcus lipidalis) as well as the tendons of the hands ("knuckle pads") and Achilles tendons.

Although therapy aimed at inserting competent LDL receptor genes into the cells of patients with homozygous FH is being designed for the future, the current approach in the treatment of heterozygotes is to attempt to increase the rate of synthesis of LDL receptors in cells pharmacologically.

Ann Jeina was treated with ezetimibe, a drug that blocks cholesterol absorption in the intestine, causing a portion of the dietary cholesterol to be carried into the feces rather than packaged into chylomicrons. This reduces the levels of chylomicron-based cholesterol and cholesterol delivered to the liver by chylomicron remnants.

HMG-CoA reductase inhibitors, such as atorvastatin, which Ann is also taking, stimulate the synthesis of additional LDL receptors by inhibiting HMG-CoA reductase, the rate-limiting enzyme for cholesterol synthesis. The subsequent decline in the intracellular free cholesterol pool also stimulates the synthesis of additional LDL receptors. These additional receptors reduce circulating LDL-cholesterol levels by increasing receptor-mediated endocytosis of LDL particles.

A combination of strict dietary and dual pharmacologic therapy, aimed at decreasing the cholesterol levels of the body, is usually quite effective in correcting the lipid abnormality and, hopefully, the associated risk of atherosclerotic cardiovascular disease in patients with heterozygous familial hypercholesterolemia.

Ivan Applebod. Low-density lipoprotein (LDL) cholesterol is the primary target of cholesterol-lowering therapy because both epidemiologic and experimental evidence strongly suggest a benefit of lowering serum LDL cholesterol in the prevention of atherosclerotic cardiovascular disease. Similar evidence for raising subnormal levels of serum HDL cholesterol is less conclusive but adequate to support such efforts, particularly in high-risk patients, such as Ivan Applebod, who have multiple cardiovascular risk factors. For individuals whose LDL levels are less than 30 points from their target, the first-line therapy in this attempt is nonpharmacologic and includes such measures as increasing aerobic exercise, weight loss in overweight patients, avoidance of excessive alcohol intake,

Vera Leizd's hirsutism was most likely the result of a problem in her adrenal cortex that caused excessive production of DHEA.

FIG. 34.26. Synthesis of active vitamin D. $1,25\text{-}(OH)_2D_3$ is produced from 7-dehydrocholesterol, a precursor of cholesterol. In the skin, ultraviolet (UV) light produces cholecalciferol, which is hydroxylated at the 25-position in the liver and at the 1-position in the kidney to form the active hormone. *PTH*, parathyroid hormone.

Ann Jeina was treated with a statin (atorvastatin) and ezetimibe. Ezetimibe reduces the percentage of absorption of free cholesterol present in the lumen of the gut and hence the amount of cholesterol available to the enterocyte to package into chylomicrons. This, in turn, reduces the amount of cholesterol returning to the liver in chylomicron remnants. The net result is a reduction in the cholesterol pool in hepatocytes. The latter induces the synthesis of an increased number of LDL receptors by the liver cells. As a consequence, the capacity of the liver to increase hepatic uptake of LDL from the circulation leads to a decrease in serum LDL levels.

reducing the intake of refined sugars, and cessation of smoking. If these efforts fail, or if the existing LDL levels are greater than 30 points from their target, drug therapy to lower serum LDL cholesterol levels must be considered.

So far, Mr. Applebod has failed in his attempts to diet and exercise. His LDL cholesterol level is 231 mg/dL. According to Table 34.1, he is a candidate for more stringent dietary therapy and for drug treatment. He should be given an HMG-CoA reductase inhibitor such as pravastatin or atorvastatin. Other lipid-lowering drugs such as the fibric acid derivatives and ezetimibe, which also decrease triacylglycerol levels and potentially increase HDL levels, could be considered (Table 34.5). A low daily dose of aspirin (81 mg) could also be prescribed (see Chapter 35). It is important to gain early control of Mr. Applebod's metabolic syndrome before the effects of insulin resistance can no longer be reversed.

Vera Leizd. Vera Leizd was born with a normal female genotype and phenotype, had normal female sexual development, spontaneous onset of puberty, and regular, although somewhat scanty, menses until the age of 20 years. At that point, she developed secondary amenorrhea (cessation of menses) and evidence of male hormone excess with early virilization (masculinization).

The differential diagnosis included an ovarian versus an adrenocortical source of the excess androgenic steroids. A screening test to determine whether the adrenal cortex or the ovary is the source of excess male hormone involves measuring the concentration of dehydroepiandrosterone sulfate (DHEAS) in the patient's plasma because the adrenal cortex makes most of the DHEA and the ovary makes little or none. Vera's plasma DHEAS level was moderately elevated, identifying her adrenal cortices as the likely source of her virilizing syndrome.

If the excess production of androgens is not the result of an adrenal tumor, but rather the result of a defect in the pathway for cortisol production, the simple treatment is to administer glucocorticoids by mouth. The rationale for such treatment can be better understood by reviewing Figure 34.23. If Vera Leizd has a genetically determined partial deficiency in the P450$_{C11}$ enzyme system needed

Table 34.5 Mechanism(s) of Action and Efficacy of Lipid-Lowering Agents

| Agent | Mechanism of Action | Total Cholesterol | Percentage Change in Serum Lipid Level (Monotherapy) | | |
			LDL Cholesterol	HDL Cholesterol	Triacylglycerols
Statins	Inhibits HMG-CoA reductase activity	↓ 15%–60%	↓ 20%–60%	↑ 5%–15%	↓ 10%–40%
Bile acid resins	Increase fecal excretion of bile salts	↓ 15%–20%	↓ 10%–25%	↑ 3%–5%	Variable, depending on pretreatment level of triacylglycerols (may increase)
Niacin	Activates LPL; reduces hepatic production of VLDL; reduces catabolism of HDL	↓ 22%–25%	↓ 10%–25%	↑ 15%–35%	↓ 20%–50%
Fibrates	Antagonizes PPARα, causing an increase in LPL activity, a decrease in apoprotein CIII production, and an increase in apoprotein AI production	↓ 12%–15%	Variable, depending on pretreatment levels of other lipids	↑ 5%–15%	↓ 20%–50%
Ezetimibe	Reduces intestinal absorption of free cholesterol from the gut lumen	↓ 10%–15%	↓ 15%–20%	↑ 1%–3%	↓ 5%–8% if triacylglycerols are high pretreatment

LPL, lipoprotein lipase; LDL, low-density lipoprotein; HMG-CoA, hydroxymethylglutaryl-CoA; HDL, high-density lipoprotein; triacylglycerols, triglycerides; PPAR, peroxisome proliferator-activated receptor; VLDL, very low-density lipoprotein.
Source: Adapted from National Cholesterol Education Program. Third report of the National Cholesterol Education Program (NCEP) Expert Panel on Detection, Evaluation, and Treatment of High Blood Cholesterol in Adults (Adult Treatment Panel III). Final Report. *Circulation.* 2002;106:3143–3457.

to convert 11-deoxycortisol to cortisol, her blood cortisol levels would fall. By virtue of the normal positive feedback mechanism, a subnormal level of cortisol in the blood would induce the anterior pituitary to make more ACTH. The latter would not only stimulate the cortisol pathway to increase cortisol synthesis to normal but, in the process, would also induce increased production of adrenal androgens such as DHEA and DHEAS. The increased levels of the adrenal androgens (although relatively weak androgens) would cause varying degrees of virilization, depending on the severity of the enzyme deficiency. The administration of a glucocorticoid by mouth would suppress the high level of secretion of ACTH from the anterior pituitary gland that occurs in response to the reduced levels of cortisol secreted from the adrenal cortex. Treatment with prednisone (a synthetic glucocorticoid), therefore, will prevent the ACTH-induced overproduction of adrenal androgens. However, when ACTH secretion returns to normal, endogenous cortisol synthesis falls below normal. The administered prednisone brings the net glucocorticoid activity in the blood back to physiologic levels. Vera's adrenal androgen levels in the blood returned to normal after several weeks of therapy with prednisone (a synthetic glucocorticoid). As a result, her menses eventually resumed, and her virilizing features slowly resolved.

Because Vera's symptoms began in adult life, her genetically determined adrenal hyperplasia is referred to as a "nonclassic" or "atypical" form of the disorder. A more severe enzyme deficiency leads to the "classic" disease, which is associated with excessive fetal adrenal androgen production in utero and manifests at birth, often with ambiguous external genitalia and virilizing features in the female neonate.

BIOCHEMICAL COMMENTS

 Drugs used to treat certain aspects of the metabolic syndrome improve insulin sensitivity and regulate lipid levels through modulation of the pathways discussed in Chapters 32 through 34. These drugs work by modifying the regulatory pathways that have been discussed so far with regard to carbohydrate and lipid metabolism.

Metformin. Metformin has been used for >30 years as a treatment for type 2 diabetes. Metformin reduces blood glucose levels by inhibiting hepatic gluconeogenesis, which is active in these patients because of the liver's resistance to the effects of insulin. Metformin also reduces lipid synthesis in the liver, which aids in modulating blood lipid levels in these patients.

Metformin accomplishes its effects by activating the adenosine monophosphate (AMP)-activated protein kinase (AMPK). It does so through activation of an upstream protein kinase, LKB1, via an unknown mechanism. As discussed previously, AMPK, when active, phosphorylates and reduces the activity of acetyl-CoA carboxylase (required for fatty acid synthesis) and HMG-CoA reductase (reducing the biosynthesis of cholesterol). Activation of AMPK also activates glucose uptake by the muscle (see Chapter 47), which is significant for reducing circulating blood glucose levels.

The activation of AMPK also leads to a cascade of transcriptional regulation that reduces the liver's ability to undergo both gluconeogenesis and lipogenesis. Activated AMPK phosphorylates a coactivator of the CREB transcription factor named *t*ransducer *of r*egulated *C*REB activity *2* (TORC2) (Fig. 34.27). When TORC2 is phosphorylated, it is sequestered in the cytoplasm, and CREB becomes very inefficient at transcribing a gene that is required to upregulate genes that code for the enzymes involved in gluconeogenesis. This important transcriptional coactivator is named peroxisome proliferator-activated receptor-γ coactivator 1α (PGC1α). PGC1α participates in the transcriptional activation of key gluconeogenic enzymes, such as glucose 6-phosphatase and phosphoenolpyruvate carboxykinase (PEPCK). Thus, in

 The LKB1 protein is a tumor suppressor; loss of LKB1 activity leads to Peutz-Jeghers syndrome (PJS). PJS exhibits the early development of vascular polyps in the gastrointestinal tract and an increased incidence of carcinomas at a relatively young age. LKB1 regulates the activity of 14 kinases that include, and are similar to, the adenosine monophosphate (AMP)-activated protein kinase. Loss of the normal regulation of these kinases, due to the absence of LKB1 activity, significantly contributes to tumor formation.

FIG. 34.27. Action of metformin on gluconeogenesis. Under normal conditions, increases of hepatic cyclic adenosine monophosphate (cAMP) levels (e.g., in response to glucagon) activate CREB, which, in combination with TORC2, leads to increased transcription of genes required for gluconeogenesis. Under conditions of insulin resistance, this pathway remains stimulated, even in the presence of insulin. Metformin stimulates the activation of AMPK, which phosphorylates TORC2 and sequesters it in the cytoplasm, thereby decreasing synthesis of gluconeogenic enzymes and reducing hepatic output of glucose. The abbreviations used are defined in this text.

the presence of metformin, hepatic gluconeogenesis is reduced and muscle uptake of blood glucose is enhanced, leading to stabilization of blood glucose levels. The physiologic regulators of LKB1 have yet to be identified.

Activation of AMPK also inhibits liver lipogenesis. In addition to phosphorylating and inhibiting acetyl-CoA carboxylase activity (which reduces malonyl-CoA levels, leading to reduced fatty acid synthesis and enhanced fatty acid oxidation), AMPK activity decreases the transcription of key lipogenic enzymes, including fatty acid synthase and acetyl-CoA carboxylase. The reduced transcriptional activity is mediated via an AMPK inhibition of the transcription of sterol-regulatory element-binding protein 1 (SREBP-1), which in addition to regulating the transcription of HMG-CoA reductase, also regulates the transcription of other lipogenic enzymes. The AMPK is discussed in more detail in the Biochemical Comments section of Chapter 36.

Fibrates. The fibrates are a class of drugs used to decrease lipid levels (principally triglycerides) in patients. A major target of the fibrates is peroxisome proliferator-activated receptor-α (PPARα). Fibrate binding to PPARα activates this transcription factor, which then leads to the transcription of a multitude of genes that degrade lipids. These targets include the genes for fatty acid transport proteins (so there is an enhanced rate of fatty acid transport into cells), fatty acid translocase (to increase mitochondrial uptake of the fatty acids), long-chain fatty acyl-CoA synthetase (activation of the fatty acids in the cytoplasm), and carnitine palmitoyl transferase I (which enhances the uptake of fatty acids into the mitochondria). In addition, PPARα activation enhances lipoprotein lipase (LPL) expression, represses apoCIII expression (apoCIII inhibits the apoCII activation of LPL), and stimulates apoAI and apoAII synthesis, the major proteins in HDL. These transcriptional changes all lead to enhanced fat use and a reduction of circulating particles.

Thiazolidinediones. A third class of drugs used for the treatment of insulin resistance and type 2 diabetes mellitus is the thiazolidinediones (TZDs), which activate the peroxisome proliferator-activated receptor-γ (PPARγ) class of transcription factors. PPARγ is expressed primarily in adipose tissue. This transcription factor is responsible for activating the transcription of adiponectin (see Chapter 33, Section VIII.B), leading to increased circulating adiponectin levels. The increase in adiponectin reduces the fat content of the liver and enhances insulin sensitivity via an AMPK-dependent pathway. Thiazolidinediones also lead to a reduction in plasma free fatty acid levels, which leads to enhanced insulin sensitivity (see the Biochemical Comments in Chapter 33).

Key Concepts

- Cholesterol regulates membrane fluidity and is a precursor of bile salts, steroid hormones (such as estrogen and testosterone), and vitamin D.
- Cholesterol, because of its hydrophobic nature, is transported in the blood as a component of lipoproteins.
- Within the lipoproteins, cholesterol can appear in its unesterified form in the outer shell of the particle or as cholesterol esters in the core of the particle.
- De novo cholesterol synthesis requires acetyl-CoA as a precursor, which is initially converted to hydroxymethylglutaryl CoA (HMG-CoA). The cholesterol synthesized in this way is packaged, along with triglyceride, into VLDL in the liver and then released into circulation.
- The conversion of HMG-CoA to mevalonic acid, catalyzed by HMG-CoA reductase, is the regulated and rate-limiting step of cholesterol biosynthesis.
- In the circulation, the triglycerides in VLDL are digested by lipoprotein lipase, which converts the particle to IDL and then to LDL.
- IDL and LDL bind specifically to receptors on the liver cell, are internalized, and the particle components are recycled.
- A third lipoprotein particle, HDL, functions to transfer apolipoprotein E and apolipoprotein CII to nascent chylomicrons and nascent VLDL.
- HDL also participates in reverse cholesterol transport, the movement of cholesterol from cell membranes to the HDL particle, which returns the cholesterol to the liver.
- Atherosclerotic plaques are associated with elevated levels of blood cholesterol levels. High levels of LDL are more strongly associated with the generation of atherosclerotic plaques, whereas high levels of HDL are protective because of their participation in reverse cholesterol transport.
- Bile salts are required for fat emulsification and micelle formation in the small intestine.
- Bile salts are recycled via the enterohepatic circulation, forming the secondary bile acids in the process.
- The steroid hormones are derived from cholesterol, which is converted to pregnenolone, which is the precursor for the mineralocorticoids (such as aldosterone), the glucocorticoids (such as cortisol), and the sex steroids (such as testosterone and estrogen).
- Lipid-lowering drugs act on a variety of targets within liver, intestine, and adipocytes.
- Diseases discussed in this chapter are summarized in Table 34.6.

Table 34.6   Diseases Discussed in Chapter 34

Disease or Disorder	Environmental or Genetic	Comments
Hypercholesterolemia	Both	Defined by elevated levels of cholesterol in the blood, often leading to coronary artery disease.
Familial hypercholesterolemia, type II	Genetic	Defect in LDL receptor, leading to elevated cholesterol levels, and premature death caused by coronary artery disease.
Virilization	Both	Excessive release of androgenic steroids due to a variety of causes.
Congenital adrenal hyperplasia (CAH)	Genetic	CAH is a constellation of disorders caused by mutations in enzymes required for cortisol synthesis. One potential consequence is excessive androgen synthesis, which may lead to prenatal masculinization of females. The different symptoms observed between patients are caused by different enzyme deficiencies in the patients.
Rickets	Environmental	Due to a lack of vitamin D, calcium metabolism is altered, leading to skeletal deformities.

1. Which of the following steps in the biosynthesis of choles-terol is the committed rate-limiting step?

    A. The condensation of acetoacetyl-CoA with a molecule of acetyl-CoA to yield β-hydroxy-β-methylglutaryl-CoA (HMG-CoA)
    B. The reduction of HMG-CoA to mevalonate
    C. The conversion of mevalonate to two activated isoprenes
    D. The formation of farnesyl pyrophosphate
    E. Condensation of six activated isoprene units to form squalene

2. Considering the final steps in cholesterol biosynthesis, when squalene is eventually converted to lanosterol, which of the following statements is correct?

    A. All of the sterols have three fused rings (the steroid nucleus) and are alcohols with a hydroxyl group at C3.
    B. The action of squalene monooxygenase oxidizes C14 of the squalene chain, forming an epoxide.
    C. Squalene monooxygenase is considered a mixed-function oxidase because it catalyzes a reaction in which only one of the oxygen atoms of O_2 is incor-porated into the organic substrate.
    D. Squalene monooxygenase uses reduced flavin nucleotides, such as FAD(2H), as the cosubstrate in the reaction.
    E. Squalene is joined at carbons 1 and 30 to form the fused-ring structure of sterols.

3. Of the major risk factors for the development of ath-erosclerotic cardiovascular disease (ASCVD), such as sedentary lifestyle, obesity, cigarette smoking, diabetes mellitus, hypertension, and hyperlipidemia, which one, if present, is the only risk factor in a given patient without a history of having had a myocardial infarction that requires that the therapeutic goal for the serum LDL cholesterol level be <100 mg/dL?

    A. Obesity
    B. Cigarette smoking
    C. Diabetes mellitus
    D. Hypertension
    E. Sedentary lifestyle

4. Which one of the following apoproteins acts as a cofactor activator of the enzyme lipoprotein lipase (LPL)?

    A. ApoCIII
    B. ApoCII
    C. ApoB$_{100}$
    D. ApoB$_{48s}$
    E. ApoE

5. Which one of the following sequences places the lipopro-teins in the order of most dense to least dense?

    A. HDL/VLDL/chylomicrons/LDL
    B. HDL/LDL/VLDL/chylomicrons
    C. LDL/chylomicrons/HDL/VLDL
    D. VLDL/chylomicrons/LDL/HDL
    E. LDL/chylomicrons/VLDL/HDL

35 Metabolism of the Eicosanoids

The *eicosanoids*, which include the **prostaglandins** *(PGs)*, **thromboxanes** *(TXs)*, and **leukotrienes** *(LTs)*, are among the most potent regulators of cellular function in nature and are produced by almost every cell in the body. They act mainly as "local" hormones, affecting the cells that produce them or neighboring cells of a different type.

Eicosanoids participate in many processes in the body, particularly the **inflammatory response** that occurs after **infection** or **injury**. The inflammatory response is the sum of the body's efforts to destroy invading organisms and to repair damage. It includes control of bleeding through the formation of blood clots. In the process of protecting the body from a variety of insults, the inflammatory response can produce **symptoms** such as **pain**, **swelling**, and **fever**. An exaggerated or inappropriate expression of the normal inflammatory response may occur in individuals who have **allergic** or **hypersensitivity** reactions.

In addition to participating in the inflammatory response, eicosanoids also regulate **smooth muscle contraction** (particularly in the intestine and uterus). They increase **water** and **sodium excretion** by the kidney and are involved in **regulating blood pressure**. They frequently serve as modulators; some eicosanoids stimulate and others inhibit the same process. For example, some serve as constrictors and others as dilators of blood vessels. They are also involved in regulating **bronchoconstriction** and **bronchodilation**.

Eicosanoids are derived from polyunsaturated fatty acids containing 20 carbon atoms, which are found in cell membranes esterified to membrane phospholipids. Arachidonic acid, derived from the diet or synthesized from linoleate, is the compound from which most eicosanoids are produced in the body. Compounds that serve as signals for eicosanoid production bind to cell membrane receptors and activate phospholipases that cleave the polyunsaturated fatty acids from cell membrane phospholipids (Fig. 35.1).

Arachidonic acid is enzymatically metabolized by three major pathways. The two pathways that have been most thoroughly studied are the **cyclooxygenase** pathway (which produces prostaglandins and thromboxanes) and the **lipoxygenase** pathway (which produces leukotrienes). The **cytochrome P450** pathway generates eicosanoids with less well-defined physiologic functions. **Isoprostanes** are a relatively new class of eicosanoids derived from nonenzymatic free radical–catalyzed reactions. The isoprostanes are similar to prostaglandins in structure and may play a role in inflammatory responses and free radical–mediated tissue injury. Isoprostane levels in blood are used to assess oxidative stress in patients. In brain tissue, arachidonic acid can be coupled to ethanolamine to generate **anandamide**. This compound can bind and activate cannabinoid receptors with actions similar to those of Δ^9-tetrahydrocannabinol (THC).

Many eicosanoids have very **short half-lives**, in the range of a few minutes or less. They are rapidly inactivated and excreted.

FIG. 35.1. Overview of eicosanoid metabolism. Eicosanoids are produced from fatty acids released from membrane phospholipids. In humans, arachidonic acid is the major precursor of the eicosanoids, which include the prostaglandins, leukotrienes, and thromboxanes. ⊖ "inhibits"; *cyt*, cytochrome; *NSAIDs*, nonsteroidal anti-inflammatory drugs.

THE WAITING ROOM

 Since her admission to the hospital for an acute myocardial infarction, **Ann Jeina** has been taking the cholesterol absorption blocking drug, ezetimibe and the hydroxymethylglutaryl coenzyme A (HMG-CoA) reductase inhibitor atorvastatin, to lower her blood cholesterol levels (see Chapter 34). She also takes 81 mg of acetylsalicylic acid (ASA; aspirin) each day. At her most recent visit to her cardiologist, she asked whether she should continue to take aspirin because she no longer has any chest pain. She was told that the use of aspirin in her case was not to alleviate pain but to reduce the risk of a second heart attack and that she should continue to take this drug for the remainder of her life unless a complication such as gastrointestinal bleeding occurred as a result of its use.

 Emma Wheezer has done well regarding her respiratory function since her earlier hospitalization for an acute asthmatic attack (see Chapter 31). She has been maintained on two puffs of triamcinolone acetonide (a potent inhaled corticosteroid) two times per day and has not required systemic steroids for months. The glucose intolerance precipitated by high intravenous and oral doses of the synthetic glucocorticoid prednisone during her earlier hospitalization resolved after this drug was discontinued. She has come to her doctor now because she is concerned that the low-grade fever and cough she has developed over the last 36 hours may trigger another acute asthma attack.

I. SOURCE OF THE EICOSANOIDS

The most abundant, and therefore the most common precursor of the eicosanoids (*eicosa* is the Greek word for 20) is *arachidonic acid* (eicosatetraenoic acid, $\omega 6,20:4$, $\Delta 5,8,11,14$), a polyunsaturated fatty acid with 20 carbons and four double bonds (see Fig. 35.1). It is esterified to phospholipids located in the lipid bilayer that constitutes the plasma membrane of the cell. Because arachidonic acid cannot be synthesized de novo in the body, the diet must contain arachidonic acid or other fatty acids from which arachidonic acid can be produced. The major dietary precursor for arachidonic acid synthesis is the essential fatty acid linoleate, which is present in plant oils (see Chapter 33). The composition of the diet affects the fatty acid content of membrane phospholipids. Individuals with a high content of saturated fatty acids in their diets have a high content of saturated fatty acids in their membrane lipids. Likewise, individuals with a high content of polyunsaturated fatty acids in their diets have a high content of polyunsaturated fatty acids in their membrane lipids.

The arachidonic acid in membrane phospholipids is released from the lipid bilayer as a consequence of the activation of membrane-bound phospholipase A2 or C (see Chapter 33, Fig. 33.30, and Fig. 35.2). This activation occurs when a variety of stimuli (agonists) such as histamine or the cytokines interact with a specific plasma membrane receptor on the target cell surface. Phospholipase A2

 Dietary deficiencies of essential fatty acids are rare. However, some cases have been reported in patients receiving total parenteral nutrition (TPN). Although the most obvious symptom is a red scaly dermatitis, deficiencies of essential fatty acids also result in a decreased availability of precursors for eicosanoid synthesis.

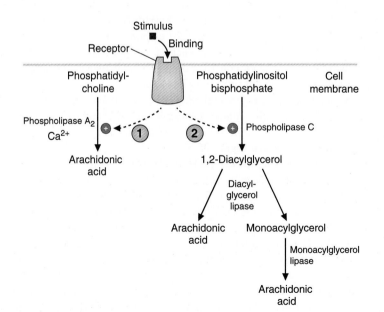

FIG. 35.2.   Release of arachidonic acid from membrane lipids. The binding of a stimulus to its receptor activates pathway 1 or 2.

FIG. 35.3. Pathways for the metabolism of arachidonic acid.

 Inflammation involving the mucosal and smooth muscle layers of the respiratory tract plays a major role in the development of acute asthmatic bronchospasm in patients such as **Emma Wheezer**. Prednisone and other potent glucocorticoids are capable of preventing or suppressing this inflammation.

In part, the glucocorticoids act by inhibiting the recruitment of leukocytes and monocytes–macrophages into affected areas. They also limit the ability of these cells to elaborate a variety of chemotactic factors and other substances, such as certain eicosanoids, which enhance the inflammatory process. Glucocorticoids, for example, suppress the transcription and translation of the inducible form of the cyclo-oxygenase enzyme, COX-2. Glucocorticoids also induce the synthesis of a protein or family of proteins (lipocortins or macrocortins) that inhibit the activity of phospholipase A2. As a result, the synthesis of prostaglandins and leukotrienes is decreased and the inflammatory response in bronchial tissues is reduced (see Figs. 35.1 and 35.2).

FIG. 35.4. Structural features common to the biologically active prostaglandins. These compounds have 20 carbons, with a carboxyl group at carbon 1. Carbons 8 through 12 form a five-membered ring with substituents (usually a hydroxyl or keto group) at carbons 9 (X) and 11 (Y). Carbon 15 contains a hydroxyl group, and a *trans* double bond connects carbons 13 and 14. Double bonds also may be present between carbons 5 and 6 and between carbons 17 and 18 (see Fig. 35.6).

is specific for the sn-2 position of phosphoacylglycerols, the site of attachment of arachidonic acid to the glycerol moiety. Phospholipase C, on the other hand, hydrolyzes phosphorylated inositol from the inositol glycerophospholipids, generating a diacylglycerol containing arachidonic acid. This arachidonic acid is subsequently released by the action of other lipases.

II. PATHWAYS FOR EICOSANOID SYNTHESIS

After arachidonic acid is released into the cytosol, it is converted to eicosanoids by a variety of enzymes with activities that vary among tissues. This variation explains why some cells, such as those in the vascular endothelium, synthesize prostaglandins E_2 and I_2 (PGE_2 and PGI_2), whereas cells such as platelets synthesize primarily thromboxane A_2 (TXA_2) and 12-hydroxyeicosatetraenoic acid (12-HETE).

Three major pathways for the metabolism of arachidonic acid occur in various tissues (Fig. 35.3). The first of these, the cyclo-oxygenase pathway, leads to the synthesis of prostaglandins and thromboxanes. The second, the lipoxygenase pathway, yields the leukotrienes, HETEs, and lipoxins. The third pathway, catalyzed by the cytochrome P450 system, is responsible for the synthesis of the epoxides, HETEs, and diHETEs.

A. Cyclo-oxygenase Pathway: Synthesis of the Prostaglandins and Thromboxanes

1. STRUCTURES OF THE PROSTAGLANDINS

Prostaglandins are fatty acids containing 20 carbon atoms, including an internal five-carbon ring. In addition to this ring, each of the biologically active prostaglandins has a hydroxyl group at carbon 15, a double bond between carbons 13 and 14, and various substituents on the ring (Fig. 35.4).

The nomenclature for the prostaglandins (PGs) involve the assignment of a capital letter (PGE), an Arabic numeral subscript (PGE_1), and for the PGF family, a Greek letter subscript (e.g., $PGF_2\alpha$). The capital letter, in this case "F," refers to the ring substituents shown in Figure 35.5.

The subscript that follows the capital letter (PGF_1) refers to the PG series 1, 2, or 3, determined by the number of unsaturated bonds present in the linear portion of the hydrocarbon chain (Fig. 35.6). It does not include double bonds in the internal ring. Prostaglandins of the 1 series have one double bond (between carbons 13 and 14). The 2 series has two double bonds (between carbons 13 and 14 and between carbons 5 and 6). The 3 series has three double bonds (between carbons 13 and 14, 5 and 6, and 17 and 18). The double bonds between carbons 13 and 14 are *trans*; the others are *cis*.

The Greek letter subscript, found only in the F series, refers to the position of the hydroxyl group at carbon 9. This hydroxyl group exists primarily in the α-position, where it lies below the plane of the ring, as does the hydroxyl group at carbon 11 (see Figs. 35.4 and 35.5).

FIG. 35.5. Ring substituents of the prostaglandins (PGs). The letter after PG denotes the configuration of the ring and its substituents. R_4, R_7, and R_8 represent the nonring portions of the molecule. R_4 contains four carbons (including the carboxyl group). R_7 and R_8 contain seven and eight carbons, respectively, and correspond to the 1, 2, or 3 series shown in Figure 35.6. Note that the prostacyclins (PGI) contain two rings.

2. STRUCTURE OF THE THROMBOXANES

The *thromboxanes*, derived from arachidonic acid via the cyclo-oxygenase pathway, closely resemble the prostaglandins in structure except that they contain a six-membered ring that includes an oxygen atom (Fig. 35.7). The most common thromboxane, TXA_2, contains an additional oxygen atom attached to both carbon 9 and carbon 11 of the ring. The thromboxanes were named for their action in producing blood clots (thrombi).

3. BIOSYNTHESIS OF THE PROSTAGLANDINS AND THROMBOXANES

Only the biosynthesis of those prostaglandins derived from arachidonic acid (e.g., the 2 series, such as PGE_2, PGI_2, TXA_2) are described because those derived from eicosatrienoic acid (the 1 series) or from eicosapentaenoic acid (the 3 series) are present in very small amounts in humans on a normal diet.

The biochemical reactions that lead to the synthesis of prostaglandins and thromboxanes are illustrated in Figure 35.8. The initial step, which is catalyzed by a cyclo-oxygenase, forms the five-membered ring and adds four atoms of oxygen (two between carbons 9 and 11, and two at carbon 15) to form the unstable endoperoxide, PGG_2. The hydroperoxy group at carbon 15 is quickly reduced to a hydroxyl group by a peroxidase to form another endoperoxide, PGH_2.

The next step is tissue specific (see Fig. 35.8). Depending on the type of cell involved, PGH_2 may be reduced to PGE_2 or PGD_2 by specific enzymes (PGE synthase and PGD synthase). PGE_2 may be further reduced by PGE 9-ketoreductase to form $PGF_2\alpha$. $PGF_2\alpha$ also may be formed directly from PGH_2 by the action of

The measurement of prostaglandin levels, in plasma or urine, is best done by radioimmunoassay (see Chapter 43, Biochemical Comments). Antibodies specific for each prostaglandin or thromboxane form are commercially available, and through competition with a standard amount of antigen, one can determine the concentration of the metabolite in the biological fluid. Recently, a more sensitive technique has been developed that can assay prostaglandin levels as low as 40 pg/mL. This technique is called fluorescent polarization immunoassay (FPIA). The method is based on the properties of small, fluorescent molecules. Molecules that fluoresce absorb light at a particular wavelength and will emit light of a lower wavelength (the fluorescence). If one excites a small fluorophore with polarized light, the fluorescence will be polarized if the molecule rotates slowly; if the molecule rotates rapidly, the emitted light will not be polarized. If, then, the fluorophore is bound to a much larger molecule, such as an antibody, its rotation would be greatly diminished and the fluorescent signal emitted will be highly polarized. One can therefore measure the polarization of the emitted light as a function of how much fluorescent standard is bound to the antibody. So for these assays, a known amount of a fluorescent prostaglandin is incubated with the samples; if the sample contains nonfluorescent prostaglandin, it will compete for binding with the fluorescent prostaglandin, relegating some fluorescent prostaglandin to being nonbound. When the excitation light hits the sample, the amount of polarization will decrease in proportion to the amount of fluorescent prostaglandin displaced from the antibody. Through use of a standard curve, one can then calculate the level of prostaglandin in the sample to very low levels.

FIG. 35.6. Prostaglandins of the 1, 2, and 3 series and their precursors. The numeral (as a subscript in the name of the compound) refers to the number of double bonds in the nonring portion of the prostaglandin. *Trans* double bonds are at position 13, and *cis* double bonds are at positions 5 and 17. The hydroxyl group at carbon 15 is required for biologic activity.

FIG. 35.7. The thromboxane ring. In contrast to the prostaglandins, which have a five-membered carbon ring, thromboxanes have a six-membered ring (*shown in red*) containing an oxygen atom. Substituents are attached to the ring at carbons 9 and 11. In the case of TXA$_2$ (shown previously), an oxygen atom connects carbons 9 and 11.

an endoperoxide reductase. Some of the major functions of the prostaglandins are listed in Table 35.1.

PGH$_2$ may be converted to the thromboxane TXA$_2$, a reaction catalyzed by TXA synthase (see Fig. 35.8). This enzyme is present in high concentration in platelets. In the vascular endothelium, however, PGH$_2$ is converted to the prostaglandin PGI$_2$ (prostacyclin) by PGI synthase (see Fig. 35.8). TXA$_2$ and PGI$_2$ have important antagonistic biologic effects on vasomotor and smooth muscle tone and on platelet aggregation. Some of the known functions of the thromboxanes are listed in Table 35.2.

FIG. 35.8. Formation of prostaglandins (including the prostacyclin PGI$_2$) and thromboxane TXA$_2$ from arachidonic acid. The conversion of arachidonic acid to PGH$_2$ is catalyzed by a membrane-bound enzyme, prostaglandin endoperoxide synthase, which has cyclo-oxygenase and peroxidase activities. The reducing agent is glutathione (GSH), which is oxidized to form a disulfide between two glutathione molecules (GSSG).

In the 1990s, the cyclo-oxygenase enzyme was found to exist as two distinct isoforms, designated COX-1 and COX-2. COX-1 is regarded as a constitutive form of the enzyme, is widely expressed in almost all tissues, is the only form expressed in mature platelets, and is involved in the production of prostaglandins and thromboxanes for "normal" physiologic functions. COX-2 is an inducible form of the enzyme regulated by a variety of cytokines and growth factors. COX-2 messenger

Table 35.1   Some Functions of the Prostaglandins

PGI$_2$, PGE$_2$, PGD$_2$	PGF$_{2\alpha}$
Increase	Increases
Vasodilation	Vasoconstriction
cAMP	Bronchoconstriction
Decrease	Smooth muscle contraction
Platelet aggregation	
Leukocyte aggregation	
IL-1[a] and IL-2	
T-cell proliferation	
Lymphocyte migration	

[a]IL, interleukin, a cytokine that augments the activity of many cells in the immune system.

Table 35.2   Some Functions of Thromboxane A$_2$

Increases
  Vasoconstriction
  Platelet aggregation
  Lymphocyte proliferation
  Bronchoconstriction

The predominant eicosanoid in platelets is TXA$_2$, a potent vasoconstrictor and a stimulator of platelet aggregation. The latter action initiates thrombus formation at sites of vascular injury as well as in the vicinity of a ruptured atherosclerotic plaque in the lumen of vessels such as the coronary arteries. Such thrombi may cause sudden total occlusion of the vascular lumen, causing acute ischemic damage to tissues distal to the block (i.e., acute myocardial infarction).

Aspirin, by covalently acetylating the active site of cyclo-oxygenase, blocks the production of TXA$_2$ from its major precursor, arachidonic acid. By causing this mild hemostatic defect, low-dose aspirin has been shown to be effective in prevention of acute myocardial infarction (see Clinical Comments). For **Ivan Applebod** (who has symptoms of coronary heart disease), aspirin is used to prevent a first heart attack (primary prevention). For **Ann Jeina** and **Cora Nari** (who have already had heart attacks), aspirin is used to prevent a second heart attack (secondary prevention).

Diets that include cold-water fish (e.g., salmon, mackerel, brook trout, herring), with a high content of polyunsaturated fatty acids, eicosapentaenoic acid (EPA), and docosahexaenoic acid (DHA) (see Chapter 33), result in a high content of these fatty acids in membrane phospholipids. It has been suggested that such diets are effective in preventing heart disease, in part because they lead to formation of more TXA$_3$ relative to TXA$_2$. TXA$_3$ is less effective in stimulating platelet aggregation than its counterpart in the 2 series, TXA$_2$.

RNA (mRNA) and protein levels are usually low in most healthy tissue but are expressed at high levels in inflamed tissue.

Because of the importance of prostaglandins in mediating the inflammatory response, drugs that block prostaglandin production should provide relief from pain. The cyclo-oxygenase enzyme is inhibited by all nonsteroidal anti-inflammatory drugs (NSAIDs) such as acetylsalicylic acid (aspirin). Aspirin transfers an acetyl group to the enzyme, **irreversibly** inactivating it (Fig. 35.9). Other NSAIDs (e.g., acetaminophen, ibuprofen) act as **reversible** inhibitors of cyclo-oxygenase. Acetaminophen is the major ingredient in Tylenol, and ibuprofen is the major ingredient in other NSAIDs such as Motrin, Nuprin, and Advil (see Fig. 35.9). Although they have some relative selectivity for inhibiting either COX-1 or COX-2, NSAIDs block the activity of both isoforms. These findings have provided the impetus for the development of selective COX-2 inhibitors, which are proposed to act as potent anti-inflammatory agents by inhibiting COX-2 activity, without the gastrointestinal (stomach ulcers) and antiplatelet side effects commonly associated with NSAID use. These adverse effects of NSAIDs are thought to be caused by COX-1 inhibition. Examples of these newer selective COX-2 inhibitors are celecoxib (Celebrex) and rofecoxib (Vioxx).

4. INACTIVATION OF THE PROSTAGLANDINS AND THROMBOXANES

Prostaglandins and thromboxanes are rapidly inactivated. Their half-lives ($t_{1/2}$) range from seconds to minutes. The prostaglandins are inactivated by oxidation of the 15-hydroxy group—which is critical for their activity—to a ketone. The double bond at carbon 13 is reduced. Subsequently, both β- and ω-oxidation of the nonring portions occur, producing dicarboxylic acids that are excreted in the urine. Active TXA$_2$ is rapidly metabolized to TXB$_2$ by cleavage of the oxygen bridge between carbons 9 and 11 to form two hydroxyl groups. TXB$_2$ has no biologic activity.

FIG. 35.9. Action of aspirin and other NSAIDs.

Table 35.3   Properties of COX-1 and COX-2

	COX-1	*COX-2*
Primary function	Platelet aggregation, stomach cytoprotection	Inflammation, hyperalgesia
Response to:		
NSAIDs	Decreased activity	Decreased activity
Steroids	No effect	Decreased synthesis and activity
COX-2 inhibitor	No effect	Decreased activity

NSAIDs, nonsteroidal anti-inflammatory drugs. Data adapted from Patrono and Baigent (see References) indicate that low-dose aspirin (50 to 100 mg/day) reduces platelet TXA$_2$ levels by 97%, with no effect on whole body PGI$_2$, thereby leading to cardioprotection. High-dose aspirin (650 to 1,300 mg/day), in addition to reducing TXA$_2$ levels, also reduced PGI$_2$ levels by 60% to 80%. COX-2 specific inhibitors, at high levels, had no effect on TXA$_2$ levels but reduced whole body PGI$_2$ levels by 60% to 80%; leading to an increased risk of myocardial infarction.

B. Lipoxygenase Pathway: Synthesis of the Leukotrienes, Hydroxyeicosatetraenoic, and Lipoxins

In addition to serving as a substrate for the cyclo-oxygenase pathway, arachidonic acid also acts as a substrate for the lipoxygenase pathway. The lipoxygenase enzymes catalyze the incorporation of an oxygen molecule into a carbon of one of several double bonds of arachidonic acid, forming a hydroperoxy (—OOH) group at these positions. With this oxygenation, the double bond isomerizes to a position one carbon removed from the hydroperoxy group and is transformed from the *cis* to the *trans* configuration (Fig. 35.10). The unstable hydroperoxy group is then converted to the more stable hydroxy group.

Lipoxygenases may act at carbons 5, 12, or 15. The type of lipoxygenase varies from tissue to tissue. For example, polymorphonuclear leukocytes contain primarily 5-lipoxygenase, platelets are rich in 12-lipoxygenase, and eosinophilic leukocytes contain primarily 15-lipoxygenase.

Although the COX-2 inhibitors did relieve the development of gastrointestinal ulcers in patients taking nonsteroidal anti-inflammatory drugs (NSAIDs), further studies indicated that specific COX-2 inhibitors may have a negative effect on cardiovascular function. Vioxx was withdrawn from the market by its manufacturer because of these negative patient studies. It has been postulated that long-term use of COX-2 inhibitors alter the balance of prostacyclin (antithrombotic, PGI$_2$) and thromboxane (prothrombotic) because platelets, the major source of the thromboxanes, do not express COX-2 and thromboxane synthesis is not reduced with COX-2 inhibitors (see Fig. 35.8, indicating that PGI$_2$ synthesis in the blood vessels will be decreased by COX-2 inhibitors). This will tilt the balance of the eicosanoids synthesized toward a thrombotic pathway. The COX-2 inhibitors that remain on the market must be used with caution, and they are contraindicated in patients with ischemic heart disease or stroke. Some properties of COX-1 and COX-2 are indicated in Table 35.3.

FIG. 35.10.   Action of lipoxygenases in the formation of HPETEs (hydroperoxyeicosatetraenoic acids) and HETEs (hydroxyeicosatetraenoic acids). Lipoxygenases add hydroperoxy groups at positions 5, 12, or 15 with rearrangement of the double bond. HPETEs are unstable and are rapidly reduced to form HETEs or are converted to leukotrienes and lipoxins (see Figs. 35.11 and 35.12).

FIG. 35.11. Formation of leukotrienes and their glutathione (GSH) derivatives. *HPETE*, hydroperoxyeicosatetraenoic acid; *LT*, leukotriene (thus, *LTA*₄ is leukotriene A₄).

FIG. 35.12. Formation of the lipoxins. These compounds contain three hydroxyl groups.

1. LEUKOTRIENE SYNTHESIS

As shown in Figure 35.11, the synthesis of the leukotrienes begins with the formation of hydroperoxyeicosatetraenoic acids (HPETEs). These products are either reduced to the corresponding hydroxy metabolites, HETEs (see Fig. 35.10), or are metabolized to form leukotrienes or lipoxins (see Figs. 35.11 and 35.12). The major leukotrienes are produced by 5-lipoxygenase. Leukotrienes are so named because they are synthesized in leukocytes and contain the typical triene structure, that is, three double bonds in series (in this case, at positions 7, 9, and 11) (see Fig. 35.11).

In leukocytes and mast cells, 5-HPETE is converted to an epoxide, leukotriene A₄ (LTA₄). The subscript 4 refers to four double bonds in the leukotriene. Three of the double bonds (at carbons 7, 9, and 11) are conjugated, that is, they form a triene.

Other functional leukotrienes are formed from LTA₄ by one of two pathways. In the first, LTA₄ is converted to LTB₄, a 5,12-dihydroxy derivative. The second metabolic pathway involves the addition of reduced glutathione to carbon 6 to form LTC₄, a reaction catalyzed by glutathione *S*-transferase. Glutamate is removed from the glutathione moiety of LTC₄ through the action of γ-glutamyl transpeptidase to form LTD₄. A dipeptidase then cleaves the glycine residue from LTD₄ to form LTE₄ (see Fig. 35.11). The major functions of some of the leukotrienes are listed in Table 35.4.

2. LIPOXIN SYNTHESIS AND ACTIONS

The lipoxins are formed through the action of 15-lipoxygenase followed by the action of 5-lipoxygenase on arachidonic acid. A series of reductions of the resultant hydroperoxy groups lead to the formation of trihydroxy derivatives of arachidonic acid known as the lipoxins (see Fig. 35.12). Lipoxins induce chemotaxis and stimulate superoxide anion production in leukocytes.

C. Cytochrome P450 Pathway: Synthesis and Actions of Epoxides, Hydroxyeicosatetraenoics, and Diol Forms Hydroxyeicosatetraenoics

A third mechanism for the oxygenation of arachidonic acid involves the cytochrome P450 pathway. The activity of the monooxygenases in this microsomal system yields epoxides, certain forms of HETEs (e.g., ω-hydroxy derivatives), and diol forms (diHETEs) (Fig. 35.13). The biologic activities of these compounds include actions in ocular, vascular, endocrine, and renal systems. Some of these actions are attributed to inhibition of the Na^+,K^+-ATPase. The physiologic role of these compounds remains to be fully characterized.

D. Isoprostane Synthesis

Isoprostanes are derived from arachidonic acid by lipid peroxidation, initiated by free radicals. There is no enzymatic mechanism for their production. Arachidonic acid, although still a component of a phospholipid, undergoes free radical damage, and then phospholipase A2 removes the altered eicosanoid from the phospholipid and releases it into circulation (Fig. 35.14). The level of isoprostanes in the urine can be used as a measure of the oxidative stress of a patient and is a useful biologic marker for patients suffering oxidative stress caused by a variety of disorders. Recall that oxidative stress results from reactive oxygen or nitrogen species that are not fully neutralized by antioxidants (see Chapter 24). The increase in reactive oxygen and nitrogen species results in protein, lipid, and nucleic acid modifications. Many neurodegenerative diseases, such as Alzheimer disease, Parkinson disease, and Lou Gehrig disease, have increased oxidative stress in common.

Surprisingly, these altered arachidonic acid molecules also have biologic activity when measured on cultured cells; it is not known whether intracellular levels reach high enough concentrations to elicit these biologic effects. The best studied isoprostane is similar to $PGF_2\alpha$, and this molecule has similar effects on cultured cells as does $PGF_2\alpha$ (see Table 35.1).

E. Endocannabinoid Synthesis

Endocannabinoids are endogenous ligands for the cannabinoid receptors (CB1 and CB2), with effects primarily in the nervous system. Anandamide was the first such ligand to be isolated and identified. Anandamide is synthesized in neurons from phosphatidylethanolamine as outlined in Figure 35.15. The biosynthetic pathway is unique in transferring an arachidonic acid group from the 2-position to the free amino group on ethanolamine, and then using a unique phospholipase D to cleave the modified ethanolamine from the phospholipid. The synthesis of anandamide is regulated, in part, by agonists that cause calcium influx into nerve cells. Once anandamide is released, it acts as a retrograde messenger, binding to receptors on the presynaptic membrane that alter ion fluxes such that neurotransmitter release from the presynaptic neuron can be increased and an analgesic effect obtained. Anandamide is degraded by the enzyme fatty acid amide hydrolase, which splits anandamide to arachidonic acid and ethanolamine. The hydrolase enzyme is a current target of drug research because inhibiting the action of this enzyme will prolong the analgesic effects induced by anandamide.

III. MECHANISM OF ACTION OF THE EICOSANOIDS

The eicosanoids have a wide variety of physiologic effects, which are generally initiated through interaction of the eicosanoid with a specific receptor on the plasma membrane of a target cell (Table 35.5). This eicosanoid-receptor binding either activates the adenylate cyclase-cAMP-protein kinase A system (PGE, PGD, and

Table 35.4   Some Functions of Leukotrienes

LTB₄
Increases
Vascular permeability
T-cell proliferation
Leukocyte aggregation
INF-γ
IL-1
IL-2

LTC₄ and LTD₄
Increase
Bronchoconstriction
Vascular permeability
INF-γ

INF, interferon; IL, interleukin.

FIG. 35.13. Examples of compounds produced from arachidonic acid by the cytochrome P450 pathway.

FIG. 35.14. Generation of an isoprostane. Free radical damage to a phospholipid on the arachidonic acid residue at position 2 generates an isoprostane, which is then removed from the damaged phospholipid by phospholipase A2. The example of an isoprostane shown in this figure is just one of many that can be produced.

FIG. 35.15. Anandamide synthesis and degradation. *TAE*, transacylase.

PGI series) or causes an increase in the level of calcium in the cytosol of target cells (PGF$_2\alpha$, TXA$_2$, the endoperoxides, and the leukotrienes).

In some systems, the eicosanoids appear to modulate the degree of activation of adenylate cyclase in response to other stimuli. In these instances, the eicosanoid may bind to a regulatory subunit of the guanosine triphosphate (GTP)-binding proteins (G proteins) within the plasma membrane of the target cell (see Chapter 11). If the eicosanoid binds to the stimulatory subunit, the effect of the stimulus is amplified. Conversely, if the eicosanoid binds to the inhibitory subunit, the cellular response to the stimulus is reduced. Through these influences on the activation of adenylate cyclase, eicosanoids contribute to the regulation of cell function.

Table 35.5   Prostaglandin and Thromboxane Receptors

Receptor	Type of Ligand	G protein Coupled	cAMP Response	Calcium Response
DP	PGD series	Yes	Increase	Increase
CRTH2	PGD series	Yes	Decrease	Increase
EP1	PGE series	Yes	None	Increase
EP2	PGE series	Yes	Increase	None
EP3	PGE series	Yes	Decrease	None
EP4	PGE series	Yes	Increase	None
FP	PGF series	Yes	None	Increase
IP	PGI series	Yes	Increase or decrease[a]	None
TP	Thromboxane A	Yes	Increase or decrease[b]	Increase

[a]Depends on the modification of the C-terminal of the receptor.
[b]Depends on cell type responding to the ligand.

Some of the biologic effects of certain eicosanoids occur as a result of a paracrine or autocrine action. One *paracrine* action is the contraction of vascular smooth muscle cells caused by TXA_2 released from circulating platelets (vasoconstriction). An *autocrine* action of eicosanoids is exemplified by platelet aggregation induced by TXA_2 produced by the platelets themselves.

The eicosanoids influence the cellular function of almost every tissue of the body. Certain organ systems are affected to a greater degree than others.

CLINICAL COMMENTS

 Ann Jeina, Cora Nari, and Ivan Applebod. In the presence of aspirin, cyclo-oxygenase is irreversibly inactivated by acetylation. New cyclo-oxygenase molecules are not produced in platelets because these cells have no nuclei and, therefore, cannot synthesize new mRNA. Thus, the inhibition of cyclo-oxygenase by aspirin persists for the life span of the platelet (7 to 10 days). When aspirin is taken daily at doses between 81 and 325 mg, new platelets are affected as they are generated. Higher doses do not improve efficacy but do increase side effects such as gastrointestinal bleeding and being bruised easily.

Patients with established or suspected atherosclerotic coronary disease such as **Ann Jeina, Cora Nari**, and **Ivan Applebod**, benefit from the action of low-dose aspirin (approximately 81 mg/day), which produces a mild defect in hemostasis. This action of aspirin helps to prevent thrombus formation in the area of an atherosclerotic plaque at critical sites in the vascular tree.

 Emma Wheezer. Corticosteroids reduce inflammation, in part, through their inhibitory effect on phospholipase A2. In addition, suppression of COX-2 induction is now thought to be a primary anti-inflammatory mechanism of action for glucocorticoids. Despite the unquestionable value of glucocorticoid therapy in a variety of diseases associated with acute inflammation of tissues, the suppression of the inflammatory response with pharmacologic doses of corticosteroids is potentially hazardous. The sudden appearance of temporary glucose intolerance when **Emma Wheezer** was treated with large doses of prednisone—a gluconeogenic steroid (glucocorticoid)—is just one of the many potential adverse effects of this class of drugs when they are given systemically in pharmacologic doses more than an extended period. The inhaled steroids, conversely, have far fewer systemic side effects because their absorption across the bronchial mucosa into the circulation is very limited. This property allows them to be used more than prolonged periods in the treatment of asthma. The fact that inhalation allows direct delivery of the agent to the primary site of inflammation adds to their effectiveness in the treatment of these patients.

 Although our knowledge of the spectrum of biologic actions of the endogenous eicosanoids is incomplete, several actions are well enough established to allow their application in a variety of clinical situations or diseases. For example, drugs that are analogs of PGE_1 and PGE_2 suppress gastric ulceration in part by inhibiting secretion of hydrochloric acid in the mucosal cells of the stomach. Analogs of PGE_1 are used in the treatment of sexual impotence. Men with certain forms of sexual impotence can self-inject this agent into the corpus cavernosum of the penis to induce immediate but temporary penile tumescence. The erection lasts for 1 to 3 hours. The stimulatory action of PGE_2 and $PGF_{2\alpha}$ on uterine muscle contraction has led to the use of these prostaglandins to induce labor and to control postpartum bleeding. PGE_1 is also used as palliative therapy in neonates with congenital heart defects to maintain patency of the ductus arteriosus until surgery can be performed. Analogs of PGI_2 have been shown to be effective in the treatment of primary pulmonary hypertension.

Although they are uncomfortable, the pain, swelling, and fever that are part of the inflammatory response serve as an important warning sign that the host is threatened and that some specific counteractions must be taken against the offending agent or process. Although the use of anti-inflammatory drugs may bring welcome to symptomatic relief, their use may, in part, diminish the effectiveness of the host's response to the inciting agent.

BIOCHEMICAL COMMENTS

The Inflammatory Process. Inflammation is the response of the body to infection or injury, directed at destroying the infectious agents and repairing the damaged areas. It involves an increase of the blood supply to the affected region by means of vasodilation. The capillaries become more permeable so that fluid, large molecules, and white blood cells can cross, leaving the blood and entering the tissue. White blood cells (particularly neutrophils and monocytes) move by chemotaxis to the injured site. Redness (rubor), heat (calor), swelling (tumor), and pain (dolor) are associated with the inflammatory process. Redness and heat are caused by the increased blood flow. Swelling is caused by the increased movement of fluid and white blood cells into the area of inflammation. Pain is caused by the release of chemical compounds and the compression of nerves in the vicinity of the inflammation.

The chemical mediators of inflammation usually are produced by activation of complement (a family of blood proteins that are cleaved to form active fragments) or of the blood clotting cascade (see Chapter 45). These processes cause the release of histamine from mast cells and the production of kinins by cleavage of kininogens. Among their other effects, both histamine and kinins increase vascular permeability. They stimulate the synthesis of eicosanoids that act on the motility and metabolism of white blood cells and cause the aggregation of platelets to arrest bleeding. Some of the prostaglandins act on thermoregulatory centers of the brain, producing fever. Cytokines are also released, which stimulate the proliferation of cells involved in the immune response.

Key Concepts

- The eicosanoids (prostaglandins, thromboxanes, and leukotrienes) are potent regulators of cellular function and are derived from polyunsaturated fatty acids containing 20 carbon atoms.
- Eicosanoids are important in the inflammatory response, smooth muscle contraction, blood pressure regulation, and bronchoconstriction and bronchodilation.
- The prostaglandins and thromboxanes require cyclo-oxygenase activity to be synthesized, whereas the leukotrienes require lipoxygenase activity.
- Eicosanoids act by binding to specific membrane receptors, which, depending on the eicosanoid, alter either protein kinase A activity or calcium levels within the target cells.
- Cyclo-oxygenase is the target of nonsteroidal anti-inflammatory drugs (NSAIDs), including aspirin, which covalently acetylates and inactivates the enzyme in platelets.
- Diseases discussed in this chapter are summarized in Table 35.6.

Table 35.6   Diseases Discussed in Chapter 35

Disease or Disorder	Environmental or Genetic	Comments
Cardiac (protection against future myocardial infarctions)	Environmental	NSAIDs such as aspirin are used to block prostaglandin production via inhibition of cyclo-oxygenase. Low-dose aspirin provides potential protective effects for those with cardiovascular disease.
Asthma	Environmental	The use of inhalants containing corticosteroids can control and reduce inflammation by inhibiting the recruitment of leukocytes and monocytes into affected areas. They also lead to a decrease in the synthesis of prostaglandins and leukotrienes.

NSAIDs, nonsteroidal anti-inflammatory drugs.

REVIEW QUESTIONS—CHAPTER 35

1. In humans, prostaglandins are derived primarily from which of the following?

    A. Glucose
    B. Acetyl-CoA
    C. Arachidonic acid
    D. Oleic acid
    E. Leukotrienes

2. Aspirin will inhibit which of the following reaction pathways?

    A. Arachidonic acid → thromboxanes
    B. Arachidonic acid → leukotrienes
    C. Arachidonic acid → phospholipids
    D. Linoleic acid → arachidonic acid
    E. Acetyl-CoA → linoleic acid

3. Which of the following drugs lead to the covalent modification and inactivation of both the COX-1 and COX-2 enzymes?

    A. Aspirin
    B. Tylenol
    C. Celebrex
    D. Vioxx
    E. Advil

4. Thromboxane A2, which is found in high levels in platelets, aids in wound repair through induction of which of the following activities?

    A. Inhibits COX-2 gene expression
    B. Inhibits COX-1 gene expression
    C. Vasoconstriction
    D. Vasodilation
    E. Bronchodilation

5. Certain prostaglandins, when binding to their receptor, induce an increase in intracellular calcium levels. The signal that leads to the elevation of intracellular calcium is initiated by which of the following enzymes?

    A. Protein kinase A
    B. Phospholipase C
    C. Phospholipase A2
    D. Protein kinase C
    E. Cyclo-oxygenase

This chapter summarizes and integrates the major pathways for the use of carbohydrates and fats as fuels. We concentrate on reviewing the regulatory mechanisms that determine the flux of metabolites in the fed and fasting states, integrating the pathways that were described separately under carbohydrate and lipid metabolism. The next section of this book covers the mechanisms by which the pathways of nitrogen metabolism are coordinated with fat and carbohydrate metabolism.

For the species to survive, it is necessary for us to store excess food when we eat and to use these stores when we are fasting. Regulatory mechanisms direct compounds through the pathways of metabolism involved in the storage and use of fuels. These mechanisms are controlled by **hormones**, by the **concentration of available fuels**, and by the **energy needs** of the body.

Changes in hormone levels, in the concentration of fuels, and in energy requirements affect the activity of key enzymes in the major pathways of metabolism. Intracellular **enzymes** are generally regulated by **activation** and **inhibition**, by **phosphorylation** and **dephosphorylation** (or other covalent modifications), by **induction** and **repression** of synthesis, and by **degradation**. Activation and inhibition of enzymes cause immediate changes in metabolism. Phosphorylation and dephosphorylation of enzymes affect metabolism slightly less rapidly. Induction and repression of enzyme synthesis are much slower processes, usually affecting metabolic flux over a period of hours. Degradation of enzymes decreases the amount available to catalyze reactions.

The pathways of metabolism have **multiple control points** and **multiple regulators** at each control point. The function of these complex mechanisms is to produce a graded response to a stimulus and to provide sensitivity to multiple stimuli so that an exact balance is maintained between flux through a given step (or series of steps) and the need or use for the product. Pyruvate dehydrogenase is an example of an enzyme that has multiple regulatory mechanisms. Regardless of insulin levels, the enzyme cannot become fully activated in the presence of products and absence of substrates.

The major hormones that regulate the pathways of fuel metabolism are **insulin** and **glucagon**. In liver, all effects of glucagon are reversed by insulin, and some of the pathways that insulin activates are inhibited by glucagon. Thus, the pathways of carbohydrate and lipid metabolism are generally regulated by changes in the **insulin/glucagon ratio**.

Although **glycogen** is a critical storage form of fuel because blood glucose levels must be carefully maintained, adipose **triacylglycerols** are quantitatively the major fuel store in humans. After a meal, both dietary glucose and fat are stored in adipose tissue as triacylglycerol. This fuel is released during fasting, when it provides the main source of energy for the tissues of the body. The length of time we can survive without food depends mainly on the size of our bodies' fat stores.

THE WAITING ROOM

Within 2 months of her surgery to remove a benign insulin-secreting β-cell tumor of the pancreas, **Bea Selmass** (see Chapter 26) was again jogging lightly. She had lost the 8 lb that she had gained in the 6 weeks before her surgery. Because her hypoglycemic episodes were no longer occurring, she had no need to eat frequent carbohydrate snacks to prevent the adrenergic and neuroglycopenic symptoms that she had experienced when her tumor was secreting excessive amounts of insulin.

A few months after her last hospitalization, **Di Abietes** was once again brought to the hospital emergency room in diabetic ketoacidosis (DKA). Blood samples for glucose and electrolytes were drawn repeatedly during the first 24 hours. The hospital laboratory reported that the serum in each of these specimens appeared opalescent rather than having its normal clear or transparent appearance. This opalescence results from light scattering caused by elevated levels of triacylglycerol-rich lipoproteins in the blood.

When **Ann Sulin** initially presented with type 2 diabetes mellitus at age 39, she was approximately 30 lb higher than her ideal weight. Her high serum glucose levels were accompanied by abnormalities in her 14-hour fasting lipid profile. Her serum total cholesterol, low-density lipoprotein (LDL) cholesterol, and triacylglycerol levels were elevated and her serum high-density lipoprotein (HDL) cholesterol level was lower than the normal range.

I. REGULATION OF CARBOHYDRATE AND LIPID METABOLISM IN THE FED STATE

A. Mechanisms That Affect Glycogen and Triacylglycerol Synthesis in Liver

After a meal, the liver synthesizes glycogen and triacylglycerol. The level of glycogen stored in the liver can increase from approximately 80 g after an overnight fast to a limit of approximately 200 to 300 g. Although the liver synthesizes triacylglycerol, it does not store this fuel but rather packages it in very low-density lipoprotein (VLDL) and secretes it in the blood. The fatty acids of the VLDL triacylglycerols secreted from the liver are stored as adipose triacylglycerols. Adipose tissue has an almost infinite capacity to store fat, limited mainly by the ability of the heart to pump blood through the capillaries of the expanding adipose mass. Although we store fat throughout our bodies, it tends to accumulate in places where it does not interfere too much with our mobility: in the abdomen, hips, thighs, and buttocks.

Both the synthesis of liver glycogen and the conversion by the liver of dietary glucose to triacylglycerol (lipogenesis) are regulated by mechanisms involving key enzymes in these pathways.

1. GLUCOKINASE

After a meal, glucose can be converted to glycogen or to triacylglycerol in the liver. For both processes, glucose is first converted to glucose 6-phosphate by glucokinase, a liver enzyme that has a high K_m for glucose (Fig. 36.1). Because of the enzyme's low affinity for glucose, this enzyme is most active in the fed state, when the concentration of glucose is particularly high because the hepatic portal vein carries digestive products directly from the intestine to the liver. Synthesis of glucokinase is also induced by insulin (which is elevated after a meal) and repressed by glucagon (which

FIG. 36.1. Regulation of glucokinase, PFK-1, and pyruvate kinase in the liver. *Fructose-1, 6-BP*, fructose 1,6-bisphosphatase; *fructose-2, 6-BP*, fructose 2,6-bisphosphate.

FIG. 36.3. Regulation of pyruvate dehydrogenase (PDH). A kinase associated with the PDH complex phosphorylates and inactivates the enzyme. ⊕, activated by; ⊖, inhibited by.

is elevated during fasting). In keeping with the liver's function in maintaining blood glucose levels, this system is set up such that the liver can metabolize glucose only when sugar levels are high and not when sugar levels are low.

2. GLYCOGEN SYNTHASE

In the conversion of glucose 6-phosphate to glycogen, the key regulatory enzyme is glycogen synthase. This enzyme is activated by the dephosphorylation that occurs when insulin is elevated and glucagon is decreased (Fig. 36.2) and by the increased level of glucose.

3. PHOSPHOFRUCTOKINASE-1 AND PYRUVATE KINASE

For lipogenesis, glucose 6-phosphate is converted through glycolysis to pyruvate. Key enzymes that regulate this pathway in the liver are *phosphofructokinase-1* (PFK-1) and pyruvate kinase. PFK-1 is allosterically activated in the fed state by fructose 2,6-bisphosphate and adenosine monophosphate (AMP) (see Fig. 36.1). *Phosphofructokinase-2* (PFK-2), the enzyme that produces the activator fructose 2,6-bisphosphate, is dephosphorylated and the kinase activity is active after a meal (see Chapter 22). Pyruvate kinase is also activated by dephosphorylation, which is stimulated by the increase of the insulin/glucagon ratio in the fed state (see Fig. 36.1).

4. PYRUVATE DEHYDROGENASE AND PYRUVATE CARBOXYLASE

The conversion of pyruvate to fatty acids requires a source of acetyl coenzyme A (acetyl-CoA) in the cytosol. Pyruvate can only be converted to acetyl-CoA in mitochondria, so it enters mitochondria and forms acetyl-CoA through the pyruvate dehydrogenase (PDH) reaction. This enzyme is dephosphorylated and most active when its supply of substrates and adenosine diphosphate (ADP) is high—its products are used and insulin is present (Fig. 36.3).

Pyruvate is also converted to oxaloacetate. The enzyme that catalyzes this reaction, pyruvate carboxylase, is activated by acetyl-CoA. Because acetyl-CoA cannot cross the mitochondrial membrane directly to form fatty acids in the cytosol, it condenses with oxaloacetate, thus producing citrate. The citrate that is not required for tricarboxylic acid (TCA) cycle activity crosses the membrane and enters the cytosol.

As fatty acids are produced under conditions of high energy, the high NADH/NAD⁺ ratio in the mitochondria inhibits isocitrate dehydrogenase, which leads to citrate accumulation within the mitochondrial matrix. As the citrate accumulates, it is transported out into the cytosol to donate carbons for fatty acid synthesis.

5. CITRATE LYASE, MALIC ENZYME, AND GLUCOSE-6-PHOSPHATE DEHYDROGENASE

In the cytosol, citrate is cleaved by *citrate lyase*, an inducible enzyme, to form oxaloacetate and acetyl-CoA (Fig. 36.4). The acetyl-CoA is used for fatty acid biosynthesis and for cholesterol synthesis—pathways that are activated by insulin. Oxaloacetate is recycled to pyruvate via cytosolic malate dehydrogenase and malic enzyme, which is inducible. Malic enzyme generates NADPH for the reactions of the fatty acid synthase complex. NADPH is also produced by the two enzymes of the pentose phosphate pathway (see Chapter 29): glucose-6-phosphate dehydrogenase and 6-phosphogluconate dehydrogenase. Glucose-6-phosphate dehydrogenase is also induced by insulin.

6. ACETYL-CoA CARBOXYLASE

Acetyl-CoA is converted to malonyl-CoA, which provides the two-carbon units for elongation of the growing fatty acyl chain on the fatty acid synthase complex. *Acetyl-CoA carboxylase*, the enzyme that catalyzes the conversion of acetyl-CoA to malonyl-CoA, is controlled by three of the major mechanisms that regulate enzyme activity (Fig. 36.5). It is activated by citrate, which causes the enzyme to polymerize,

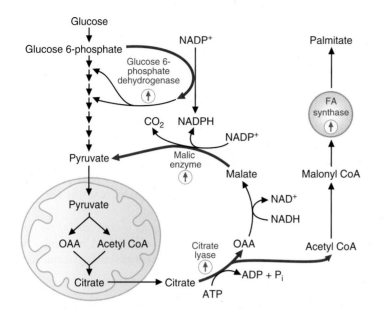

FIG. 36.4. Regulation of citrate lyase, malic enzyme, glucose-6-phosphate dehydrogenase, and fatty acid synthase. Citrate lyase, which provides acetyl-CoA for fatty acid biosynthesis, the enzymes that provide NADPH (malic enzyme, glucose-6-phosphate dehydrogenase), as well as fatty acid synthase are inducible ↑. *FA*, fatty acid.

and inhibited by long-chain fatty acyl-CoA. A phosphatase stimulated by insulin activates the enzyme by dephosphorylation. The third means by which this enzyme is regulated is induction: the quantity of the enzyme increases in the fed state.

Malonyl-CoA, the product of the acetyl-CoA carboxylase reaction, provides the carbons for the synthesis of palmitate on the fatty acid synthase complex. Malonyl-CoA also inhibits *carnitine palmitoyl transferase I* (CPTI, also known as *carnitine acyltransferase I*), the enzyme that prepares long-chain fatty acyl-CoA for transport

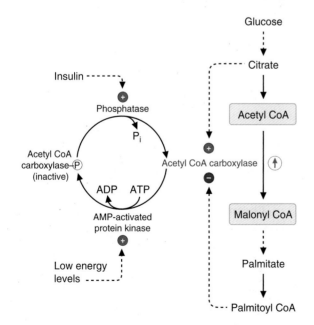

FIG. 36.5. Regulation of acetyl-CoA carboxylase (ACC). ACC is regulated by activation and inhibition, by phosphorylation (mediated by the AMP-activated protein kinase) and dephosphorylation (via an insulin-stimulated phosphatase), and by induction and repression. It is active in the fed state.

FACoA

Palmitate

FA synthase

FACoA
Carnitine

CPTI ⊖ ◄---- Malonyl CoA

FA-carnitine

CPTII

FACoA   CoASH

β-Oxidation

Acetyl CoA

FIG. 36.6. Inhibition of transport of fatty acids (*FAs*) into mitochondria by malonyl-CoA. In the fed state, malonyl-CoA (the substrate for fatty acid synthesis produced by acetyl-CoA carboxylase) is elevated. It inhibits carnitine palmitoyl transferase I (CPTI), preventing the transport of long-chain fatty acids into mitochondria. Therefore, substrate is not available for β-oxidation and ketone body synthesis.

The measurement of triglycerides in blood samples is performed using a coupled assay. The sample is incubated with a lipase that converts the triglyceride to glycerol and three fatty acids. The glycerol is then converted to glycerol 3-phosphate by glycerol kinase and ATP, and the glycerol 3-phosphate is then oxidized by a bacterial glycerol-3-phosphate dehydrogenase to produce DHAP and hydrogen peroxide. The hydrogen peroxide, in the presence of peroxidase, will oxidize a colorless substrate, which turns color when oxidized. Measurement of the color change is directly proportional to the amount of glycerol generated in the sample.

Di Abietes has *type 1 diabetes mellitus* (insulin dependent), a disease associated with a severe deficiency or absence of insulin production by the β-cells of the pancreas. One of the effects of insulin is to stimulate production of LPL. Because of low insulin levels, **Di Abietes** tends to have low levels of this enzyme. Hydrolysis of the triacylglycerols in chylomicrons and in VLDL is decreased and hypertriglyceridemia results.

into mitochondria (Fig. 36.6). In the fed state, when acetyl-CoA carboxylase is active and malonyl-CoA levels are elevated, newly synthesized fatty acids are converted to triacylglycerols for storage, rather than being transported into mitochondria for oxidation and formation of ketone bodies.

7. FATTY ACID SYNTHASE COMPLEX

In a well-fed individual, the quantity of the fatty acid synthase complex is increased (see Fig. 36.4). The genes that produce this enzyme complex are induced by increases in the insulin/glucagon ratio. The amount of the complex increases slowly after a few days of a high-carbohydrate diet.

Glucose-6-phosphate dehydrogenase which generates NADPH in the pentose phosphate pathway and malic enzyme which produces NADPH are also induced by the increase of insulin.

The palmitate produced by the synthase complex is converted to palmitoyl-CoA and elongated and desaturated to form other fatty acyl-CoA molecules, which are converted to triacylglycerols. These triacylglycerols are packaged and secreted into the blood as VLDL.

B. Mechanisms That Affect the Fate of Chylomicrons and VLDL

The lipoprotein triacylglycerols in chylomicrons and VLDL are hydrolyzed to fatty acids and glycerol by *lipoprotein lipase* (LPL), an enzyme attached to endothelial cells of capillaries in muscle and adipose tissue. The enzyme found in muscle, particularly heart muscle, has a low K_m for these blood lipoproteins. Therefore, it acts even when these lipoproteins are present at very low concentrations in the blood. The fatty acids enter muscle cells and are oxidized for energy. The enzyme found in adipose tissue has a higher K_m and is most active after a meal when blood lipoprotein levels are elevated.

C. Mechanisms That Affect Triacylglycerol Storage in Adipose Tissue

Insulin stimulates adipose cells to synthesize and secrete LPL, which hydrolyzes the chylomicron and VLDL triacylglycerols. Apoprotein CII (apoCII), donated to chylomicrons and VLDL by HDL, activates LPL (Fig. 36.7).

Fatty acids released from chylomicrons and VLDL by LPL are stored as triacylglycerols in adipose cells. The glycerol released by LPL is not used by adipose cells because they lack glycerol kinase. Glycerol can be used by liver cells, however, because these cells do contain glycerol kinase. In the fed state, liver cells convert

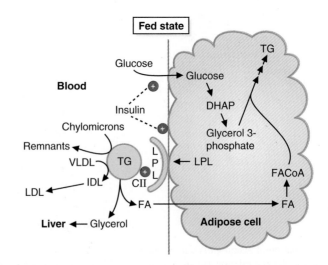

FIG. 36.7. Regulation of the storage of triacylglycerols (TGs) in adipose tissue. Insulin stimulates the secretion of LPL from adipose cells and the transport of glucose into these cells. ApoCII activates LPL. *FA*, fatty acids.

glycerol to the glycerol moiety of the triacylglycerols of VLDL, which is secreted from the liver to distribute the newly synthesized triglycerides to the tissues.

Insulin causes the number of glucose transporters in adipose cell membranes to increase. Glucose enters these cells and is oxidized, producing energy and providing the glycerol 3-phosphate moiety for triacylglycerol synthesis (via the dihydroxyacetone phosphate intermediate of glycolysis).

II. REGULATION OF CARBOHYDRATE AND LIPID METABOLISM DURING FASTING

A. Mechanisms in Liver That Serve to Maintain Blood Glucose Levels

During fasting, the insulin/glucagon ratio decreases. Liver glycogen is degraded to produce blood glucose because enzymes of glycogen degradation are activated by cAMP-directed phosphorylation (Fig. 36.8). Glucagon stimulates adenylate

Why does **Ann Sulin** have a hyper-triglyceridemia?

The 20% to 30% of patients with an insulinoma gain weight as part of their syndrome. **Bea Selmass** gained 8 lb 6 weeks before her surgery. Although she was primed by her high insulin levels both to store and to use fuel more efficiently, she would not have gained weight if she had not consumed more calories than what was required for her daily energy expenditure during her illness (see Chapter 1). Bea consumed extra carbohydrate calories—mostly as hard candies and table sugar—to avoid the symptoms of hypoglycemia.

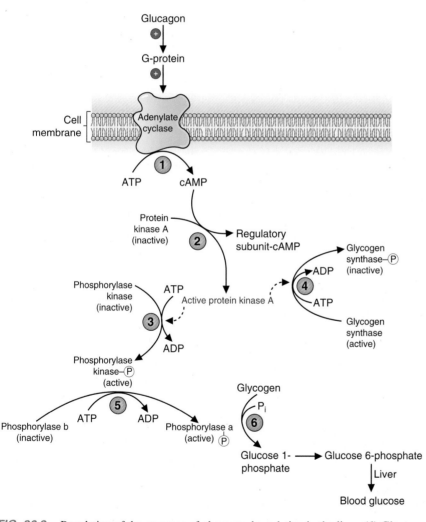

FIG. 36.8. Regulation of the enzymes of glycogen degradation in the liver. (*1*) Glucagon (or epinephrine) binds to its cell membrane receptor, initially activating a G protein, which activates adenylate cyclase. (*2*) As cAMP levels rise, inhibitory subunits are removed from protein kinase A, which now phosphorylates phosphorylase kinase. (*3*) (*4*) The cAMP-dependent protein kinase also phosphorylates glycogen synthase, inactivating the enzyme. (*5*) Phosphorylated phosphorylase kinase phosphorylates glycogen phosphorylase. (*6*) Phosphorylated glycogen phosphorylase catalyzes the phosphorolysis of glycogen, producing glucose 1-phosphate. These events occur during fasting and produce glucose to maintain a relatively constant level of blood glucose.

Ann Sulin has type 2 diabetes mellitus. She produces insulin, but her adipose tissue is partially resistant to its actions. Therefore, her adipose tissue does not produce as much LPL as a normal person, which is one of the reasons why VLDL and chylomicrons remain elevated in her blood.

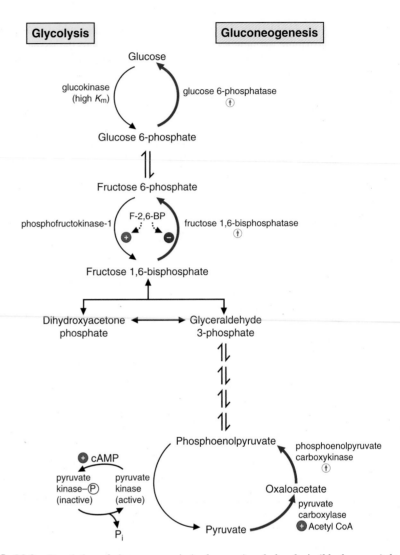

FIG. 36.9.   Regulation of gluconeogenesis (*red arrows*) and glycolysis (*black arrows*) during fasting. The gluconeogenic enzymes phosphoenolpyruvate carboxykinase, fructose 1,6-bisphosphatase, and glucose 6-phosphatase are induced ↑. Fructose 1,6-bisphosphatase is also active because, during fasting, the level of its inhibitor, fructose 2,6-bisphosphate, is low. The corresponding enzymes of glycolysis are not very active during fasting. The rate of glucokinase is low because it has a high K_m for glucose and the glucose concentration is low. PFK-1 is not very active because the concentration of its activator fructose 2,6-bisphosphate is low. Pyruvate kinase is inactivated by cAMP-mediated phosphorylation. *F-2,6-BP*, fructose 2,6-bisphosphate.

Di Abietes suffers from hyperglycemia because her insulin levels tend to be low and her glucagon levels tend to be high. Her muscle and adipose cells do not take up glucose at a normal rate, and she produces glucose by glycogenolysis and gluconeogenesis. As a result, her blood glucose levels are elevated. **Ann Sulin** is in a similar metabolic state. However, in her case, she produces insulin but her tissues are resistant to its actions.

cyclase to produce cAMP, which activates protein kinase A. Protein kinase A phosphorylates phosphorylase kinase, which then phosphorylates and activates glycogen phosphorylase. Protein kinase A also phosphorylates but, in this case, inactivates glycogen synthase.

Gluconeogenesis is stimulated because the synthesis of phosphoenolpyruvate carboxykinase, fructose 1,6-bisphosphatase, and glucose 6-phosphatase is induced and because there is an increased availability of precursors. Fructose 1,6-bisphosphatase is also activated because the levels of its inhibitor, fructose 2,6-bisphosphate, are low (Fig. 36.9). During fasting, the activities of the corresponding enzymes of glycolysis are decreased.

Induction of enzyme synthesis requires activation of transcription factors. One of the factors that is activated is CREB, which stands for cAMP response element–binding protein. CREB is phosphorylated and activated by the cAMP-dependent

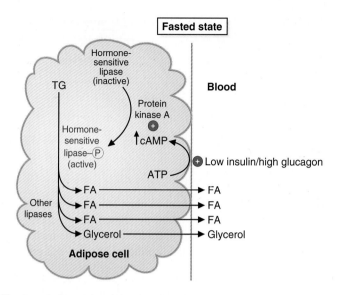

FIG. 36.10. Regulation of hormone-sensitive lipase (HSL) in adipose tissue. During fasting, the glucagon/insulin ratio rises causing cAMP levels to be elevated. Protein kinase A is activated and phosphorylates HSL, activating this enzyme. HSL-P initiates the mobilization of adipose triacylglycerol by removing a fatty acid (*FA*). Other lipases then act, producing fatty acids and glycerol. Insulin stimulates the phosphatase that inactivates HSL in the fed state.

protein kinase, which itself is activated on glucagon or epinephrine stimulation. A second set of transcription factors activated are the C/EPBs (CCAAT enhancer–binding proteins), although the regulation of their activity is still under investigation and is quite complex.

B. Mechanisms That Affect Lipolysis in Adipose Tissue

During fasting, as blood insulin levels fall and glucagon levels rise, the level of cAMP rises in adipose cells. Consequently, protein kinase A is activated and causes phosphorylation of hormone-sensitive lipase (HSL). The phosphorylated form of this enzyme is active and cleaves fatty acids from triacylglycerols (Fig. 36.10). Other hormones (e.g., epinephrine, adrenocorticotropic hormone [ACTH], growth hormone) also activate this enzyme (see Chapter 43). Glyceroneogenesis and resynthesis of triglyceride by the adipocyte regulate the rate of release of fatty acids during fasting.

C. Mechanisms That Affect Ketone Body Production by the Liver

As fatty acids are released from adipose tissue during fasting, they travel in the blood complexed with albumin. These fatty acids are oxidized by various tissues, particularly muscle. In the liver, fatty acids are transported into mitochondria because acetyl-CoA carboxylase is inactive, malonyl-CoA levels are low, and CPTI is active (see Fig. 36.6). Acetyl-CoA, produced by β-oxidation, is converted to ketone bodies. Ketone bodies are used as an energy source by many tissues (Table 36.1) to spare the use of glucose and the necessity of degrading muscle protein to provide the precursors for gluconeogenesis. The high levels of acetyl-CoA in the liver (derived from fat oxidation) inhibit pyruvate dehydrogenase (which prevents pyruvate from being converted to acetyl-CoA) and activate pyruvate carboxylase, which produces oxaloacetate for gluconeogenesis. The oxaloacetate does not condense with acetyl-CoA to form citrate for two reasons. The first is that under these conditions (a high rate of fat oxidation in the liver mitochondria), energy levels in the mitochondrial matrix are high; that is, there are high levels of NADH

 Insulin normally inhibits lipolysis by decreasing the lipolytic activity of hormone-sensitive lipase (HSL) in the adipocyte. Individuals such as **Di Abietes**, who have a deficiency of insulin, have increased lipolysis and a subsequent increase in the concentration of free fatty acids in the blood. The liver, in turn, uses some of these fatty acids to synthesize triacylglycerols, which then are used in the hepatic production of VLDL. VLDL is not stored in the liver but is secreted into the blood, raising its serum concentration. Di also has low levels of LPL because of decreased insulin levels. Her hypertriglyceridemia is the result, therefore, of both overproduction of VLDL by the liver and decreased breakdown of VLDL triacylglycerol for storage in adipose cells.

The serum begins to appear cloudy when the triacylglycerol level reaches 200 mg/dL. As the triacylglycerol level increases further, the degree of serum opalescence increases proportionately.

Table 36.1 Fuel Use by Various Tissues during Starvation (Fasting)[a]

Tissue	Glucose	Fatty Acids	Ketone Bodies
Nervous system	++	−	++
Skeletal muscle	−	++	++
Heart muscle	−	++	++
Liver	−	++	−
Intestinal epithelial cells	−	−	++
Kidney	−	+	+

[a]—Indicates no substrate utilization; +, a low level of substrate utilization; ++, a high level of substrate utilization.

and ATP present. The high NADH level inhibits isocitrate dehydrogenase. As a result, citrate accumulates and inhibits citrate synthase from producing more citrate. The second reason that citrate synthesis is depressed is that the high NADH/NAD$^+$ ratio also diverts oxaloacetate into malate, so the malate can exit the mitochondria (via the malate/aspartate shuttle) for use in gluconeogenesis.

D. Regulation of the Use of Glucose and Fatty Acids by Muscle

During exercise, the fuel that is used initially by muscle cells is muscle glycogen. As exercise continues and the blood supply to the tissue increases, glucose is taken up from the blood and is oxidized. Liver glycogenolysis and gluconeogenesis replenish the blood glucose supply. However, because insulin levels drop, the concentration of the GLUT4 glucose transporters in the membrane is reduced, thereby reducing glucose entry from the circulation into the muscle.

Thus, as fatty acids become available because of increased lipolysis of adipose triacylglycerols, the exercising muscle begins to oxidize fatty acids. β-Oxidation produces NADH and acetyl-CoA, which slows the flow of carbon from glucose through the reaction catalyzed by pyruvate dehydrogenase (see Fig. 36.3). Thus, the oxidation of fatty acids provides a major portion of the increased demand for ATP generation and spares blood glucose.

III. THE IMPORTANCE OF AMP AND FRUCTOSE 2,6-BISPHOSPHATE

The switch between catabolic and anabolic pathways is often regulated by the levels of AMP and fructose 2,6-bisphosphate in cells, particularly the liver. It is logical for AMP to be a critical regulator. Because a cell uses ATP in energy-requiring pathways, the levels of AMP accumulate more rapidly than that of ADP because of the adenylate kinase reaction (2 ADP → ATP and AMP). The rise in AMP levels then signals that more energy is required (usually through allosteric binding sites on enzymes and the activation of the AMP-activated protein kinase), and the cell switches to the activation of catabolic pathways. As AMP levels drop, and ATP levels rise, the anabolic pathways are activated to store the excess energy.

The levels of fructose 2,6-bisphosphate are also critical in regulating glycolysis versus gluconeogenesis in the liver. Under conditions of high blood glucose and insulin release, fructose 2,6-bisphosphate levels are high because PFK-2 is in its activated state. The fructose 2,6-bisphosphate activates PFK-1 and inhibits fructose 1,6-bisphosphatase, thereby allowing glycolysis to proceed. When blood glucose levels are low, and glucagon is released, PFK-2 is phosphorylated by the cAMP-dependent protein kinase and is inhibited, thereby lowering fructose 2,6-bisphosphate levels and inhibiting glycolysis, whereas favoring gluconeogenesis.

IV. GENERAL SUMMARY

All of the material in this chapter was presented previously. However, because this information is so critical for understanding biochemistry in a way that will

Because **Di Abietes** produces very little insulin, she is prone to developing ketoacidosis. When insulin levels are low, HSL of adipose tissue is very active, resulting in increased lipolysis. The fatty acids that are released travel to the liver, where they are converted to the triacylglycerols of VLDL. They also undergo β-oxidation and conversion to ketone bodies. If Di does not take exogenous insulin or if her insulin levels decrease abruptly for some physiologic reason, she may develop ketoacidosis (diabetic ketoacidosis [DKA]). In fact, she has had repeated bouts of DKA.

For reasons that are not as well understood, individuals with type 2 diabetes mellitus such as **Ann Sulin** do not tend to develop ketoacidosis. One possible explanation is that the insulin resistance is tissue specific; the insulin sensitivity of adipocytes may be greater than that of muscle and liver. It has been suggested that the level of insulin required to suppress lipolysis is only 10% that required to enhance glucose use by muscle and adipocyte. Such a tissue-specific sensitivity would lead to less fatty acids being released from adipocytes in type 2 diabetes than in type 1 diabetes, although in both cases, the release of fatty acids would be greater than that of an individual without the disease. If, however, a person with type 2 diabetes has a precipitating event, such as the release of stress hormones (see Chapter 43), then ketoacidosis is more likely to be found as the stress hormones counteract the effects of insulin on the adipocyte.

allow it to be used in interpreting clinical situations, it has been summarized in this chapter. In addition, the information presented previously under carbohydrate metabolism has been integrated with lipid metabolism. We have—for the most part—left out the role of allosteric modifiers and other regulatory mechanisms that finely coordinate these processes to an exquisite level. Because such details may be important for specific clinical situations, we hope this summary will serve as a framework to which the details can be fitted as students advance in their clinical studies.

Figure 36.11 is a comprehensive figure, and Tables 36.2 and 36.3 provide a list of the major regulatory enzymes of carbohydrate and lipid metabolism in

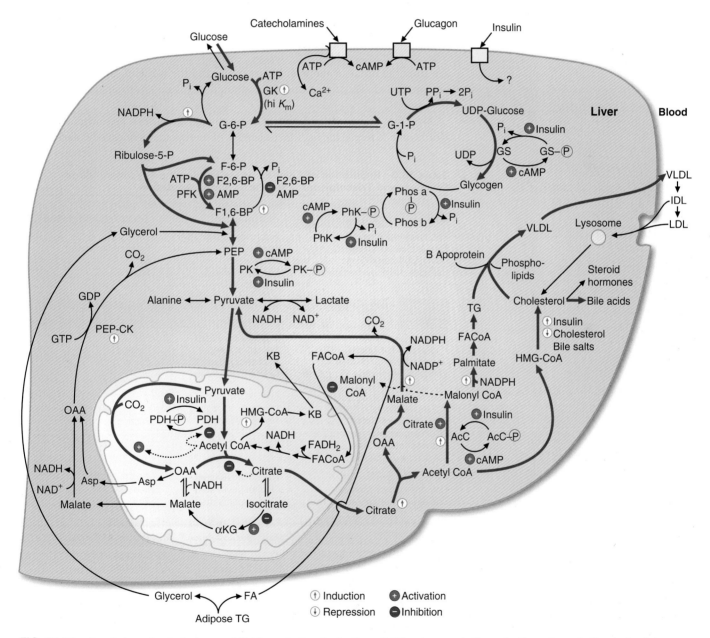

FIG. 36.11. Regulation of carbohydrate and lipid metabolism in the liver. *Solid red arrows* indicate the flow of metabolites in the fed state. *Solid black arrows* indicate the flow during fasting. *ACC*, acetyl-CoA carboxylase; *αKG*, α-ketoglutarate; *F1,6-BP*, fructose 1,6-phosphate; *F2,6-BP*, fructose 2,6-bisphosphate; *F-6-P*, fructose 6-phosphate; *G-6-P*, glucose 6-phosphate; *FA*, fatty acid or fatty acyl group; *GK*, glucokinase; *GS*, glycogen synthase; *OAA*, oxaloacetate; *circled P*, phosphate group; *PEP*, phosphoenolpyruvate; *PFK*, phosphofructokinase-1; *Phos*, glycogen phosphorylase; *PhK*, phosphorylase kinase; *PK*, pyruvate kinase; *TG*, triacylglycerol.

Table 36.2 Flowchart of Changes in Liver Metabolism

When blood sugar increases:	When blood sugar decreases:
Insulin is released, which leads to the **dephosphorylation** of:	Glucagon is released, which leads to the **phosphorylation** of:
• PFK-2 (kinase activity now active)	• PFK-2 (phosphatase activity now active)
• Pyruvate kinase (now active)	• Pyruvate kinase (now inactive)
• Glycogen synthase (now active)	• Glycogen synthase (now inactive)
• Phosphorylase kinase (now inactive)	• Phosphorylase kinase (now active)
• Glycogen phosphorylase (now inactive)	• Glycogen phosphorylase (now active)
• Pyruvate dehydrogenase (now active)	• Pyruvate dehydrogenase (now inactive)
• Acetyl-CoA carboxylase (now active)	• Acetyl-CoA carboxylase (now inactive)
Which leads to **active**	Which leads to **active**
• Glycolysis	• Glycogenolysis
• Fatty acid synthesis	• Fatty acid oxidation
• Glycogen synthesis	• Gluconeogenesis

Note. PKF-2, phosphofructokinase-2.

the liver, an order of the events that occur and the mechanisms by which they are controlled. This figure and tables should help students to integrate this mass of material.

Now that many of the details of the pathways have been presented, it may be worthwhile to reread the first three chapters of this book. A student who understands

Table 36.3 Regulation of Liver Enzymes Involved in Glycogen, Blood Glucose, and Triacylglycerol Synthesis and Degradation

Liver Enzymes Regulated by Activation/Inhibition		
Enzyme	*Activated by*	*State in which Active*
Phosphofructokinase-1	Fructose 2,6-bisP, AMP	Fed
Pyruvate carboxylase	Acetyl-CoA	Fed and fasting
Acetyl-CoA carboxylase	Citrate	Fed
Carnitine palmitoyl transferase I	Loss of inhibitor (malonyl-CoA)	Fasting

Liver Enzymes Regulated by Phosphorylation/Dephosphorylation		
Enzyme	*Active form*	*State in which Active*
Glycogen synthase	Dephosphorylated	Fed
Phosphorylase kinase	Phosphorylated	Fasting
Glycogen phosphorylase	Phosphorylated	Fasting
Phosphofructokinase-2/fructose 2,6-bisphosphatase (acts as a kinase, increasing fructose 2,6-bisP levels)	Dephosphorylated	Fed
Phosphofructokinase-2/fructose 2,6-bisphosphatase (acts as a phosphatase, decreasing fructose 2,6-bisP levels)	Phosphorylated	Fasting
Pyruvate kinase	Dephosphorylated	Fed
Pyruvate dehydrogenase	Dephosphorylated	Fed
Acetyl-CoA carboxylase	Dephosphorylated	Fed.

Liver Enzymes Regulated by Induction/Repression		
Enzyme	*State in which Induced*	*Process Affected*
Glucokinase	Fed	Glucose → TG
Citrate lyase	Fed	Glucose → TG
Acetyl-CoA carboxylase	Fed	Glucose → TG
Fatty acid synthase	Fed	Glucose → TG
Malic enzyme	Fed	Production of NADPH
Glucose-6-phosphate dehydrogenase	Fed	Production of NADPH
Glucose 6-phosphatase	Fasted	Production of blood glucose
Fructose 1,6-bisphosphatase	Fasted	Production of blood glucose
Phosphoenolpyruvate carboxykinase	Fasted	Production of blood glucose

AMP, adenosine monophosphate; fructose 2,6-bisP, fructose 2,6-bisphosphate; TG, triacylglycerol.

biochemistry within the context of fuel metabolism is in a very good position to solve clinical problems that involve metabolic derangements.

CLINICAL COMMENTS

 Bea Selmass. **Bea Selmass's** younger sister was very concerned that Bea's pancreatic tumor might be genetically determined or potentially malignant, so she accompanied Bea to her second postoperative visit to the endocrinologist. The doctor explained that insulinomas may be familial in up to 20% of cases and that in 10% of patients with insulinomas, additional secretory neoplasms may occur in the anterior pituitary or the parathyroid glands (a genetically determined syndrome known as *multiple endocrine neoplasia*, type I, or simply MEN I). Bea's tumor showed no evidence of malignancy, and the histologic slides—although not always definitive—showed a benign-appearing process. The doctor was careful to explain, however, that close observation for recurrent hypoglycemia and for the signs and symptoms suggestive of other facets of MEN I would be necessary for the remainder of Bea's and her immediate family's life.

 Di Abietes. **Diabetes mellitus** is a well-accepted risk factor for the development of coronary artery disease; the risk is three to four times higher in the population with diabetes than in the population without diabetes. Although chronically elevated serum levels of chylomicrons and very low-density lipoprotein (VLDL) may contribute to this atherogenic predisposition, the premature vascular disease seen in **Di Abietes** and other patients with type 1 diabetes mellitus, as well as **Ann Sulin** and other patients with type 2 diabetes mellitus, is also related to other abnormalities in lipid metabolism. Among these are the increase in glycation (nonenzymatic attachment of glucose molecules to proteins) of low-density lipoprotein (LDL) apoproteins as well as glycation of the proteins of the LDL receptor, which occurs when serum glucose levels are chronically elevated. These glycations interfere with the normal interaction or "fit" of the circulating LDL particles with their specific receptors on cell membranes. As a consequence, the rate of uptake of circulating LDL by the normal target cells is diminished. The LDL particles, therefore, remain in the circulation and eventually bind nonspecifically to "scavenger" receptors located on macrophages adjacent to the endothelial surfaces of blood vessels—one of the early steps in the process of atherogenesis.

BIOCHEMICAL COMMENTS

 AMPK. The *AMP-activated protein kinase* (AMPK) is a pivotal regulatory molecule in the metabolism of carbohydrates and fats. The hepatic targets of AMPK include the following proteins:

- Acetyl-CoA carboxylase (phosphorylation reduces activity, leading to reduced fatty acid synthesis)
- eEF2 kinase (this protein is activated when phosphorylated, and it will lead to a reduction in protein synthesis)
- Glycerol 3-phosphate acyltransferase (GPAT) (phosphorylation reduces activity, leading to reduced triglyceride synthesis)
- HMG-CoA reductase (phosphorylation reduces activity, leading to reduced cholesterol synthesis)
- Malonyl-CoA decarboxylase (MCD; active when phosphorylated, reduces malonyl CoA levels, allowing fatty acid oxidation to occur)
- Mammalian target of rapamycin (mTOR) (reduced activity when phosphorylated, leading to reduced protein synthesis)

- Tuberous sclerosis complex 2 (TSC2; increased activity when phosphorylated, leading to reduced protein synthesis)
- Target of rapamycin complex 2 (TORC2) (the protein is sequestered in the cytoplasm when phosphorylated, leading to decreased expression—at the transcriptional level—of gluconeogenic enzymes)

The overall effect of AMPK activation is reduced fatty acid and triglyceride synthesis (via effects on acetyl-CoA carboxylase, GPAT, and MCD), reduced cholesterol synthesis (via inhibition of HMG-CoA reductase), and reduced protein synthesis (via effects on mTOR and TSC2). There is a concommitant increase in fatty acid oxidation to raise ATP levels. Because the processes described previously are all highly energy-dependent, it makes sense to turn them off when energy levels are low, as exemplified by increased AMP levels.

mTOR (a drug that is a potent immunosuppressant) is a protein kinase, which, when active, phosphorylates key proteins that regulate and initiate protein synthesis. AMPK phosphorylation of mTOR blocks the activation of mTOR. mTOR can be activated by TSC2 through a complex pathway involving the GTP-binding protein Rheb (ras homolog enriched in brain). The TSC complex (consisting of TSC1 and TSC2) acts as a GTPase activating protein for Rheb. Rheb-GTP activates mTOR, whereas Rheb-GDP does not. Phosphorylation of TSC2 by the AMPK activates the GTPase-activating activity of TSC2, leading to Rheb-GDP formation, and reduced mTOR activity. The reduced mTOR activity leads to a reduction of protein synthesis.

mTOR also plays a critical role in transmitting the signal from the insulin receptor to an increase in protein synthesis within the cell. Insulin receptor activation leads to Akt activation (see Fig. 11.14). The protein kinase Akt (protein kinase B) will phosphorylate the TSC1/TSC2 complex and inactivate the GTPase activating component of the complex. Under these conditions, Rheb-GTP will be long lived and mTOR will be active, leading to an enhancement of protein synthesis in the cell. The interaction of TSC1/TSC2, mTOR, and its regulatory kinases is depicted in Figure 36.12.

The AMPK can be activated in several ways, all of which depend on increased AMP levels within the cell. As the concentration of AMP increases, AMPK is activated by allosteric means, by phosphorylation by LKB1 (see Chapter 34), or by phosphorylation by a calmodulin kinase kinase. AMPK is inactivated by dephosphorylation by protein phosphatases or by a decrease in AMP levels. Small changes in intracellular AMP levels can have profound effects on AMPK activity because of these multiple regulatory pathways.

AMPK is a heterotrimeric complex that consists of a catalytic subunit (α) and two regulatory subunits (β and γ). The allosteric activation of AMPK occurs via AMP binding to the α-subunit; the phosphorylation activation of AMPK occurs via threonine phosphorylation on the α-subunit. Different tissues express different isoforms of the α-, β-, and γ-subunits, giving rise to a wide variety of isozymes of AMPK in the different tissues.

Key Concepts

- Three key controlling elements determine whether a fuel is metabolized or stored: hormones, concentration of available fuels, and energy needs of the body.
- Key intracellular enzymes are generally regulated by allosteric activation and inhibition, by covalent modification, by transcriptional control, and by degradation.
- Regulation is complex to allow sensitivity and feedback to multiple stimuli so that an exact balance can be maintained between synthesis of a product and need for the product.
- The insulin/glucagon ratio is primarily responsible for the hormonal regulation of carbohydrate and lipid metabolism.
- The key enzymes of glycolysis, fatty acid synthesis, fatty acid degradation, glycogen synthesis, glycogenolysis, and gluconeogenesis are all regulated in a coordinated manner, allowing the appropriate pathways to be activated and inhibited without the creation of futile cycles.
- This chapter summarizes—in one package—all of the major regulatory events discussed in the previous 17 chapters.
- Diseases discussed in this chapter are summarized in Table 36.4.

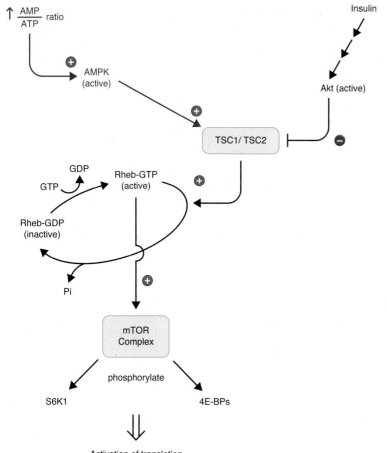

FIG. 36.12.   Central role of mTOR and the TSC1/TSC2 complex in regulating protein synthesis. The TSC1/TSC2 complex acts as a GTPase-activating protein for the G protein Rheb. When active, Rheb-GTP activates the mTOR kinase, leading to phosphorylation events that promote protein synthesis (S6K1 and 4E-BPs are phosphorylated). AMPK phosphorylation of the TSC1/TSC2 complex activates the complex such that the GTPase activity of Rheb is enhanced, leading to Rheb inactivation and loss of mTOR kinase activity. This will lead to a decrease in protein synthesis. Insulin binding to its receptor leads to the activation of the protein kinase Akt (see Fig. 11.14). Akt will phosphorylate the TSC1/TSC2 complex at sites distinct from AMPK, which inhibits the GTPase-activating activity of the complex. This allows Rheb-GTP to be active for extended periods of time, activating mTOR, and increasing protein synthesis in the cell in response to insulin.

Table 36.4   Diseases Discussed in Chapter 36

Disease or Disorder	Environmental or Genetic	Comments
Insulinoma	Environmental (10%–20% genetic)	A tumor of the pancreas leading to excessive, episodic insulin secretion, usually coupled with weight gain to avoid hypoglycemia.
Diabetic ketoacidosis	Environmental	Diabetic ketoacidosis occurs due to an elevation of ketone body levels caused by reduced levels of insulin in a person with type 1 diabetes. Diabetic ketoacidosis is not normally seen in persons with type 2 diabetes because only a partial resistance of adipocytes to circulating insulin.
Type 2 diabetes	Both	Reduced ability of tissues to respond to insulin even though insulin is being produced. Different tissues may display a differential sensitivity to insulin, particularly fat cells as compared to muscle cells.

1. A 20-year-old woman with diabetes mellitus was admitted to the hospital in a semiconscious state with fever, nausea, and vomiting. Her breath smelled of acetone. A urine sample was strongly positive for ketone bodies. Which one of the following statements about this woman is correct?

    A. A blood glucose test will probably show that her blood glucose level is much lower than 80 mg/dL.
    B. An injection of insulin will decrease her ketone body production.
    C. She should be given a glucose infusion so she will regain consciousness.
    D. Glucagon should be administered to stimulate glycogenolysis and gluconeogenesis in the liver.
    E. The acetone was produced by decarboxylation of the ketone body β-hydroxybutyrate.

2. A woman was told by her physician to go on a low-fat diet. She decided to continue to consume the same number of calories by increasing her carbohydrate intake while decreasing her fat intake. Which of the following blood lipoprotein levels would be decreased as a consequence of her diet?

    A. VLDL
    B. IDL
    C. HDL
    D. Chylomicrons
    E. HDL

3. Assume that an individual has been eating excess calories daily such that he will gain weight. Under which of the following conditions will the person gain weight most rapidly?

    A. If all the excess calories are due to carbohydrate.
    B. If all the excess calories are due to triacylgycerol.

    C. If all the excess calories are split 50%/50% between carbohydrate and triacylglycerol.
    D. If all the excess calories are split 25%/75% between carbohydrate and triacylglycerol.
    E. It makes no difference what form the excess calories are in.

4. A chronic alcoholic has been admitted to the hospital because of a severe hypoglycemic episode brought about by excessive alcohol consumption for the past 5 days. A blood lipid analysis indicates much higher than expected VLDL levels. The elevated VLDL is attributable to which of the following underlying cause?

    A. Alcohol-induced inhibition of lipoprotein lipase
    B. Elevated NADH levels in the liver
    C. Alcohol-induced transcription of the apo B-100 gene
    D. NADH activation of phosphoenolpyruvate carboxykinase
    E. Acetaldehyde induction of enzymes on the endoplasmic reticulum

5. Certain patients with abetalipoproteinemia frequently have difficulty maintaining blood volume; their blood has trouble clotting. This symptom is attributable to which of the following?

    A. Inability to produce chylomicrons
    B. Inability to produce VLDL
    C. Inability to synthesize clotting factors
    D. Inability to synthesize fatty acids
    E. Inability to absorb short-chain fatty acids

Nitrogen Metabolism

Dietary proteins are the primary source of the nitrogen that is metabolized by the body (Fig. VII.1). Amino acids, produced by digestion of dietary proteins, are absorbed through intestinal epithelial cells and enter the blood. Various cells take up these amino acids, which enter the cellular pools. They are used for the synthesis of proteins and other nitrogen-containing compounds or they are oxidized for energy.

Protein synthesis, the translation of mRNA on ribosomes (see Chapter 15), is a dynamic process. Within the body, proteins are constantly being synthesized and degraded, partially draining and then refilling the cellular amino acid pools.

Compounds derived from amino acids include cellular proteins, hormones, neurotransmitters, creatine phosphate, the heme of hemoglobin and the cytochromes, the skin pigment melanin, and the purine and pyrimidine bases of nucleotides and nucleic acids. In fact, all of the nitrogen-containing compounds of the body are synthesized from amino acids. Many of these pathways are outlined in the following chapters.

In addition to serving as the precursors for the nitrogen-containing compounds of the body and as the building blocks for protein synthesis, amino acids are also a source of energy. Amino acids are either oxidized directly or the amino acid carbons are converted to glucose and then oxidized or stored as glycogen. The amino acid carbons may also be converted to fatty acids and stored as adipose triacylglycerols. Glycogen and triacylglycerols are oxidized during periods of fasting. The liver is the major site of amino acid oxidation. However, most tissues can oxidize the branched-chain amino acids (leucine, isoleucine, and valine).

Before the carbon skeletons of amino acids are oxidized, the nitrogen must be removed. Amino acid nitrogen forms ammonia, which is toxic to the body. In the liver, ammonia and the amino groups from amino acids are converted to urea, which is nontoxic, water-soluble, and readily excreted in the urine. The process by which urea is produced is known as the *urea cycle*. The liver is the organ responsible for producing urea. Branched-chain amino acids can be oxidized in many tissues, but the nitrogen must always travel to the liver for disposal.

Although urea is the major nitrogenous excretory product of the body, nitrogen is also excreted in other compounds (Table VII.1). Uric acid is the degradation product of the purine bases, creatinine is produced from creatine phosphate, and ammonia is released from glutamine particularly by the kidney, where it helps to buffer the urine by reacting with protons to form ammonium ions (NH_4^+). These compounds are excreted mainly in the urine, but substantial amounts are also lost in the feces and through the skin. Small amounts of nitrogen-containing metabolites are formed from the degradation of neurotransmitters, hormones, and other specialized amino acid products and excreted in the urine. Some of these degradation products, such as bilirubin (formed from the degradation of heme), are excreted mainly in the feces.

Eleven of the 20 amino acids used to form proteins are synthesized in the body if an adequate amount is not present in the diet (Table VII.2). Ten of these amino acids can be produced from glucose; the 11th, tyrosine, is synthesized from the essential amino acid phenylalanine. It should be noted that cysteine, one of the

FIG. VII.1. Summary of amino acid metabolism. Dietary proteins are digested to amino acids in the stomach and intestine, which are absorbed by the intestinal epithelium, transferred to the circulation, and taken up by cells. Amino acids are used to synthesize proteins and other nitrogen-containing compounds. The carbon skeletons of amino acids are also oxidized for energy, and the nitrogen is converted to urea and other nitrogenous excretory products.

 The healthy human adult is in nitrogen balance; in other words, the amount of nitrogen excreted each day (mainly in the urine) equals the amount consumed (mainly as dietary protein). Negative nitrogen balance occurs when the amount of nitrogen excreted is greater than the amount consumed, and positive nitrogen balance occurs when the amount excreted is less than that consumed (see Chapter 1).

693

Table VII.1   Major Nitrogenous Urinary Excretory Products

Amount Excreted in Urine Per Day[a]		
Urea[b]	12–20 g urea nitrogen (12,000–20,000 mg)	
NH_4^+	140–1,500 mg ammonia nitrogen	
Creatinine	Men	14–26 mg/kg
	Women	11–20 mg/kg
Uric acid	250–750 mg	

[a]The amounts are expressed in the units that are generally reported by clinical laboratories. Note that the amounts for creatinine and uric acid are for the whole compound, whereas those for urea and ammonia are for the nitrogen content.
[b]Under normal circumstances, approximately 90% of the nitrogen excreted in the urine is in the form of urea. The exact amounts of each component vary, however, depending on dietary protein intake and physiologic state. For instance, NH_4^+ excretion increases during acidosis because the kidney secretes ammonia to bind protons in the urine.

10 amino acids produced from glucose, obtains its sulfur atom from the essential amino acid methionine.

Certain amino acids are essential in humans. "Essential" means that the carbon skeleton cannot be synthesized and, therefore, these amino acids are required in the diet (Table VII.3). The essential amino acids are also called the *indispensable amino acids*. Arginine is essential during periods of growth; in adults it is no longer considered essential.

Table VII.3   Amino Acids Essential in the Diet

Histidine
Isoleucine
Leucine
Lysine
Methionine
Phenylalanine
Threonine
Tryptophan
Valine
Arginine (not required by the adult but required for growth)

Table VII.2   Amino Acids Synthesized in the Body[a]

From Glucose	*From an Essential Amino Acid*
Alanine	Tyrosine (from phenylalanine)
Arginine	
Asparagine	
Aspartate	
Cysteine[b]	
Glutamate	
Glutamine	
Glycine	
Proline	
Serine	

[a]These amino acids are called "nonessential" or "dispensable," terms that refer to dietary requirements. Of course, within the body, they are necessary. We cannot survive without them.
[b]Although the carbons of cysteine can be derived from glucose, its sulfur is obtained from the essential amino acid methionine.

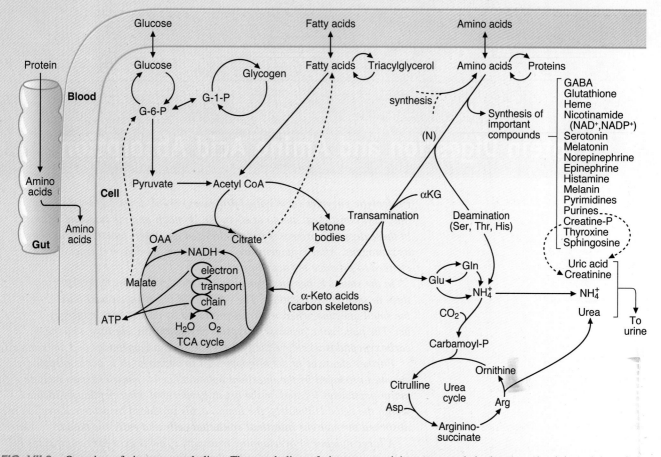

FIG. VII.2. Overview of nitrogen metabolism. The metabolism of nitrogen-containing compounds is shown on the right and that of glucose and fatty acids is shown on the left. This figure shows a hypothetical, composite cell. No single-cell type has all of these pathways. Many of the pathways shown are described in the next few chapters. α-*KG*, α-ketoglutarate; *OAA*, oxaloacetate; *G-6-P*, glucose 6-phosphate; *G-1-P*, glucose 1-phosphate.

After nitrogen is removed from amino acids, the carbon skeletons are oxidized (Fig. VII.2). Most of the carbons are converted to pyruvate, intermediates of the tricarboxylic acid (TCA) cycle, or to acetyl coenzyme A (acetyl-CoA). In the liver, particularly during fasting, these carbons may be converted to glucose or to ketone bodies and released into the blood. Other tissues then oxidize the glucose and ketone bodies. Ultimately, the carbons of the amino acids are converted to CO_2 and H_2O.

Proteolytic enzymes (also called **proteases**) break down dietary proteins into their constituent amino acids in the **stomach** and the **intestine**. Many of these digestive proteases are synthesized as larger, inactive forms known as **zymogens**. After zymogens are secreted into the digestive tract, they are cleaved to produce the active proteases.

In the stomach, **pepsin** begins the digestion of proteins by hydrolyzing them to smaller polypeptides. The contents of the stomach pass into the small intestine, where enzymes produced by the exocrine pancreas act. The pancreatic proteases (**trypsin**, **chymotrypsin**, **elastase**, and the **carboxypeptidases**) cleave the polypeptides into oligopeptides and amino acids.

Further cleavage of the oligopeptides to amino acids is accomplished by enzymes produced by the intestinal epithelial cells. These enzymes include **aminopeptidases** located on the brush border and other peptidases located within the cells. Ultimately, the amino acids produced by protein digestion are absorbed through the **intestinal epithelial cells** and enter the **blood**.

A large number of overlapping transport systems exist for amino acids in cells. Some systems contain **facilitative transporters**, whereas others express **sodium-linked transporters**, which allow the **active transport** of amino acids into cells. Defects in amino acid transport can lead to disease.

Proteins are also continually synthesized and degraded (**turnover**) in cells. A wide variety of proteases in cells carry out this activity. **Lysosomal proteases (cathepsins)** degrade proteins that enter lysosomes. Cytoplasmic proteins targeted for turnover are covalently linked to the small protein **ubiquitin**, which then interacts with a large protein complex, the **proteasome**, to degrade the protein in an adenosine triphosphate (ATP)-dependent process. The amino acids released from proteins during turnover can then be used for the synthesis of new proteins or for energy generation.

THE WAITING ROOM

Sissy Fibrosa, a young child with cystic fibrosis (see Chapter 17), has had repeated bouts of bronchitis caused by *Pseudomonas aeruginosa*. With each of these infections, her response to aerosolized antibiotics has been good. However, her malabsorption of food continues, resulting in foul-smelling, glistening, bulky stools. Her growth records show a slow decline. She is now in the 24th percentile for height and the 20th percentile for weight. She is often listless and irritable, and she tires easily. When her pediatrician discovered that her levels of the serum proteins albumin and prealbumin were low to low normal (indicating protein malnutrition), Sissy was given enteric-coated microspheres of pancreatic enzymes. Almost immediately, the character of Sissy's stools became more normal and she began gaining weight. Over the next 6 months, her growth curves showed improvement, and she seemed brighter, more active, and less irritable.

For the first few months after a painful episode of renal colic, during which he passed a kidney stone (see Chapter 6), **Cal Kulis** had faithfully maintained a high daily fluid intake and had taken the medication required to increase the pH of his urine. Because he has cystinuria, these measures were necessary to increase the solubility of the large amounts of cystine present in his urine and thereby to prevent further formation of kidney stones (calculi). With time, however, he became increasingly complacent about his preventive program. After failing to take his medication for a month, he experienced another severe episode of renal colic with grossly bloody urine. Fortunately, he passed the stone spontaneously, after which he vowed to comply faithfully with his prescribed therapy.

His mother heard that some dietary amino acids were not absorbed in patients with cystinuria and asked whether any dietary changes would reduce Cal's chances of developing additional renal stones.

I. PROTEIN DIGESTION

The digestion of protein begins in the stomach and is completed in the intestine (Fig. 37.1). The enzymes that digest proteins are produced as inactive precursors (zymogens) that are larger than the active enzymes. The inactive zymogens are secreted from the cells in which they are synthesized and enter the lumen of the digestive tract, where they are cleaved to smaller forms that have proteolytic activity (Fig. 37.2). These active enzymes have different specificities; no single enzyme can completely digest a protein. However, by acting in concert, they can digest dietary proteins to amino acids and small peptides, which are cleaved by peptidases associated with intestinal epithelial cells.

A. Digestion of Proteins in the Stomach

Pepsinogen is secreted by the chief cells of the stomach. The gastric parietal cells secrete HCl. The acid in the stomach lumen alters the conformation of pepsinogen so that it can cleave itself, producing the active protease pepsin. Thus, the activation of pepsinogen is autocatalytic.

Dietary proteins are denatured by the acid in the stomach. This inactivates the proteins and partially unfolds them so that they are better substrates for proteases. However, at the low pH of the stomach, pepsin is not denatured and acts as an endopeptidase, cleaving peptide bonds at various points within the protein chain.

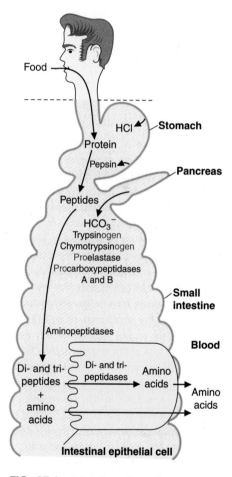

FIG. 37.1. Digestion of proteins. The proteolytic enzymes, trypsin, chymotrypsin, elastase, and the carboxypeptidases are produced as zymogens (the [*pro*] and [*ogen*], in *red*, accompanying the enzyme name) that are activated by cleavage after they enter the gastrointestinal lumen (see Fig. 37.2). Pepsinogen is produced within the stomach and is activated within the stomach (to pepsin) as the pH drops due to HCl secretion.

Kwashiorkor, a common problem of children in third world countries, is caused by a deficiency of protein in a diet that is adequate in calories. Children with kwashiorkor suffer from muscle wasting and decreased concentration of plasma proteins, particularly albumin. The result is an increase in interstitial fluid that causes edema and a distended abdomen, which makes the children appear "plump" (see Chapter 44). The muscle wasting is caused by the lack of essential amino acids in the diet; existing proteins must be broken down to produce these amino acids for new protein synthesis. These problems may be compounded by a decreased ability to produce digestive enzymes and new intestinal epithelial cells because of a decreased availability of amino acids for the synthesis of new proteins.

FIG. 37.2. Activation of the gastric and pancreatic zymogens. Pepsinogen catalyzes its own cleavage as the pH of the stomach drops. Trypsinogen is cleaved by enteropeptidase in the intestine to form the active protease trypsin. Trypsin then plays a key role by catalyzing the cleavage and activation of the other pancreatic zymogens.

Elastase is also found in neutrophils, which are white blood cells that engulf and destroy invading bacteria. Neutrophils frequently act in the lung, and elastase is sometimes released into the lung as the neutrophils work. In normal individuals, the released elastase is blocked from destroying lung cells by the action of circulating α-1-antitrypsin, a protease inhibitor that is synthesized and secreted by the liver. Certain individuals have a genetic mutation that leads to the production of an inactive α-1-antitrypsin protein (α-1-antitrypsin deficiency). The lack of this enzyme activity leads to the development of emphysema caused by proteolytic destruction of lung cells, which results in a reduction in the expansion/contraction capability of the lungs. Deficiency of α-1-antitrypsin can be measured using a dried blood spot. The blood is solubilized using a buffer, and then various amounts of the blood sample are incubated with antibodies specific for α-1-antitrypsin. The antigen–antibody complexes formed will disperse light, and the extent of light scattering is proportional to the concentration of α-1-antitrypsin in the solution. This procedure is known as *rate nephelometry*. Obtaining blood samples from a finger prick and allowing the blood to dry on a card enables rapid screening of individuals for this disorder.

Although pepsin has fairly broad specificity, it tends to cleave peptide bonds in which the carboxyl group is provided by an aromatic or acidic amino acid (Fig. 37.3). Smaller peptides and some free amino acids are produced.

B. Digestion of Proteins by Enzymes from the Pancreas

As the gastric contents empty into the intestine, they encounter the secretions from the exocrine pancreas. Recall that the exocrine pancreas secretes amylase for starch digestion, and lipase and colipase for dietary triacylglycerol digestion. Another pancreatic secretion is bicarbonate, which, in addition to neutralizing stomach acid, raises the pH so that the pancreatic proteases, which are also present in pancreatic secretions, can be active. As secreted, these pancreatic proteases are in the inactive proenzyme form (zymogens). Because the active forms of these enzymes can digest each other, it is important for their zymogen forms all to be activated within a short span of time. This is accomplished by the cleavage of trypsinogen to the active enzyme trypsin, which then cleaves the other pancreatic zymogens, producing their active forms (see Fig. 37.2).

The zymogen trypsinogen is cleaved to form trypsin by *enteropeptidase* (a protease, formerly called *enterokinase*) secreted by the brush border cells of the small intestine. Trypsin catalyzes the cleavages that convert chymotrypsinogen to the active enzyme chymotrypsin, proelastase to elastase, and the procarboxypeptidases to the carboxypeptidases. Thus, trypsin plays a central role in digestion because it both cleaves dietary proteins and activates other digestive proteases produced by the pancreas.

Trypsin, chymotrypsin, and elastase are serine proteases (see Chapter 9) that act as endopeptidases. Trypsin is the most specific of these enzymes, cleaving peptide bonds in which the carboxyl (carbonyl) group is provided by lysine or arginine (see Fig. 37.3). Chymotrypsin is less specific but favors residues that contain hydrophobic amino acids. Elastase cleaves not only elastin (for which it was named) but also other proteins at bonds in which the carboxyl group is contributed by amino acid residues with small side chains (alanine, glycine, and serine). The actions of these pancreatic endopeptidases continue the digestion of dietary proteins begun by pepsin in the stomach.

The smaller peptides formed by the action of trypsin, chymotrypsin, and elastase are attacked by exopeptidases, which are proteases that cleave one amino acid at a time from the end of the chain. Procarboxypeptidases, zymogens produced by the pancreas, are converted by trypsin to the active carboxypeptidases. These exopeptidases remove amino acids from the carboxyl ends of peptide chains. Carboxypeptidase A preferentially releases hydrophobic amino acids, whereas carboxypeptidase B releases basic amino acids (arginine and lysine).

C. Digestion of Proteins by Enzymes from Intestinal Cells

Exopeptidases produced by intestinal epithelial cells act within the brush border and also within the cell. Aminopeptidases, located on the brush border, cleave one amino acid at a time from the amino end of peptides. Intracellular peptidases act on small peptides that are absorbed by the cells.

The concerted action of the proteolytic enzymes produced by cells of the stomach, pancreas, and intestine cleaves dietary proteins to amino acids. The digestive enzymes digest themselves as well as dietary protein. They also digest the intestinal cells that are regularly sloughed off into the lumen. These cells are replaced by cells that mature from precursor cells in the duodenal crypts. The amount of protein that is digested and absorbed each day from digestive juices and cells released into the intestinal lumen may be equal to or greater than the amount of protein consumed in the diet (50 to 100 g).

II. ABSORPTION OF AMINO ACIDS

Amino acids are absorbed from the intestinal lumen through secondary active Na^+-dependent transport systems and through facilitated diffusion.

A. Cotransport of Na^+ and Amino Acids

Amino acids are absorbed from the lumen of the small intestine principally by semispecific Na^+-dependent transport proteins in the luminal membrane of the intestinal cell brush border, similar to that already seen for carbohydrate transport (Fig. 37.4). The cotransport of Na^+ and the amino acid from the outside of the apical membrane to the inside of the cell is driven by the low intracellular Na^+ concentration. Low intracellular

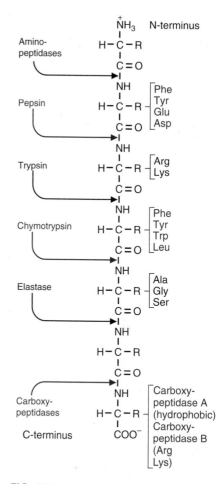

FIG. 37.3. Action of the digestive proteases. Pepsin, trypsin, chymotrypsin, and elastase are endopeptidases; they hydrolyze peptide bonds within chains. The others are exopeptidases; aminopeptidases remove the amino acid at the N-terminus and the carboxypeptidases remove the amino acid at the C-terminus. For each proteolytic enzyme, the amino acid residues involved in the peptide bond that is cleaved are listed beside the R group to the right of the enzyme name.

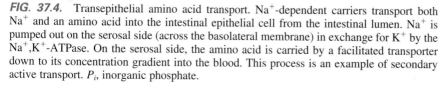

FIG. 37.4. Transepithelial amino acid transport. Na^+-dependent carriers transport both Na^+ and an amino acid into the intestinal epithelial cell from the intestinal lumen. Na^+ is pumped out on the serosal side (across the basolateral membrane) in exchange for K^+ by the Na^+,K^+-ATPase. On the serosal side, the amino acid is carried by a facilitated transporter down to its concentration gradient into the blood. This process is an example of secondary active transport. P_i, inorganic phosphate.

 Patients with cystic fibrosis, such as **Sissy Fibrosa**, have a genetically determined defect in the function of the chloride channels. In the pancreatic secretory ducts, which carry pancreatic enzymes into the lumen of the small intestines, this defect causes inspissation (drying and thickening) of pancreatic exocrine secretions, leading eventually to obstruction of these ducts. One result of this problem is the inability of pancreatic enzymes to enter the intestinal lumen to digest dietary proteins.

The pancreas synthesizes and stores the zymogens in secretory granules. The pancreas also synthesizes a secretory trypsin inhibitor. The need for the inhibitor is to block any trypsin activity that may occur from accidental trypsinogen activation. If the inhibitor were not present, trypsinogen activation would lead to the activation of all of the zymogens in the pancreas, which would lead to the digestion of intracellular pancreatic proteins. Such episodes can lead to pancreatitis.

 Hartnup disease is another genetically determined and relatively rare autosomal recessive disorder. It is caused by a defect in the transport of neutral amino acids across both intestinal and renal epithelial cells (system B^0, gene SLC6A19, where SLC refers to the solute carrier family of transport proteins, of which there are 55, with a total of 362 different genes). The signs and symptoms are caused, in part, by a deficiency of essential amino acids (see Clinical Comments). Cystinuria (system $B^{0,+}$, genes involved are SLC7A9 and SLC3A1, as the transporter is a heteromeric complex) and Hartnup disease involve defects in two different transport proteins. In each case, the defect is present both in intestinal cells, causing malabsorption of the amino acids from the digestive products in the intestinal lumen, and in kidney tubular cells, causing a decreased resorption of these amino acids from the glomerular filtrate and an increased concentration of the amino acids in the urine.

 Why do patients with cystinuria and Hartnup disease have hyperaminoaciduria without associated hyperaminoacidemia?

Na^+ results from the pumping of Na^+ out of the cell by a Na^+,K^+-ATPase on the serosal membrane. Thus, the primary transport mechanism is the creation of a sodium gradient; the secondary transport process is the coupling of amino acids to the influx of sodium. This mechanism allows the cells to concentrate amino acids from the intestinal lumen. The amino acids are then transported out of the cell into the interstitial fluid, principally by facilitated transporters in the serosal membrane (see Fig. 37.4).

At least six different Na^+-dependent amino acid carriers are located in the apical brush border membrane of the epithelial cells. These carriers have overlapping specificity for different amino acids. One carrier preferentially transports neutral amino acids, another transports proline and hydroxyproline, a third preferentially transports acidic amino acids, and a fourth transports basic amino acids (lysine, arginine, the urea-cycle intermediate ornithine) and cystine (two cysteine residues linked by a disulfide bond). In addition to these Na^+-dependent carriers, some amino acids are transported across the luminal membrane by facilitated transport carriers. Most amino acids are transported by more than one transport system.

As with glucose transport, the Na^+-dependent carriers of the apical membrane of the intestinal epithelial cells are also present in the renal epithelium. However, different isozymes are present in the cell membranes of other tissues. Conversely, the facilitated transport carriers in the serosal membrane of the intestinal epithelia are similar to those found in other cell types in the body. During starvation, the intestinal epithelia, like these other cells, take up amino acids from the blood to use as an energy source. Thus, amino acid transport across the serosal membrane is bidirectional.

B. Transport of Amino Acids into Cells

Amino acids that enter the blood are transported across cell membranes of the various tissues principally by Na^+-dependent cotransporters and, to a lesser extent, by facilitated transporters (Table 37.1). In this respect, amino acid transport differs from glucose transport, which is Na^+-dependent transport in the intestinal and renal epithelium but facilitated transport in other cell types. The Na^+ dependence of amino acid transport in liver, muscle, and other tissues allows these cells to concentrate amino acids from the blood. These transport proteins have different genetic bases, amino acid compositions, and somewhat different specificities than those in the luminal membrane of intestinal epithelia. They also differ somewhat

Table 37.1   A Partial Listing of Amino Acid Transport Systems[a]

System Name	Sodium Dependent?	Specificity	Tissues Expressed
A	Yes	Small and polar neutral amino acids (Ala, Ser, Gln, Gly, Pro, Cys, Asn, His, Met)	Many
ASC	Yes	Small amino acids (Ala, Ser, Cys)	Many
N	Yes	Gln, Asn, His	Liver, basolateral membrane of kidney
L	No	Branched and aromatic amino acids (His, Met, Leu, Ile, Val, Phe, Tyr, Trp)	Many[b]
$B^{0,+}$	Yes	Basic amino acids	Intestine (brush border)[c] and kidney
B^0	Yes	Zwitterionic amino acids (monoamino, monocarboxylic acid amino acids)	Intestine and kidney[d]
X_{AG}^-	Yes	Anionic amino acids (Asp, Glu)	Intestine (brush border) and kidney
Imino	Yes	Pro, hydroxyproline, Gly	Intestine (brush border) and kidney

[a]Not all transport systems are listed.
[b]This transport system will be exploited in a treatment for PKU, see Chapter 39.
[c]This system is most likely defective in cystinuria.
[d]This system is most likely defective in Hartnup disease.

among tissues. For instance, the N-system for glutamine uptake is present in the liver but either is not present in other tissues or is present as an isoform with different properties. There is also some overlap in specificity of the transport proteins, with most amino acids being transported by more than one carrier.

III. PROTEIN TURNOVER AND REPLENISHMENT OF THE INTRACELLULAR AMINO ACID POOL

The amino acid pool within cells is generated both from dietary amino acids and from the degradation of existing proteins within the cell. All proteins within cells have a *half-life* ($t_{1/2}$), a time at which 50% of the protein that was synthesized at a particular time will have been degraded. Some proteins are inherently short-lived, with half-lives of 5 to 20 minutes. Other proteins are present for extended periods, with half-lives of many hours or even days. Thus, proteins are continuously being synthesized and degraded in the body, using a variety of enzyme systems to do so (Table 37.2). Examples of proteins that undergo extensive synthesis and degradation are hemoglobin, muscle proteins, digestive enzymes, and the proteins of cells sloughed off from the gastrointestinal tract. Hemoglobin is produced in reticulocytes and reconverted to amino acids by the phagocytic cells that remove mature red blood cells from the circulation on a daily basis. Muscle protein is degraded during periods of fasting, and the amino acids are used for gluconeogenesis. After ingestion of protein in the diet, muscle protein is resynthesized. Adults cannot increase the amount of muscle or other body proteins by eating an excess amount of protein. If dietary protein is consumed in excess of our needs, it is converted to glycogen and triacylglycerols, which are then stored.

A large amount of protein is recycled daily in the form of digestive enzymes, which are themselves degraded by digestive proteases. In addition, approximately one-fourth of the cells lining the walls of the gastrointestinal tract are lost each day and replaced by newly synthesized cells. As cells leave the gastrointestinal wall, their proteins and other components are digested by enzymes in the lumen of the gut, and the products are absorbed. Additionally, red blood cells have a life span of about 120 days. Every day, 3×10^{11} red blood cells die and are phagocytosed. The hemoglobin in these cells is degraded to amino acids by lysosomal proteases, and their amino acids are reused in the synthesis of new proteins. Only approximately 6% (roughly 10 g) of the protein that enters the digestive tract (including dietary proteins, digestive enzymes, and the proteins in sloughed-off cells) is excreted in the feces each day. The remainder is recycled.

Proteins are also recycled within cells. The differences in amino acid composition of the various proteins of the body, the vast range in turnover times ($t_{1/2}$), and the recycling of amino acids are all important factors that help to determine the requirements for specific amino acids and total protein in the diet. The synthesis

 Trace amounts of polypeptides pass into the blood. They may be transported through intestinal epithelial cells, probably by pinocytosis, or they may slip between the cells that line the gut wall. This process is particularly troublesome for premature infants because it can lead to allergies caused by proteins in their food.

 Patients with cystinuria and Hartnup disease have defective transport proteins in both the intestine and the kidney. These patients do not absorb the affected amino acids at a normal rate from the digestive products in the intestinal lumen. They also do not readily resorb these amino acids from the glomerular filtrate into the blood. Therefore, they do not have *hyperaminoacidemia* (a high concentration in the blood). Normally, only a few percentage of the amino acids that enter the glomerular filtrate are excreted in the urine; most are resorbed. In these diseases, much larger amounts of the affected amino acids are excreted in the urine, resulting in hyperaminoaciduria.

 Cal Kulis and other patients with cystinuria have a genetically determined defect in the transport of cystine and the basic amino acids—lysine, arginine, and ornithine—across the brush border membranes of cells in both their small intestine and renal tubules (system $B^{0,+}$). However, they do not appear to have any symptoms of amino acid deficiency, in part because the amino acids cysteine (which is oxidized in blood and urine to form the disulfide cystine) and arginine can be synthesized in the body (i.e., they are "nonessential" amino acids). *Ornithine* (an amino acid that is not found in proteins but serves as an intermediate of the urea cycle) can also be synthesized. The most serious problem for these patients is the insolubility of cystine, which can form kidney stones that may lodge in the ureter, causing genitourinary bleeding and severe pain known as *renal colic*.

Table 37.2   Proteases Involved in Protein Turnover/Degradation

Classification	Mechanism	Role
Cathepsins	Cysteine proteases	Lysosomal enzymes
Caspases	Cysteine proteases, which cleave after aspartate	Apoptosis; activated from procaspases (see Chapter 18)
Matrix metalloproteinases	Require zinc for catalysis	Model extracellular matrix components; regulated by TIMPs (tissue inhibitors of matrix metalloproteinases)
Proteasome	Large complex that degrades ubiquitin-tagged proteins	Protein turnover
Serine proteases	Active-site serine in a catalytic triad with histidine and aspartic acid	Digestion and blood clotting; activated usually from zymogens (see Chapter 45)
Calpains	Calcium-dependent cysteine proteases	Many different cellular roles

of many enzymes is induced in response to physiologic demand (such as fasting or feeding). These enzymes are continuously being degraded. Intracellular proteins are also damaged by oxidation and other modifications that limit their function. Mechanisms for intracellular degradation of unnecessary or damaged proteins involve lysosomes and the ubiquitin/proteasome system.

A. Lysosomal Protein Turnover

Lysosomes participate in the process of autophagy, in which intracellular components are surrounded by membranes that fuse with lysosomes and endocytosis (see Chapter 10). *Autophagy* is a complex regulated process in which cytoplasm is sequestered into vesicles and delivered to the lysosomes. Within the lysosomes, the cathepsin family of proteases degrades the ingested proteins to individual amino acids. The recycled amino acids can then leave the lysosome and rejoin the intracellular amino acid pool. Although the details of how autophagy is induced are still being unraveled, starvation of a cell is a trigger to induce this process. This allows old proteins to be recycled and the newly released amino acids to be used for new protein synthesis, to enable the cell to survive starvation conditions. The mammalian target of rapamycin (mTOR) (see Chapter 36) plays a key role in regulating autophagy, as outlined in Figure 37.5.

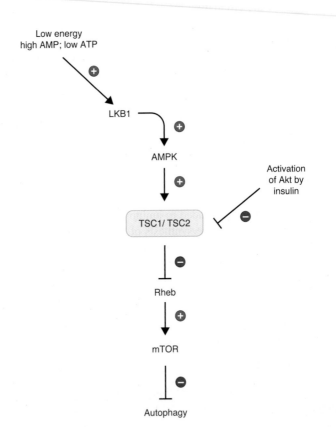

FIG. 37.5. Overview of mTOR participation in autophagy. When active, the mTOR kinase will phosphorylate a protein crucial to the initiation of phagosome formation, which will inhibit autophagy. mTOR kinase is activated by Rheb-GTP (ras homolog enriched in brain, bound to GTP). Under low energy conditions (starvation), autophagy is favored as the AMP-activated protein kinase (AMPK) is activated, which phosphorylates the tuberous sclerosis complexes 1 and 2 (TSC1/TSC2) activating its Rheb-GTPase activating activity. This leads to the inactivation of Rheb (Rheb-GTP is converted to the inactive Rheb-GDP), which leads to the inactivation of mTOR. When inactive, mTOR does not block autophagy, and self-proteolysis is favored, as is an inhibition of protein synthesis. In the presence of growth factors that activate the Akt kinase, Akt phosphorylates the TSC1/TSC2 complex at a site distinct from the AMPK site. The phosphorylation event by Akt leads to an inhibition of the TSC1/TSC2 Rheb-GTPase activating activity, which allows Rheb to be active for extended periods. Active Rheb leads to activation of mTOR, inhibition of autophagy, and activation of protein synthesis.

FIG. 37.6.   The proteasome and cap proteins. The cap proteins (PA700 and PA28) regulate the activity of this proteolytic complex by recruiting to the complex the substrates for proteolysis. The ATP requirement is to unfold and denature the proteins targeted for destruction.

B. The Ubiquitin–Proteasome Pathway

Ubiquitin is a small protein (76 amino acids) that is highly conserved. Its amino acid sequence in yeast and humans differs by only three residues. Ubiquitin targets intracellular proteins for degradation by covalently binding to the ε-amino group of lysine residues. This is accomplished by a three-enzyme system that adds ubiquitin to proteins targeted for degradation. Often, the target protein is *polyubiquitinylated*, a process in which additional ubiquitin molecules are added to previous ubiquitin molecules, forming a long ubiquitin tail on the target protein. After polyubiquitinylation is complete, the targeted protein is released from the three-enzyme complex and is directed to the proteasome via a variety of mechanisms.

A protease complex, known as the *proteasome*, then degrades the targeted protein, releasing intact ubiquitin that can again mark other proteins for degradation (Fig. 37.6). The basic proteasome is a cylindrical 20S protein complex with multiple internal proteolytic sites. Adenosine triphosphate (ATP) hydrolysis is used both to unfold the tagged protein and to push the protein into the core of the cylinder. The complex is regulated by 19S regulatory particles (cap complexes), which bind the ubiquinylated protein (a step that requires ATP) and deliver them to the complex. After the target protein is degraded, the ubiquitin is released intact and recycled. The resulting amino acids join the intracellular pool of free amino acids.

Many proteins that contain regions rich in the amino acids proline (P), glutamate (E), serine (S), and threonine (T) have short half-lives. These regions are known as *PEST sequences*, based on the one-letter abbreviations used for these amino acids. Most of the proteins that contain PEST sequences are hydrolyzed by the ubiquitin–proteasome system.

CLINICAL COMMENTS

Sissy Fibrosa. Sissy Fibrosa's growth and weight curves were both subnormal until her pediatrician added pancreatic enzyme supplements to her treatment plan. These supplements digest dietary protein, releasing essential and other amino acids from the dietary protein, which are then absorbed by the epithelial cells of Sissy's small intestine, through which they are transported into the blood. A discernable improvement in Sissy's body weight and growth curves was noted within months of starting this therapy.

Besides the proportions of essential amino acids present in various foods, the quality of a dietary protein is also determined by the rate at which it is digested and, in a more general way, by its capacity to contribute to the growth of the infant. In this regard, the proteins in foods of animal origin are more digestible than are those derived from plants. For example, the digestibility of proteins in eggs is approximately 97%; that of meats, poultry, and fish is 85% to 100%; and that from wheat, soybeans, and other legumes ranges from 75% to 90%.

The official daily dietary "protein requirement" accepted by the United States and Canadian government is 0.8 g of protein per kilogram of desirable body weight for adults (approximately 56 g for an adult man and 44 g for an adult woman). On an average weight basis, the requirement per kilogram is much greater for infants and children. This fact underscores the importance of improving **Sissy Fibrosa's** protein digestion to optimize her potential for normal growth and development.

 Cal Kulis. In patients with cystinuria, such as Cal Kulis, the inability to absorb cystine and basic amino acids from the gut and the increased loss of these amino acids in the urine may be expected to cause a deficiency of these compounds in the blood. However, because three of these amino acids can be synthesized in the body (i.e., they are nonessential amino acids), their concentrations in the plasma remain normal, and clinical manifestations of a deficiency state do not develop. It is not clear why symptoms related to a lysine deficiency have not been observed.

In a disorder that was first observed in the Hartnup family and bears their name, the intestinal and renal transport defect involves the neutral amino acids (mono-amine, monocarboxylic acids), including several essential amino acids (isoleucine, leucine, phenylalanine, threonine, tryptophan, and valine) as well as certain nonessential amino acids (alanine, serine, and tyrosine). A reduction in the availability of these essential amino acids may be expected to cause a variety of clinical disorders. Yet children with the Hartnup disorder identified by routine newborn urine screening almost always remain clinically normal.

However, some patients with the Hartnup biochemical phenotype eventually develop pellagra-like manifestations, which usually include a photosensitivity rash, ataxia, and neuropsychiatric symptoms. Pellagra results from a dietary deficiency of the vitamin niacin or the essential amino acid tryptophan, which are both precursors for the nicotinamide moiety of NAD and NADP. In asymptomatic patients, the transport abnormality may be incomplete and so subtle as to allow no phenotypic expression of Hartnup disease. These patients also may be capable of absorbing some small peptides that contain the neutral amino acids.

The only rational treatment for patients who have pellagra-like symptoms is to administer niacin (nicotinic acid) in oral doses up to 300 mg/day. Although the rash, ataxia, and neuropsychiatric manifestations of niacin deficiency may disappear, the hyperaminoaciduria and intestinal transport defect do not respond to this therapy. In addition to niacin, a high-protein diet may benefit some patients.

BIOCHEMICAL COMMENTS

The γ-Glutamyl Cycle. The γ-glutamyl cycle is necessary for the synthesis of *glutathione*, a compound that protects cells from oxidative damage (see Chapter 24). When it was first discovered, the cycle was thought to be important in amino acid transport, but its involvement in such transport is now thought to be limited to salvage of cysteine. The enzymes of the cycle are present in many tissues, although certain tissues lack one or more of the enzymes of the cycle.

The entire cycle is presented in Figure 37.7. In this case, the extracellular amino acid reacts with glutathione (γ-glutamyl-cysteinyl-glycine) in a reaction catalyzed by a transpeptidase present in the cell membrane. A γ-glutamyl amino acid is

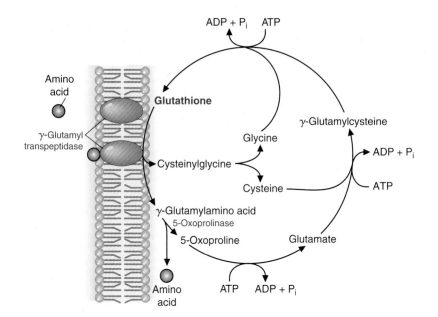

FIG. 37.7.   The γ-glutamyl cycle. In cells of the intestine and kidney, amino acids can be trans-ported across the cell membrane by reacting with glutathione (γ-glutamyl-cysteinyl-glycine) to form a γ-glutamyl amino acid. The amino acid is released into the cell, and glutathione is resyn-thesized. However, the major role of this cycle is glutathione synthesis because many tissues lack the transpeptidase and 5-oxoprolinase activities. P_i, inorganic phosphate.

formed, which travels across the cell membrane and releases the amino acid into the cell. The other products of these two reactions are reconverted to glutathione.

The reactions that convert glutamate to glutathione in the γ-glutamyl cycle are the same reactions as those required for the synthesis of glutathione. The enzymes for glutathione synthesis, but not the transpeptidase, are found in most tissues. The oxoprolinase is also missing from many tissues, so the major role of this pathway is one of glutathione synthesis from glutamate, cysteine, and glycine. The trans-peptidase is the only protease in the cell that can break the γ-glutamyl linkage in glutathione. Glutathione is also involved in reducing compounds such as hydrogen peroxide (see Chapter 21). It also protects cells, particularly erythrocytes, from oxidative damage through formation of oxidized glutathione—two glutathione residues connected by a disulfide bond (see Chapter 24).

Key Concepts

- Proteases (proteolytic enzymes) break down dietary proteins into peptides and then their constituent amino acids in the stomach and intestine.
- Pepsin initiates protein breakdown in the stomach.
- Upon entering the small intestine, inactive zymogens secreted from the pancreas are activated to continue protein digestion.
- Enzymes produced by the intestinal epithelial cells are also required to fully degrade proteins.
- The amino acids generated by proteolysis in the intestinal lumen are transported into the intestinal epithelial cells, from which they enter the circulation for use by the tissues.
- Transport systems for amino acids are similar to transport systems for monosaccharides; both facilitative and active transport systems exist.
- There are several overlapping transport systems for amino acids in cells.
- Protein degradation (turnover) occurs continuously in all cells.
- Proteins can be degraded by lysosomal enzymes (cathepsins).
- Proteins are also targeted for destruction by being covalently linked to the small protein ubiquitin.
- The ubiquitin-tagged proteins interact with the proteasome, a large complex that degrades proteins to small peptides in an ATP-dependent process.
- Amino acids released from proteins during turnover can be used for the synthesis of new proteins, for energy generation, or for gluconeogenesis.
- Diseases discussed in this chapter are summarized in Table 37.3.

Table 37.3   Diseases Discussed in Chapter 37

Disease or Disorder	Genetic or Environmental	Comments
Cystic fibrosis	Genetic	Patients with cystic fibrosis often experience a blockage of the pancreatic duct, which necessitates oral ingestion of digestive enzymes for appropriate nutrient degradation and absorption.
Cystinuria	Genetic	A mutation in a membrane transport protein (B^{0+}) for basic amino acids, including cystine, which is expressed in kidney and intestine. Kidney stones may develop due to this disorder.
Kwashiorkor	Environmental	Protein–calorie malnutrition (diet is adequate in calories but lacking in protein), leading to excessive protein degradation in the extremities and edema.
Hartnup disease	Genetic	A mutation in a membrane transport protein (B^{0}) for neutral amino acids, including tryptophan, which is expressed in both the kidney and intestine. Some patients may develop pellagra-like symptoms due to the lack of tryptophan.

REVIEW QUESTIONS—CHAPTER 37

1. An individual with a deficiency in the conversion of trypsinogen to trypsin would be expected to experience a more detrimental effect on protein digestion than an individual who was defective in any of the other digestive proteases. This is a result of which of the following?

   A. Trypsin has a greater and wider range of substrates on which to act.
   B. Trypsin activates pepsinogen, so digestion can begin in the stomach.
   C. Trypsin activates the other zymogens that are secreted by the pancreas.
   D. Trypsin activates enteropeptidase, which is needed to activate the other pancreatic zymogens.
   E. Trypsin inhibits intestinal motility, so the substrates can be hydrolyzed for longer periods.

2. An individual has been shown to have a deficiency in an intestinal epithelial cell amino acid transport system for leucine. However, the individual shows no symptoms of amino acid deficiency. This could be due to which of the following?

   A. The body synthesizes leucine to compensate for the transport defect.
   B. The kidney reabsorbs leucine and sends it to other tissues.
   C. There are multiple transport systems for leucine.
   D. Isoleucine takes the place of leucine in proteins.
   E. Leucine is not necessary for bulk protein synthesis.

3. Kwashiorkor can result from which of the following?

   A. Consuming a calorie-deficient diet that is also deficient in protein.
   B. Consuming a calorie-adequate diet that is deficient in carbohydrates.
   C. Consuming a calorie-adequate diet that is deficient in fatty acids.
   D. Consuming a calorie-adequate diet that is deficient in proteins.
   E. Consuming a calorie-deficient diet that is primarily proteins.

4. Which of the following enzymes is activated through an autocatalytic process?

   A. Enteropeptidase
   B. Trypsinogen
   C. Pepsinogen
   D. Aminopeptidase
   E. Proelastase

5. Children with kwashiorkor usually have a fatty liver. This is due to which of the following?

   A. The high-fat content of their diet
   B. The high-carbohydrate content of their diet
   C. The high-protein content of their diet
   D. The lack of substrates for gluconeogenesis in the liver
   E. The lack of substrates for protein synthesis in the liver
   F. The lack of substrates for glycogen synthesis in the liver

38 Fate of Amino Acid Nitrogen: Urea Cycle

In comparison with carbohydrate and lipid metabolism, the metabolism of amino acids is complex. We must be concerned not only with the fate of the carbon atoms of the amino acids but also with the fate of the **nitrogen**. During their metabolism, amino acids travel in the blood from one tissue to another. Ultimately, most of the nitrogen is converted to **urea** in the **liver** and the carbons are oxidized to CO_2 and H_2O by several tissues (Fig. 38.1).

After a meal that contains protein, amino acids released by digestion (see Chapter 37) pass from the gut through the hepatic portal vein to the liver (see Fig. 38.2A). In a normal diet containing 60 to 100 g protein, most of the amino acids are used for the synthesis of proteins in the liver and in other tissues. Excess amino acids may be converted to glucose or triacylglycerol.

During fasting, muscle protein is cleaved to amino acids. Some of the amino acids are partially oxidized to produce energy (see Fig. 38.2B). Portions of these amino acids are converted to **alanine** and **glutamine**, which, along with other amino acids, are released into the blood. Glutamine is oxidized by various tissues, including the **lymphocytes**, **gut**, **and kidney**, which convert some of the carbons and nitrogen to alanine. Alanine and other amino acids travel to the liver, where the carbons are converted to glucose and ketone bodies, and the nitrogen is converted to urea, which is excreted by the kidneys. Glucose, produced by gluconeogenesis, is subsequently oxidized to CO_2 and H_2O by many tissues, and ketone bodies are oxidized by tissues such as muscle and kidney.

Several enzymes are important in the process of interconverting amino acids and in removing nitrogen so that the carbon skeletons can be oxidized. These include **dehydratases**, **transaminases**, **glutamate dehydrogenases**, **glutaminases**, and **deaminases**.

The conversion of amino acid nitrogen to urea occurs mainly in the liver. Urea is formed in the urea cycle from NH_4^+, bicarbonate, and the nitrogen of **aspartate** (see Fig. 38.1). Initially, NH_4^+, bicarbonate, and adenosine triphosphate (ATP) react to produce **carbamoyl phosphate**, which reacts with **ornithine** to form **citrulline**. Aspartate then reacts with citrulline to form **argininosuccinate**, which releases **fumarate**, forming **arginine**. Finally, **arginase** cleaves arginine to release urea and regenerate ornithine. The cycle is regulated in a **feed-forward** manner, such that when amino acid degradation is occurring, the rate of the cycle is increased.

FIG. 38.1. Fate of amino acid carbons and nitrogen. Amino acid carbon can be used either for energy storage (glycogen, fatty acids) or for energy. Amino acid nitrogen is used for urea synthesis. One nitrogen of urea comes from NH_4^+, the other from aspartate.

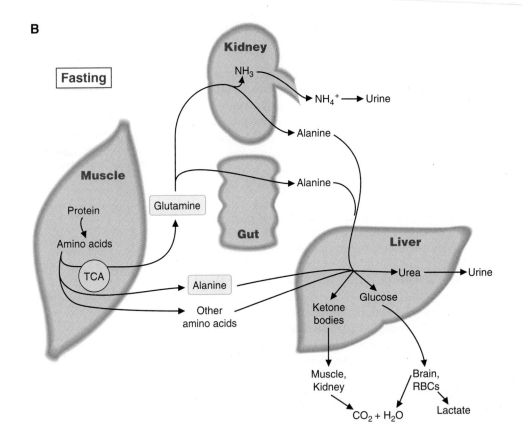

FIG. 38.2. Roles of various tissues in amino acid metabolism. **A.** In the fed state, amino acids released by digestion of dietary proteins travel through the hepatic portal vein to the liver, where they are used for the synthesis of proteins, particularly the blood proteins, such as serum albumin. The carbon skeletons of excess amino acids are converted to glucose or to triacylglycerols. The latter are then packaged and secreted in very low-density lipoproteins (VLDLs). The glucose produced from amino acids in the fed state is stored as glycogen or released into the blood if blood glucose levels are low. Amino acids that pass through the liver are converted to proteins in cells of other tissues. **B.** During fasting, amino acids are released from muscle protein. Some enter the blood directly. Others are partially oxidized and the nitrogen is stored in the form of alanine and glutamine, which enter the blood. In the kidney, glutamine releases ammonia into the urine and is converted to alanine and serine. In the cells of the gut, glutamine is converted to alanine. Alanine (the major gluconeogenic amino acid) and other amino acids enter the liver, where their nitrogen is converted to urea, which is excreted in the urine, and their carbons are converted to glucose and ketone bodies, which are oxidized by various tissues for energy. *RBCs,* red blood cells; *TCA,* tricarboxylic acid.

THE WAITING ROOM

Percy Veere and his high school friend decided to take a Caribbean cruise, during which they sampled the cuisine of many of the islands on their itinerary. One month after their return to the United States, Percy complained of severe malaise, loss of appetite, nausea, vomiting, and arthralgias (joint pains). He had a low-grade fever and noted a persistent and increasing pain in the area of his liver. His friend noted a yellow discoloration of the whites of Percy's eyes and skin. Percy's urine turned the color of iced tea, and his stool became a light-clay color. His doctor found his liver to be enlarged and tender. Liver function tests were ordered.

Serologic testing for viral hepatitis types B, C, and D were nonreactive, but fecal studies showed "shedding" of hepatitis virus type A. Tests for antibodies to antigens of the hepatitis A virus (anti-HAV) in the serum were positive for the immunoglobulin M type.

A diagnosis of acute viral hepatitis type A was made, probably contracted from virus-contaminated food Percy had eaten while on his cruise. His physician explained that there was no specific treatment for type A viral hepatitis but recommended symptomatic and supportive care and prevention of transmission to others by the fecal–oral route. Percy took acetaminophen three to four times a day for fever and arthralgias throughout his illness.

I. FATE OF AMINO ACID NITROGEN

A. Transamination Reactions

Transamination is the major process for removing nitrogen from amino acids. In most instances, the nitrogen is transferred as an amino group from the original amino acid to α-ketoglutarate, forming glutamate, whereas the original amino acid is converted to its corresponding α-keto acid (Fig. 38.3). For example, the amino acid aspartate can be transaminated to form its corresponding α-keto acid, oxaloacetate. In the process, the amino group is transferred to α-ketoglutarate, which is converted to its corresponding amino acid, glutamate.

All amino acids except lysine and threonine have the ability to undergo transamination reactions. The enzymes that catalyze these reactions are known as *transaminases* or *aminotransferases*. For most of these reactions, α-ketoglutarate and glutamate serve as one of the α-keto acid–amino acid pairs. Pyridoxal phosphate is the required cofactor for these reactions. Pyridoxal phosphate is derived from vitamin B_6 (pyridoxine), as shown in Figure 38.4.

Overall, in a transamination reaction, an amino group from one amino acid becomes the amino group of a second amino acid. Because these reactions are readily reversible, they can be used to remove nitrogen from amino acids or to transfer nitrogen to α-keto acids to form amino acids. Thus, they are involved both in amino acid degradation and in amino acid synthesis.

B. Removal of Amino Acid Nitrogen as Ammonia

Cells in the body and bacteria in the gut release the nitrogen of certain amino acids as ammonia or ammonium ion (NH_4^+) (Fig. 38.5). Because these two forms of nitrogen can be interconverted, the terms are sometimes used interchangeably. The ammonium ion releases a proton to form ammonia by a reaction with a pK_a of 9.3 (Fig. 38.6). Therefore, at physiologic pH, the equilibrium favors NH_4^+ by a factor of approximately 100/1 (see Chapter 4, the Henderson–Hasselbalch equation).

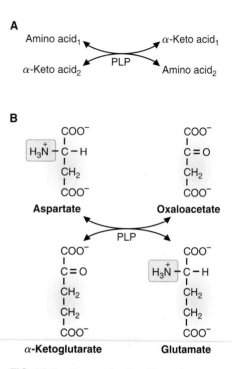

FIG. 38.3. Transamination. The amino group from one amino acid is transferred to another. Pairs of amino acids and their corresponding α-keto acids are involved in these reactions. α-Ketoglutarate and glutamate are usually one of the pairs. The reactions, which are readily reversible, use pyridoxal phosphate (PLP) as a cofactor. The enzymes are called transaminases or aminotransferases. **A.** A generalized reaction. **B.** The aspartate transaminase reaction.

FIG. 38.4.   Activation of vitamin B_6 to pyridoxal phosphate. The two steps are an oxidation and a phosphorylation.

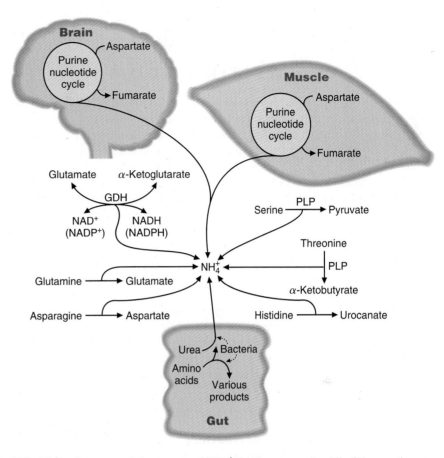

FIG. 38.5.   Summary of the sources of NH_4^+ for the urea cycle. All of the reactions are irreversible except that of glutamate dehydrogenase (GDH). Only the dehydratase reactions, which produce NH_4^+ from serine and threonine, require pyridoxal phosphate as a cofactor. The reactions that are not shown occurring in the muscle or the gut can all occur in the liver, where the NH_4^+ generated can be converted to urea. The purine nucleotide cycle of the brain and muscle is described further in Chapter 41. *PLP*, pyridoxal phosphate.

However, it is important to note that NH_3 is also present in the body because this is the form that can cross cell membranes. For example, NH_3 passes into the urine from kidney tubule cells and decreases the acidity of the urine by binding protons, forming NH_4^+. Once the NH_4^+ is formed, the compound can no longer freely diffuse across membranes.

Glutamate can be oxidatively deaminated by a reaction catalyzed by glutamate dehydrogenase that produces ammonium ion and α-ketoglutarate (Fig. 38.7). Either

$$NH_4^+ \rightleftharpoons NH_3 + H^+$$
$$pK_a = 9.3$$

FIG. 38.6.   Formation of ammonia from an ammonium ion. Because the pK_a is 9.3, the concentration of NH_4^+ at physiologic pH is almost 100 times that of NH_3.

FIG. 38.7.   Reaction catalyzed by glutamate dehydrogenase. This reaction is readily reversible and can use either NAD^+ or $NADP^+$ as a cofactor. The oxygen on α-ketoglutarate is derived from H_2O.

NAD$^+$ or NADP$^+$ can serve as the cofactor. This reaction, which occurs in the mitochondria of most cells, is readily reversible; it can incorporate ammonia into glutamate or release ammonia from glutamate. Glutamate can collect nitrogen from other amino acids as a consequence of transamination reactions and then release ammonia through the glutamate dehydrogenase reaction. This process provides one source of the ammonia that enters the urea cycle. Glutamate dehydrogenase is one of three mammalian enzymes that can "fix" ammonia into organic molecules. The other two are glutamine synthetase and carbamoyl phosphate synthetase I (CPSI).

In addition to glutamate, several amino acids release their nitrogen as NH$_4^+$ (see Fig. 38.5). Histidine may be directly deaminated to form NH$_4^+$ and urocanate. The deaminations of serine and threonine are dehydration reactions that require pyridoxal phosphate and are catalyzed by serine dehydratase. Serine forms pyruvate, and threonine forms α-ketobutyrate. In both cases, NH$_4^+$ is released.

Glutamine and asparagine contain R-group amides that may be released as NH$_4^+$ by deamidation. Asparagine is deamidated by asparaginase, yielding aspartate and NH$_4^+$. Glutaminase acts on glutamine, forming glutamate and NH$_4^+$. The glutaminase reaction is particularly important in the kidney, where the ammonium ion produced is excreted directly into the urine, where it forms salts with metabolic acids, facilitating their removal in the urine.

In muscle and brain, but not in liver, the purine nucleotide cycle allows NH$_4^+$ to be released from amino acids (see Fig. 38.5). Nitrogen is collected by glutamate from other amino acids by means of transamination reactions. Glutamate then transfers its amino group to oxaloacetate to form aspartate, which supplies nitrogen to the purine nucleotide cycle (see Chapter 41). The reactions of the cycle release fumarate and NH$_4^+$. The ammonium ion formed can leave the muscle in the form of glutamine.

In summary, NH$_4^+$ that enters the urea cycle is produced in the body by deamination or deamidation of amino acids (see Fig. 38.5). A significant amount of NH$_4^+$ is also produced by bacteria that live in the lumen of the intestinal tract. This ammonium ion enters the hepatic portal vein and travels to the liver.

C. Role of Glutamate in the Metabolism of Amino Acid Nitrogen

Glutamate plays a pivotal role in the metabolism of amino acids. It is involved in both synthesis and degradation.

Glutamate provides nitrogen for amino acid synthesis (Fig. 38.8). In this process, glutamate obtains its nitrogen either from other amino acids by transamination

FIG. 38.8. Role of glutamate in amino acid synthesis. Glutamate transfers nitrogen by means of transamination reactions to α-keto acids to form amino acids. This nitrogen is either obtained by glutamate from transamination of other amino acids or from NH$_4^+$ by means of the glutamate dehydrogenase (GDH) reaction. *PLP*, pyridoxal phosphate, the active form of vitamin B$_6$ (pyridoxine).

 Percy Veere's laboratory studies showed that his serum alanine transaminase (ALT) level was 675 U/L (reference range, 5 to 30 U), and his serum aspartate transaminase (AST) level was 601 U/L (reference range, 10 to 30 U). His serum alkaline phosphatase level was 284 U/L (reference range for an adult male, 40 to 125 U), and his serum total bilirubin was 9.6 mg/dL (reference range, 0.2 to 1.0 mg/dL). Bilirubin is a degradation product of heme, as described in Chapter 44.

Cellular enzymes such as AST, ALT, and alkaline phosphatase leak into the blood through the membranes of hepatic cells that have been damaged as a result of the inflammatory process. In acute viral hepatitis, the serum ALT level is often elevated to a greater extent than the serum AST level. Alkaline phosphatase, which is present on membranes between liver cells and the bile duct, is also elevated in the blood in acute viral hepatitis.

The rise in serum total bilirubin occurs as a result of the inability of the infected liver to conjugate bilirubin and of a partial or complete occlusion of the hepatic biliary drainage ducts caused by inflammatory swelling within the liver. In fulminant hepatic failure, the serum bilirubin level may exceed 20 mg/dL, a poor prognostic sign.

 Vitamin B$_6$ deficiency symptoms include dermatitis, a microcytic, hypochromic anemia, weakness, irritability, and, in some cases, convulsions. Xanthurenic acid (a degradation product of tryptophan) and other compounds appear in the urine because of an inability to metabolize amino acids completely. A decreased ability to synthesize heme from glycine may cause the microcytic anemia (see Chapter 44), and decreased decarboxylation of amino acids to form neurotransmitters (see Chapter 48) may explain the convulsions. Although vitamin B$_6$ is required for a large number of reactions involved in amino acid metabolism, it is also required for the glycogen phosphorylase reaction (see Chapter 28).

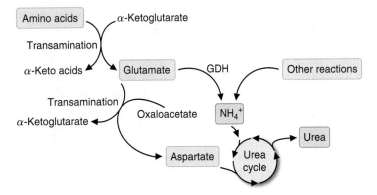

FIG. 38.9. Role of glutamate in urea production. Glutamate collects nitrogen from other amino acids by transamination reactions. This nitrogen can be released as NH_4^+ by glutamate dehydrogenase (GDH). NH_4^+ is also produced by other reactions (see Fig. 38.5). NH_4^+ provides one of the nitrogens for urea synthesis. The other nitrogen comes from aspartate, which is obtained from glutamate by transamination of oxaloacetate.

reactions or from NH_4^+ by the glutamate dehydrogenase reaction. Transamination reactions then serve to transfer amino groups from glutamate to α-keto acids to produce their corresponding amino acids.

When amino acids are degraded and urea is formed, glutamate collects nitrogen from other amino acids by transamination reactions. Some of this nitrogen is released as ammonia by the glutamate dehydrogenase reaction, but much larger amounts of ammonia are produced from the other sources shown in Figure 38.5. NH_4^+ is one of the two forms in which nitrogen enters the urea cycle (Fig. 38.9).

The second form of nitrogen for urea synthesis is provided by aspartate (see Fig. 38.9). Glutamate can be the source of the nitrogen. Glutamate transfers its amino group to oxaloacetate, and aspartate and α-ketoglutarate are formed.

D. Role of Alanine and Glutamine in Transporting Amino Acid Nitrogen to the Liver

Protein turnover and amino acid degradation occur in all tissues; however, the urea-cycle enzymes are active primarily in the liver (the intestine expresses low levels of activity of these enzymes; see Chapter 42). Thus, a mechanism needs to be in place to transport amino acid nitrogen to the liver. Alanine and glutamine are the major carriers of nitrogen in the blood. Alanine is exported primarily by muscle. Because muscle is metabolizing glucose through glycolysis, pyruvate is available in the muscle. The pyruvate is transaminated by glutamate to form alanine, which travels to the liver (Fig. 38.10). The glutamate is formed by transamination of an amino

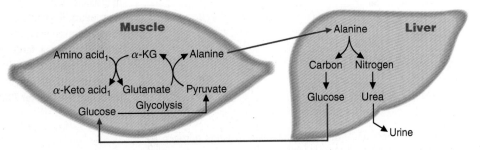

FIG. 38.10. The glucose/alanine cycle. Within the muscle, amino acid degradation leads to the transfer of nitrogens to α-ketoglutarate (α-KG) and pyruvate. The alanine formed travels to the liver, where the carbons of alanine are used for gluconeogenesis and the alanine nitrogen is used for urea biosynthesis. This could occur during exercise when the muscle uses blood-borne glucose (see Chapter 47).

FIG. 38.11. Synthesis of glutamine in peripheral tissues and its transport to the liver. Within the liver, glutaminase converts glutamine to glutamate. Note how α-ketoglutarate can accept two molecules of ammonia to form glutamine. α-*KG*, α-ketoglutarate; *GDH*, glutamate dehydrogenase; P_i, inorganic phosphate.

acid that is being degraded. Upon arriving at the liver, alanine is transaminated to pyruvate, and the nitrogen is used for urea synthesis. The pyruvate formed is used for gluconeogenesis, and the glucose is exported to the muscle for use as energy. This cycle of moving carbons and nitrogen between the muscle and liver is known as the *glucose/alanine cycle*.

Glutamine is synthesized from glutamate by the fixation of ammonia, requiring energy (adenosine triphosphate [ATP]) and the enzyme glutamine synthetase (Fig. 38.11), which is a cytoplasmic enzyme found in all cells. In the liver, glutamine synthetase is located in cells surrounding the portal vein. Its major role is to convert any ammonia that has escaped from urea production into glutamine, so that free ammonia does not leave the liver and enters the circulation.

Under conditions of rapid amino acid degradation within a tissue, so that ammonia levels increase, the glutamate that has been formed from transamination reactions accepts another nitrogen molecule to form glutamine. The glutamine travels to the liver, kidney, or intestines, where glutaminase (see Fig. 38.11) removes the amide nitrogen to form glutamate plus ammonia. In the kidney, the release of ammonia, and the formation of ammonium ion, serves to form salts with metabolic acids in the urine. In the intestine, the glutamine is used as a fuel (see Chapter 42). In the liver, the ammonia is used for urea biosynthesis.

II. UREA CYCLE

The normal human adult is in nitrogen balance; that is, the amount of nitrogen ingested each day, mainly in the form of dietary protein, is equal to the amount of nitrogen excreted. The major nitrogenous excretory product is urea, which exits from the body in the urine. This innocuous compound, produced mainly in the liver by the urea cycle, serves as the disposal form of ammonia, which is toxic, particularly to the brain and central nervous system. Normally, little ammonia (or NH_4^+) is present in the blood. The concentration ranges between 30 and 60 μM. Ammonia is rapidly removed from the blood and converted to urea by the liver. Nitrogen travels in the blood mainly in amino acids, particularly alanine and glutamine. The urea cycle was proposed in 1932 by Hans Krebs and a medical student, Kurt Henseleit, based on their laboratory observations. It was originally called the *Krebs–Henseleit cycle*. Subsequently, Krebs used this concept of metabolic cycling to explain a second process that also bears his name, the Krebs (or tricarboxylic acid [TCA]) cycle.

A. Reactions of the Urea Cycle

Nitrogen enters the urea cycle as NH_4^+ and aspartate (Fig. 38.12). NH_4^+ forms carbamoyl phosphate, which reacts with ornithine to form citrulline. Ornithine is

Percy Veere's symptoms and laboratory abnormalities did not slowly subside over the next 6 weeks as they usually do in uncomplicated viral hepatitis A infections. Instead, his serum total bilirubin, ALT, AST, and alkaline phosphatase levels increased further. His vomiting became intractable, and his friend noted jerking motions of his arms (asterixis), facial grimacing, restlessness, slowed mentation, and slight disorientation. He was admitted to the hospital with a diagnosis of hepatic failure with incipient hepatic encephalopathy (brain dysfunction caused by accumulation of various toxins in the blood), a rare complication of acute type A viral hepatitis alone. The possibility of a superimposed acute hepatic toxicity caused by the use of acetaminophen was considered.

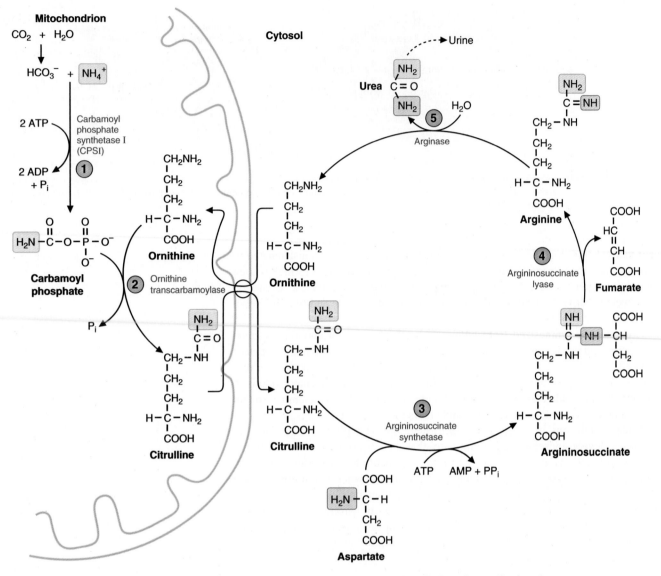

FIG. 38.12.   Urea cycle. The steps of the cycle are numbered 1 through 5. P_i, inorganic phosphate.

the compound that both initiates and is regenerated by the cycle (similar to oxalo-acetate in the TCA cycle). Aspartate reacts with citrulline, eventually donating its nitrogen for urea formation. Arginine is formed in two successive steps. Cleavage of arginine by arginase releases urea and regenerates ornithine.

1. SYNTHESIS OF CARBAMOYL PHOSPHATE

In the first step of the urea cycle, NH_4^+, bicarbonate, and ATP react to form carbamoyl phosphate (see Fig. 38.12). The cleavage of two molecules of ATP is required to form the high-energy phosphate bond of carbamoyl phosphate. CPSI, the enzyme that catalyzes this first step of the urea cycle, is found mainly in mitochondria of the liver and intestine. The Roman numeral suggests that another carbamoyl phosphate synthetase exists, and indeed, CPSII, located in the cytosol, produces carbamoyl phosphate for pyrimidine biosynthesis, using nitrogen from glutamine (see Chapter 41).

2. PRODUCTION OF ARGININE BY THE UREA CYCLE

Carbamoyl phosphate reacts with ornithine to form citrulline (see Fig. 38.12). The high-energy phosphate bond of carbamoyl phosphate provides the energy required for this reaction, which occurs in mitochondria and is catalyzed by ornithine transcarbamoylase (OTC). The product citrulline is transported across the mitochondrial membranes in exchange for cytoplasmic ornithine and enters the cytosol. The carrier for this transport reaction catalyzes an electroneutral exchange of the two compounds.

In the cytosol, citrulline reacts with aspartate, the second source of nitrogen for urea synthesis, to produce argininosuccinate (see Fig. 38.12). This reaction, catalyzed by argininosuccinate synthetase, is driven by the hydrolysis of ATP to adenosine monophosphate (AMP) and pyrophosphate. Aspartate is produced by transamination of oxaloacetate.

Argininosuccinate is cleaved by argininosuccinate lyase to form fumarate and arginine (see Fig. 38.12). Fumarate is produced from the carbons of argininosuccinate provided by aspartate. Fumarate is converted to malate (using cytoplasmic fumarase), which is used either for the synthesis of glucose by the gluconeogenic pathway or for the regeneration of oxaloacetate by cytoplasmic reactions similar to those observed in the TCA cycle (Fig. 38.13). The oxaloacetate that is formed is transaminated to generate the aspartate that carries nitrogen into the urea cycle. Thus, the carbons of fumarate can be recycled to aspartate.

3. CLEAVAGE OF ARGININE TO PRODUCE UREA

Arginine, which contains nitrogens derived from NH_4^+ and aspartate, is cleaved by arginase, producing urea and regenerating ornithine (see Fig. 38.12). Urea is produced from the guanidinium group on the side chain of arginine. The portion of arginine originally derived from ornithine is reconverted to ornithine.

The reactions by which citrulline is converted to arginine and arginine is cleaved to produce urea occur in the cytosol. Ornithine, the other product of the arginase reaction, is transported into the mitochondrion in exchange for citrulline, where it can react with carbamoyl phosphate, initiating another round of the cycle.

B. Origin of Ornithine

Ornithine is an amino acid. However, it is not incorporated into proteins during the process of protein synthesis because no genetic codon exists for this amino

When ornithine transcarbamoylase (OTC) is deficient, the carbamoyl phosphate that normally would enter the urea cycle accumulates and floods the pathway for pyrimidine biosynthesis. Under these conditions, excess orotic acid (orotate), an intermediate in pyrimidine biosynthesis, is excreted in the urine. It produces no ill effects but is indicative of a problem in the urea cycle.

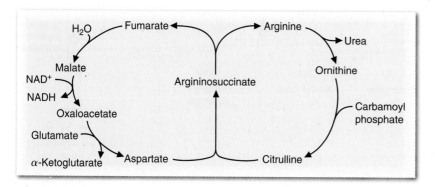

FIG. 38.13.   The Krebs bi-cycle, indicating the common steps between the TCA and urea cycles. All reactions shown occur in the cytoplasm except for the synthesis of citrulline, which occurs in the mitochondria.

FIG. 38.14. The ornithine aminotransferase reaction. This is a reversible reaction that depends on pyridoxal phosphate, which normally favors ornithine degradation. *PLP*, pyridoxal phosphate.

 The precise pathogenesis of the central nervous system (CNS) signs and symptoms that accompany liver failure (hepatic encephalopathy) in patients such as **Percy Veere** is not completely understood. These changes are, however, attributable in part to toxic materials that are derived from the metabolism of nitrogenous substrates by bacteria in the gut that circulate to the liver in the portal vein. These materials "bypass" their normal metabolism by the liver cells, however, because the acute inflammatory process of viral hepatitis severely limits the ability of liver cells to degrade these compounds to harmless metabolites. As a result, these toxins are "shunted" into the hepatic veins unaltered and eventually reach the brain through the systemic circulation ("portal–systemic encephalopathy").

acid. Although ornithine is normally regenerated by the urea cycle (as one of the products of the arginase reaction), ornithine also can be synthesized de novo if needed. The reaction is an unusual transamination reaction catalyzed by ornithine aminotransferase under specific conditions in the intestine (Fig. 38.14). The usual direction of this reaction is the formation of glutamate semialdehyde, which is the first step of the degradation pathway for ornithine.

C. Regulation of the Urea Cycle

The human liver has a vast capacity to convert amino acid nitrogen to urea, thereby preventing toxic effects from ammonia, which would otherwise accumulate. In general, the urea cycle is regulated by substrate availability; the higher the rate of ammonia production, the higher is the rate of urea formation. Regulation by substrate availability is a general characteristic of disposal pathways, such as the urea cycle, which remove toxic compounds from the body. This is a type of "feed-forward" regulation, in contrast to the "feedback" regulation characteristic of pathways that produce functional end products.

Two other types of regulation control the urea cycle: allosteric activation of CPSI by *N*-acetylglutamate (NAG) and induction/repression of the synthesis of urea-cycle enzymes. NAG is formed specifically to activate CPSI; it has no other known function in mammals. The synthesis of NAG from acetyl coenzyme A (acetyl-CoA) and glutamate is stimulated by arginine (Fig. 38.15). Thus, as arginine levels increase within the liver, two important reactions are stimulated. The first is the synthesis of NAG, which increases the rate at which carbamoyl phosphate is produced. The second is to produce more ornithine (via the arginase reaction), so that the cycle can operate more rapidly.

The induction of urea-cycle enzymes occurs in response to conditions that require increased protein metabolism, such as a high-protein diet or prolonged fasting. In both of these physiologic states, as amino acid carbon is converted to glucose, amino acid nitrogen is converted to urea. The induction of the synthesis of urea-cycle enzymes under these conditions occurs even though the uninduced enzyme levels are far in excess of the capacity required. The ability of a high-protein diet to increase urea-cycle enzyme levels is another type of "feed-forward" regulation.

FIG. 38.15. Activation of carbamoyl phosphate synthetase I (CPSI). Arginine stimulates the synthesis of *N*-acetylglutamate, which activates CPSI. P_i, inorganic phosphate.

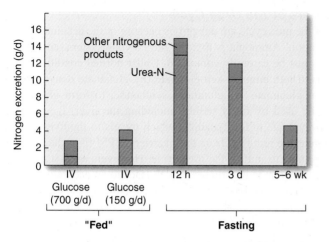

FIG. 38.16. Nitrogen excretion during fasting. Human subjects were initially given intravenous (IV) glucose as indicated, then fasted. Total nitrogen excretion was measured as well as the nitrogen in urea (*brown* area). (Based on Ruderman NB, Aoki TT, Cahill GF Jr. Gluconeogenesis and its disorders in man. In: Hanson RW, Mehlman MA, eds. *Gluconeogenesis: Its Regulation in Mammalian Species.* New York, NY: John Wiley & Sons; 1976:518.)

D. Function of the Urea Cycle during Fasting

During fasting, the liver maintains blood glucose levels. Amino acids from muscle protein are a major carbon source for the production of glucose by the pathway of gluconeogenesis. As amino acid carbons are converted to glucose, the nitrogens are converted to urea. Thus, the urinary excretion of urea is high during fasting (Fig. 38.16). As fasting progresses, however, the brain begins to use ketone bodies, sparing blood glucose. Less muscle protein is cleaved to provide amino acids for gluconeogenesis, and decreased production of glucose from amino acids is accompanied by decreased production of urea (see Chapter 31).

The major amino acid substrate for gluconeogenesis is alanine, which is synthesized in peripheral tissues to act as a nitrogen carrier (see Fig. 38.10). Glucagon release, which is expected during fasting, stimulates alanine transport into the liver by activating the transcription of transport systems for alanine. Two molecules of alanine are required to generate one molecule of glucose. The nitrogen from the two molecules of alanine is converted to one molecule of urea (Fig. 38.17).

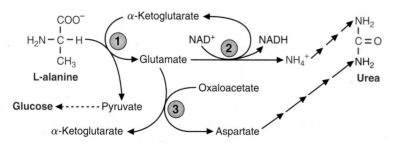

FIG. 38.17. Conversion of alanine to glucose and urea. *(1)* Alanine, the key gluconeogenic amino acid, is transaminated to form pyruvate, which is converted to glucose. The nitrogen, now in glutamate, can be released as NH_4^+ *(2)* or transferred to oxaloacetate to form aspartate *(3)*. NH_4^+ and aspartate enter the urea cycle, which produces urea. In summary, the carbons of alanine form glucose, and the nitrogens form urea. Two molecules of alanine are required to produce one molecule of glucose and one molecule of urea.

 NH_4^+ is one of the toxins that results from the degradation of urea or proteins by intestinal bacteria and is not metabolized by the infected liver. The subsequent elevation of ammonia concentrations in the fluid bathing the brain causes depletion of tricarboxylic acid (TCA) cycle intermediates and adenosine triphosphate (ATP) in the central nervous system. α-Ketoglutarate, a TCA cycle intermediate, combines with ammonia to form glutamate in a reaction catalyzed by glutamate dehydrogenase. Glutamate subsequently reacts with ammonia to form glutamine.

The absolute level of ammonia and its metabolites, such as glutamine, in the blood or cerebrospinal fluid in patients with hepatic encephalopathy correlates only roughly with the presence or severity of the neurologic signs and symptoms. γ-Aminobutyric acid (GABA), an important inhibitory neurotransmitter in the brain, is also produced in the gut lumen and is shunted into the systemic circulation in increased amounts in patients with hepatic failure. In addition, other compounds (such as aromatic amino acids, false neurotransmitters, and certain short-chain fatty acids) bypass liver metabolism and accumulate in the systemic circulation, adversely affecting central nervous system function. Their relative importance in the pathogenesis of hepatic encephalopathy remains to be determined.

 In addition to producing urea, the reactions of the urea cycle also serve as the pathway for the biosynthesis of arginine. Therefore, this amino acid is not required in the diet of the adult; however, it is required in the diet for growth. Urea is not cleaved by human enzymes. However, bacteria, including those in the human digestive tract, can cleave urea to ammonia and CO_2 using the enzyme urease. Urease is not produced by humans.

To some extent, humans excrete urea into the gut and saliva. Intestinal bacteria convert urea to ammonia. This ammonia, as well as ammonia produced by other bacterial reactions in the gut, is absorbed into the hepatic portal vein. It is normally extracted by the liver and converted to urea. Approximately one-fourth of the total urea released by the liver each day is recycled by bacteria.

Blood ammonia levels can be determined in several ways. One is to use an ammonia-specific electrode. Another is to use enzyme-coupled reactions that result in either a color change or an absorbance change. One enzyme-coupled system takes advantage of glutamate dehydrogenase. The unknown sample is incubated with glutamate dehydrogenase, α-ketoglutarate, and NADPH. If ammonia is present, glutamate will be produced, as will NADP$^+$. As NADPH is converted to NADP$^+$, the absorbance of light at 340 nm will decrease, and because one NADP$^+$ is formed per ammonia molecule used, the concentration of ammonia can be determined.

Blood urea nitrogen (BUN) is a measurement for the urea content of the blood. The key to measuring BUN is to split urea into carbon dioxide and two ammonia molecules by the bacterial enzyme urease. The ammonia levels are then determined as described previously, or via a colorimetric assay based on pH indicator dyes. As ammonia is generated, it binds protons, forming ammonium ions, which raises the pH. The extent of the pH change will be proportional to the amount of ammonia generated. Once BUN is determined, the urea concentration can be determined (in milligrams per deciliter) by multiplying the nitrogen value by 2.14.

E. Disorders of the Urea Cycle

Disorders of the urea cycle are dangerous because of the accumulation of ammonia in the circulation. Ammonia is toxic to the nervous system, and its concentration in the body must be carefully controlled. Under normal conditions, free ammonia is rapidly fixed into either α-ketoglutarate (by glutamate dehydrogenase, to form glutamate) or glutamate (by glutamine synthetase, to form glutamine). The glutamine can be used by many tissues, including the liver; the glutamate donates nitrogens to pyruvate to form alanine, which travels to the liver. Within the liver, as the nitrogens are removed from their carriers, CPSI fixes the ammonia into carbamoyl phosphate to initiate the urea cycle. However, when a urea-cycle enzyme is defective, the cycle is interrupted, which leads to an accumulation of urea-cycle intermediates before the block. Because of the block in the urea cycle, glutamine levels increase in the circulation, and because α-ketoglutarate is no longer being regenerated by removal of nitrogen from glutamine, the α-ketoglutarate levels are too low to fix more free ammonia, leading to elevated ammonia levels in the blood.

Therefore, defects in any urea-cycle enzyme lead to elevated glutamine and ammonia levels in the circulation. However, the extent of the elevation depends on which enzyme is defective; see Question 1 at the end of this chapter.

Ammonia toxicity will lead to brain swelling due, in part, to an osmotic imbalance caused by high levels of both ammonia and glutamine in the astrocytes. As ammonia levels increase in the astrocytes, more glutamine is produced (via glutamine synthetase), which only exacerbates the osmotic imbalance. The ammonia levels inhibit glutaminase, leading to glutamine elevation. Additionally, high levels of glutamine alter the permeability of the mitochondrial membrane, leading to an opening of the mitochondrial permeability transition pore, which leads to cell death (see Chapter 21). Another toxic effect of ammonia is a lowering of glutamate levels (due to the high activity of the glutamine synthetase reaction). Glutamate is a neurotransmitter, and glutamatergic neurotransmission is impaired, causing brain dysfunction. As glutamate is one of the excitatory neurotransmitters, the absence of glutamate neurotransmission can result in lethargy and reduced nervous system activity.

The most common urea-cycle defect is OTC deficiency, which is an X-linked disorder. This disorder occurs with a frequency of between 1 in 20,000 and 1 in 80,000 live births. The reason for the range of values is that there is a late-onset form of OTC deficiency that may be underrepresented in the data used to determine the frequency of the disorder in the population.

The major clinical problem in treating patients with urea-cycle defects is reducing the effects of excessive blood ammonia on the nervous system. High ammonia levels can lead to irreversible neuronal damage and mental retardation. So how is hyperammonemia treated?

The key to treating patients with urea-cycle defects is to diagnose the disease early and then treat aggressively with compounds that can aid in nitrogen removal. Low-protein diets are essential to reduce the potential for excessive amino acid degradation. If the enzyme defect in the urea cycle comes after the synthesis of argininosuccinate, massive arginine supplementation has proved beneficial. Once argininosuccinate has been synthesized, the two nitrogen molecules destined for excretion have been incorporated into the substrate; the problem is that ornithine cannot be regenerated. If ornithine could be replenished to allow the cycle to continue, argininosuccinate could be used as the carrier for nitrogen excretion from the body. Thus, ingesting large levels of arginine leads to ornithine production by the arginase reaction, and nitrogen excretion via argininosuccinate in the urine can be enhanced.

Arginine therapy will not work for enzyme defects that exist in steps before the synthesis of argininosuccinate. For these disorders, drugs are used that form conjugates with amino acids. The conjugated amino acids are excreted, and the body then has to use its nitrogen to resynthesize the excreted amino acid. The two compounds most frequently used are benzoic acid and phenylbutyrate. (The active component

FIG. 38.18.   The metabolism of benzoic acid (**A**) and phenylbutyrate (**B**), two agents used to reduce nitrogen levels in patients with urea-cycle defects.

of phenylbutyrate is phenylacetate, its oxidation product. Phenylacetate has a bad odor, which makes it difficult to take orally.) As indicated in Figure 38.18A, benzoic acid, after activation, reacts with glycine to form hippuric acid, which is excreted. As glycine is synthesized from serine, the body now uses nitrogens to synthesize serine, so more glycine can be produced. Phenylacetate (see Fig. 38.18B) forms a conjugate with glutamine, which is excreted. This conjugate removes two nitrogens per molecule and requires the body to resynthesize glutamine from glucose, thereby using another two nitrogen molecules.

Urea-cycle defects are excellent candidates for treatment by gene therapy. This is because the defect has to be repaired in only one cell type (in this case, the hepatocyte), which makes it easier to target the vector carrying the replacement gene. Preliminary gene therapy experiments had been carried out on individuals with OTC deficiency (the most common inherited defect of the urea cycle), but the experiments came to a halt when one of the patients died of a severe immunologic reaction to the vector used to deliver the gene. This incident has placed gene replacement therapy in the United States "on hold" for the foreseeable future.

CLINICAL COMMENTS

Percy Veere. The two most serious complications of acute viral hepatitis found in patients such as **Percy Veere** are massive hepatic necrosis leading to fulminant liver failure and the eventual development of chronic hepatitis. Both complications are rare in acute viral hepatitis type A, however, suggesting that acetaminophen toxicity may have contributed to Percy's otherwise unexpectedly severe hepatocellular dysfunction and early hepatic encephalopathy.

Fortunately, bed rest, rehydration, parenteral nutrition, and therapy directed at decreasing the production of toxins that result from bacterial degradation of nitrogenous substrates in the gut lumen (e.g., administration of lactulose, which reduces gut ammonia levels by a variety of mechanisms; the use of enemas and certain antibiotics, such as rifaximin, to decrease the intestinal flora, a low-protein diet) prevented Percy from progressing to the later stages of hepatic encephalopathy. As with most patients who survive an episode of fulminant hepatic failure, recovery to his previous state of health occurred over the next 3 months. Percy's liver function studies returned to normal, and a follow-up liver biopsy showed no histologic abnormalities.

BIOCHEMICAL COMMENTS

Pyridoxal Phosphate. Pyridoxal phosphate is a key coenzyme for amino acid metabolism. This cofactor participates in a wide variety of reactions involving amino acids, such as transamination, deamination, decarboxylation, β-elimination, racemization, and γ-elimination. The type of reaction that takes place is dictated by the amino acid substrate and the enzymes that catalyze the reaction.

All amino acid reactions that require pyridoxal phosphate occur with the amino group of the amino acid bonded covalently to the aldehyde carbon of the coenzyme (Fig. 38.19). As an example of a mechanism through which pyridoxal

FIG. 38.19. Pyridoxal phosphate attached covalently to an amino acid substrate. The *arrows* indicate which bonds are broken for the various types of reactions in which pyridoxal phosphate is involved. X and Y represent chemical leaving groups that may be present on the amino acid (such as the hydroxyl group on serine or threonine).

FIG. 38.20. Function of pyridoxal phosphate (*PLP*) in transamination reactions. The order in which the reactions occur is 1 to 4. Pyridoxal phosphate (enzyme-bound) reacts with amino acid$_1$, forming a Schiff base (a carbon–nitrogen double bond). After a shift of the double bond, α-keto acid$_1$ is released through hydrolysis of the Schiff base, and pyridoxamine phosphate is produced. Pyridoxamine phosphate then forms a Schiff base with α-keto acid$_2$. After the double bond shifts, amino acid$_2$ is released through hydrolysis of the Schiff base and enzyme-bound pyridoxal phosphate is regenerated. The net result is that the amino group from amino acid$_1$ is transferred to α-keto acid$_2$.

phosphate aids catalysis, Figure 38.20 indicates how a transamination reaction occurs. The other reaction types that require pyridoxal phosphate follow similar mechanisms.

Key Concepts

- Amino acid catabolism generates urea, which is a nontoxic carrier of nitrogen atoms.
- Urea synthesis occurs in the liver. The amino acids alanine and glutamine carry amino acid nitrogen from peripheral tissues to the liver.
- Key enzymes involved in nitrogen disposal are transaminases, glutamate dehydrogenase, and glutaminase.
- The urea cycle consists of four steps and incorporates a nitrogen from ammonia and one from aspartate into urea.
- Disorders of the urea cycle lead to hyperammonemia, a condition that is toxic to nervous system health and development.
- Diseases discussed in this chapter are summarized in Table 38.1.

Table 38.1   Diseases Discussed in Chapter 38

Disease or Disorder	Genetic or Environmental	Comments
Viral hepatitis	Environmental	Infection of the liver by viral hepatitis may lead to liver failure.
Pyridoxamine deficiency	Environmental	The lack of vitamin B_6 affects many systems, such as heme synthesis, glycogen phosphorylase activity, and neurotransmitter synthesis, leading to possibly dementia, dermatitis, anemia, weakness, and convulsions.
Hepatic encephalopathy	Environmental	Liver failure leading to brain dysfunction due to the liver's inability to rid the body of toxins, including ammonia
Ammonia toxicity	Both	Ammonia accumulation interferes with energy production and neurotransmitter synthesis in the brain, altering brain function.
Ornithine transcarbamoylase deficiency	Genetic	Most common urea-cycle defect, leading to elevated blood ammonia and orotic acid levels, and will lead to mental impairment if not treated.
CPSI deficiency, argininosuccinate synthetase deficiency, argininosuccinate lyase deficiency, and arginase deficiency	All genetic	Mutations in urea cycle enzymes, leading to various degrees of hyperammonemia and inability to synthesize urea. Can be distinguished by the type of urea cycle intermediates that accumulate in the blood.

CPSI, carbamoyl phosphate synthetase I.

REVIEW QUESTIONS—CHAPTER 38

1. Deficiency diseases have been described that involve each of the five enzymes of the urea cycle. Clinical manifestations may appear in the neonatal period. Infants with defects in the first four enzymes usually appear normal at birth, but after 24 hours, progressively develop lethargy, hypothermia, and apnea. They have high blood ammonia levels, and the brain becomes swollen. One possible explanation for the swelling is the osmotic effect of the accumulation of glutamine in the brain produced by the reactions of ammonia with α-ketoglutarate and glutamate. Arginase deficiency is not as severe as deficiencies of the other urea-cycle enzymes.

    Given the following information about five newborn infants (identified as I through V) who appeared normal at birth but developed hyperammonemia after 24 hours, determine which urea-cycle enzyme might be defective in each case (for each infant, choose from the same five answers, lettered A through E). All infants had low levels of blood urea nitrogen (BUN). (Normal citrulline levels are 10 to 20 μM.)

Infant	Urine Orotate	Blood Citrulline	Blood Arginine	Blood NH₃
I	Low	Low	Low	High
II	—	High (>1,000 μM)	Low	High
III	—	—	High	Moderately high
IV	High	Low	Low	High
V	—	High (200 μM)	Low	High

—, Value not determined; low, below normal; high, above normal.

   A. Carbamoyl phosphate synthetase I
   B. Ornithine transcarbamoylase
   C. Argininosuccinate synthetase
   D. Argininosuccinate lyase
   E. Arginase

2. The nitrogens in urea are derived directly from which of the following compounds?

   A. Ornithine and carbamoyl phosphate
   B. Ornithine and aspartate
   C. Ornithine and glutamate
   D. Carbamoyl phosphate and aspartate
   E. Carbamoyl phosphate and glutamine
   F. Aspartate and glutamine

3. Which one of the following enzymes can fix ammonia into an organic molecule?

   A. Alanine–pyruvate aminotransferase
   B. Glutaminase
   C. Glutamate dehydrogenase
   D. Arginase
   E. Argininosuccinate synthetase

4. Pyridoxal phosphate, which is required for transaminations, is also required for which of the following pathways?

   A. Glycolysis
   B. Gluconeogenesis
   C. Glycogenolysis
   D. The TCA cycle
   E. Fatty acid oxidation

5. The major regulated step of the urea cycle is which one of the following?

   A. Carbamoyl phosphate synthetase I
   B. Ornithine transcarbamoylase
   C. Argininosuccinate synthetase
   D. Argininosuccinate lyase
   E. Arginase

Because each of the 20 common amino acids has a unique structure, their metabolic pathways differ. Despite this, some generalities do apply to both the synthesis and degradation of all amino acids. These are summarized in the following sections. Because several amino acid pathways are clinically relevant, we present most of the diverse pathways that occur in humans. However, we will be as succinct as possible.

Important Coenzymes. Pyridoxal phosphate (derived from vitamin B_6) is the quintessential coenzyme of amino acid metabolism. In degradation, it is involved in the removal of amino groups, principally through **transamination reactions** and in donation of amino groups for various amino acid biosynthetic pathways. It is also required for certain reactions that involve the carbon skeleton of amino acids. **Tetrahydrofolate (FH_4)** is a coenzyme that is used to transfer one-carbon groups at various oxidation states. FH_4 is used in both amino acid degradation (e.g., serine and histidine) and biosynthesis (e.g., glycine). **Tetrahydrobiopterin (BH_4)** is a cofactor that is required for ring hydroxylation reactions (e.g., phenylalanine to tyrosine).

Synthesis of the Amino Acids. Eleven of the 20 common amino acids can be synthesized in the body (Fig. 39.1). The other nine are considered **"essential"** and must be obtained from the diet. Almost all of the amino acids that can be synthesized by humans are amino acids used for the synthesis of additional nitrogen-containing compounds. Examples include glycine, which is used for porphyrin and purine synthesis; glutamate, which is required for neurotransmitter and purine synthesis; and aspartate, which is required for both purine and pyrimidine biosynthesis.

Nine of the 11 **"nonessential" amino acids** can be produced from glucose plus, of course, a source of nitrogen such as another amino acid or ammonia. The other two nonessential amino acids, tyrosine and cysteine, require an essential amino acid for their synthesis (phenylalanine for tyrosine, methionine for cysteine). The carbons for cysteine synthesis come from glucose; the methionine donates only the sulfur.

The carbon skeletons of the 10 nonessential amino acids derived from glucose are produced from intermediates of **glycolysis** and the **tricarboxylic acid (TCA) cycle** (see Fig. 39.1). Four amino acids (**serine, glycine, cysteine, and alanine**) are produced from glucose through components of the **glycolytic pathway**. TCA cycle intermediates (which can be produced from glucose) provide carbon for synthesis of the six remaining nonessential amino acids. α-Ketoglutarate is the precursor for the synthesis of glutamate, glutamine, proline, and arginine. Oxaloacetate provides carbon for the synthesis of aspartate and asparagine.

Regulation of the biosynthesis of individual amino acids can be quite complex, but the overriding feature is that the **pathways are feedback-regulated** such that as the **concentration of free amino acid increases**, a key biosynthetic **enzyme is allosterically or transcriptionally inhibited**. Amino acid levels, however, are always maintained at a level such that the aminoacyl-tRNA synthetases can remain active, and protein synthesis can continue.

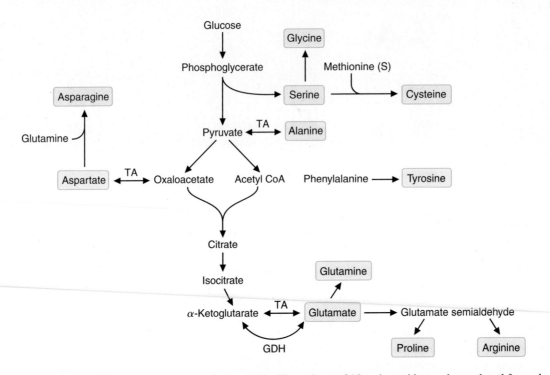

FIG. 39.1. Overview of the synthesis of the nonessential amino acids. The carbons of 10 amino acids may be produced from glucose through intermediates of glycolysis or the TCA cycle. The 11th nonessential amino acid, tyrosine, is synthesized by hydroxylation of the essential amino acid phenylalanine. Only the sulfur of cysteine comes from the essential amino acid methionine; its carbons and nitrogen come from serine. Transamination (TA) reactions involve pyridoxal phosphate (PLP) and another amino acid/α-keto acid pair.

*Degradation of Amino Acids. The **degradation pathways** for amino acids are, in general, **distinct from biosynthetic pathways**. This allows for separate regulation of the anabolic and catabolic pathways. Because protein is a fuel, almost every amino acid has a degradative pathway that can generate NADH, which is used as an electron source for oxidative phosphorylation. However, the energy-generating pathway may involve direct oxidation, oxidation in the TCA cycle, conversion to glucose and then oxidation, or conversion to **ketone bodies**, which are then oxidized.*

*The fate of the carbons of the amino acids depends on the physiologic state of the individual and the tissue in which the degradation occurs. For example, in the liver during fasting, the carbon skeletons of the amino acids produce glucose, ketone bodies, and CO₂. In the fed state, the liver can convert intermediates of amino acid metabolism to glycogen and triacylglycerols. Thus, the **fate of the carbons of the amino acids parallels that of glucose and fatty acids**. The **liver** is the only tissue that has all of the pathways of amino acid synthesis and degradation.*

*As amino acids are degraded, their **carbons** are converted to (1) **CO₂**, (2) compounds that produce **glucose** in the liver (pyruvate and the TCA cycle intermediates α-ketoglutarate, succinyl coenzyme A [succinyl-CoA], fumarate, and oxaloacetate), and (3) **ketone bodies** or their precursors (acetoacetate and acetyl-CoA) (Fig. 39.2). For simplicity, amino acids are considered to be **glucogenic** if their carbon skeletons can be converted to a precursor of glucose and **ketogenic** if their carbon skeletons can be converted directly to acetyl-CoA or acetoacetate. Some amino acids contain carbons that produce a glucose precursor and other carbons that produce acetyl-CoA or acetoacetate. These amino acids are both glucogenic and ketogenic.*

*The amino acids that are synthesized from intermediates of glycolysis (**serine, alanine, and cysteine**) plus certain amino acids (**threonine, glycine,***

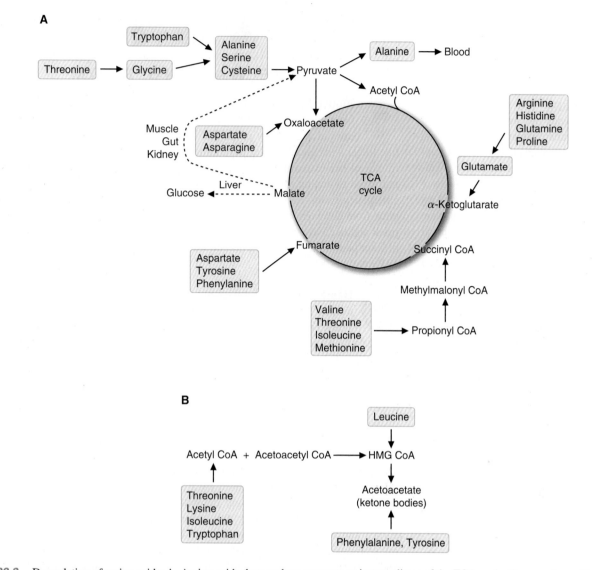

FIG. 39.2. Degradation of amino acids. **A.** Amino acids that produce pyruvate or intermediates of the TCA cycle. These amino acids are considered glucogenic because they can produce glucose in the liver. The fumarate group of amino acids produces cytoplasmic fumarate. Potential mechanisms whereby the cytoplasmic fumarate can be oxidized are presented in Section III.C.1. **B.** Amino acids that produce acetyl-CoA or ketone bodies. These amino acids are considered ketogenic.

*and tryptophan) produce **pyruvate** when they are degraded. The amino acids synthesized from TCA cycle intermediates (**aspartate, asparagine, glutamate, glutamine, proline,** and **arginine**) are reconverted to these intermediates during degradation. **Histidine** is converted to **glutamate** and then to the TCA cycle intermediate α-**ketoglutarate**. **Methionine, threonine, valine,** and **isoleucine** form **succinyl CoA**, and **phenylalanine** (after conversion to **tyrosine**) forms **fumarate**. Because pyruvate and the TCA cycle intermediates can produce glucose in the liver, these amino acids are glucogenic.*

*Some amino acids with carbons that produce glucose also contain other carbons that produce ketone bodies. **Tryptophan, isoleucine,** and **threonine** produce **acetyl-CoA**, and **phenylalanine and tyrosine** produce **acetoacetate**. These amino acids are both glucogenic and ketogenic.*

*Two of the essential amino acids (**lysine** and **leucine**) are strictly **ketogenic**. They do not produce glucose, only acetoacetate and acetyl-CoA.*

THE WAITING ROOM

All states have enacted legislation requiring that newborns be screened for various metabolic abnormalities, of which phenylketonuria (PKU) is one. A common screening procedure is the Guthrie bacterial inhibition assay. In this assay, spores of the organism *Bacillus subtilis* are plated on an agar plate containing β_2-thienylalanine, an inhibitor of *B. subtilis* growth. The blood sample obtained from the infant (in the form of a dried blood spot on a filter disk) is placed on the agar plate. If the phenylalanine content of the blood is greater than 2 to 4 mg/dL, the phenylalanine will counteract the effects of the β_2-thienylalanine, and bacterial growth will occur. An alternative assay is a microfluorometric determination of phenylalanine, via its incorporation into a ninhydrin–copper complex with the dipeptide L-leucyl-L-alanine. Positive results with either assay then require verification and actual measurement of phenylalanine levels, using either high-performance liquid chromatography (HPLC) separation of the components of the blood or enzymatic and fluorometric assays.

Piquet Yuria, a 4-month-old female infant, emigrated from the Soviet Union with her French mother and Russian father 1 month ago. She was normal at birth but in the last several weeks was less than normally attentive to her surroundings. Her psychomotor maturation seemed to be delayed, and a tremor of her extremities had recently appeared. When her mother found her having gross twitching movements in her crib, she brought the infant to the hospital emergency room. A pediatrician examined Piquet and immediately noted a musty odor from the baby's wet diaper. A drop of her blood was obtained from a heel prick and used to perform a Guthrie bacterial inhibition assay using a special type of filter paper. This screening procedure was positive for an excess of phenylalanine in Piquet's blood.

Homer Sistine, a 14-year-old boy, had a sudden grand mal seizure (with jerking movements of the torso and head) in his eighth-grade classroom. The school physician noted mild weakness of the muscles of the left side of Homer's face and of his left arm and leg. Homer was hospitalized with a tentative diagnosis of a cerebrovascular accident involving the right cerebral hemisphere, which presumably triggered the seizure.

Homer's past medical history was normal, except for slight mental retardation requiring placement in a special education group. He also had a downward partial dislocation of the lenses of both eyes, for which he had had a surgical procedure (a peripheral iridectomy).

Homer's left-sided neurologic deficits cleared spontaneously within 3 days, but a computerized axial tomogram (CAT) showed changes consistent with a small infarction (a damaged area caused by a temporary or permanent loss of adequate arterial blood flow) in the right cerebral hemisphere. A neurologist noted that Homer had a slight waddling gait, which his mother said began several years earlier and was progressing with time. Further studies confirmed the decreased mineralization (decreased calcification) of the skeleton (called osteopenia if mild and osteoporosis if more severe) and high methionine and homocysteine but low cystine levels in the blood.

All of this information, plus the increased length of the long bones of Homer's extremities and a slight curvature of his spine (scoliosis), caused his physician to suspect that Homer might have an inborn error of metabolism.

I. THE ROLE OF COFACTORS IN AMINO ACID METABOLISM

Amino acid metabolism requires the participation of three important cofactors. Pyridoxal phosphate (PLP) is the quintessential coenzyme of amino acid metabolism (see Biochemical Comments in Chapter 38).

The coenzyme tetrahydrofolate (FH$_4$) is required in certain amino acid pathways to either accept or donate a one-carbon group. The carbon can be in various states of oxidation. Chapter 40 describes the reactions of FH$_4$ in much more detail.

The coenzyme tetrahydrobiopterin (BH$_4$) is required for ring hydroxylations. The reactions involve molecular oxygen, and one atom of oxygen is incorporated into the product. The second is found in water (see Chapter 24). BH$_4$ is important for the synthesis of tyrosine and neurotransmitters (see Chapter 48).

II. AMINO ACIDS DERIVED FROM INTERMEDIATES OF GLYCOLYSIS

Four amino acids are synthesized from intermediates of glycolysis: serine, glycine, cysteine, and alanine. Serine, which produces glycine and cysteine, is synthesized from 3-phosphoglycerate; and alanine is formed by transamination of pyruvate, the product of glycolysis (Fig. 39.3). When these amino acids are degraded, their carbon atoms are converted to pyruvate or to intermediates of the glycolytic/gluco-neogenic pathway and, therefore, can produce glucose or be oxidized to CO_2.

A. Serine

In the biosynthesis of serine from glucose, 3-phosphoglycerate is first oxidized to a 2-keto compound (3-phosphohydroxypyruvate), which is then transaminated to form phosphoserine (Fig. 39.4). Phosphoserine phosphatase removes the phosphate, forming serine. The major sites of serine synthesis are the liver and kidney.

Serine can be used by many tissues and is generally degraded by transamination to hydroxypyruvate, followed by reduction and phosphorylation to form 2-phosphoglycerate, an intermediate of glycolysis that forms phosphoenolpyruvate (PEP) and, subsequently, pyruvate. Serine also can undergo β-elimination of its hydroxyl group, catalyzed by serine dehydratase, to form pyruvate directly.

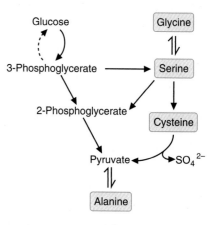

FIG. 39.3. Amino acids derived from intermediates of glycolysis. These amino acids can be synthesized from glucose. Their carbons can be reconverted to glucose in the liver.

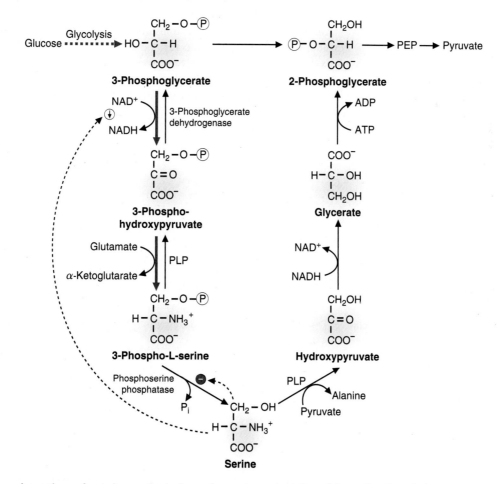

FIG. 39.4. The major pathway for serine synthesis from glucose is on the left, and for serine degradation on the right. Serine levels are maintained because serine causes repression (⊕) of 3-phosphoglycerate dehydrogenase synthesis. Serine also inhibits (⊖) phosphoserine phosphatase. *PEP*, phosphoenolpyruvate; P_i, inorganic phosphate; *PLP*, pyridoxal phosphate.

Regulatory mechanisms maintain serine levels in the body. When serine levels fall, serine synthesis is increased by induction of 3-phosphoglycerate dehydrogenase and by release of the feedback inhibition of phosphoserine phosphatase (caused by higher levels of serine). When serine levels rise, synthesis of serine decreases because synthesis of the dehydrogenase is repressed and the phosphatase is inhibited (see Fig. 39.4).

B. Glycine

Glycine can be synthesized from serine and, to a minor extent, threonine. The major route from serine is by a reversible reaction that involves FH_4 and PLP (Fig. 39.5). *Tetrahydrofolate* is a coenzyme that transfers one-carbon groups at different levels of oxidation. It is derived from the vitamin folate and is discussed in more detail in Chapter 40. The minor pathway for glycine production involves threonine degradation (this is an aldolase-like reaction because threonine contains a hydroxyl group located two carbons from the carbonyl group).

The conversion of glycine to glyoxylate by the enzyme D-amino acid oxidase is a degradative pathway of glycine that is clinically relevant. Once glyoxylate is formed, it can be oxidized to oxalate, which is sparingly soluble and tends to precipitate in kidney tubules, leading to formation of kidney stones. Approximately 40% of oxalate formation in the liver comes from glycine metabolism. Dietary oxalate accumulation has been estimated to be a low contributor to excreted oxalate in the urine because of poor absorption of oxalate in the intestine.

Although glyoxalate can be transaminated back to glycine, this is not really considered a biosynthetic route for "new" glycine because the primary route for glyoxylate formation is from glycine oxidation.

Generation of energy from glycine occurs through a dehydrogenase (glycine cleavage enzyme) that oxidizes glycine to CO_2, ammonia, and a carbon that is donated to FH_4.

Oxalate, produced from glycine or obtained from the diet, forms precipitates with calcium. Kidney stones (renal calculi) are often composed of calcium oxalate. A lack of the transaminase that can convert glyoxylate to glycine (see Fig. 39.5) leads to the disease primary oxaluria type I (PH 1). This disease has a consequence of renal failure attributable to excessive accumulation of oxalate in the kidney.

FIG. 39.5. Metabolism of glycine. Glycine can be synthesized from serine (major route) or threonine. Glycine forms serine or CO_2 and NH_4^+ by reactions that require tetrahydrofolate (FH_4). Glycine also forms glyoxylate, which is converted to oxalate or to CO_2 and H_2O. N^5, N^{10}–CH_2–FH_4, N^5, N^{10}-methylene tetrahydrofolate (see Chapter 40); *TPP*, thiamine pyrophosphate.

FIG. 39.6. Synthesis and degradation of cysteine. Cysteine is synthesized from the carbons and nitrogen of serine and the sulfur of homocysteine (which is derived from methionine). During the degradation of cysteine, the sulfur is converted to sulfate and either excreted in the urine or converted to PAPS (universal sulfate donor; 3′-phosphoadenosine 5′-phosphosulfate), and the carbons are converted to pyruvate. *PLP*, pyridoxal phosphate.

C. Cysteine

The carbons and nitrogen for cysteine synthesis are provided by serine, and the sulfur is provided by methionine (Fig. 39.6). Serine reacts with homocysteine (which is produced from methionine) to form cystathionine. This reaction is catalyzed by cystathionine β-synthase. Cleavage of cystathionine by cystathionase

Cystathioninuria, the presence of cystathionine in the urine, is relatively common in premature infants. As they mature, cystathionase levels rise, and the levels of cystathionine in the urine decrease. In adults, a genetic deficiency of cystathionase causes cystathioninuria. Individuals with a genetically normal cystathionase can also develop cystathioninuria from a dietary deficiency of pyridoxine (vitamin B_6) because cystathionase requires the cofactor pyridoxal phosphate (PLP). No characteristic clinical abnormalities have been observed in individuals with cystathionase deficiency, and it is probably a benign disorder.

Cystinuria and cystinosis are disorders involving two different transport proteins for cystine, the disulfide formed from two molecules of cysteine. Cystinuria is caused by a defect in the transport protein that carries cystine, lysine, arginine, and ornithine into intestinal epithelial cells and that permits resorption of these amino acids by renal tubular cells. Cystine, which is not very soluble in the urine, forms renal calculi (stones). **Cal Kulis**, a patient with cystinuria, developed cystine stones (see Chapter 37).

Cystinosis is a rare disorder caused by a defective carrier that normally transports cystine across the lysosomal membrane from lysosomal vesicles to the cytosol. Cystine accumulates in the lysosomes in many tissues and forms crystals, leading to a depletion of intracellular cysteine levels. Children with this disorder develop renal failure by 6 to 12 years of age, through a mechanism that has not yet been fully elucidated.

produces cysteine and α-ketobutyrate, which forms succinyl-CoA via propionyl-CoA. Both cystathionine β-synthase (β-elimination) and cystathionase (γ-elimination) require PLP.

Cysteine inhibits cystathionine β-synthase and, therefore, regulates its own production to adjust for the dietary supply of cysteine. Because cysteine derives its sulfur from the essential amino acid methionine, cysteine becomes essential if the supply of methionine is inadequate for cysteine synthesis. Conversely, an adequate dietary source of cysteine "spares" methionine; that is, it decreases the amount that must be degraded to produce cysteine.

When cysteine is degraded, the nitrogen is converted to urea, the carbons to pyruvate, and the sulfur to sulfate, which has two potential fates (see Fig. 39.6; see also Chapter 43). Sulfate generation, in an aqueous medium, is essentially generating sulfuric acid, and both the acid and sulfate needs to be disposed of in the urine. Sulfate is also used in most cells to generate an activated form of sulfate known as PAPS (3'-phosphoadenosine 5'-phosphosulfate), which is used as a sulfate donor in modifying carbohydrates or amino acids in various structures (glycosaminoglycans) and proteins in the body.

The conversion of methionine to homocysteine and homocysteine to cysteine is the major degradative route for these two amino acids. Because this is the only degradative route for homocysteine, vitamin B_6 deficiency or congenital cystathionine β-synthase deficiency can result in homocystinemia, which has been reported to be associated with cardiovascular disease.

D. Alanine

Alanine is produced from pyruvate by a transamination reaction catalyzed by alanine aminotransaminase (ALT) and may be converted back to pyruvate by a reversal of the same reaction (see Fig. 39.3). Alanine is the major gluconeogenic amino acid because it is produced in many tissues for the transport of nitrogen to the liver.

III. AMINO ACIDS RELATED TO TCA CYCLE INTERMEDIATES

Two groups of amino acids are synthesized from TCA cycle intermediates; one group from α-ketoglutarate and one from oxaloacetate (see Fig. 39.1). During degradation, four groups of amino acids are converted to the TCA cycle intermediates: α-ketoglutarate, oxaloacetate, succinyl-CoA, and fumarate (see Fig. 39.2A).

A. Amino Acids Related through α-Ketoglutarate/Glutamate

1. GLUTAMATE

The five carbons of glutamate are derived from α-ketoglutarate either by transamination or by the glutamate dehydrogenase reaction (see Chapter 38). Because α-ketoglutarate can be synthesized from glucose, all of the carbons of glutamate can be obtained from glucose (see Fig. 39.1). When glutamate is degraded, it is likewise converted back to α-ketoglutarate either by transamination or by glutamate dehydrogenase. In the liver, α-ketoglutarate leads to the formation of malate, which produces glucose via gluconeogenesis. Thus, glutamate can be derived from glucose and reconverted to glucose (Fig. 39.7).

Glutamate is used for the synthesis of several other amino acids (glutamine, proline, ornithine, and arginine) (see Fig. 39.7) and for providing the glutamyl moiety of glutathione (γ-glutamyl-cysteinyl-glycine; see Biochemical Comments in Chapter 37). Glutathione is an important antioxidant, as has been described previously (see Chapter 24).

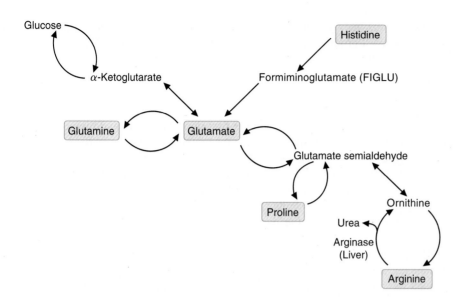

FIG. 39.7. Amino acids related through glutamate. These amino acids contain carbons that can be reconverted to glutamate, which can be converted to glucose in the liver. All of these amino acids except histidine can be synthesized from glucose.

2. GLUTAMINE

Glutamine is produced from glutamate by glutamine synthetase, which adds NH_4^+ to the carboxyl group of the side chain, forming an amide (Fig. 39.8). This is one of only three human enzymes that can fix free ammonia into an organic molecule; the other two are glutamate dehydrogenase and carbamoyl phosphate synthetase I (see Chapter 38). Glutamine is reconverted to glutamate by

FIG. 39.8. Synthesis and degradation of glutamine. Different enzymes catalyze the addition and the removal of the amide nitrogen of glutamine. P_i, inorganic phosphate.

 Homocysteine is oxidized to a disulfide—homocystine. To indicate that both forms are being considered, the term "homocyst(e)ine" is used.

Because a colorimetric screening test for urinary homocystine was positive, the doctor ordered several biochemical studies on **Homer Sistine's** serum, which included tests for methionine, homocyst(e)ine (both free and protein-bound), cystine, vitamin B_{12}, and folate. The level of homocystine in a 24-hour urine collection was also measured.

The results were as follows: The serum methionine level was 980 μM (reference range, <30 μM); serum homocyst(e)ine (both free and protein-bound) was markedly elevated; cystine was not detected in the serum; and the serum B_{12} and folate levels were normal. A 24-hour urine homocystine level was elevated.

Based on these measurements, **Homer Sistine's** doctor concluded that Homer had homocystinuria caused by an enzyme deficiency. What was the rationale for this conclusion?

If the blood levels of methionine and homocysteine are very elevated and cystine is low, cystathionine β-synthase could be defective, but a cystathionase deficiency is also a possibility. With a deficiency of either of these enzymes, cysteine could not be synthesized, and levels of homocysteine would rise. Homocysteine would be converted to methionine by reactions that require vitamin B_{12} and tetrahydrofolate (FH_4) (see Chapter 40). In addition, it would be oxidized to homocystine, which would appear in the urine. The levels of cysteine (measured as its oxidation product cystine) would be low. A measurement of serum cystathionine levels would help to distinguish between a cystathionase or cystathionine β-synthase deficiency.

FIG. 39.9. Synthesis and degradation of proline. Reactions 1, 3, and 4 occur in mitochondria. Reaction 2 occurs in the cytosol. Synthesis and degradation involve different enzymes. The cyclization reaction (formation of a Schiff base) is nonenzymatic; that is, it is spontaneous. P_i, inorganic phosphate.

a different enzyme, glutaminase, which is particularly important in the kidney. The ammonia it produces enters the urine and can be used as an expendable cation to aid in the excretion of metabolic acids ($NH_3 + H^+ \rightarrow NH_4^+$), as discussed in Chapter 38.

3. PROLINE

In the synthesis of proline, glutamate is first phosphorylated and then converted to glutamate 5-semialdehyde by reduction of the side-chain carboxyl group to an aldehyde (Fig. 39.9). This semialdehyde spontaneously cyclizes (forming an internal Schiff base between the aldehyde and the α-amino group). Reduction of this cyclic compound yields proline. Hydroxyproline is formed only after proline has been incorporated into collagen (see Chapter 49) by the prolyl hydroxylase system, which uses molecular oxygen, iron, α-ketoglutarate, and ascorbic acid (vitamin C).

Proline is converted back to glutamate semialdehyde, which is oxidized to form glutamate. The synthesis and degradation of proline use different enzymes even though the intermediates are the same. Hydroxyproline, however, has an entirely different degradative pathway (not shown). The presence of the hydroxyl group in hydroxyproline allows an aldolase-like reaction to occur once the ring has been hydrolyzed, which is not possible with proline.

4. ARGININE

Arginine is synthesized from glutamate via glutamate semialdehyde, which is transaminated to form ornithine, an intermediate of the urea cycle (see Fig. 38.14). This activity (ornithine aminotransferase) appears to be greatest in the epithelial cells of the small intestine (see Chapter 42). The reactions of the urea cycle then produce arginine. However, the quantities of arginine generated by the urea cycle are adequate only for the adult and are insufficient to support growth. Therefore, during periods of growth, arginine becomes an essential amino acid. It is important to realize that if arginine is used for protein synthesis, the levels of ornithine will drop, thereby slowing the urea cycle. This will stimulate the formation of ornithine from glutamate.

Arginine is cleaved by arginase to form urea and ornithine. If ornithine is present in amounts in excess of those required for the urea cycle, it is transaminated to glutamate semialdehyde, which is reduced to glutamate. The conversion of an aldehyde to a primary amine is a unique form of a transamination reaction and requires PLP.

5. HISTIDINE

Although histidine cannot be synthesized in humans, five of its carbons form glutamate when it is degraded. In a series of steps, histidine is converted to formiminoglutamate (FIGLU). The subsequent reactions transfer one carbon of FIGLU to the FH_4 pool (see Chapter 40) and release NH_4^+ and glutamate (Fig. 39.10).

B. Amino Acids Related to Oxaloacetate (Aspartate and Asparagine)

Aspartate is produced by transamination of oxaloacetate. This reaction is readily reversible, so aspartate can be reconverted to oxaloacetate (Fig. 39.11).

Asparagine is formed from aspartate by a reaction in which glutamine provides the nitrogen for formation of the amide group. Thus, this reaction differs from the synthesis of glutamine from glutamate, in which NH_4^+ provides the nitrogen. However, the reaction catalyzed by asparaginase, which hydrolyzes asparagine to NH_4^+ and aspartate, is analogous to the reaction catalyzed by glutaminase.

C. Amino Acids That Form Fumarate

1. ASPARTATE

Although the major route for aspartate degradation involves its conversion to oxaloacetate, carbons from aspartate can form fumarate in the urea cycle (see Chapter 38). This reaction generates cytosolic fumarate, which must be converted to malate (using cytoplasmic fumarase) for transport into the mitochondria for oxidative or anaplerotic purposes. An analogous sequence of reactions occurs in the purine nucleotide cycle. Aspartate reacts with inosine monophosphate (IMP) to form an intermediate (adenylosuccinate) that is then cleaved, forming adenosine monophosphate (AMP) and fumarate (see Chapter 41).

2. PHENYLALANINE AND TYROSINE

Phenylalanine is converted to tyrosine by a hydroxylation reaction. Tyrosine, produced from phenylalanine or obtained from the diet, is oxidized, ultimately forming acetoacetate and fumarate. The oxidative steps required to reach this point are, surprisingly, not energy generating. The conversion of fumarate to malate, followed by the action of malic enzyme, allows the carbons to be used for gluconeogenesis. The conversion of phenylalanine to tyrosine and the production of acetoacetate are considered further in Section IV of this chapter.

D. Amino Acids That Form Succinyl-CoA

The essential amino acids methionine, valine, isoleucine, and threonine are degraded to form propionyl-CoA. The conversion of propionyl-CoA to succinyl-CoA is common to their degradative pathways. Propionyl-CoA is also generated from the oxidation of odd-chain fatty acids.

 Certain types of tumor cells, particularly leukemic cells, require asparagine for their growth. Therefore, asparaginase has been used as an antitumor agent. It acts by converting asparagine to aspartate in the blood, decreasing the amount of asparagine available for tumor cell growth. Asparaginase has been used for more than 30 years to treat acute lymphoblastic leukemia.

FIG. 39.10. Degradation of histidine. The highlighted portion of histidine forms glutamate. The remainder of the molecule provides one carbon for the tetrahydrofolate (FH$_4$) pool (see Chapter 40) and releases NH$_4^+$.

FIG. 39.11. Synthesis and degradation of aspartate and asparagine. Note that the amide nitrogen of asparagine is derived from glutamine. (The amide nitrogen of glutamine comes from NH$_4^+$; see Fig. 38.11.)

A biopsy specimen from **Homer Sistine's** liver was sent to the hospital's biochemistry research laboratory for enzyme assays. Cystathionine β-synthase activity was reported to be 7% of that found in normal liver.

Homocystinuria is caused by deficiencies in the enzymes cystathionine β-synthase and cystathionase as well as by deficiencies of methyltetrahydrofolate (CH$_3$-FH$_4$) or of methyl-B$_{12}$. The deficiencies of CH$_3$-FH$_4$ or of methyl-B$_{12}$ are caused by either an inadequate dietary intake of folate or vitamin B$_{12}$ or by defective enzymes involved in joining methyl groups to tetrahydrofolate (FH$_4$), transferring methyl groups from FH$_4$ to B$_{12}$, or passing them from B$_{12}$ to homocysteine to form methionine (see Chapter 40).

Is **Homer Sistine's** homocystinuria caused by any of these problems?

Propionyl-CoA is carboxylated in a reaction that requires biotin and forms D-methylmalonyl-CoA. The D-methylmalonyl-CoA is racemized to L-methylmalonyl-CoA, which is rearranged in a vitamin B$_{12}$-requiring reaction to produce succinyl-CoA, a TCA cycle intermediate (see Fig. 23.11).

1. METHIONINE

Methionine is converted to S-adenosylmethionine (SAM), which donates its methyl group to other compounds to form S-adenosylhomocysteine (SAH). SAH is then converted to homocysteine (Fig. 39.12). Methionine can be regenerated from homocysteine by a reaction that requires both FH$_4$ and vitamin B$_{12}$ (a topic that is considered in more detail in Chapter 40). Alternatively, by reactions that require PLP, homocysteine can provide the sulfur needed for the synthesis of cysteine (see Fig. 39.6). Carbons of homocysteine are then metabolized to α-ketobutyrate, which undergoes oxidative decarboxylation to propionyl-CoA. The propionyl-CoA is then converted to succinyl-CoA (see Fig. 39.12).

2. THREONINE

In humans, threonine is primarily degraded by a PLP-requiring dehydratase to ammonia and α-ketobutyrate, which subsequently undergoes oxidative decarboxylation to form propionyl-CoA, just as in the case for methionine (see Fig. 39.12).

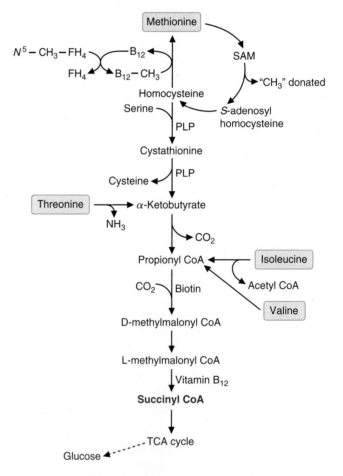

FIG. 39.12. Conversion of amino acids to succinyl-CoA. The amino acids methionine, threonine, isoleucine, and valine—all of which form succinyl-CoA via methylmalonyl-CoA—are essential in the diet. The carbons of serine are converted to cysteine and do not form succinyl-CoA by this pathway. *PLP*, pyridoxal phosphate; *SAM*, S-adenosylmethionine; *B$_{12}$-CH$_3$*, methylcobalamin; *N^5-CH$_3$-FH$_4$*, N^5-methyltetrahydrofolate.

3. VALINE AND ISOLEUCINE

The branched-chain amino acids (valine, isoleucine, and leucine) are universal fuels, and the degradation of these amino acids occurs at low levels in the mitochondria of most tissues, but the muscle carries out the highest level of branched-chain amino acid oxidation. The branched-chain amino acids make up almost 25% of the content of the average protein, so their use as fuel is quite significant. The degradative pathway for valine and isoleucine has two major functions, the first being energy generation and the second to provide precursors to replenish TCA cycle intermediates (anaplerosis). Valine and isoleucine, two of the three branched-chain amino acids, contain carbons that form succinyl-CoA. The initial step in the degradation of the branched-chain amino acids is a transamination reaction. Although the enzyme that catalyzes this reaction is present in most tissues, the level of activity varies from tissue to tissue. However, its activity is particularly high in muscle. In the second step of the degradative pathway, the α-keto analogs of these amino acids undergo oxidative decarboxylation by the α-keto acid dehydrogenase complex in a reaction similar in its mechanism and cofactor requirements to pyruvate dehydrogenase and α-ketoglutarate dehydrogenase (see Chapter 20). As with the first enzyme of the pathway, the highest level of activity for this dehydrogenase is found in muscle tissue. Subsequently, the pathways for degradation of these amino acids follow parallel routes (Fig. 39.13). The steps are analogous to those for β-oxidation of fatty acids, so NADH and FAD(2H) are generated for energy production.

Homer Sistine's methionine levels are elevated, and his vitamin B_{12} and folate levels are normal. Therefore, he does not have a deficiency of dietary folate or vitamin B_{12} or of the enzymes that transfer methyl groups from tetrahydrofolate to homocysteine to form methionine. In these cases, homocysteine levels are elevated but methionine levels are low.

Thiamine deficiency will lead to an accumulation of α-keto acids in the blood because of an inability of pyruvate dehydrogenase, α-ketoglutarate dehydrogenase, and branched-chain α-keto acid dehydrogenase to catalyze their reactions (see Chapter 8). **Al Martini** had a thiamine deficiency resulting from his chronic alcoholism. His ketoacidosis resulted partly from the accumulation of these α-keto acids in his blood and partly from the accumulation of ketone bodies used for energy production.

Q: What compounds form succinyl-CoA via propionyl-CoA and methylmalonyl-CoA?

FIG. 39.13. Degradation of the branched-chain amino acids. Valine forms propionyl-CoA. Isoleucine forms propionyl-CoA and acetyl-CoA. Leucine forms acetoacetate and acetyl-CoA.

In maple syrup urine disease, the branched-chain α-keto acid dehydrogenase that oxidatively decarboxylates the branched-chain amino acids is defective. As a result, the branched-chain amino acids and their α-keto analogs (produced by transamination) accumulate. They appear in the urine, giving it the odor of maple syrup or burnt sugar. The accumulation of α-keto analogs leads to neurologic complications. This condition is difficult to treat by dietary restriction because abnormalities in the metabolism of three essential amino acids contribute to the disease.

In addition to methionine, threonine, isoleucine, and valine (see Fig. 39.14), the last three carbons at the ω-end of odd-chain fatty acids form succinyl-CoA by this route (see Chapter 23).

Alcaptonuria occurs when homogentisate, an intermediate in tyrosine metabolism, cannot be further oxidized because the next enzyme in the pathway, homogentisate oxidase, is defective. Homogentisate accumulates and auto-oxidizes, forming a dark pigment, which discolors the urine and stains the diapers of affected infants. Later in life, the chronic accumulation of this pigment in cartilage may cause arthritic joint pain.

Valine and isoleucine are converted to succinyl-CoA (see Fig. 39.12). Isoleucine also forms acetyl-CoA. Leucine, the third branched-chain amino acid, does not produce succinyl-CoA. It forms acetoacetate and acetyl-CoA and is strictly ketogenic.

IV. AMINO ACIDS THAT FORM ACETYL CoA AND ACETOACETATE

Seven amino acids produce acetyl-CoA or acetoacetate and, therefore, are categorized as ketogenic. Of these, isoleucine, threonine, and the aromatic amino acids (phenylalanine, tyrosine, and tryptophan) are converted to compounds that produce both glucose and acetyl-CoA or acetoacetate (Fig. 39.14). Leucine and lysine do not produce glucose; they produce acetyl-CoA and acetoacetate.

A. Phenylalanine and Tyrosine

Phenylalanine is converted to tyrosine, which undergoes oxidative degradation (Fig. 39.15). The last step in the pathway produces both fumarate and the ketone body acetoacetate. Deficiencies of different enzymes in the pathway result in phenylketonuria, tyrosinemia, and alcaptonuria.

Phenylalanine is hydroxylated to form tyrosine by a mixed-function oxidase, phenylalanine hydroxylase (PAH), which requires molecular oxygen and BH_4 (Fig. 39.16). The cofactor BH_4 is converted to quinonoid dihydrobiopterin by this reaction. BH_4 is not synthesized from a vitamin; it can be

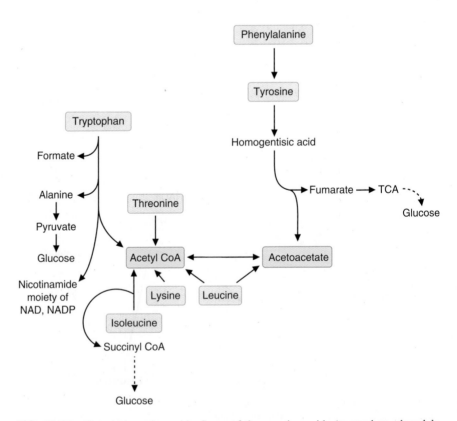

FIG. 39.14. Ketogenic amino acids. Some of these amino acids (tryptophan, phenylalanine, and tyrosine) also contain carbons that can form glucose. Leucine and lysine are strictly ketogenic; they do not form glucose.

Transient tyrosinemia is frequently observed in newborn infants, especially those that are premature. For the most part, the condition appears to be benign, and dietary restriction of protein returns plasma tyrosine levels to normal. The biochemical defect is most likely a low level, attributable to immaturity, of 4-hydroxyphenylpyruvate dioxygenase. Because this enzyme requires ascorbate, ascorbate supplementation also aids in reducing circulating tyrosine levels.

Other types of tyrosinemia are related to specific enzyme defects (see Fig. 39.15). Tyrosinemia II is caused by a genetic deficiency of tyrosine aminotransferase (TAT) and may lead to lesions of the eye and skin as well as neurologic problems. Patients are treated with a low-tyrosine, low-phenylalanine diet.

Tyrosinemia I (also called tyrosinosis) is caused by a genetic deficiency of fumarylacetoacetate hydrolase. The acute form is associated with liver failure, a cabbage-like body odor, and death within the first year of life.

FIG. 39.15. Degradation of phenylalanine and tyrosine. The carboxyl carbon forms CO_2, and the other carbons form fumarate or acetoacetate as indicated. Deficiencies of enzymes (*dark bars*) result in the indicated diseases. *PKU*, phenylketonuria; *PLP*, pyridoxal phosphate.

A small subset of patients with hyperphenylalaninemia shows an appropriate reduction in plasma phenylalanine levels with dietary restriction of this amino acid; however, these patients still develop progressive neurologic symptoms and seizures and usually die within the first 2 years of life ("malignant" hyperphenylalaninemia). These infants exhibit normal phenylalanine hydroxylase (PAH) activity but have a deficiency in dihydropteridine reductase (DHPR), an enzyme required for the regeneration of tetrahydrobiopterin (BH_4), a cofactor of PAH (see Fig. 39.16). Less frequently, DHPR activity is normal but a defect in the biosynthesis of BH_4 exists. In either case, dietary therapy corrects the hyperphenylalaninemia. However, BH_4 is also a cofactor for two other hydroxylations required in the synthesis of neurotransmitters in the brain: the hydroxylation of tryptophan to 5-hydroxytryptophan and of tyrosine to L-dopa (see Chapter 48). It has been suggested that the resulting deficit in central nervous system neurotransmitter activity is, at least in part, responsible for the neurologic manifestations and eventual death of these patients.

synthesized in the body from guanosine triphosphate (GTP). However, as is the case with other cofactors, the body contains limited amounts. Therefore, dihydrobiopterin must be reconverted to BH_4 for the reaction to continue to produce tyrosine.

B. Tryptophan

Tryptophan is oxidized to produce alanine (from the nonring carbons), formate, and acetyl-CoA. Tryptophan is, therefore, both glucogenic and ketogenic (Fig. 39.17).

NAD^+ and $NADP^+$ can be produced from the ring structure of tryptophan. Therefore, tryptophan "spares" the dietary requirement for niacin. The higher the dietary levels of tryptophan, the lower are the levels of niacin required to prevent symptoms of deficiency.

FIG. 39.16. Hydroxylation of phenylalanine. Phenylalanine hydroxylase (PAH) is a mixed-function oxidase; that is, molecular oxygen (O_2) donates one atom to water and one to the product, tyrosine. The cofactor tetrahydrobiopterin (BH_4) is oxidized to dihydrobiopterin (BH_2) and must be reduced back to BH_4 for PAH to continue forming tyrosine. BH_4 is synthesized in the body from GTP. PKU results from deficiencies of PAH (the classic form), dihydropteridine reductase, or enzymes in the biosynthetic pathway for BH_4.

If the dietary levels of niacin and tryptophan are insufficient, the condition known as pellagra results. The symptoms of pellagra are dermatitis, diarrhea, dementia, and, finally, death. In addition, abnormal metabolism of tryptophan occurs in a vitamin B_6 deficiency. Kynurenine intermediates in tryptophan degradation cannot be cleaved because kynureninase requires PLP derived from vitamin B_6. Consequently, these intermediates enter a minor pathway for tryptophan metabolism that produces xanthurenic acid, which is excreted in the urine.

FIG. 39.17. Degradation of tryptophan. One of the ring carbons (*in red*) produces formate. The nonring portion (*indicated by the box*) forms alanine. Kynurenine is an intermediate, which can be converted to several urinary excretion products (e.g., xanthurenate), degraded to CO_2 and acetyl-CoA, or converted to the nicotinamide moiety of NAD and NADP, which also can be formed from the vitamin niacin. *PLP*, pyridoxal phosphate.

C. Threonine, Isoleucine, Leucine, and Lysine

As discussed previously, the major route of threonine degradation in humans is by threonine dehydratase (see Section III.D.2). In a minor pathway, threonine degradation by threonine aldolase produces glycine and acetyl-CoA in the liver.

Isoleucine produces both succinyl-CoA and acetyl-CoA (see Section III.D.3).

Leucine is purely ketogenic and produces hydroxymethylglutaryl CoA (HMG-CoA), which is cleaved to form acetyl-CoA and the ketone body acetoacetate (see Figs. 39.13 and 39.14). Most of the tissues in which it is oxidized can use ketone bodies, with the exception of the liver. As with valine and isoleucine, leucine is a universal fuel, with its primary metabolism occurring in muscle.

Lysine cannot be directly transaminated at either of its two amino groups. Lysine is degraded by a complex pathway in which saccharopine, α-ketoadipate, and crotonyl-CoA are intermediates. During the degradation pathway, NADH and FADH₂ are generated for energy. Ultimately, lysine generates acetyl-CoA (see Fig. 39.14) and is strictly ketogenic.

CLINICAL COMMENTS

Piquet Yuria. The overall incidence of PKU, leading to hyperphenylalaninemia, is approximately 100 per million births, with a wide geographic and ethnic variation. PKU occurs by autosomal recessive transmission of a defective phenylalanine hydroxylase (PAH) gene, causing accumulation of phenylalanine in the blood that is much higher than the normal concentration in young children and adults (<1 to 2 mg/dL). In the newborn, the upper limit of normal is almost twice this value. Values greater than 20 mg/dL are usually found in patients, such as Piquet, who have "classic" PKU.

Patients with classic PKU usually appear normal at birth. If the disease is not recognized and treated within the first month of life, the infant gradually develops varying degrees of irreversible mental retardation (IQ scores frequently less than 50), delayed psychomotor maturation, tremors, seizures, eczema, and hyperactivity. The neurologic sequelae may result in part from the competitive interaction of phenylalanine with brain amino acid transport systems and inhibition of neurotransmitter synthesis. A successful dietary therapy for PKU, in addition to phenylalanine reduction, is supplementation of the diet with large, neutral amino acids (such as tryptophan, tyrosine, histidine, and leucine). These large, neutral amino acids share a transport system (the L system) with phenylalanine, and can overcome the high levels of phenylalanine in the blood, allowing the neurotransmitter precursors to enter the nervous system. If the disease is not recognized in time, the biochemical alterations lead to impaired myelin synthesis and delayed neuronal development, which result in the clinical picture in patients such as Piquet. Because of the simplicity of the test for PKU (elevated phenylalanine levels in the blood), all newborns in the United States are required to have a PKU test at birth. Early detection of the disease can lead to early treatment, and the neurologic consequences of the disease can be bypassed.

To restrict dietary levels of phenylalanine, special semisynthetic preparations such as Lofenalac or PKU aid are used in the United States. Use of these preparations reduces dietary intake of phenylalanine to 250 to 500 mg/day while maintaining normal intake of all other dietary nutrients. Although it is generally agreed that scrupulous adherence to this regimen is mandatory for the first decade of life, less consensus exists regarding its indefinite use. Evidence suggests, however, that without lifelong compliance with dietary restriction of phenylalanine, even adults

On more definitive testing of **Piquet Yuria's** blood, the plasma level of phenylalanine was elevated at 25 mg/dL (reference range, <1.2). Several phenyl ketones and other products of phenylalanine metabolism, which give the urine a characteristic odor, were found in significant quantities in the baby's urine.

A liver biopsy was sent to the special chemistry research laboratory, where it was determined that the level of activity of PAH in Piquet's blood was less than 1% of that found in normal infants. A diagnosis of "classic" PKU was made.

Until gene therapy allows substitution of the defective PAH gene with its normal counterpart in vivo, the mainstay of therapy in classic PKU is to maintain levels of phenylalanine in the blood between 3 and 12 mg/dL through dietary restriction of this essential amino acid.

will develop at least neurologic sequelae of PKU. A pregnant woman with PKU must be particularly careful to maintain satisfactory plasma levels of phenylalanine throughout gestation to avoid the adverse effects of hyperphenylalaninemia on the fetus. The use of glycomacropeptide from whey is a promising development in PKU treatment. This protein—when pure—contains no phenylalanine, but as isolated has a very low phenylalanine content, while providing adequate levels of the other amino acids. The use of glycomacropeptide in PKU diet preparation is expanding and provides alternatives to the dietary therapy not previously available.

Piquet's parents were given thorough dietary instruction, which they followed carefully. Although her pediatrician was not optimistic, it was hoped that the damage done to her nervous system before dietary therapy was minimal and that her subsequent psychomotor development would allow her to lead a relatively normal life.

The pathologic findings that underlie the clinical features manifested by **Homer Sistine** are presumed (but not proved) to be the consequence of chronic elevations of homocysteine (and perhaps other compounds, e.g., methionine) in the blood and tissues. The zonular fibers that normally hold the lens of the eye in place become frayed and break, causing dislocation of the lens. The skeleton reveals a loss of bone ground substance (i.e., osteoporosis), which may explain the curvature of the spine. The elongation of the long bones beyond their normal genetically determined length leads to tall stature.

Animal experiments suggest that increased concentrations of homocysteine and methionine in the brain may trap adenosine as S-adenosylhomocysteine, diminishing adenosine levels. Because adenosine normally acts as a central nervous system depressant, its deficiency may be associated with a lowering of the seizure threshold as well as a reduction in cognitive function.

Homer Sistine. The most characteristic biochemical features of the disorder that affects **Homer Sistine**, a cystathionine β-synthase deficiency, are the presence of an accumulation of both homocyst(e)ine and methionine in the blood. Because renal tubular reabsorption of methionine is highly efficient, this amino acid may not appear in the urine. Homocystine, the disulfide of homocysteine, is less efficiently reabsorbed, and amounts in excess of 1 mmol may be excreted in the urine each day.

In the type of homocystinuria in which the patient is deficient in cystathione β-synthase, the elevation in serum methionine levels is presumed to be the result of enhanced rates of conversion of homocysteine to methionine because of increased availability of homocysteine (see Fig. 39.12). In type II and type III homocystinuria, in which there is a deficiency in the synthesis of methyl cobalamin and of N^5-methyltetrahydrofolate, respectively (both required for the methylation of homocysteine to form methionine), serum homocysteine levels are elevated but serum methionine levels are low (see Fig. 39.12).

Acute vascular events are common in these patients. Thrombi (blood clots) and emboli (clots that have broken off and traveled to a distant site in the vascular system) have been reported in almost every major artery and vein as well as in smaller vessels. These clots result in infarcts in vital organs such as the liver, the myocardium (heart muscle), the lungs, the kidneys, and many other tissues. Although increased serum levels of homocysteine have been implicated in enhanced platelet aggregation and damage to vascular endothelial cells (leading to clotting and accelerated atherosclerosis), no generally accepted mechanism for these vascular events has yet emerged.

Treatment is directed toward early reduction of the elevated levels of homocysteine and methionine in the blood. In addition to a diet that is low in methionine, very high oral doses of pyridoxine (vitamin B_6) have significantly decreased the plasma levels of homocysteine and methionine in some patients with cystathionine β-synthase deficiency. (Genetically determined "responders" to pyridoxine treatment make up approximately 50% of type I homocystinurics.) Pyridoxal phosphate (PLP) serves as a cofactor for cystathionine β-synthase; however, the molecular properties of the defective enzyme that confer the responsiveness to vitamin B_6 therapy are not known.

The terms hypermethioninemia, homocystinuria (or -emia), and cystathioninuria (or -emia) designate biochemical abnormalities and are not specific clinical diseases. Each may be caused by more than one specific genetic defect. For example, at least seven distinct genetic alterations can cause increased excretion of homocystine in the urine. A deficiency of cystathionine β-synthase is the most common cause of homocystinuria; more than 600 such proven cases have been studied.

Table 39.1   Genetic Disorders of Amino Acid Metabolism

Amino Acid Degradation Pathway	Missing Enzyme	Product That Accumulates	Disease	Symptoms
Phenylalanine	Phenylalanine hydroxylase	Phenylalanine	PKU (classical)	Mental retardation
	Dihydropteridine reductase	Phenylalanine	PKU (nonclassical)	Mental retardation
	Homogentisate oxidase	Homogentisic acid	Alcaptonuria	Black urine, arthritis
	Fumarylacetoacetate hydrolase	Fumarylacetoacetate	Tyrosinemia I	Liver failure, early death
Tyrosine	Tyrosine aminotransferase	Tyrosine	Tyrosinemia II	Neurologic defects
Methionine	Cystathionase	Cystathionine	Cystathioninuria	Benign
	Cystathionine β-synthase	Homocysteine	Homocysteinemia	Cardiovascular complications and neurologic problems
Glycine	Glycine transaminase	Glyoxylate	Primary oxaluria type I	Renal failure because of stone formation
Branched-chain amino acids (leucine, isoleucine, valine)	Branched-chain α-keto acid dehydrogenase	α-Keto acids of the branched chain amino acids	Maple syrup urine disease	Mental retardation

BIOCHEMICAL COMMENTS

Phenylketonuria. Many enzyme deficiency diseases have been discovered that affect the pathways of amino acid metabolism. These deficiency diseases have helped researchers to elucidate the pathways in humans, in whom experimental manipulation is, at best, unethical. These spontaneous mutations ("experiments" of nature), although devastating to patients, have resulted in an understanding of these diseases that now permit treatment of inborn errors of metabolism that were once considered to be untreatable.

Classic phenylketonuria (PKU) is caused by mutations in the gene located on chromosome 12 that encodes the enzyme phenylalanine hydroxylase (PAH). This enzyme normally catalyzes the hydroxylation of phenylalanine to tyrosine, the rate-limiting step in the major pathway by which phenylalanine is catabolized.

In early experiments, sequence analysis of mutant clones indicated a single base substitution in the gene, with a G-to-A transition at the canonical 5' donor splice site of intron 12 and expression of a truncated unstable protein product. This protein lacked the C-terminal region, a structural change that yielded less than 1% of the normal activity of PAH.

Since these initial studies, DNA analysis has shown more than 100 mutations (missense, nonsense, insertions, and deletions) in the PAH gene, associated with PKU and non-PKU hyperphenylalaninemia. That PKU is a heterogeneous phenotype is supported by studies measuring PAH activity in needle biopsy samples taken from the livers of a large group of patients with varying degrees of hyperphenylalaninemia. PAH activity varied from less than 1% of normal in patients with classic PKU to up to 35% of normal in those with a non-PKU form of hyperphenylalaninemia (such as a defect in BH_4 production; see Chapter 48).

The genetic diseases affecting amino acid degradation that have been discussed in this chapter are summarized in Table 39.1. This is just a partial listing of disorders in amino acid metabolism; there are many others that are less common and were not discussed in this chapter.

Key Concepts

- Humans can synthesize only 11 of the 20 amino acids required for protein synthesis; the other 9 are considered to be essential amino acids in the diet.
- Amino acid metabolism uses, to a large extent, the cofactors pyridoxal phosphate, tetrahydrobiopterin (BH_4), and tetrahydrofolate (FH_4).
  - Pyridoxal phosphate is required primarily for transamination reactions.
  - BH_4 is required for ring hydroxylation reactions.
  - FH_4 is required for one-carbon metabolism and is discussed further in Chapter 40.

- The nonessential amino acids can be synthesized from glycolytic intermediates (serine, glycine, cysteine, and pyruvate), TCA cycle intermediates (aspartate, asparagine, glutamate, glutamine, proline, arginine, and ornithine), or from existing amino acids (tyrosine from phenylalanine).
- When amino acids are degraded, the nitrogen is converted to urea, and the carbon skeletons are classified as either glucogenic (a precursor of glucose) or ketogenic (a precursor of ketone bodies).
- Defects in amino acid degradation pathways can lead to disease.
  - Glycine degradation can lead to oxalate production, which may lead to one class of kidney stone formation.
  - Defects in methionine degradation can lead to hyperhomocysteinemia, which has been linked to blood-clotting disorders and heart disease.
  - A defect in branched-chain amino acid degradation leads to maple syrup urine disease, which has severe neurologic consequences.
  - Defects in phenylalanine and tyrosine degradation lead to phenylketonuria (PKU), alcaptonuria, and albinism.
- Table 39.2 summarizes, in a slightly different format than Table 39.1, the diseases discussed in this chapter.

Table 39.2   Diseases Discussed in Chapter 39

Disease or Disorder	Environmental or Genetic	Comments
PKU	Genetic	Classical PKU is caused by a defect in phenylalanine hydroxylase whereas nonclassical PKU is caused by a defect in dihydropteridine reductase (or an inability to synthesize tetrahydrobiopterin). Both forms of PKU will lead to mental retardation if treatment is not initiated at an early age.
Alcaptonuria	Genetic	Alcaptonuria is caused by a defect in homogentisate oxidase, leading to an accumulation of homogentisic acid. Arthritis may develop later in life.
Tyrosinemia	Genetic	Tyrosinemia type I is a defect in fumarylacetoacetate hydrolase, leading to liver failure and early death. Tyrosinemia type II is a defect in tyrosine aminotransferase, leading to neurologic defects.
Cystathioninuria	Genetic	Defect in cystathionase, leading to an accumulation of cystathionine. No major complications result from this mutation.
Homocysteinemia	Genetic	A defect in cystathionine β-synthase leads to accumulation of homocysteine, which can result in cardiologic and neurologic complications in the patient.
Primary oxaluria type I	Genetic	Defect in glycine transaminase leading to oxalate accumulate, and renal failure because of stone formation within the kidney.
Maple syrup urine disease	Genetic	A defect in the branched-chain α-keto acid dehydrogenase, leading to an accumulation of the α-keto acids of the branched-chain amino acids, resulting in mental retardation.
Cystinosis	Genetic	A defect in the transport protein that carries cystine across lysosomal membranes. Cystine accumulates in lysosomes, interfering with and ultimately destroying their function.
Thiamine deficiency	Environmental	A thiamine deficiency leads to accumulation of α-keto acids because the enzymes that catalyze oxidative decarboxylation reactions will not function in the absence of this vitamin. This will interfere with energy production, and lead to ketoacidosis.

1. If an individual has a vitamin B_6 deficiency, which of the following amino acids could still be synthesized and be considered nonessential?

    A. Tyrosine
    B. Serine
    C. Alanine
    D. Cysteine
    E. Aspartate

2. The degradation of amino acids can be classified into families, which are named after the end product of the degradative pathway. Which of the following is such an end product?

    A. Citrate
    B. Glyceraldehyde 3-phosphate
    C. Fructose 6-phosphate
    D. Malate
    E. Succinyl-CoA

3. A newborn infant has elevated levels of phenylalanine and phenylpyruvate in her blood. Which of the following enzymes might be deficient in this baby?

    A. Phenylalanine dehydrogenase
    B. Phenylalanine oxidase
    C. Dihydropteridine reductase
    D. Tyrosine hydroxylase
    E. Tetrahydrofolate synthase

4. Pyridoxal phosphate is required for which of the following reaction pathways or individual reactions?

    A. Phenylalanine → tyrosine
    B. Methionine → cysteine + α-ketobutyrate
    C. Propionyl-CoA → succinyl-CoA
    D. Pyruvate → acetyl-CoA
    E. Glucose → glycogen

5. A folic acid deficiency would interfere with the synthesis of which of the following amino acids from the indicated precursors?

    A. Aspartate from oxaloacetate and glutamate
    B. Glutamate from glucose and ammonia
    C. Glycine from glucose and alanine
    D. Proline from glutamate
    E. Serine from glucose and alanine

40 Tetrahydrofolate, Vitamin B_{12}, and S-Adenosylmethionine

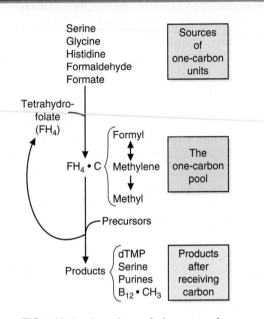

FIG. 40.1. Overview of the one-carbon pool. $FH_4 \cdot C$ indicates tetrahydrofolate (FH_4) containing a one-carbon unit that is at the formyl, methylene, or methyl level of oxidation (see Fig. 40.3). The origin of the carbons is indicated, as are the final products after a one-carbon transfer.

Groups that contain a single carbon atom can be transferred from one compound to another. These carbon atoms may be in several different oxidation states. The most oxidized form, CO_2, is transferred by biotin. One-carbon groups at lower levels of oxidation than CO_2 are transferred by reactions involving tetrahydrofolate (FH_4), vitamin B_{12}, and S-adenosylmethionine (SAM).

***Tetrahydrofolate**. Tetrahydrofolate, which is produced from the vitamin **folate**, is the primary one-carbon carrier in the body. This vitamin obtains one-carbon units from serine, glycine, histidine, formaldehyde, and formate (Fig. 40.1). While these carbons are attached to FH_4, they can be either oxidized or reduced. As a result, folate can exist in a variety of chemical forms. Once a carbon has been reduced to the methyl level (methyl-FH_4), however, it cannot be reoxidized. Collectively, these one-carbon groups attached to their carrier FH_4 are known as the **one-carbon pool**. The term "folate" is used to represent a water-soluble B-complex vitamin that functions in transferring single-carbon groups at various stages of oxidation.*

*The one-carbon groups carried by FH_4 are used for many biosynthetic reactions. For example, one-carbon units are transferred to the pyrimidine base of deoxyuridine monophosphate (**dUMP**) to form deoxythymidine monophosphate (**dTMP**), to the amino acid **glycine** to form **serine**, to precursors of the purine bases to produce carbons C2 and C8 of the **purine ring**, and to **vitamin B_{12}**.*

***Vitamin B_{12}**. Vitamin B_{12} is involved in two reactions in the body. It participates in the rearrangement of the methyl group of L-methylmalonyl coenzyme A (L-methylmalonyl-CoA) to form succinyl-CoA, and it transfers a methyl group, obtained from FH_4, to homocysteine, forming methionine.*

***S-adenosylmethionine**. SAM, produced from methionine and adenosine triphosphate (ATP), transfers the methyl group to precursors that form several compounds, including creatine, phosphatidylcholine, epinephrine, melatonin, methylated nucleotides, and methylated DNA.*

*Methionine metabolism is very dependent on both FH_4 and vitamin B_{12}. **Homocysteine** is derived from methionine metabolism and can be converted back into methionine by using both methyl-FH_4 and vitamin B_{12}. This is the only reaction in which methyl-FH_4 can donate the methyl group. If the enzyme that catalyzes this reaction is defective, or if vitamin B_{12} or FH_4 levels are insufficient, homocysteine will accumulate. Elevated homocysteine levels have been linked to cardiovascular and neurologic disease. A vitamin B_{12} deficiency can be brought about by the lack of **intrinsic factor**, a gastric protein required for the absorption of dietary B_{12}. A consequence of vitamin B_{12} deficiency is the accumulation of methyl-FH_4 and a decrease in other folate derivatives. This is known as the **methyl-trap hypothesis**, in which,* *because of the B_{12} deficiency, most of the carbons in the FH_4 pool are trapped in the methyl-FH_4 form, which is the most stable. The carbons cannot be released from the folate because the one reaction in which they participate cannot occur because of the B_{12} deficiency. This leads to a functional folate deficiency, even though total levels of folate are normal. A folate deficiency (whether functional or actual) leads to* **megaloblastic anemia** *caused by an inability of blood cell precursors to synthesize DNA and, therefore, to divide. This leads to large, partially replicated cells being released into the blood to attempt to replenish the cells that have died. Folate deficiencies also have been linked to an increased incidence of* **neural tube defects**, *such as spina bifida, in mothers who become pregnant while folate deficient.*

THE WAITING ROOM

After resection of the cancer in his large intestine and completion of a course of postoperative chemotherapy with 5-fluorouracil (5-FU), **Colin Tuma** returned to his gastroenterologist for a routine follow-up colonoscopy. His colon was completely normal, with excellent healing at the site of the anastomosis. His physician expressed great optimism about a possible cure of Colin's previous malignancy but cautioned him about the need for regular colonoscopic examinations over the next few years. The 5-FU treatment had also reduced the growth of the metastatic tumors so they may be able to be resected in the future.

Bea Twelvlow, a 75-year-old woman, went to see her physician because of numbness and tingling in her legs. A diet history indicated a normal and healthy diet, but Bea was not taking any supplemental vitamin pills. Laboratory results indicated a slight elevation of methylmalonic acid, and this led the physician to suspect a vitamin B_{12} deficiency. Direct measurement of serum B_{12} levels did indicate a deficiency, but the results of a Schilling test were normal.

The initial laboratory profile, determined when **Jean Ann Tonich** first presented to her physician with evidence of early alcohol-induced hepatitis, included a hematologic analysis that showed that Jean Ann was anemic. Her hemoglobin was 11 g/dL (reference range, 12 to 16 g/dL for an adult woman). The erythrocyte (red blood cell) count was 3.6 million cells/mm³ (reference range, 4.0 to 5.2 million cells/mm³ for an adult woman). The average volume of her red blood cells (mean corpuscular volume or MCV) was 108 fL (reference range, 80 to 100 fL; 1 fL = 10^{-12} mL), and the hematology laboratory reported a striking variation in the size and shape of the red blood cells in a smear of her peripheral blood (see Chapter 44). The nuclei of the circulating granulocytic leukocytes had increased nuclear segmentation (polysegmented neutrophils). Because these findings are suggestive of a macrocytic anemia (in which blood cells are larger than normal), measurements of serum folate and vitamin B_{12} (cobalamin) levels were ordered.

I. TETRAHYDROFOLATE
A. Structure and Forms of Tetrahydrofolate

Folates exist in many chemical forms. The coenzyme form that functions in accepting one-carbon groups is tetrahydrofolate polyglutamate (Fig. 40.2), generally referred to as just tetrahydrofolate or FH_4. It has three major structural components,

The Schilling test involves the patient ingesting radioactive (^{60}Co) crystalline vitamin B_{12}, after which a 24-hour urine sample is collected. The radioactivity in the urine sample is compared with the input radioactivity, and the difference represents the amount of B_{12} not absorbed through the digestive tract. Such tests can distinguish between problems in removing B_{12} from bound dietary proteins or if the deficiency is caused by a lack of intrinsic factor or other proteins involved in transporting B_{12} throughout the body. Another method to determine if intrinsic factor activity is reduced is to determine the levels of anti-intrinsic antibodies in the blood. Autoantibodies toward intrinsic factor commonly develop in individuals with lack of intrinsic factor activity, and the levels of such antibodies can be determined in an enzyme-linked immunosorbent assay (ELISA) using recombinant human intrinsic factor bound to plastic wells as the antigen.

Folate deficiencies occur frequently in chronic alcoholics. Several factors are involved: inadequate dietary intake of folate; direct damage to intestinal cells and brush border enzymes, which interferes with absorption of dietary folate; a defect in the enterohepatic circulation, which reduces the absorption of folate; liver damage that causes decreased hepatic production of plasma proteins; and interference with kidney reabsorption of folate.

Because of the possibility of a direct toxic effect of alcohol on hematopoietic tissues in **Jean Ann Tonich**, a bone marrow aspirate was performed. The aspirate contained a greater than normal number of red and white blood cell precursors, most of which were larger than normal. The large red blood cells are called *megaloblasts*.

These hematopoietic precursor cells, when exposed to too little folate and/or vitamin B_{12}, show slowed cell division, but cytoplasmic development occurs at a normal rate. Hence, the megaloblastic cells tend to be large, with an increased ratio of RNA to DNA. Megaloblastic erythroid progenitors are usually destroyed in the bone marrow (although some reach the circulation). Thus, marrow cellularity is often increased but production of red blood cells is decreased, a condition called *ineffective erythropoiesis*.

Therefore, Jean Ann has megaloblastic anemia, characteristic of folate or B_{12} deficiency.

Jean Ann Tonich's serum folic acid level was 3.1 ng/mL (reference range, 6 to 15 ng/mL), and her serum B_{12} level was 154 pg/mL (reference range, 150 to 750 pg/mL). Her serum iron level was normal. It was clear, therefore, that Jean Ann's megaloblastic anemia was caused by a folate deficiency (although her B_{12} levels were in the low range of normal). The management of a pure folate deficiency in an alcoholic patient includes cessation of alcohol intake and a diet that is rich in folate.

Sulfa drugs, which are used to treat certain bacterial infections, are analogs of *para*-aminobenzoic acid. They prevent growth and cell division in bacteria by interfering with the synthesis of folate. Because we cannot synthesize folate, sulfa drugs do not affect human cells in this way.

The current U.S. Recommended Dietary Allowance (RDA) for folate equivalents is approximately 400 μg for adult men and women. In addition to being prevalent in green leafy vegetables, other good sources of this vitamin are liver, yeast, legumes, and some fruits. Protracted cooking of these foods, however, can destroy up to 90% of their folate content. A standard U.S. diet provides 50 to 500 μg of absorbable folate each day. Folate deficiency in pregnant women, especially during the month before conception and the month after, increases the risk of neural tube defects, such as spina bifida, in the fetus. To reduce the potential risk of neural tube defects for women who are capable of becoming pregnant, the recommendation is to take 400 μg of folic acid daily in a multivitamin pill. If the women have a history of having a child with a neural tube defect, this amount is increased to 4,000 μg/day for the month before and the month after conception. Flour-containing products in the United States are now supplemented with folate to reduce the risk of neural tube defects in newborns.

FIG. 40.2. Reduction of folate to tetrahydrofolate (FH_4). The same enzyme, dihydrofolate reductase (DHFR), catalyzes both reactions. Multiple glutamate residues are added within cells (n ~ 5). Plants can synthesize folate but humans cannot. Therefore, folate is a dietary requirement. R is the portion of the folate molecule shown to the right of N^{10}. The different precursors of FH_4 are indicated in the figure. *PABA*, *para*-aminobenzoic acid.

a bicyclic pteridine ring, *para*-aminobenzoic acid, and a polyglutamate tail consisting of several glutamate residues joined in amide linkage. The one-carbon group that is accepted by the coenzyme and then transferred to another compound is bound to N^5, to N^{10}, or both.

Different forms of folate may differ in the oxidation state of the one-carbon group, in the number of glutamate residues attached, or in the degree of oxidation of the pteridine ring. When the term "folate" or "folic acid" is applied to a specific chemical form, it is the most oxidized form of the pteridine ring (see Fig. 40.2). Folate is reduced to dihydrofolate (FH_2) and then to FH_4 by dihydrofolate reductase (DHFR) present in cells. Reduction is the favored direction of the reaction; therefore, most of the folate present in the body is present as the reduced coenzyme form, FH_4.

B. The Vitamin Folate

Folates are synthesized in bacteria and higher plants and ingested in green leafy vegetables, fruits, and legumes in the diet. The vitamin was named for its presence in green, leafy vegetables (foliage). Most of the dietary folate derived from natural food sources is present in the reduced coenzyme form. However, vitamin supplements and fortified foods contain principally the oxidized form of the pteridine ring.

As dietary folates pass into the proximal third of the small intestine, folate conjugases in the brush border of the lumen cleave off glutamate residues to produce the monoglutamate form of folate, which is then absorbed (see Fig. 40.2, upper structure, when n = 1). Within the intestinal cells, folate is converted principally to N^5-methyl-FH$_4$, which enters the portal vein and goes to the liver. Smaller amounts of other forms of folate also follow this route.

The liver, which stores half of the body's folate, takes up much of the folate from the portal circulation; uptake may be through active transport or receptor-mediated endocytosis. Within the liver, FH$_4$ is reconjugated to the polyglutamate form before being used in reactions. A small amount of the folate is partially degraded, and the components enter the urine. A relatively large portion of the folate enters the bile and is subsequently reabsorbed (very similar to the fate of bile salts in the enterohepatic circulation).

N^5-Methyl-FH$_4$, the major form of folate in the blood, is loosely bound to plasma proteins, particularly serum albumin.

C. Oxidation and Reduction of the One-Carbon Groups of Tetrahydrofolate

One-carbon groups transferred by FH$_4$ are attached either to N^5 or N^{10}, or they form a bridge between N^5 and N^{10}. The collection of one-carbon groups attached to FH$_4$ is known as the *one-carbon pool*. While they are attached to FH$_4$, these one-carbon units can be oxidized and reduced (Fig. 40.3). Thus, reactions that require a carbon in a particular oxidation state may use carbon from the one-carbon pool that was donated in a different oxidation state.

The individual steps for reduction of the one-carbon group are shown in Figure 40.3. The most oxidized form is N^{10}-formyl-FH$_4$. The most reduced form is N^5-methyl-FH$_4$. Once the methyl group is formed, it is not readily reoxidized back to N^5,N^{10}-methylene-FH$_4$, and thus N^5-methyl-FH$_4$ tends to accumulate in the cell.

D. Sources of One-Carbon Groups Carried by FH$_4$

Carbon sources for the one-carbon pool include serine, glycine, formaldehyde, histidine, and formate (Fig. 40.4). These donors transfer the carbons to folate in different oxidation states. *Serine* is the major carbon source of one-carbon groups in the human. Its hydroxymethyl group is transferred to FH$_4$ in a reversible reaction, catalyzed by the enzyme serine hydroxymethyltransferase. This reaction produces glycine and N^5,N^{10}-methylene-FH$_4$. Because serine can be synthesized from *3-phosphoglycerate*, an intermediate of glycolysis, dietary carbohydrate can serve as a source of carbon for the one-carbon pool. The glycine that is produced may be further degraded by donation of a carbon to folate. Additional donors that form N^5,N^{10}-methylene-FH$_4$ are listed in Table 40.1.

Histidine and formate provide examples of compounds that donate carbon in different oxidation levels (see Fig. 40.4). Degradation of histidine produces formiminoglutamate (FIGLU), which reacts with FH$_4$ to donate a carbon and nitrogen (generating N^5-formimino-FH$_4$), thereby releasing glutamate. Formate, produced from tryptophan oxidation, can react with FH$_4$ and generate N^{10}-formyl-FH$_4$, the most oxidized folate derivative.

E. Recipients of One-Carbon Groups

The one-carbon groups on FH$_4$ may be oxidized or reduced (see Fig. 40.3) and then transferred to other compounds (see Fig. 40.4 and Table 40.1). Transfers of this sort are involved in the synthesis of glycine from serine, the synthesis of the base thymine required for DNA synthesis, the purine bases required for both DNA and RNA synthesis, and the transfer of methyl groups to vitamin B$_{12}$.

Because the conversion of serine to glycine is readily reversible, glycine can be converted to serine by drawing carbon from the one-carbon pool.

Hereditary folate malabsorption is a rare disease caused by a mutation in a proton-coupled folate transporter (PCFT, gene *SLC46A1*). Loss of PCFT activity in the intestinal proximal jejunum and duodenum lead to systemic folate deficiency. Newborns begin to exhibit symptoms of folate deficiency after a few months of life, after the folate obtained from the mother has been excreted. The children develop anemia, diarrhea, and become immunocompromised (because of the reduction in blood cell differentiation). High-dose oral folate can be used to treat the patients, as another folate transporter (the reduced folate carrier, gene *SLC19A1*) can absorb sufficient folate when folate is present at high concentrations.

A deficiency of folate results in the accumulation of formiminoglutamate (FIGLU), which is excreted in the urine. A histidine load test can be used to detect folate deficiency. Patients are given a test dose of histidine (a histidine load), and the amount of FIGLU that appears in the urine is measured and compared to normal values. Values greater than normal indicate folate deficiency.

The concentration of folate in serum can also be determined by a microbiologic test. Certain strains of bacteria require folate for growth, and if these bacteria are plated on a medium that lacks folate, they will not grow. Folate levels can be quantitated by preparing a standard curve using plates containing different levels of folate and determining the level of growth of the bacteria at that folate level. The unknown sample is then tested for bacterial growth and the extent of growth compared to the standard curve to determine the amount of folate in the unknown sample. Other tests for folate include measuring the binding of folate to certain proteins and use of immunologic reagents that specifically bind to and identify folate.

Tetrahydrofolate (FH$_4$) is required for the synthesis of deoxythymidine monophosphate (dTMP) and the purine bases used to produce the precursors for DNA replication. Therefore, FH$_4$ is required for cell division. Blockage of the synthesis of thymine and the purine bases, either by a dietary deficiency of folate or by drugs that interfere with folate metabolism, results in a decreased rate of cell division and growth.

FIG. 40.3. One-carbon units attached to tetrahydrofolate (FH$_4$). **A.** The active form of FH$_4$. For definition of R, see Figure 40.2. **B.** Interconversions of one-carbon units of FH$_4$. Only the portion of FH$_4$ from N^5 to N^{10} is shown, which is indicated by the *green box* in A. After a formyl group forms a bridge between N^5 and N^{10}, two reductions can occur. Note that N^5-methyl-FH$_4$ cannot be reoxidized. The most oxidized form of FH$_4$ is at the top of the figure, whereas the most reduced form is at the bottom.

The nucleotide deoxythymidine monophosphate (dTMP) is produced from deoxyuridine monophosphate (dUMP) by a reaction in which dUMP is methylated to form dTMP (Fig. 40.5). The source of carbon is N^5,N^{10}-methylene-FH$_4$. Two hydrogen atoms from FH$_4$ are used to reduce the donated carbon to the methyl level. Consequently, FH$_2$ is produced. Reduction of FH$_2$ by NADPH in a reaction catalyzed by DHFR regenerates FH$_4$. This is the only reaction involving FH$_4$ in which

FIG. 40.4. Sources of carbon (*reactions 1 to 4*) for the tetrahydrofolate (FH₄) pool and the recipients of carbon (*reactions 5 to 8*) from the pool. See Figure 40.3 to view the FH₄ derivatives involved in each reaction.

the folate group is oxidized as the one-carbon group is donated to the recipient. Recall that DHFR is also required to reduce the oxidized form of the vitamin, which is obtained from the diet (see Fig. 40.2). Thus, DHFR is essential for regenerating FH₄ both in the tissues and from the diet. These reactions contribute to the effect of folate deficiency on DNA synthesis because dTMP is required only for the synthesis of DNA.

During the synthesis of the purine bases, carbons 2 and 8 are obtained from the one-carbon pool (see Chapter 41). N^{10}-formyl-FH₄ provides both carbons. Folate deficiency also hinders these reactions, contributing to an inability to replicate DNA because of the lack of precursors.

After the carbon group carried by FH₄ is reduced to the methyl level, it is transferred to vitamin B₁₂. This is the only reaction through which the methyl group can leave FH₄ (recall that the reaction that creates N^5-methyl-FH₄ is not reversible).

Individuals with non-Hodgkin lymphoma receive several drugs to treat the tumor, including methotrexate. The structure of methotrexate is shown in the following:

Methotrexate

What compound does methotrexate resemble?

Table 40.1   One-Carbon Pool: Sources and Recipients of Carbon

Source[a]	Form of One-Carbon Donor Produced[b]	Recipient	Final Product
Formate	N^{10}-formyl-FH₄	Purine precursor	Purine (C2 and C8)
Serine	N^5, N^{10}-methylene-FH₄	dUMP	dTMP
Glycine		Glycine	Serine
Formaldehyde			
N^5, N^{10}-methylene-FH₄	N^5-methyl-FH₄	Vitamin B₁₂	Methylcobalamin
Histidine	N^5-formimino-FH₄ is converted to N^5, N^{10}-methenyl-FH₄		
Choline	Betaine	Homocysteine	Methionine and dimethylglycine
Methionine	SAM	Glycine (there are many others; see Fig. 40.9B)	N-methylglycine (sarcosine)

dUMP, deoxyuridine monophosphate; dTMP, deoxythymidine monophosphate; SAM, S-adenosylmethionine.

[a]The major source of carbon is serine.

[b]The carbon unit attached to FH₄ can be oxidized and reduced (see Fig. 40.3). At the methyl level, reoxidation does not occur.

A better understanding of the structure and function of the purine and pyrimidine bases and of folate metabolism led to the development of compounds having antimetabolic and antifolate action useful for treatment of neoplastic disease. For example, **Colin Tuma** was successfully treated for colon cancer with 5-fluorouracil (5-FU) (see Chapter 12 and Fig. 40.5). *5-FU* is a pyrimidine analog, which is converted in cells to the nucleotide fluorodeoxyuridylate (FdUMP). FdUMP causes a "thymineless death," especially for tumor cells that have a rapid turnover rate. It prevents the growth of cancer cells by blocking the thymidylate synthase reaction, that is, the conversion of deoxyuridine monophosphate (dUMP) to dTMP.

A: Methotrexate has the same structure as folate except that it has an amino group on C4 and a methyl group on N^{10}. Anticancer drugs such as methotrexate are folate analogs that act by inhibiting dihydrofolate reductase (DHFR), thereby preventing the conversion of FH$_2$ to tetrahydrofolate (FH$_4$) (see Fig. 40.5). Thus, the cellular pools of FH$_4$ are not replenished, and reactions that require FH$_4$ cannot proceed.

Jean Ann Tonich's megaloblastic anemia was treated, in part, with folate supplements (see Clinical Comments section). Within 48 hours of the initiation of folate therapy, megaloblastic or "ineffective" erythropoiesis usually subsides, and effective erythropoiesis begins.

Megaloblastic anemia is caused by a decrease in the synthesis of thymine and the purine bases. These deficiencies lead to an inability of hematopoietic (and other) cells to synthesize DNA and, therefore, to divide. Their persistently thwarted attempts at normal DNA replication, DNA repair, and cell division produce abnormally large cells (called *megaloblasts*) with abundant cytoplasm capable of protein synthesis but with clumping and fragmentation of nuclear chromatin (see Chapter 44). Some of these large cells, although immature, are released early from the marrow in an attempt to compensate for the anemia. Thus, peripheral blood smears also contain megaloblasts. Many of the large immature cells, however, are destroyed in the marrow and never reach the circulation.

The average daily diet in Western countries contains 5 to 30 μg of vitamin B$_{12}$, of which 1 to 5 μg is absorbed into the blood. (The Recommended Dietary Allowance [RDA] is 2.4 μg/day.) Total body content of this vitamin in an adult is approximately 2 to 5 mg, of which 1 mg is present in the liver. As a result, a dietary deficiency of B$_{12}$ is uncommon and is observed only after several years on a diet that is deficient in this vitamin.

In spite of **Jean Ann Tonich's** relatively malnourished state because of her chronic alcoholism, her serum cobalamin level was still within the low-to-normal range. If her undernourished state had continued, a cobalamin deficiency would eventually have developed.

FIG. 40.5. Transfer of a one-carbon unit from N^5,N^{10}-methylene-FH$_4$ to deoxyuridine monophosphate (dUMP) to form deoxythymidine monophosphate (dTMP). FH$_4$ (tetrahydrofolate) is oxidized to FH$_2$ (dihydrofolate) in this reaction. FH$_2$ is reduced to FH$_4$ by dihydrofolate reductase (DHFR) and FH$_4$ is converted to N^5,N^{10}-methylene-FH$_4$ using serine as a carbon donor. *Shaded bars* indicate the steps at which the antimetabolites 5-fluorouracil (5-FU) and methotrexate act. 5-FU inhibits thymidylate synthase. Methotrexate inhibits DHFR.

II. VITAMIN B$_{12}$

A. Structure and Forms of Vitamin B$_{12}$

The structure of vitamin B$_{12}$ (also known as *cobalamin*) is complex (Fig. 40.6). It contains a corrin ring, which is similar to the porphyrin ring found in heme. The corrin ring differs from heme, however, in that two of the four pyrrole rings are joined directly rather than by a methylene bridge. Its most unusual feature is the presence of cobalt, coordinated with the corrin ring (similar to the iron coordinated with the porphyrin ring). This cobalt can form a bond with a carbon atom. In the body, it reacts with the carbon of a methyl group, forming methylcobalamin, or with the 5′-carbon of 5′-deoxyadenosine, forming 5′-deoxyadenosylcobalamin (note that in this case, the "deoxy" designation refers to the 5′-carbon, not the 2′-carbon as is the case in the sugar found in DNA). The form of B$_{12}$ found in vitamin supplements is cyanocobalamin in which a CN group is linked to the cobalt.

B. Absorption and Transport of Vitamin B$_{12}$

Although vitamin B$_{12}$ is produced by bacteria, it cannot be synthesized by higher plants or animals. The major source of vitamin B$_{12}$ is dietary meat, eggs, dairy products, fish, poultry, and seafood. The animals that serve as the source of these foods obtain B$_{12}$ mainly from the bacteria in their food supply. The absorption of B$_{12}$ from the diet is a complex process (Fig. 40.7).

Ingested B$_{12}$ can exist in two forms, either free or bound to dietary proteins. If free, the B$_{12}$ binds to proteins known as *R-binders* (haptocorrins, also known as *transcobalamin I*), which are secreted by the salivary glands and the gastric mucosa, in either the saliva or the stomach. If the ingested B$_{12}$ is bound to proteins, it must be released from the proteins by the action of digestive proteases in both the stomach and small intestine. Once the B$_{12}$ is released from its bound protein, it binds to the haptocorrins. In the small intestine, the pancreatic proteases digest the haptocorrins, and the released B$_{12}$ then binds to *intrinsic factor*, a glycoprotein secreted by the parietal cells of the stomach when food enters the stomach. The intrinsic factor-B$_{12}$ complex attaches to specific receptors in the terminal segment of the small intestine known as the *ileum*, after which the complex is internalized.

FIG. 40.6. Vitamin B₁₂. X, 5′-deoxyadenosine in deoxyadenosylcobalamin; X = CH₃ in methylcobalamin; X = CN in cyanocobalamin (the commercial form found in vitamin tablets).

Pernicious anemia, a deficiency of intrinsic factor, is a relatively common problem that is caused by malabsorption of dietary cobalamin. It may result from an inherited defect that leads to decreased ability of gastric parietal cells to synthesize intrinsic factor or from partial resection of the stomach or of the ileum. Production of intrinsic factor often declines with age and may be low in elderly individuals. An alternative circumstance that leads to the development of a B₁₂ deficiency is pancreatic insufficiency or a high intestinal pH, which results from too little acid being produced by the stomach. Both of these conditions prevent the degradation of the R-binder–B₁₂ complex; as a result, B₁₂ is not released from the R-binder protein and, therefore, cannot bind to intrinsic factor. The protein receptor for the B₁₂-intrinsic factor complex is named *cubilin*, and the internalization of the B₁₂-intrinsic factor-cubilin complex requires the activity of a transmembrane protein named *amnionless*. Congenital malabsorption of B₁₂ can also arise from inherited mutations in either cubilin or amnionless.

The B₁₂ within the enterocyte complexes with transcobalamin II and then released into circulation. The transcobalamin II-B₁₂ complex delivers B₁₂ to the tissues, which contain specific receptors for this complex. The liver takes up approximately 50% of the vitamin B₁₂, and the remainder is transported to other tissues. The amount of the vitamin stored in the liver is large enough that 3 to 6 years pass before symptoms of a dietary deficiency occur.

C. Functions of Vitamin B₁₂

Vitamin B₁₂ is involved in two reactions in the body: the transfer of a methyl group from N^5-methyl-FH₄ to homocysteine to form methionine and the rearrangement of L-methylmalonyl-CoA to form succinyl-CoA (Fig. 40.8).

FH₄ receives a one-carbon group from serine or from other sources. This carbon is reduced to the methyl level and transferred to vitamin B₁₂, forming methyl-B₁₂ (or methylcobalamin). Methylcobalamin transfers the methyl group to homocysteine, which is converted to methionine by the enzyme methionine synthase. Methionine can then be activated to *S*-adenosylmethionine (SAM) to transfer the methyl group to other compounds (Fig. 40.9).

Vitamin B₁₂ also participates in the conversion of L-methylmalonyl-CoA to succinyl-CoA. In this case, the active form of the coenzyme is 5′-deoxyadenosylcobalamin.

How should vitamin B₁₂ be administered to a patient with pernicious anemia?

A: Because the problem in pernicious anemia is a lack of intrinsic factor, which results in an inability to absorb vitamin B_{12} from the gastrointestinal tract, B_{12} cannot be administered orally to treat this condition. In the past, it was usually given by injection. An effective nasal spray containing B_{12} has recently been marketed, however, and its use precludes the need for lifelong injections of this vitamin.

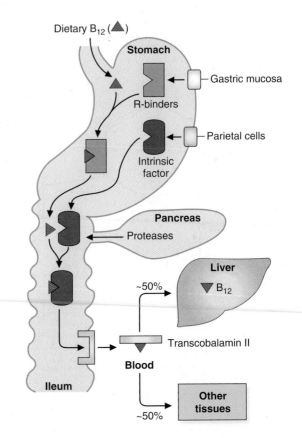

FIG. 40.7. Absorption, transport, and storage of vitamin B_{12}. Dietary B_{12} binds to R-binders (haptocorrins) in the stomach and travels to the intestine, where the R-binders are destroyed by pancreatic proteases. The freed B_{12} then binds to intrinsic factor (IF). B_{12} is absorbed in the ileum and carried by proteins named transcobalamins (TC) to the liver, where B_{12} is stored.

FIG. 40.8. The two reactions involving vitamin B_{12} in humans.

This reaction is part of the metabolic route for the conversion of carbons from valine, isoleucine, threonine, and the last three carbons of odd-chain fatty acids, all of which form propionyl-CoA, to the tricarboxylic acid (TCA) cycle intermediate succinyl-CoA (see Chapter 39).

III. S-ADENOSYLMETHIONINE

SAM participates in the synthesis of many compounds that contain methyl groups. It is used in reactions that add methyl groups to either oxygen or nitrogen atoms in the acceptor (contrast that to folate derivatives, which can add one-carbon groups to sulfur or to carbon). As examples, SAM is required for the conversion of phosphatidylethanolamine to phosphatidylcholine, guanidinoacetate to creatine, norepinephrine to epinephrine, acetylserotonin to melatonin, and nucleotides to methylated nucleotides (see Fig. 40.9B). It is also required for the inactivation of catecholamines and serotonin (see Chapter 48). More than 35 reactions in humans require methyl donation from SAM.

SAM is synthesized from methionine and adenosine triphosphate (ATP). As with the activation of vitamin B_{12}, ATP donates the adenosine. With the transfer of its methyl group, SAM forms S-adenosylhomocysteine (SAH), which is subsequently hydrolyzed to form homocysteine and adenosine.

Methionine, required for the synthesis of SAM, is obtained from the diet or produced from homocysteine, which accepts a methyl group from vitamin B_{12} (see Fig. 40.9A). Thus, the methyl group of methionine is regenerated. The portion

A

B

Precursor		Methylated product
Norepinephrine	SAM	Epinephrine
Guanidinoacetate	SAM	Creatine
Nucleotides	SAM	Methylated nucleotides
Phosphatidylethanolamine	SAM	Phosphatidylcholine
Acetylserotonin	SAM	Melatonin

FIG. 40.9. Relationships among tetrahydrofolate (FH₄), B₁₂, and S-adenosymelthionine (SAM). **A.** Overall scheme. **B.** Some specific reactions that require SAM.

of methionine that is essential in the diet is the homocysteine moiety. If we had an adequate dietary source of homocysteine, methionine would not be required in the diet. However, there is no good dietary source of homocysteine, whereas methionine is plentiful in the diet.

Homocysteine provides the sulfur atom for the synthesis of cysteine (see Chapter 39). In this case, homocysteine reacts with serine to form cystathionine, which is cleaved, yielding cysteine and α-ketobutyrate. The first reaction in this sequence is inhibited by cysteine. Thus, methionine, via homocysteine, is not used for cysteine synthesis unless the levels of cysteine in the body are lower than required for its metabolic functions. An adequate dietary supply of cysteine, therefore, can "spare" (or reduce) the dietary requirement for methionine.

IV. RELATIONSHIPS AMONG FOLATE, VITAMIN B₁₂, AND S-ADENOSYLMETHIONINE

A. The Methyl-Trap Hypothesis

If one analyzes the flow of carbon in the folate cycle, the equilibrium lies in the direction of the N^5-methyl-FH₄ form. This appears to be the most stable form of carbon attached to the vitamin. However, in only one reaction can the methyl group be removed from N^5-methyl-FH₄, and that is the methionine synthase reaction, which requires vitamin B₁₂. Thus, if vitamin B₁₂ is deficient, or if the methionine synthase enzyme is defective, N^5-methyl-FH₄ accumulates. Eventually, most folate forms in the body become "trapped" in the N^5-methyl form. A functional folate deficiency results because the carbons cannot be removed from the folate. The appearance of a functional folate deficiency caused by a lack of vitamin B₁₂ is known as the *methyl-trap hypothesis*, and its clinical implications are discussed in following sections.

 There are two major clinical manifestations of cobalamin (B₁₂) deficiency. One such presentation is hematopoietic (caused by the adverse effects of a B₁₂ deficiency on folate metabolism), and the other is neurologic (caused by hypomethylation in the nervous system). The hemopoietic problems associated with a B₁₂ deficiency are identical to those observed in a folate deficiency and, in fact, result from a folate deficiency secondary to (i.e., caused by) the B₁₂ deficiency (i.e., the methyl-trap hypothesis). As the tetrahydrofolate (FH₄) pool is exhausted, deficiencies of the FH₄ derivatives needed for purine and dTMP biosynthesis develop, leading to the characteristic megaloblastic anemia.

The classical clinical presentation of the neurologic dysfunction associated with a B₁₂ deficiency includes symmetric numbness and tingling of the hands and feet, diminishing vibratory and position sense, and progression to a spastic gait disturbance. The patient may become somnolent or may become extremely irritable ("megaloblastic madness"). Eventually, blind spots in the central portions of the visual fields develop, accompanied by alterations in gustatory (taste) and olfactory (smell) function. This is believed to be caused by hypomethylation within the nervous system brought about by an inability to recycle homocysteine to methionine and from there to S-adenosylmethionine (SAM). The latter is the required methyl donor in these reactions. The nervous system lacks the betaine pathway of methionine regeneration (see Fig. 40.10) and is dependent on the B₁₂ system. With a B₁₂ deficiency, this pathway is inoperable in the nervous system.

Many health food stores now sell SAMe, a stabilized version of SAM. SAMe has been hypothesized to relieve depression because the synthesis of certain neurotransmitters requires methylation by SAM (see Chapter 48). This has led to the hypothesis that by increasing SAM levels in the nervous system, the biosynthesis of these neurotransmitters will be accelerated. This in turn might alleviate the feelings of depression. There have been reports in the literature indicating that this may occur, but its efficacy as an antidepressant must be confirmed. The major questions that must be addressed include the stability of SAMe in the digestive system and the level of uptake of SAMe by cells of the nervous system.

B. Hyperhomocysteinemia

Elevated homocysteine levels have been linked to cardiovascular and neurologic disease. Homocysteine levels can accumulate in several ways, which are related to both folic acid and vitamin B_{12} metabolism. Homocysteine is derived from SAM, which arises when SAM donates a methyl group (Fig. 40.10). Because SAM is frequently donating methyl groups, there is constant production of SAH, which leads to constant production of homocysteine. Recall from Chapter 39 that homocysteine has two biochemical fates. The homocysteine produced can be either remethylated to methionine or condensed with serine to form cystathionine. There are two routes to methionine production. The major one is methylation by N^5-methyl-FH_4, which requires vitamin B_{12}. The liver also contains a second pathway in which *betaine* (a degradation product of choline) can donate a methyl group to homocysteine to form methionine, but this is a minor pathway. The conversion of homocysteine to cystathionine requires pyridoxal phosphate (PLP). Thus, if an individual is deficient in vitamin B_{12}, the conversion of homocysteine to methionine by the major route is inhibited. This directs homocysteine to produce cystathionine, which eventually produces cysteine. As cysteine levels accumulate, the enzyme that makes cystathionine undergoes feedback inhibition, and that pathway is also inhibited (see Fig. 40.10). This, overall, leads to accumulation of homocysteine, which is released into the blood.

Homocysteine also accumulates in the blood if a mutation is present in the enzyme that converts N^5,N^{10}-methylene-FH_4 to N^5-methyl-FH_4. When this occurs, the levels of N^5-methyl-FH_4 are too low to allow homocysteine to be converted to methionine. The loss of this pathway, coupled with the feedback inhibition by cysteine on cystathionine formation, also leads to elevated homocysteine levels in the blood.

A third way in which serum homocysteine levels can be elevated is by a mutated cystathionine β-synthase or a deficiency in vitamin B_6, the required cofactor for that enzyme. These defects block the ability of homocysteine to be converted to cystathionine, and the homocysteine that does accumulate cannot

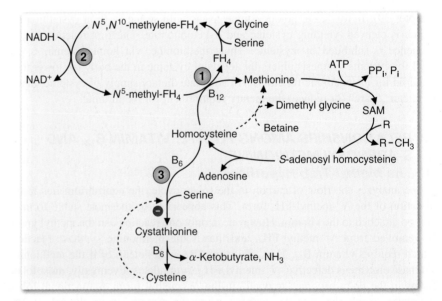

FIG. 40.10. Reaction pathways that involve homocysteine. Defects in numbered enzymes (*1*, methionine synthase; *2*, N^5,N^{10}-methylene-FH_4 reductase; *3*, cystathionine β-synthase) lead to elevated homocysteine. Recall that as cysteine accumulates, there is feedback inhibition on cystathionine β-synthase to stop further cysteine production.

all be accommodated by conversion to methionine. Thus, an accumulation of homocysteine results.

C. Neural Tube Defects

Folate deficiency during pregnancy has been associated with an increased risk of neural tube defects in the developing fetus. This risk is significantly reduced if women take folic acid supplements periconceptually. The link between folate deficiency and neural tube defects was first observed in women with hyperhomocysteinemia brought about by a thermolabile variant of N^5,N^{10}-methylene-FH$_4$ reductase. This form of the enzyme, which results from a single nucleotide change (C to T) in position 677 of the gene that encodes the protein, is less active at body temperature than at lower temperatures. This results in a reduced level of N^5-methyl-FH$_4$ being generated and, therefore, an increase in the levels of homocysteine. Along with the elevated homocysteine, the women were also folate deficient. The folate deficiency and the subsequent inhibition of DNA synthesis leads to neural tube defects. The elevated homocysteine is one indication that such a deficit is present. These findings have led to the recommendation that women considering getting pregnant begin taking folate supplements before conception occurs, and for at least 1 month after conception. The US Department of Agriculture has, in fact, mandated that folate be added to flour-containing products in the United States.

D. Folate Deficiencies and DNA Synthesis

Folate deficiencies result in decreased availability of the deoxythymidine and purine nucleotides that serve as precursors for DNA synthesis. The decreased concentrations of these precursors affect not only the DNA synthesis that occurs during replication before cell division, but also the DNA synthesis that occurs as a step in the processes that repair damaged DNA.

Decreased methylation of dUMP to form dTMP, a reaction that requires N^5,N^{10}-methylene-FH$_4$ as a coenzyme (see Fig. 40.5), leads to an increase in the intracellular dUTP/deoxythymidine triphosphate (dTTP) ratio. This change causes a significant increase in the incorporation of uracil into DNA. Although much of this uracil can be removed by DNA-repair enzymes, the lack of available dTTP blocks the step of DNA repair that is catalyzed by DNA polymerase. The result is fragmentation of DNA as well as blockade of normal DNA replication.

These abnormal nuclear processes are responsible for the clumping and polysegmentation seen in the nuclei of neutrophilic leukocytes in the bone marrow and in the peripheral blood of patients with megaloblastic anemia caused either by a primary folate deficiency or one that is secondary to B$_{12}$ deficiency. The abnormalities in DNA synthesis and repair lead to an irreversible loss of the capacity for cell division and eventually to cell death.

V. CHOLINE AND ONE-CARBON METABOLISM

Other compounds involved in one-carbon metabolism are derived from degradation products of choline. *Choline*, an essential component of certain phospholipids, is oxidized to form betaine aldehyde, which is further oxidized to betaine (trimethylglycine). In the liver, betaine can donate a methyl group to homocysteine to form methionine and dimethyl glycine. This allows the liver to have two routes for homocysteine conversion to methionine. This is in contrast to the nervous system, which only expresses the primary B$_{12}$-requiring pathway. Under conditions in which SAM accumulates, glycine can be methylated to form sarcosine (*N*-methyl glycine). This route is used when methionine levels are high and excess methionine needs to be metabolized (Fig. 40.11).

FIG. 40.11. Choline and one-carbon metabolism.

CLINICAL COMMENTS

Jean Ann Tonich. Jean Ann Tonich developed a folate deficiency and is on the verge of developing a cobalamin (vitamin B_{12}) deficiency as a consequence of prolonged, moderately severe malnutrition related to chronic alcoholism. Before folate therapy is started, the physician must ascertain that the megaloblastic anemia is not caused by a pure B_{12} deficiency or a combined deficiency of folate and B_{12}.

If folate is given without cobalamin to a B_{12}-deficient patient, the drug only partially corrects the megaloblastic anemia because it will "bypass" the methyl folate trap and provide adequate tetrahydrofolate (FH_4) coenzyme for the conversion of deoxyuridine monophosphate (dUMP) to deoxythymidine monophosphate (dTMP) and for a resurgence of purine synthesis. As a result, normal DNA synthesis, DNA repair, and cell division occur. However, the neurologic syndrome resulting from hypomethylation in nervous tissue may progress unless the physician realizes that B_{12} supplementation is required. In Jean Ann's case, in which the serum B_{12} concentration was borderline low and in which the dietary history supported the possibility of a B_{12} deficiency, a combination of folate and B_{12} supplements is required to avoid this potential therapeutic trap.

Colin Tuma. Colin Tuma continued to do well and returned faithfully for his regular colonoscopic examinations.

Bea Twelvlow. Bea Twelvlow was diagnosed with an inability to absorb dietary B_{12} but not crystalline B_{12} (the Schilling test results were normal). One of the consequences of aging is a reduced acid production by the gastric mucosa (atrophic gastritis), which limits the ability of pepsin to work on dietary protein. Reduced pepsin efficiency then reduces the amount of bound B_{12} released from dietary protein as a result of which the B_{12} is not available for absorption. Because Bea absorbs crystalline B_{12} without a problem, her condition can be easily treated by taking vitamin B_{12} supplements orally.

BIOCHEMICAL COMMENTS

 A potential mechanism relating to folate deficiencies and neural tube defects. As indicated in Section IV.C of this chapter, neural tube defects in newborns have been associated with folate deficiency during pregnancy. Although the mechanism leading to neural tube defects is vague, new research has indicated that the induction of micro RNAs (miRNAs) may play a role in altering the normal developmental pattern of neural tube closure.

Under conditions of a folate deficiency, hypomethylation occurs in the nervous system, affecting membrane phospholipid biosynthesis (such as phosphatidylcholine), myelin basic protein (see Chapter 48), and neurotransmitter biosynthesis (see Chapter 48). The reduced levels of neurotransmitters may interfere with normal gene expression during embryogenesis. DNA methylation is also reduced because of reduced *S*-adenosylmethionine (SAM) levels when folate is limiting. Hypomethylation is also the result of increased levels of *S*-adenosylhomocysteine (SAH), which accumulates during a folate deficiency. SAH will inhibit DNA methyltransferase enzymes by tightly binding to the enzyme and preventing the normal substrate, SAM, from binding to the enzyme. The enzymes affinity for SAH is higher than that of SAM, contributing to the hypomethylation observed.

MiRNA genes are frequently near CpG islands in DNA, and it has been predicted that alterations in cytosine methylation may be a means of regulating miRNA expression. Experimentally, a cell line in which two DNA methyltransferase genes were knocked out (inactivated) resulted in a significant reduction in global genomic methylation and the differential expression of 13 miRNAs (seven of those genes were overexpressed, whereas the other 6 displayed a reduction in expression). A similar result was obtained with another cell line that was placed in folate-deficient media; global hypomethylation and alterations in miRNA expression were observed.

As an example, miR-222 was identified as a potential miRNA that is upregulated under conditions of folate deprivation. A predicted target of miR-222 is the *DNMT1* gene (a DNA methyltransferase), whose activity is critical for the maintenance of methylation patterns in DNA. Overexpression of miR-222 would reduce *DNMT1* gene expression, thereby altering methylation patterns in the cell. A reduction of *DNMT1* activity has been shown to increase the expression of several genes, including β-catenin (see Chapter 18). This will lead to enhanced cell proliferation and inhibition of differentiation in the nervous system (all leading to a failure to close the neural tube).

Such studies as those described previously are in their infancy but produced a promising start for unraveling the effects of DNA methylation and miRNA expression on cell growth and differentiation in the nervous system.

Key Concepts

- One-carbon groups at lower oxidation states than carbon dioxide (which is carried by biotin) are transferred by reactions that involve tetrahydrofolate (FH₄), vitamin B₁₂, and *S*-adenosylmethionine (SAM).
- FH₄ is produced from the vitamin folate and obtains one-carbon units from serine, glycine, histidine, formaldehyde, and formic acid.
- The carbon attached to FH₄ can be oxidized or reduced, thus producing several different forms of FH₄. However, once a carbon has been reduced to the methyl level, it cannot be reoxidized.
- The carbons attached to FH₄ are known collectively as the *one-carbon pool*.
- The carbons carried by folate are used in a limited number of biochemical reactions, but they are very important in forming deoxythymidine monophosphate (dTMP) and the purine rings.
- Vitamin B₁₂ participates in two reactions in the body: conversion of L-methylmalonyl-CoA to succinyl-CoA and conversion of homocysteine to methionine.

Table 40.2   Diseases Discussed in Chapter 40

Disease or Disorder	Environmental or Genetic	Comments
Colon cancer	Both	Colon cancer can be treated by drugs, which block the action of thymidylate synthase, blocking DNA synthesis by reducing the supply of dTTP.
Pernicious anemia	Both	Pernicious anemia is caused by the lack of intrinsic factor, which leads to a B_{12} deficiency. The B_{12} deficiency indirectly interferes with DNA synthesis. In cells of the erythroid lineage, cell size increases without cell division leading to megaloblastic anemia.
Alcohol-induced megaloblastic anemia	Environmental	Alcohol-induced malnutrition that can lead to folate and/or B_{12} deficiencies. The folate and/or B_{12} deficiency will lead to the development of megaloblastic anemia.
Neural tube defects	Both	A lack of folate derivatives leads to reduced methylation in the nervous system, altering gene expression and increasing the risk of neural tube defects.

dTTP, deoxythymidine triphosphate.

- SAM, formed from adenosine triphosphate (ATP) and methionine, transfers the methyl group to precursors of a variety of methylated compounds.
- Both vitamin B_{12} and methyl-FH_4 are required in methionine metabolism; a deficiency of vitamin B_{12} leads to overproduction and trapping of folate in the methyl form, leading to a functional folate deficiency. Such deficiencies can lead to
  - Megaloblastic anemia
  - Neural tube defects in newborns
- Diseases discussed in this chapter are summarized in Table 40.2.

REVIEW QUESTIONS—CHAPTER 40

1. Which of the following reactions requires N^5,N^{10}-methylene-FH_4 as a carbon donor?

   A. Homocysteine to methionine
   B. Serine to glycine
   C. Betaine to dimethylglycine
   D. dUMP to dTMP
   E. The de novo biosynthesis of the purine ring

2. Propionic acid accumulation from amino acid degradation will result from a deficiency of which of the following vitamins?

   A. Vitamin B_6
   B. Biotin
   C. Folic acid
   D. Vitamin B_{12}
   E. Vitamin B_1
   F. Vitamin B_2

3. A dietary vitamin B_{12} deficiency can result from which of the following?

   A. Excessive intrinsic factor production by the gastric parietal cells
   B. Eating a diet that is high in animal protein

   C. Pancreatic insufficiency
   D. Increased absorption of folic acid
   E. Inability to conjugate the vitamin with glutamic acid

4. Which of the following forms of tetrahydrofolate is required for the synthesis of methionine from homocysteine?

   A. N^5,N^{10}-methylene tetrahydrofolate
   B. N^5-methyl tetrahydrofolate
   C. N^5,N^{10}-methenyl tetrahydrofolate
   D. N^{10}-formyl tetrahydrofolate
   E. N^5-formimino tetrahydrofolate

5. An alternative method to methylate homocysteine to form methionine is which of the following?

   A. Using glycine and FH_4 as the methyl donor
   B. Using dimethylglycine as the methyl donor
   C. Using choline as the methyl donor
   D. Using sarcosine as the methyl donor
   E. Using betaine as the methyl donor

41 Purine and Pyrimidine Metabolism

Purines and pyrimidines are required for synthesizing **nucleotides** and **nucleic acids**. These molecules can be synthesized either from scratch, **de novo**, or **salvaged** from existing bases. Dietary uptake of purine and pyrimidine bases is low because most of the ingested nucleic acids are metabolized by the intestinal epithelial cells.

The de novo pathway of purine synthesis is complex, consisting of 11 steps, and requiring six molecules of adenosine triphosphate (ATP) for every purine synthesized. The precursors that donate components to produce purine nucleotides include **glycine, ribose 5-phosphate, glutamine, aspartate, carbon dioxide**, and **N^{10}-formyl-FH$_4$** (Fig. 41.1). Purines are synthesized as **ribonucleotides**, with the initial purine synthesized being **inosine monophosphate (IMP)**. Adenosine monophosphate (AMP) and guanosine monophosphate (GMP) are each derived from IMP in two-step reaction pathways.

The purine nucleotide salvage pathway allows free purine bases to be converted into nucleotides, nucleotides into nucleosides, and nucleosides into free bases. Enzymes included in this pathway are **AMP** and **adenosine deaminase, adenosine kinase, purine nucleoside phosphorylase, adenine phosphoribosyltransferase (APRT)**, and **hypoxanthine-guanine phosphoribosyltransferase (HGPRT)**. Mutations in a number of these enzymes lead to serious diseases. Deficiencies in purine nucleoside phosphorylase and adenosine deaminase lead to **immunodeficiency disorders**. A deficiency in HGPRT leads to **Lesch–Nyhan syndrome**. The **purine nucleotide cycle**, in which aspartate carbons are converted to fumarate to replenish tricarboxylic acid (TCA) cycle intermediates in working muscle, and the aspartate nitrogen is released as ammonia, uses components of the purine nucleotide salvage pathway.

Pyrimidine bases are first synthesized as the free base and then converted to a nucleotide. **Aspartate** and **carbamoyl phosphate** form all components of the pyrimidine ring. Ribose 5-phosphate, which is converted to **phosphoribosyl pyrophosphate (PRPP)**, is required to donate the sugar phosphate to form a nucleotide. The first pyrimidine nucleotide produced is **orotate monophosphate (OMP)**. The OMP is converted to **uridine monophosphate (UMP)**, which becomes the precursor for both **cytidine triphosphate (CTP)** and **deoxythymidine monophosphate (dTMP)** production.

The formation of deoxyribonucleotides requires **ribonucleotide reductase** activity, which catalyzes the reduction of ribose on nucleotide diphosphate substrates to 2'-deoxyribose. Substrates for the enzyme include adenosine diphosphate (ADP), guanosine diphosphate (GDP), cytidine diphosphate (CDP), and uridine diphosphate (UDP). Regulation of the enzyme is complex. There are two major allosteric sites. One controls the overall activity of the enzyme, whereas the other determines the substrate specificity of the enzyme. All deoxyribonucleotides are synthesized using this one enzyme.

The **regulation** of de novo purine nucleotide biosynthesis occurs at four points in the pathway. The enzymes **PRPP synthetase, amidophosphoribosyl transferase, IMP dehydrogenase**, and **adenylosuccinate synthetase** are regulated by allosteric modifiers, as they occur at key branch points through the

FIG. 41.1. Origin of the atoms of the purine base. *FH$_4$*, tetrahydrofolate; *RP*, ribose 5'-phosphate.

*pathway. Pyrimidine synthesis is regulated at the first committed step, which is the synthesis of cytoplasmic carbamoyl phosphate, by the enzyme **carbamoyl phosphate synthetase II (CPSII)**.*

*Purines, when degraded, cannot generate energy, nor can the purine ring be substantially modified. The end product of purine ring degradation is **uric acid**, which is excreted in the urine. Uric acid has limited solubility, and if it were to accumulate, uric acid crystals would precipitate in tissues of the body that have a reduced temperature (such as the big toe). This condition of acute painful inflammation of specific soft tissues and joints is called **gout**. Pyrimidines, when degraded, however, give rise to water-soluble compounds such as urea, carbon dioxide, and water and do not lead to a disease state if pyrimidine catabolism is increased.*

THE WAITING ROOM

The initial acute inflammatory process that caused **Lotta Topaigne** to experience a painful attack of gouty arthritis responded quickly to colchicine therapy (see Chapter 10). Several weeks after the inflammatory signs and symptoms in her right great toe subsided, Lotta was placed on allopurinol, a drug that reduces uric acid synthesis. Her serum uric acid level gradually fell from a pretreatment level of 9.2 mg/dL into the normal range (2.5 to 8.0 mg/dL). She remained free of gouty symptoms when she returned to her physician for a follow-up office visit.

I. PURINES AND PYRIMIDINES

As has been seen in previous chapters, nucleotides serve numerous functions in different reaction pathways. For example, nucleotides are the activated precursors of DNA and RNA. Nucleotides form the structural moieties of many coenzymes (examples include NADH, FAD, and coenzyme A). Nucleotides are critical elements in energy metabolism (adenosine triphosphate [ATP], guanosine triphosphate [GTP]). Nucleotide derivatives are frequently activated intermediates in many biosynthetic pathways. For example, uridine diphosphate (UDP)-glucose and cytidine diphosphate (CDP)-diacylglycerol are precursors of glycogen and phosphoglycerides, respectively. S-Adenosylmethionine carries an activated methyl group. In addition, nucleotides act as second messengers in intracellular signaling (e.g., cyclic adenosine monophosphate [cAMP], cyclic guanosine monophosphate [cGMP]). Finally, nucleotides and nucleosides act as metabolic allosteric regulators. Think about all of the enzymes that have been studied that are regulated by levels of ATP, adenosine diphosphate (ADP), and adenosine monophosphate (AMP).

Dietary uptake of purine and pyrimidine bases is minimal. The diet contains nucleic acids and the exocrine pancreas secretes deoxyribonuclease and ribonuclease, along with the proteolytic and lipolytic enzymes. This enables digested nucleic acids to be converted to nucleotides. The intestinal epithelial cells contain alkaline phosphatase activity, which converts nucleotides to nucleosides. Other enzymes within the epithelial cells tend to metabolize the nucleosides to uric acid (which is released into the circulation) or to salvage them for their own needs. Approximately 5% of ingested nucleotides make it into the circulation, either as the free base or as a nucleoside. Because of the minimal dietary uptake of these important molecules, de novo synthesis of purines and pyrimidines is required.

II. PURINE BIOSYNTHESIS

The purine bases are produced de novo by pathways that use amino acids as precursors and produce nucleotides. Most de novo synthesis occurs in the liver (Fig. 41.2), and the nitrogenous bases and nucleosides are then transported to other tissues by red blood cells. The brain also synthesizes significant amounts of nucleotides. Because the de novo pathway requires at least six high-energy bonds per purine produced, a salvage pathway, which is used by many cell types, can convert free bases and nucleosides to nucleotides.

A. De Novo Synthesis of the Purine Nucleotides

1. SYNTHESIS OF INOSINE MONOPHOSPHATE

As purines are built on a ribose base (see Fig. 41.2), an activated form of ribose is used to initiate the purine biosynthetic pathway. 5-Phosphoribosyl-1-pyrophosphate (PRPP) is the activated source of the ribose moiety. It is synthesized from ATP and ribose 5'-phosphate (Fig. 41.3), which is produced from glucose through the pentose phosphate pathway (see Chapter 29). The enzyme that catalyzes this reaction, PRPP synthetase, is a regulated enzyme (see Section II.A.5); however, this step is not the committed step of purine biosynthesis. PRPP has many other uses, which are described as the chapter progresses.

In the first committed step of the purine biosynthetic pathway, PRPP reacts with glutamine to form 5-phosphoribosyl 1-amine (Fig. 41.4). This reaction, which produces nitrogen 9 of the purine ring, is catalyzed by glutamine phosphoribosyl amidotransferase, a highly regulated enzyme.

In the next step of the pathway, the entire glycine molecule is added to the growing precursor. Glycine provides carbons 4 and 5 and nitrogen 7 of the purine ring (Fig. 41.5). This step requires energy in the form of ATP.

Subsequently, carbon 8 is provided by N^{10}-formyl-FH$_4$, nitrogen 3 by glutamine, carbon 6 by CO_2, nitrogen 1 by aspartate, and carbon 2 by N^{10}-formyltetrahydrofolate (see Fig. 41.1). Note that six high-energy bonds of ATP are required (starting with ribose 5-phosphate) to synthesize the first purine nucleotide, inosine monophosphate (IMP). This nucleotide contains the base hypoxanthine joined by an *N*-glycosidic bond from nitrogen 9 of the purine ring to carbon 1 of the ribose (Fig. 41.6). Hypoxanthine is not found in DNA, but it is the precursor for the other purine bases.

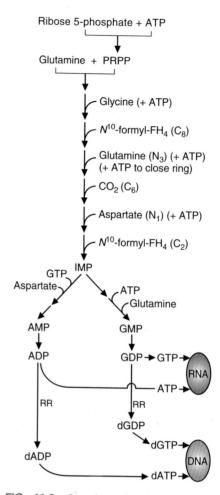

FIG. 41.2. Overview of purine production, starting with glutamine, ribose 5-phosphate, and ATP. The steps that require ATP are also indicated in this figure. *FH$_4$*, tetrahydrofolate; *PRPP*, 5-phosphoribosyl-1-pyrophosphate; *RR*, ribonucleotide reductase.

FIG. 41.3. Synthesis of PRPP. Ribose 5-phosphate is produced from glucose by the pentose phosphate pathway.

PRPP

Glutamine
phosphoribosyl
amidotransferase

H₂O

Glutamine

Glutamate

PP$_i$

5-Phosphoribosyl 1-amine

FIG. 41.4. The first step in purine biosynthesis. The purine base is built on the ribose moiety. The availability of the substrate PRPP is a major determinant of the rate of this reaction.

5-Phosphoribosyl 1-amine

ATP

Phosphoribosylglycinamide
synthetase

ADP + P$_i$

Glycine

**Glycinamide
ribosyl 5-phosphate**

FIG. 41.5. Incorporation of glycine into the purine precursor. The ATP is required for the condensation of the glycine carboxylic acid group with the 1′-amino group of phosphoribosyl 1-amine.

**Inosine monophosphate
(IMP)**

FIG. 41.6. Structure of inosine monophosphate (IMP). The base is hypoxanthine.

However, hypoxanthine is found in the anticodon of transfer RNA (tRNA) molecules (see Chapter 15) and is a critical component for allowing wobble base pairs to form.

2. SYNTHESIS OF ADENOSINE MONOPHOSPHATE

IMP serves as the branch point from which both adenine and guanine nucleotides can be produced (see Fig. 41.2). AMP is derived from IMP in two steps (Fig. 41.7). In the first step, aspartate is added to IMP to form adenylosuccinate, a reaction similar to the one catalyzed by argininosuccinate synthetase in the urea cycle. Note that this reaction requires a high-energy bond, donated by GTP. Fumarate is then released from the adenylosuccinate by the enzyme adenylosuccinase to form AMP. This is similar to the aspartate-to-fumarate conversion seen in the urea cycle (see Chapter 38). In both cases, aspartate donates a nitrogen to the product, while the carbons of aspartate are released as fumarate.

3. SYNTHESIS OF GUANOSINE MONOPHOSPHATE

Guanosine monophosphate (GMP) is also synthesized from IMP in two steps (Fig. 41.8). In the first step, the hypoxanthine base is oxidized by IMP dehydrogenase to produce the base xanthine and the nucleotide xanthosine monophosphate (XMP). Glutamine then donates the amide nitrogen to XMP to form GMP in a reaction that is catalyzed by GMP synthetase. This second reaction requires energy in the form of ATP.

4. PHOSPHORYLATION OF AMP AND GMP

AMP and GMP can be phosphorylated to the diphosphate and triphosphate levels. The production of nucleoside diphosphates requires specific nucleoside monophosphate kinases, whereas the production of nucleoside triphosphates requires nucleoside diphosphate kinases, which are active with a wide range of nucleoside diphosphates. The purine nucleoside triphosphates are also used for energy-requiring processes in the cell and also as precursors for RNA synthesis (see Fig. 41.2).

5. REGULATION OF PURINE SYNTHESIS

Regulation of purine synthesis occurs at several sites (Fig. 41.9). Four key enzymes are regulated: PRPP synthetase, amidophosphoribosyl transferase, adenylosuccinate synthetase, and IMP dehydrogenase. The first two enzymes regulate IMP synthesis; the last two regulate the production of AMP and GMP, respectively.

FIG. 41.7. The conversion of IMP to AMP. Note that GTP is required for the synthesis of AMP. *R5P*, ribose 5-phosphate.

FIG. 41.8. The conversion of IMP to GMP. Note that ATP is required for the synthesis of GMP.

A primary site of regulation is the synthesis of PRPP. PRPP synthetase is negatively affected by guanosine diphosphate (GDP) and, at a distinct allosteric site, by ADP. Thus, the simultaneous binding of an oxypurine (e.g., GDP) and an aminopurine (e.g., ADP) can occur, with the result being a synergistic inhibition of the enzyme. This enzyme is not the committed step of purine biosynthesis; PRPP is also used in pyrimidine synthesis and both the purine and pyrimidine salvage pathways.

The committed step of purine synthesis is the formation of 5-phosphoribosyl 1-amine by glutamine phosphoribosyl amidotransferase. This enzyme is strongly inhibited by GMP and AMP (the end products of the purine biosynthetic pathway). The enzyme is also inhibited by the corresponding nucleoside diphosphates and triphosphates, but under cellular conditions, these compounds probably do not play a central role in regulation. The active enzyme is a monomer of 133,000 Da but is converted to an inactive dimer (270,000 Da) by binding of the end products. Cellular concentrations of PRPP and glutamine are usually below their K_m for glutamine phosphoribosyl amidotransferase. Thus, any situation that leads to an increase in their concentration can lead to an increase in de novo purine biosynthesis.

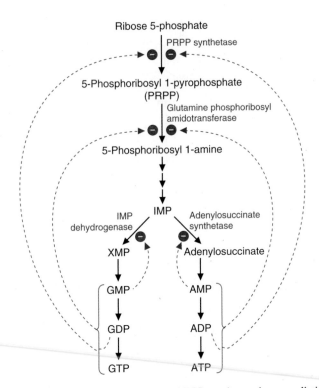

FIG. 41.9. The regulation of purine synthesis. PRPP synthetase has two distinct allosteric sites: one for ADP, the other for GDP. Glutamine phosphoribosyl amidotransferase contains adenine nucleotide– and guanine nucleotide–binding sites; the monophosphates are the most important, although the diphosphates and triphosphates will also bind to and inhibit the enzyme. Adenylosuccinate synthetase is inhibited by AMP; IMP dehydrogenase is inhibited by GMP.

The enzymes that convert IMP to XMP and adenylosuccinate are both regulated. GMP inhibits the activity of IMP dehydrogenase, and AMP inhibits adenylosuccinate synthetase. Note that the synthesis of AMP is dependent on GTP (of which GMP is a precursor), whereas the synthesis of GMP is dependent on ATP (which is made from AMP). This serves as a type of positive regulatory mechanism to balance the pools of these precursors: When the levels of ATP are high, GMP will be made; when the levels of GTP are high, AMP synthesis will take place. GMP and AMP act as negative effectors at these branch points, a classic example of feedback inhibition.

B. Purine Salvage Pathways

Most of the de novo synthesis of the bases of nucleotides occurs in the liver and to some extent in the brain, neutrophils, and other cells of the immune system. Within the liver, nucleotides can be converted to nucleosides or free bases, which can be transported to other tissues via the red blood cells in the circulation. In addition, the small amounts of dietary bases or nucleosides that are absorbed also enter cells in this form. Thus, most cells can salvage these bases to generate nucleotides for RNA and DNA synthesis. For certain cell types such as lymphocytes, the salvage of bases is the major form of nucleotide generation.

The overall picture of salvage is shown in Figure 41.10. The pathways allow free bases, nucleosides, and nucleotides to be easily interconverted. The major enzymes required are purine nucleoside phosphorylase, phosphoribosyl transferases, and deaminases.

Purine nucleoside phosphorylase catalyzes a phosphorolysis reaction of the *N*-glycosidic bond that attaches the base to the sugar moiety in the nucleosides guanosine and inosine (Fig. 41.11). Thus, guanosine and inosine are converted to

A deficiency in purine nucleoside phosphorylase activity leads to an immune disorder in which T-cell immunity is compromised. B-cell immunity, conversely, may be only slightly compromised or even normal. Children who lack this activity have recurrent infections and more than half display neurologic complications. Symptoms of the disorder first appear at between 6 months and 4 years of age.

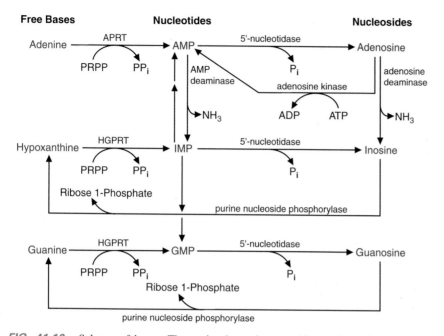

FIG. 41.10. Salvage of bases. The purine bases hypoxanthine and guanine react with PRPP to form the nucleotides inosine and guanosine monophosphate, respectively. The enzyme that catalyzes the reaction is hypoxanthine-guanine phosphoribosyltransferase (HGPRT). Adenine forms AMP in a reaction that is catalyzed by adenine phosphoribosyltransferase (APRT). Nucleotides are converted to nucleosides by 5′-nucleotidase. Free bases are generated from nucleosides by purine nucleoside phosphorylase (although adenosine is not a substrate of this enzyme). Deamination of the base adenine occurs with AMP and adenosine deaminase. Of the purines, only adenosine can be phosphorylated directly back to a nucleotide by adenosine kinase.

Adenosine deaminase activity is measured by coupling the deamination of adenosine (to inosine) with purine nucleoside phosphorylase, which will generate hypoxanthine and ribose 1-phosphate from inosine. The hypoxanthine generated then reacts with xanthine oxidase, generating uric acid and hydrogen peroxide. The hydrogen peroxide produced is then measured in the presence of peroxidase and a colorless dye. The oxidation of the colorless dye creates a colored dye, and the intensity of the color (which is directly proportional to the amount of inosine produced) can be determined spectrophotometrically.

Lesch–Nyhan syndrome is caused by a defective hypoxanthine-guanine phosphoribosyltransferase (HGPRT) (see Fig. 41.12). In this condition, purine bases cannot be salvaged. Instead, they are degraded, forming excessive amounts of uric acid. Individuals with the severe form of this syndrome suffer from mental retardation. They are also prone to chewing off their fingers and performing other acts of self-mutilation.

guanine and hypoxanthine, respectively, along with ribose 1-phosphate. The ribose 1-phosphate can be isomerized to ribose 5-phosphate, and the free bases then salvaged or degraded, depending on cellular needs.

The phosphoribosyl transferase enzymes catalyze the addition of a ribose 5-phosphate group from PRPP to a free base, generating a nucleotide and pyrophosphate (Fig. 41.12). Two enzymes do this for purine metabolism: adenine phosphoribosyl transferase (APRT) and hypoxanthine-guanine phosphoribosyltransferase (HGPRT). The reactions they catalyze are the same, differing only in their substrate specificity.

Adenosine and AMP can be deaminated by adenosine deaminase and AMP deaminase, respectively, to form inosine and IMP (see Fig. 41.10). Adenosine is also the only nucleoside to be directly phosphorylated to a nucleotide by adenosine kinase. Guanosine and inosine must be converted to free bases by purine nucleoside phosphorylase before they can be converted to nucleotides by HGPRT.

A portion of the salvage pathway that is important in muscle is the purine nucleotide cycle (Fig. 41.13). The net effect of these reactions is the deamination of aspartate to fumarate (as AMP is synthesized from IMP and then deaminated back to IMP by AMP deaminase). Under conditions in which the muscle must generate energy, the fumarate derived from the purine nucleotide cycle is used anaplerotically to replenish tricarboxylic acid (TCA) cycle intermediates and to allow the cycle to operate at high speed. Deficiencies in enzymes of this cycle lead to muscle fatigue during exercise.

III. SYNTHESIS OF THE PYRIMIDINE NUCLEOTIDES

A. De Novo Pathways

In the synthesis of the pyrimidine nucleotides, the base is synthesized first, and then it is attached to the ribose 5′-phosphate moiety (Fig. 41.14). The origin of the atoms

FIG. 41.11. The purine nucleoside phosphorylase reaction, which converts guanosine or inosine to ribose 1-phosphate plus the free base guanine or hypoxanthine.

5-Phosphoribosyl 1-pyrophosphate (PRPP)

Phosphoribosyl-
transferase

Nucleotide

FIG. 41.12. The phosphoribosyltransferase reaction. APRT uses the free base adenine; HGPRT can use either hypoxanthine or guanine as a substrate.

of the ring (aspartate and carbamoyl phosphate, which is derived from carbon dioxide and glutamine) is shown in Figure 41.15. In the initial reaction of the pathway, glutamine combines with bicarbonate and ATP to form carbamoyl phosphate. This reaction is analogous to the first reaction of the urea cycle, except that it uses glutamine as the source of the nitrogen (rather than ammonia) and it occurs in the cytosol (rather than in mitochondria). The reaction is catalyzed by carbamoyl phosphate synthetase II (CPSII), which is the regulated step of the pathway. The analogous reaction in urea synthesis is catalyzed by carbamoyl phosphate synthetase I (CPSI), which is activated by *N*-acetylglutamate. The similarities and differences between these two carbamoyl phosphate synthetase enzymes are described in Table 41.1.

In the next step of pyrimidine biosynthesis, the entire aspartate molecule adds to carbamoyl phosphate in a reaction that is catalyzed by aspartate transcarbamoylase (Fig. 41.16). The molecule subsequently closes to produce a ring (catalyzed by dihydroorotase), which is oxidized to form orotic acid (or its anion, orotate) through the actions of dihydroorotate dehydrogenase. The enzyme orotate phosphoribosyl transferase catalyzes the transfer of ribose 5-phosphate from PRPP to orotate, producing

FIG. 41.13. The purine nucleotide cycle. Using a combination of biosynthetic and salvage enzymes, the net effect is the conversion of aspartate to fumarate plus ammonia, with the fumarate playing an anaplerotic role in the muscle. *AS*, adenylosuccinate.

FIG. 41.14. Synthesis of the pyrimidine bases. *CPS-II*, carbamoyl phosphate synthetase II; *FH₂* and *FH₄*, forms of folate; *RR*, ribonucleotide reductase; ⊕, stimulated by; ⊖, inhibited by.

FIG. 41.15. The origin of the atoms in the pyrimidine ring.

orotidine 5′-phosphate, which is decarboxylated by orotidylic acid decarboxylase to form uridine monophosphate (UMP) (see Fig. 41.16). In mammals, the first three enzymes of the pathway (CPSII, aspartate transcarbamoylase, and dihydroorotase) are located on the same polypeptide, designated as CAD. The last two enzymes of the pathway are similarly located on a polypeptide known as UMP synthase (the orotate phosphoribosyl transferase and orotidylic acid decarboxylase activities).

UMP is phosphorylated to UTP. An amino group, derived from the amide of glutamine, is added to carbon 4 to produce cytidine triphosphate (CTP) by the enzyme CTP synthetase (this reaction cannot occur at the nucleotide monophosphate level). UTP and CTP are precursors for the synthesis of RNA (see Fig. 41.14). The synthesis of thymidine triphosphate (TTP) is described in Section IV.

Table 41.1   Comparison of Carbamoyl Phosphate Synthetases (CPSI and CPSII)

	CPSI	*CPSII*
Pathway	Urea cycle	Pyrimidine biosynthesis
Source of nitrogen	NH_4^+	Glutamine
Location	Mitochondria	Cytosol
Activator	*N*-Acetylglutamate	PRPP
Inhibitor	—	UTP

PRPP, phosphoribosyl pyrophosphate; UTP, uridine triphosphate.

Aspartate

Carbamoyl phosphate

→ Pi

Carbamoyl aspartate

Orotic acid (orotate)

Orotate phosphoribosyl-transferase

⟨ PRPP
→ PPi

OMP

Orotidine 5'-P decarboxylase

→ CO_2

UMP

■■■ Block in hereditary orotic aciduria

FIG. 41.16. Conversion of carbamoyl phosphate and aspartate to UMP. The defective enzymes in hereditary orotic aciduria are indicated by the *dark bar*.

B. Salvage of Pyrimidine Bases

Pyrimidine bases are normally salvaged by a two-step route. First, a relatively nonspecific pyrimidine nucleoside phosphorylase converts the pyrimidine bases to their respective nucleosides (Fig. 41.17). Notice that the preferred direction for this reaction is the reverse phosphorylase reaction, in which phosphate is released and is not being used as a nucleophile to release the pyrimidine base from the nucleoside. The more specific nucleoside kinases then react with the nucleosides, forming nucleotides (Table 41.2). As with purines, further phosphorylation is carried out by increasingly more specific kinases. The nucleoside phosphorylase–nucleoside kinase route for synthesis of pyrimidine nucleoside monophosphates is relatively inefficient for salvage of pyrimidine bases because of the very low concentration of the bases in plasma and tissues.

Pyrimidine phosphorylase can use all of the pyrimidines but has a preference for uracil and is sometimes called *uridine phosphorylase*. The phosphorylase uses cytosine fairly well but has a very, very low affinity for thymine; therefore, a ribonucleoside containing thymine is almost never made in vivo. A second phosphorylase, thymidine phosphorylase, has a much higher affinity for thymine and adds a deoxyribose residue (see Fig. 41.17).

Of the various ribonucleosides and deoxyribonucleoside kinases, one that merits special mention is thymidine kinase (TK). This enzyme is allosterically inhibited by deoxythymidine triphosphate (dTTP). Activity of TK in a given cell is closely related to the proliferative state of that cell. During the cell cycle, the activity of TK rises dramatically as cells enter S-phase, and in general, rapidly dividing cells have high levels of this enzyme. Radiolabeled thymidine is widely used for isotopic labeling of DNA, for example, in radioautographic investigations or to estimate rates of intracellular DNA synthesis.

C. Regulation of De Novo Pyrimidine Synthesis

The regulated step of pyrimidine synthesis in humans is CPSII. The enzyme is inhibited by UTP and activated by PRPP (see Fig. 41.14). Thus, as pyrimidines decrease in concentration (as indicated by UTP levels), CPSII is activated and pyrimidines are synthesized. The activity is also regulated by the cell cycle. As cells approach S-phase, CPSII becomes more sensitive to PRPP activation and less sensitive to UTP inhibition. At the end of S-phase, the inhibition by UTP is more pronounced, and the activation by PRPP is reduced. These changes in the allosteric properties of CPSII are related to its phosphorylation state. Phosphorylation of the enzyme at a specific site by a MAP kinase leads to a more easily activated enzyme. Phosphorylation at a second site by the cAMP-dependent protein kinase leads to a more easily inhibited enzyme.

IV. THE PRODUCTION OF DEOXYRIBONUCLEOTIDES

For DNA synthesis to occur, the ribose moiety must be reduced to deoxyribose (Fig. 41.18). This reduction occurs at the diphosphate level and is catalyzed by ribonucleotide reductase, which requires the protein thioredoxin. The deoxyribonucleoside diphosphates can be phosphorylated to the triphosphate level and used as precursors for DNA synthesis (see Figs. 41.2 and 41.14).

Table 41.2   Salvage Reactions for Conversion of Pyrimidine Nucleosides to Nucleotides

Enzyme	Reaction
Uridine-cytidine kinase	Uridine + ATP → UMP + ADP
	Cytidine + ATP → CMP + ADP
Deoxythymidine kinase	Deoxythymidine + ATP → dTMP + ADP
Deoxycytidine kinase	Deoxycytidine + ATP → dCMP + ADP

ATP, adenosine triphosphate; UMP, uridine monophosphate; ADP, adenosine diphosphate; CMP, cytidine monophosphate; dTMP, deoxythymidine monophosphate; dCMP, deoxycytidine monophosphate.

The regulation of ribonucleotide reductase is quite complex. The enzyme contains two allosteric sites: one controlling the activity of the enzyme and the other controlling the substrate specificity of the enzyme. ATP bound to the activity site activates the enzyme; deoxyadenosine triphosphate (dATP) bound to this site inhibits the enzyme. Substrate specificity is more complex. ATP bound to the substrate site activates the reduction of pyrimidines (CDP and UDP) to form deoxycytidine diphosphate (dCDP) and deoxyuridine diphosphate (dUDP). The dUDP is not used for DNA synthesis; rather, it is used to produce deoxythymidine monophosphate (dTMP) (see the following discussions). Once dTMP is produced, it is phosphorylated to dTTP, which then binds to the substrate site and induces the reduction of GDP. As dGTP accumulates, it replaces dTTP in the substrate site and allows ADP to be reduced to deoxyadenosine diphosphate (dADP). This leads to the accumulation of dATP, which inhibits the overall activity of the enzyme. These allosteric changes are summarized in Table 41.3.

dUDP can be dephosphorylated to form deoxyuridine monophosphate (dUMP), or, alternatively, deoxycytidine monophosphate (dCMP) can be deaminated to form dUMP. Methylene tetrahydrofolate transfers a methyl group to dUMP to form dTMP (see Fig. 40.5). Phosphorylation reactions produce dTTP, a precursor for DNA synthesis and a regulator of ribonucleotide reductase.

V. DEGRADATION OF PURINE AND PYRIMIDINE BASES

A. Purine Bases

The degradation of the purine nucleotides (AMP and GMP) occurs mainly in the liver (Fig. 41.19). Salvage enzymes are used for most of these reactions. AMP is first deaminated to produce IMP (AMP deaminase). Then IMP and GMP are dephosphorylated (5′-nucleotidase), and the ribose is cleaved from the base by purine nucleoside phosphorylase. Hypoxanthine, the base produced by cleavage of IMP, is converted by xanthine oxidase to xanthine, and guanine is deaminated by the enzyme guanase to produce xanthine. The pathways for the degradation of adenine and guanine merge at this point. Xanthine is converted by xanthine oxidase to uric acid, which is excreted in the urine. Xanthine oxidase is a molybdenum-requiring enzyme

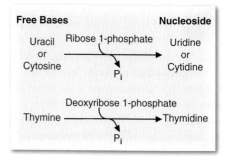

FIG. 41.17. Salvage reactions for pyrimidine nucleoside production. Thymine phosphorylase uses deoxyribose 1-phosphate as a substrate, so ribothymidine is rarely formed.

In hereditary orotic aciduria, orotic acid is excreted in the urine because the enzymes that convert it to uridine monophosphate, orotate phosphoribosyltransferase and orotidine 5′-phosphate decarboxylase, are defective (see Fig. 41.16). Pyrimidines cannot be synthesized and, therefore, normal growth does not occur. Oral administration of uridine is used to treat this condition. Uridine, which is converted to uridine monophosphate (UMP), bypasses the metabolic block and provides the body with a source of pyrimidines, as both cytidine triphosphate (CTP) and deoxythymidine monophosphate (dTMP) can be produced from UMP.

When ornithine transcarbamoylase is deficient (urea-cycle disorder), excess carbamoyl phosphate from the mitochondria leaks into the cytoplasm. The elevated levels of cytoplasmic carbamoyl phosphate lead to pyrimidine production, as the regulated step of the pathway, the reaction catalyzed by carbamoyl phosphate synthetase II, is being bypassed. Thus, orotic aciduria results.

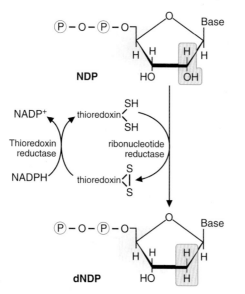

FIG. 41.18. Reduction of ribose to deoxyribose. Reduction occurs at the nucleoside diphosphate level. A ribonucleoside diphosphate (NDP) is converted to a deoxyribonucleoside diphosphate (dNDP). Thioredoxin is oxidized to a disulfide, which must be reduced for the reaction to continue producing dNDP.

Q: Gout is caused by excessive uric acid levels in the blood and tissues. To determine whether a person with gout has developed this problem because of overproduction of purine nucleotides or because of a decreased ability to excrete uric acid, an oral dose of a ^{15}N-labeled amino acid is sometimes used. Which amino acid would be most appropriate to use for this purpose?

Uric acid has a pK of 5.4. It is ionized in the body to form urate. Urate is not very soluble in an aqueous environment. The quantity in normal human blood is very close to the solubility constant.

Table 41.3   Effectors of Ribonucleotide Reductase Activity

Preferred Substrate	Effector Bound to Overall Activity Site	Effector Bound to Substrate Specificity Site
None	dATP	Any nucleotide
CDP	ATP	ATP or dATP
UDP	ATP	ATP or dATP
GDP	ATP	dTTP
ADP	ATP	dGTP

CDP, cytidine diphosphate; UDP, uridine diphosphate; GDP, guanosine diphosphate; ADP, adenosine diphosphate; dATP, deoxyadenosine triphosphate; ATP, adenosine triphosphate; dTTP, deoxythymidine triphosphate; dGTP, deoxyguanosine triphosphate.

that uses molecular oxygen and produces hydrogen peroxide (H_2O_2). Another form of xanthine oxidase uses NAD^+ as the electron acceptor (see Chapter 24).

Note how little energy is derived from the degradation of the purine ring. Thus, it is to the cell's advantage to recycle and salvage the ring because it costs energy to produce and not much is obtained in return.

FIG. 41.19. Degradation of the purine bases. The reactions inhibited by allopurinol are indicated. A second form of xanthine oxidase exists that uses NAD^+ instead of O_2 as the electron acceptor.

B. Pyrimidine Bases

The pyrimidine nucleotides are dephosphorylated, and the nucleosides are cleaved to produce ribose 1-phosphate and the free pyrimidine bases cytosine, uracil, and thymine. Cytosine is deaminated, forming uracil, which is converted to CO_2, NH_4^+, and β-alanine. Thymine is converted to CO_2, NH_4^+, and β-aminoisobutyrate (Fig. 41.20). These products of pyrimidine degradation are excreted in the urine or converted to CO_2, H_2O, and NH_4^+ (which forms urea). They do not cause any problems for the body, in contrast to urate, which is produced from the purines and can precipitate, causing gout. As with the purine degradation pathway, little energy can be generated by pyrimidine degradation.

CLINICAL COMMENTS

Lotta Topaigne. Hyperuricemia in **Lotta Topaigne's** case arose as a consequence of overproduction of uric acid. Treatment with allopurinol not only inhibits xanthine oxidase, lowering the formation of uric acid with an increase in the excretion of hypoxanthine and xanthine, but also decreases the overall synthesis of purine nucleotides. Hypoxanthine and xanthine produced by purine degradation are salvaged (i.e., converted to nucleotides) by a process that requires the consumption of phosphoribosyl pyrophosphate (PRPP). PRPP is a substrate for the glutamine phosphoribosyl amidotransferase reaction that initiates purine biosynthesis. Because the normal cellular levels of PRPP and glutamine are below the K_m of the enzyme, changes in the level of either substrate can accelerate or reduce the rate of the reaction. Therefore, decreased levels of PRPP cause decreased synthesis of purine nucleotides.

BIOCHEMICAL COMMENTS

Adenosine Deaminase Deficiency. A deficiency in adenosine deaminase activity leads to severe combined immunodeficiency disease, or SCID. In the severe form of combined immunodeficiency, both T cells (which provide cell-based immunity, see Chapter 44) and B cells (which produce antibodies) are deficient, leaving the individual without a functional immune system. Children born with this disorder do not develop a mature thymus gland and suffer from many opportunistic infections because of their lack of a functional immune system. Death results if the child is not placed in a sterile environment. Administration of polyethylene glycol–modified adenosine deaminase has been successful in treating the disorder, and the ADA gene was the first to be used in gene therapy in treating the disorder. The question that remains, however, is that even though all the cells of the body lack ADA activity, why are the immune cells specifically targeted for destruction?

The specific immune disorder is not caused by any defect in purine salvage pathways, as children with Lesch–Nyhan syndrome have a functional immune system, although there are other major problems in those children. This suggests that perhaps the accumulation of precursors to ADA lead to toxic effects. Three hypotheses have been proposed and are outlined in the following section.

In the absence of ADA activity, both adenosine and deoxyadenosine accumulate. When deoxyadenosine accumulates, adenosine kinase can convert it to dAMP. Other kinases then allow deoxyadenosine triphosphate (dATP) to accumulate in the lymphocytes. Why specifically the lymphocytes? The other cells of the body secrete the deoxyadenosine they cannot use, and it accumulates in the circulation. As the lymphocytes are present in the circulation, they tend to accumulate this compound more so than cells that are not constantly present in the blood. As dATP accumulates, ribonucleotide reductase becomes inhibited, and the cells can no

The entire glycine molecule is incorporated into the precursor of the purine nucleotides. The nitrogen of this glycine also appears in uric acid, the product of purine degradation. ^{15}N-labeled glycine could be used, therefore, to determine whether purines are being overproduced.

Normally, as cells die, their purine nucleotides are degraded to hypoxanthine and xanthine, which are converted to uric acid by xanthine oxidase (see Fig. 41.19). Allopurinol (a structural analog of hypoxanthine) is a substrate for xanthine oxidase. It is converted to oxypurinol (also called *alloxanthine*), which remains tightly bound to the enzyme, preventing further catalytic activity (see Fig. 8.18). Thus, allopurinol is a suicide inhibitor. It reduces the production of uric acid and hence its concentration in the blood and tissues (e.g., the synovial lining of the joints in **Lotta Topaigne's** great toe). Xanthine and hypoxanthine accumulate, and urate levels decrease. Overall, the amount of purine being degraded is spread over three products rather than appearing in only one. Therefore, none of the compounds exceeds its solubility constant, precipitation does not occur, and the symptoms of gout gradually subside.

FIG. 41.20. Water-soluble end products of pyrimidine degradation.

Once nucleotide biosynthesis and salvage was understood at the pathway level, it was quickly realized that one way to inhibit cell proliferation would be to block purine or pyrimidine synthesis. Thus, drugs were developed that would interfere with a cell's ability to generate precursors for DNA synthesis, thereby inhibiting cell growth. This is particularly important for cancer cells, which have lost their normal growth-regulatory properties. Such drugs have been introduced previously with a number of different patients. **Colin Tuma** was treated with 5-fluorouracil, which inhibits thymidylate synthase (dUMP-to-TMP synthesis). **Arlyn Foma** was treated with a combination of drugs (R-CHOP) for his leukemia. These drugs all interfere with DNA synthesis via a variety of mechanisms. **Mannie Weitzels** was treated with hydroxyurea to block ribonucleotide reductase activity, with the goal of inhibiting DNA synthesis in the leukemic cells. Development of these drugs would not have been possible without an understanding of the biochemistry of both purine and pyrimidine salvage and synthesis and DNA replication. Such drugs also affect rapidly dividing normal cells, which brings about several side effects of chemotherapeutic regimens.

Table 41.4   Gene Disorders in Purine and Pyrimidine Metabolism

Disease	Gene Defect	Metabolite That Accumulates	Clinical Symptoms
Gout	Multiple causes	Uric acid	Painful joints
Severe combined immunodeficiency disease (SCID)	Adenosine deaminase (purine salvage pathway)	Deoxyadenosine and derivatives thereof	Loss of immune system function, including absence of T and B cells
Immunodeficiency disease	Purine nucleoside phosphorylase	Purine nucleosides	Partial loss of immune system; no T cells, but B cells are present
Lesch–Nyhan syndrome	Hypoxanthine-guanine phosphoribosyl-transferase	Purines, uric acid	Mental retardation, self-mutilation
Hereditary orotic aciduria	UMP synthase	Orotic acid	Growth retardation

UMP, uridine monophosphate.

longer produce deoxyribonucleotides for DNA synthesis. Thus, when cells are supposed to grow and differentiate in response to cytokines, they cannot, and they die.

A second hypothesis suggests that the accumulation of deoxyadenosine in lymphocytes leads to an inhibition of *S*-adenosylhomocysteine hydrolase, the enzyme that converts *S*-adenosylhomocysteine to homocysteine and adenosine. This leads to hypomethylation in the cell and an accumulation of *S*-adenosylhomocysteine. *S*-Adenosylhomocysteine accumulation has been linked to the triggering of apoptosis.

The third hypothesis suggested is that elevated adenosine levels lead to inappropriate activation of adenosine receptors. Adenosine is also a signaling molecule, and stimulation of the adenosine receptors results in activation of protein kinase A and elevated cAMP levels in thymocytes. Elevated levels of cAMP in these cells trigger both apoptosis and developmental arrest of the cell.

Although it is still not clear which potential mechanism best explains the arrested development of immune cells, it is clear that elevated levels of adenosine and deoxyadenosine are toxic. The biochemical disorders of purine and pyrimidine metabolism discussed in this chapter are summarized in Table 41.4.

Key Concepts

- Purine and pyrimidine nucleotides can both be synthesized from scratch (de novo) or salvaged from existing bases.
- De novo purine synthesis is complex, requiring 11 steps and six molecules of ATP for every purine synthesized. Purines are initially synthesized in the ribonucleotide form.
- The precursors for de novo purine synthesis are glycine, ribose 5-phosphate, glutamine, aspartate, carbon dioxide, and N^{10}-formyl-FH$_4$.
- The initial purine ribonucleotide synthesized is inosine monophosphate (IMP). AMP and GMP are each derived from IMP.
- Since de novo purine synthesis requires a large amount of energy, purine nucleotide salvage pathways exist such that free purine bases can be converted to nucleotides.
- Mutations in purine salvage enzymes are associated with severe diseases, such as Lesch–Nyhan syndrome and severe combined immunodeficiency disease (SCID).
- Pyrimidine bases are initially synthesized as the free base and then converted to nucleotides.
- Aspartate and cytoplasmic carbamoyl phosphate are the precursors for pyrimidine ring synthesis.
- The initial pyrimidine nucleotide synthesized is orotate monophosphate, which is converted to uridine monophosphate. The other pyrimidine nucleotides are derived from a uracil-containing intermediate.
- Deoxyribonucleotides are derived by reduction of ribonucleotides, as catalyzed by ribonucleotide reductase. The regulation of ribonucleotide reductase is complex.
- Degradation of purine containing nucleotides results in production of uric acid, which is eliminated in the urine. Elevated uric acid levels in the blood lead to gout.
- Diseases discussed in this chapter are summarized in Table 41.5.

Table 41.5   Diseases Discussed in Chapter 41

Disease or Disorder	Environmental or Genetic	Comments
Gout	Both	Painful joints caused by the precipitation of uric acid in the blood.
PNP (purine nucleoside phosphorylase) deficiency	Genetic	A defect in a purine salvage enzyme, leading to a loss of T-cell function, and a partial immunodeficiency disease.
Lesch–Nyhan syndrome (lack of hypoxanthine-guanine phosphoribosyl transferase activity)	Genetic	The loss of HGPRT activity leads to the accumulation of purines and uric acid, with mental retardation and self-mutilation resulting in severe cases.
Hereditary orotic aciduria	Genetic	A defect in UMP synthase, leading to orotic acid accumulation and growth retardation.
Adenosine deaminase deficiency	Genetic	The loss of adenosine deaminase activity leads to SCID (severe combined immunodeficiency disease), with a loss of both T- and B-cell function.
Cancer	Both	The use of drugs that interfere with DNA replication will destroy rapidly dividing cells at a faster rate than normal cells.

HGPRT, hypoxanthine-guanine phosphoribosyltransferase; UMP, uridine monophosphate.

REVIEW QUESTIONS–CHAPTER 41

1. Similarities between carbamoyl phosphate synthetase I and carbamoyl phosphate synthetase II include which one of the following?

    A. Carbon source
    B. Intracellular location
    C. Nitrogen source
    D. Regulation by *N*-acetyl glutamate
    E. Regulation by UMP

2. Gout can result from a reduction in activity of which one of the following enzymes?

    A. Glutamine phosphoribosyl amidotransferase
    B. Glucose 6-phosphatase
    C. Glucose-6-phosphate dehydrogenase
    D. PRPP synthetase
    E. Purine nucleoside phosphorylase

3. Lesch–Nyhan syndrome is due to an inability to catalyze which of the following reactions?

    A. Adenine to AMP
    B. Adenosine to AMP
    C. Guanine to GMP
    D. Guanosine to GMP
    E. Thymine to TMP
    F. Thymidine to TMP

4. Allopurinol can be used to treat gout because of its ability to inhibit which one of the following reactions?

    A. AMP to XMP
    B. Xanthine to uric acid
    C. Inosine to hypoxanthine
    D. IMP to XMP
    E. XMP to GMP

5. The regulation of ribonucleotide reductase is quite complex. Assuming that an enzyme deficiency leads to highly elevated levels of dGTP, what effect would you predict on the reduction of ribonucleotides to deoxyribonucleotides under these conditions?

    A. Elevated levels of dCDP will be produced.
    B. The formation of dADP will be favored.
    C. AMP will begin to be reduced.
    D. Reduced thioredoxin will become rate-limiting, thereby reducing the activity of ribonucleotide reductase.
    E. Deoxy-GTP will bind to the overall activity site and inhibit the functioning of the enzyme.

42 Intertissue Relationships in the Metabolism of Amino Acids

The body maintains a relatively large free amino acid pool in the blood, even during fasting. As a result, tissues have continuous access to individual amino acids for the synthesis of proteins and essential amino acid derivatives, such as neurotransmitters. The amino acid pool also provides the liver with **amino acid substrates** for **gluconeogenesis** and provides several other cell types with a source of **fuel**. The **free amino acid pool** is derived from **dietary amino acids** and the **turnover of proteins** in the body. During an **overnight fast** and during **hypercatabolic states**, **degradation** of labile **protein** particularly that in **skeletal muscle** is the major source of free amino acids.

The liver is the major site of amino acid metabolism in the body and the major site of **urea synthesis**. The liver is also the major site of amino acid degradation. Hepatocytes partially oxidize most amino acids, converting the carbon skeleton to glucose, ketone bodies, or CO_2. Because ammonia is toxic, the liver converts most of the nitrogen from amino acid degradation to urea, which is excreted in the urine. The nitrogen derived from amino acid catabolism in other tissues is transported to the liver as **alanine** or **glutamine** and converted to urea.

The **branched-chain amino acids**, or BCAAs (valine, isoleucine, and leucine), are oxidized principally in **skeletal muscle** and other tissues and not in the liver. In skeletal muscle, the carbon skeletons and some of the nitrogen are converted to glutamine, which is released into the blood. The remainder of the nitrogen is incorporated into alanine, which is taken up by the liver and converted to urea and glucose.

The formation and release of glutamine from skeletal muscle and other tissues serves several functions. In the kidney, the NH_4^+ carried by glutamine is excreted into the urine. This process removes protons formed during fuel oxidation and helps to maintain the body's pH, especially during metabolic acidosis. **Glutamine** also provides a **fuel** for the **kidney** and **gut**. In rapidly dividing cells (e.g., lymphocytes and macrophages), glutamine is required as a fuel, as a nitrogen donor for biosynthetic reactions, and as a substrate for protein synthesis.

During conditions of **sepsis** (the presence of various pathogenic organisms or their toxins in the blood or tissues), **trauma**, **injury**, or **burns**, the body enters a **catabolic state** characterized by a **negative nitrogen balance** (Fig. 42.1). Increased net protein degradation in skeletal muscle increases the availability of glutamine and other amino acids for cell division and protein synthesis in cells involved in the immune response and wound healing. In these conditions, increased release of glucocorticoids from the adrenal cortex stimulates proteolysis.

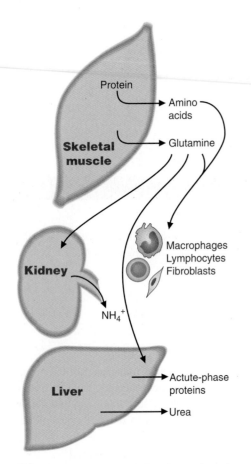

FIG. 42.1. Amino acid flux in sepsis and trauma. In sepsis and traumatic injury, glutamine and other amino acids are released from skeletal muscle for uptake by tissues involved in the immune response and tissue repair, such as macrophages, lymphocytes, fibroblasts, and the liver. Nitrogen excretion as urea and NH_4^+ results in negative nitrogen balance.

THE WAITING ROOM

Katta Bolic, a 62-year-old homeless woman, was found by a neighborhood child who heard Katta's moans coming from an abandoned building. The child's mother called the police who took Katta to the hospital emergency room. The patient was semicomatose, incontinent of urine, and her clothes were stained with vomitus. She had a fever of 103°F, was trembling uncontrollably, appeared to be severely dehydrated, and had marked muscle wasting. Her heart rate was very rapid, and her blood pressure was low (85/46 mm Hg). Her abdomen was distended and without bowel sounds. She responded to moderate pressure on her abdomen with moaning and grimacing.

Blood was sent for a broad laboratory profile, and cultures of her urine and blood were taken. Intravenous saline with glucose, thiamine and folate, and parenteral broad-spectrum antibiotics were begun. Radiography performed after her vital signs were stabilized suggested a bowel perforation. These findings were compatible with a diagnosis of a ruptured viscus (e.g., an infected colonic diverticulum that perforated, allowing colonic bacteria to infect the tissues of the peritoneal cavity, causing peritonitis). Further studies confirmed that a diverticulum had ruptured, and appropriate surgery was performed. All of the blood cultures grew out *Escherichia coli*, indicating that Katta also had a gram-negative infection of her blood (septicemia) that had been seeded by the proliferating organisms in her peritoneal cavity. Intensive fluid and electrolyte therapy and antibiotic coverage were continued. The medical team (surgeons, internists, and nutritionists) began developing a complex therapeutic plan to reverse Katta's severely catabolic state.

I. MAINTENANCE OF THE FREE AMINO ACID POOL IN BLOOD

The body maintains a relatively large free amino acid pool in the blood, even in the absence of an intake of dietary protein. The large free amino acid pool ensures the continuous availability of individual amino acids to tissues for the synthesis of proteins, neurotransmitters, and other nitrogen-containing compounds (Fig. 42.2). In a normal, well-fed, healthy individual, approximately 300 to 600 g of body protein is degraded per day. At the same time, roughly 100 g of protein is consumed in the diet per day, which adds additional amino acids. From this pool, tissues use amino acids for the continuous synthesis of new proteins (300 to 600 g) to replace those degraded. The continuous turnover of proteins in the body makes the complete complement of amino acids available for the synthesis of new and different proteins, such as antibodies. Protein turnover allows shifts in the quantities of different proteins produced in tissues in response to changes in physiologic state and continuously removes modified or damaged proteins. It also provides a complete pool of specific amino acids that can be used as oxidizable substrates; precursors for gluconeogenesis and for heme, creatine phosphate, purine, pyrimidine, and neurotransmitter synthesis; for ammoniagenesis to maintain blood pH levels; and for numerous other functions.

The concentration of free amino acids in the blood is not nearly as rigidly controlled as blood glucose levels. The free amino acid pool in the blood is only a small part (0.5%) of the total amino acid pool in whole-body protein. Because of the large skeletal muscle mass, approximately 80% of the body's total protein is in skeletal muscle. Consequently, the concentration of individual amino acids in the blood is strongly affected by the rates of protein synthesis and degradation in skeletal muscle, as well as the rate of uptake and utilization of individual amino acids for metabolism in liver and other tissues. For the most

FIG. 42.2. Maintenance of the blood amino acid pool. Dietary protein *(1)* and degradation of endogenous protein *(2)* provide a source of essential amino acids (those that cannot be synthesized in the human). *(3)* The synthesis of new protein is the major use of amino acids from the free amino acid pool. *(4)* Compounds synthesized from amino acid precursors are essential for physiologic functions. Many of these compounds are degraded to nitrogen-containing urinary metabolites and do not return to the free amino acid pool. *(5)* In tissues, the nitrogen is removed from amino acids by transamination and deamination reactions. *(6)* The nitrogen from amino acid degradation appears in the urine primarily as urea or NH_4^+, the ammonium ion. Ammonia excretion is necessary to maintain the pH of the blood. *(7)* Amino acids are used as fuels either directly or after being converted to glucose by gluconeogenesis. *(8)* Some amino acids can be synthesized in humans provided that glucose and a nitrogen source are available.

part, changes in the rate of protein synthesis and degradation take place over a span of hours.

A. Interorgan Flux of Amino Acids in the Postabsorptive State

The fasting state provides an example of the interorgan flux of amino acids necessary to maintain the free amino acid pool in the blood and supply tissues with their required amino acids (Fig. 42.3). During an overnight fast, protein synthesis in the liver and other tissues continues but at a diminished rate compared with the postprandial state. Net degradation of labile protein occurs in skeletal muscle (which contains the body's largest protein mass) and other tissues.

Q: What changes in hormone levels and fuel metabolism occur during an overnight fast?

1. RELEASE OF AMINO ACIDS FROM SKELETAL MUSCLE DURING FASTING

The efflux of amino acids from skeletal muscle supports the essential amino acid pool in the blood (see Fig. 42.3). Skeletal muscle oxidizes the branched-chain amino acids (BCAAs) (valine, leucine, isoleucine) to produce energy and glutamine. The amino groups of the BCAAs and of aspartate and glutamate are transferred out of skeletal muscle in alanine and glutamine. Alanine and glutamine account for approximately 50% of the total α-amino nitrogen released by skeletal muscle (Fig. 42.4).

The release of amino acids from skeletal muscle is stimulated during an overnight fast by the decrease of insulin and increase of glucocorticoid levels in the blood (see Chapters 31 and 43). Insulin promotes the uptake of amino acids and the general synthesis of proteins. The mechanisms for the stimulation of protein synthesis in human skeletal muscle are not all known but probably include an activation of the A system for amino acid transport (a modest effect), a general effect on initiation of translation, and an inhibition of lysosomal proteolysis. The fall of blood insulin levels during an overnight fast results in net proteolysis

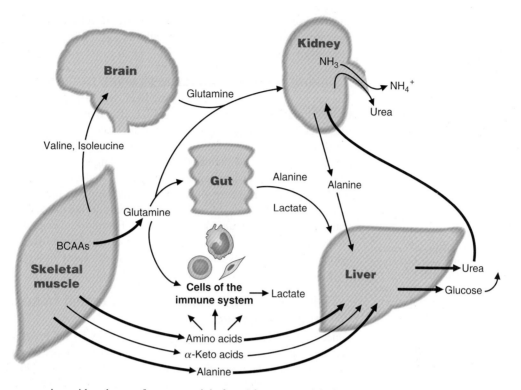

FIG. 42.3. Interorgan amino acid exchange after an overnight fast. After an overnight fast (the postabsorptive state), the use of amino acids for protein synthesis, for fuels, and for the synthesis of essential functional compounds continues. The free amino acid pool is supported largely by net degradation of skeletal muscle protein. Glutamine and alanine serve as amino-group carriers from skeletal muscle to other tissues. Glutamine brings NH_4^+ to the kidney for the excretion of protons and serves as a fuel for the kidney, gut, and cells of the immune system. Alanine transfers amino groups from the skeletal muscle, the kidney, and the gut to the liver, where they are converted to urea for excretion. The brain continues to use amino acids for neurotransmitter synthesis.

FIG. 42.4. Amino acid release from skeletal muscle. The *arteriovenous difference* (the concentration in arterial blood minus the concentration in venous blood) across the human forearm has been measured for many amino acids. This graph compares the amount of alanine, glutamine, and branched-chain amino acids (BCAAs) released with their composition in the average protein. Alanine and glutamine represent a much higher percentage of total nitrogen released than originally present in the degraded protein, evidence that they are being synthesized in the skeletal muscle. The BCAAs (leucine, valine, and isoleucine) are released in much lower amounts than those present in the degraded protein, evidence that they are being catabolized. Aspartate and glutamate also contribute nitrogen to the formation of alanine and glutamine.

A: The hormonal changes that occur during an overnight fast include a decrease of blood insulin levels and an increase of glucagon relative to levels after a high-carbohydrate meal. Glucocorticoid levels also increase in the blood. These hormones coordinate the changes of fat, carbohydrate, and amino acid metabolism. Fatty acids are released from adipose triacylglycerols and are used as the major fuel by heart, skeletal muscle, liver, and other tissues. The liver converts some of the fatty acids to ketone bodies. Liver glycogen stores are diminished and gluconeogenesis becomes the major support of blood glucose levels for glucose-dependent tissues. The major precursors of gluconeogenesis include amino acids released from skeletal muscle, lactate, and glycerol.

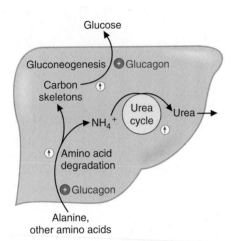

FIG. 42.5. Hormonal regulation of hepatic amino acid metabolism in the postabsorptive state. ⊕, glucagon-mediated activation of enzymes or proteins; ⬆, induction of enzyme synthesis mediated by glucagon and glucocorticoids. Induction of urea cycle enzymes occurs both during fasting and after a high-protein meal. Because many individuals in the United States normally have a high-protein diet, the levels of urea cycle enzymes may not fluctuate to any great extent.

 The body normally produces approximately 1 mmol of protons per kilogram of body weight per day. Nevertheless, the pH of the blood and extracellular fluid is normally maintained between 7.36 and 7.44. The narrow range is maintained principally by the bicarbonate (HCO_3^-), phosphate (HPO_4^-), and hemoglobin buffering systems and by the excretion of an amount of acid equal to that produced. The excretion of protons by the kidney regenerates bicarbonate, which can be reclaimed from the glomerular filtrate.

The acids are produced from normal fuel metabolism. The major acid is carbonic acid, which is formed from water and CO_2 produced in the tricarboxylic acid (TCA) cycle and other oxidative pathways. The oxidation of sulfur-containing amino acids (methionine and cysteine) ultimately produces sulfuric acid (H_2SO_4), which dissociates into $2H^+ + SO_4^{2-}$, and the protons and sulfate are excreted. The hydrolysis of phosphate esters produces the equivalent of phosphoric acid. What other acids produced during metabolism appear in the blood?

and release of amino acids. As glucocorticoid release from the adrenal cortex increases, induction of ubiquitin synthesis and increase of ubiquitin-dependent proteolysis also occur.

2. AMINO ACID METABOLISM IN LIVER DURING FASTING

The major site of alanine uptake is the liver, which disposes of the amino nitrogen by incorporating it into urea (see Fig. 42.3). The liver also extracts free amino acids, α-keto acids, and some glutamine from the blood. Alanine and other amino acids are oxidized and their carbon skeletons converted principally to glucose. Glucagon and glucocorticoids stimulate the uptake of amino acids into liver and increase gluconeogenesis and ureagenesis (Fig. 42.5). Alanine transport into the liver, in particular, is enhanced by glucagon. The induction of the synthesis of gluconeogenic enzymes by glucagon and glucocorticoids during the overnight fast correlates with an induction of many of the enzymes of amino acid degradation (e.g., tyrosine aminotransferase) and an induction of urea cycle enzymes (see Chapter 38). Urea synthesis also increases because of the increased supply of NH_4^+ from amino acid degradation in the liver.

3. METABOLISM OF AMINO ACIDS IN OTHER TISSUES DURING FASTING

Glucose, produced by the liver, is used for energy by the brain and other glucose-dependent tissues, such as erythrocytes. The muscle, under conditions of exercise, when the adenosine monophosphate (AMP)-activated protein kinase is active, also oxidizes some of this glucose to pyruvate, which is used for the carbon skeleton of alanine (the glucose–alanine cycle; see Chapter 38).

Glutamine is generated in skeletal muscle from the oxidation of BCAAs and by the lungs and brain for the removal of NH_4^+ formed from amino acid catabolism or entering from the blood. The kidney, the gut, and the cells with rapid turnover rates such as those of the immune system are the major sites of glutamine uptake (see Fig. 42.3). Glutamine serves as a fuel for these tissues, as a nitrogen donor for purine synthesis, and as a substrate for ammoniagenesis in the kidney. Much of the unused nitrogen from glutamine is transferred to pyruvate to form alanine in these tissues. Alanine then carries the unused nitrogen back to the liver.

The brain is glucose dependent but, like many cells in the body, can use BCAAs for energy. The BCAAs also provide a source of nitrogen for neurotransmitter synthesis during fasting. Other amino acids released from skeletal muscle protein degradation also serve as precursors of neurotransmitters.

B. Principles Governing Amino Acid Flux between Tissues

The pattern of interorgan flux of amino acids is strongly affected by conditions that change the supply of fuels (e.g., the overnight fast, a mixed meal, a high-protein meal) and by conditions that increase the demand for amino acids (metabolic acidosis, surgical stress, traumatic injury, burns, wound healing, and sepsis). The flux of amino acid carbon and nitrogen in these different conditions is dictated by several considerations.

1. Ammonia (NH_3) is toxic. Consequently, it is transported between tissues as alanine or glutamine. *Alanine* is the principal carrier of amino acid nitrogen from other tissues back to the liver, where the nitrogen is converted to urea and subsequently excreted into the urine by the kidneys. The amount of urea synthesized is proportional to the amount of amino acid carbon that is being oxidized as a fuel.

   The differences in amino acid metabolism between tissues are dictated by the types and amounts of different enzyme and transport proteins present in each tissue and the ability of each tissue to respond to different regulatory messages (hormones and neural signals).

2. The pool of glutamine in the blood serves several essential metabolic functions (Table 42.1). It provides ammonia for excretion of protons in the urine as NH_4^+. It serves as a fuel for the gut, the kidney, and the cells of the immune system. Glutamine is also required by the cells of the immune system and other rapidly dividing cells in which its amide group serves as the source of nitrogen for biosynthetic reactions. In the brain, the formation of glutamine from glutamate and NH_4^+ provides a means of removing ammonia and of transporting glutamate between different cell types within the brain. The use of the blood glutamine pool is prioritized. During metabolic acidosis, the kidney becomes the predominant site of glutamine uptake at the expense of glutamine use in other tissues. Conversely, during sepsis, in the absence of acidosis, cells involved in the immune response (macrophages, hepatocytes) become the preferential sites of glutamine uptake.

3. BCAAs (valine, leucine, and isoleucine) form a significant portion of the composition of the average protein and can be converted to tricarboxylic acid (TCA) cycle intermediates and used as fuels by almost all tissues. Valine and isoleucine are also the major precursors of glutamine. Except for the BCAAs and alanine, aspartate, and glutamate, the catabolism of amino acids occurs principally in the liver.

   The ability to convert four-carbon intermediates of the TCA cycle to pyruvate is required for oxidation of both BCAAs and glutamine. This sequence of reactions requires phosphoenolpyruvate (PEP) carboxykinase or decarboxylating malate dehydrogenase (malic enzyme). Most tissues have one, or both, of these enzymes.

4. Amino acids are major gluconeogenic substrates, and most of the energy obtained from their oxidation is derived from oxidation of the glucose formed from their carbon skeletons. A much smaller percentage of amino acid carbon is converted to acetyl coenzyme A (acetyl-CoA) or to ketone bodies and oxidized. The use of amino acids for glucose synthesis for the brain and other glucose-requiring tissues is subject to the hormonal regulatory mechanisms of glucose homeostasis (see Chapters 31 and 36).

5. The relative rates of protein synthesis and degradation (protein turnover) determine the size of the free amino acid pools available for the synthesis of new proteins and for other essential functions. For example, the synthesis of new proteins to mount an immune response is supported by the net degradation of other proteins in the body.

II. UTILIZATION OF AMINO ACIDS IN INDIVIDUAL TISSUES

Because tissues differ in their physiologic functions, they have different amino acid requirements and contribute differently to whole-body nitrogen metabolism. However, all tissues share a common requirement for essential amino acids for protein synthesis, and protein turnover is an ongoing process in all cells.

A. The Kidney

One of the primary roles of amino acid nitrogen is to provide ammonia in the kidney for the excretion of protons in the urine. NH_4^+ is released from glutamine by glutaminase and by glutamate dehydrogenase, resulting in the formation of α-ketoglutarate (Fig. 42.6). α-Ketoglutarate is used as a fuel by the kidney and is oxidized to CO_2, converted to glucose for use in cells in the renal medulla or converted to alanine to return ammonia to the liver for urea synthesis.

1. USE OF GLUTAMINE NITROGEN TO BUFFER URINE

The rate of glutamine uptake from the blood and its use by the kidney depends principally on the amount of acid that must be excreted to maintain a normal pH

Katta Bolic was in a severe stage of negative nitrogen balance on admission, which was caused by both her malnourished state and her intra-abdominal infection complicated by sepsis. The physiologic response to advanced catabolic status includes a degradation of muscle protein with the release of amino acids into the blood. This release is coupled with increased uptake of amino acids for acute-phase protein synthesis by the liver (systemic response) and other cells involved in the immune response to general and severe infection.

Table 42.1   Functions of Glutamine

Protein synthesis
Ammoniagenesis for proton excretion
Nitrogen donor for synthesis of
  purines,
  pyrimidines,
  NAD^+,
  amino sugars,
  asparagine, and
  other compounds
Glutamate donor for synthesis of
  glutathione,
  GABA,
  ornithine,
  arginine,
  proline, and
  other compounds

GABA, γ-aminobutyric acid.

Lactic acid is produced from glucose and amino acid metabolism. The ketone bodies (acetoacetate and β-hydroxybutyrate) produced during fatty acid oxidation are also acids. Many α-keto acids, formed from transamination reactions, are also found in the blood.

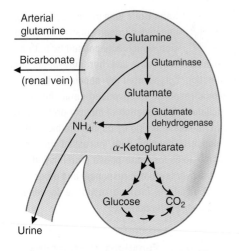

FIG. 42.6. Renal glutamine metabolism. Renal tubule cells preferentially oxidize glutamine. During metabolic acidosis, it is the major fuel for the kidney. Conversion of glutamine to α-ketoglutarate generates NH_4^+. Ammonium ion excretion helps to buffer systemic acidemia.

Table 42.2   Excretion of Compounds in the Urine

Component	g/24 h	Nitrogen (mmol)
H_2O	1,000	—
SO_4^{2-}	2–5	—
PO_4^{2-}	2–5	—
K^+	1–2	—
Urea	12–20	400–650
Creatinine	1–1.8	25–50
Uric acid	0.2–0.8	4–16
NH_4^+	0.2–1	11–55
	(up to 10 in acidosis)	(up to 550 in acidosis)

in the blood. In metabolic acidosis, the excretion of NH_4^+ by the kidney increases severalfold (Table 42.2). Because glutamine nitrogen provides approximately two-thirds of the NH_4^+ excreted by the kidney, glutamine uptake by the kidney also increases. Renal glutamine use for proton excretion takes precedence over the requirements of other tissues for glutamine.

Ammonia increases proton excretion by providing a buffer for protons that are transported into the renal tubular fluid (which is transformed into urine as it passes through the tubules of the kidney) (Fig. 42.7). Specific transporters in the membranes of the renal tubular cells transport protons from these cells into the tubular lumen in exchange for Na^+. The protons in the tubular fluid are buffered by phosphate, by bicarbonate, and by ammonia. Ammonia (NH_3), which is uncharged, enters the urine by free diffusion through the cell membrane. As it combines with a proton in the fluid, it forms ammonium ion (NH_4^+), which cannot be transported back into the cells and is excreted in the urine.

2. GLUTAMINE AS A FUEL FOR THE KIDNEY

Glutamine is used as a fuel by the kidney in the normal fed state and, to a greater extent, during fasting and metabolic acidosis (Table 42.3). The carbon skeleton forms α-ketoglutarate, which is oxidized to CO_2, converted to glucose or released as the carbon skeleton of serine or alanine (Fig. 42.8). α-Ketoglutarate can be converted to oxaloacetate by TCA cycle reactions, and oxaloacetate is converted to PEP by PEP carboxykinase. PEP can then be converted to pyruvate and subsequently acetyl-CoA, alanine, serine, or glucose. The glucose is used principally by the cells of the renal medulla, which have a relatively high dependence on anaerobic glycolysis because of their lower oxygen supply and mitochondrial capacity. The lactate released from anaerobic glycolysis in these cells is taken up and oxidized in the renal cortical cells, which have a higher mitochondrial capacity and a greater blood supply.

B. Skeletal Muscle

Skeletal muscle, because of its large mass, is a major site of protein synthesis and degradation in the human. After a high-protein meal, insulin promotes the uptake of certain amino acids and stimulates net protein synthesis. The insulin stimulation of protein synthesis is dependent on an adequate supply of amino acids to undergo protein synthesis. During fasting and other catabolic states, a net degradation of skeletal muscle protein and release of amino acids occur (see Fig. 42.3). The net degradation of protein affects functional proteins, such as myosin, which are sacrificed to meet more urgent demands for amino acids in other tissues. During sepsis, degradation of skeletal muscle protein is stimulated by the glucocorticoid cortisol. The effect of cortisol is exerted through the activation of ubiquitin-dependent proteolysis. During fasting, the decrease of blood insulin levels and the increase of blood cortisol levels increase net protein degradation.

FIG. 42.7. Ammonia excretion by the kidney. Ammonia increases proton excretion by combining with a proton to form ammonium ion in the renal tubular fluid, which is transformed into urine as it passes through the tubules of the kidney. As blood is filtered in the capillary bed of the glomerulus, urea, sugars, amino acids, ions, and H_2O enter the renal tubular fluid (glomerular filtrate). As this fluid passes through a progression of tubules (the proximal convoluted tubule, the loop of Henle, the distal convoluted tubule, and the collecting duct) on its way to becoming urine, various components are reabsorbed or added to the filtrate by the epithelial cells lining the tubules. Specific transporters in the membranes of the renal tubule cells transport protons into the tubule lumen in exchange for Na^+ so that the glomerular filtrate becomes more acidic as it is transformed into urine. The protons in the tubule fluid are buffered by phosphate, by bicarbonate, and by NH_3. The ammonia, which is uncharged, is able to diffuse through the membrane of the renal tubule cells into the urine. As it combines with a proton in the urine, it forms NH_4^+, which cannot be transported back into the cells. The removal of protons as NH_4^+ decreases the requirement for bicarbonate excretion to buffer the urine.

Skeletal muscle is a major site of glutamine synthesis, thereby satisfying the demand for glutamine during the postabsorptive state, during metabolic acidosis, and during septic stress and trauma. The carbon skeleton and nitrogen of glutamine are derived principally from the metabolism of BCAAs. Amino acid degradation in skeletal muscle is also accompanied by the formation of alanine, which transfers amino groups from skeletal muscle to the liver in the glucose–alanine cycle.

Table 42.3   Major Fuel Sources for the Kidney

	Percentage of Total CO_2 Formed in Different Physiologic States		
Fuel	Normal	Acidosis	Fasted
Lactate	45	20	15
Glucose[a]	25	20	0
Fatty acids	15	20	60
Glutamine	15	40	25

[a]Glucose used in the renal medulla is produced in the renal cortex.

FIG. 42.8. Metabolism of glutamine and other fuels in the kidney. To completely oxidize glutamate carbon to CO_2, it must enter the tricarboxylic acid (TCA) cycle as acetyl-CoA. Carbon entering the TCA cycle as α-ketoglutarate (α-KG) exits as oxaloacetate and is converted to phosphoenolpyruvate (PEP) by PEP carboxykinase. PEP is converted to pyruvate, which may be oxidized to acetyl-CoA. PEP also can be converted to serine, glucose, or alanine. *GDH*, glutamate dehydrogenase; *OAA*, oxaloacetate; *PEPCK*, phosphoenolpyruvate carboxykinase; *TA*, transaminase.

1. OXIDATION OF BRANCHED-CHAIN AMINO ACIDS IN SKELETAL MUSCLE

The BCAAs play a special role in muscle and most other tissues because they are the major amino acids that can be oxidized in tissues other than the liver. However, all tissues can interconvert amino acids and TCA cycle intermediates through transaminase reactions, that is, alanine $\leftrightarrow$ pyruvate, aspartate $\leftrightarrow$ oxaloacetate, and α-ketoglutarate $\leftrightarrow$ glutamate. The first step of the pathway, transamination of the BCAAs to α-keto acids, occurs principally in brain, heart, kidney, and skeletal muscles. These tissues have a high content of BCAA transaminase relative to the low levels in liver. The α-keto acids of the BCAAs are then either released into the blood and taken up by liver or oxidized to CO_2 or glutamine within the muscle or other tissue (Fig. 42.9). They can be oxidized by all tissues that contain mitochondria.

The oxidative pathways of the BCAAs convert the carbon skeleton to either succinyl-CoA or acetyl-CoA (see Chapter 39 and Fig. 42.9). The pathways generate NADH and FAD(2H) for adenosine triphosphate (ATP) synthesis before the conversion of carbon into intermediates of the TCA cycle, thus providing the muscle with energy without loss of carbon as CO_2. Leucine is "ketogenic" in that it is converted to acetyl-CoA and acetoacetate. Skeletal muscle, adipocytes, and most other tissues are able to use these products and, therefore, oxidize leucine directly to CO_2. The portion of isoleucine that is converted to acetyl-CoA is also oxidized directly to CO_2. For the portion of valine and isoleucine that enters the TCA cycle as succinyl-CoA to be completely oxidized to CO_2, it must first be converted to acetyl-CoA. To form acetyl-CoA, succinyl-CoA is oxidized to malate in the TCA cycle, and malate is then converted to pyruvate by malic enzyme (malate + $NADP^+$ → pyruvate + NADPH + H^+) (see Fig. 42.9). Pyruvate can then be oxidized to acetyl-CoA. Alternatively, pyruvate can form alanine or lactate.

When the carbon skeleton of alanine is derived from glucose, the efflux of alanine from skeletal muscle and its uptake by liver provide no net transfer of amino acid carbon to the liver for gluconeogenesis. However, some of the alanine carbon is derived from sources other than glucose. Which amino acids can provide carbon for alanine formation? (Hint: See Fig. 42.9.)

Some of the alanine released from skeletal muscle is derived directly from protein degradation. The carbon skeletons of valine, isoleucine, aspartate, and glutamate, which are converted to malate and oxaloacetate in the TCA cycle, can be converted to pyruvate and subsequently transaminated to alanine. The extent to which these amino acids contribute carbon to alanine efflux differs between different types of muscles in the human. These amino acids also may contribute to alanine efflux from the gut.

FIG. 42.9.   Metabolism of the carbon skeletons of BCAAs in skeletal muscle. *(1)* The first step in the metabolism of BCAAs is transamination (TA). *(2)* Carbon from valine and isoleucine enters the tricarboxylic acid (TCA) cycle as succinyl-CoA and is converted to pyruvate by decarboxylating malate dehydrogenase (malic enzyme). *(3)* The oxidative pathways generate NADH and FAD(2H) even before the carbon skeleton enters the TCA cycle. The rate-limiting enzyme in the oxidative pathways is the α-keto acid dehydrogenase complex. The carbon skeleton also can be converted to glutamate and alanine, shown in *red*.

2. CONVERSION OF BRANCHED-CHAIN AMINO ACIDS TO GLUTAMINE

The major route of valine and isoleucine catabolism in skeletal muscle is to enter the TCA cycle as succinyl-CoA and exit as α-ketoglutarate to provide the carbon skeleton for glutamine formation (see Fig. 42.9). Some of the glutamine and CO_2 that is formed from net protein degradation in skeletal muscle may also arise from the carbon skeletons of aspartate and glutamate. These amino acids are transaminated and become part of the pool of four-carbon intermediates of the TCA cycle.

Glutamine nitrogen is derived principally from the BCAAs (Fig. 42.10). The α-amino group arises from transamination reactions that form glutamate from α-ketoglutarate, and the amide nitrogen is formed from the addition of free ammonia to glutamate by glutamine synthetase. Free ammonia in skeletal muscle arises principally from the deamination of glutamate by glutamate dehydrogenase or from the purine nucleotide cycle.

The purine nucleotide cycle is found in skeletal muscle and brain but is absent in the liver and in many other tissues. One of its functions in skeletal muscle is to respond to the rapid use of adenosine triphosphate (ATP) during exercise. During exercise, the rapid hydrolysis of ATP increases adenosine monophosphate (AMP) levels, resulting in an activation of AMP deaminase (see Fig. 42.11). As a consequence, the cellular concentration of inosine monophosphate (IMP) increases and ammonia is generated. IMP, like AMP, activates muscle glycogen phosphorylase during exercise (see Chapter 22). The ammonia that is generated may help to buffer the increased lactic acid production that occurs in skeletal muscles during strenuous exercise.

FIG. 42.10. Formation of glutamine from the amino groups of BCAAs. The BCAAs are first transaminated with α-ketoglutarate to form glutamate and the branched-chain α-keto acids. The glutamate nitrogen can then follow either of two paths leading to glutamine formation. *α-KG*, α-ketoglutarate; *OAA*, oxaloacetate; *TA*, transamination.

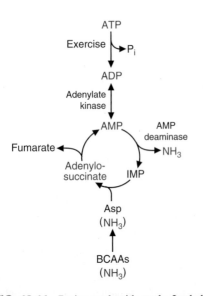

FIG. 42.11 Purine nucleotide cycle. In skeletal muscle, the purine nucleotide cycle can convert the amino groups of the branched-chain acids (BCAAs) to NH_3, which is incorporated into glutamine. Compare this to Figure 41.13, in which the fumarate generated is used in an anaplerotic role in the muscle.

In the purine nucleotide cycle (Fig. 42.11), the deamination of AMP to inosine monophosphate (IMP) releases NH_4^+. AMP is resynthesized with amino groups provided from aspartate. The aspartate amino groups can arise from the BCAAs through transamination reactions. The fumarate can be used to replenish TCA cycle intermediates (see Fig. 41.13).

3.   THE GLUCOSE–ALANINE CYCLE

The nitrogen arising from the oxidation of BCAAs in skeletal muscle can also be transferred back to the liver as alanine in the glucose–alanine cycle (Fig. 42.12; see also Fig. 38.10). The amino group of the BCAAs is first transferred to α-ketoglutarate to form glutamate and then transferred to pyruvate to form alanine by sequential transamination reactions. The pyruvate arises principally from glucose via the glycolytic pathway. The alanine released from skeletal muscle is taken up principally by the liver, where the amino group is incorporated into urea, and the carbon skeleton can be converted back to glucose through gluconeogenesis. Although

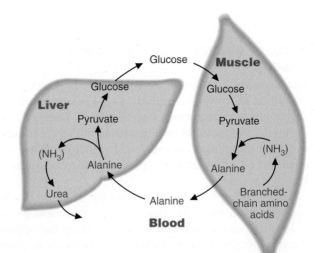

FIG. 42.12. Glucose–alanine cycle. The pathway for transfer of the amino groups from BCAAs in skeletal muscle to urea in the liver is shown in *red*.

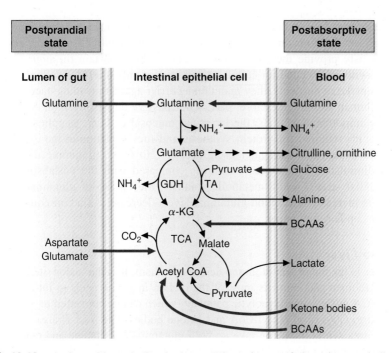

FIG. 42.13.   Amino acid metabolism in the gut. The pathways of glutamine metabolism in the gut are the same whether it is supplied by the diet (postprandial state) or from the blood (postabsorptive state). Cells of the gut also metabolize aspartate, glutamate, and BCAAs. Glucose is converted principally to the carbon skeleton of alanine. *α-KG*, α-ketoglutarate; *GDH*, glutamate dehydrogenase; *TA*, transaminase.

the amount of alanine formed varies with dietary intake and physiologic state, the transport of nitrogen from skeletal muscle to liver as alanine occurs almost continuously throughout our daily fasting–feeding cycle.

C. THE GUT

Amino acids are an important fuel for the intestinal mucosal cells after a protein-containing meal and in catabolic states such as fasting or surgical trauma (Fig. 42.13). During fasting, glutamine is one of the major amino acids used by the gut. The principal fates of glutamine carbon in the gut are oxidation to CO_2 and conversion to the carbon skeletons of lactate, citrulline, and ornithine. The gut also oxidizes BCAAs. Nitrogen derived from amino acid degradation is converted to citrulline, alanine, NH_4^+, and other compounds that are released into the blood and taken up by the liver. Although most of the carbon in this alanine is derived from glucose, the oxidation of glucose to CO_2 is not a major fuel pathway for the gut. Fatty acids are also not a significant source of fuel for the intestinal mucosal cells, although they do use ketone bodies.

Even though the liver is the organ that generates urea, the intestine also contains the enzymes for the urea cycle (including carbamoyl synthetase I). However, within the intestine, the V_{max} values for argininosuccinate synthetase and argininosuccinate lyase are very low, suggesting that the primary role of the urea cycle enzymes in the gut is to produce citrulline from the carbons of glutamine (glutamine → glutamate → glutamate semialdehyde → ornithine → citrulline). The citrulline is released in the circulation for use by the liver.

After a protein meal, dietary glutamine is a major fuel for the gut, and the products of glutamine metabolism are similar to those seen in the postabsorptive state. The gut also uses dietary aspartate and glutamate, which enter the TCA cycle. *Colonocytes* (the cells of the colon) also use short-chain fatty acids, derived from bacterial action in the lumen.

The importance of the gut in whole-body nitrogen metabolism arises from the high rate of division and death of intestinal mucosal cells and the need to continuously provide these cells with amino acids to sustain the high rates of protein synthesis needed for cellular division. Not only are these cells important for the uptake of nutrients, they maintain a barrier against invading bacteria from the gut lumen and are, therefore, part of our passive defense system. As a result of these important functions, the intestinal mucosal cells are supplied with the amino acids required for protein synthesis and fuel oxidation at the expense of the more expendable skeletal muscle protein. However, glutamine use by the gut is diminished by metabolic acidosis compared with the postabsorptive or postprandial state. During metabolic acidosis, the uptake of glutamine by the kidney is increased and blood glutamine levels decrease. As a consequence, the gut takes up less glutamine.

D. The Liver

The liver is the major site of amino acid metabolism. It is the major site of amino acid catabolism and converts most of the carbon in amino acids to intermediates of the TCA cycle or the glycolytic pathway (which can be converted to glucose or oxidized to CO_2) or to acetyl-CoA and ketone bodies. The liver is also the major site for urea synthesis. It can take up both glutamine and alanine and convert the nitrogen to urea for disposal (see Chapter 38). Other pathways in the liver give it an unusually high amino acid requirement. The liver synthesizes plasma proteins, such as serum albumin, transferrin, and the proteins of the blood-coagulation cascade. It is a major site for the synthesis of nonessential amino acids, the conjugation of xenobiotic compounds with glycine, the synthesis of heme and purine nucleotides, and the synthesis of glutathione.

E. Brain and Nervous Tissue

1. THE AMINO ACID POOL AND NEUROTRANSMITTER SYNTHESIS

A major function of amino acid metabolism in neural tissue is the synthesis of neurotransmitters. More than 40 compounds are believed to function as neurotransmitters, and all of these contain nitrogen derived from precursor amino acids. They include amino acids, which are themselves neurotransmitters (e.g., glutamate, glycine), the catecholamines derived from tyrosine (dopamine, epinephrine, and norepinephrine), serotonin (derived from tryptophan), γ-aminobutyric acid (GABA, derived from glutamate), acetylcholine (derived from choline synthesized in the liver and acetyl-CoA), and many peptides. In general, neurotransmitters are formed in the presynaptic terminals of axons and stored in vesicles until they are released by a transient change in electrochemical potential along the axon. Subsequent catabolism of some of the neurotransmitters results in the formation of a urinary excretion product. The rapid metabolism of neurotransmitters requires the continuous availability of a precursor pool of amino acids for de novo neurotransmitter synthesis (see Chapter 48).

2. METABOLISM OF GLUTAMINE IN THE BRAIN

The brain is a net glutamine producer, owing principally to the presence of glutamine synthetase in astroglial cells (see Chapter 48). Glutamate and aspartate are synthesized in these cells, using amino groups donated by the BCAAs (principally valine) and TCA cycle intermediates formed from glucose and from the carbon skeletons of BCAAs (Fig. 42.14). The glutamate is converted to glutamine by glutamine synthetase, which incorporates NH_4^+ released from deamination of amino acids and deamination of AMP in the purine nucleotide cycle in the brain. This glutamine may efflux from the brain, carrying excess NH_4^+ into the blood, or serve as a precursor of glutamate in neuronal cells.

FIG. 42.14. Role of glutamine in the brain. Glutamine serves as a nitrogen transporter in the brain for the synthesis of many different neurotransmitters. Different neurons convert glutamine to γ-aminobutyric acid (GABA) or to glutamate. Glutamine also transports excess NH_4^+ from the brain into the blood. *α-KG*, α-ketoglutarate; *BCKA*, branched-chain keto acids.

Glutamine synthesized in the astroglial cells is a precursor of *glutamate* (an excitatory neurotransmitter) and *GABA* (an inhibitory neurotransmitter) in the neuronal cells (see Fig. 42.14). It is converted to glutamate by a neuronal glutaminase isozyme. In GABAergic neurons, glutamate is then decarboxylated to GABA, which is released during excitation of the neuron. GABA is one of the neurotransmitters that is recycled; a transaminase converts it to succinaldehyde, which is then oxidized to succinate. Succinate enters the TCA cycle.

III. CHANGES IN AMINO ACID METABOLISM WITH DIETARY AND PHYSIOLOGIC STATE

The rate and pattern of amino acid use by different tissues change with dietary and physiologic state. Two such states, the postprandial period following a high-protein meal and the hypercatabolic state produced by sepsis or surgical trauma, differ from the postabsorptive state with respect to the availability of amino acids and other fuels and the levels of different hormones in the blood. As a result, the pattern of amino acid use is somewhat different.

A. High-Protein Meal

After the ingestion of a high-protein meal, the gut and the liver use most of the absorbed amino acids (Fig. 42.15). Glutamate and aspartate are used as fuels by the gut, and very little enters the portal vein. The gut also may use some BCAAs. The liver takes up 60% to 70% of the amino acids present in the portal vein. These amino acids, for the most part, are converted to glucose in the gluconeogenic pathway.

After a pure protein meal, the increased levels of dietary amino acids reaching the pancreas stimulate the release of glucagon above fasting levels, thereby increasing amino acid uptake into the liver and stimulating gluconeogenesis. Insulin release is also stimulated, but not nearly to the levels found after a high-carbohydrate meal. In general, the insulin released after a high-protein meal is sufficiently high that the uptake of BCAAs into skeletal muscle and net protein synthesis is stimulated, but gluconeogenesis in the liver is not inhibited. The higher the carbohydrate content of the meal, the higher is the insulin/glucagon ratio and the greater the shift of amino acids away from gluconeogenesis into biosynthetic pathways in the liver such as the synthesis of plasma proteins.

Most of the amino acid nitrogen entering the peripheral circulation after a high-protein meal or a mixed meal is present as BCAAs. Because the liver has low levels of transaminases for these amino acids, it cannot oxidize them to a significant

During hyperammonemia, ammonia (NH_3) can diffuse into the brain from the blood. The ammonia is able to inhibit the neural isozyme of glutaminase, thereby decreasing additional ammonia formation in the brain and inhibiting the formation of glutamate and its subsequent metabolism to γ-aminobutyric acid (GABA). This effect of ammonia might contribute to the lethargy associated with the hyperammonemia found in patients with hepatic disease.

The levels of transthyretin (binds to vitamin A and thyroid hormones in the blood) and serum albumin in the blood may be used as indicators of the degree of protein malnutrition. In the absence of hepatic disease, decreased levels of these proteins in the blood indicate insufficient availability of amino acids to the liver for synthesis of serum proteins. The levels of transthyretin can be determined by immunologic means. The levels of albumin are rapidly determined using a hydrophobic dye-binding assay and determining the amount of colored dye bound to albumin. The dye that is used binds specifically to the hydrophobic pocket of albumin and not to other proteins in the serum.

Q: In what ways does liver metabolism after a high-protein meal resemble liver metabolism in the fasting state?

A: Both of these dietary states are characterized by an elevation of glucagon. Glucagon stimulates amino acid transport into the liver, stimulates gluconeogenesis through decreasing levels of fructose 2,6-bisphosphate, and induces the synthesis of enzymes in the urea cycle, the gluconeogenic pathway, and the pathways for degradation of some of the amino acids.

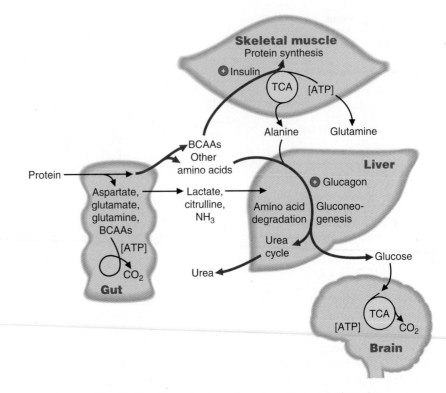

FIG. 42.15. Flux of amino acids after a high-protein meal.

extent, and they enter the systemic circulation. The BCAAs are slowly taken up by skeletal muscle and other tissues. These peripheral nonhepatic tissues use the amino acids derived from the diet principally for net protein synthesis.

High-protein, low-carbohydrate diets are based on the premise that ingesting high-protein, low-carbohydrate meals will keep circulating insulin levels low, so that energy storage is not induced, and glucagon release will point the insulin/glucagon ratio to energy mobilization, particularly fatty acid release from the adipocyte and oxidation by the tissues. The lack of energy storage coupled with the loss of fat leads to weight loss.

B. Hypercatabolic States

Surgery, trauma, burns, and septic stress are examples of hypercatabolic states characterized by increased fuel use and a negative nitrogen balance (Fig. 42.16). The mobilization of body protein, fat, and carbohydrate stores serves to maintain normal tissue function in the presence of a limited dietary intake, as well as to support the energy and amino acid requirements for the immune response and wound healing. The negative nitrogen balance that occurs in these hypercatabolic states results from accelerated protein turnover and an increased rate of net protein degradation, primarily in skeletal muscle.

The catabolic state of sepsis (acute, generalized, febrile infection) is one of enhanced mobilization of fuels and amino acids to provide the energy and precursors required by cells of the immune system, host defense mechanisms, and wound healing. The amino acids must provide the substrates for new protein synthesis and cell division. Glucose synthesis and release are enhanced to provide fuel for these cells, and the patient may become mildly hyperglycemic.

In these hypercatabolic states, skeletal muscle protein synthesis decreases and protein degradation increases. Oxidation of BCAAs is increased, and glutamine production enhanced. Amino acid uptake is diminished. Cortisol is the major hormonal mediator of these responses, although certain cytokines may also have direct effects on skeletal muscle metabolism. As occurs during fasting and metabolic

The degree of the body's hypercatabolic response depends on the severity and duration of the trauma or stress. After an uncomplicated surgical procedure in an otherwise healthy patient, the net negative nitrogen balance may be limited to about 1 week. The mild nitrogen losses are usually reversed by dietary protein supplementation as the patient recovers. With more severe traumatic injury or septic stress, the body may catabolize body protein and adipose tissue lipids for a prolonged period, and the negative nitrogen balance may not be corrected for weeks.

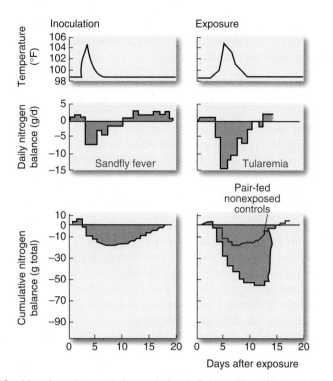

FIG. 42.16. Negative nitrogen balance during infection. The effects of experimentally induced infections on nitrogen balance were determined in human volunteers. After inoculation with sandfly fever, increased amino acid catabolism produced a negative nitrogen balance. A few days after exposure, the daily nitrogen balance became positive, until the volunteers returned to their original state. Experiments with patients exposed to tularemia showed that the negative nitrogen balance was much larger than could be expected from a decreased appetite alone. Volunteers who ate the same amount of food as the infected individuals (pair-fed nonexposed controls) had a much smaller cumulative negative nitrogen balance than the infected volunteers. (From Beisel WR. Magnitude of the host nutritional responses to infection. *Am J Clin Nutr.* 1977;30:1236–1247. Copyright 1977 American Society for Clinical Nutrition.)

acidosis, increased levels of cortisol stimulate ubiquitin-mediated proteolysis, induce the synthesis of glutamine synthetase, and enhance release of amino acids and glutamine from the muscle cells.

The amino acids released from skeletal muscle during periods of hypercatabolic stress are used in a prioritized manner, with the cellular components of the immune system receiving top priority. For example, the uptake of amino acids by the liver for the synthesis of acute-phase proteins, which are part of the immune system, is greatly increased. Conversely, during the early phase of the acute response, the synthesis of other plasma proteins (e.g., albumin) is decreased. The increased availability of amino acids and the increased cortisol levels also stimulate gluconeogenesis, thereby providing fuel for the glucose-dependent cells of the immune system (e.g., lymphocytes). An increase of urea synthesis accompanies the acceleration of amino acid degradation.

The increased efflux of glutamine from skeletal muscle during sepsis serves several functions (see Fig. 42.1). It provides the rapidly dividing cells of the immune system with an energy source. Glutamine is available as a nitrogen donor for purine synthesis, for NAD^+ synthesis (to convert nicotinic acid to nicotinamide), and for other biosynthetic functions that are essential to growth and division of the cells. Increased production of metabolic acids may accompany stress such as sepsis, so there is increased use of glutamine by the kidney.

Under the influence of elevated levels of glucocorticoids, epinephrine, and glucagon, fatty acids are mobilized from adipose tissue to provide alternate fuels

 Katta Bolic's severe negative nitrogen balance was caused by both her malnourished state and her intra-abdominal infection complicated by sepsis. The systemic and diverse responses the body makes to insults such as an acute febrile illness are termed the *acute-phase response*. An early event in this response is the stimulation of phagocytic activity (see Fig. 42.17). Stimulated macrophages release cytokines, which are regulatory proteins that stimulate the release of cortisol, insulin, and growth hormone. Cytokines also directly mediate the acute-phase response of the liver and skeletal muscle to sepsis.

for other tissues and spare glucose. Under these conditions, fatty acids are the major energy source for skeletal muscle, and glucose uptake is decreased. These changes may lead to mild hyperglycemia.

CLINICAL COMMENTS

 Katta Bolic. The clinician can determine whether a patient such as **Katta Bolic** is mounting an acute-phase response to some insult, however subtle, by determining whether several unique acute-phase proteins are being secreted by the liver. C-reactive protein, so named because of its ability to interact with the C-polysaccharide of pneumococci, and serum amyloid A protein, a precursor of the amyloid fibril found in secondary amyloidosis, are elevated in patients who are undergoing the acute-phase response and as compared with healthy individuals. Other proteins normally found in the blood of healthy individuals are present in increased concentrations in patients undergoing an acute-phase response. These include haptoglobin, certain protease inhibitors, complement components, ceruloplasmin, and fibrinogen. The elevated concentration of these proteins in the blood increases the erythrocyte sedimentation rate (ESR), another laboratory measure of the presence of an acute-phase response.

To determine the ESR, the patient's blood is placed vertically in a small-bore glass tube. The speed with which the red blood cells sediment toward the bottom of the tube depends on what percentage of the red blood cells clump together and thereby become more dense. The degree of clumping is directly correlated with the presence of one or more of the acute-phase proteins listed previously. These proteins interfere with what is known as the *zeta-potential of the red blood cells*, which normally prevents the red blood cells from clumping. Because many different proteins can individually alter the zeta-potential, the ESR is a nonspecific test for the presence of acute inflammation.

The weight loss often noted in septic patients is caused primarily by a loss of appetite resulting from the effect of certain cytokines on the medullary appetite center. Other causes include increased energy expenditure due to fever and enhanced muscle proteolysis.

BIOCHEMICAL COMMENTS

Amino acid metabolism in trauma and sepsis. After a catabolic insult such as injury, trauma, infection, or cancer, the interorgan flow of glutamine and fuels is altered dramatically. Teleologically, the changes in metabolism that occur give first priority to cells that are part of the immune system. Evidence suggests that the changes in glutamine and fuel metabolism are mediated by the insulin counterregulatory hormones, such as cortisol and epinephrine, and several different cytokines (see Chapter 11 for a review of cytokines). Cytokines appear to play a more important role than hormones during sepsis, although they exert their effects, in part, through hormones (Fig. 42.17). Although cytokines can be released from a variety of cells, macrophages are the principal source during trauma and sepsis.

Two cytokines that are important in sepsis are interleukin 1 (IL-1) and tumor necrosis factor (TNF). IL-1 and TNF affect amino acid metabolism both through regulation of the release of glucocorticoids and through direct effects on tissues. Although cytokines are generally considered to be paracrine, with their effects being exerted over cells in the immediate vicinity, TNF and IL-1 increase in the blood during sepsis. Other cytokines, such as IL-6, also may be involved.

During sepsis, TNF, IL-1, and possibly other cytokines, bacterial products, or mediators act on the brain to stimulate the release of glucocorticoids from the adrenal cortex (a process mediated by adrenocorticotropic hormone [ACTH]), epinephrine

FIG. 42.17. Cytokines and hormones mediate amino acid flux during sepsis. Bacterial products act on macrophages to stimulate the release of cytokines and on the brain to stimulate the sympathoadrenal response. The result is a stimulation of the release of the insulin counter-regulatory hormones, epinephrine, glucagon, and glucocorticoids. The glucocorticoid cortisol may be the principal mediator of net muscle protein degradation during sepsis. Hepatic protein synthesis, particularly that of acute-phase proteins, is stimulated by both cortisol and cytokines. Amino acid metabolism in the gut is also probably affected by glucocorticoids and cytokines. Because of the release of the counterregulatory hormones, muscle and other tissues become resistant to insulin action, as indicated by the bar on the figure. (Adapted with permission from Fischer JE, Hasselgren PO. Cytokines and glucocorticoids in the regulation of the hepato-skeletal muscle axis in sepsis. *Am J Surg.* 1991;161:266–271.)

from the adrenal medulla, and both insulin and glucagon from the pancreas. Although insulin is elevated during sepsis, the tissues exhibit an insulin resistance that is similar to that of the patient with non–insulin-dependent diabetes mellitus, possibly resulting from the elevated levels of the insulin counterregulatory hormones (glucocorticoids, epinephrine, and glucagon). Changes in the rate of acute-phase protein synthesis are mediated, at least in part, by effects of TNF, IL-1, and IL-6 on the synthesis of groups of proteins in the liver.

The molecular mechanism whereby sepsis/trauma leads to reduced muscle protein synthesis involves, in part, mammalian target of rapamycin (mTOR; see Chapter 36, Figure 36.12). Sepsis reduces translational efficiency, primarily at the translation initiation step. Initiation is regulated by, and requires, specific eukaryotic initiation factors (eIFs, see Chapter 15). eIF4E is a multifactor complex required to assemble the charged initiator tRNA$_i^{Met}$– 40S small ribosomeal subunit complex onto the capped mRNA. The activity of eIF4E is regulated by the eIF4E binding protein, 4E-BP1. When eIF4E is bound to 4E-BP1, translation initiation is reduced. mTOR, when active, will phosphorylate 4E-BP1, causing the binding protein to dissociate from the eIF4E complex, thereby stimulating translation initiation. Sepsis, and/or release of TNF-α, leads to the inactivation of mTOR and reduced phosphorylation of 4E-BP1, resulting in a decrease in translation. The reduced translation, coupled with enhanced protein turnover, allows the muscle to export amino acids for use by other tissues.

 Hypercatabolic states may be accompanied by varying degrees of insulin resistance caused, in part, by the release of counterregulatory hormones into the blood. Thus, patients with diabetes mellitus may require higher levels of exogenous insulin during sepsis.

Table 42.4   Diseases Discussed in Chapter 42

Disease or Disorder	Environmental of Genetic	Comments
Catabolic state	Environmental	The body adapts to a catabolic state by degrading proteins to enhance survival. This change in metabolism is initiated through the stress response, as mediated by cortisol, epinephrine, and norepinephrine, among other signaling molecules
Hyperammonemia	Both	Hyperammonemia can result from mutations in urea cycle enzymes or due to a failing liver as caused by a variety of conditions (one of which is alcohol abuse over many years).

Key Concepts

- The body maintains a large free amino acid pool in the blood, even during fasting, allowing tissues continuous access to these building blocks.
- Amino acids are used for gluconeogenesis by the liver as a fuel source for the gut and as neurotransmitter precursors in the nervous system. They are also required by all organs for protein synthesis.
- During an overnight fast and during hypercatabolic states, degradation of labile protein (primarily from skeletal muscle) is the major source of free amino acids.
- The liver is the major site for urea synthesis. Nitrogen from other tissues travels to the liver in the form of glutamine and alanine.
- Branched-chain amino acids (BCAAs) are oxidized primarily in the skeletal muscle.
- Glutamine in the blood serves several roles:
  - The kidney uses the ammonium ion carried by glutamine for excretion in the urine to act as a buffer against acidotic conditions.
  - The kidney and the gut use glutamine as a fuel source.
  - All tissues use glutamine for protein synthesis.
- The body can enter a catabolic state, characterized by negative nitrogen balance, under the following conditions:
  - Sepsis (the presence of various pathogenic organisms or their toxins in the blood or tissues)
  - Trauma
  - Injury
  - Burns
- The negative nitrogen balance results from increased net protein degradation in skeletal muscle brought about by the release of glucocorticoids. The released amino acids are used for protein synthesis and cell division in cells involved in the immune response and wound healing.
- Diseases discussed in this chapter are summarized in Table 42.4.

REVIEW QUESTIONS—CHAPTER 42

1. Which of the profiles indicated in the following would occur within 2 hours after eating a meal that was very high in protein and low in carbohydrates?

	Blood Glucagon Levels	Liver Gluconeogenesis	BCAA Oxidation in Muscle
A.	↓	↓	↑
B.	↓	↓	↑
C.	↓	↑	↑
D.	↑	↑	↑
E.	↓	↓	↓
F.	↑	↓	↓
G.	↓	↑	↓
H.	↑	↑	↓

2. The gut uses glutamine as an energy source, but it can also secrete citrulline, synthesized from the carbons of glutamine. Which of the following compounds is an obligatory intermediate in this conversion (consider only the carbon atoms of glutamine while answering this question)?

A. Aspartate
B. Succinyl-CoA
C. Glutamate
D. Serine
E. Fumarate

3. The signal that indicates to muscle that protein degradation needs to be initiated is which of the following?

    A. Insulin
    B. Glucagon
    C. Epinephrine
    D. Cortisol
    E. Glucose

4. The skeletal muscles convert branched-chain amino acid (BCAA) carbons to glutamine for export to the rest of the body. An obligatory intermediate, which carries carbons originally from the BCAAs, in the conversion of BCAAs to glutamine, is which of the following?

    A. Urea
    B. Pyruvate
    C. Lactate
    D. Isocitrate
    E. Phosphoenolpyruvate

5. An individual in sepsis will display which of the following metabolic patterns?

	Nitrogen Balance	Gluconeogenesis	Fatty Acid Oxidation
A.	Positive	↑	↓
B.	Negative	↑	↑
C.	Positive	↑	↓
D.	Negative	↑	↓
E.	Positive	↓	↑
F.	Negative	↓	↓

Tissue Metabolism

Although many of the pathways described previously are present in all tissues of the body, many tissues also carry out specialized functions and contain unique biochemical pathways. This section describes a number of such tissues and, in some cases, how the tissues interact with the rest of the body to coordinate their functions. Previous chapters have focused primarily on insulin and glucagon as the major mediators for regulating metabolic pathways; however, a large number of other hormones also regulate the storage and use of metabolic fuels (see Chapter 43). These hormones primarily counteract the effects of insulin and are called *counterregulatory hormones*. They include growth hormone, thyroid hormone, glucocorticoids such as cortisol, small peptides such as the somatostatins, and small molecules such as the catecholamines. Growth hormone works, in part, by inducing the synthesis of the insulin-like growth factors. These hormones can exert their effects rapidly (through covalent modification of selected enzymes) or long term (through alterations in the rate of synthesis of selected enzymes). The interplay of these hormones with insulin and glucagon is discussed, as are the synthesis, secretion, and conditions leading to secretion of each hormone.

The proteins and cells in the blood form their own tissue system (see Chapter 44). All blood cells are derived from a common precursor—the stem cell—in the bone marrow. Different cytokine signals trigger differentiation of a particular blood cell lineage. For example, when oxygen supply to the tissues is decreased, the kidney responds by releasing erythropoietin. This hormone specifically stimulates the production of red blood cells.

Red blood cells have limited metabolic functions, owing to their lack of internal organelles. Their main function is to deliver oxygen to the tissues through the binding of oxygen to hemoglobin. When the number of red blood cells is decreased, that, by definition, represents anemia. This can be attributable to many causes, including nutritional deficiencies or mutations (hereditary anemias). The morphology of the red blood cell can sometimes aid in distinguishing the various types of anemia.

Red blood cell metabolism is geared toward preserving the ability of these cells to transport oxygen, as well as to regulate oxygen binding to hemoglobin. Glycolysis provides energy and NADH to protect the oxidation state of the heme-bound iron. The hexose monophosphate shunt pathway generates NADPH to protect red blood cell membranes from oxidation. Heme synthesis, which uses succinyl coenzyme A (succinyl-CoA) and glycine for all of the carbon and nitrogen atoms in the structure, occurs in the precursors of red blood cells. Inherited defects in heme synthesis leads to a class of diseases known as the *porphyrias*. Because red blood cells normally pass through the very narrow capillaries, their membranes must be easily deformable. This deformability is, in part, attributable to the complex cytoskeletal structure that surrounds the erythrocyte. Mutations in these structural proteins can lead to less deformable cells, which are more easily lysed as they circulate in the bloodstream. This, in turn, can result in hemolytic anemia.

Among other functions, the hematologic system is responsible for hemostasis as well as for maintaining a constant blood volume (see Chapter 45). A tear in the wall of a vessel can lead to blood loss, which, when extensive, can be fatal. Repairing vessel damage, whether internal or external, is accomplished by a complicated series of zymogen activations of circulating blood proteins resulting in the formation of a fibrin clot (the coagulation cascade). Platelets play a critical role in hemostasis not only through their release of procoagulants but through their ability to form aggregates within the thrombus (clot) as well. Clots function as a plug, allowing defects or rents in vessel walls to repair and thereby preventing further blood loss. Conversely, inappropriate or accelerated clot formation in the lumen of vessels that supply blood to vital organs or tissues can cause an intraluminal obstruction to flow that may lead to an acute cerebral or myocardial infarction. Because clotting must be tightly controlled, intricate mechanisms exist that regulate this important hematologic function.

The liver is an altruistic organ that provides multiple services for other tissues (see Chapter 46). It supplies glucose and ketone bodies to the rest of the body when fuel stores are limited. It disposes of ammonia as urea when amino acid degradation occurs. It is the site of detoxification of xenobiotics, and it synthesizes many of the proteins found in the blood. The liver synthesizes triacylglycerols and cholesterol and distributes them to other tissues in the form of very low-density lipoprotein (VLDL). The liver also synthesizes bile acids for fat digestion in the intestine. The liver recycles cholesterol and triglyceride through its uptake of intermediate-density lipoprotein (IDL), chylomicron and VLDL remnants, and low-density lipoprotein (LDL) particles. Because of its protective nature and its strategic location between the gut and the systemic circulation, the liver has "first crack" at all compounds that enter the blood through the enterohepatic circulation. Thus, xenobiotic compounds can be detoxified as they enter the liver, before they have a chance to reach other tissues.

Muscle cells contain unique pathways that allow them to store energy as creatine phosphate and to regulate closely their use of fatty acids as an energy source (see Chapter 47). The adenosine monophosphate (AMP)-activated protein kinase is an important regulator of muscle energy metabolism. Muscle is composed of different types of contractile fibers that derive their energy from different sources. For example, the slow-twitch type I fibers use oxidative energy pathways, whereas the type II fast-twitch fibers use the glycolytic pathway for their energy requirements.

The nervous system consists of various cell types that are functionally interconnected so as to allow efficient signal transmission throughout the system (see Chapter 48). The cells of the central nervous system are protected from potentially toxic compounds by the blood–brain barrier, which restricts entry of potentially toxic compounds into the nervous system (ammonia, however, is a notable exception). The brain cells communicate with each other and with other organs through the synthesis of neurotransmitters and neuropeptides. Many of the neurotransmitters are derived from amino acids, most of which are synthesized within the nerve cells. Because the pathways of amino acid and neurotransmitter biosynthesis require cofactors (such as pyridoxal phosphate, thiamine pyrophosphate, and vitamin B_{12}), deficiencies of these cofactors can lead to neuropathies (dysfunction of specific neurons in the nervous system).

Because of the restrictions imposed by the blood–brain barrier, the brain also must synthesize its own lipids. An adequate supply of lipids is vital to the central nervous system because lipids are constituents of the myelin sheath that surrounds the neurons and allows them to conduct impulses normally. The neurodegenerative disorders, such as multiple sclerosis, are a consequence of varying degrees of demyelination of the neurons.

Connective tissue, which consists primarily of fibroblasts, produces extracellular matrix materials that surround cells and tissues, determining their appropriate position within the organ (see Chapter 49). These materials include structural proteins (collagen and elastin), adhesive proteins (fibronectin), and glycosaminoglycans (heparan sulfate and chondroitin sulfate). The unique structures of the proteins and carbohydrates in the extracellular matrix allow tissues and organs to carry out their many functions. Loss of these supportive and barrier functions of connective tissue sometimes lead to significant clinical consequences, such as those that result from the microvascular alterations that lead to blindness or renal failure, or peripheral neuropathies in patients with diabetes mellitus.

43 Actions of Hormones That Regulate Fuel Metabolism

Many hormones affect fuel metabolism, including those that regulate appetite as well as those that influence absorption, transport, and oxidation of foodstuffs. The major hormones that influence nutrient metabolism and their actions on muscle, liver, and adipose tissue are listed in Table 43.1.

__Insulin__ is the major __anabolic hormone__. It promotes the __storage__ of __nutrients__ as __glycogen__ in liver and muscle and as __triacylglycerols__ in adipose tissue. It also stimulates the __synthesis__ of __proteins__ in tissues such as muscle. At the same time, insulin acts to inhibit fuel mobilization.

__Glucagon__ is the major __counterregulatory__ hormone. The term "counter-regulatory" means that its actions are generally opposed to those of insulin (__contrainsular__). The major action of glucagon is to __mobilize fuel reserves__ by stimulating __glycogenolysis__ and __gluconeogenesis__. These actions ensure that glucose will be available to glucose-dependent tissues between meals.

__Epinephrine__, __norepinephrine__, __cortisol__, __somatostatin__, and __growth hormone__ (GH) also have contrainsular activity. __Thyroid hormone__ also must be classified as an insulin-counterregulatory hormone because it __increases__ the rate of __fuel consumption__ and also increases the sensitivity of the target cells to other insulin-counterregulatory hormones.

Insulin and the counterregulatory hormones exert two types of metabolic regulation (see Chapter 26). The first type of control occurs within minutes to hours of the hormone–receptor interaction and usually results from changes in the catalytic activity or kinetics of key preexisting enzymes caused by phosphorylation or dephosphorylation of these enzymes. The second type of control involves regulation of the __synthesis of key enzymes__ by mechanisms that stimulate or inhibit transcription and translation of messenger RNA (mRNA). These processes are slow and require hours to days.

Table 43.1 Major Hormones That Regulate Fuel Metabolism

Hormones	Muscle Glucose Uptake	Glucose Use	Protein Synthesis	Glucose Output	Keto-genesis	Liver Gluconeo-genesis	Glyco-genolysis	Glyco-genesis	Protein Synthesis	Adipose Fat Synthesis	Tissue Lipolysis
Anabolic hormones											
Insulin	↑↑	↑↑	↑↑	↓↓	↓↓	↓↓	↓↓	↑	↑	↑↑	↓↓
Counterregulatory hormones[a]											
Glucagon	—	—	—	↑↑	↑	↑	↑↑	↓	—	—	↑ (at large doses)
Epinephrine and norepinephrine	↓	↑	—	↑↑	—	↑	↑↑ (initial)	↓	—	—	↑↑
Glucocorticoid	↓	↓	↓	↑	↑	↑ (mainly permissive)	—	↑	↑	—	↑ (permissive)
Growth hormone	↓ (weakly)	↓ (weakly)	↑	↑	↑	↑	—	—	↑	—	↑ (mainly permissive)
Thyroid hormone	—	↑	↑	↑	↑	↑	—	—	—	—	↑ (permissive)
Somatostatin[b]	—	—	—	—	—	—	—	—	—	—	—

[a]Hormones with actions that are generally opposed to those of insulin.
[b]Somatostatin's effects on metabolism are indirect via suppression of secretion of insulin, glucagon, growth hormone, and thyroid hormone and by effects on gastric acid secretion, gastric emptying time, and pancreatic exocrine secretion (see text).
↑↑, pronounced increased effect; ↑, moderate increased effect; ↓, moderate decreased effect; —, no effect.

THE WAITING ROOM

Otto Shape, now a third-year medical student, was assigned to do a history and physical examination on a newly admitted 47-year-old patient named **Corti Solemia**. Mr. Solemia had consulted his physician for increasing weakness and fatigue and was found to have a severely elevated serum glucose level. While he was examining the patient, Otto noted marked redness of Mr. Solemia's facial skin, as well as reddish purple stripes (striae) in the skin of his lower abdomen and thighs. The patient's body fat was unusually distributed in that it appeared to be excessively deposited centrally in his face, neck, upper back, chest, and abdomen, whereas the distal portions of his arms and legs appeared to be almost devoid of fat. Mr. Solemia's skin appeared thinned and large bruises were present over many areas of his body for which Mr. Solemia had no explanation. The neurologic examination showed severe muscle weakness especially in the proximal arms and legs, where the muscles seemed to have atrophied.

Sam Atotrope, a 42-year-old jeweler, noted increasingly severe headaches behind his eyes that were sometimes associated with a "flash of light" in his visual field. At times his vision seemed blurred, making it difficult to perform some of the intricate work required of a jeweler. He consulted his ophthalmologist, who was impressed with the striking change in Sam's facial features that had occurred since he last saw the patient 5 years earlier. The normal skin creases in Sam's face had grown much deeper, his skin appeared to be thickened, his nose and lips appeared more bulbous, and his jaw seemed more prominent. The doctor also noted that Sam's hands appeared bulky, and his voice had deepened. An eye examination showed that Sam's optic nerves appeared slightly atrophied and there was a loss of the upper outer quadrants of his visual fields.

I. PHYSIOLOGIC EFFECTS OF INSULIN

The effects of insulin on fuel metabolism and substrate flux were considered in many of the earlier chapters of this book, particularly in Chapter 26. Insulin stimulates the storage of glycogen in liver and muscle and the synthesis of fatty acids and triacylglycerols and their storage in adipose tissue. In addition, insulin stimulates the synthesis in various tissues of >50 proteins, some of which contribute to the growth of the organism. In fact, it is difficult to separate the effects of insulin on cell growth from those of a family of proteins known as the somatomedins or the insulin-like growth factors I and II (IGF-I and IGF-II) (see Section III.B.6).

Finally, insulin has paracrine actions within the pancreatic islet cells. When insulin is released from the β-cells, it suppresses glucagon release from the α-cells.

II. PHYSIOLOGIC EFFECTS OF GLUCAGON

Glucagon is one of several counterregulatory (contrainsular) hormones. It is synthesized as part of a large precursor protein called *proglucagon*. Proglucagon is produced in the α-cells of the islets of Langerhans in the pancreas and in the L-cells of the intestine. It contains several peptides linked in tandem: glicentin-related peptide, glucagon, glucagon-like peptide 1 (GLP-1), and glucagon-like peptide 2 (GLP-2). Proteolytic cleavage of proglucagon releases various combinations of its constituent peptides. Glucagon is cleaved from proglucagon in the pancreas and constitutes 30% to 40% of the immunoreactive glucagon in the blood. The remaining immunoreactivity is caused by other cleavage products of proglucagon released

 The measurement of hormone levels in blood is best performed using immunologic reagents that specifically recognize the hormone being measured. Such techniques are further described in the Biochemical Comments of this chapter.

from the pancreas and the intestine. Pancreatic glucagon has a plasma half-life of 3 to 6 minutes and is removed mainly by the liver and kidney.

Glucagon promotes glycogenolysis, gluconeogenesis, and ketogenesis by stimulating the generation of cyclic adenosine monophosphate (cAMP) in target cells. The liver is the major target organ for glucagon, in part because the concentrations of this hormone bathing the liver cells in the portal blood are higher than in the peripheral circulation. Levels of glucagon in the portal vein may reach concentrations as high as 500 pg/mL.

Finally, glucagon stimulates insulin release from the β-cells of the pancreas. Whether this is a paracrine effect or an endocrine effect has not been established. The pattern of blood flow in the pancreatic islet cells is believed to bathe the β-cells first and then the α-cells. Therefore, the β-cells may influence α-cell function by an endocrine mechanism, whereas the influence of α-cell hormone on β-cell function is more likely to be paracrine.

III. PHYSIOLOGIC EFFECTS OF OTHER COUNTERREGULATORY HORMONES

A. Somatostatin

1. BIOCHEMISTRY

Preprosomatostatin, a 116-amino acid peptide, is encoded by a gene located on the long arm of chromosome 3. Somatostatin (SS-14), a cyclic peptide with a molecular weight of 1,600 Da, is produced from the 14 amino acids at the C-terminus of this precursor molecule. SS-14 was first isolated from the hypothalamus and named for its ability to inhibit the release of growth hormone (GH, somatotropin) from the anterior pituitary. It also inhibits the release of insulin. In addition to the hypothalamus, somatostatin is also secreted from the D-cells (δ-cells) of the pancreatic islets, many areas of the central nervous system (CNS) outside of the hypothalamus, and gastric and duodenal mucosal cells. SS-14 predominates in the CNS and is the sole form secreted by the δ-cells of the pancreas. In the gut, however, prosomatostatin (SS-28), which has 14 additional amino acids extending from the C-terminal portion of the precursor, makes up 70% to 75% of the immunoreactivity (the amount of hormone that reacts with antibodies to SS-14). The prohormone SS-28 is 7 to 10 times more potent in inhibiting the release of GH and insulin than SS-14.

2. SECRETION OF SOMATOSTATIN

Tolbutamide, a sulfonylurea drug that increases insulin secretion, also increases the secretion of pancreatic somatostatin.

The secretagogues for somatostatin are similar to those that cause secretion of insulin. The metabolites that increase somatostatin release include glucose, arginine, and leucine. The hormones that stimulate somatostatin secretion include glucagon, vasoactive intestinal polypeptide (VIP), and cholecystokinin (CCK). Insulin, however, does not influence somatostatin secretion directly.

3. PHYSIOLOGIC EFFECTS OF SOMATOSTATIN

Five somatostatin receptors have been identified and characterized, all of which are members of the G protein coupled-receptor superfamily. Four of the five receptors do not distinguish between SS-14 and SS-28. Somatostatin binds to its plasma membrane receptors on target cells. These "activated" receptors interact with a variety of intracellular signaling pathways, depending on the cell type expressing the receptor, and which somatostatin receptor is being expressed. These pathways include inactivation of adenylate cyclase (via an inhibitory G protein), regulation of phosphotyrosine phosphatases and mitogen-activated protein (MAP) kinases, and alterations of intracellular ion concentrations (calcium [Ca^{2+}] and potassium). The inactivation of adenylate cyclases reduces the production of cAMP, and protein kinase A is not activated. This inhibitory effect suppresses secretion of GH and thyroid-stimulating hormone (TSH) from the anterior pituitary gland as well as the secretion of insulin and glucagon from the pancreatic islets. If one were to summarize the action of somatostatin in one phrase, it would be "somatostatin inhibits the secretion of many other hormones." As such, it acts to regulate the effects of those other hormones. In addition to these effects on hormones that regulate fuel metabolism, somatostatin also reduces nutrient absorption from the gut by prolonging gastric emptying time (through a decrease in the secretion of gastrin, which reduces gastric acid secretion), by diminishing pancreatic exocrine secretions (i.e., digestive enzymes, bicarbonate, and water), and by decreasing visceral blood flow. Thus, somatostatin exerts a broad, albeit indirect, influence on nutrient absorption and, therefore, on the use of fuels.

Somatostatin and its synthetic analogs are used clinically to treat a variety of secretory neoplasms such as GH-secreting tumors of the pituitary. Such tumors can cause gigantism if GH is secreted in excess before the closure of the growth centers of the ends of long bones or acromegaly if excess GH is chronically secreted after the closure of these centers (as in **Sam Atotrope**).

B. Growth Hormone

1. BIOCHEMISTRY

GH is a polypeptide that, as its name implies, stimulates growth. Many of its effects are mediated by insulin-like growth factors (IGFs, also known as somatomedins) that are produced by cells in response to the binding of GH to its cell membrane receptors (see Section III.B.6). However, GH also has direct effects on fuel metabolism.

Human GH is a water-soluble 22-kDa polypeptide with a plasma half-life of 20 to 50 minutes. It is composed of a single chain of 191 amino acids having two intramolecular disulfide bonds (Fig. 43.1). The gene for GH is located on chromosome 17. It is secreted by the *somatotroph cells* (the cells that synthesize and release GH) in the lateral areas of the anterior pituitary. GH is structurally related to human prolactin and to *human chorionic somatomammotropin* (hCS) from the placenta—a polypeptide that stimulates growth of the developing fetus. Yet the hCS peptide has only 0.1% of the growth-inducing potency of GH. GH is the most abundant trophic hormone in the anterior pituitary, being present in concentrations of 5 to 15 mg/g of tissue. The other anterior pituitary hormones are present in quantities of micrograms per gram of tissue.

The actions of GH can be classified as those that occur as a consequence of the hormone's direct effect on target cells and those that occur indirectly through the ability of GH to generate other factors, particularly IGF-I.

The IGF-I–independent actions of GH are exerted primarily in hepatocytes. GH administration is followed by an early increase in the synthesis of 8 to 10 proteins, among which are IGF-I, α_2-macroglobulin, and the serine protease inhibitors Spi 2.1 and Spi 2.3. Expression of the gene for ornithine decarboxylase, an enzyme that is active in polyamine synthesis (and, therefore, in the regulation of cell proliferation), is also significantly increased by GH.

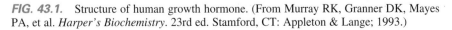

Human growth hormone

FIG. 43.1. Structure of human growth hormone. (From Murray RK, Granner DK, Mayes PA, et al. *Harper's Biochemistry.* 23rd ed. Stamford, CT: Appleton & Lange; 1993.)

 In addition to its effects on normal GH secretion, somatostatin also suppresses the pathologic increase in GH that occurs in acromegaly (caused by a GH-secreting pituitary tumor), diabetes mellitus, and carcinoid tumors (tumors that secrete serotonin). Somatostatin also suppresses the basal secretion of TSH, thyrotropin-releasing hormone (TRH), insulin, and glucagon. The hormone also has a suppressive effect on a wide variety of nonendocrine secretions.

The major limitation in the clinical use of native somatostatin is its short half-life of less than 3 minutes in the circulation. Analogs of native somatostatin, however, have been developed that are resistant to degradation and, therefore, have a longer half-life. One such analog is octreotide, an octapeptide variant of somatostatin with a half-life of approximately 110 minutes.

 A magnetic resonance imaging (MRI) scan of **Sam Atotrope's** brain showed a macroadenoma (a tumor >10 mm in diameter) in the pituitary gland, with superior extension that compressed the optic nerve as it crossed above the sella turcica, causing his visual problems. The skeletal and visceral changes noted by the ophthalmologist are characteristic of acromegalic patients with chronically elevated serum levels of GH and IGF-I.

Therapeutic alternatives for acromegaly caused by a GH-secreting tumor of the anterior pituitary gland include surgery if the mass is amenable or lifelong medical therapy with a somatostatin analog, such as octreotide; or a dopamine agonist that inhibits the secretion of GH, such as cabergoline; or a GH-receptor antagonist, such as pegvisomant. Another therapeutic option is stereotactic radiation therapy. If the excessive secretion of GH is controlled successfully, some of the visceral or soft tissue changes of acromegaly may slowly subside to varying degrees. The skeletal changes, however, cannot be reversed.

The ophthalmologist ordered a morning fasting serum GH level on **Sam Atotrope**, which was elevated at 56 ng/mL (normal, 0 to 5 ng/mL), as well as a determination of circulating insulin-like growth factor I (IGF-I) levels.

Sam Atotrope was given an oral dose of 100 g glucose syrup. This dose would suppress serum GH levels to <2 ng/mL in normal subjects, but not in patients with acromegaly who have an autonomously secreting pituitary tumor making GH. Because Sam's serum GH level was 43 ng/mL after the oral glucose load, a diagnosis of acromegaly was made. The patient was referred to an endocrinologist for further evaluation.

GH stimulates IGF-I gene expression not only in the liver but in several extrahepatic tissues as well. In acromegalics, rising levels of IGF-I cause a gradual generalized increase in skeletal, muscular, and visceral growth. As a consequence, a diffuse increase occurs in the bulk of all tissues ("megaly" means enlargement) especially in the "acral" (most peripheral) tissues of the body such as the face, the hands, and the feet; hence the term "acromegaly."

Sam Atotrope's coarse facial features and bulky hands are typical of patients with acromegaly.

Muscle and adipocyte cell membranes contain GH receptors that mediate direct, rapid metabolic effects on glucose and amino acid transport as well as on lipolysis. These receptors use associated cytoplasmic tyrosine kinases for signal transduction (such as the janus kinases; see Chapter 11, Section III.C). STAT (signal transducer and activator of transcription) transcription factors are activated and, depending on the tissue, the MAP kinase pathway and/or the AKT pathway is also activated. For example, in adipose tissue, GH has acute insulin-like effects followed by increased lipolysis, inhibition of lipoprotein lipase, stimulation of hormone-sensitive lipase, decreased glucose transport, and decreased lipogenesis. In muscle, GH causes increased amino acid transport, increased nitrogen retention, increased fat-free (lean) tissue, and increased energy expenditure. GH also has growth-promoting effects. GH receptors are present on a variety of tissues in which GH increases IGF-I gene expression. The subsequent rise in IGF-I levels contributes to cell multiplication and differentiation by autocrine or paracrine mechanisms. These, in turn, lead to skeletal, muscular, and visceral growth. These actions are accompanied by a direct anabolic influence of GH on protein metabolism with a diversion of amino acids from oxidation to protein synthesis and a shift to a positive nitrogen balance.

2. CONTROL OF SECRETION OF GROWTH HORMONE

Although the regulation of GH secretion is complex, the major influence is hormonal (Fig. 43.2). The pulsatile pattern of GH secretion reflects the interplay of two hypothalamic regulatory peptides. Release is stimulated by growth hormone-releasing hormone (GHRH, also called somatocrinin). The structure of GHRH was identified in 1982 (Fig. 43.3). It exists as both a 40- and a 44-amino acid peptide encoded on chromosome 20 and produced exclusively in cells of the arcuate nucleus. Its C-terminal leucine residue is amidated. Full biologic activity of this releasing hormone resides in the first 29 amino acids of the N-terminal portion of the molecule. GHRH interacts with specific receptors on the plasma membranes of the somatotrophs. The intracellular signaling mechanisms that result in GH synthesis and release appear to be multiple, as cAMP and calcium-calmodulin both stimulate GH release.

Conversely, GH secretion is suppressed by growth hormone release–inhibiting hormone (GHRIH, the same as somatostatin, which has already been discussed). In addition, IGF-I, produced primarily in the liver in response to the action of GH on hepatocytes, feeds back negatively on the somatotrophs to limit GH secretion. Other physiologic factors (e.g., exercise and sleep) and many pathologic factors also control its release (Table 43.2).

In addition, GH release is modulated by plasma levels of all of the metabolic fuels, including proteins, fats, and carbohydrates. A rising level of glucose in the blood normally suppresses GH release, whereas hypoglycemia increases GH secretion in normal subjects. Amino acids, such as arginine, stimulate release of GH when their concentrations rise in the blood. Rising levels of fatty acids may blunt the GH response to arginine or a rapidly dropping blood glucose level. However, prolonged fasting, in which fatty acids are mobilized in an effort to spare protein, is associated with a rise in GH secretion. Some of the physiologic, pharmacologic, and pathologic influences on GH secretion are given in Table 43.2. These modulators of GH secretion provide the basis for clinical suppression and stimulation tests in patients suspected of having excessive or deficient GH secretion.

3. EFFECTS OF GROWTH HORMONE ON ENERGY METABOLISM

GH affects the uptake and oxidation of fuels in adipose tissue, muscle, and liver and indirectly influences energy metabolism through its actions on the islet cells of the pancreas. In summary, GH increases the availability of fatty acids, which are oxidized for energy. This and other effects of GH spare glucose and protein; that is, GH indirectly decreases the oxidation of glucose and amino acids (Fig. 43.4).

4. EFFECTS OF GROWTH HORMONE ON ADIPOSE TISSUE

GH increases the sensitivity of the adipocyte to the lipolytic action of the catecholamines and decreases its sensitivity to the lipogenic action of insulin. These actions lead to the release of free fatty acids and glycerol into the blood to be metabolized by the liver. GH also decreases esterification of fatty acids, thereby reducing triacylglycerol synthesis within the fat cell. Recent evidence suggests that GH may impair glucose uptake by both fat and muscle cells by a postreceptor inhibition of insulin action. As a result of the metabolic effects of GH, the clinical course of acromegaly (increased GH secretion) may be complicated by impaired glucose tolerance or even overt diabetes mellitus.

5. EFFECTS OF GROWTH HORMONE ON MUSCLE

The lipolytic effects of GH increase free fatty acid levels in the blood that bathes muscle. These fatty acids are used preferentially as fuel, indirectly suppressing glucose uptake by muscle cells. Through the effects on glucose uptake, the rate of glycolysis is proportionately reduced.

GH increases the transport of amino acids into muscle cells, providing substrate for protein synthesis. Through a separate mechanism, GH increases the synthesis of DNA and RNA. The positive effect on nitrogen balance is reinforced by the protein-sparing effect of GH-induced lipolysis that makes fatty acids available to muscle as an alternative fuel source.

6. EFFECTS OF GROWTH HORMONE ON THE LIVER

When plasma insulin levels are low, as in the fasting state, GH enhances fatty acid oxidation to acetyl coenzyme A (acetyl-CoA). This effect, in concert with the increased flow of fatty acids from adipose tissue, enhances ketogenesis. The increased amount of glycerol reaching the liver as a consequence of enhanced lipolysis acts as a substrate for gluconeogenesis.

Hepatic glycogen synthesis is also stimulated by GH in part because of the increased gluconeogenesis in the liver. Finally, glucose metabolism is suppressed by GH at several steps in the glycolytic pathway.

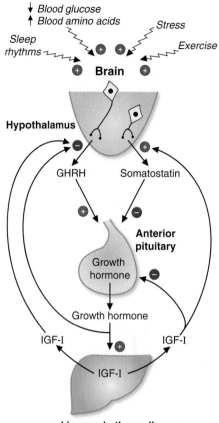

FIG. 43.2. Control of GH secretion. Various factors stimulate the release of GHRH from the hypothalamus. The hypothalamus also releases somatostatin in response to other stimuli. GHRH stimulates and somatostatin inhibits the release of growth hormone from the anterior pituitary. GH causes the release of IGF-I from liver and other tissues. IGF-I inhibits GHRH release and stimulates somatostatin release.

Growth hormone–releasing hormone (GHRH)

Growth hormone release–inhibiting hormone (GHRIH) (Somatostatin)

FIG. 43.3. Structures of growth hormone-releasing hormone (GHRH) and growth hormone release–inhibiting hormone (GHRIH, the same as somatostatin). GHRH has an amide at the C-terminal (in *box*).

 While **Sam Atotrope** was trying to decide which of the major alternatives for the treatment of his growth hormone (GH)–secreting pituitary tumor to choose, he noted progressive fatigue and the onset of increasing urinary frequency associated with a marked increase in thirst. In addition, he had lost 4 lb over the course of the last 6 weeks in spite of a good appetite. His physician suspected that Mr. Atotrope had developed diabetes mellitus, perhaps related to the chronic hypersecretion of GH. This suspicion was confirmed when Sam's serum glucose level—drawn before breakfast—was reported to be 236 mg/dL.

Table 43.2   Some Factors Affecting Growth Hormone Secretion

	Stimulate	*Suppress*
Physiologic	Low blood glucose after meals High blood amino acids after meals Exercise Sleep Stress	High blood glucose after meals High blood fatty acids
Pharmacologic	GHRH Estrogens α-Adrenergic agonists β-Adrenergic antagonists Dopamine agonists Serotonin precursors K$^+$ infusion	Somatostatin Progesterone α-Adrenergic antagonists β-Adrenergic agonists Dopamine antagonists Growth hormone and IGF-I
Pathologic	Starvation Anorexia nervosa Ectopic GHRH production Acromegaly Chronic renal failure Hypoglycemia	Obesity Hypothyroidism Hyperthyroidism

GHRH, growth hormone-releasing hormone; IGF-I, insulin-like growth factor I.

A major effect of GH on liver is to stimulate production and release of IGFs. The IGFs are also known as somatomedins. The two somatomedins in humans share structural homologies with proinsulin, and both have substantial insulin-like growth activity—hence the designations insulin-like growth factor I (human IGF-I, or somatomedin-C) and insulin-like growth factor II (human IGF-II, or somatomedin-A). IGF-I is a single chain basic peptide that has 70 amino acids, and IGF-II is slightly acidic with 67 amino acids. These two peptides are identical to insulin in half of their residues. In addition, they contain a structural domain that is homologous to the C-peptide of proinsulin.

A broad spectrum of normal cells respond to high doses of insulin by increasing thymidine uptake and initiating cell propagation. In most instances, IGF-I

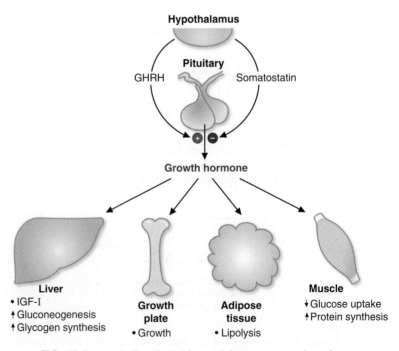

FIG. 43.4.   Anabolic effects of growth hormone on various tissues.

causes the same response as insulin in these cells but at significantly smaller, more physiologic concentrations. Thus, the IGFs are more potent than insulin in their growth-promoting actions.

Evidence suggests that the IGFs exert their effects through either an endocrine or a paracrine/autocrine mechanism. IGF-I appears to stimulate cell propagation and growth by binding to specific IGF-I receptors on the plasma membrane of target cells, rather than binding to GH receptors (Fig. 43.5).

Like insulin, the intracellular portion of the plasma membrane receptor for IGF-I (but not IGF-II) has intrinsic tyrosine kinase activity. The fact that the receptors for insulin and several other growth factors have intrinsic tyrosine kinase activity indicates that tyrosine phosphorylation initiates the process of cellular replication and growth. Subsequently, a chain of kinases is activated, which include several proto-oncogene products (see Chapters 11 and 18).

Most cells of the body have mRNA for IGF, but the liver has the greatest concentration of these messages, followed by kidney and heart. The synthesis of IGF-I is regulated, for the most part, by GH whereas hepatic production of IGF-II is independent of GH levels in the blood.

C. Catecholamines (Epinephrine, Norepinephrine, Dopamine)

The catecholamines belong to a family of bioamines and are secretory products of the sympathoadrenal system. They are required for the body to adapt to a great variety of acute and chronic stresses. Epinephrine (80% to 85% of stored catecholamines) is synthesized primarily in the cells of the adrenal medulla, whereas norepinephrine (15% to 20% of stored catecholamines) is synthesized and stored not only in the adrenal medulla but also in various areas of the CNS and in the nerve endings of the adrenergic nervous system. Dopamine, another catecholamine, acts primarily as a neurotransmitter and has little effect on fuel metabolism.

The first total chemical synthesis of epinephrine was accomplished by Stolz et al. in 1904. In 1950, Sutherland was the first to demonstrate that epinephrine (and glucagon) induces glycogenolysis. This marked the beginning of our understanding of the molecular mechanisms through which hormones act.

1. SYNTHESIS OF THE CATECHOLAMINES

Tyrosine is the precursor of the catecholamines. The pathway for the biosynthesis of these molecules is described in Chapter 48.

2. SECRETION OF THE CATECHOLAMINES

Secretion of epinephrine and norepinephrine from the adrenal medulla is stimulated by a variety of stresses, including pain, hemorrhage, exercise, hypoglycemia, and hypoxia. Release is mediated by stress-induced transmission of nerve impulses emanating from adrenergic nuclei in the hypothalamus. These impulses stimulate the release of the neurotransmitter acetylcholine from preganglionic neurons that innervate the adrenomedullary cells. Acetylcholine depolarizes the plasma membranes of these cells, allowing the rapid entry of extracellular Ca^{2+} into the cytosol. Ca^{2+} stimulates the synthesis and release of epinephrine and norepinephrine from the chromaffin granules into the extracellular space by exocytosis.

3. PHYSIOLOGIC EFFECTS OF EPINEPHRINE AND NOREPINEPHRINE

The catecholamines act through two major types of receptors on the plasma membrane of target cells: the α-adrenergic and the β-adrenergic receptors (see Chapter 26, Section IV.C).

The actions of epinephrine and norepinephrine in the liver, the adipocyte, the skeletal muscle cell, and the α- and β-cells of the pancreas directly influence fuel metabolism (Fig. 43.6). These catecholamines are counterregulatory hormones that have metabolic effects directed toward mobilization of fuels from their storage sites for oxidation by cells to meet the increased energy requirements of acute and

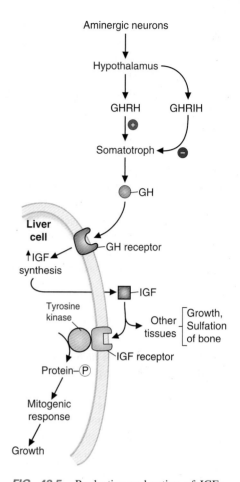

FIG. 43.5. Production and action of IGFs. The hypothalamus produces GHRH, which stimulates somatotrophs in the anterior pituitary to release GH. GHRIH inhibits GH release. GH binds to cell surface receptors and stimulates IGF production and release by liver and other tissues. IGF binds to cell surface receptors and stimulates the phosphorylation of proteins that lead to cell division and growth.

 High levels of circulating IGF-I have been linked to the development of breast, prostate, colon, and lung cancer. Additionally, experimental modulation of IGF-I receptor activity can alter the growth of different types of tumor cells. Current research is aimed at targeting the interaction of IGF-I and its receptor to reduce tumor cell proliferation.

In patients suspected of having a neoplasm of the adrenal medulla that is secreting excessive quantities of epinephrine or norepinephrine (a pheochromocytoma), either the catecholamines themselves (epinephrine, norepinephrine, and dopamine) or their metabolites (the metanephrines and vanillylmandelic acid [VMA]) may be measured in a 24-hour urine collection, or the level of catecholamines in the blood may be measured. A patient who has consistently elevated levels in the blood or urine should be considered to have a pheochromocytoma, particularly if the patient has signs and symptoms of catecholamine excess such as excessive sweating, palpitations, tremulousness, and hypertension.

A relatively rare form of secondary hypertension (high blood pressure) is caused by a catecholamine-secreting neoplasm of the adrenal medulla, known as a pheochromocytoma. Patients with this kind of tumor periodically secrete large amounts of epinephrine and norepinephrine into the bloodstream. Symptoms related to this secretion include a sudden and often severe increase in blood pressure, heart palpitations, a throbbing headache, and inappropriate and diffuse sweating. In addition, chronic hypersecretion of these catecholamines may lead to impaired glucose tolerance or even overt diabetes mellitus. Describe the actions of these hormones that lead to the significant rise in glucose levels.

chronic stress. They simultaneously suppress insulin secretion, which ensures that fuel fluxes will continue in the direction of fuel use rather than storage as long as the stressful stimulus persists.

In addition, norepinephrine works as a neurotransmitter and affects the sympathetic nervous system in the heart, lungs, blood vessels, bladder, gut, and other organs. These effects of catecholamines on the heart and blood vessels increase cardiac output and systemic blood pressure, hemodynamic changes that facilitate the delivery of blood-borne fuels to metabolically active tissues.

Epinephrine has a short half-life in the blood and, to be effective pharmacologically, it must be administered parenterally. It may be used clinically to support the beating of the heart, to dilate inflamed bronchial muscles, and even to decrease bleeding from organs during surgery.

4. METABOLISM AND INACTIVATION OF CATECHOLAMINES

Catecholamines have a relatively low affinity for both α- and β-receptors. After binding, the catecholamine disassociates from its receptor quickly, causing the duration of the biologic response to be brief. The free hormone is degraded in several ways as outlined in Chapter 48.

D. Glucocorticoids
1. BIOCHEMISTRY

Cortisol (hydrocortisone) is the major physiologic glucocorticoid (GC) in humans, although corticosterone also has some GC activity. GCs, such as cortisol, were

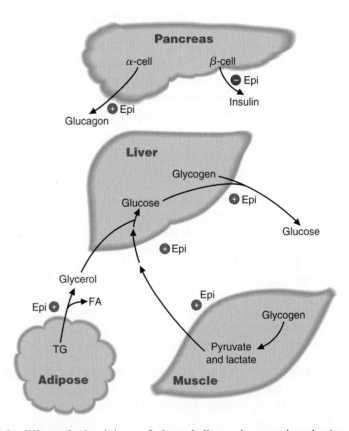

FIG. 43.6. Effects of epinephrine on fuel metabolism and pancreatic endocrine function. Epinephrine (*Epi*) stimulates glycogen breakdown in muscle and liver, gluconeogenesis in liver, and lipolysis in adipose tissue. Epi further reinforces these effects because it increases the secretion of glucagon, a hormone that shares many of the same effects as epinephrine. Epi also inhibits insulin release while stimulating glucagon release from the pancreas. *FA*, fatty acid; *TG*, triglyceride.

named for their ability to raise blood glucose levels. These steroids are among the "counterregulatory" hormones that protect the body from insulin-induced hypoglycemia. The biosynthesis of steroid hormones and their basic mechanism of action has been described in Chapters 16 and 34.

2. SECRETION OF GLUCOCORTICOIDS

The synthesis and secretion of cortisol are controlled by a cascade of neural and endocrine signals linked in tandem in the cerebrocortical–hypothalamic–pituitary–adrenocortical axis. Cerebrocortical signals to the midbrain are initiated in the cerebral cortex by "stressful" signals such as pain, hypoglycemia, hemorrhage, and exercise (Fig. 43.7). These nonspecific "stresses" elicit the production of monoamines in the cell bodies of neurons of the midbrain. Those that stimulate the synthesis and release of corticotropin-releasing hormone (CRH) are acetylcholine and serotonin. These neurotransmitters then induce the production of CRH by neurons originating in the paraventricular nucleus. These neurons discharge CRH into the hypothalamico-hypophyseal portal blood. CRH is delivered through these portal vessels to specific receptors on the cell membrane of the adrenocorticotropic hormone (ACTH)-secreting cells of the anterior pituitary gland (corticotrophs). This hormone–receptor interaction causes ACTH to be released into the general circulation, eventually to interact with specific receptors for ACTH on the plasma membranes of cells in the zona fasciculata and zona reticulosum of the adrenal cortex. The major trophic influence of ACTH on cortisol synthesis is at the level of the conversion of cholesterol to pregnenolone, from which the adrenal steroid hormones are derived (see Chapter 34 for the biosynthesis of the steroid hormones).

Cortisol is secreted from the adrenal cortex in response to ACTH. The concentration of free (unbound) cortisol that bathes the CRH-producing cells of the hypothalamus and the ACTH-producing cells of the anterior pituitary acts as a negative feedback signal that has a regulatory influence on the release of CRH and ACTH (see Fig. 43.7). High cortisol levels in the blood suppress CRH and ACTH secretion, and low cortisol levels stimulate secretion. In severe stress, however, the negative feedback signal on ACTH secretion exerted by high cortisol levels in the blood is overridden by the stress-induced activity of the higher portions of the axis (see Fig. 43.7).

The effects of GCs on fuel metabolism in liver, skeletal muscle, and adipose tissue are outlined in Table 43.1 and in Figure 43.8. Their effects on other tissues are diverse and, in many instances, essential for life. Some of the nonmetabolic actions of GCs are listed in Table 43.3.

3. EFFECTS OF GLUCOCORTICOIDS

GCs have diverse actions that affect most tissues of the body. At first glance, some of these effects may appear to be contradictory (such as inhibition of glucose uptake by certain tissues), but taken together they promote survival in times of stress.

In many tissues, GCs inhibit DNA, RNA, and protein synthesis and stimulate the degradation of these macromolecules. In response to chronic stress, GCs act to make fuels available, so that when the acute alarm sounds and epinephrine is released, the organism can fight or flee. When GCs are elevated, glucose uptake by the cells of many tissues is inhibited, lipolysis occurs in peripheral adipose tissue, and proteolysis occurs in skin, lymphoid cells, and muscle. The fatty acids that are released are oxidized by the liver for energy, and the glycerol and amino acids serve in the liver as substrates for the production of glucose, which is converted to glycogen and stored. The alarm signal of epinephrine stimulates liver glycogen breakdown, making glucose available as fuel to combat the acute stress.

The mechanism by which GCs exert these effects involves binding of the steroid to intracellular receptors, interaction of the steroid–receptor complex with

 The catecholamines are counterregulatory hormones that mobilize fuels from their storage sites for oxidation in target cells to meet the increased energy requirements that occur during acute or chronic stress, or in this case, the release of catecholamines by a tumor in the adrenal medulla. These actions provide the liver, for example, with increased levels of substrate needed for gluconeogenesis. Although in normal individuals, most of the glucose generated through this mechanism is oxidized—blood glucose levels rise in the process. In addition, the catecholamines suppress insulin secretion to ensure that fuels will continue to flow in the direction of use rather than storage under these circumstances. Hence, blood glucose levels may rise in patients who have a pheochromocytoma.

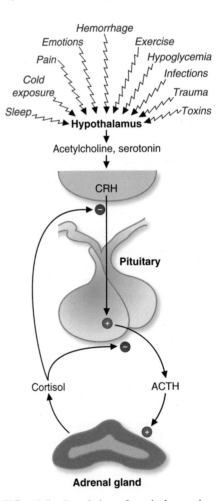

FIG. 43.7. Regulation of cortisol secretion. Various factors act on the hypothalamus to stimulate the release of CRH. CRH stimulates the release of ACTH from the anterior pituitary, which stimulates the release of cortisol from the adrenal cortex. Cortisol inhibits the release of CRH and ACTH via negative feedback loops.

When **Otto Shape** was writing his list of differential diagnoses to explain the clinical presentation of **Corti Solemia**, he suddenly thought of a relatively rare endocrine disorder that could explain all of the presenting signs and symptoms. He made a provisional diagnosis of excessive secretion of cortisol secondary to an excess secretion of ACTH (Cushing "disease") or by a primary increase of cortisol production by an adrenocortical tumor (Cushing syndrome).

Otto suggested that resting, fasting plasma cortisol and ACTH levels be measured at 8:00 the next morning. These studies showed that Mr. Solemia's morning plasma ACTH and cortisol levels were both significantly higher than the reference range. Therefore, Otto concluded that Mr. Solemia probably had a tumor that was producing ACTH autonomously (i.e., not subject to normal feedback inhibition by cortisol). The high plasma levels of ACTH were stimulating the adrenal cortex to produce excessive amounts of cortisol. Additional laboratory and imaging studies indicated that the hypercortisolemia was caused by a benign ACTH-secreting adenoma of the anterior pituitary gland (Cushing "disease").

Otto Shape was now able to explain the mechanism for most of **Corti Solemia's** signs and symptoms. For example, Otto knew the metabolic explanation for the patient's hyperglycemia. Some of Mr. Solemia's muscle wasting and weakness were caused by the catabolic effect of hypercortisolemia on protein stores, such as those in skeletal muscle, to provide amino acids as precursors for gluconeogenesis. This catabolic action also resulted in the degradation of elastin, a major supportive protein of the skin, as well as an increased fragility of the walls of the capillaries of the cutaneous tissues. These changes resulted in the easy bruisability and the torn subcutaneous tissues of the lower abdomen, which resulted in red striae or stripes. The plethora (redness) of Mr. Solemia's facial skin was also caused in part by the thinning of the skin as well as by a cortisol-induced increase in the bone marrow production of red blood cells, which enhanced the "redness" of the subcutaneous tissues.

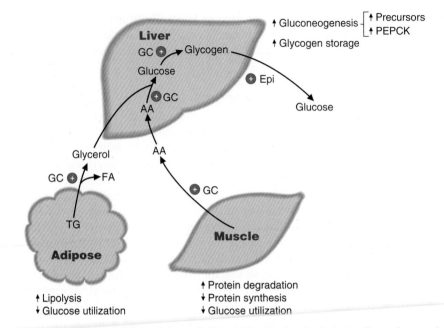

FIG. 43.8.   Effects of GCs on fuel metabolism. GCs stimulate lipolysis in adipose tissue and the release of amino acids from muscle protein. In liver, GCs stimulate gluconeogenesis and the synthesis of glycogen. The breakdown of liver glycogen is stimulated by epinephrine. *AA*, amino acid; *Epi*, epinephrine; *PEPCK*, phosphoenolpyruvate carboxykinase; *TG*, triglyceride.

GC response elements on DNA, transcription of genes, and synthesis of specific proteins (see Chapter 16, Section III.C.2). In some cases, the specific proteins responsible for the GC effect are known (e.g., the induction of phosphoenolpyruvate carboxykinase that stimulates gluconeogenesis). In other cases, the proteins responsible for the GC effect have not yet been identified.

Table 43.3   Some Nonmetabolic Physiologic Actions of Glucocorticoids

On electrolyte and water balance:
  Increase sodium and water retention (1/3,000 the potency of aldosterone)
  Increase renal glomerular filtration rate to maintain water excretion rate
On cardiovascular system:
  Indirect effect of glucocorticoid actions on sodium and water metabolism (above)
  Maintain volume of microcirculation to tissues (cardiac output)
  Maintain normal vasomotor response to vasoconstricting agents
On skeletal muscle:
  Maintain muscle function by providing normal microcirculation to muscle
  Influence muscle mass by enhancing protein catabolism and suppressing protein synthesis
On central nervous system:
  Indirect
    Maintain normal cerebral microcirculation
  Direct
    Influence mood, behavior
    Influence sensitivity of special senses to stimuli
    Suppress CRH, ACTH, and ADH secretion
On formed elements in blood:
  Increase red blood cell mass and granulocyte proliferation
  Decrease lymphocyte, monocyte, and basophil proliferation
Anti-inflammatory actions:
  Inhibit early inflammatory process (i.e., edema, fibrin deposition, capillary dilation, leukocyte migration, and phagocytic action)
  Inhibit late inflammatory process (proliferation of capillaries and fibroblasts, deposition of collagen, and later scar formation)
Immune-suppressant actions (of questionable significance at physiologic levels):
  Prevent manifestations of humoral and cellular immunity
  Interfere with production of cytokines needed for immune competence via cell-to-cell communication

CRH, corticotropin-releasing hormone; ACTH, adrenocorticotropic hormone; ADH, antidiuretic hormone.

E. Thyroid Hormone

1. BIOCHEMISTRY

The secretory products of the thyroid acinar cells are tetra-iodothyronine (thyroxine, T_4) and triiodothyronine (T_3). Their structures are shown in Figure 43.9. The basic steps in the synthesis of T_3 and T_4 in these cells involve the transport or trapping of iodide from the blood into the thyroid acinar cell against an electrochemical gradient; the oxidation of iodide to form an iodinating species; the iodination of tyrosyl residues on the protein, thyroglobulin (Tgb), to form iodotyrosines; and the coupling of residues of monoiodotyrosine and diiodotyrosine in Tgb to form residues of T_3 and T_4 (Fig. 43.10). Proteolytic cleavage of Tgb releases free T_3 and T_4. The steps in thyroid hormone synthesis are stimulated by TSH, a glycoprotein produced by the anterior pituitary. Approximately 35% of T_4 is deiodinated at the 5'-position to form T_3, and 43% is deiodinated at the 5'-position to form the inactive "reverse" T_3. Further deiodination or oxidative deamination leads to formation of compounds that have no biologic activity.

Iodide transport from the blood into the thyroid acinar cell is accomplished through an energy-requiring, iodide-trapping mechanism that requires symport with sodium (Na^+). The sodium–iodide symporter (NIS, encoded by the SLC5A5 gene) is driven by the electrochemical gradient across the membrane that is established by the Na^+,K^+-ATPase. For each iodide anion transported across the membrane, two Na^+ ions are cotransported to facilitate and drive the translocation of the ions. Loss of NIS activity leads to congenital iodide transport defect.

The rate of iodide transport is influenced by the absolute concentration of iodide within the thyroid cell. An internal autoregulatory mechanism decreases transport of iodide into the cell when the intracellular iodide concentration exceeds a certain threshold and increases transport when intracellular iodide falls lower than this threshold level. The iodide-concentrating or trapping process in the plasma membrane of thyroid acinar cells create iodide levels within the thyroid cell that are several hundredfold greater than those in the blood, depending on the current size of the total body iodide pool and the present need for new hormone synthesis.

The oxidation of intracellular iodide is catalyzed by thyroid peroxidase (located at the apical border of the thyroid acinar cell) in what may be a two-electron oxidation step forming I^+ (iodinium ion). I^+ may react with a tyrosine residue in the protein Tgb to form a tyrosine quinoid and then a 3'-monoiodotyrosine (MIT) residue. It has been suggested that a second iodide is added to the ring by similar mechanisms to form a 3,5-diiodotyrosine (DIT) residue. Because iodide is added to these organic compounds, iodination is also referred to as the "organification of iodide."

 If **Corti Solemia's** problem had been caused by a neoplasm of the adrenal cortex, what would his levels of blood ACTH and cortisol have been?

 Once iodide anion enters the thyroid follicular cell, it must be transported across the apical membrane to react with thyroid peroxidase and thyroglobulin (Tgb). The apical iodide transporter is pendrin (encoded by the SLC26A4 gene), and mutations in pendrin lead to Pendred syndrome. Children with this syndrome display a total loss of hearing, goiter (swelling of the thyroid gland), and metabolic defects in iodide organification.

FIG. 43.9. Thyroid hormones T_3 and T_4.

Tgb with Tyr residues

Tgb with DIT

Tgb with T₄

Colloid

H_2O_2

I^+

Iodination

Coupling

PD

Exocytosis

Pinocytosis

Tgb with T_4 ($+ T_3$)

Lysosomes

Tgb

Digestion by lysosomal proteases

Tgb with T_4 ($+ T_3$)

Protein synthesis

I^-

RER

Thyroid follicular cell

T_3 T_4

Blood

Iodine pump

NIS

I^-

T_3 T_4

FIG. 43.10. Synthesis of the thyroid hormones (T_3 and T_4). The protein thyroglobulin (Tgb) is synthesized in thyroid follicular cells and secreted into the colloid. Iodination and coupling of tyrosine residues in Tgb produce T_3 and T_4 residues, which are released from Tgb by pinocytosis (endocytosis) and lysosomal action. The coupling of a monoiodotyrosine (MIT) with a diiodotyrosine (DIT) to form triiodothyronine (T_3) is not depicted here. *RER*, rough endoplasmic reticulum; *NIS*, sodium–iodide symporter; *PD*, pendrin.

A: If **Corti Solemia's** problem had resulted from primary hypersecretion of cortisol by a neoplasm of the adrenal cortex, his blood cortisol levels would have been elevated. The cortisol would have acted on the CRH-producing cells of the hypothalamus and the ACTH-secreting cells of the anterior pituitary by a negative feedback mechanism to decrease ACTH levels in the blood.

Because his cortisol and ACTH levels were both high, Mr. Solemia's tumor was most likely in the pituitary gland or possibly in neoplastic extrapituitary tissue that was secreting ACTH "ectopically." ("Ectopic" means that the tumor or neoplasm is producing and secreting a substance that is not ordinarily made or secreted by the tissue from which the tumor developed.) Mr. Solemia's tumor was in the anterior pituitary, not in an extrapituitary ACTH-producing site.

The biosynthesis of thyroid hormone proceeds with the coupling of an MIT and a DIT residue to form a T_3 residue or of two DIT residues to form a T_4 residue. T_3 and T_4 are stored in the thyroid follicle as amino acid residues in Tgb. Under most circumstances, the T_4/T_3 ratio in Tgb is approximately 13:1. Normally, the thyroid gland secretes 80 to 100 μg of T_4 and approximately 5 μg of T_3 per day. The additional 22 to 25 μg of T_3 "produced" daily is the result of the deiodination of the 5'-carbon of T_4 in peripheral tissues. T_3 is believed to be the predominant biologically active form of thyroid hormone in the body. The thyroid gland is unique in that it has the capacity to store large amounts of hormone as amino acid residues in Tgb within its colloid space. This storage accounts for the low overall turnover rate of T_3 and T_4 in the body.

The plasma half-life of T_4 is approximately 7 days, and that of T_3 is 1 to 1.5 days. These relatively long plasma half-lives result from binding of T_3 and T_4 to several transport proteins in the blood. Of these transport proteins, thyroid-binding globulin (TBG) has the highest affinity for these hormones and carries approximately 70% of bound T_3 and T_4. Only 0.03% of total T_4 and 0.3% of total T_3 in the blood are in the unbound state. This free fraction of hormone has biologic activity because it is the only form that is capable of diffusing across target cell membranes to interact with intracellular receptors. The transport proteins, therefore, serve as a large reservoir of hormone that can release additional free hormone as the metabolic need arises.

The thyroid hormones are degraded in liver, kidney, muscle, and other tissues by deiodination, which produces compounds with no biologic activity.

2. SECRETION OF THYROID HORMONE

The release of T_3 and T_4 from Tgb is controlled by TSH from the anterior pituitary. TSH stimulates the endocytosis of Tgb to form endocytic vesicles within the thyroid acinar cells (see Fig. 43.10). Lysosomes fuse with these vesicles, and lysosomal proteases hydrolyze Tgb, releasing free T_4 and T_3 into the blood in a 10:1 ratio. In various tissues, T_4 is deiodinated, forming T_3, which is the active form of the hormone.

TSH is synthesized in the thyrotropic cells of the anterior pituitary. Its secretion is regulated primarily by a balance between the stimulatory action of hypothalamic thyrotropin-releasing hormone (TRH) and the inhibitory (negative feedback) influence of thyroid hormone (primarily T_3) at levels higher than a critical threshold in the blood bathing the pituitary thyrotrophs. TSH secretion occurs in a circadian pattern, a surge beginning late in the afternoon and peaking before the onset of sleep. In addition, TSH is secreted in a pulsatile fashion, with intervals of 2 to 6 hours between peaks.

TSH stimulates all phases of thyroid hormone synthesis by the thyroid gland, including iodide trapping from the plasma, organification of iodide, coupling of MIT and DIT, endocytosis of Tgb, and proteolysis of Tgb to release T_3 and T_4 (see Fig. 43.10). In addition, the vascularity of the thyroid gland increases as TSH stimulates hypertrophy and hyperplasia of the thyroid acinar cells.

The predominant mechanism of action of TSH is mediated by binding of TSH to its G protein coupled-receptor on the plasma membrane of the thyroid acinar cell, leading to an increase in the concentration of cytosolic cAMP (through $G\alpha s$) and Ca^{2+} (through $G\alpha q$). The increase in Ca^{2+} is brought about by activation of phospholipase C, eventually leading to the activation of the MAP kinase pathway.

The large protein Tgb, which contains T_3 and T_4 in peptide linkage, is stored extracellularly in the colloid that fills the central space of each thyroid follicle. Each of the biochemical reactions that leads to the release and eventual secretion of T_3 and T_4, such as those that lead to their formation in Tgbs, is TSH-dependent. Rising levels of serum TSH stimulate the endocytosis of stored Tgb into the thyroid acinar cell. Lysosomal enzymes then cleave T_3 and T_4 from Tgb. T_3 and T_4 are secreted into the bloodstream in response to rising levels of TSH.

As the free T_3 level in the blood bathing the thyrotrophs of the anterior pituitary gland rises, the feedback loop is closed. Secretion of TSH is inhibited until the free T_3 levels in the systemic circulation fall just below a critical level, which once again signals the release of TSH. This feedback mechanism ensures an uninterrupted supply of biologically active free T_3 in the blood (Fig. 43.11). High levels of T_3 also inhibit the release of TRH from the hypothalamus.

3. PHYSIOLOGIC EFFECTS OF THYROID HORMONE

Only those physiologic actions of thyroid hormone that influence fuel metabolism are considered here. It is important to stress the term "physiologic" because the effects of supraphysiologic concentrations of thyroid hormone on fuel metabolism may not be simple extensions of their physiologic effects. For example, when T_3 is present in excess, it has severe catabolic effects that increase the flow of amino acids from muscle into the blood and eventually to the liver. In general, the following comments apply to the effects of thyroid hormone on energy metabolism in individuals who have normal thyroid hormone levels in their blood.

i. Effects of Thyroid Hormone on the Liver

Several of the actions of thyroid hormone affect carbohydrate and lipid metabolism in the liver. Thyroid hormone increases glycolysis and cholesterol synthesis and increases the conversion of cholesterol to bile salts. Through its action of increasing

The "central" deposition of fat in patients, such as **Corti Solemia**, with Cushing "disease" or syndrome is not readily explained because GCs actually cause lipolysis in adipose tissue. The increased appetite caused by an excess of GC and the lipogenic effects of the hyperinsulinemia that accompanies the GC-induced chronic increase in blood glucose levels have been suggested as possible causes. Why the fat is deposited centrally under these circumstances, however, is not understood. This central deposition leads to the development of a large fat pad at the center of the upper back ("buffalo hump"), to accumulation of fat in the cheeks and jaws ("moon facies") and neck area, as well as a marked increase in abdominal fat. Simultaneously, there is a loss of adipose and muscle tissue below the elbows and knees, exaggerating the appearance of "central obesity" in Cushing "disease" or syndrome.

In areas of the world in which the soil is deficient in iodide, hypothyroidism is common. The thyroid gland enlarges (forms a goiter) in an attempt to produce more thyroid hormone. In the United States, table salt (NaCl) enriched with iodide (iodized salt) is used to prevent hypothyroidism caused by iodine deficiency.

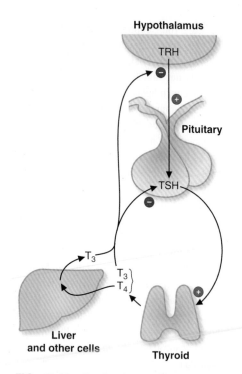

Hypothalamus

TRH

Pituitary

TSH

T₃

T₃
T₄

Liver
and other cells

Thyroid

FIG. 43.11. Feedback regulation of thyroid hormone levels. TRH from the hypothalamus stimulates the release of TSH from the anterior pituitary, which stimulates the release of T₃ and T₄ from the thyroid. T₄ is converted to T₃ in the liver and other cells. T₃ inhibits the release of TSH from the anterior pituitary and of TRH from the hypothalamus.

A patient presents with the following clinical and laboratory profile: The serum free and total T₃ and T₄ and the serum TSH levels are elevated, but the patient has symptoms of mild hypothyroidism, including a diffuse, palpable goiter. What single abnormality in the pituitary–thyroid–thyroid hormone target cell axis would explain all of these findings?

the sensitivity of the hepatocyte to the gluconeogenic and glycogenolytic actions of epinephrine, T₃ indirectly increases hepatic glucose production (permissive or facilitatory action). Because of its ability to sensitize the adipocyte to the lipolytic action of epinephrine, T₃ increases the flow of fatty acids to the liver and thereby indirectly increases hepatic triacylglycerol synthesis. The concurrent increase in the flow of glycerol to the liver (as a result of increased lipolysis) further enhances hepatic gluconeogenesis.

ii. Effects of Thyroid Hormone on the Adipocyte

T₃ has an amplifying or facilitatory effect on the lipolytic action of epinephrine on fat cells. Yet thyroid hormone has a bipolar effect on lipid storage because it increases the availability of glucose to the fat cells, which serves as a precursor for fatty acid and glycerol 3-phosphate synthesis. The major determinant of the rate of lipogenesis, however, is not T₃, but rather the amount of glucose and insulin available to the adipocyte for triacylglycerol synthesis.

iii. Effects of Thyroid Hormone on Muscle

In physiologic concentrations, T₃ increases glucose uptake by muscle cells. It also stimulates protein synthesis and, therefore, growth of muscle, through its stimulatory actions on gene expression.

In physiologic concentrations, thyroid hormone sensitizes the muscle cell to the glycogenolytic actions of epinephrine. Glycolysis in muscle is increased by this action of T₃.

iv. Effects of Thyroid Hormone on the Pancreas

Thyroid hormone increases the sensitivity of the β-cells of the pancreas to those stimuli that normally promote insulin release and is required for optimal insulin secretion.

4. CALORIGENIC EFFECTS OF THYROID HORMONE

The oxidation of fuels convert approximately 25% of the potential energy present in the foods ingested by humans to adenosine triphosphate (ATP). This relative inefficiency of the human "engine" leads to the production of heat as a consequence of fuel use. This inefficiency, in part, allows homeothermic animals to maintain a constant body temperature in spite of rapidly changing environmental conditions. The acute response to cold exposure is shivering, which is probably secondary to increased activity of the sympathetic nervous system in response to this "stressful" stimulus.

Thyroid hormone participates in this acute response by sensitizing the sympathetic nervous system to the stimulatory effect of cold exposure. The ability of T₃ to increase heat production is related to its effects on the pathways of fuel oxidation, which both generate ATP and release energy as heat. The effects of T₃ on the sympathetic nervous system increases the release of norepinephrine. Norepinephrine stimulates the uncoupling protein thermogenin in brown adipose tissue (BAT), resulting in increased heat production from the uncoupling of oxidative phosphorylation (see Chapter 21). Very little residual brown fat persists in normal adult human beings, however.

Norepinephrine also increases the permeability of BAT and skeletal muscle to Na⁺. Because an increase of intracellular Na⁺ is potentially toxic to cells, Na⁺,K⁺-ATPase is stimulated to transport Na⁺ out of the cell in exchange for K⁺. The increased hydrolysis of ATP by Na⁺,K⁺-ATPase stimulates the oxidation of fuels and the regeneration of more ATP and heat from oxidative phosphorylation. Over a longer time course, thyroid hormone also increases the level of Na⁺,K⁺-ATPase and many of the enzymes of fuel oxidation. Because even at normal room temperature ATP use by Na⁺,K⁺-ATPase accounts for 20% or more of our basal metabolic rate (BMR), changes in its activity can cause relatively large increases in heat production.

Thyroid hormone also may increase heat production by stimulating ATP use in futile cycles (in which reversible ATP-consuming conversions of substrate to product and back to substrate use fuels and, therefore, produce heat).

F. Gastrointestinal-Derived Hormones That Affect Fuel Metabolism

In addition to insulin and the counterregulatory hormones discussed so far, a variety of peptides synthesized in the endocrine cells of the pancreatic islets, or the cells of the enteric nervous system, or the endocrine cells of the stomach, small bowel and large bowel, as well as certain cells of the central and peripheral nervous system influence fuel metabolism directly. Some of these peptides and their tissues of origin, their actions on fuel metabolism, and the factors that stimulate (or suppress) their secretion are listed in Table 43.4. In addition to these peptides, others such as gastrin, motilin, pancreatic polypeptide (PP), peptide YY (PYY), and secretin may also influence fuel metabolism by indirect effects on the synthesis or secretion of insulin or the counterregulatory hormones (Table 43.5). For example, gastrin induces gastric acid secretion, which ultimately affects nutrient absorption and metabolism. Motilin, secreted by enteroendocrine M-cells of the proximal small bowel, stimulates gastric and pancreatic enzyme secretion, which in turn influences nutrient digestion. PP from the pancreatic islets reduces gastric emptying and slows upper intestinal motility. PYY from the α-cells in the mature pancreatic islets inhibits gastric acid secretion. Finally, secretin, produced by the enteroendocrine S-cells in the proximal small bowel, regulates pancreatic enzyme secretion and inhibits gastrin release and secretion of gastric acid. Although these "gut" hormones do not influence fuel metabolism directly, they have a significant impact on how ingested nutrients are digested and prepared for absorption. If digestion or absorption of fuels is altered through a disturbance in the delicate interplay among all of the peptides, fuel metabolism will be altered as well.

Several of these gastrointestinal peptides, such as GLP-1 and gastric inhibitory polypeptide/glucose-dependent insulinotropic polypeptide (GIP), do not act as direct insulin secretagogues when blood glucose levels are normal but do so after a meal large enough to cause an increase in the blood glucose concentration. The release of these peptides may explain why the modest postprandial increase in serum glucose that is seen in normal subjects has a relatively robust stimulatory effect on insulin release, whereas a similar glucose concentration in vitro elicits a significantly smaller increase in insulin secretion. Likewise, this effect (certain factors potentiating insulin release), known as the "incretin effect," could account for the greater β-cell response seen after an oral glucose load as opposed to that seen after the administration of glucose intravenously. This phenomenon is estimated to account for approximately 50% to 70% of the total insulin secreted after oral glucose administration. It is clear then that the gastrointestinal tract plays a critical role in peripheral energy homeostasis through its ability to influence the digestion, absorption, and assimilation of ingested nutrients. Importantly, the incretin hormones also regulate the amount of nutrients ingested through their central action as satiety signals.

In Table 43.6, the actions of GLP-1 and GIP on key target organs that are important for the control of glucose homeostasis are given. Both GLP-1 and GIP enhance the synthesis and release of insulin as well as exerting a positive influence on the survival of pancreatic islet cells. In addition, GLP-1 contributes to the regulation of glucose homeostasis by inhibiting the secretion of glucagon from the α-cells of the pancreas as well as by slowing the rate of gastric emptying. GIP, but not GLP-1, interacts with GIP receptors on adipocytes, an interaction that is coupled to energy storage. Figure 43.12 summarizes the key effects of GLP-1 and GIP on energy metabolism.

A generalized (i.e., involving all of the target cells for thyroid hormone in the body) but incomplete resistance of cells to the actions of thyroid hormone could explain the profile of the patient. In Refetoff disorder, a mutation in the portion of the gene that encodes the ligand-binding domain of the β-subunit of the thyroid hormone–receptor protein (expressed in all thyroid hormone responsive cells) causes a relative resistance to the suppressive action of thyroid hormone on the secretion of TSH by the thyrotrophs of the anterior pituitary gland. Therefore, the gland releases more TSH than normal into the blood. The elevated level of TSH causes an enlargement of the thyroid gland (goiter) as well as an increase in the secretion of thyroid hormone into the blood. As a result, the serum levels of both T_3 and T_4 rise in the blood. The increase in the secretion of thyroid hormone may or may not be adequate to fully compensate for the relative resistance of the peripheral tissues to thyroid hormone. If the compensatory increase in the secretion of thyroid hormone is inadequate, the patient may develop the signs and symptoms of hypothyroidism.

In hypothyroid patients, insulin release may be suboptimal, although glucose intolerance on this basis alone is uncommon.

In hyperthyroidism, the degradation and the clearance of insulin are increased. These effects, plus the increased demand for insulin caused by the changes in glucose metabolism, may lead to varying degrees of glucose intolerance in these patients (a condition called metathyroid diabetes mellitus). A patient with uncomplicated hyperthyroidism, however, rarely develops significant diabetes mellitus.

Ghrelin, a hormone identified as a growth hormone secretagogue, has recently been linked to appetite stimulation. The mechanism whereby this occur is through the activation of the AMP-activated protein kinase in the hypothalamus. The activation of this kinase leads to the release of neuropeptide Y, which increases appetite. Research geared toward interrupting the ghrelin/ghrelin receptor signaling system is increasing to develop new antiobesity agents.

Table 43.4   Gastrointestinal-Derived Hormones That Affect Fuel Metabolism Directly

Hormone	Primary Cell/Tissue of Origin	Actions	Secretory Stimuli (and Inhibitors)
Amylin	Pancreatic β-cell, endocrine cells of stomach and small intestine	1. Inhibits arginine-stimulated and post-prandial glucagon secretion 2. Inhbits insulin secretion	Co-secreted with insulin in response to oral nutrients
CGRP	Enteric neurons and enteroendocrine cells of the rectum	Inhibits insulin secretion	Oral glucose intake and gastric acid secretion
Galanin	Nervous system, pituitary, neurons of gut, pancreas, thyroid, and adrenal gland	Inhibits secretion of insulin, somatostatin, enteroglucagon, pancreatic polypeptide, and others	Intestinal distension
GIP	Neuroendocrine K-cells of duodenum and proximal jejunum	1. Increases insulin release via an "incretin" effect 2. Regulates glucose and lipid metabolism	Oral nutrient ingestion, especially long-chain fatty acids
GRP	Enteric nervous system and pancreas	Stimulates release of cholecystokinin; GIP, gastrin, glucagon, GLP-1, GLP-2, and somatostatin	
Ghrelin	Central nervous system, stomach, small intestine, and colon	Stimulates growth hormone release	Fasting
Glucagon	Pancreatic α-cell, central nervous system	Primary counter-regulatory hormone that restores glucose levels in hypoglycemic state (increases glycogenolysis and gluconeogenesis as well as protein–lipid flux in liver and muscle)	Neural and humoral factors released in response to hypoglycemia
GLP-1	Enteroendocrine L-cells in ileum, colon, and central nervous system	1. Enhances glucose disposal after meals by inhibiting glucagon secretion and stimulating insulin secretion 2. Acts through second messengers in β-cells to increase sensitivity of these cells to glucose (an incretin)	1. Oral nutrient ingestion 2. Vagus nerve 3. GRP and GIP 4. Somatostatin inhibits secretion
GLP-2	Same as for GLP-1	Stimulates intestinal hexose transport	Same as GLP-1
Neuropeptide Y	Central and peripheral nervous system, pancreatic islet cells	Inhibits glucose-stimulated insulin secretion	Oral nutrient ingestion and activation of sympathetic nervous system
NT	Small intestine N-cells (especially ileum), enteric nervous system, adrenal gland, pancreas	In brain, modulates dopamine neuro-transmission and anterior pituitary secretions	1. Luminal lipid nutrients 2. GRP 3. Somatostatin inhibits secretion
PACAP	Brain, lung, and enteric nervous system	Stimulates insulin and catecholamine release	Activation of central nervous system
Somatostatin	Central nervous system, pancreatic δ-cells, and enteroendocrine δ-cells	1. Inhibits secretion of insulin, glucagon and PP (islets), and gastrin, secretin, GLP-1, and GLP-2 (in gut) 2. Reduces carbohydrate absorption from gut lumen	1. Luminal nutrients 2. GLP-1 3. GIP 4. PACAP 5. VIP 6. β-Adrenergic stimulation
VIP	Widely expressed in the central and peripheral nervous systems	May regulate release of insulin and pancreatic glucagon	1. Mechanical stimulation of gut 2. Activation of central and peripheral nervous systems

CGRP, calcitonin gene-related peptide; GIP, gastric inhibitory polypeptide/glucose-dependent insulinotropic polypeptide; GRP, gastrin-releasing peptide; GLP-1, glucagon-like peptide-1; GLP-2, glucagon-like peptide-2; NT, neurotensin; PACAP, pituitary adenylate cyclase activating peptide; PP, pancreatic polypeptide; VIP, vasoactive intestinal peptide.

As the biological effects of the incretins were being discovered, it was hypothesized that agents which would increase the levels of the incretins, or increase their half-life in circulation, may provide an effective means of treating type 2 diabetes by increasing insulin secretion from the pancreas. The half-lives of GIP and GLP-1 in the circulation are on the order of 2.5 minutes. The protease DPP-4 (dipeptidyl protease 4) found on the surface of kidneys, intestine, liver, and many other tissues is responsible for inactivating GIP and GLP-1. If one wants to increase the efficacy of the incretins, synthetic incretin mimetics with longer half-lives could be developed, along with drugs which inhibit DPP-4, thereby increasing the serum half-lives of GIP and GLP-1. Such drugs have been developed and are used for the treatment of type 2 diabetes

Table 43.5   Gastrointestinal-Derived Hormones That Affect Fuel Metabolism Indirectly

Hormone	Primary Cell/Tissue of Origin	Actions	Secretory Stimuli (and Inhibitors)
CCK	Enteroendocrine I-cells, enteric nerves, others	1. Inhibits proximal gastric motility 2. Increases antral and pyloric contractions 3. Regulates nutrient-stimulated enzyme secretion and gallbladder contraction 4. Increases postprandial satiety	1. Oral nutrient ingestion 2. GGRP and bombesin from gut
Gastrin	Enteroendocrine G-cells of the stomach, duodenal bulb, and other cells	Induces gastric acid secretion	1. Luminal contents, especially aromatic amino acids, calcium, coffee, and ethanol 2. Vagus nerve stimulation; activation of β-adrenergic and GABA neurons 3. Somatostatin inhibits secretion
Motilin	Enteroendocrine M-cells in upper small bowel and other cells	1. Induces phase III contractions in stomach 2. Stimulates gastric secretion and pancreatic enzyme secretion 3. Induces gallbladder contraction	1. Duodenal alkalinization 2. Gastric distension 3. Secretion suppressed by nutrients in duodenum
PP	Endocrine cells in periphery of islets in the head of the pancreas	1. Reduces CCK-mediated gastric acid secretion 2. Increases intestinal transit time (slows motility)	Stimulated by intraluminal nutrients, hypoglycemia, and vagal nerve stimulation
PYY	Enteroendocrine cells, developing pancreas; alpha cells in mature islets	1. Inhibits both gastric acid secretion and gastric motility 2. Slows intestinal motility 3. Inhibits pancreatic exocrine secretion	1. Oral nutrient ingestion 2. Bile acids and fatty acids 3. Amino acids in colon
Secretin	Enteroendocrine S-cells in upper small bowel	1. Stimulates pancreatic and biliary bicarbonate and water secretion 2. Regulates pancreatic enzyme secretion 3. Inhibits postprandial gastric emptying, gastrin release, and gastric acid secretion	1. Gastric acid, bile salts, fatty acids, peptides, and ethanol 2. Somatostatin inhibits secretion
Tachykinins	Neurons localized in the submucous and myenteric plexuses; enterochromaffin cells in gut epithelium	1. Regulates vasomotor and gastrointestinal smooth muscle contraction 2. Mucus secretion and water absorption	Direct and indirect activation of neurons in submucosa and myenteric plexuses in gut epithelium
TRH	Enteric nervous system, colon, G-cells of stomach, and pancreatic β-cells	1. Suppresses hormone-stimulated gastric acid secretion 2. Inhibits cholesterol synthesis within the intestinal mucosa	In the stomach, histamine and serotonin stimulate secretion

CCK, cholecystokinin; GGRP, gastric gastrin releasing peptide; GABA, γ-aminobutyric acid; PP, pancreatic polypeptide; PYY, peptide YY; TRH, thyrotropin-releasing hormone.

Table 43.6   Actions of GLP-1 and GIP Relevant to Glucose Control

	GLP-1	GIP
Pancreas		
Stimulates glucose-dependent insulin release	+	+
Increase insulin biosynthesis	+	+
Inhibits glucagon secretion	+	−
Stimulates somatostatin secretion	+	−
Induces β-cell proliferation	+	+
Inhibits β-cell apoptosis	+	+
Gastrointestinal tract		
Inhibits gastric emptying	+	−
Inhibits gastric acid secretion	+	+
Central nervous system		
Inhibits food and water intake	+	−
Promotes satiety and weight loss	+	−
Cardiovascular system		
Improves cardiovascular function after ischemia	+	−
Adipose tissue		
Insulin-like lipogenic actions	−	+
Lipid storage	−	+

GLP-1, glucagon-like peptide-1; GIP, gastric inhibitory polypeptide/glucose-dependent insulinotropic polypeptide.

FIG. 43.12. Actions of selected peptides on vital tissues involved in glucose homeostasis. Both GLP-1 and GIP increase insulin secretion and β-cell survival. GLP-1 has additional actions related to glucose metabolism. In contrast, gastrin and CCK do not acutely regulate plasma glucose levels, but appear to increase β-cell proliferation.

mellitus. The first are potent GLP-1 receptor agonists. Exendin-4 or exenatide (Byetta) isolated from the venom of a lizard—*Heloderma suspectum*—was the first drug approved for such treatment. This agonist of the GLP-1 receptor must be administered subcutaneously, but because of its relative resistance to enzymatic cleavage by dipeptidyl peptidase 4 (unlike native GLP-1, which is rapidly cleaved by this enzyme), its biologic half-life in the plasma allows it to be administered only twice daily. DPP-4 cleaves GLP-1 after amino acid 2 (alanine) and breaks the alanine–glutamate peptide bond at that position. Exenatide has a glycine–glutamate sequence at amino acids 2 and 3, rendering this peptide more resistant to DPP-4 action than GLP-1. A second GLP-1 receptor agonist is liraglutide, which is a modified version of GLP-1. Liraglutide has a substitution at position 34 of the peptide, of an arginine for a lysine (K34R), along with the addition of a palmitate at position K26 (covalently linked to the lysine side chain). Addition of the fatty acid to the peptide allows liraglutide to bind to albumin in the circulation, protecting it from DPP-4, and allowing just a single daily dosing.

The second class of agents (first marketed in October 2006 as sitagliptin [Januvia]) are orally administered inhibitors of DPP-4. Through this action, sitagliptin slows the rate of catalytic cleavage of GIP and GLP-1 by DPP-4 and, therefore, prolongs their half-lives in the blood, allowing sitagliptin to be administered just twice daily. The contrasting actions of GLP-1 receptor agonists and the DPP-4 inhibitors are listed in Table 43.7. Since the introduction of sitagliptin, other DPP-4 inhibitors have been introduced, including alogliptin, saxagliptin, and vildagliptin. Only sitagliptin and saxagliptin are approved by the FDA for use in the United States.

Early estimates of their glucose-lowering efficacy in patients with type 2 diabetes mellitus suggests that the drugs which boost incretin action lowers the blood hemoglobin A1c level to approximately the same extent as does the other currently available oral antidiabetic agents (see the Biochemical Comments in Chapter 34) such as the sulfonylureas, metformin, and the thiazolidinediones (e.g., rosiglitazone [Avandia] and pioglitazone [Actos]).

Table 43.7 Similarities and Differences in GLP-1 Receptor Agonists and DPP-4 Inhibitors

Characteristic	GLP-1 Receptor Agonists	DPP-4 Inhibitors
Administration	Injection	Oral
GLP-1 concentrations	Pharmacologic	Physiologic
Increased insulin secretion	Yes	Yes
Reduced glucagon secretion	Yes	Yes
Activation of portal glucose sensor	No	Yes
Gastric emptying inhibited	Yes	No
Weight loss	Yes	No
Loss of appetite, nausea	Yes	No
Proliferation of β-cells	Yes	Yes
Potential immunogenicity	Yes	No

GLP-1, glucagon-like peptide-1; DPP-4, dipeptidyl peptidase 4.

G. Neural Factors That Control Secretion of Insulin and Counterregulatory Hormones

Although a full treatment is beyond the scope of this section, the gastrointestinal neuroendocrine system is described briefly here with regard to its effects on fuel metabolism. The pancreatic islet cells are innervated by both the adrenergic and the cholinergic limbs of the autonomic nervous system. Although stimulation of both the sympathetic and the parasympathetic systems increases glucagon secretion, insulin secretion is increased by vagus nerve fibers and suppressed by sympathetic fibers via the α-adrenoreceptors. Evidence also suggests that the sympathetic nervous system regulates pancreatic β-cell function indirectly through stimulation or suppression of the secretion of somatostatin, β_2-adrenergic receptor number, and the neuropeptides—neuropeptide Y and galanin.

A tightly controlled interaction between the hormonal and neural factors that control nutrient metabolism is necessary to maintain normal fuel and, hence, energy homeostasis.

H. The Endocannabinoid System and Energy Homeostasis

The discovery of the endocannabinoid system (ECS) dates to 4,000 years ago, when the psychotropic and therapeutic properties of the plant *Cannabis sativa* were first described in India. Research into the functional characteristics of the ECS led to the characterization of Δ^9-tetrahydrocannabinol (Δ^9-THC), the major psychoactive substance in marijuana (an exogenous cannabinoid). With this discovery, the biochemical and physiologic properties of this novel endogenous signaling system were described. The ECS warrants further discussion here because of its many influences on energy homeostasis (see Chapter 35 for the biosynthesis of endogenous endocannabinoids).

Exogenous ligands (e.g., Δ^9-THC) and endogenous ligands (e.g., anandamide or AEA, and 2-arachidonoylglycerol or 2-AG) interact with two basic receptors of the seven-transmembrane G protein–coupled family of receptors. Only the cannabinoid receptor 1 (CB1) receptor will be discussed. The CB2 receptor is found primarily in cells related to immune function and does not affect energy homeostasis.

The CB1 receptor is expressed in many tissues, including adipose tissue, muscle, liver, gastrointestinal tract, pancreas, and the CNS. The functions of the ECS in the brain influence energy metabolism via two major mechanisms.

The first mechanism involves the ability of the cannabinoids to modulate signaling from hypothalamic nuclei to most of the trophic hormone-producing cells of the anterior pituitary gland. For example, these ligands modulate the rate of secretion of GH, ACTH, luteinizing hormone (LH), follicle-stimulating hormone (FSH), and TSH. All of these pituitary trophic hormones, in turn, trigger the release of hormones from peripheral endocrine organs (e.g., IGF-I, cortisol, sex steroids, and thyroid hormone, respectively), all of which directly or indirectly influence nutrient intake and energy use or storage (see earlier text).

To establish the diagnosis of a secretory tumor of an endocrine gland, one must first demonstrate that basal serum levels of the hormone in question are regularly elevated. More important, one must show that the hypersecretion of the hormone (and hence its elevated level in the peripheral blood) cannot be adequately inhibited by "maneuvers" that are known to suppress secretion from a normally functioning gland (i.e., one must show that the hypersecretion is "autonomous").

To ensure that both the basal and the postsuppression levels of the specific hormone to be tested will reflect the true secretory rate of the suspected endocrine tumor, all of the known factors that can stimulate the synthesis of the hormone must be eliminated. For GH, for example, the secretagogues (stimulants to secretion) include nutritional factors; the patient's level of activity, consciousness, and stress; and certain drugs. GH secretion is stimulated by a high-protein meal or by a low level of fatty acids or glucose in the blood. Vigorous exercise; stage III to IV sleep; psychologic and physical stress; and levodopa, clonidine, and estrogens also increase GH release.

The suppression test used to demonstrate the autonomous hypersecretion of GH involves giving the patient an oral glucose load and measuring GH levels subsequently. A sudden rise in blood glucose suppresses serum GH to 2 ng/mL or less in normal subjects, but not in patients with active acromegaly.

If one attempts to demonstrate autonomous hypersecretion of GH in a patient suspected of having acromegaly, therefore, before drawing the blood for both the basal (pre-glucose load) serum GH level and the post-glucose load serum GH level, one must be certain that the patient has not eaten for 6 to 8 hours, has not done vigorous exercise for at least 4 hours, remains fully awake during the entire testing period (in a nonstressed state to the extent possible), and has not taken any drugs known to increase GH secretion for at least 1 week.

Under these carefully controlled circumstances, if both the basal and postsuppression serum levels of the suspect hormone are elevated, one can conclude that autonomous hypersecretion is probably present. At this point, localization procedures (such as an MRI of the pituitary gland in an acromegalic suspect) are performed to further confirm the diagnosis.

Endocannabinoid receptors have also been found in the thyroid gland and in adrenal cortical cells of rodents, but their importance in energy homeostasis remains to be elucidated in these animals.

The second "central" energy-related response to CB1 receptor activation is to induce hyperphagia, particularly for highly palatable foods even in satiated animals (increase in incentive value of food regardless of the quality of the macronutrient) (the "incentive hypothesis"). Importantly, this orexigenic action of the endocannabinoids is fully inhibited if the animals are given CB1-specific antagonists prior to receiving the endocannabinoid. In this regard, CB1 receptor blockade has also been shown to decrease the "reward" potential of addictive drugs. The most significant reward pathway appears to be part of the mesolimbic-dopaminergic system in the brain. It has been demonstrated that inhibitors of the enzyme fatty acid synthase have significant anorexigenic actions. Because CB1 receptor activation modulates the fatty acid synthase pathway in the hypothalamus, the inhibition of hypothalamic expression by the CB1 receptor antagonist rimonabant (Acomplia) may explain, in part, the anorexigenic properties of the endocannabinoid antagonists in general.

In addition to these "central" effects of the exogenous and endogenous cannabinoids on energy homeostasis, there are "peripheral" effects on metabolic functions as well. The administration of CB1 receptor antagonists is associated with reduction in body weight that persists beyond the duration of the anorexigenic action of the agent. To explain this phenomenon, a direct stimulating effect of CB1 receptor antagonists on energy expenditure has been suggested. The expression of CB1 receptors in adipose tissue and the capacity of CB1 receptor antagonists to inhibit cannabinoid-induced lipogenesis suggests that the ECS also operates via peripheral pathways that, when activated, alter energy balance as well. More specifically, CB1 receptor antagonists appear to reduce adipose mass. This lipolytic action is the result of induction of enzymes involved in β-oxidation of fatty acids as well as enzymes of the tricarboxylic acid (TCA) cycle. Glucose homeostasis has also been shown to be more tightly regulated in that CB1 receptor antagonists increase the expression of the insulin-responsive glucose transporter 4 (GLUT 4), suggesting an antidiabetogenic action of these antagonists. All of this is supported by data showing that the chronic administration of CB1 receptor antagonists increases the level of adiponectin in the blood of rodents and, in addition, increases the production of uncoupling proteins (UCPs) (e.g., UCP-1 and UCP-3 mRNA in BAT of mice). The latter suggests that CB1 receptor blockade may stimulate thermogenesis and increase oxygen consumption in adipocytes. Taken together, these findings suggest that the ECS plays a major role in the regulation of energy homeostasis in fat tissue.

Hepatocytes contain about twice the amount of 2-AG as the cells of other peripheral organs, suggesting that liver cells are also targets of the cannabinoids. For example, the cannabinoid receptor agonist H4210 stimulates the expression of genes that code for lipogenic enzymes such as lipogenic transcription factor SREBP-1c and its targets, acetyl-CoA carboxylase-1 and fatty acid synthase. It is likely, therefore, that blockade of the hepatic ECS protects liver cells from the damaging effect of a chronically high-fat diet (e.g., hepatic steatosis).

Finally, evidence suggests that the ECS in gastrointestinal cells may modulate nutrient intake and thereby affect energy homeostasis. The concentration of AEA in intestinal cells increases sharply when caloric intake is significantly restricted. This increase, together with that which occurs in the CNS, may synergize to increase appetite under these experimental conditions.

These findings suggest that cannabinoid antagonists may have therapeutic value in the treatment of obesity. SR141716, also known as rimonabant (Acomplia) has been studied in multicenter phase III trials to determine its efficacy as an anorexiant. Approval by the U.S. Food and Drug Administration for the marketing of rimonabant was not forthcoming, however, because the advisory committee considering rimonabant has advised against its marketing due to reports of psychiatric side effects in patients treated with this agent.

CLINICAL COMMENTS

 Corti Solemia. One of the functions of cortisol is to prepare the body to deal with periods of stress. In response to cortisol, the body re-sorts its fuel stores so that they can rapidly be made available for the "fight-or-flight" response to the alarm signal sounded by epinephrine. Cortisol causes gluconeogenic substrates to move from peripheral tissues to the liver, where they are converted to glucose and stored as glycogen. The release of epinephrine stimulates the breakdown of glycogen, increasing the supply of glucose to the blood. Thus, fuel becomes available for muscle to fight or flee.

Cushing "disease," the cause of **Corti Solemia's** current problems, results from prolonged hypersecretion of ACTH from a benign pituitary tumor. ACTH stimulates the adrenal cortex to produce cortisol, and blood levels of this steroid hormone rise.

Other nonpituitary causes of Cushing syndrome, however, include a primary tumor of the adrenal cortex secreting excessive amounts of cortisol directly into the bloodstream. This disorder also can result from the release of ACTH from secretory nonendocrine, nonpituitary neoplasms ("ectopic" ACTH syndrome). Cushing syndrome is often caused by excessive doses of synthetic GCs used to treat a variety of disorders because of their potent anti-inflammatory effects (iatrogenic Cushing syndrome).

 Sam Atotrope. The diabetogenic potential of chronically elevated GH levels in the blood is manifested by the significant incidence of diabetes mellitus (25%) and impaired glucose tolerance (33%) in patients with acromegaly such as **Sam Atotrope**. Under normal circumstances, however, physiologic concentrations of GH (as well as of cortisol and thyroid hormone) have a facilitatory or permissive effect on the quantity of insulin released in response to hyperglycemia and other insulin secretagogues. This "proinsular" effect is probably intended to act as a "brake" to dampen any potentially excessive "contrainsular" effects that increments in GH and the other counterregulatory hormones exerted.

BIOCHEMICAL COMMENTS

Radioimmunoassays. Most hormones are present in body fluids in picomolar to nanomolar amounts, requiring highly sensitive assays to determine their concentration in the blood or urine. Radioimmunoassays (RIAs), developed in the 1960s, use an antibody, generated in animals, against a specific antigen (the hormone to be measured). Determining the concentration of the hormone in the sample involves incubating the plasma or urine sample with the antibody and then quantifying the level of antigen–antibody complex formed during the incubation by one of several techniques.

The classic RIA uses very high-affinity antibodies, which have been fixed (immobilized) on the inner surface of a test tube, a Teflon bead, or a magnetized particle. A standard curve is prepared, using a set amount of the antibody and various known concentrations of the unlabeled hormone to be measured. In addition to a known concentration of the unlabeled hormone, each tube contains the same small, carefully measured amount of radiolabeled hormone. The labeled hormone and the unlabeled hormone compete for binding to the antibody. The higher the amount of unlabeled hormone in the sample, the less radiolabeled

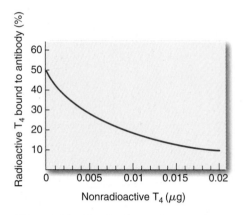

FIG. 43.13. Standard curve for a radioimmunoassay. A constant amount of radioactive T_4 is added to a series of tubes, each of which contains a different amount of nonradioactive T_4. The amount of radioactive hormone that binds to an antibody that is specific for the hormone is measured and plotted against the nonradioactive hormone concentration. When more nonradioactive T_4 is present in the tube, less radioactive T_4 binds to the antibody.

hormone is bound. A standard curve is plotted (Fig. 43.13). The unknown sample from the patient's blood or urine, containing the unlabeled hormone to be measured, is incubated with the immobilized antibody in the presence of the same small, carefully measured amount of radiolabeled hormone. The amount of radiolabeled hormone bound to the antibody is determined, and the standard curve is used to quantitate the amount of unlabeled hormone in the patient sample.

The same principle is used in immunoradiometric assays (IRMAs), but with this technique, the antibody, rather than the antigen to be measured, is radiolabeled.

The sensitivity of RIAs can be enhanced using a "sandwich technique." This method uses two different monoclonal antibodies (antibodies generated by a single clone of plasma cells rather than multiple clones), each of which recognizes a different specific portion of the hormone's structure. The first antibody, attached to a solid support matrix such as a plastic culture dish, binds the hormone to be assayed. After exposure of the patient sample to this first antibody, the excess plasma is washed away, and the second antibody (which is radiolabeled) is then incubated with the first antibody–hormone complex. The amount of binding of the second (labeled) antibody to the first complex is proportional to the concentration of the hormone in the sample.

The sandwich technique can be improved even further if the second antibody is attached to an enzyme, such as alkaline phosphatase. The enzyme rapidly converts an added colorless substrate into a colored product or a nonfluorescent substrate into a highly fluorescent product. These changes can be quantitated if the degree of change in color or fluorescence is proportional to the amount of hormone present in the patient sample. Less than a nanogram (10^{-9} g) of a protein can be measured by such an enzyme-linked immunosorbent assay (ELISA).

Key Concepts

- Insulin is the major anabolic hormone of the body.
- Hormones that counteract the action of insulin are known as counterregulatory (contrainsular) hormones.
- Glucagon is the major counterregulatory hormone.
- Other contrainsular hormones are
  - Epinephrine
  - Norepinephrine
  - Cortisol
  - Somatostatin
  - Growth hormone
  - Thyroid hormone
- Somatostatin inhibits insulin secretion, as well as the secretion of a large number of other hormones.
- Growth hormone (GH) exhibits a wide variety of effects.
  - GH increases lipolysis in adipose tissue, which increases the availability of fatty acids for oxidation, thereby reducing the oxidation of glucose and amino acids.
  - GH increases amino acid uptake into muscle cells, thereby increasing muscle protein synthesis.
  - GH stimulates gluconeogenesis (from amino acid substrates) and glycogen production in the liver.
- The catecholamines have metabolic effects directed toward mobilization of fuels from their storage sites for oxidation by cells while simultaneously suppressing insulin secretion.
- Cortisol (a glucocorticoid) promotes survival in times of stress, primarily via alteration of gene expression.
  - ATP-requiring processes such as DNA, RNA, and protein synthesis are inhibited.
    - Fuels are made available.
    - Fat-cell lipolysis is stimulated.
    - Muscle proteolysis is stimulated.
    - Glucose uptake by many tissues is inhibited to provide the nervous system with the glucose.
  - The liver uses the carbons of the amino acids for gluconeogenesis and glycogen storage.

Table 43.8   Diseases Discussed in Chapter 43

Disease or Disorder	Environmental or Genetic	Comments
Hypercortisolemia	Both	Excessive cortisol secretion, leading to inappropriate catabolic responses
Acromegaly	Environmental	Excessive secretion of growth hormone, most often caused by ACTH- or GH-secreting neoplasms
Cushing disease	Environmental	A pituitary adenoma leading to excessive secretion of ACTH, which leads to excessive cortisol secretion.
Cushing syndrome	Environmental or genetic (MEN)	Exposure to high levels of cortisol for prolonged periods with its subsequent effects
Hypothyroidism	Environmental	Reduced secretion of thyroid hormone, weight gain

ACTH, adrenocorticotropic hormone; GH, growth hormone; MEN, multiple endocrine neoplasia 1.

- Thyroid hormone secretion is regulated by thyroid-stimulating hormone (TSH) and thyrotropin-releasing hormone (TRH).
- Thyroid hormone effects in the liver include:
  ○ Increases in glycolysis and cholesterol synthesis
  ○ Increase in the synthesis of bile salts
  ○ Increase in triglyceride synthesis
- Thyroid hormone effects on fat cells include:
  ○ Increased lipolysis
  ○ Increased glycerol release to the liver
- Thyroid hormone also stimulates heat production via a variety of mechanisms.
- The intestine and stomach (the gut) also secrete a variety of factors that affect fuel metabolism by working with (or against) the other hormones already described.
- The incretins glucagon-like peptide-1 (GLP-1) and glucose-dependent insulinotropic peptide (GIP) are synthesized in specialized cells of the gastrointestinal tract.
- GLP-1 and GIP influence nutrient homeostasis by increasing insulin release from the pancreatic β-cells in a glucose-dependent manner.
- Incretin action facilitates the uptake of glucose by muscle tissue and by the liver while simultaneously suppressing glucagon secretion by the α-cells of the pancreas.
- The incretins also increase the levels of cAMP in the islets leading to expansion of β-cell mass and resistance to β-cell apoptosis.
- Diseases discussed in this chapter are summarized in Table 43.8.

REVIEW QUESTIONS—CHAPTER 43

1. As a third-year medical student, you examine your first patient. You find that he is 52 years old, has a round face, acne, and a large hump of fat on the back of his neck. He complains that he is too weak to "mow his lawn." His fasting blood glucose level is 170 mg/dL (reference range, 80 to 100 mg/dL). His plasma cortisol levels are 62 μg/mL (reference range, 3 to 31μg/mL). His plasma ACTH levels are 0 pg/mL (reference range, 0 to 100 pg/mL).

   Based on the information given, if the patient's problem is attributable to a single cause, the most likely diagnosis is which of the following?

   A. Non–insulin-dependent diabetes mellitus
   B. Insulin-dependent diabetes mellitus
   C. A secretory tumor of the anterior pituitary
   D. A secretory tumor of the posterior pituitary
   E. A secretory tumor of the adrenal cortex

2. A woman was scheduled for a growth hormone suppression test. If each of the following events occurred the morning of the test, which one of the events would be most likely to cause a decrease in growth hormone levels?

   A. She ate four large doughnuts for breakfast.
   B. She was on estrogen replacement therapy and took her tablets after breakfast.
   C. While unlocking her car, she was chased by the neighbor's vicious dog.
   D. She fell asleep at the start of the test and slept soundly until it was completed 1.5 hours later.
   E. She forgot to eat breakfast before the test.

3. A dietary deficiency of iodine will lead to which of the following?

    A. A direct effect on the synthesis of thyroglobulin on ribosomes

    B. An increased secretion of TSH

    C. Decreased production of TRH

    D. Increased heat production

    E. Weight loss

4. A woman whose thyroid gland was surgically removed was treated with 0.10 mg of thyroxine daily (tablet form). After 3 months of treatment, serial serum TSH levels ranged between 10 and 15 mIU/mL (reference range, 0.3 to 5.0 mIU/mL). She complained of fatigue, weight gain, and hoarseness. Her dose of thyroid hormone should be adjusted in which direction?

    A. More thyroid hormone should be given

    B. Less thyroid hormone should be given

    C. No adjustment is needed

5. A patient complains of nervousness, palpitations, sweating, and weight loss without loss of appetite, and has a goiter. Suspecting a defect in thyroid function, the physician orders a total serum T_4. The test is performed by radioimmunoassay. The standard curve for the assay, which measures T_4 in 0.1 mL serum, is shown in Figure 43.13. Normal levels of $T_4 = 4$ to 10 $\mu g/dL$. In an assay of 0.1 mL of the patient's serum, 15% of the radioactive T_4 was bound by the antibody. According to the radioimmunoassay, the approximate blood level of T_4 is which of the following?

    A. 0.015 $\mu g/dL$

    B. 0.15 $\mu g/dL$

    C. 15 $\mu g/dL$

    D. 20 $\mu g/dL$

    E. 30 $\mu g/dL$

The Biochemistry of Erythrocytes and Other Blood Cells

*The cells of the blood are classified as **erythrocytes**, **leukocytes**, or **thrombocytes**. The erythrocytes (**red blood cells**) carry oxygen to the tissues and are the most numerous cells in the blood. The leukocytes (**white blood cells**) are involved in defense against infection, and the thrombocytes (**platelets**) function in blood clotting. All of the cells in the blood can be generated from hematopoietic stem cells in the bone marrow on demand. For example, in response to infection, leukocytes secrete **cytokines** called **interleukins** that stimulate the production of additional leukocytes to fight the infection. Decreased supply of oxygen to the tissues signals the kidney to release **erythropoietin**, a hormone that stimulates the production of red blood cells.*

*The red blood cell has limited metabolic function, owing to its lack of internal organelles. **Glycolysis** is the main energy-generating pathway, with lactate production regenerating NAD^+ for glycolysis to continue. The NADH produced in glycolysis is also used to reduce the ferric form of hemoglobin, **methemoglobin**, to the normal ferrous state. Glycolysis also leads to a side pathway in which **2,3-bisphosphoglycerate** is produced, which is a major allosteric effector for oxygen binding to hemoglobin. The **hexose monophosphate shunt** pathway generates **NADPH** to protect red blood cell membrane lipids and proteins from oxidation, through regeneration of reduced glutathione. **Heme synthesis** occurs in the precursors of red blood cells and is a complex pathway that originates from succinyl coenzyme A (succinyl-CoA) and glycine. Mutations in any of the steps of heme synthesis lead to a group of diseases known collectively as **porphyrias**.*

*The red blood cell membrane must be highly deformable to allow it to travel throughout the capillary system in the body. This is because of a complex **cytoskeletal** structure that consists of the major proteins spectrin, ankyrin, and **band 3 protein**. Mutations in these proteins lead to improper formation of the membrane cytoskeleton, ultimately resulting in malformed red blood cells, **spherocytes**, in the circulation. Spherocytes have a shortened life span, leading to loss of blood cells.*

*When the body does not have sufficient red blood cells, the patient is said to be **anemic**. Anemia can result from many causes. **Nutritional deficiencies** of iron, folate, or **vitamin B_{12}** prevent the formation of adequate numbers of red blood cells. **Mutations** in the genes that encode red blood cell metabolic **enzymes**, **membrane structural proteins**, and **globins** cause **hereditary anemias**. The appearance of red blood cells on a blood smear frequently provides clues to the cause of an anemia. Because the mutations that give rise to hereditary anemias also provide some protection against malaria, hereditary anemias are some of the most common genetic diseases known.*

*The human alters globin gene expression during development, a process known as **hemoglobin switching**. The switch between expression of one gene to another is regulated by transcription factor binding to the promoter regions of these genes. Current research is attempting to reactivate fetal hemoglobin genes to combat sickle cell disease and thalassemia.*

THE WAITING ROOM

Anne Niemick, who has β^+-thalassemia, complains of pain in her lower spine (see Chapters 14 and 15). A quantitative computed tomogram (CT) of the vertebral bodies of the lumbar spine shows evidence of an area of early spinal cord compression in the upper lumbar region. She is suffering from severe anemia, resulting in stimulation of production of red blood cell precursors (the erythroid mass) from the stem cells in her bone marrow. This expansion of marrow volume causes osteoporosis leading to compression fractures in the lumbar spine, which, in turn, causes pain. Local irradiation to reduce the marrow volume in the lumbar spine is considered, as is a program of regular blood transfusions to maintain the oxygen-carrying capacity of circulating red blood cells. The results of special studies related to the genetic defect underlying her thalassemia are pending, although preliminary studies have shown that she has elevated levels of fetal hemoglobin, which, in part, moderates the manifestations of her disease. **Anne Niemick's** parents have returned to the clinic to discuss the results of these tests.

Spiro Site is a 21-year-old college student who complains of feeling tired all the time. Two years previously he had had gallstones removed, which consisted mostly of bilirubin. His spleen is palpable, and jaundice (icterus) is evidenced by yellowing of the whites of his eyes. His hemoglobin is low (8 g/dL; reference value, 13.5 to 17.5 g/dL). A blood smear showed dark, rounded, abnormally small red blood cells called spherocytes as well as an increase in the number of circulating immature red blood cells known as reticulocytes.

I. CELLS OF THE BLOOD

The blood, together with the bone marrow, makes up the organ system that makes a significant contribution to achieving homeostasis, the maintenance of the normal composition of the body's internal environment. Blood can be considered a liquid tissue consisting of water, proteins, and specialized cells. The most abundant cells in the blood are the erythrocytes or red blood cells, which transport oxygen to the tissues and contribute to buffering of the blood through the binding of protons by hemoglobin (see Section IV of this chapter, and the material in Chapter 4, Section IV.B, and Chapter 7, Section VII). Red blood cells lose all internal organelles during the process of differentiation. The white blood cells (leukocytes) are nucleated cells present in blood that function in the defense against infection. The platelets (thrombocytes), which contain cytoplasmic organelles but no nucleus, are involved in the control of bleeding by contributing to normal thrombus (clot) formation within the lumen of the blood vessel. The average concentration of these cells in the blood of normal individuals is presented in Table 44.1.

A. Classification and Functions of Leukocytes and Thrombocytes

The leukocytes can be classified either as polymorphonuclear leukocytes (granulocytes) or mononuclear leukocytes, depending on the morphology of the nucleus in these cells. The mononuclear leukocyte has a rounded nucleus, whereas the polymorphonuclear leukocytes have a multilobed nucleus.

1. THE GRANULOCYTES

The granulocytes, so named because of the presence of secretory granules visible on staining, are the neutrophils, eosinophils, and basophils. When these

Table 44.1 Normal Values of Blood Cell Concentrations in Adults

Cell Type	Mean (cells/mm³)
Erythrocytes	5.2×10^6 (men); 4.6×10^6 (women)
Neutrophils	4,300
Lymphocytes	2,700
Monocytes	500
Eosinophils	230
Basophils	40

cells are activated in response to chemical stimuli, the vesicle membranes fuse with the cell plasma membrane, resulting in the release of the granule contents (degranulation). The granules contain many cell-signaling molecules that mediate inflammatory processes. The granulocytes, in addition to displaying segmented nuclei (are polymorphonuclear), can be distinguished from each other by their staining properties (caused by different granular contents) in standard hematologic blood smears: neutrophils stain pink, eosinophils stain red, and basophils stain blue.

Neutrophils are phagocytic cells that migrate rapidly to areas of infection or tissue damage. As part of the response to acute infection, neutrophils engulf foreign bodies and destroy them, in part, by initiating the respiratory burst (see Chapter 24). The respiratory burst creates oxygen radicals that rapidly destroy the foreign material found at the site of infection.

A primary function of eosinophils is to fight viral infections (eosinophils release RNase from their granules), to remove fibrin during inflammation, and to protect against parasites such as worms. The eosinophilic granules are lysosomes containing hydrolytic enzymes and cationic proteins, which are toxic to parasitic worms. Eosinophils have also been implicated in asthma and allergic responses, as well as antigen presentation to T cells. Elucidating the function of eosinophils is currently an active area of research.

Basophils, the least abundant of the leukocytes, participate in hypersensitivity reactions such as allergic responses. Histamine, produced by the decarboxylation of histidine, is stored in the secretory granules of basophils. Release of histamine during basophil activation stimulates smooth muscle cell contraction and increases vascular permeability. The granules also contain enzymes such as proteases, β-glucuronidase, and lysophospholipase. These enzymes degrade microbial structures and assist in the remodeling of damaged tissue.

2. MONONUCLEAR LEUKOCYTES

The mononuclear leukocytes consist of various classes of lymphocytes and the monocytes. Lymphocytes are small, round cells that were originally identified in lymph fluid. These cells have a high ratio of nuclear volume to cytoplasmic volume and are the primary antigen (foreign body)-recognizing cells. There are three major types of lymphocytes: T cells, B cells, and NK cells. The precursors of T cells (thymus-derived lymphocytes) are produced in the bone marrow and then migrate to the thymus, where they mature before being released to the circulation. Several subclasses of T cells exist. These subclasses are identified by different surface membrane proteins, the presence of which correlate with the function of the subclass. Lymphocytes that mature in the bone marrow are the B cells, which secrete antibodies in response to antigen binding. The third class of lymphocytes is the natural killer cells (NK cells), which target virally infected and malignant cells for destruction.

Circulatory monocytes are the precursors of tissue macrophages. Macrophages ("large eaters") are phagocytic cells that enter inflammatory sites and consume microorganisms, and necrotic host cell debris left behind by granulocyte attack of the foreign material. Macrophages in the spleen play an important role in maintaining the oxygen-delivering capabilities of the blood by removing damaged red blood cells that have a reduced oxygen-carrying capacity.

3. THE THROMBOCYTES

Platelets are heavily granulated disc-like cells that aid in intravascular clotting. Like the erythrocyte, platelets lack a nucleus. Their function is discussed in the following chapter. Platelets arise by budding of the cytoplasm of megakaryocytes, multinucleated cells that reside in the bone marrow.

Table 44.2 Normal Hemoglobin Levels in Blood (g/dL)

Adult	
Males	13.5–17.5
Females	11.5–15.5
Children	
Newborns	15.0–21.0
3–12 mo	9.5–12.5
1 y to puberty	11.0–13.5

Table 44.3 Classification of the Anemias on the Basis of Red Cell Morphology

Red Cell Morphology	Functional Deficit	Possible Causes
Microcytic, hypochromic	Impaired hemoglobin synthesis	Iron deficiency, mutation leading to thalassemia, lead poisoning
Macrocytic, normochromic	Impaired DNA synthesis	Vitamin B_{12} or folic acid deficiency, erythroleukemia
Normocytic, normochromic	Red cell loss	Acute bleeding, sickle cell disease, red cell metabolic defects, red cell membrane defects

B. Anemia

The major function of erythrocytes is to deliver oxygen to the tissues. To do this, a sufficient concentration of hemoglobin in the red blood cells is necessary for efficient oxygen delivery to occur. When the hemoglobin concentration falls below normal values (Table 44.2), the patient is classified as anemic. Anemias can be categorized based on red cell size and hemoglobin concentration. Red blood cells can be of normal size (normocytic), small (microcytic), or large (macrocytic). Cells containing a normal hemoglobin concentration are termed normochromic; those with decreased concentration are hypochromic. This classification system provides important diagnostic tools (Table 44.3) that enable one to properly classify, diagnose, and treat the anemia.

Other measurements used to classify the type of anemia present include the mean corpuscular volume (MCV) and the mean corpuscular hemoglobin concentration (MCHC). The MCV is the average volume of the red blood cell, expressed in femtoliters (10^{-15} L). Normal MCV values range from 80 to 100 fL. The MCHC is the average concentration of hemoglobin in each individual erythrocyte, expressed in grams per liter. The normal range is 32 to 37 g/L; a value of <32 g/L indicates hypochromic cells. Thus, microcytic, hypochromic red blood cells have an MCV of <80 fl and an MCHC of <32 g/L. Macrocytic, normochromic cells have an MCV of >100 fl, with an MCHC between 32 and 37 g/L.

II. ERYTHROCYTE METABOLISM

A. The Mature Erythrocyte

To understand how the erythrocyte can carry out its major function, a discussion of erythrocyte metabolism is required. Mature erythrocytes contain no intracellular organelles, so the metabolic enzymes of the red blood cell are limited to those found in the cytoplasm. In addition to hemoglobin, the cytosol of the red blood cell contains enzymes necessary for the prevention and repair of damage done by reactive oxygen species (see Chapter 24) and the generation of energy (Fig. 44.1). Erythrocytes can only generate adenosine triphosphate (ATP) by glycolysis (see Chapter 22). The ATP is used for ion transport across the cell membrane (primarily Na^+, K^+, and Ca^+), the phosphorylation of membrane proteins, and the priming reactions of glycolysis. Erythrocyte glycolysis also uses the Rapoport–Luebering shunt to generate 2,3-bisphosphoglycerate (2,3-BPG). Red cells contain 4 to 5 mM 2,3-BPG, compared with trace amounts in other cells. The trace amounts of 2,3-BPG found in cells other than erythrocytes is required for the phosphoglycerate mutase reaction of glycolysis, in which 3-phosphoglycerate is isomerized to 2-phosphoglycerate. As the 2,3-BPG is regenerated during each reaction cycle, it is required in only catalytic amounts. As discussed in more detail in Section IV, 2,3-BPG is a modulator of oxygen binding to hemoglobin that stabilizes the deoxy form of hemoglobin, thereby facilitating the release of oxygen to the tissues.

To bind oxygen, the iron of hemoglobin must be in the ferrous (+2) state. Reactive oxygen species can oxidize the iron to the ferric (+3) state, producing

A complete blood count (CBC) is ordered when a physician suspects a problem in the cellular composition of a patient's blood. The cells within the collected blood are counted and typed using an automated analyzer based on flow cytometry (counting cells one at a time as they flow through a detector). As each cell flows through the machine, a laser shines light at the cell, which leads to predictable light scattering and absorbance depending on the cell type. Based on the light-scattering and absorption pattern, the machine keeps track of the results of each cell that flows through the machine, leading to a very accurate count of each cell type present in the sample. The data from this analysis will include the total number of red blood cells per liter, the amount of hemoglobin in the red blood cells (in grams per liter), the hematocrit (the fraction of whole blood that consists of red blood cells), the mean corpuscular volume, the total number of white blood cells, as well as a count of the different types of white blood cells (neutrophils, lymphocytes, monocytes, eosinophils, and basophils).

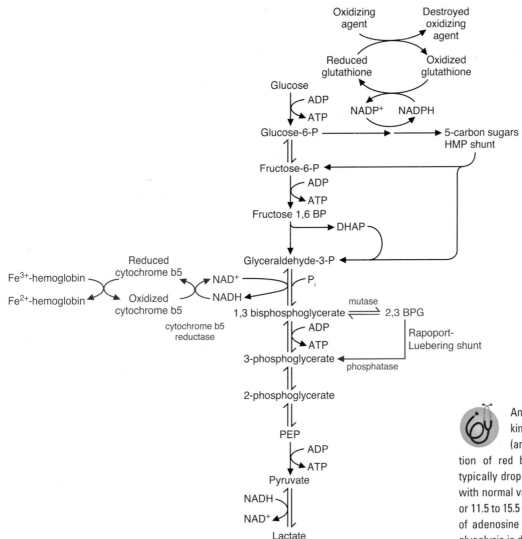

FIG. 44.1. Overview of erythrocyte metabolism. Glycolysis is the major pathway, with branches for the hexose monophosphate shunt (for protection against oxidizing agents) and the Rapoport–Luebering shunt (which generates 2,3-bisphosphoglycerate, which moderates oxygen binding to hemoglobin). The NADH generated from glycolysis can be used to reduce methemoglobin (Fe^{3+}) to normal hemoglobin (Fe^{2+}), or to convert pyruvate to lactate, so that NAD^+ can be regenerated and used for glycolysis. Pathways that are unique to the erythrocyte are indicated in *red*. See text for abbreviations.

methemoglobin. Some of the NADH produced by glycolysis is used to regenerate hemoglobin from methemoglobin by the NADH-cytochrome b_5 methemoglobin reductase system. Cytochrome b_5 reduces the Fe^{3+} of methemoglobin. The oxidized cytochrome b_5 is then reduced by a flavin-containing enzyme, cytochrome b_5 reductase (also called methemoglobin reductase), using NADH as the reducing agent.

Approximately 5% to 10% of the glucose metabolized by red blood cells is used to generate NADPH by way of the hexose monophosphate shunt. The NADPH is used to maintain glutathione in the reduced state. The glutathione cycle is the red blood cell's chief defense against damage to proteins and lipids by reactive oxygen species (see Chapter 24).

The enzyme that catalyzes the first step of the hexose monophosphate shunt is glucose-6-phosphate dehydrogenase (G6PD). The lifetime of the red blood cell correlates with G6PD activity. Lacking ribosomes, the red blood cell cannot

An inherited deficiency in pyruvate kinase leads to hemolytic anemia (an anemia caused by the destruction of red blood cells; hemoglobin values typically drop to 4 to 10 g/dL in this condition, with normal values being 13.5 to 17.5 in males, or 11.5 to 15.5 in females). Because the amount of adenosine triphosphate (ATP) formed from glycolysis is decreased by 50%, red blood cell ion transporters cannot function effectively. The red blood cells tend to gain Ca^{2+} and lose K^+ and water. The water loss increases the intracellular hemoglobin concentration. With the increase in intracellular hemoglobin concentration, the internal viscosity of the cell is increased to the point that the cell becomes rigid and, therefore, more susceptible to damage by shear forces in the circulation. Once they are damaged, the red blood cells are removed from circulation, leading to the anemia. However, the effects of the anemia are frequently moderated by the twofold to threefold elevation in 2,3-bisphosphoglycerate (2,3-BPG) concentration that results from the blockage of the conversion of phosphoenolpyruvate to pyruvate. Because 2,3-BPG binding to hemoglobin decreases the affinity of hemoglobin for oxygen, the red blood cells that remain in circulation are highly efficient in releasing their bound oxygen to the tissues.

Congenital methemoglobinemia, the presence of excess methemoglobin, is found in people with an enzymatic deficiency in cytochrome b_5 reductase or in people who have inherited hemoglobin M. In hemoglobin M, a single amino acid substitution in the heme-binding pocket stabilizes the ferric (Fe^{3+}) oxygen. Individuals with congenital methemoglobinemia appear cyanotic but have few clinical problems. Methemoglobinemia can be acquired by ingestion of certain oxidants such as nitrites, quinones, aniline, and sulfonamides. Acquired methemoglobinemia can be treated by the administration of reducing agents, such as ascorbic acid or methylene blue.

 Glucose-6-phosphate dehydrogenase (G6PD) deficiency is the most common enzyme deficiency in humans, probably, in part, because individuals with G6PD deficiency are resistant to malaria. The resistance to malaria counterbalances the deleterious effects of the deficiency. G6PD-deficient red cells have a shorter life span and are more likely to lyse under conditions of oxidative stress. When soldiers during the Korean War were given the antimalarial drug primaquine prophylactically, approximately 10% of the soldiers of African ancestry developed spontaneous anemia. Because the gene for G6PD is found on the X chromosome, these men had only one copy of a variant G6PD gene.

 All known glucose-6-phosphate dehydrogenase (G6PD) variant genes contain small in-frame deletions or missense mutations. The corresponding proteins, therefore, have decreased stability or lowered activity, leading to a reduced half-life or life span for the red cell. No mutations have been found that result in complete absence of G6PD. Based on studies with knockout mice, those mutations would be expected to result in embryonic lethality.

 Pyridoxine (vitamin B_6) deficiencies are often associated with a microcytic, hypochromic anemia. Why would a B_6 deficiency result in small (microcytic), pale (hypochromic) red blood cells?

FIG. 44.2. Structure of heme. The side chains can be abbreviated as MVMVMPPM. M, methyl (—CH_3); P, propionyl (—CH_2—CH_2—COO^-); V, vinyl (—CH=CH_2).

synthesize new G6PD protein. Consequently, as the G6PD activity decreases, oxidative damage accumulates, leading to lysis of the erythrocyte. When red blood cell lysis (hemolysis) substantially exceeds the normal rate of red blood cell production, the number of erythrocytes in the blood drops below normal values, leading to hemolytic anemia.

B. The Erythrocyte Precursor Cells and Heme Synthesis

1. HEME STRUCTURE

Heme consists of a porphyrin ring coordinated with an atom of iron (Fig. 44.2). Four pyrrole rings are joined by methenyl bridges (–CH–) to form the porphyrin ring (see Fig. 7.12). Eight side chains serve as substituents on the porphyrin ring, two on each pyrrole. These side chains may be acetyl (A), propionyl (P), methyl (M), or vinyl (V) groups. In heme, the order of these groups is M V M V M P P M. This order, in which the position of the methyl group is reversed on the fourth ring, is characteristic of the porphyrins of the type III series, the most abundant in nature.

Heme is the most common porphyrin found in the body. It is complexed with proteins to form hemoglobin, myoglobin, and the cytochromes (see Chapters 7 and 21), including cytochrome P450 (see Chapter 24).

2. SYNTHESIS OF HEME

Heme is synthesized from glycine and succinyl coenzyme A (succinyl-CoA) (Fig. 44.3), which condense in the initial reaction to form δ-aminolevulinic acid (δ-ALA) (Fig. 44.4). The enzyme that catalyzes this reaction, δ-ALA synthase, requires the participation of pyridoxal phosphate, as the reaction is an amino acid decarboxylation reaction (glycine is decarboxylated; see Chapter 39).

The next reaction of heme synthesis is catalyzed by δ-ALA dehydratase, in which two molecules of δ-ALA condense to form the pyrrole, porphobilinogen (Fig. 44.5). Four of these pyrrole rings condense to form a linear chain and then a series of porphyrinogens. The side chains of these porphyrinogens initially contain acetyl (A) and propionyl (P) groups. The acetyl groups are decarboxylated to form methyl groups. Then the first two propionyl side chains are decarboxylated and oxidized to vinyl groups, forming a protoporphyrinogen. The methylene bridges are subsequently oxidized to form protoporphyrin IX (see Fig. 44.3). Heme is red and is responsible for the color of red blood cells and of muscles that contain a large number of mitochondria.

In the final step of the pathway, iron (as Fe^{2+}) is incorporated into protoporphyrin IX in a reaction catalyzed by ferrochelatase (also known as heme synthase).

In a B_6 deficiency, the rate of heme production is slow because the first reaction in heme synthesis requires pyridoxal phosphate (see Fig. 44.4). Thus, less heme is synthesized, causing red blood cells to be small and pale. Iron stores are usually elevated.

δ-Aminolevulinic acid (δ-ALA) dehydratase, which contains zinc, and ferrochelatase are inactivated by lead. Thus, in lead poisoning, δ-ALA and protoporphyrin IX accumulate, and the production of heme is decreased. Anemia results from a lack of hemoglobin, and energy production decreases because of the lack of cytochromes for the electron-transport chain.

FIG. 44.3. Synthesis of heme. To produce one molecule of heme, eight molecules each of glycine and succinyl-CoA are required. A series of porphyrinogens is generated in sequence. Finally, iron is added to produce heme. Heme regulates its own production by repressing the synthesis of δ-aminolevulinic acid (δ-ALA) synthase ($\downarrow$) and by directly inhibiting the activity of this enzyme ($-$). Deficiencies of enzymes in the pathway result in a series of diseases known as porphyrias (listed on the right, beside the deficient enzyme).

3. SOURCE OF IRON

Iron, which is obtained from the diet, has a U.S. Recommended Dietary Allowance (RDA) of 10 mg for men and postmenopausal women, and 15 mg for premenopausal women. The average U.S. diet contains 10 to 50 mg of iron. However, only 10% to 15% is normally absorbed, and iron deficiencies are fairly common. The iron in meats is in the form of heme, which is readily absorbed. The nonheme iron in plants is not as readily absorbed, in part, because plants often contain oxalates, phytates, tannins, and other phenolic compounds that chelate or form insoluble precipitates with iron, preventing its absorption. Conversely, vitamin C (ascorbic acid) increases the uptake of nonheme iron from the digestive tract. The uptake of iron is also increased in times of need by mechanisms that are not yet understood. Iron is absorbed in the ferrous (Fe^{2+}) state (Fig. 44.6), but is oxidized to the ferric state by a ferroxidase known as ceruloplasmin (a copper-containing enzyme) for transport through the body.

Because free iron is toxic, it is usually found in the body bound to proteins (see Fig. 44.6). Iron is carried in the blood (as Fe^{3+}) by the protein apotransferrin, with which it forms a complex known as transferrin. Transferrin is usually only one-third saturated with iron. The total iron-binding capacity of blood, due mainly to its content of transferrin, is approximately 300 μg/dL. Transferrin, with bound iron, binds to the transferrin receptor on the cell surface and the complex is internalized into the cell. The internalized membrane develops into an endosome, with a slightly

FIG. 44.4. Synthesis of δ-aminolevulinic acid (δ-ALA). The atoms in *red* in δ-aminolevulinic acid are derived from glycine. *PLP*, pyridoxal phosphate.

Porphyrias are a group of rare inherited disorders resulting from deficiencies of enzymes in the pathway for heme biosynthesis (see Fig. 44.3). Intermediates of the pathway accumulate and may have toxic effects on the nervous system that cause neuropsychiatric symptoms. When porphyrinogens accumulate, they may be converted by light to porphyrins, which react with molecular oxygen to form oxygen radicals. These radicals may cause severe damage to the skin. Thus, individuals with excessive production of porphyrins are photosensitive. The scarring and increased growth of facial hair seen in some porphyrias may have contributed to the rise of the werewolf legends.

FIG. 44.5. Two molecules of δ-ALA condense to form porphobilinogen.

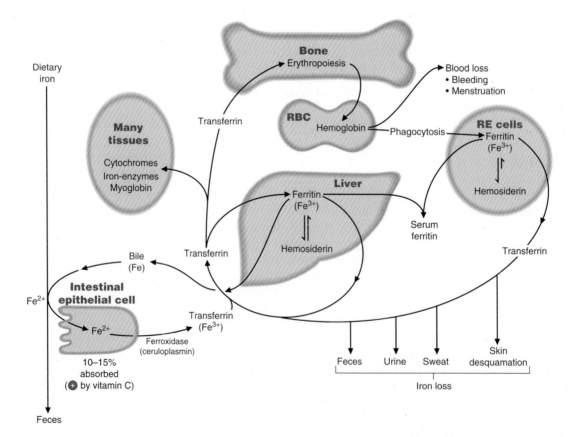

FIG. 44.6. Iron metabolism. Iron is absorbed from the diet, transported in the blood by transferrin, stored in ferritin, and used for the synthesis of cytochromes, iron-containing enzymes, hemoglobin, and myoglobin. It is lost from the body with bleeding and sloughed-off cells, sweat, urine, and feces. Hemosiderin is the protein in which excess iron is stored. Small amounts of ferritin enter the blood and can be used to measure the adequacy of iron stores. *RE*, reticuloendothelial.

acidic pH. The iron (in the ferrous form) is transported out of the endosome into the cytoplasm via the divalent metal ion transporter 1 (DMT-1). Once in the cytoplasm, the iron is oxidized and binds to ferritin for long-term storage.

Storage of iron occurs in most cells but especially those of the liver, spleen, and bone marrow. In these cells, the storage protein, apoferritin, forms a complex with iron (Fe^{3+}) known as ferritin. Normally, ferritin is present in the blood in small amounts. The level increases, however, as iron stores increase. Therefore, the amount of ferritin in the blood is the most sensitive indicator of the amount of iron in the body's stores.

Iron can be drawn from ferritin stores, transported in the blood as transferrin, and taken up via receptor-mediated endocytosis by cells that require iron (e.g., by reticulocytes that are synthesizing hemoglobin). When excess iron is absorbed from the diet, it is stored as hemosiderin, a form of ferritin complexed with additional iron that cannot be readily mobilized.

 An inherited mutation in *SLC11A2* (the gene encoding divalent metal ion transporter 1 [DMT-1]) leads to an iron deficiency anemia, as indicated by a refractory hypochromic microcytic anemia. The iron is trapped in endosomal vesicles and cannot be released to bind to ferritin, or used in other necessary biosynthetic reactions. This leads to reduced heme synthesis, reduced globin synthesis, and anemia.

4. REGULATION OF HEME SYNTHESIS

Heme regulates its own synthesis by mechanisms that affect the first enzyme in the pathway, δ-ALA synthase (see Fig. 44.3). Heme represses the synthesis of this enzyme, and also directly inhibits the activity of the enzyme (an allosteric modifier). Thus, heme is synthesized when heme levels fall. As heme levels rise, the rate of heme synthesis decreases.

Heme also regulates the synthesis of hemoglobin by stimulating synthesis of the protein globin. Heme maintains the ribosomal initiation complex for globin synthesis in an active state (see Chapter 15).

5. DEGRADATION OF HEME

Heme is degraded to form bilirubin, which is conjugated with glucuronic acid and excreted in the bile (Fig. 44.7). Although heme from cytochromes and myoglobin

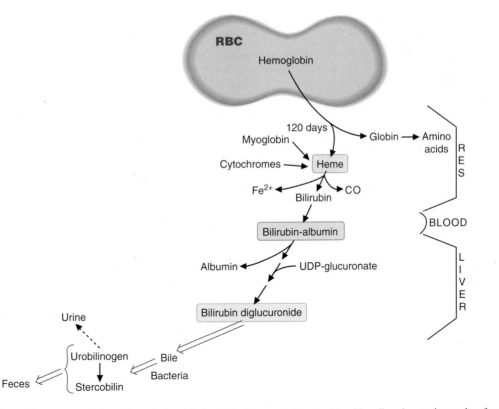

FIG. 44.7. Overview of heme degradation. Heme is degraded to bilirubin, carried in the blood by albumin, conjugated to form the diglucuronide in the liver, and excreted in the bile. The iron is returned to the body's iron stores. *RBC*, red blood cells; *RES*, reticuloendothelial system.

FIG. 44.8. Conversion of heme to bilirubin. A methylene bridge in heme is cleaved, releasing carbon monoxide (CO) and iron. Then the center methylene bridge is reduced.

The iron lost by adult men (approximately 1 mg/day) by desquamation of the skin and in bile, feces, urine, and sweat is replaced by iron absorbed from the diet. Men are not as likely to suffer from iron deficiencies as premenopausal adult women, who also lose iron during menstruation and who must supply iron to meet the needs of a growing fetus during pregnancy. If a man eating a Western diet has iron deficiency anemia, his physician should suspect bleeding from the gastrointestinal tract as a result of ulcers or colon cancer.

Drugs, such as phenobarbital, induce enzymes of the drug-metabolizing systems of the endoplasmic reticulum that contain cytochrome P450. Because heme is used for synthesis of cytochrome P450, free heme levels fall and δ-aminolevulinic acid (δ-ALA) synthase is induced to increase the rate of heme synthesis.

Q: In an iron deficiency, what characteristics will blood exhibit?

also undergoes conversion to bilirubin, the major source of this bile pigment is hemoglobin. After red blood cells reach the end of their life span (approximately 120 days), they are phagocytosed by cells of the reticuloendothelial system. Globin is cleaved to its constituent amino acids, and iron is returned to the body's iron stores. Heme is oxidized and cleaved to produce carbon monoxide and biliverdin (Fig. 44.8). Biliverdin is reduced to bilirubin, which is transported to the liver complexed with serum albumin.

In the liver, bilirubin is converted to a more water-soluble compound by reacting with UDP-glucuronate to form bilirubin monoglucuronide, which is converted to the diglucuronide (see Fig. 30.5). This conjugated form of bilirubin is excreted into the bile.

In the intestine, bacteria deconjugate bilirubin diglucuronide and convert the bilirubin to urobilinogens (see Fig. 44.7). Some urobilinogen is absorbed into the blood and excreted in the urine. However, most of the urobilinogen is oxidized to urobilins, such as stercobilin, and excreted in the feces. These pigments give feces their brown color.

III. THE RED BLOOD CELL MEMBRANE

Under the microscope, the red blood cell appears to be a red disc with a pale central area (biconcave disc) (Fig. 44.9). The biconcave disc shape (as opposed to a spherical shape) serves to facilitate gas exchange across the cell membrane. The membrane proteins that maintain the shape of the red blood cell also allow the red blood cell to traverse the capillaries with very small luminal diameters to deliver oxygen to the tissues. The interior diameters of many capillaries are smaller than the approximately 7.5-μm diameter of the red cell. Furthermore, in passing through the kidney, red blood cells traverse hypertonic areas that are up to six times the normal isotonicity, and back again, causing the red cell to shrink and expand during its travels. The spleen is the organ responsible for determining the viability of the red blood cells. Erythrocytes pass through the spleen 120 times per day. The elliptical passageways through the spleen are approximately 3 μm in diameter, and normal red cells traverse them in approximately 30 seconds. Thus, to survive in the circulation, the red cell must be highly deformable. Damaged red cells that are no longer deformable become trapped in the passages in the spleen, where they are destroyed by macrophages. The reason for the erythrocyte's deformability lies in its shape and in the organization of the proteins that make up the red blood cell membrane.

The surface area of the red cell is approximately 140 μm^2, which is greater than the surface of a sphere needed to enclose the contents of the red cell (98 μm^2). The presence of this extra membrane and the cytoskeleton that supports it allows the red cell to be stretched and deformed by mechanical stresses as the cell passes through narrow vascular beds. On the cytoplasmic side of the membrane, proteins form a two-dimensional lattice that gives the red cell its flexibility (Fig. 44.10). The major proteins are spectrin, actin, band 4.1, band 4.2, and ankyrin. Spectrin, the major

FIG. 44.9.   The shape of the red blood cell. **A.** Wright-stained cells, displaying the pale staining in the center. **B.** Scanning electron micrograph, showing the biconcave disc structure of the cells. The stacks of erythrocytes in this preparation (collected from a blood tube) are not unusual. These photographs were obtained, with permission, from Cohen BJ, Wood DL. *Memmler's the Human Body in Health and Disease*. 9th ed. Philadelphia, PA: Lippincott Williams & Wilkins; 2000 (Panel A) and Alberts B, Johnson A, Lewis J, et al. *Molecular Biology of the Cell*. 4th ed. New York, NY: Garland Science; 2002:600 (Panel B).

A: Iron deficiency will result in a microcytic, hypochromic anemia. Red blood cells will be small and pale. In contrast to a vitamin B$_6$ deficiency, which also results in a microcytic, hypochromic anemia, iron stores are low in an iron deficiency anemia.

FIG. 44.10.   A generalized view of the erythrocyte cytoskeleton. **A.** The major protein, spectrin, is linked to the plasma membrane either through interactions with ankyrin and band 3, or with actin, band 4.1, and glycophorin. Other proteins in this complex, not shown, are tropomyosin and adducin. **B.** A view from inside the cell, looking up at the cytoskeleton. This view displays the cross-linking of the spectrin dimers to actin and band 3 anchor sites.

Defects in erythrocyte cytoskeletal proteins lead to hemolytic anemia. Shear stresses in the circulation result in the loss of pieces of the red cell membrane. As the membrane is lost, the red blood cell becomes more spherical and loses its deformability. As these cells become more spherical, they are more likely to lyse in response to mechanical stresses in the circulation, or to be trapped and destroyed in the spleen.

protein, is a heterodimer composed of α- and β-subunits wound around each other. The dimers self-associate at the heads. At the opposite end of the spectrin dimers, actin and band 4.1 bind near to each other. Multiple spectrins can bind to each actin filament, resulting in a branched membrane cytoskeleton.

The spectrin cytoskeleton is connected to the membrane lipid bilayer by ankyrin, which interacts with β-spectrin and the integral membrane protein, band 3. Band 4.2 helps to stabilize this connection. Band 4.1 anchors the spectrin skeleton with the membrane by binding the integral membrane protein glycophorin C and the actin complex, which has bound multiple spectrin dimers.

When the red blood cell is subjected to mechanical stress, the spectrin network rearranges. Some spectrin molecules become uncoiled and extended; others become compressed, thereby changing the shape of the cell, but not its surface area.

The mature erythrocyte cannot synthesize new membrane proteins or lipids. However, membrane lipids can be freely exchanged with circulating lipoprotein lipids. The glutathione system protects the proteins and lipids from oxidative damage.

The unusual names for some erythrocyte membrane proteins, such as band 4.1, arose through analysis of red blood cell membranes by polyacrylamide gel electrophoresis. The stained bands observed in the gel were numbered according to molecular weight (band 1, band 2, etc.), and as functions were assigned to the proteins, more common names were assigned to the proteins (e.g., spectrin is actually band 1).

IV. AGENTS THAT AFFECT OXYGEN BINDING

The major agents that affect oxygen binding to hemoglobin are shown in Figure 44.11.

A. 2,3-Bisphosphoglycerate

2,3-Bisphosphoglycerate (2,3-BPG) is formed in red blood cells from the glycolytic intermediate 1,3-bisphosphoglycerate, as indicated in Figure 44.1. 2,3-BPG binds to hemoglobin in the central cavity formed by the four subunits, increasing the energy required for the conformational changes that facilitate the binding of oxygen. Thus, 2,3-BPG lowers the affinity of hemoglobin for oxygen. Therefore, oxygen is less readily bound (i.e., is more readily released in tissues) when hemoglobin contains 2,3-BPG.

B. Proton Binding (Bohr Effect)

The binding of protons by hemoglobin lowers its affinity for oxygen (Fig. 44.12), contributing to a phenomenon known as the Bohr effect (Fig. 44.13). The pH of the blood decreases as it enters the tissues (and the proton concentration rises) because the CO_2 produced by metabolism is converted to carbonic acid by the reaction catalyzed by carbonic anhydrase in red blood cells. Dissociation of carbonic acid produces protons that react with several amino acid residues in hemoglobin, causing conformational changes that promote the release of oxygen.

In the lungs, this process is reversed. Oxygen binds to hemoglobin, causing a release of protons, which combine with bicarbonate to form carbonic acid. This decrease of protons causes the pH of the blood to rise. Carbonic anhydrase cleaves the carbonic acid to H_2O and CO_2, and the CO_2 is exhaled. Thus, in tissues in which the pH of the blood is low because of the CO_2 produced by metabolism, oxygen is released from hemoglobin. In the lungs, where the pH of the blood is higher because CO_2 is being exhaled, oxygen binds to hemoglobin.

C. Carbon Dioxide

Although most of the CO_2 produced by metabolism in the tissues is carried to the lungs as bicarbonate, some of the CO_2 is covalently bound to hemoglobin (Fig. 44.14). In the tissues, CO_2 forms carbamate adducts with the N-terminal amino groups of

FIG. 44.11. Agents that affect oxygen binding by hemoglobin. Binding of hydrogen ions, 2,3-bisphosphoglycerate, and carbon dioxide to hemoglobin decrease its affinity for oxygen.

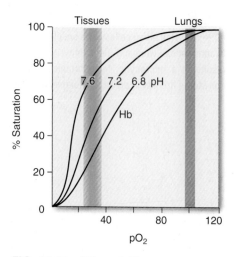

FIG. 44.12. Effect of pH on oxygen saturation curves. As the pH decreases, the affinity of hemoglobin for oxygen decreases, producing the Bohr effect.

FIG. 44.13. Effect of H^+ on oxygen binding by hemoglobin (Hb). **A.** In the tissues, CO_2 is released. In the red blood cell, this CO_2 forms carbonic acid, which releases protons. The protons bind to Hb, causing it to release oxygen to the tissues. **B.** In the lungs, the reactions are reversed. O_2 binds to protonated Hb, causing the release of protons. They bind to bicarbonate (HCO_3^-), forming carbonic acid, which is cleaved to water and CO_2, which is exhaled. *RBC*, red blood cell.

deoxyhemoglobin and stabilizes the deoxy conformation. In the lungs, where the P_{O_2} is high, oxygen binds to hemoglobin and this bound CO_2 is released.

V. HEMATOPOIESIS

The various types of cells (lineages) that make up the blood are constantly being produced in the bone marrow. All cell lineages are descended from hematopoietic stem cells, cells that are renewable throughout the life of the host. The population of hematopoietic stem cells is quite small. Estimates vary between 1 and 10 per 10^5 bone marrow cells. In the presence of the appropriate signals, hematopoietic

FIG. 44.14. Binding of CO_2 to hemoglobin. CO_2 forms carbamates with the N-terminal amino groups of hemoglobin (Hb) chains. Approximately 15% of the CO_2 in blood is carried to the lungs bound to Hb. The reaction releases protons, which contribute to the Bohr effect. The overall effect is stabilization of the deoxy form of hemoglobin.

Populations of hematopoietic cells enriched with stem cells can be isolated by fluorescence-activated cell sorting, based on the expression of specific cell-surface markers. Increasing the population of stem cells in cells used for a bone marrow transplantation increases the chances of success of the transplantation.

stem cells proliferate, differentiate, and mature into any of the types of cells that make up the blood (Fig. 44.15).

Hematopoietic differentiation is hierarchical. The number of fates a developing blood cell may adopt becomes progressively restricted. Hematopoietic progenitors are designated colony-forming unit–lineage, or colony-forming unit–erythroid (CFU-E). Progenitors that form very large colonies are termed burst-forming units.

A. Cytokines and Hematopoiesis
Developing progenitor cells in the marrow grow in proximity with marrow stromal cells. These include fibroblasts, endothelial cells, adipocytes, and macrophages.

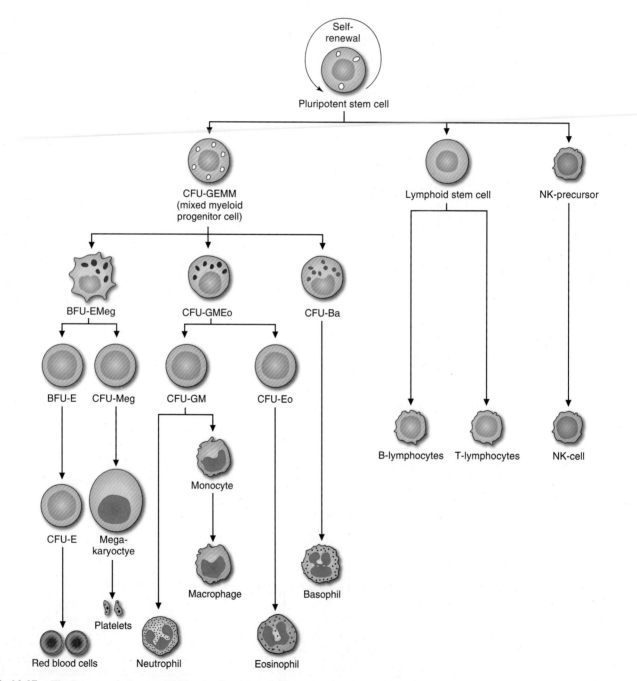

FIG. 44.15. The hematopoietic tree. All blood cells arise from the self-renewing pluripotent stem cell. Different cytokines are required at each step for these events to occur. *BFU*, burst-forming unit; *CFU*, colony-forming unit.

The stromal cells form an extracellular matrix and secrete growth factors that regulate hematopoietic development.

The hematopoietic growth factors have multiple effects. An individual growth factor may stimulate proliferation, differentiation, and maturation of the progenitor cells and also may prevent apoptosis. These factors also may activate various functions within the mature cell. Some hematopoietic growth factors act on multiple lineages, whereas others have more limited targets.

Most hematopoietic growth factors are recognized by receptors belonging to the cytokine receptor superfamily. Binding of ligand to receptor results in receptor aggregation, which induces phosphorylation of Janus kinases (JAKs). The JAKs are a family of cytoplasmic tyrosine kinases that are active when phosphorylated (see Chapter 11, Section III.C, and Fig. 11.15). The activated JAKs then phosphorylate the cytokine receptor. Phosphorylation of the receptor creates docking regions where additional signal transduction molecules bind, including members of the signal transducer and activator of transcription (STAT) family of transcription factors. The JAKs phosphorylate the STATs, which dimerize and translocate to the nucleus, where they activate target genes. Additional signal transduction proteins bind to the phosphorylated cytokine receptor, leading to activation of the Ras/Raf/MAP kinase pathways. Other pathways are also activated, some of which lead to an inhibition of apoptosis (see Chapter 18).

The response to cytokine binding is usually transient because the cell contains multiple negative regulators of cytokine signaling. The family of *silencer of cytokine signaling* (SOCS) proteins is induced by cytokine binding. One member of the family binds to the phosphorylated receptor and prevents the docking of signal transduction proteins. Other SOCS proteins bind to JAKs and inhibit them. Whether SOCS inhibition of JAKs is a consequence of steric inhibition or whether SOCS recruit phosphatases that then dephosphorylate the JAKs (Fig. 44.16) is uncertain.

SHP-1 is a tyrosine phosphatase found primarily in hematopoietic cells that is necessary for proper development of myeloid and lymphoid lineages. Its function is to dephosphorylate JAK2, thereby inactivating it.

STATs are also inactivated. The *protein inhibitors of activated STAT* (PIAS) family of proteins bind to phosphorylated STATs and prevent their dimerization

 Leukemias, malignancies of the blood, arise when a differentiating hematopoietic cell does not complete its developmental program but remains in an immature, proliferative state. Leukemias have been found in every hematopoietic lineage.

 In X-linked severe combined immuno-deficiency (SCID) disease, the most common form of SCID, circulating T lymphocytes are not formed, and B lymphocytes are not active. The affected gene encodes the γ-chain of the interleukin-2 receptor. Mutant receptors are unable to activate Janus kinase 3 (JAK3), and the cells are unresponsive to the cytokines that stimulate growth and differentiation. Recall also that adenosine deaminase deficiency (see Chapter 41), which is not X-linked, also leads to a form of SCID, but for different reasons.

FIG. 44.16. Cytokine signaling through the JAK/STAT pathway. *(1)* Cytokine binding to receptors initiates dimerization and activation of the JAK kinase, which phosphorylates the receptor on tyrosine residues. *(2)* STAT proteins bind to the activated receptors and are themselves phosphorylated. *(3)* Phosphorylated STAT proteins dimerize, travel to the nucleus, and initiate gene transcription. *(4)* One family of proteins whose synthesis is stimulated by STATs is the SOCS (**s**uppressor **o**f **c**ytokine **s**ignaling) family, which inhibits further activation of STAT proteins *(5)* by a variety of mechanisms.

Families have been identified whose members have a mutant erythropoietin (EPO) receptor that is unable to bind SHP-1. Erythropoietin is the hematopoietic cytokine that stimulates production of red blood cells. Individuals with the mutant EPO receptor have a higher than normal percentage of red blood cells in the circulation because the mutant EPO receptor cannot be deactivated by SHP-1. Erythropoietin causes sustained activation of Janus kinase 2 (JAK2) and STAT 5 in these cases.

Perturbed JAK/STAT signaling is associated with development of lymphoid and myeloid leukemias, severe congenital neutropenia (a condition in which levels of circulating neutrophils are severely reduced), and Fanconi anemia, which is characterized by bone marrow failure and increased susceptibility to malignancy.

A complication of sickle cell disease is an increased formation of gallstones. A sickle cell crisis accompanied by the intravascular destruction of red blood cells (hemolysis) experienced by patients with sickle cell disease, such as **Will Sichel**, increases the amount of unconjugated bilirubin that is transported to the liver. If the concentration of this unconjugated bilirubin exceeds the capacity of the hepatocytes to conjugate it to the more soluble diglucuronide through interaction with hepatic UDP-glucuronate, both the total and the unconjugated bilirubin levels in the blood increase. More unconjugated bilirubin is then secreted by the liver into the bile. The increase in unconjugated bilirubin (which is not very water-soluble) results in its precipitation within the gallbladder lumen, leading to the formation of pigmented (calcium bilirubinate) gallstones.

or promote the dissociation of STAT dimers. STATs also may be inactivated by dephosphorylation, although the specific phosphatases have not yet been identified, or by targeting activated STATs for proteolytic degradation.

B. Erythropoiesis

The production of red cells is regulated by the demands of oxygen delivery to the tissues. In response to reduced tissue oxygenation, the kidney releases the hormone erythropoietin, which stimulates the multiplication and maturation of erythroid progenitors. The progression along the erythroid pathway begins with the stem cell and passes through the mixed myeloid progenitor cell (CFU-GEMM, colony-forming unit–granulocyte, erythroid, monocyte, megakaryocyte), burst-forming unit–erythroid (BFU-E), CFU-E, and to the first recognizable red cell precursor, the normoblast. Each normoblast undergoes four more cycles of cell division. During these four cycles, the nucleus becomes smaller and more condensed. After the last division, the nucleus is extruded. The red cell at this state is called a reticulocyte. Reticulocytes still retain ribosomes and messenger RNA (mRNA) and are capable of synthesizing hemoglobin. They are released from the bone marrow and circulate for 1 to 2 days. Reticulocytes mature in the spleen, where the ribosomes and mRNA are lost (Fig. 44.17).

C. Nutritional Anemias

Each person produces approximately 10^{12} red blood cells per day. Because so many cells must be produced, nutritional deficiencies in iron, vitamin B_{12}, and folate prevent adequate red blood cell formation. The physical appearance of the cells in the case of a nutritional anemia frequently provides a clue as to the nature of the deficiency.

In the case of iron deficiency, the cells are smaller and paler than normal. The lack of iron results in decreased heme synthesis, which in turn affects globin synthesis. Maturing red cells following their normal developmental program divide until their hemoglobin has reached the appropriate concentration. Iron (and hemoglobin)-deficient developing red blood cells continue dividing past their normal stopping point, resulting in small (microcytic) red cells. The cells are also pale—because of the lack of hemoglobin—compared with normal cells (thus, a pale, microcytic anemia results).

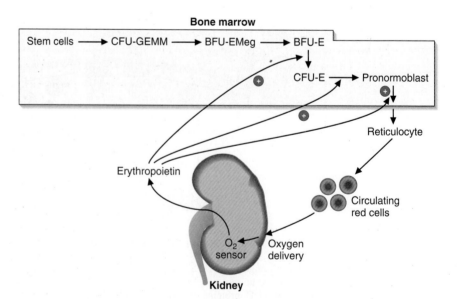

FIG. 44.17. Erythropoietin stimulation of erythrocyte maturation. The abbreviations are described in the text.

Deficiencies of folate or vitamin B_{12} can cause megaloblastic anemia, in which the cells are larger than normal. Folate and B_{12} are required for DNA synthesis (see Chapters 40 and 41). When these vitamins are deficient, DNA replication and nuclear division do not keep pace with the maturation of the cytoplasm. Consequently, the nucleus is extruded before the requisite number of cell divisions has taken place, and the cell volume is greater than it should be, and fewer blood cells are produced.

VI. HEMOGLOBINOPATHIES, HEREDITARY PERSISTENCE OF FETAL HEMOGLOBIN, AND HEMOGLOBIN SWITCHING

A. Hemoglobinopathies: Disorders in the Structure or Amount of the Globin Chains

More than 700 different mutant hemoglobins have been discovered. Most arise from a single base substitution, resulting in a single amino acid replacement. Many have been discovered during population screenings and are not clinically significant. However, in patients with hemoglobin S (HbS, sickle cell anemia), the most common hemoglobin mutation, the amino acid substitution has a devastating effect in the homozygote (see **Will Sichel** in Chapter 6). Another common hemoglobin variant, hemoglobin C (HbC), results from a glu-to-lys replacement in the same position as the HbS mutation. This mutation has two effects. It promotes water loss from the cell by activating the K^+ transporter by an unknown mechanism, resulting in a higher than normal concentration of hemoglobin within the cell. The amino acid replacement also substantially lowers the hemoglobin solubility in the homozygote, resulting in a tendency of the mutant hemoglobin to precipitate within the red cell, although, unlike sickle cells, the cell does not become deformed. Homozygotes for the HbC mutation have a mild hemolytic anemia. Heterozygous individuals are clinically unaffected.

B. Thalassemias

For optimum function, the hemoglobin α- and β-globin chains must have the proper structure and be synthesized in a 1:1 ratio. A large excess of one subunit over the other results in the class of diseases called thalassemias. These anemias are clinically very heterogeneous, as they can arise by multiple mechanisms. Like sickle cell anemia, the thalassemia mutations provide resistance to malaria in the heterozygous state.

Hemoglobin single amino acid replacement mutations that give rise to a globin subunit of decreased stability is one mechanism by which thalassemia arises. More common, however, are mutations that result in decreased synthesis of one subunit. The α-thalassemias usually arise from complete gene deletions. Two copies of the α-globin gene are found on each chromosome 16, for a total of four α-globin genes per precursor cell. If one copy of the gene is deleted, the size and hemoglobin concentration of the individual red blood cells is minimally reduced. If two copies are deleted, the red blood cells are of decreased size (microcytic) and reduced hemoglobin concentration (hypochromic). However, the individual is usually not anemic. The loss of three α-globin genes causes a moderately severe microcytic hypochromic anemia (hemoglobin, 7 to 10 g/dL) with splenomegaly (enlarged spleen). The absence of four α-globin genes (hydrops fetalis) is usually fatal in utero.

As discussed in Chapter 14, β-thalassemia is a very heterogeneous genetic disease. Insufficient β-globin synthesis can result from deletions, promoter mutations, and splice-junction mutations. Heterozygotes for β^+ (some globin chain synthesis) or β-null (β^0, no globin chain synthesis) are generally asymptomatic, although they typically have microcytic, hypochromic red blood cells and may have mild anemia. β^+/β^+ homozygotes have anemia of variable severity, β^+/β^0 compound heterozygotes tend to be more severely affected, and β^0/β^0 homozygotes have severe disease. In general, diseases of β-chain deficiency are more severe than

Hemoglobin C (HbC) is found in high frequency in West Africa, in regions with a high frequency of hemoglobin S (HbS). Consequently, compound heterozygotes for HbS and HbC are not uncommon both in some African regions and among African Americans. HbS/HbC individuals have significantly more hematopathology than individuals with sickle cell trait (adult hemoglobin [HbA]/HbS). Polymerization of deoxygenated HbS is dependent on the HbS concentration within the cell. The presence of HbC in the compound heterozygote increases the HbS concentration by stimulating K^+ and water efflux from the cell. Because the HbC globin tends to precipitate, the proportion of HbS tends to be higher in HbS/HbC cells than in the cells of individuals with sickle cell trait (HbS/HbA). The way in which multiple mutations ameliorate or exacerbate hematologic diseases has provided insights into the molecular mechanisms of hemoglobin function and developmental regulation.

There are two ways in which an individual might have two α-globin genes deleted. In one case, one copy of chromosome 16 might have both α-globin genes deleted, whereas the other copy had two functional α-globin genes. In the second case, both chromosomes might have lost one of their two copies of the α-globin gene. The former possibility is more common among Asians, the latter among Africans.

diseases of α-chain deficiency. Excess β-chains form a homotetramer, hemoglobin H (HbH), which is ineffective for delivering oxygen to the tissues because of its high oxygen affinity. As red blood cells age, HbH precipitates in the cells, forming inclusion bodies. Red blood cells with inclusion bodies have shortened life spans because they are more likely to be trapped and destroyed in the spleen. Excess α-chains are unable to form a stable tetramer. However, excess α-chains precipitate in erythrocytes at every developmental stage. The α-chain precipitation in erythroid precursors results in their widespread destruction, a process called ineffective erythropoiesis. The precipitated α-chains also damage red blood cell membranes through the heme-facilitated lipid oxidation by reactive oxygen species. Both lipids and proteins, particularly band 4.1, are damaged.

C. Hereditary Persistence of Fetal Hemoglobin

Fetal hemoglobin (HbF), the predominant hemoglobin of the fetal period, consists of two α-chains and two γ-chains, whereas adult hemoglobin (HbA) consists of two α- and two β-chains. The process that regulates the conversion of HbF to HbA is called hemoglobin switching. Hemoglobin switching is not 100%; most individuals continue to produce a small amount of HbF throughout life. However, some people, who are clinically normal, produce abnormally high levels (up to 100%) of HbF in place of HbA. Patients with hemoglobinopathies such as β-thalassemia or sickle cell anemia frequently have less severe illnesses if their levels of HbF are elevated. One goal of much research on hemoglobin switching is to discover a way to reactivate transcription of the γ-globin genes to compensate for defective β-globin synthesis. Individuals who express HbF past birth have hereditary persistence of fetal hemoglobin (HPFH).

1. NONDELETION FORMS OF HEREDITARY PERSISTENCE OF FETAL HEMOGLOBIN

The nondeletion forms of HPFH are those that derive from point mutations in the Aγ and Gγ promoters. When these mutations are found with sickle cell or β-thalassemia mutations, they have an ameliorating effect on the disease because of the increased production of γ-chains.

2. DELETION FORMS OF HEREDITARY PERSISTENCE OF FETAL HEMOGLOBIN

In deletion HPFH, both the entire δ- and β-genes have been deleted from one copy of chromosome 11 and only HbF can be produced. In some individuals, the fetal globins remain activated after birth, and enough HbF is produced that the individual is clinically normal. Other individuals with similar deletions that remove the entire δ- and β-genes do not produce enough fetal hemoglobin to compensate for the deletion and are considered to have $\delta^0\beta^0$-thalassemia. The difference between these two outcomes is believed to be the site at which the deletions end within the β-globin gene cluster. In deletion HPFH, powerful enhancer sequences $3'$ of the β-globin gene are resituated because of the deletion so that they activate the γ-promoters. In individuals with $\delta^0\beta^0$-thalassemia, the enhancer sequences have not been relocated so that they can interact with the γ-promoters.

D. Hemoglobin Switching: A Developmental Process Controlled by Transcription Factors

In humans, embryonic megaloblasts (the embryonic red blood cell is large and is termed a "blast" because it retains its nucleus) are first produced in the yolk sac approximately 15 days after fertilization. After 6 weeks, the site of erythropoiesis shifts to the liver. The liver and to a lesser extent the spleen are the major sites of fetal erythropoiesis. In the last few weeks before birth, the bone marrow begins producing red blood cells. By 8 to 10 weeks after birth, the bone marrow is the sole site of erythrocyte production. The composition of the hemoglobin also changes with

The difference in amino acid composition between the β-chains of HbA and the γ-chains of fetal hemoglobin (HbF) results in structural changes that cause HbF to have a lower affinity for 2,3-bisphosphoglycerate (2,3-BPG) than adult hemoglobin (HbA) and thus a greater affinity for oxygen. Therefore, the oxygen released from the mother's hemoglobin (HbA) is readily bound by HbF in the fetus. Thus, the transfer of oxygen from the mother to the fetus is facilitated by the structural difference between the hemoglobin molecule of the mother and that of the fetus.

development because both the α-globin locus and the β-globin locus have multiple genes that are differentially expressed during development (Fig. 44.18).

E. Structure and Transcriptional Regulation of the α- and β-Globin Gene Loci

The α-globin locus on chromosome 16 contains the embryonic ζ (zeta) gene and two copies of the α-gene, α_2 and α_1. The β-globin locus on chromosome 11 contains the embryonic ε-gene; two copies of the fetal β-globin gene, Gγ and Aγ (which differ by one amino acid); and two adult genes, δ and β. The order of the genes along the chromosome parallels the order of expression of the genes during development (see Fig. 44.18). The embryonic hemoglobins are $\zeta_2\varepsilon_2$ (Gower 1), $\zeta_2\gamma_2$ (Portland), and $\alpha_2\gamma_2$ (Gower 2). Fetal hemoglobin is predominantly α_2Gγ_2. The major adult species is $\alpha_2\beta_2$ (hemoglobin A); the minor adult species is $\alpha_2\delta_2$ (hemoglobin A$_2$). The fetal hemoglobin found in adult cells is α_2Aγ_2. The timing of hemoglobin switching is controlled by a developmental clock that is not significantly altered by environmental conditions and is related to changes in expression of specific transcription factors. Premature newborns convert from HbF to HbA on schedule with their gestational ages.

A Chromosome 16

Embryo: $\zeta_2\varepsilon_2$ = Gower 1

$\zeta_2\gamma_2$ = Portland

$\alpha_2\varepsilon_2$ = Gower 2

Fetus: $\alpha_2\gamma_2$ = HbF

Adult: $\alpha_2\gamma_2$ = HbF

$\alpha_2\delta_2$ = A$_2$

$\alpha_2\beta_2$ = A

B

FIG. 44.18. Globin gene clusters and expression during development. **A.** The globin gene clusters with the α-genes on chromosome 16 and the β-genes on chromosome 11. *LCR,* locus control region. **B.** The switching of globin chain synthesis during development.

CLINICAL COMMENTS

Spiro Site. Spiro Site's red blood cells are deficient in spectrin. This deficiency impairs the ability of his erythrocytes to maintain the redundant surface area necessary to maintain deformability. Mechanical stresses in the circulation cause progressive loss of pieces of membrane. As membrane components are lost, Spiro Site's red blood cells become spherical and unable to deform. His spleen is enlarged because of the large number of red blood cells that have become trapped within it. His erythrocytes are lysed by mechanical stresses in the circulation and by macrophages in the spleen. Consequently, this hemolytic process results in anemia. His gallstones were the result of the large amounts of bilirubin that were produced and stored in the gallbladder as a result of the hemolysis. The abnormally rounded red cells seen on a blood smear are characteristic of hereditary spherocytosis.

Mutations in the genes for ankyrin, β-spectrin, or band 3 account for three quarters of the cases of hereditary spherocytosis, whereas mutations in the genes for α-spectrin or band 4.2 account for the remainder. The result of defective synthesis of any of the membrane cytoskeletal proteins results in improper formation of the membrane cytoskeleton. Excess membrane proteins are catabolized, resulting in a net deficiency of spectrin. **Spiro Site** underwent a splenectomy. Because the spleen was the major site of destruction of his red blood cells, his anemia improved significantly after surgery. He was discharged with the recommendation to take a folate supplement daily. It was explained to Mr. Site that because the spleen plays a major role in protection against certain bacterial agents, he would require immunizations against *Pneumococcus*, *Meningococcus*, and *Haemophilus influenzae* type b.

Anne Niemick. Anne Niemick was found to be a compound heterozygote for mutations in the β-globin gene. On one gene, a mutation in position 6 of intron 1 converted a T to a C. The presence of this mutation, for unknown reasons, raises HbF production. The other β-globin gene had a mutation in position 110 of exon 1 (a C-to-T mutation). Both β-globin chains have reduced activity, but combined with the increased expression of HbF, the result is a β^+-thalassemia.

BIOCHEMICAL COMMENTS

Control of Hemoglobin Switching. How is hemoglobin switching controlled? Although there are still many unanswered questions, some of the molecular mechanisms have been identified. The α-globin locus covers ~100 kb (kilobases). The major regulatory element, HS40, is a nuclease-sensitive region of DNA that lies 5' of the ζ-gene (see Fig. 44.18). HS40 acts as an erythroid-specific enhancer that interacts with the upstream regulatory regions of the ζ- and α-genes, and stimulates their transcription. The region immediately 5' of the ζ-gene contains the regulatory sequences responsible for silencing ζ-gene transcription. However, the exact sequences and transcription factors responsible for this silencing have not yet been identified. Even after silencing, low levels of ζ-gene transcripts are still produced after the embryonic period; however, they are not translated. This is because both the ζ-globin and α-globin transcripts have regions that bind to a messenger ribonucleoprotein (mRNP) stability-determining complex. Binding to this complex prevents the messenger RNA (mRNA) from being degraded. The α-globin messenger RNA has a much higher affinity for the mRNP than the ζ-globin message, which leads to the ζ-globin message being rapidly degraded.

The β-globin locus covers ~100 kb. From 5 to 25 kb upstream of the ε-gene is the locus control region (LCR), containing five DNAse hypersensitive sites. The LCR is necessary for the function of the β-globin locus. It maintains the chromatin of the entire locus in an active configuration and acts as an enhancer and entry point for the factors that transcribe the genes of the β-globin locus. One model of the control of hemoglobin switching postulates that proteins bound at the promoters of the ε-, γ-, and β-globin genes compete to interact with the enhancers of the LCR.

Each gene in the β-globin locus has individual regulatory elements—a promoter, silencers, or enhancers that control its developmental regulation. The promoters that control the γ- and β-globin genes have been intensively studied because of their clinical relevance.

The ε-globin gene, like the ζ-globin gene, has silencers in the 5′-regulatory region. Binding of proteins to these regions turns off the ε-gene.

The proximal region of the γ-globin gene promoter has multiple transcription factor–binding sites (Fig. 44.19). Many hereditary persistence of fetal hemoglobin (HPFH) mutations map to these transcription factor–binding sites, either by destroying a site or by creating a new one, but the exact mechanisms are still not understood. Two sites that appear to be significant in the control of hemoglobin switching are the stage-selector protein-binding (SSP) site and the CAAT box region. When the SSP complex is bound to the promoter, the γ-globin gene has a competitive advantage over the β-globin promoter for interaction with the LCR. A second transcription factor, Sp1, also binds at the SSP-binding site, where it may act as a repressor, and competition between these two protein complexes for the SSP-binding site helps to determine the activity of the γ-globin gene. A similar

FIG. 44.19. **A.** The γ-globin gene promoter, indicating some of the transcription factor–binding sites associated with hereditary persistence of fetal hemoglobin. **B.** The β-globin gene locus. When *BCL11A* is expressed, the interaction between the LCR and the γ-gene promoter is blocked, turning off γ-gene expression. NURD is a chromatin remodeling complex containing histone deacetylase activity.

mechanism appears to be operating at the CAAT box. CP1, thought to be a transcription activator, binds at the CAAT box. CAAT displacement protein (CDP) is a repressor that binds at the CAAT site and displaces CP1. Part of the mechanism of hemoglobin switching appears to be the binding of repressors at the β-globin and γ-globin upstream regulatory regions.

The β-globin gene also has binding sites for multiple transcription factors in its regulatory regions. Mutations that affect binding of transcription factors can produce thalassemia by reducing the activity of the β-globin promoter. There is also an enhancer 3' of the poly A signal that seems to be required for stage-specific activation of the β-globin promoter.

Further insights into the control of hemoglobin switching indicate that the transcription factor *BCL11A* is a strong repressor of γ-globin gene expression. *BCL11A* interacts with a variety of other transcription factors (GATA-1, FOG1, and the NURD repressor complex [nucleosome remodeling and histone deacetylase]) to repress γ-globin expression. This appears to be caused by *BCL11A* interfering with LCR interactions with the γ-globin gene promoter. Experiments that reduce, or eliminate, *BCL11A* expression lead to an increase in γ-globin synthesis. *BCL11A* expression is regulated by the transcription factor KLF1, which is essential for β-globin expression. KLF1 increases *BCL11A* expression, which blocks γ-globin gene expression, while KFL1 stimulates β-globin gene expression. These recent results suggest that drugs, which interfere with KLF1 action, would enhance and activate fetal globin gene expression in individuals with either β-thalassemia or sickle cell disease (see Fig. 44.19B).

Key Concepts

- The blood contains a wide variety of distinct cell types, each of whose function is necessary for maintaining the body's internal environment.
- Erythrocytes transport oxygen throughout the body and return carbon dioxide back to the lung.
  - Erythrocytes lack nuclei and carry out limited metabolic reactions.
    - Glycolysis provides energy and NADH.
    - The NADH maintains the iron in hemoglobin in the ferrous state.
    - The HMP shunt provides NADPH to regenerate reduced glutathione to protect the membrane from oxidative damage.
    - 1,3-Bisphosphoglycerate is converted to 2,3-bisphosphoglycerate as a by-product of glycolysis to regulate oxygen binding to hemoglobin.
  - Heme synthesis occurs in the erythrocyte precursor, using succinyl-CoA and glycine. Inherited defects in heme synthesis lead to porphyrias.
  - Iron, a critical part of heme, is carried throughout the body on protein carriers because free iron is toxic.
  - The erythrocyte membrane is flexible as a result of its unique cytoskeletal structure, which allows erythrocytes to deform in order to travel through narrow capillaries.
  - Oxygen binding to hemoglobin in the erythrocyte is modulated by a variety of factors.
    - 2,3-Bisphosphoglycerate stabilizes the deoxy form of hemoglobin.
    - Proton binding to hemoglobin stabilizes the deoxy form of hemoglobin (the Bohr effect).
    - Carbon dioxide links covalently to the amino termini of the four globin chains in a hemoglobin molecule, further stabilizing the deoxy form of hemoglobin.
- Hematopoiesis is the generation of the unique blood cell types from a single precursor stem cell in the bone marrow.
- Polymorphonuclear leukocytes consist of a variety of cell types that release chemical signals when activated (granulocytes), phagocytose foreign bodies (neutrophils), destroy parasites (eosinophils), and are involved in the allergic response (basophils).
- Mononuclear leukocytes include the lymphocytes (necessary for the immune response) and monocytes (which develop into macrophages, which engulf debris left behind after granulocytes attack foreign material).
- A wide variety of mutations can lead to alterations in hemoglobin function (hemoglobinopathies):
  - Sickle cell anemia
  - Thalassemias
  - Hereditary persistence of fetal hemoglobin (hemoglobin switching and its regulation)
- Diseases discussed in this chapter are summarized in Table 44.4.

Table 44.4   Diseases Discussed in Chapter 44

Disease or Disorder	Environmental or Genetic	Comments
Thalassemias	Genetic	Unbalanced synthesis of alpha and beta chains of hemoglobin, leading to anemia.
Pyruvate kinase deficiency	Genetic	Red cell hemolysis, leading to fewer red cells. An increase in 2,3-BPG levels often masks the effects of the anemia.
Congenital methemoglobinemia	Genetic	Oxidation of the iron in heme to the ferric state, which will not bind oxygen, although many individuals with this disorder are asymptomatic.
Glucose-6-phosphate dehydrogenase deficiency	Genetic	Affects red blood cell membrane stability through an inability to protect membrane proteins and lipids against oxidation.
Porphyrias	Genetic	Inherited defects in almost any step of heme synthesis leading to a series of diseases with different symptoms and outcomes.
Iron deficiency	Both	Reduced iron leads to reduced heme synthesis and reduced oxygen delivery to the tissues.
X-linked severe-combined immunodeficiency syndrome	Genetic	Loss of a cytokine receptor subunit, leading to a complete loss of B- and T-cell maturation and proliferation, and no functional immune system.
Defective erythropoietin receptor	Genetic	Red blood cell formation is reduced under conditions in which red blood cell production should be increased (such as reduced oxygen delivery to the tissues).
Hemoglobin C	Genetic	A point mutation in hemoglobin leading to a lysine for a glutamic acid at position 6 of the beta chain, leading to hemolytic anemia in the homozygous state.
Hereditary persistence of fetal hemoglobin	Genetic	Mutations in promoter and enhancer regions leading to misexpression of the globin gamma gene, and constant expression of the gene
Spherocytosis	Genetic	Mutations in any of several red blood cell membrane proteins (such as spectrin), leading to instability of the red cells, destruction of the red blood cells, and an anemia.

2,3-BPG, 2,3-bisphosphoglycerate.

REVIEW QUESTIONS—CHAPTER 44

1. A compensatory mechanism to allow adequate oxygen delivery to the tissues at high altitudes, where oxygen concentrations are low, is which of the following?

   A. An increase in 2,3-bisphosphoglycerate synthesis by the red cell
   B. A decrease in 2,3-bisphosphoglycerate synthesis by the red cell
   C. An increase in hemoglobin synthesis by the red cell
   D. A decrease in hemoglobin synthesis by the red cell
   E. Decreasing the blood pH

2. A 2-year-old boy of normal weight and height is brought to a clinic because of excessive fatigue. Blood work indicates anemia, with microcytic hypochromic red cells. The boy lives in a 100-year-old apartment building and has been caught ingesting paint chips. His parents indicate that the child eats a healthy diet and takes a Flintstones vitamin supplement every day. His anemia is most likely attributable to a deficiency in which of the following?

   A. Iron
   B. Vitamin B_{12}
   C. Folate
   D. Heme
   E. Vitamin B_6

3. Drugs are being developed that will induce the transcription of globin genes, which are normally silent in patients affected with sickle cell disease. A good target gene for such therapy in this disease would be which of the following?

   A. The α_1-gene
   B. The α_2-gene
   C. The γ-gene
   D. The β-gene
   E. The ζ-gene

4. A mature blood cell that lacks a nucleus is which of the following?

    A. Lymphocyte
    B. Basophil
    C. Eosinophil
    D. Platelet
    E. Neutrophil

5. A family has two children, one with a mild case of thalassemia and a second with a severe case of thalassemia, requiring frequent blood transfusions as part of the treatment plan. One parent is of Mediterranean descent, the other is of Asian descent. Neither parent exhibits clinical signs of thalassemia. Both children express 20% of the expected level of β-globin; the more severely affected child expresses normal levels of α-globin, whereas the less severely affected child expresses only 50% of the normal levels of α-globin. Why is the child who has a deficiency in α-globin expression less severely affected?

    A. Thalassemia is caused by a mutation in the α-gene, and the more severely affected child expresses more of it.
    B. The less severely affected child must be synthesizing the ζ-gene to make up for the deficiency in α-chain synthesis.
    C. The more severely affected child also has HPFH.
    D. The more severely affected child produces more inactive globin tetramers than the less severely affected child.
    E. Thalassemia is caused by an iron deficiency, and when the child is synthesizing normal levels of α-globin, there is insufficient iron to populate all of the heme molecules synthesized.

45 Blood Plasma Proteins, Coagulation, and Fibrinolysis

*The blood is the body's main transport system. Although the transport and delivery of oxygen to the cells of the tissues is carried out by specialized cells, other vital components such as nutrients, metabolites, electrolytes, and hormones are all carried in the noncellular fraction of the blood, the **plasma**. Some components, such as glucose, are dissolved in the plasma; others, for example, lipids and steroid hormones, are bound to carrier proteins for transport. The **osmotic pressure** exerted by the plasma proteins regulates the distribution of water between the blood and the tissues. Plasma proteins in conjunction with platelets maintain the integrity of the circulatory system through the process of clotting.*

*Blood normally circulates through endothelium-lined blood vessels. When a blood vessel is severed, a **blood clot** (called a **thrombus**, which is formed by the process of **thrombosis**) forms as part of **hemostasis**, the physiologic response that stops bleeding. Blood clots also form to repair damage to the endothelial lining in which components of the **subendothelial layer** become accessible to plasma proteins.*

*In hemostasis and thrombosis, a primary hemostatic plug, consisting of **aggregated platelets** and a **fibrin clot**, forms at the site of injury. Platelets are attached to the subendothelial layer of the vessel principally through the protein **von Willebrand factor** (vWF) and are activated to bind fibrinogen. **Fibrinogen** binds the platelets to each other to form a platelet aggregate. The platelet aggregate is rapidly covered with layers of **fibrin**, which are formed from fibrinogen by the proteolytic enzyme **thrombin**.*

*Injury to the endothelium and exposure of **tissue factor** on the **subendothelial layer** to plasma proteins also activate the blood coagulation cascade, which ultimately activates thrombin and **factor XIII**. Factor XIII **cross-links** strands of polymerized fibrin monomers to form a stable clot (the **secondary hemostatic plug**). The blood coagulation cascade consists of a series of enzymes (such as **factor X**), which are inactive until they are proteolytically cleaved by the preceding enzyme in the cascade. Other proteins (**factor V** and **factor VIII**) serve as binding proteins, which assemble factor complexes at the site of injury. Ca^{2+} and **γ-carboxyglutamate** residues in the proteins (formed by a vitamin K–dependent process in the liver) attach the factor complexes to **phospholipids** exposed on platelet membranes. Consequently, thrombus formation is rapidly accelerated and localized to the site of injury.*

***Regulatory mechanisms** within the blood coagulation cascade and **antifibrinolytic mechanisms** prevent random coagulation within blood vessels that might obstruct blood flow. Impairments in these mechanisms lead to thrombosis.*

There are two basic assays for measuring the activity of factor VIII in a blood sample: the first is a functional (clotting) assay and the second is a coupled (to factor X activation) enzyme system leading to the cleavage of a chromogenic substrate, generating a colored product.

For the functional assay, a sample of the patient's plasma is added to a factor VIII-deficient sample of plasma (which can be obtained commercially), and the time to generate clot formation is determined. Although clot formation is the end product of this assay, one is measuring the eventual activation of factor II to IIa, which allows clot formation to initiate.

In the automated, chromogenic assay, a sample of the unknown is mixed with purified factor IXa, Ca^{2+}, phospholipid vesicles, the chromogenic substrate, and purified factor X. If the unknown sample contains factor VIII, the factors VIII and IXa will synergize and activate factor X to Xa. The factor Xa will cleave the chromogenic substrate, forming a colored product, whose concentration can be determined spectrophotometrically. Comparison to a standard curve of factor VIII addition enables an accurate estimate of the level of active factor VIII in the sample.

In cases of severe protein malnutrition (*kwashiorkor*), the concentration of the plasma proteins decreases as a result of which the osmotic pressure of the blood decreases. As a result, fluid is not drawn back to the blood and instead accumulates in the interstitial space (edema). The distended bellies of famine victims are the result of fluid accumulation in the extravascular tissues because of the severely decreased concentration of plasma proteins, particularly albumin. Albumin synthesis decreases fairly early under conditions of protein malnutrition.

THE WAITING ROOM

Sloe Klotter, a 6-month-old male infant, was brought to his pediatrician's office with a painful, expanding mass in his right upper thigh that was first noted just hours after he fell down three uncarpeted steps in his home. The child appeared to be in severe distress.

A radiograph showed no fractures, but a soft tissue swelling, consistent with a hematoma (bleeding into the tissues), was noted. Sloe's mother related that soon after he began to crawl, his knees occasionally became swollen and seemed painful.

The pediatrician suspected a disorder of coagulation. A screening coagulation profile suggested a possible deficiency of *factor VIII*, a protein involved in the formation of blood clots. Sloe's plasma factor VIII level was found to be only 3% of the average level found in normal subjects. A diagnosis of hemophilia A was made.

I. PLASMA PROTEINS MAINTAIN PROPER DISTRIBUTION OF WATER BETWEEN BLOOD AND TISSUES

When cells are removed from the blood, the remaining plasma is composed of water, nutrients, metabolites, hormones, electrolytes, and proteins. Plasma has essentially the same electrolyte composition as other extracellular fluids and constitutes approximately 25% of the body's total extracellular fluid. The plasma proteins serve several functions, including maintaining the proper distribution of water between the blood and the tissues; transporting nutrients, metabolites, and hormones throughout the body; defending against infection; and maintaining the integrity of the circulation through clotting. Many diseases alter the amounts of plasma proteins produced and hence their concentration in the blood. These changes can be determined by electrophoresis of plasma proteins over the course of a disease.

A. Body Fluid Maintenance between Tissues and Blood

As the arterial blood enters the capillaries, fluid moves from the intravascular space into the interstitial space (that surrounding the capillaries) because of what are known as *Starling forces*. The hydrostatic pressure in the arteriolar end of the capillaries (~37 mm Hg) exceeds the sum of the tissue pressure (~1 mm Hg) and the osmotic pressure of the plasma proteins (~25 mm Hg). Thus, water tends to leave the capillaries and enter extravascular spaces. At the venous end of the capillaries, the hydrostatic pressure falls to approximately 17 mm Hg while the osmotic pressure and the tissue pressure remain constant, resulting in movement of fluid back from the extravascular (interstitial) spaces and into the blood. Thus, most of the force bringing water back from the tissues into the plasma is the osmotic pressure mediated by the presence of proteins in the plasma.

B. The Major Serum Protein, Albumin

As indicated in Table 45.1, the liver produces several transport or binding proteins and secretes them into the blood. The major protein synthesized is albumin, which constitutes approximately 60% of the total plasma protein, but because of its relatively small size (69 kDa), it is thought to contribute 70% to 80% of the total osmotic pressure of the plasma. *Albumin*, like most plasma proteins, is a glycoprotein and is a carrier of free fatty acids, calcium, zinc, steroid hormones, copper, and bilirubin. Many drugs also bind to albumin, which may have important pharmacologic implications. For example, when a drug binds to albumin, such binding will

Table 45.1   Specific Plasma-Binding Proteins Synthesized in the Liver

Albumin	Binds free fatty acids, calcium, zinc, steroid hormones, copper, bilirubin
Ceruloplasmin	Binds copper; appears to be more important as a copper storage pool than as a transport protein; integrates iron and copper homeostasis
Corticosteroid-binding globulin	Binds cortisol
Haptoglobin	Binds extracorpuscular heme
Lipoproteins	Transport cholesterol and fatty acids
Retinol-binding protein	Binds vitamin A
Sex hormone–binding globulin	Binds estradiol and testosterone
Transferrin	Transports iron
Transthyretin	Binds thyroxine (T_4); also forms a complex with retinol-binding protein

likely lower the effective concentration of that drug and may lengthen its lifetime in the circulation. Drug dosimetry may need to be recalculated if a patient's plasma protein concentration is abnormal.

II. THE PLASMA CONTAINS PROTEINS THAT AID IN IMMUNE DEFENSE

Two different sets of proteins aid in the immune response: the immunoglobulins and the complement proteins. The immunoglobulins are secreted by a subset of differentiated B lymphocytes termed *plasma cells* and bind antigens at binding sites formed by the hypervariable regions of the proteins (see Chapter 7). Once the antibody–antigen complex is formed, it must be cleared from the circulation. The complement system participates in this function. The complement system consisting of approximately 20 proteins becomes activated in either of two ways: The first is interaction with antigen–antibody complexes, and the second, specific for bacterial infections, is through interaction of bacterial cell polysaccharides with complement protein C3b. Activation of the complement system by either trigger results in a proteolytic activation cascade of the proteins of the complement system, resulting in the release of biologically active peptides or polypeptide fragments. These peptides mediate the inflammatory response, attract phagocytic cells to the area, initiate degranulation of granulocytes, and promote clearance of antigen–antibody complexes.

Protease inhibitors in plasma serve to carefully control the inflammatory response. Activated neutrophils release lysosomal proteases from their granules that can attack elastin, the various types of collagen, and other extracellular matrix proteins. The plasma proteins α_1-antiproteinase (α_1-antitrypsin) and α_2-macroglobulin limit proteolytic damage by forming noncovalent complexes with the proteases, thereby inactivating them. However, the product of neutrophil myeloperoxidase, HOCl, inactivates the protease inhibitors, thereby ensuring that the proteases are active at the site of infection.

III. PLASMA PROTEINS MAINTAIN THE INTEGRITY OF THE CIRCULATORY SYSTEM

Blood is lost from the circulation when the endothelial lining of the blood vessels is damaged and the vessel wall is partly or wholly severed. When this occurs, the subendothelial cell layer is exposed, consisting of the basement membrane of the endothelial cells and smooth muscle cells. In response to the damage, a barrier (the hemostatic plug, a fibrin clot) initiated by platelet binding to the damaged area is formed at the site of injury. Regulatory mechanisms limit clot formation to the site of injury and control its size and stability. As the vessel heals, the clot is degraded (fibrinolysis). Plasma proteins are required for these processes to occur.

 In spite of the importance of albumin in the maintenance of osmotic pressure in the blood, individuals who lack albumin (*analbuminemia*) have only moderate edema. Apparently, the concentration of other plasma proteins is increased to compensate for the lack of albumin. The frequency of analbuminemia is less than one per million individuals.

 α_1-Antiproteinase (AAP) is the main serine protease inhibitor of human plasma. Individuals with a point mutation in exon 5 of the AAP gene, which results in a single amino acid substitution in the protein, have diminished secretion of AAP from the liver. These individuals are at increased risk for developing emphysema. When neutrophils degranulate in the lungs as part of the body's defense against microorganisms, insufficient levels of AAP are present to neutralize the elastase and other proteases released. The excess proteolytic activity damages lung tissue, leading to loss of alveolar elasticity and emphysema.

Methionine 358 of AAP is necessary for AAP binding to the proteases. Oxidation of this methionine destroys AAP's protease-binding capacity. Cigarette smoke oxidizes Met-358, thereby increasing the risk of emphysema.

Idiopathic thrombocytopenic purpura (ITP) is an autoimmune disease in which antibodies to platelet glycoproteins are produced. Antibody binding to platelets results in their clearance by the spleen. An early symptom of the disorder is the appearance of small red spots on the skin (petechial hemorrhages) caused by blood leakage from capillaries. Minor damage to vascular endothelial cells is constantly being caused by mechanical forces related to blood flow. In patients with ITP, few platelets are available to repair the damage.

von Willebrand factor (vWF) is a large multimeric glycoprotein with a subunit molecular weight of 220,000 Da. Its size in the circulation ranges between 500 and 20,000 kDa, and its role in circulation is to stabilize factor VIII and protect it from degradation. The high-molecular-weight (HMW) forms are concentrated in the endothelium of blood vessels and are released in response to stress hormones and endothelial damage. HMW vWF released by the endothelium is cleaved by a specific metalloprotease in the serum, reducing the size of the circulating vWF. Large vWF multimers are more effective at forming complexes with platelets than are small vWF multimers.

vWF deficiency is the most common cause of inherited bleeding disorders. Both platelet adherence and the clotting cascade are affected because levels of factor VIII are low. In the absence of vWF, factor VIII is rapidly cleared from the system. The vWF gene is large, covering approximately 180 kilobases and contains 52 exons. Multiple mutations are known with varying clinical presentations.

A. Formation of the Hemostatic Plug

1. THE PLATELET

Platelets are nonnucleated cells in the blood whose major role is to form mechanical plugs at the site of vessel injury and to secrete regulators of the clotting process and vascular repair. In the absence of platelets, leakage of blood from rents in small vessels is common. Platelets are derived from megakaryocytes in the bone marrow. Megakaryocytes differentiate from the hematopoietic stem cell. As the megakaryocyte matures, it undergoes synchronous nuclear replication without cellular division to form a cell with a multilobed nucleus and enlarged cytoplasm. At approximately the eight-nucleus stage, the cytoplasm becomes granular, and the platelets are budded off the cytoplasm. A single megakaryocyte gives rise to approximately 4,000 platelets.

In the *nonactivated platelet* (a platelet that is not involved in forming a clot), the plasma membrane invaginates extensively into the interior of the cell, forming an open membrane (canalicular) system. Because the plasma membrane contains receptors and phospholipids that accelerate the clotting process, the canalicular structure substantially increases the membrane surface area that is potentially available for clotting reactions. The platelet interior contains microfilaments and an extensive actin/myosin system. Platelet activation in response to endothelial injury causes Ca^{2+}-dependent changes in the contractile elements, which, in turn, substantially change the architecture of the plasma membrane. Long pseudopodia are generated, increasing the surface area of the membrane as clot formation is initiated.

Platelets contain three types of granules. The first are electron-dense granules, which contain calcium, adenosine diphosphate (ADP), adenosine triphosphate (ATP), and serotonin. The second type of granule is the α-granule, which contains a heparin antagonist (heparin interferes with blood clotting; see the Biochemical Comments section), platelet-derived growth factor, β-thromboglobulin, fibrinogen, *von Willebrand factor* (vWF), and other clotting factors. The third type of granule is the lysosomal granule, which contains hydrolytic enzymes. During activation, the contents of these granules, which modulate platelet aggregation and clotting, are secreted.

2. PLATELET ACTIVATION

Three fundamental mechanisms are involved in platelet function during blood coagulation: adhesion, aggregation, and secretion. Adhesion sets off a series of reactions termed *platelet activation*, which leads to platelet aggregation and secretion of platelet granule contents.

1. The adhesion step refers primarily to the platelet-subendothelial interaction that occurs when platelets initially adhere to the sites of blood vessel injury (Fig. 45.1). Blood vessel injury exposes collagen, subendothelial matrix-bound vWF, and other matrix components. *vWF* is a protein synthesized in endothelial cells and megakaryocytes and is located in the subendothelial matrix, in specific platelet granules, and in the circulation bound to factor VIII. The platelet cell membrane contains glycoproteins (Gps) that bind to collagen and to vWF, causing the platelet to adhere to the subendothelium. Binding to collagen by GpIa (integrin $\alpha_2\beta_1$) causes the platelet to change its shape from a flat disc to a spherical cell. The latter extrudes long pseudopods, which promote platelet/platelet interactions. Binding of subendothelial vWF by GpIb causes changes in the platelet membrane that expose GpIIb-IIIa (integrin $\alpha_{IIb}\beta_3$)-binding sites to fibrinogen and vWF.

2. The initial adherence of platelets sets off a series of reactions (platelet activation) that result in more platelets being recruited and aggregated at the site of injury. After initial adherence, some of the platelets release the contents of their dense granules and their α-granules, with ADP release being of particular

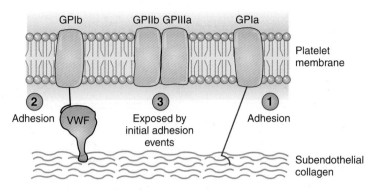

FIG. 45.1.   Adhesion of platelets to the subendothelial cell layer. (*1*) GpIa initially binds to the exposed collagen, which results in changes in the three-dimensional configuration of the complex, allowing GpIb to bind to von Willebrand factor (vWF) (*2*). (*3*) This second binding event exposes the GpIIb-GpIIIa complex, which also can bind to vWF and fibrinogen.

importance because ADP is a potent platelet activator. ADP released from the platelets and from damaged red blood cells binds to a receptor on the platelet membrane, which leads to the further unmasking of GpIIb-IIIa-binding sites. Aggregation of platelets cannot take place without ADP stimulation because ADP induces swelling of the activated platelets, promoting platelet/platelet contact and adherence.

Fibrinogen is a protein that circulates in the blood and is also found in platelet granules. It consists of two triple helices held together with disulfide bonds (Fig. 45.2). Binding of fibrinogen to activated platelets is necessary for aggregation, providing, in part, the mechanism by which platelets adhere to one another. Cleavage of fibrinogen by thrombin (a protease that is activated by the coagulation cascade) produces fibrin monomers that polymerize and, together with platelets, form a "soft clot." Thrombin itself is a potent activator of platelets, through binding to a specific receptor on the platelet surface.

B. The Blood Coagulation Cascade

Thrombus (clot) formation is enhanced by thrombin activation, which is mediated by the complex interaction that constitutes the blood coagulation cascade. This cascade (Fig. 45.3) consists primarily of proteins that serve as enzymes or cofactors, which function to accelerate thrombin formation and localize it at the site of injury. These proteins are listed in Table 45.2. All of these proteins are present in the plasma as proproteins (zymogens). These precursor proteins are activated by cleavage of the polypeptide chain at one or more sites. The key to successful and appropriate thrombus formation is the regulation of the proteases that activate these zymogens.

The *proenzymes* (factors VII, IX, X, XI, and prothrombin) are serine proteases that, when activated by cleavage, cleave the next proenzyme in the cascade. Because of the sequential activation, great acceleration and amplification of the response is achieved. That cleavage and activation have occurred is indicated by the addition of an "a" to the name of the proenzyme (e.g., factor IX is cleaved to form the active factor IXa).

The cofactor proteins (tissue factor, factors V and VIII) serve as binding sites for other factors. Tissue factor is not related structurally to the other blood coagulation cofactors and is an integral membrane protein that does not require cleavage for active function. Factors V and VIII serve as procofactors, which, when activated by cleavage, function as binding sites for other factors.

Two additional proteins that are considered part of the blood coagulation cascade, protein S and protein C, are regulatory proteins. Only protein C is

 Defects in GpIb cause a bleeding disorder known as *Bernard–Soulier syndrome*. Platelet aggregation is affected because of the inability of GpIb to adhere to subendothelial vWF.

Thrombotic thrombocytopenic purpura (TTP) is a disease characterized by the formation in the circulation of microclots (microthrombi) consisting of aggregated platelets. The microthrombi collect in the microvasculature and damage red blood cells, resulting in hemolytic anemia. They also damage vascular endothelium, exposing collagen and releasing HMW vWF promoting more platelet aggregation. The subsequent depletion of platelets renders the patient susceptible to internal hemorrhage. Mortality in untreated TTP can approach 90%.

Familial TTP is associated with mutations in the vWF-specific metalloprotease, although not all individuals with defective protease develop TTP. Sporadic cases of TTP are associated with the development of an antibody to the metalloprotease.

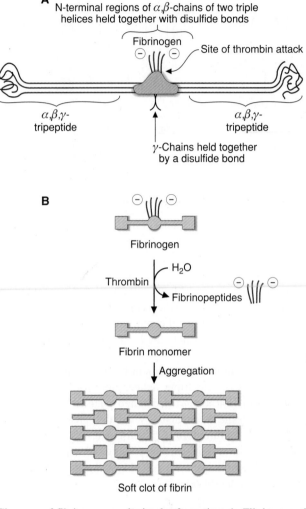

A
N-terminal regions of α,β-chains of two triple
helices held together with disulfide bonds

Fibrinogen

Site of thrombin attack

α,β,γ-
tripeptide

α,β,γ-
tripeptide

γ-Chains held together
by a disulfide bond

B

Fibrinogen

Thrombin   H₂O

Fibrinopeptides

Fibrin monomer

Aggregation

Soft clot of fibrin

FIG. 45.2. Cleavage of fibrinogen results in clot formation. **A.** Fibrinogen, the precursor protein of fibrin, is formed from two triple helices joined together at their N-terminal ends. The α,β-peptides are held together by disulfide bonds, and the γ-peptides are joined to each other by disulfide bonds. The terminal α,β-peptide regions, shown in *red*, contain negatively charged glutamate and aspartate residues that repel each other and prevent aggregation. **B.** Thrombin, a serine protease, cleaves the terminal portions of fibrinogen that contain negative charges. The fibrin monomers can then aggregate and form a "soft" clot. The soft clot is subsequently cross-linked by another enzyme.

regulated by proteolytic cleavage, and when it is activated, it is itself a serine protease.

Additionally, in response to collagen and thrombin, platelets release vasoconstrictors. Serotonin is released from the dense granules of the platelets, and the synthesis of thromboxane A_2 is stimulated. This reduces blood flow to the damaged area. Platelet-derived growth factor, which stimulates proliferation of vascular cells, is also released into the environment surrounding the damage.

C. The Process of Blood Coagulation

Activation of the blood coagulation cascade is triggered by the reaction of plasma proteins with the subendothelium at the same time that platelets are adhering to the subendothelial layer. Historically, two different pathways were discovered, one dependent on external stimuli (such as blunt trauma, which initiates the extrinsic

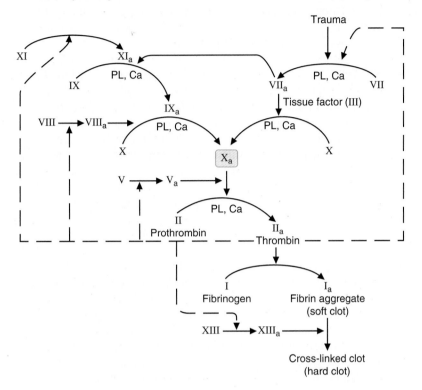

FIG. 45.3. The blood coagulation cascade. Activation of clot formation occurs through interlocking pathways, termed the *intrinsic* and *extrinsic pathways*. The intrinsic pathway is activated when factor XI is converted to factor XIa by thrombin. The extrinsic pathway (external damage, such as a cut) is activated by tissue factor. The reactions designated by "PL, Ca" are occurring through cofactors bound to phospholipids (PLs) on the platelet and blood vessel endothelial cell surface in a Ca^{2+}-coordination complex. Factors VIIa, IXa, Xa, XIa and thrombin are serine proteases. Note the positive feedback regulation of thrombin on the activation of proteases earlier in the cascade sequence (indicated by the *dashed lines*).

Table 45.2 Proteins of Blood Coagulation

Factor	Descriptive Name	Function/Active Form
Coagulation factors		
I	Fibrinogen	Fibrin
II	Prothrombin	Serine protease
III	Tissue factor	Receptor and cofactor
IV	Ca^{2+}	Cofactor
V	Proaccelerin, labile factor	Cofactor
VII	Proconvertin	Serine protease
VIII	Antihemophilia factor A	Cofactor
IX	Antihemophilia factor B, Christmas factor	Serine protease
X	Stuart-Prower factor	Serine protease
XI	Plasma thromboplastin antecedent	Serine protease
XIII	Fibrin-stabilizing factor	Ca^{2+}-dependent transglutaminase
Regulatory proteins		
Thrombomodulin	Endothelial cell receptor, binds thrombin	
Protein C	Activated by thrombomodulin-bound thrombin;	
Protein S	protease cofactor; binds activated protein C	

The use of an active-site serine to cleave a peptide bond is common to a variety of enzymes referred to as *serine proteases*. Serine proteases are essential for activating the formation of a blood clot from fibrin. Fibrin and many of the other proteins involved in blood coagulation are present in the blood as inactive precursors or zymogens, which must be activated by proteolytic cleavage. *Thrombin*, the serine protease that converts fibrinogen to fibrin, has the same aspartate–histidine–serine catalytic triad found in chymotrypsin and trypsin.

Thrombin is activated by proteolytic cleavage of its precursor protein, prothrombin. The sequence of proteolytic cleavages leading to thrombin activation requires factor VIII, the blood clotting protein that is deficient in **Sloe Klotter**.

pathway) and one using internal stimuli (the intrinsic pathway). As our understanding of blood clotting has expanded, it has become obvious that these distinctions are no longer correct because there is overlap between the pathways, but the terms have persisted in the description of the pathways.

In the case of external trauma, damaged tissues present tissue factor to the blood at the injured site, thereby triggering the extrinsic phase of blood coagulation. Circulating factor VII binds to tissue factor, which autocatalyzes its own activation to factor VIIa. Factor VIIa then activates factor X (to Xa) in the extrinsic pathway and factor IX (to IXa) in the intrinsic pathway. Factor IXa, as part of the intrinsic pathway, also activates factor X. Therefore, activation of both the extrinsic and intrinsic pathways results in the conversion of factor X to factor Xa. All of these conversions require access to membranes and calcium; the platelet membrane, which had adhered to the damaged site, is used as a scaffold for the activation reactions to occur. The γ-carboxylated clotting proteins are chelated to membrane surfaces via electrostatic interactions with calcium and negatively charged phospholipids of the platelet membrane. The protein cofactors VIIIa and Va serve as sites for assembling enzyme–cofactor complexes on the platelet surface, thereby accelerating and localizing the reaction. The result is thrombin formation, which augments its own formation by converting factors V, VIII, and XI into activated cofactors and stimulating platelet degranulation. The initial activation of prothrombin is slow because the activator cofactors, VIIIa and Va, are present only in small amounts. However, once a small amount of thrombin is activated, it accelerates its own production by cleaving factors V and VIII to their active forms. Note that these factors are in the intrinsic pathway. The intrinsic pathway is thought to sustain the coagulation response initiated by the extrinsic pathway. The major substrate of thrombin is fibrinogen, which is hydrolyzed to form fibrin monomers that undergo spontaneous polymerization to form the fibrin clot. This is considered a "soft" clot because the fibrin monomers are not cross-linked. Cross-linking requires factor XIIIa, which is activated by thrombin cleavage of factor XIII.

1. CROSS-LINKING OF FIBRIN

Factor XIIIa catalyzes a transamidation reaction between glutamine and lysine side chains on adjacent fibrin monomers. The covalent cross-linking takes place in three dimensions, creating a strong network of fibers that is resistant to mechanical and proteolytic damage. This network of fibrin fibers traps the aggregated platelets and other cells, forming the clot that plugs the vent in the vascular wall (Fig. 45.4). Factor XIIIa is the only enzyme in the blood coagulation cascade that is not a serine protease.

2. FACTOR COMPLEXES

In several of the essential steps in the blood coagulation cascade, the activated protease is bound in a complex attached to the surfaces of the platelets that have aggregated at the site of injury. Factors VII, IX, X, and prothrombin contain a domain in which one or more glutamate residues are carboxylated to γ-carboxyglutamate in a reaction that requires vitamin K (Fig. 45.5). Prothrombin and factor X both contain 10 or more γ-carboxyglutamate residues that bind Ca^{2+}. The Ca^{2+} forms a coordination complex with the negatively charged platelet membrane phospholipids and the γ-carboxyglutamates, thereby localizing the complex assembly and thrombin formation to the platelet surface.

Cofactor Va contains a binding site for both factor Xa and prothrombin, the zymogen substrate of factor Xa. Upon binding to the factor Va–platelet complex, prothrombin undergoes a conformational change, rendering it more susceptible to enzymatic cleavage. Binding of factor Xa to the factor Va–prothrombin–platelet complex allows the prothrombin-to-thrombin conversion. Complex assembly

FIG. 45.4. The transamidation reaction catalyzed by factor XIIIa, transglutaminase. This reaction cross-links fibrin monomers, allowing "hard" clots to form.

FIG. 45.5. **A.** Structures of vitamin K derivatives. Phylloquinone is found in green leaves, and intestinal bacteria synthesize menaquinone. Humans convert menadione to a vitamin K active form. **B.** Vitamin K-dependent formation of γ-carboxyglutamate residues. Thrombin, factor VII, factor IX, and factor X are bound to their phospholipid activation sites on cell membranes by Ca^{2+}. The vitamin K-dependent carboxylase, which adds the extra carboxyl group, uses a reduced form of vitamin K (KH_2) as the electron donor and converts vitamin K to an epoxide. Vitamin K epoxide is reduced, in two steps, back to its active form by the enzymes vitamin K epoxide reductase and vitamin K reductase.

accelerates the rate of this conversion 10,000- to 15,000-fold as compared with noncomplex formation.

Factor VIIIa forms a similar type of complex on the surface of activated platelets but binds factor IXa and its zymogen substrate, factor X. Tissue factor works slightly different because it is an integral membrane protein. However, once it is exposed by injury, it also binds factor VIIa and initiates complex formation.

Complex assembly has two physiologically important consequences. First, it enhances the rate of thrombin formation by as much as several hundred thousand-fold, enabling the clot to form rapidly enough to preserve hemostasis. Second, such explosive thrombin formation is localized to the site of vascular injury at which the negatively charged phospholipids are exposed. From our knowledge of the location of such phospholipids in cellular and subcellular organelle membranes, these surface-binding sites are only exposed at an injury site in which cell rupture exposes the internal membrane surface (recall that certain phospholipids face only the cytoplasm; if these lipids are now exposed to the environment, substantial cell damage must have occurred).

Warfarin (Coumadin) is a slow- and long-acting blood anticoagulant with a structure resembling that of vitamin K. The structural similarity allows the compound to compete with vitamin K and prevent γ-carboxylation of glutamate residues in factors II, VII, IX, X, and proteins C and S. The noncarboxylated blood clotting protein precursors increase in both the blood and plasma, but they are unable to promote blood coagulation because they cannot bind calcium and thus cannot bind to their phospholipid membrane sites of activation.

Warfarin

Warfarin is a commonly used rat poison and thus is occasionally encountered in emergency departments in cases of accidental poisoning. It is effective as a rat poison because it takes many hours to develop pathologic symptoms, which allows one poisoned trap to kill more than one rat.

Deficiency in the amount or functionality of protein C or protein S increases the risk of venous thromboembolism. Individuals who are homozygous for these mutations do not survive the neonatal period unless they are given replacement therapy.

3. VITAMIN K REQUIREMENT FOR BLOOD COAGULATION

The formation of the γ-carboxyglutamate residues on blood coagulation factors takes place in the hepatocyte before release of the protein. Within the hepatocyte, vitamin K (which is present in the quinone form) is reduced to form vitamin KH_2 by a microsomal quinone reductase (see Fig. 45.5). *Vitamin KH_2* is a cofactor for carboxylases that add a carboxyl group to the appropriate glutamate residues in the proenzyme to form the carboxylated proenzyme (e.g., prothrombin). In the same reaction, vitamin K is converted to vitamin K epoxide. To recover active vitamin KH_2, vitamin K is first reduced to the quinone form by vitamin K epoxide reductase and then to the active hydroquinone form.

D. Regulation through Feedback Amplification and Inhibition

Once the formation of the clot (thrombus) begins, clot formation is accelerated in an almost explosive manner by several processes that are collectively termed *feedback amplification*.

1. THE ROLE OF THROMBIN IN REGULATION

Thrombin has both a prothrombotic regulatory role (feedback amplification) and an antithrombotic regulatory role (feedback inhibition). The prothrombotic action is initiated when thrombin stimulates its own formation by activating factors V, VIII, and XI, thereby accelerating the rate of clot formation (see Fig. 45.3). Thrombin also promotes clot formation by activating platelet aggregation, stimulating the release of factor VIII from vWF and cleaving factor XIII to factor XIIIa.

Antithrombotic effects of thrombin result from its binding to an endothelial cell receptor called *thrombomodulin* (Fig. 45.6). Thrombomodulin abolishes the clotting function of thrombin and allows thrombin to activate protein C, which has anticoagulant effects.

2. PROTEINS S AND C

Protein C and its cofactor protein S serve to suppress the activity of the coagulation cascade. After activation, protein C forms a complex with protein S. Protein S anchors the activated protein C (APC) complex to the clot through Ca^{2+}/γ-carboxyglutamate binding to platelet phospholipids. The APC destroys the active blood coagulation cofactors factor VIIIa and Va by proteolytic cleavage, decreasing the production of thrombin. The APC also stimulates endothelial cells to increase secretion of the prostaglandin I_2 (PGI_2), which reduces platelet aggregation.

FIG. 45.6. Antithrombotic effects of thrombin. Thrombin, bound to thrombomodulin on the endothelial cell surface, activates protein C. Activated protein C (APC) in complex with protein S binds to the platelet membrane, and the activated complex destroys factors Va and VIIIa, thereby inhibiting the coagulation cascade.

3. SERPINS

Many proteases of the blood coagulation enzyme system are serine proteases. Because uncontrolled proteolytic activity would be destructive, modulating mechanisms control and limit intravascular proteolysis. The *serine protease inhibitors* (serpins) are a group of naturally occurring inhibitory proteins that are present in the plasma at high concentration (approximately 10% of the plasma proteins are serpins). At least eight major inhibitors have been found that share a common mechanism of action and inhibit proteases involved in coagulation and clot dissolution (fibrinolysis). Each inhibitor possesses a reactive site that appears to be an ideal substrate for a specific serine protease and thus acts as a trap for that protease. The bound serine protease attacks a peptide bond located at a critical amino acid residue within the serpin and forms a tight enzyme–inhibitor complex.

The activity of thrombin is controlled by the serpin antithrombin III (ATIII). Regulation of blood coagulation at the level of thrombin is critical because this enzyme affects the pathways of both coagulation and fibrinolysis (see Section III.F). One molecule of ATIII irreversibly inactivates one molecule of thrombin through reaction of an arginine residue in ATIII with the active-site serine residue of thrombin. ATIII–thrombin complex formation is markedly enhanced in the presence of heparin. *Heparin* is a glycosaminoglycan (see Chapter 49) found in the secretory granules of mast cells and in the loose connective tissue around small vascular beds. Heparin binds to lysyl residues on ATIII and dramatically accelerates its rate of binding to thrombin. This is because of an allosteric alteration in ATIII such that the position of the critical arginine residue of ATIII is more readily available for interaction with thrombin. The formation of the ATIII–thrombin complex releases the heparin molecule so that it can be reused and, therefore, the function of heparin is catalytic. Thrombin that is attached to a surface, for example, to thrombomodulin on the endothelial cell membrane, is no longer participating in clot formation and is not readily attacked by ATIII or the ATIII–heparin complex. The ATIII–heparin complex also can inactivate the serine protease factors XIIIa, XIa, IXa, and Xa but has no effect on factor VIIa or APC.

E. Thromboresistance of Vascular Endothelium

Endothelial cells of blood vessels provide a selectively permeable barrier between the circulating blood and the tissues. The normal endothelial cell lining neither activates coagulation nor supports platelet adhesion; thus, it is called a *nonthrombogenic surface*. The thromboresistance of normal vascular endothelium is contributed to by several properties. Endothelial cells are highly negatively charged, a feature that may repel the negatively charged platelets. Endothelial cells synthesize PGI$_2$ and nitric oxide, vasodilators, and powerful inhibitors of platelet aggregation. PGI$_2$ synthesis is stimulated by thrombin, epinephrine, and local vascular injury. Endothelial cells also synthesize two cofactors that each inhibits the action of thrombin, thrombomodulin, and heparan sulfate. *Heparan sulfate* is a glycosaminoglycan similar to heparin that potentiates ATIII but not as efficiently. The inactivation of thrombin is accelerated by heparan sulfate present on the endothelial cell surface. Thus, the intact endothelium has the capability of modifying thrombin action and inhibiting platelet aggregation.

F. Fibrinolysis

After successful formation of a hemostatic plug, further propagation of the clot must be prevented. This is accomplished in part by switching off blood coagulation and in part by turning on fibrinolysis. Fibrinolysis involves the degradation of fibrin in a clot by *plasmin*, a serine protease that is formed from its zymogen, plasminogen. *Plasminogen* is a circulating serum protein that has a high affinity for fibrin, promoting the incorporation of plasminogen in the developing clot. The activity of plasminogen is mediated by proteins known as *plasminogen activators*.

In European populations, a point mutation in the factor V gene (factor V Leiden) causes the replacement of an arginine with a glutamine in the preferred site for cleavage by activated protein C (APC), rendering factor Va Leiden resistant to APC. Heterozygous individuals have a sixfold to eightfold increased risk of deep vein thromboses, and homozygous individuals have a 30- to 140-fold increased risk. The factor V Leiden mutation does not appear to be associated with increased risk of arterial thrombosis, such as myocardial infarction, except in young women who smoke.

Genetic studies suggest that the factor V Leiden mutation arose after the separation of the European, Asian, and African populations. The frequency of this variant indicates that it conferred some selective advantage at one time. In the developed world, inherited APC resistance is the most prevalent risk factor for familial thrombotic disease.

The conversion of plasminogen to plasmin by plasminogen activators can occur both in the liquid phase of the blood and at the clot surface; however, the latter process is by far more efficient. APC, in addition to turning off the blood coagulation cascade, also stimulates the release of plasminogen activator from tissues (tPA, tissue plasminogen activator) and simultaneously inactivates an inhibitor of plasminogen activator, PAI-1.

Plasminogen activator release can lead to plasmin formation in the circulation. However, the circulating plasmin is rapidly inactivated by binding with α_2-*antiplasmin*, a circulating protease inhibitor. Clot-bound plasmin is not readily inactivated by α_2-antiplasmin. Thus, plasminogen binding to fibrin facilitates its activation to plasmin, protects it from blood serpins, and localizes it on the fibrin substrate for subsequent efficient proteolytic attack. This mechanism allows for dissolution of fibrin in pathologic thrombi or oversized hemostatic plugs and at the same time prevents degradation of fibrinogen in the circulating blood.

Two endogenous plasminogen activators are most important; both are synthesized in a variety of cells. tPA is produced chiefly by the vascular endothelial cells, has a high binding affinity for fibrin, and plays a major role in fibrinolysis. Single-chain urokinase (U-PA) is synthesized in most cells and tissues and has a moderate affinity for fibrin. *Streptokinase*, the bacterial exogenous plasminogen activator from β-hemolytic streptococci, is not an enzyme but an allosteric modifier of human plasminogen that allows an autocatalytic reaction such that plasmin is formed. In vivo, physical stress, hypoxia, and large numbers of low-molecular-weight (LMW) organic compounds promote increased synthesis and release of tPA and U-PA from tissues into the blood. The balance between release of plasminogen activators, the availability of fibrin, and inhibitors of the activators and plasmin determine regulation of the fibrinolytic response, as indicated in Figure 45.7.

G. Regulation of Fibrinolysis

Antiactivators regulate interaction of plasminogen in blood with plasminogen activators in a dynamic equilibrium. Even if minute amounts of plasmin are generated (e.g., after release of vascular plasminogen activator after stress), the enzyme is probably inactivated by antiplasmin. Upon activation of the blood coagulation system, a fibrin clot is formed, which not only strongly binds tPA and plasminogen from blood but also accelerates the rate of plasmin activation. The clot-bound plasmin is protected from inhibitors while attached to fibrin. The enzyme is inactivated by α_2-antiplasmin and α_2-macroglobulin after proteolytic dissolution of fibrin and its liberation into the liquid phase of blood. Thus, the fibrin network catalyzes both initiation and regulation of fibrinolysis.

Both streptokinase and tissue plasminogen activator (tPA) have been approved for the treatment of myocardial infarction. The rationale is that the enzyme will lead to clot dissolution, thereby restoring blood flow to the heart. The use of both drugs reduces mortality. Although there are more side effects associated with the use of streptokinase, it is substantially cheaper than tPA.

FIG. 45.7. Regulation of plasmin activation. Plasminogen can be activated by either tissue plasminogen activator (tPA) or single-chain urokinase (U-PA) (⊕). PAI-1 blocks tPA action (⊖). Streptokinase binding to plasminogen allows autocatalysis to form plasmin. Circulating α_2-antiplasmin blocks (⊖) the activity of any soluble plasmin that may be in the blood.

CLINICAL COMMENTS

Sloe Klotter. **Sloe Klotter** has hemophilia A, the most frequently encountered serious disorder of blood coagulation in humans, occurring in 1 in every 10,000 males. The disease is transmitted with an X-linked pattern of inheritance.

The most common manifestations of hemophilia A are those caused by bleeding into soft tissues (*hematomas*) such as muscle or into body spaces such as the peritoneal cavity, joint spaces, or the lumen of the gastrointestinal tract. When bleeding occurs repeatedly into joints (*hemarthrosis*), the joint may eventually become deformed and immobile.

In the past, bleeding episodes have been managed primarily by administration of factor VIII, sometimes referred to as *antihemophilia cofactor*. Unfortunately, the concentration of factor VIII in plasma is quite low (0.3 nM, compared with 8,800 nM for fibrinogen), requiring that it be prepared from multiple human donors. Before donor screening and virus inactivation procedures during preparation essentially eliminated transmission with blood transfusions, >50% of patients with hemophilia treated with factor VIII during the 1980s in Western Europe or North America became infected with HIV and hepatitis C. Recombinant factor VIII is now available for clinical use and mitigates the threat of HIV/hepatitis C transmission in these patients.

Another X-linked bleeding disorder is hemophilia B, which is caused by mutations in the gene for factor IX. Lack of factor IX activity leads to an inability to convert prothrombin to thrombin and impaired clotting.

BIOCHEMICAL COMMENTS

Drugs That Inhibit Blood Coagulation. Several drugs have been developed that inhibit the blood coagulation cascade. Such drugs are useful in cases in which patients develop spontaneous thrombi, which, if left untreated, would result in a fatal pulmonary embolism. There are three major classes of such drugs: the heparins, vitamin K antagonists, and specific inhibitors of thrombin.

Heparin binds to and activates antithrombin III (ATIII), which leads to thrombin inactivation. ATIII also blocks the activity of factors VIIIa, IXa, Xa, and XIa. Heparin can be administered in either of two forms: unfractionated or high-molecular-weight (HMW) heparin and fractionated or LMW heparin. HMW heparin is a heterogenous mixture of glycosaminoglycans, with an average chain length of 45 monosaccharides with an average molecular weight of 15 kDa (the range is 3 to 30 kDa). LMW heparins are fragments of HMW heparin, containing fewer than 18 monosaccharides with an average molecular weight of 4 to 5 kDa.

HMW heparin binds to plasma proteins and cell surfaces in addition to its prime target, ATIII. Because different individuals synthesize different levels of plasma proteins, the use of this form of heparin as an anticoagulant requires constant monitoring of the patient to ensure that the correct dosage has been given so that spontaneous thrombi do not develop but not so much that spontaneous bleeding occurs. LMW heparin has fewer nonspecific interactions than HMW heparin, and its effects are easier to predict on patients, so constant monitoring is not required.

A major complication of heparin therapy is *heparin-induced thrombocytopenia* (HIT, excessive blood clotting with a reduction in the number of circulating platelets). This unexpected result of heparin treatment is caused by heparin binding to a platelet protein, *platelet factor 4* (PF4), which induces a conformational change in PF4 such that the immune system believes the complex is foreign. Thus, antibodies are developed against the heparin–PF4 complex. When the antibodies bind to the platelets, the platelets become activated, and thrombi develop. Treatment consists of removing the heparin and using a different form of antithrombotic agent.

The classic vitamin K antagonist is warfarin. Warfarin acts by blocking the vitamin K reductase enzymes required to regenerate active vitamin K

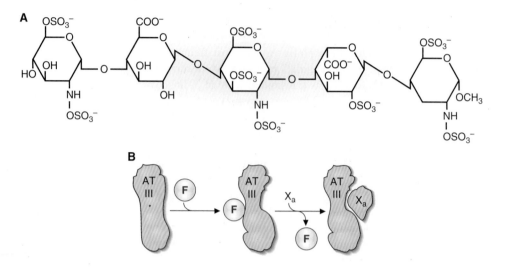

FIG. 45.8.   **A.** Structure of fondaparinux. **B.** Mechanism of fondaparinux action. The drug (shown in *blue*) binds to ATIII, which induces a conformational change so that factor Xa can now bind to ATIII. Once factor Xa binds and is inactivated, the drug is released and can activate another molecule of ATIII.

(see Fig. 45.5). This results in reduced γ-carboxylation of factors II, VII, IX, and X. In the absence of γ-carboxylation, the factors cannot bind calcium nor form the complexes necessary for the coagulation cascade to be initiated. However, warfarin also blocks the activity of proteins S and C, so both blood clotting and the regulation of clotting are impaired by warfarin administration.

Both heparin and warfarin therapy suffer from their lack of specificity, so drugs specific for single steps in the blood coagulation pathway have been sought and identified. Analysis of heparin potentiation of factor Xa binding to ATIII showed that a unique pentasaccharide sequence was required. An appropriate pentasaccharide, named *fondaparinux*, was developed that would specifically enhance ATIII interactions with factor Xa (Fig. 45.8). Fondaparinux stimulates the binding of ATIII to factor Xa by 300-fold and is specific for factor Xa inhibition. Fondaparinux does not affect thrombin or platelet activity, and it is not an activating agent of platelets. Because fondaparinux does not bind to PF4, HIT is not a complication with this therapy.

Direct thrombin inhibitors are based on the hirudin molecules, which were initially discovered in leeches and other blood-sucking organisms. These organisms would not be able to feed if the blood clotted at the site of the puncture wound, so the organisms secrete thrombin inhibitors to prevent clotting from occurring. Hirudin treatment itself is dangerous in that formation of the hirudin–thrombin complex is irreversible, and use of the drug requires constant monitoring of the patient. Thus, to overcome this problem, rational drug design based on the hirudin structure was used, and a synthetic 20-amino acid peptide known as *bivalirudin* was synthesized. This agent has a high binding affinity and specificity for thrombin although its effects on thrombin are transient (not irreversible), making this a safer agent for long-term use.

Key Concepts

- The plasma contains water, nutrients, metabolites, hormones, electrolytes, and proteins.
- Plasma proteins provide osmotic pressure to maintain fluid balance between the tissues and the blood.
- The plasma proteins provide transport for many molecules and also aid in immune defense.
- The plasma proteins, in association with platelets, maintain the integrity of the circulatory system.
  - Platelets form mechanical plugs at the site of vessel injury and secrete regulators of the blood clotting process.
  - Platelets become activated when bound to a site of injury, which leads to more platelet binding and aggregation at the injured site.
  - Circulating fibrinogen also binds to the activated platelets at sites of injury.

- Clot formation is carefully regulated such that overclotting (thrombosis) or underclotting (bleeding) does not occur.
  - The clotting cascade consists of a series of protease activation steps leading to the activation of thrombin, which converts fibrinogen to fibrin.
  - Thrombin also activates transglutaminase, which cross-links the fibrin and leads to "hard clot" formation.
  - Proteins S and C regulate the clotting cascade and are activated by thrombin.
  - In order to form a clot, protein complexes must adhere to the activated platelets, which occurs via γ-carboxyglutamate binding to calcium and platelet membranes.
  - Serpins are serine protease inhibitors; the serpin antithrombin III (ATIII) aids in regulating blood coagulation by modulating thrombin activity.
  - Heparin enhances the interaction of thrombin with ATIII.
  - Plasmin, the active product of plasminogen, is the only protease that can dissolve fibrin clots.
  - Hemophilia A is caused by a lack of factor VIII, an essential factor required for thrombin activation.
- Diseases discussed in this chapter are summarized in Table 45.3.

Table 45.3   Diseases Discussed in Chapter 45

Disease or Disorder	Environmental or Genetic	Comments
Factor V Leiden	Genetic	Factor V is altered such that it cannot be inactivated by activated protein C, leading to hypercoagulation and deep vein thrombosis (excessive clotting).
Hemophilia B	Genetic	Lack of factor IX in the blood clotting cascade such that clots cannot be formed.
Hemophilia A	Genetic	Lack of factor VIII in blood clotting cascade, leading to a bleeding disorder (reduced clot formation).
α_1-Antiproteinase deficiency	Genetic	Lack of α_1-antitrypsin leads to elastase destruction of lung tissue, progressing to emphysema and chronic obstructive pulmonary disease (COPD).
Kwashiorkor	Environmental	Protein deficiency in a calorie-sufficient diet leads to a reduction in circulating blood proteins, resulting in edema.
Thrombocytopenic purpura (TPP)	Both	Formation of microscopic thrombi, which lead to hemolysis and organ failure if untreated. The idiopathic type may be caused by autoimmune destruction of platelets.
vWF deficiency	Both	A defect in von Willebrand factor, a necessary factor for initiation of the blood clotting cascade. In its absence, clotting will not occur, and bleeding disorders will result.
Bernard-Soulier syndrome	Genetic	Lack of GpIb, the receptor for von Willebrand factor (vWF). Leads to lack of function of vWF and a bleeding disorder as the coagulation cascade cannot be fully initiated.

1. The edema observed in patients with noncalorie protein malnutrition is caused by which of the following?

   A. Loss of muscle mass
   B. Ingestion of excess carbohydrates
   C. Increased fluid uptake
   D. Reduced protein synthesis in the liver
   E. Increased production of ketone bodies

2. A recent surgery patient receiving warfarin therapy was found to be bleeding internally. The clotting process is impaired in this patient primarily because of which of the following?

   A. Inability of the liver to synthesize clotting factors
   B. Specific inhibition of factor XIII activation
   C. Inability to form clotting factor complexes on membranes
   D. Reduction of plasma calcium levels
   E. Enhancement of protein C activity

3. An inactivating mutation in which of the following pro-enzymes would be expected to lead to thrombosis, uncontrolled blood clotting?

   A. Factor XIII
   B. Prothrombin
   C. Protein C
   D. Factor VIII
   E. Tissue factor

4. Classical hemophilia A results in an inability to directly activate which of the following factors?

   A. Factor II
   B. Factor IX
   C. Factor X
   D. Protein S
   E. Protein C

5. Hemophilia B results in an inability to directly activate which of the following factors?

   A. Factor II
   B. Factor IX
   C. Factor X
   D. Protein S
   E. Protein C

46 Liver Metabolism

*The liver is strategically interposed between the general circulation and the digestive tract. It receives 20% to 25% of the volume of blood leaving the heart each minute (the cardiac output) through the portal vein (which delivers absorbed nutrients and other substances from the gastrointestinal tract to the liver) and through the hepatic artery (which delivers blood from the general circulation back to the liver). Potentially toxic agents absorbed from the gut or delivered to the liver by the hepatic artery must pass through this **metabolically active organ** before they can reach the other organs of the body. The liver's relatively large size (approximately 3% of total body weight) allows extended residence time in the liver for nutrients to be properly metabolized as well as for potentially harmful substances to be detoxified and prepared for excretion into the urine or feces. Among other functions, therefore, the liver, along with the kidney and gut, is an **excretory organ** equipped with a broad spectrum of detoxifying mechanisms. It can, for example, carry out **metabolic conversion pathways** and use **secretory systems** that allow the excretion of potentially toxic compounds. Concurrently, the liver contains highly specific and selective **transport mechanisms** for essential nutrients that are required not only to sustain its own energy but also to provide physiologically important substrates for the systemic needs of the organism. In addition to the myriad of transport processes within the sinusoidal and canalicular plasma membrane sheets, intracellular hepatocytic transport systems exist in organelles such as **endosomes**, **mitochondria**, **lysosomes**, as well as the **nucleus**. The sequential transport steps carried out by these organelles include (1) **uptake**, (2) **intracellular binding and sequestration**, (3) **metabolism**, (4) **sinusoidal secretion**, and (5) **biliary excretion**. The rate of hepatobiliary transport is determined, in part, by the rate of activity of each of these steps. The overall transport rate is also determined by such factors as hepatic blood flow, plasma protein binding, and the rate of canalicular reabsorption. The various aspects of the major metabolic processes performed by the liver have been discussed in greater detail elsewhere in this book. These previous sources will be referred to as the broad spectrum of the liver's contributions to overall health and diseases are described.*

THE WAITING ROOM

Jean Ann Tonich's family difficulties continued and in spite of a period of sobriety that lasted 6 months, she eventually started drinking increasing amounts of gin again in an effort to deal with her anxieties. Her appetite for food declined slowly as well. She gradually withdrew from much of the social support system that her doctors and friends had attempted to build during her efforts for rehabilitation. Upper mid-abdominal pain became almost constant, and she noted increasing girth and distention of her abdomen. Early one morning, she was awakened in excruciating pain in her upper abdomen. She vomited a dark-brown "coffee ground" material followed by copious amounts of bright red blood. She called a friend, who rushed her to the hospital emergency room.

Amy Biasis, a 23-year-old missionary, was brought to the hospital emergency department complaining of the abrupt onset of fever, chills, and severe pain in the right upper quadrant of her abdomen. The pain was constant and radiated to her right shoulder top. She vomited undigested food twice in the hour before arriving at the emergency department. This did not relieve her pain.

Her medical history indicated that, while serving as a missionary in western Belize, Central America, 2 months earlier, she had a 3-day illness that included fever, chills, and mild but persistent diarrhea. A friend of Amy's there, a medical missionary, had given her an unidentified medication for 7 days. Amy's diarrhea slowly resolved, and she felt well again until her current abdominal symptoms began.

On physical examination, she appeared toxic and had a temperature of 101°F. She was sweating profusely. Her inferior-anterior liver margin was palpable three fingerbreadths below the right rib cage, suggestive of an enlarged liver. The liver edge was rounded and tender. Gentle fist percussion of the lower posterior right rib cage caused severe pain. Routine laboratory studies were ordered, and a computed tomogram (CT) of the upper abdomen was scheduled to be done immediately.

I. LIVER ANATOMY

The human liver consists of two lobes, each containing multiple lobules and sinusoids. The liver receives 75% of its blood supply from the portal vein, which carries blood returning to the heart from the small intestine, stomach, pancreas, and spleen. The remaining 25% of the liver's blood supply is arterial, carried to the liver by the hepatic artery.

Blood from both the portal vein and hepatic artery empty into a common conduit, mixing their contents as they enter the liver sinusoids (Fig. 46.1). The sinusoids are expandable vascular channels that run through the hepatic lobules. They are lined with endothelial cells that have been described as "leaky" because, as blood flows through the sinusoids, the contents of the plasma have relatively free access to the hepatocytes, which are located on the other side of the endothelial cells.

The liver is also an exocrine organ, secreting bile into the biliary drainage system. The hepatocytes secrete bile into the bile canniculus, whose contents flow parallel to that in the sinusoids but in the opposite direction. The canniculi empty into the bile ducts. The lumina of the bile ducts then fuse, forming the common bile duct. The common duct then releases bile into the duodenum. Some of the liver's effluent is stored in the gallbladder and discharged into the duodenum postprandially to aid in digestion.

The entire liver surface is covered by a capsule of connective tissue that branches and extends throughout the liver. This capsule provides support for the blood

Liver lobule

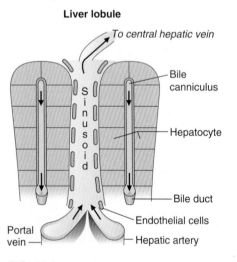

FIG. 46.1. Schematic view of liver anatomy.

vessels, lymphatic vessels, and bile ducts that permeate the liver. In addition, this connective tissue sheet subdivides the liver lobes into the smaller lobules.

II. LIVER CELL TYPES

The primary cell type of the liver is the *hepatocyte*. Hepatocytes, also known as *hepatic parenchymal cells*, form the liver lobules. Eighty percent of the liver volume is composed of hepatocytes, but only 60% of the total number of cells in the liver are hepatocytes. The other 40% of the cells are nonparenchymal cells and constitute the lining cells of the walls of the sinusoids. The lining cells comprise the endothelial cells, Kupffer cells, and hepatic stellate cells. In addition, intrahepatic lymphocytes, which include pit cells (liver-specific natural killer cells) are also present in the sinusoidal lining.

A. Hepatocytes

The hepatocyte is the cell that carries out the many functions of the liver. Almost all pathways of metabolism are represented in the hepatocyte, and these pathways are controlled through the actions of hormones that bind to receptors located on the plasma membrane of their cells. Although hepatocytes are normally quiescent cells with low turnover and a long life span, they can be stimulated to grow if damage occurs to other cells in the liver. The liver mass has a relatively constant relationship to the total body mass of adult individuals. Deviation from the normal or optimal ratio (caused, for example, by a partial hepatectomy or significant hepatic cell death or injury) is rapidly corrected by hepatic growth caused by a proportional increase in hepatocyte replication.

B. Endothelial Cells

The sinusoidal endothelial cells constitute the lining cells of the sinusoid. Unlike endothelial cells in other body tissues, these cells contain fenestrations with a mean diameter of 100 nm. They do not, therefore, form a tight basement membrane barrier between themselves and the hepatocytes. In this way, they allow free diffusion of small molecules to the hepatocytes but not of particles the size of chylomicrons (chylomicron remnants, however, which are smaller than chylomicrons, do have free passage to the hepatocyte). The endothelial cells are capable of endocytosing many ligands and also may secrete cytokines when appropriately stimulated. Because of their positioning, lack of tight junctions, and absence of a tight basement membrane, the liver endothelial cells do not present a significant barrier to the movement of the contents of the sinusoids into hepatocytes. Their fenestrations or pores further promote the free passage of blood components through this membrane into the liver parenchymal cells.

C. Kupffer Cells

Kupffer cells are located within the sinusoidal lining. They contain almost one-quarter of all the lysosomes of the liver. The Kupffer cells are tissue macrophages with both endocytotic and phagocytic capacity. They phagocytose many substances such as denatured albumin, bacteria, and immune complexes. They protect the liver from gut-derived particulate materials and bacterial products. On stimulation by immunomodulators, these cells secrete potent mediators of the inflammatory response and play a role in liver immune defense through the release of cytokines that lead to the inactivation of substances considered foreign to the organism. The Kupffer cells also remove damaged erythrocytes from the circulation.

D. Hepatic Stellate Cells

The stellate cells are also called *perisinusoidal* or *Ito cells*. There are approximately 5 to 20 of these cells per 100 hepatocytes. The stellate cells are lipid-filled cells and also serve as the primary storage site for vitamin A. They also control the turnover

The reports of **Amy Biasis's** initial laboratory studies showed an elevation in her serum hepatic transaminases, her serum alkaline phosphatases, as well as her serum total bilirubin level.

The CT scan of **Amy Biasis's** upper abdomen showed an elevated right hemidiaphragm as well as several cystic masses in her liver, the largest of which was located in the superior portion of the right lobe. Her clinical history as well as her history of possible exposure to various parasites while working in a part of Belize, Central America, that is known to practice substandard sanitation, prompted her physicians to order a titer of serum antibodies against the parasite *Entamoeba histolytica*, in addition to measuring serum antibodies against other invasive parasites.

of hepatic connective tissue and extracellular matrix and regulate the contractility of the sinusoids. When cirrhosis of the liver is present, the stellate cells are stimulated by various signals to increase their synthesis of extracellular matrix material. This, in turn, diffusely infiltrates the liver, eventually interfering with the function of the hepatocytes.

E. Pit Cells

The hepatic pit cells, also known as *liver-associated lymphocytes*, are natural killer cells, which are a defense mechanism against the invasion of the liver by potentially toxic agents, such as tumor cells or viruses.

III. MAJOR FUNCTIONS OF THE LIVER

A. The Liver Is a Central Receiving and Recycling Center for the Body

The liver can carry out a multitude of biochemical reactions. This is necessary because of its role in constantly monitoring, recycling, modifying, and distributing all of the various compounds absorbed from the digestive tract and delivered to the liver. If any portion of an ingested compound is potentially useful to that organism, the liver retrieves this portion and converts it to a substrate that can be used by hepatic and nonhepatic cells. At the same time, the liver removes many of the toxic compounds that are ingested or produced in the body and targets them for excretion in the urine or in the bile.

As mentioned previously, the liver receives nutrient-rich blood from the enteric circulation through the portal vein; thus, all of the compounds that enter the blood from the digestive tract pass through the liver on their way to other tissues. The enterohepatic circulation allows the liver first access to nutrients to fulfill specific functions (such as the synthesis of blood coagulation proteins, heme, purines, and pyrimidines) and first access to ingested toxic compounds (such as ethanol) and to such potentially harmful metabolic products (such as NH_4^+ produced from bacterial metabolism in the gut).

In addition to the blood supply from the portal vein, the liver receives oxygen-rich blood through the hepatic artery; this arterial blood mixes with the blood from the portal vein in the sinusoids. This unusual mixing process gives the liver access to various metabolites ingested and produced in the periphery and secreted into the peripheral circulation, such as glucose, individual amino acids, certain proteins, iron–transferrin complexes, and waste metabolites as well as potential toxins produced during substrate metabolism. As mentioned, fenestrations in the endothelial cells, combined with gaps between the cells, the lack of a basement membrane between the endothelial cells and the hepatocytes, and low portal blood pressure (which results in slow blood flow) contribute to the efficient exchange of compounds between sinusoidal blood and the hepatocyte and clearance of unwanted compounds from the blood. Thus, large molecules targeted for processing, such as serum proteins and chylomicron remnants, can be removed, degraded, and their components recycled by hepatocytes. Similarly, newly synthesized molecules, such as very low-density lipoprotein (VLDL) and serum proteins, can be easily secreted into the blood. In addition, the liver can convert all of the amino acids found in proteins into glucose, fatty acids, or ketone bodies. The secretion of VLDL by the liver not only delivers excess calories to adipose tissue for storage of fatty acids in triacylglycerol, it also delivers phospholipids and cholesterol to tissues that are in need of these compounds for synthesis of cell walls as well as other functions. The secretion of glycoproteins by the liver is accomplished through the liver's gluconeogenic capacity and its access to a variety of dietary sugars to form the oligosaccharide chains, as well as its access to dietary amino acids with which it synthesizes proteins. Thus, the liver has the capacity to carry out a large number of biosynthetic reactions. It has the biochemical wherewithal to synthesize a myriad of compounds from a broad spectrum of precursors. At the same time, the liver metabolizes compounds into biochemically useful products. Alternatively, it has the ability to degrade and excrete those compounds presented to it that cannot be further used by the body.

Each of the liver cells described contains specialized transport and uptake mechanisms for enzymes, infectious agents, drugs, and other xenobiotics that specifically target these substances to certain liver cell types. These are accomplished by linking these agents covalently by way of biodegradable bonds to their specific carrier. The latter then determines the particular fate of the drug by using specific cell recognition, uptake, transport, and biodegradation pathways.

B. Inactivation and Detoxification of Xenobiotic Compounds and Metabolites

Xenobiotics are compounds that have no nutrient value (cannot be used by the body for energy requirements) and are potentially toxic. They are present as natural components of foods or they may be introduced into foods as additives or through processing. Pharmacologic and recreational drugs are also xenobiotic compounds. The liver is the principal site in the body for the degradation of these compounds. Because many of these substances are lipophilic, they are oxidized, hydroxylated, or hydrolyzed by enzymes in phase I reactions. Phase I reactions introduce or expose hydroxyl groups or other reactive sites that can be used for conjugation reactions (the phase II reactions). The conjugation reactions add a negatively charged group such as glycine or sulfate to the molecule. Many xenobiotic compounds are transformed through several different pathways. A general scheme of inactivation is shown in Figure 46.2.

The conjugation and inactivation pathways are similar to those used by the liver to inactivate many of its own metabolic waste products. These pathways are intimately related to the biosynthetic cascades that exist in the liver. The liver can synthesize the precursors that are required for conjugation and inactivation reactions from other compounds. For example, sulfation is used by the liver to clear steroid hormones from the circulation. The sulfate used for this purpose can be obtained from the degradation of cysteine or methionine.

The liver, kidney, and intestine are the major sites in the body for biotransformation of xenobiotic compounds. Many xenobiotic compounds contain aromatic rings (such as benzopyrene in tobacco smoke) or heterocyclic ring structures (such as the nitrogen-containing rings of nicotine or pyridoxine) that we are unable to degrade or recycle into useful components. These structures are hydrophobic, causing the molecules to be retained in adipose tissue unless they are sequestered by the liver, kidney, or intestine for biotransformation reactions. Sometimes, however, the phase I and II reactions backfire, and harmless hydrophobic molecules are converted to toxins or potent chemical carcinogens.

1. CYTOCHROME P450 AND XENOBIOTIC METABOLISM

The toxification/detoxification of xenobiotics is accomplished through the activity of a group of enzymes with a broad spectrum of biologic activity. Some examples

 A knowledge of functional characteristics of liver cells has been used to design diagnostic agents to determine the normalcy of specific biochemical pathways of the hepatocytes. These "tailor-made" pharmaceuticals can be designed to be taken up by one or more of the transport mechanisms available to the liver. For example, receptor-related endocytic processes can be used as targets to probe specific receptor-mediated transport functions of the liver cells. The asialoglycoprotein receptor, also known as the *hepatic-binding protein*, has been used in this diagnostic approach. The substrate $^{99}T_c{}^m$-galactosyl-neoglycoalbumin (NGA) was developed as a specific ligand for selective uptake via this specific hepatic receptor. The timing and extent of the assimilation of this probe into the hepatocytes, as determined by imaging the liver at precise intervals after the administration of this isotope, yields an estimate of hepatic blood flow as well as the transport capacity of this specific hepatic transporter protein.

 Antibody titers against *Entamoeba histolytica* by use of an enzyme immunoassay were strongly reactive in **Amy Biasis's** blood. A diagnosis of **amoebiasis** was made. Her physicians started a nitroimidazole amoebicide (metronidazole) orally in a dose of 500 mg every 6 hours for 10 days. By the third day of treatment, Amy began to feel noticeably better. Her physicians told her that they expected a full clinical response in 95% of patients with amoebic liver abscesses treated in this way, although her multiple hepatic abscesses adversely affected her prognosis to a degree. After her response to oral therapy for the liver abcess, she was also treated with a "luminal agent" to clear the organism from her intestine.

FIG. 46.2. General scheme of xenobiotic detoxification. The toxic compound RH has been converted to a sulfated derivative suitable for excretion.

Table 46.1   Examples of Enzymes Used in Biotransformation of Xenobiotic Compounds

Acetyltransferase
Amidase-esterase
Dehydrogenase
Flavin-containing monooxygenase
Glutathione *S*-transferase
Methyltransferase
Mixed-function oxidase
Reductase
Sulfotransferase
UDP-glucosyltransferase
UDP-glucuronosyltransferase

UDP, uridine diphosphate.

of enzymes involved in xenobiotic transformation are described in Table 46.1. Of the wide variety of enzymes that are involved in xenobiotic metabolism, only the cytochrome P450–dependent monooxygenase system is discussed here. The cytochrome P450–dependent monooxygenase enzymes are determinants in oxidative, peroxidative, and reductive degradation of exogenous (chemicals, carcinogens, pollutants, etc.) and endogenous (steroids, prostaglandins, retinoids, etc.) substances. The key enzymatic constituents of this system are the flavoprotein NADPH-cytochrome P450 oxidoreductase and cytochrome P450 (Fig. 46.3). The latter is the terminal electron acceptor and substrate-binding site of the microsomal mixed-function oxidase complex, a very versatile catalytic system. The system got its name in 1962, when Omura and Sato found a pigment with unique spectral characteristics derived from liver microsomes of rabbits. When reduced and complexed with carbon monoxide, it exhibited a spectral absorbance maximum at 450 nm.

The major role of the cytochrome P450 enzymes (see Chapter 25) is to oxidize substrates and introduce oxygen to the structure. Similar reactions can be carried out by other flavin monooxygenases that do not contain cytochrome P450.

The human cytochrome P450 enzyme family contains 57 functional genes, which produce proteins with at least 40% sequence homology. These isozymes have different but overlapping specificities. The human enzymes are generally divided into nine major subfamilies, and each of these is further subdivided. For example, in the naming of the principal enzyme involved in the oxidation of ethanol to acetaldehyde, CYP2E1, the CYP denotes the cytochrome P450 family, the 2 denotes the subfamily, the E denotes ethanol, and the 1 denotes the specific isozyme.

The CYP3A4 isoform accounts for 30% to 40% of CYP450 enzymes in the liver and 70% of cytochrome enzymes in gut wall enterocytes. It metabolizes the greatest number of drugs in humans. Specific drugs are substrates for CYP3A4. The concomitant ingestion of two CYP3A4 substrates could potentially induce competition for the binding site, which, in turn, could alter the blood levels of these two agents. The drug with the highest affinity for the enzyme will be preferentially metabolized, whereas the metabolism (and degradation) of the other drug will be reduced. The latter drug's concentration in the blood will then rise.

Moreover, many substances or drugs impair or inhibit the activity of the CYP3A4 enzyme, thereby impairing the body's ability to metabolize a drug. Some of the lipid-lowering agents known as the statins (HMG-CoA reductase inhibitors) require CYP3A4 for degradation. Appropriate drug treatment and dosing takes into account the normal degradative pathway of the drug. However, grapefruit juice is a potent inhibitor of CYP3A4-mediated drug metabolism. Evidence suggests that if a statin is regularly taken with grapefruit juice, its level in the blood may increase as much as 15-fold. This marked increase in plasma concentration could increase the muscle and liver toxicity of the statin in question because side effects of the statins appear to be dose-related.

The cytochrome P450 isozymes all have certain features in common:

1. They all contain cytochrome P450, oxidize the substrate, and reduce oxygen.
2. They all have a flavin-containing reductase subunit that uses NADPH, and not NADH, as a substrate.
3. They are all found in the smooth endoplasmic reticulum and are referred to as *microsomal enzymes* (e.g., CYP2E1 is also referred to as the *microsomal ethanol-oxidizing system*, MEOS).
4. They are all bound to the lipid portion of the membrane, probably to phosphatidylcholine.
5. They are all inducible by the presence of their own best substrate and somewhat less inducible by the substrates for other P450 isozymes.
6. They all generate a reactive free radical compound as an intermediate in the reaction.

FIG. 46.3. General structure of the P450 enzymes. O_2 binds to the P450 Fe-heme in the active site and is activated to a reactive form by accepting electrons. The electrons are donated by the cytochrome P450 reductase, which contains an FAD plus an FMN or Fe–S center to facilitate the transfer of single electrons from NADPH to O_2. The P450 enzymes involved in steroidogenesis have a somewhat different structure. For CYP2E1, RH is ethanol (CH_3CH_2OH), and ROH is acetaldehyde (CH_3COH).

FIG. 46.4.   Detoxification of vinyl chloride.

2. EXAMPLES OF CYTOCHROME P450 DETOXIFICATION REACTIONS

i. Vinyl Chloride

The detoxification of vinyl chloride provides an example of effective detoxification by a P450 isozyme (ethanol detoxification was discussed in Chapter 25). Vinyl chloride is used in the synthesis of plastics and can cause angiosarcoma in the liver of exposed workers. It is activated in a phase I reaction to a reactive epoxide by a hepatic P450 isozyme (CYP2E1), which can react with guanine in DNA or other cellular molecules. However, it also can be converted to chloroacetaldehyde, conjugated with reduced glutathione, and excreted in a series of phase II reactions (Fig. 46.4).

ii. Aflatoxin B$_1$

Aflatoxin B$_1$ is an example of a compound that is made more toxic by a cytochrome P450 reaction (CYP2A1). Current research suggests that ingested aflatoxin B$_1$ in contaminated food (it is produced by a fungus [*Aspergillus flavus*] that grows on peanuts that may have been stored in damp conditions) is directly involved in hepatocarcinogenesis in humans by introducing a G → T mutation into the *p53* gene. Aflatoxin is metabolically activated to its 8,9-epoxide by two different isozymes of cytochrome P450. The epoxide modifies DNA by forming covalent adducts with guanine residues. In addition, the epoxide can combine with lysine residues in proteins and thus is also a hepatotoxin.

iii. Acetaminophen

Acetaminophen (Tylenol) is an example of a xenobiotic that is metabolized by the liver for safe excretion; however, it can be toxic if ingested in high doses. The pathways for acetaminophen metabolism are shown in Figure 46.5. As shown in the figure, acetaminophen can be glucuronylated or sulfated for safe excretion by the kidney. However, a cytochrome P450 enzyme produces the toxic intermediate *N*-acetyl-*p*-benzoquinone imine (NAPQI), which can be excreted safely in the urine after conjugation with glutathione.

NAPQI is a dangerous and unstable metabolite that can damage cellular proteins and lead to death of the hepatocyte. Under normal conditions, when acetaminophen is taken in the correct therapeutic amounts, <10% of the drug forms NAPQI, an amount that can be readily handled by the glutathione detoxifying system (phase II reactions). However, when taken in doses that are potentially toxic, the sulfotransferase and glucuronyl transferase systems are overwhelmed, and more acetaminophen is metabolized through the NAPQI route. When this occurs, the levels of glutathione in the hepatocyte are insufficient to detoxify NAPQI, and hepatocyte death can result.

The enzyme that produces NAPQI—CYP2E1—is induced by alcohol (see Chapter 25, MEOS). Thus, individuals who chronically abuse alcohol have increased sensitivity to acetaminophen toxicity because a higher percentage of

FIG. 46.5. Pathways of acetaminophen detoxification. *N*-acetyl cysteine stimulates the production of glutathione, thereby reducing the levels of NAPQI, which can damage cellular proteins. Ethanol upregulates CYP2E1 activity (the MEOS).

acetaminophen metabolism is directed toward NAPQI, compared with an individual with low levels of CYP2E1. Therefore, even recommended therapeutic doses of acetaminophen can be toxic to these individuals.

An effective treatment for acetaminophen poisoning involves the use of *N*-acetyl cysteine. This compound supplies cysteine as a precursor for increased glutathione production, which in turn enhances the phase II reactions, which reduces the levels of the toxic intermediate.

C. Regulation of Blood Glucose Levels

One of the primary functions of the liver is to maintain blood glucose concentrations within the normal range. The manner in which the liver accomplishes this has been the subject of previous chapters (Chapters 26, 31, and 36). In brief, the pancreas monitors blood glucose levels and secretes insulin when blood glucose levels rise and glucagon when such levels decrease. These hormones initiate regulatory cascades that affect liver glycogenolysis, glycogen synthesis, glycolysis, and gluconeogenesis. In addition, sustained physiologic increases in growth hormone, cortisol, and catecholamine secretion help to sustain normal blood glucose levels during fasting (see Chapter 43).

When blood glucose levels drop, glycolysis and glycogen synthesis are inhibited, and gluconeogenesis and glycogenolysis are activated. Concurrently, fatty acid oxidation is activated to provide energy for glucose synthesis. During an overnight fast, blood glucose levels are maintained primarily by glycogenolysis and, if gluconeogenesis is required, the energy (six ATP molecules are required to produce one molecule of glucose from two molecules of pyruvate) is obtained by fatty acid oxidation. On insulin release, the opposing pathways are activated such that excess fuels can be stored either as glycogen or fatty acids. The pathways are regulated by the activation or inhibition of two key kinases, the cyclic adenosine monophosphate (cAMP)–dependent protein kinase, and the AMP-activated protein kinase (see Fig. 36.11 for a review of these pathways). Recall that the liver can export glucose because it is one of only two tissues that express glucose 6-phosphatase.

D. Synthesis and Export of Cholesterol and Triacylglycerol

When food supplies are plentiful, hormonal activation leads to fatty acid, triacylglycerol, and cholesterol synthesis. High dietary intake and intestinal absorption of cholesterol compensatorily reduces the rate of hepatic cholesterol synthesis, in which case the liver acts as a recycling depot for sending excess dietary cholesterol to the peripheral tissue when needed as well as accepting cholesterol from these tissues when required. The pathways of cholesterol metabolism were discussed in Chapter 34.

E. Ammonia and the Urea Cycle

The liver is the primary organ for synthesizing urea and thus is the central depot for the disposition of ammonia in the body. Ammonia groups travel to the liver on glutamine and alanine, and the liver converts these ammonia nitrogens to urea for excretion in the urine. The reactions of the urea cycle were discussed in Chapter 38.

Table 46.2 lists some of the important nitrogen-containing compounds that are primarily synthesized or metabolized by the liver.

F. Formation of Ketone Bodies

The liver is the only organ that can produce ketone bodies, yet it is one of the few that cannot use these molecules for energy production. Ketone bodies are produced when the rate of glucose synthesis is limited (i.e., substrates for gluconeogenesis are limited) and fatty acid oxidation is occurring rapidly. Ketone bodies can cross the

Table 46.2   Nitrogen-Containing Products Produced by the Liver

Product	Precursors	Tissues	Function
Creatine	Arginine, glycine, and SAM	Liver	Forms creatine phosphate in muscle for energy storage. Excreted as creatinine.
Glutathione	Glutamate, cysteine, glycine	All tissues, but highest use in the liver	Protection against free radical injury by reduction of hydrogen peroxide and lipid peroxides. In liver and kidney, forms mercapturic acids.
Purines	Glycine, glutamine, aspartate, carbon dioxide, tetrahydrofolate, PRPP	Liver, small amounts in brain and cells of the immune system	Adenine and guanine nucleosides and nucleotides. DNA, RNA, and coenzymes and energy-transferring nucleotides
Pyrimidines	Aspartate, glutamine, carbon dioxide	Liver, small amounts in brain and cells of the immune system	Uracil, thymine, and cytosine
Sialic acid (NANA), other amino sugars	Glutamine	Most cells	In the liver, synthesis of oligosaccharide chains on secreted proteins. Most cells, glycoproteins, proteoglycans, and glycolipids
Sulfated compounds	Cysteine	Liver and kidney produce sulfate	Many cells use sulfate in blood for formation of PAPS, which transfers sulfate to proteoglycans, drugs, and xenobiotics.
Taurine	Cysteine	Liver	Conjugated bile salts
Glycocholic acid, and glycochenodeoxycholic acid	Glycine, bile salts	Liver	Conjugated bile salts are excreted into the bile and assists in the absorption of lipids and fat-soluble vitamins through the formation of micelles.
Sphingosine	Serine and palmitoyl-CoA	Liver, brain, and other tissues	Precursor of sphingolipids found in myelin and other membranes.
Heme	Glycine and succinyl-CoA	Liver, bone marrow cytochromes. Heme from bone marrow	Heme from liver is incorporated into hemoglobin.
Glycine conjugates of xenobiotic compounds	Glycine, medium-size hydrophobic carboxylic acids	Liver, kidney	Inactivation and targeting toward urinary excretion.
Niacin	Tryptophan, glutamine	Liver	NAD, NADP coenzymes for oxidation reactions
One-carbon methyl donors for tetrahydrofolate and SAM	Glycine, serine, histidine, methionine	Most cells, but highest in liver	Choline, phosphatidylcholine, purine and pyrimidine synthesis, inactivation of waste metabolites and xenobiotics through methylation

SAM, *S*-adenosyl methionine; NANA, *N*-acetylneuraminic acid; PRPP, 5′-phosphoribosyl 1′-pyrophosphate; PAPS, 3′-phosphoadenosine 5′-phosphosulfate.

Cirrhosis of the liver results in portal hypertension, which, because of increasing back pressure into the esophageal veins, promotes the development of dilated thin-walled esophageal veins (varices). At the same time, synthesis of blood coagulation proteins by the liver and required vitamin K-dependent reactions are greatly diminished (resulting in a prolonged prothrombin time, which, in turn, increases clotting time). When the esophageal varices rupture, massive bleeding into the thoracic or abdominal cavity as well as the stomach may occur. Much of the protein content of the blood entering the gastrointestinal tract is metabolized by intestinal bacteria, releasing ammonium ion, which enters the portal vein. Because hepatocellular function has been compromised, the urea cycle capacity is inadequate, and the ammonium ion enters the peripheral circulation, thereby contributing to hepatic encephalopathy (brain toxicity caused by elevated ammonia levels).

blood–brain barrier and become a major fuel for the nervous system under conditions of starvation. Synthesis and metabolism of ketone bodies have been described in Chapter 23.

G. Nucleotide Biosynthesis

The liver can synthesize and salvage all ribonucleotides and deoxyribonucleotides for other cells to use. Certain cells have lost the capacity to produce nucleotides de novo but can use the salvage pathways to convert free bases to nucleotides. The liver can secrete free bases into the circulation for these cells to use for this purpose. Nucleotide synthesis and degradation are discussed in Chapter 41.

H. Synthesis of Blood Proteins

The liver is the primary site of the synthesis of circulating proteins such as albumin and the clotting factors. When liver protein synthesis is compromised, the protein levels in the blood are reduced. Hypoproteinemia may lead to edema because of a decrease in the protein-mediated osmotic pressure in the blood. This, in turn, causes plasma water to leave the circulation and enter (and expand) the interstitial space, causing edema.

Most circulating plasma proteins are synthesized by the liver. Therefore, the hepatocyte has a well-developed endoplasmic reticulum, Golgi system, and cellular cytoskeleton, all of which function in the synthesis, processing, and secretion of proteins. The most abundant plasma protein produced by the liver is albumin, which represents 55% to 60% of the total plasma protein pool. Albumin serves as a carrier for a large number of hydrophobic compounds such as fatty acids, steroids, hydrophobic amino acids, vitamins, and pharmacologic agents. It is also an important osmotic regulator in the maintenance of normal plasma osmotic pressure. The other proteins synthesized by the liver are, for the most part, glycoproteins. They function in hemostasis, transport, protease inhibition, and ligand binding and as secretagogues for hormone release. The acute-phase proteins that are part of the immune response and the body's response to many forms of "injury" are also synthesized in the liver. Table 46.3 lists some of the proteins and their functions.

I. The Synthesis of Glycoproteins and Proteoglycans

The liver, because it is the site of synthesis of most of the blood proteins (including the glycoproteins), has a high requirement for the sugars that go into the oligosaccharide portion of glycoproteins (the synthesis of glycoproteins is discussed in Chapter 30). These include mannose, fructose, galactose, and amino sugars.

One of the intriguing aspects of the hepatic biosynthetic pathways that use carbohydrate in the synthesis of these compounds is that the liver is not dependent on either dietary glucose or hepatic glucose to generate the precursor intermediates for these pathways. This is because the liver can generate carbohydrates from dietary amino acids (which enter gluconeogenesis generally as pyruvate or an intermediate of the tricarboxylic acid [TCA] cycle), lactate (generated from anaerobic glycolysis in other tissues), and glycerol (generated by the release of free fatty acids from the adipocyte). Of course, if dietary carbohydrate is available, the liver can use that source as well.

Most of the sugars secreted by the liver are *O*-linked, that is, the carbohydrate is attached to the protein at its anomeric carbon through a glycosidic link to the

Table 46.3 A Partial List of Proteins Synthesized in the Liver

Type of Protein	Examples
Blood coagulation	Blood coagulation factors: fibrinogen; prothrombin; factors V, VII, IX, and X. Also α_2-macroglobulin
Metal-binding proteins	Transferrin (iron), ceruloplasmin (copper), haptoglobin (heme), hemopexin (heme)
Lipid transport	Apoprotein B100, apoprotein A1
Protease inhibitor	α_1-Antitrypsin

A. O-linked   **B. N-linked**

GalNAc   Serine   GlcNAc   Asparagine

FIG. 46.6. The general configuration of *O*-linked (**A**) and *N*-linked (**B**) glycoproteins.

–OH of a serine or a threonine residue. This is in contrast to the *N*-linked arrangement in which there is an *N*-glycosyl link to the amide nitrogen of an asparagine residue (Fig. 46.6). A particularly important *O*-linked sugar is *N*-acetylneuraminic acid (NANA or sialic acid), a nine-carbon sugar that is synthesized from fructose 6-phosphate and phosphoenolpyruvate (see Fig. 30.8). As circulating proteins age, NANA (sialic acid) residues are lost from the serum proteins. This change signals their removal from the circulation and their eventual degradation. An asialoglycoprotein receptor on the liver cell surface binds such proteins, and the receptor–ligand complex is endocytosed and transported to the lysosomes. The amino acids from the degraded protein are then recycled within the liver.

J. The Pentose Phosphate Pathway

The major functions of the pentose phosphate pathway (see Chapter 29) are the generation of NADPH and five-carbon sugars. All cell types, including red blood cells, can carry out this pathway because they need to generate NADPH so that the activity of glutathione reductase, the enzyme that catalyzes the conversion of oxidized glutathione (GSSG) back to reduced glutathione (GSH), can be maintained. Without the activity of this enzyme, the protection against free radical injury is lost. All cells also need this pathway for the generation of ribose, especially those cells that are dividing rapidly or that have high rates of DNA synthesis.

The liver has a much greater demand for NADPH than do most other organs. It uses NADPH for the biosynthesis of fatty acids and cholesterol, which the liver must make to produce phospholipids, and for the synthesis of VLDL and bile salts. It also uses NADPH for other biosynthetic reactions such as proline synthesis. NADPH is also used by mixed-function oxidases such as cytochrome P450 that are involved in the metabolism of xenobiotics and of a variety of pharmaceuticals. Because the liver participates in so many reactions that are capable of generating free radicals, the liver uses more glutathione and NADPH to maintain glutathione reductase and catalase activity than any other tissue. Consequently, the concentration of glucose-6-phosphate dehydrogenase (the rate-limiting and regulated enzyme in the pentose phosphate pathway) is high in the liver, and the rate of flux through this pathway may be as high as 30% of the rate of flux through glycolysis.

IV. FUELS FOR THE LIVER

The reactions used to modify and inactivate dietary toxins and waste metabolites are energy-requiring, as are the reactions used by anabolic (biosynthetic) pathways such as gluconeogenesis and fatty acid synthesis. Thus, the liver has a high energy requirement and consumes approximately 20% of the total oxygen used by the body. The principal forms in which energy is supplied to these reactions are the high-energy phosphate bonds of adenosine triphosphate (ATP), uridine triphosphate (UTP), and guanosine triphosphate (GTP), reduced NADPH, and acyl coenzyme A (acyl-CoA) thioesters. The energy for the formation of these compounds is obtained directly from oxidative metabolism, the TCA cycle, or the electron-transport chain and oxidative phosphorylation. After a mixed meal containing carbohydrate, the major fuels used by the liver are glucose, galactose, and fructose. If ethanol is consumed, the liver is the major site of ethanol oxidation, yielding principally acetate and then acetyl-CoA. During an overnight fast, fatty acids become the major fuel for the liver. They are oxidized to carbon dioxide or ketone bodies. The liver also can use all of the amino acids as fuels (although its use of branched-chain amino acids is small compared to the muscles), converting many of them to glucose. The urea cycle disposes of the ammonia that is generated from amino acid oxidation.

A. Carbohydrate Metabolism in the Liver

After a carbohydrate-containing meal, glucose, galactose, and fructose enter the portal circulation and flow to the liver. This organ serves as the major site in the body for the use of dietary galactose and fructose. It metabolizes these compounds by converting them to glucose and intermediates of glycolysis. Their fate is essentially the same as that of glucose (Table 46.4).

B. Glucose as a Fuel

The entry of glucose into the liver is dependent on a high concentration of glucose in the portal vein after a high-carbohydrate meal. Because the K_m for both the glucose transporter (GLUT2) and glucokinase is so high (approximately 10 mM), glucose enters the liver principally after its concentration rises to 10 to 40 mM in the portal blood and not at the lower 5-mM concentration in the hepatic artery. The increase in insulin secretion that follows a high-carbohydrate meal promotes the conversion of glucose to glycogen. In addition, the rate of glycolysis is increased (phosphofructokinase-2 [PFK-2] kinase activity is active; thus phosphofructokinase-1 [PFK-1] is activated by fructose 2,6-bisphosphate) so that acetyl-CoA can be produced for fatty acid synthesis (acetyl-CoA carboxylase is activated by citrate; see Chapter 33). Thus, after a high-carbohydrate meal, the liver uses glucose as its major fuel while activating the pathways for glycogen and fatty acid synthesis.

The rate of glucose use by the liver is determined, in part, by the level of activity of glucokinase. Glucokinase activity is regulated by a glucokinase regulatory protein (RP, Fig. 46.7), which is located in the nucleus. In the absence of glucose, glucokinase is partially sequestered within the nucleus, bound to RP in an inactive form. High concentrations of fructose 6-phosphate promote the interaction of glucokinase with RP, whereas high levels of either glucose or fructose 1-phosphate block glucokinase from binding to RP and promote the dissociation of the complex.

Table 46.4 Major Fates of Carbohydrates in the Liver

Storage as glycogen
Glycolysis to pyruvate
  Followed by oxidation to carbon dioxide in the TCA cycle
  Precursors for the synthesis of glycerol 3-phosphate (the backbone of triacylglycerols and other glycolipids), sialic acid, and serine
  Entry into the TCA cycle and exit as citrate, followed by conversion to acetyl-CoA, malonyl-CoA, and entry into fatty acid synthesis and secretion as VLDL
  Synthesis of phospholipids and other lipids from triacylglycerols
Conversion to mannose, sialic acid, and other sugars necessary for the synthesis of oligosaccharides for glycoproteins, including those secreted into blood.
Synthesis of acid sugars for proteoglycan synthesis and formation of glucuronides
Oxidation in the pentose phosphate pathway for the formation of NADPH (necessary for biosynthetic reactions such as fatty acid synthesis, glutathione reduction, and other NADPH-utilizing detoxification reactions)

TCA, tricarboxylic acid; VLDL, very low-density lipoprotein.

A

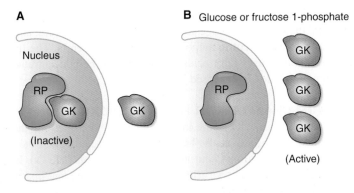

B Glucose or fructose 1-phosphate

FIG. 46.7. Regulation of glucokinase (GK) by regulatory protein (RP). RP is localized to the nucleus, and in the absence of glucose or presence of fructose 6-phosphate, most glucokinase is translocated to the nucleus and binds RP. This leads to the formation of the inactive form of glucokinase. When glucose or fructose 1-phosphate levels rise, glucokinase is released from RP. It then translocates to the cytoplasm and actively converts glucose to glucose 6-phosphate.

Thus, as glucose levels rise in the cytoplasm and nucleus (e.g., because of increased blood glucose levels after a meal), there is a significant enhancement of glucose phosphorylation as glucokinase is released from the nucleus, travels to the cytoplasm, and phosphorylates glucose.

The role of glucokinase RP is very complex. Mice that have been genetically engineered so that they do not express the RP (knockout mice) display reduced levels of total glucokinase activity in the liver. This is attributable to the finding that RP is important in the posttranscriptional processing of the mRNA for glucokinase. In the absence of RP, less glucokinase is produced. These mice, therefore, have no glucokinase in the nucleus, reduced cytoplasmic glucokinase content, and inefficient glucose phosphorylation in the liver when glucose levels rise.

The major regulatory step for liver glycolysis is the PFK-1 step. Even under fasting conditions, the ATP concentration in the liver (approximately 2.5 mM) is sufficiently high to inhibit PFK-1 activity. Thus, liver glycolysis is basically controlled by modulating the levels of fructose 2,6-bisphosphate—the product of the PFK-2 reaction. As fructose 2,6-bisphosphate levels increase (which will occur in the presence of insulin), the rate of glycolysis increases; when glucagon levels increase and protein kinase A is activated so that PFK-2 is phosphorylated and its kinase activity inactive, glycolysis slows down and gluconeogenesis is enhanced (see Chapters 22 and 31).

C. Lipid Metabolism

Long-chain fatty acids are a major fuel for the liver during periods of fasting, when they are released from adipose tissue triacylglycerols and travel to the liver as fatty acids bound to albumin. In the liver, they bind to fatty acid–binding proteins and are then activated on the outer mitochondrial membrane, the peroxisomal membrane, and the smooth endoplasmic reticulum by fatty acyl-CoA synthetases. The fatty acyl group is transferred from CoA to carnitine for transport through the inner mitochondrial membrane, where it is reconverted back into fatty acyl-CoA and oxidized to acetyl-CoA in the β-oxidation spiral (see Chapter 23).

The enzymes in the pathways of fatty acid activation and β-oxidation (the synthetases, the carnitine acyltransferases, and the dehydrogenases of β-oxidation) are somewhat specific for the length of the fatty acid carbon chain. The chain-length specificity is divided into enzymes for long-chain (C20 to approximately C12), medium-chain (approximately C12 to C4), and short-chain fatty acids (C4 to C2). The major lipids oxidized in the liver as fuels are the long-chain fatty acids (pal-

Q: Why would you expect fructose 1-phosphate levels to promote the dissociation of glucokinase from regulatory protein (RP)?

Glucokinase activators are being investigated as potential drugs to lower blood glucose levels in type 2 diabetes. The activators will enhance glucose metabolism in the pancreas, resulting in increased insulin release. These drugs are currently in clinical trials.

A: Fructose 1-phosphate is produced from fructose metabolism. The major dietary source of fructose, the ingestion of which would lead to increased fructose 1-phosphate levels, is sucrose. Sucrose is a disaccharide of glucose and fructose. Thus, an elevation of fructose 1-phosphate usually indicates an elevation of glucose levels as well.

Medium-chain triglycerides (MCTs) are important components of nutritional supplements used in patients with digestive disorders. They, therefore, can be employed as an easily absorbed source of calories in patients who have a gastrointestinal (GI) disorder that may result in malabsorption of nutrients. These diseases include pancreatic insufficiency, intraluminal bile salt deficiency caused by cholestatic liver disease, biliary obstruction, ileal disease or resection, and disease that causes obstruction of intestinal lymphatics. Remember, however, that MCTs do not contain polyunsaturated fatty acids that can be used for synthesis of eicosanoids (see Chapter 35).

Zellweger (cerebrohepatorenal) syndrome occurs in individuals with a rare inherited absence of peroxisomes in all tissues. Patients accumulate C26 to C38 polyenoic acids in brain tissue because of defective peroxisomal oxidation of the very long-chain fatty acids synthesized in the brain for myelin formation. In liver, bile acid and ether lipid synthesis are affected, as is the oxidation of very long-chain fatty acids.

mitic, stearic, and oleic acids) because these are the lipids that are synthesized in the liver, are the major lipids ingested from meat or dairy sources, and are the major form of fatty acids present in adipose tissue triacylglycerols. The liver, as well as many other tissues, uses fatty acids as fuels when the concentration of the fatty acid–albumin complex is increased in the blood.

1. MEDIUM-CHAIN-LENGTH FATTY ACID OXIDATION

The liver and certain cells in the kidney are the major sites for the oxidation of medium-chain-length fatty acids. These fatty acids usually enter the diet of infants in maternal milk as medium-chain-length triacylglycerols (MCTs). In the intestine, the MCTs are hydrolyzed by gastric lipase, bile salt–dependent lipases, and pancreatic lipase more readily than long-chain triacylglycerols. In the enterocytes, they are neither reconverted to triacylglycerols nor incorporated into chylomicrons. Instead, they are released directly into the portal circulation (fatty acids of approximately eight-carbon chain lengths or less are water-soluble). In the liver, they diffuse through the inner mitochondrial membrane and are activated to acyl-CoA derivatives by medium-chain-length fatty acid–activating enzyme (MMFAE), a family of similar isozymes present only in liver and kidney. The medium-chain fatty acyl-CoA is then oxidized by the normal route beginning with medium-chain-length acyl-CoA dehydrogenase (MCAD; see Chapter 23).

2. PEROXISOMAL OXIDATION OF VERY LONG-CHAIN FATTY ACIDS

Peroxisomes are present in greater numbers in the liver than in other tissues. Liver peroxisomes contain the enzymes for the oxidation of very long-chain fatty acids such as C24:0 and phytanic acid, for the cleavage of the cholesterol side chain necessary for the synthesis of bile salts, for a step in the biosynthesis of ether lipids, and for several steps in arachidonic acid metabolism. Peroxisomes also contain catalase and are capable of detoxifying hydrogen peroxide.

Very long-chain fatty acids of C20 to C26 or greater are activated to CoA derivatives by very long-chain acyl-CoA synthetase present in the peroxisomal membrane. The very long-chain acyl-CoA derivatives are then oxidized in liver peroxisomes to the eight-carbon octanoyl-CoA level. In contrast to mitochondrial β-oxidation, the first enzyme in peroxisomal β-oxidation introduces a double bond and generates hydrogen peroxide instead of FAD(2H). The remainder of the cycle, however, remains the same, releasing NADH and acetyl-CoA. Peroxisomal catalase inactivates the hydrogen peroxide, and the acetyl-CoA can be used in biosynthetic pathways such as those of cholesterol and dolichol synthesis.

The octanoyl-CoA that is the end product of peroxisomal oxidation leaves the peroxisomes and the octanoyl group is transferred through the inner mitochondrial membrane by medium-chain-length acylcarnitine transferase. In the mitochondria, it enters the regular β-oxidation pathway, beginning with MCAD.

3. PEROXISOME PROLIFERATOR–ACTIVATED RECEPTORS

The peroxisome proliferator–activated receptors (PPARs) play an important role in liver metabolism. These receptors obtained their name from the finding that certain agonists were able to induce the proliferation of peroxisomes in the liver. These agonists included hypolipidemic agents, nonsteroidal anti-inflammatory agents, and environmental toxins. The receptors that bind these agents, the PPARs, are members of a nuclear receptor family and, when activated, stimulate new gene transcription. In the liver, the major form of PPAR regulates directly the activity of genes that are involved in fatty acid uptake and β- and ω-oxidation of fatty acids.

Although the roles of the PPARs have been discussed previously (see Section VI of this book), it is worth reviewing them here. There are three major PPAR isoforms: α, δ/β, and γ. The major form found in the liver is the α-form. Fatty

Table 46.5 Genes Regulated by Activation of PPARα

Fatty acid transport proteins (upregulated)
The mitochondrial and peroxisomal enzymes of fatty acid oxidation (upregulated)
Carnitine palmitoyl transferase I (upregulated)
Lipoprotein lipase (upregulated)
Apoproteins A1 and A2 (upregulated, leading to increased HDL production)
Apoprotein CIII (downregulated)
Acyl-Coenzyme A synthetase (upregulated)

HDL, high-density lipoprotein.

acids are an endogenous ligand for PPARα, such that when the level of fatty acids in the circulation is increased (with a concurrent increase in the fatty acid content of hepatocytes), there is increased gene transcription for those proteins involved in regulating fatty acid metabolism (Table 46.5). Genetically altered mice have been generated that lack PPARα. These knockout mice exhibit no abnormal phenotype when they are fed a normal diet. When they are fasted, however, or when they are fed a high-fat diet, these mice develop severe fatty infiltration of the liver. The inability to increase the rate of fatty acid oxidation in this organ leads to excessive fatty acid buildup in the hepatocytes. It also leads to an insufficient energy supply with which to make glucose (leading to hypoglycemia) as well as an inability to produce ketone bodies. In normal fasted mice or mice fed a high-fat diet, fatty acids will eventually stimulate their own oxidation via peroxisome proliferation and by induction of other enzymes needed for their oxidation. The knockout mice cannot make these compensations.

4. XENOBIOTICS METABOLIZED AS FATTY ACIDS

The liver uses the pathways of fatty acid metabolism to detoxify very hydrophobic and lipid-soluble xenobiotics that, like fatty acids, either have carboxylic acid groups or can be metabolized to compounds that contain carboxylic acids. Benzoate and salicylate are examples of xenobiotics that are metabolized in this way. Benzoate is naturally present in plant foods and is added to foods such as sodas as a preservative. Its structure is similar to that of salicylic acid (which is derived from the degradation of aspirin). Salicylic acid and benzoate are similar in size to medium-chain–length fatty acids and are activated to an acyl-CoA derivative by MMFAE (Fig. 46.8). The acyl group is then conjugated with glycine, which targets the compound for urinary excretion. The glycine derivatives of salicylate and benzoate are called *salicylurate* and *hippurate*, respectively. Salicylurate is the major urinary metabolite of aspirin in humans. Benzoate has been administered to treat hyperammonemia associated with congenital defects because urinary hippurate excretion tends to lower the free ammonia pool. Aspirin cannot be used for this purpose because it is toxic in the large doses required.

5. THE METABOLISM OF LIPIDS IN LIVER DISEASE

Chronic parenchymal liver disease is associated with relatively predictable changes in plasma lipids and lipoproteins. Some of these changes are related to a reduction in the activity of lecithin-cholesterol acyltransferase (LCAT). This plasma enzyme is synthesized and glycosylated in the liver; then enters the blood, where it catalyzes the transfer of a fatty acid from the 2-position of lecithin to the 3-β-OH group of free cholesterol to produce cholesterol ester and lysolecithin. As expected, in severe parenchymal liver disease, in which LCAT activity is decreased, plasma levels of cholesterol ester are reduced and free cholesterol levels are normal or increased.

Plasma triacylglycerols are normally cleared by peripheral lipases (lipoprotein lipase [LPL] and hepatic triglyceride lipase [HTGL]). Because the activities of both LPL and HTGL are reduced in patients with hepatocellular disease, a relatively high level of plasma triacylglycerols may be found in both acute and chronic hepatitis,

The fibrates (e.g., clofibrate) are a class of drugs that bind to PPARs to elicit changes in lipid metabolism. They are typically prescribed for individuals with elevated triglyceride levels because they increase the rate of triglyceride oxidation. This, in turn, leads to a reduction in serum triacylglycerol levels. Fibrates, through PPARα stimulation, also suppress apoprotein CIII (apoCIII) synthesis and stimulate lipoprotein lipase (LPL) activity. ApoCIII normally inhibits LPL activity, so by reducing CIII synthesis overall, LPL activity is increased. ApoCIII also blocks apoprotein E (apoE) on intermediate-density lipoprotein (IDL) particles, causing the IDL particles to accumulate because they cannot be taken up by the apoE receptor in the liver. The suppression of apoCIII levels allows more IDL to be endocytosed, thereby also reducing circulating triacylglycerol levels.

Reye's syndrome is characterized clinically by vomiting with signs of progressive central nervous system damage. In addition, there are signs of hepatic injury and hypoglycemia. There is mitochondrial dysfunction with decreased activity of hepatic mitochondrial enzymes. Hepatic coma may occur as serum ammonia levels rise. It is associated epidemiologically with the consumption of aspirin by children during a viral illness, but it may occur in the absence of exposure to salicylates. The incidence in the United States has decreased dramatically since the 1980s, when parents were made aware of the dangers of giving aspirin to children to reduce fever. Reye's syndrome is not necessarily confined to children. In patients who die of this disease, the liver at autopsy shows swollen and disrupted mitochondria and extensive accumulation of lipid droplets with fatty vacuolization of cells in both the liver and the renal tubules.

FIG. 46.8. Benzoate and salicylate metabolism.

in patients with cirrhosis of the liver, and in patients with other diffuse hepatocellular disorders.

With low LCAT activity and elevated triacylglycerol level described, low-density lipoprotein (LDL) particles have an abnormal composition. They are relatively triacylglycerol-rich and cholesterol ester–poor.

High-density lipoprotein (HDL) metabolism may be abnormal in chronic liver disease as well. For example, because the conversion of HDL_3 (less antiatherosclerotic) to HDL_2 (more antiatherosclerotic) is catalyzed by LCAT, the reduced activity of LCAT in patients with cirrhosis leads to a decrease in the $HDL_2:HDL_3$ ratio. Conversely, the conversion of HDL_2 to HDL_3 requires hepatic lipases. If the activity of this lipase is reduced, one would expect an elevation in the $HDL_2:HDL_3$ ratio. Because the $HDL_2:HDL_3$ ratio is usually elevated in cirrhosis, the lipase deficiency appears to be the more dominant of the two mechanisms. These changes may result in an overall increase in serum total HDL levels. How this affects the efficiency of the reverse cholesterol transport mechanism and the predisposition to atherosclerosis is not fully understood.

With regard to triacylglycerol levels in patients with severe parenchymal liver disease, the hepatic production of the triacylglycerol-rich, VLDL particle is impaired. Yet the total level of plasma triacylglycerols remains relatively normal because the LDL particle in such patients is triacylglycerol-rich, for reasons that have not been fully elucidated.

Nonesterified fatty acid (NEFA) levels are elevated in patients with cirrhosis. This change might be expected because basal hepatic glucose output is low in these patients. As a result, more NEFA are presumably required (via increased lipolysis) to meet the fasting energy requirements of peripheral tissues.

D. Amino Acid Metabolism in the Liver

The liver is the principal site of amino acid metabolism in humans. It essentially balances the free amino acid pool in the blood through the metabolism of amino acids supplied by the diet after a protein-containing meal and through metabolism

M The level of nonesterified fatty acid (NEFA) levels in blood samples can be determined using enzyme-coupled reactions. The unknown sample is incubated with coenzyme A (CoA) and acyl-CoA synthetase, which adds the coenzyme to the nonesterified fatty acids, creating acyl-CoA. The acyl-CoA produced is oxidized by acyl-CoA oxidase, which generates hydrogen peroxide. The hydrogen peroxide is used as a source of electrons by peroxidase to reduce a chromogenic substrate, which produces a colored reaction product. The concentration of the reaction product is determined spectrophotometrically and is directly proportional to the level of NEFA in the sample.

of amino acids supplied principally by skeletal muscles during an overnight fast. In an adult who is no longer growing linearly, the total protein content of the body on a daily basis is approximately constant, so the net degradation of amino acids (either to other compounds or used for energy) is approximately equal to the amount consumed. The key points concerning hepatic amino acid metabolism are the following:

1. The liver contains all the pathways for catabolism of all of the amino acids (although its metabolism of the branched-chain amino acids is low) and can oxidize most of the carbon skeletons to carbon dioxide. A small proportion of the carbon skeletons are converted to ketone bodies. The liver also contains the pathways for converting amino acid carbon skeletons to glucose (gluconeogenesis) that can be released into the blood.

2. Because the liver is the principal site of amino acid catabolism, it also contains the urea cycle, the pathway that converts toxic ammonium ion to nontoxic urea. The urea is then excreted in the urine.

3. After a mixed or high-protein meal, the gut uses dietary aspartate, glutamate, and glutamine as fuel (during fasting, the gut uses glutamine from the blood as a major fuel). Thus, the ingested acidic amino acids do not enter the general circulation. The nitrogen from gut metabolism of these amino acids is passed to the liver as citrulline or ammonium ion via the portal vein.

4. The branched-chain amino acids (valine, leucine, and isoleucine) can be used as a fuel by most cell types, including cells of the gut and skeletal muscle. After a high-protein meal, most of the branched-chain amino acids are not oxidized by the liver (because of very low activity of the branched-chain amino acid transaminase) and instead enter the peripheral circulation to be used as a fuel by other tissues or for protein synthesis (these amino acids are essential amino acids). The liver does, however, take up whatever amino acids it needs to carry out its own protein synthesis.

5. Most tissues transfer the amino acid nitrogen to the liver to dispose of as urea. They, therefore, produce either alanine (from the pyruvate–glucose–alanine cycle, in skeletal muscle, kidney, and intestinal mucosa) or glutamine (skeletal muscle, lungs, neural tissues) or serine (kidney), which are released into the blood and taken up by the liver.

6. The liver uses amino acids for the synthesis of proteins that it requires as well as for the synthesis of proteins to be used elsewhere. For example, the liver uses the carbon skeletons and nitrogens of amino acids for the synthesis of nitrogen-containing compounds such as heme, purines, and pyrimidines. The amino acid precursors for these compounds are all nonessential because they can be synthesized in the liver.

E. Amino Acid Metabolism in Liver Disease

The concentration of amino acids in the blood of patients with liver disease is often elevated. This change is, in part, attributable to a significantly increased rate of protein turnover (a general catabolic effect seen in severely ill patients) as well as to impaired amino acid uptake by the diseased liver. It is unlikely that the increased levels are caused by degradation of liver protein and the subsequent release of amino acids from the failing hepatocyte into the blood. This is true because the total protein content of the liver is only approximately 300 g. To account for the elevated amino acid levels in the blood, the entire protein content of the liver would have to be degraded within 6 to 8 hours to account for the increased protein turnover rates found. Because 18 to 20 times more protein is present in skeletal muscle (greater mass), the muscle is probably the major source of the elevated plasma levels of amino acids seen in catabolic states such as cirrhosis of the liver.

In cirrhotic patients, such as **Jean Ann Tonich**, the fasting blood α-amino nitrogen level is elevated as a result of reduced clearance. Urea synthesis is reduced as well.

 Unlike **Amy Biasis**, whose hepatic amoebic disorder was more localized (abscesses), **Jean Anne Tonich** had a diffuse hepatic disease, known as *alcohol-induced cirrhosis* (referred to historically as *Laennec's cirrhosis*). The latter is characterized by diffuse fine scarring, a fairly uniform loss of hepatic cells, and the formation of small regenerative nodules (sometimes referred to as *micronodular cirrhosis*). With continued alcohol intake, fibroblasts and activated stellate cells deposit collagen at the site of persistent injury. This leads to the formation of web-like septa of connective tissue in periportal and pericentral zones. These eventually connect portal triads and central veins. With further exposure to alcohol, the liver shrinks and then becomes nodular and firm as end-stage cirrhosis develops. Unless they are successfully weaned from alcohol, these patients eventually die of liver failure. **Amy Biasis**, however, can probably look forward to enjoying a normal liver function after successful amebicidal therapy without evidence of residual hepatic scarring.

The plasma profile of amino acids in cirrhosis characteristically shows an elevation in aromatic amino acids, phenylalanine and tyrosine, and in free tryptophan and methionine. The latter changes may be caused by impaired hepatic use of these amino acids as well as by portosystemic shunting. Although the mechanism is not known, a reduction in fasting plasma levels of the branched-chain amino acids (BCAAs) is also seen in cirrhotic patients. These findings, however, must be interpreted with caution because most of the free amino acid pool in humans is found in the intracellular space. Therefore, changes seen in their plasma concentrations do not necessarily reflect their general metabolic fate. Yet the elevation in aromatic amino acids and the suppression of the level of BCAAs in the blood of cirrhotics have been implicated in the pathogenesis of hepatic encephalopathy.

V. DISEASES OF THE LIVER

Diseases of the liver can be clinically and biochemically devastating because no other organ can compensate for the loss of the multitude of functions that the liver normally performs. Alcohol-induced liver disease has been discussed in Chapter 25. Several diseases can lead to hepatic fibrosis (see Biochemical Comments) and cirrhosis. When this occurs to a great enough extent, liver function becomes inadequate for life. Signs and symptoms of liver disease include elevated levels of the enzymes alanine aminotransferase (ALT) and aspartate aminotransferase (AST) in the plasma (caused by hepatocyte injury or death with a consequent release of these enzymes into the blood), jaundice (an accumulation of bilirubin in the blood caused by inefficient bilirubin glucuronidation by the liver; see Chapter 45), increased clotting times (the liver has difficulty producing clotting factors for secretion), edema (reduced albumin synthesis by the liver leads to a reduction in osmotic pressure in the blood), and hepatic encephalopathy (reduced urea cycle activity leading to excessive levels of ammonia and other toxic compounds in the central nervous system).

CLINICAL COMMENTS

Jean Ann Tonich. Patients with cirrhosis of the liver who have no known genetic propensity to glucose intolerance, such as **Jean Ann Tonich**, tend to have higher blood glucose levels than do normal subjects in both fasting and fed states. The mechanisms that may increase glucose levels in the fasting state include a reduction in the metabolic clearance rate of glucose by 25% to 40% compared with normal subjects. This reduction in glucose clearance results, in part, from increased oxidation of fatty acids and ketone bodies and the consequent decrease in glucose oxidation by peripheral tissues in cirrhosis patients. This is suggested by the discovery that plasma nonesterified fatty acid (NEFA) levels are high in many patients with hepatocellular dysfunction, in part because of decreased hepatic clearance of NEFA and in part because of increased adipose tissue lipolysis. Another possible explanation for the reduction in whole-body glucose use in cirrhotic patients relates to the finding that ketone body production is increased in some patients with cirrhosis. This could lead to enhanced use of ketone bodies for fuel by the central nervous system in such patients, thereby reducing the need for glucose oxidation by the highly metabolically active brain.

After glucose ingestion (fed state), many patients with liver disease have abnormally elevated blood glucose levels ("hepatogenous diabetes"). Using World Health Organization (WHO) criteria, 60% to 80% of cirrhotic patients have varying degrees of glucose intolerance, and overt diabetes mellitus occurs two to four times as often in cirrhotics than it does in subjects without liver disease. The proposed mechanisms include a degree of insulin resistance in peripheral tissues; however, as the cirrhotic process progresses, these patients develop a marked impairment of insulin secretion as well. Although the mechanisms are not well understood, this decrease in insulin secretion leads to increased hepatic glucose output (leading to fasting hyperglycemia) and reduced suppression of hepatic glucose output after meals, leading to postprandial hyperglycemia as well. If the patient has an underlying genetic predisposition to diabetes mellitus, the superimposition of the mechanisms outlined previously will lead to an earlier and more significant breakdown in glucose tolerance in these specific patients.

BIOCHEMICAL COMMENTS

Hepatic Fibrosis. Extensive and progressive fibrosis of the hepatic parenchyma leads to cirrhosis of the liver, a process that has many causes. The development of fibrosis requires the activities of hepatic stellate cells, cytokines, proteases, and protease inhibitors.

A major change that occurs when fibrosis is initiated is that the normally "sparse" or "leaky" basement membrane between the endothelial cell and the hepatocyte is replaced with a high-density membrane containing fibrillar collagen. This occurs because of both increased synthesis of a different type of collagen than is normally produced and a reduction in the turnover rate of existing extracellular matrix components.

The supportive tissues of the normal liver contain an extracellular matrix that, among other proteins, includes type IV collagen (which does not form fibers), glycoproteins, and proteoglycans. After a sustained insult to the liver, a threefold to eightfold increase occurs in extracellular matrix components, some of which contain fibril-producing collagen (types I and III), glycoproteins, and proteoglycans. The accumulation of these fibril-producing compounds leads to a loss of endothelial cell fenestrations and, therefore, a loss of the normal sievelike function of the basement membranes. These changes interfere with normal transmembrane metabolic exchanges between the blood and hepatocytes.

The hepatic stellate cell is the source of the increased and abnormal collagen production. These cells are activated by growth factors whose secretion is induced by injury to the hepatocytes or endothelial cells. Growth factors involved in cellular activation include transforming growth factor β_1 (TGF-β_1) (which is derived from the endothelial cells, Kupffer cells, and platelets) and platelet-derived growth factor (PDGF) and epidermal growth factor (EGF) from platelets. The release of PDGF stimulates stellate cell proliferation and, in the process, increases their synthesis and release of extracellular matrix materials and remodeling enzymes. These enzymes include matrix metalloproteinases (MMPs) and tissue inhibitors of MMPs, as well as converting (activating) enzymes. This cascade leads to the degradation of the normal extracellular matrix and replacement with a much denser and more rigid type of matrix material. These changes are in part the result of an increase in the activity of tissue inhibitors of MMPs for the new collagen relative to the original collagen in the extracellular matrix.

One consequence of the increasing stiffness of the hepatic vascular channels through which hepatic blood must flow is a greater resistance to the free flow of blood through the liver as a whole. Resistance to intrahepatic blood flow is also increased by a loss of vascular endothelial cell fenestrations, loss of free space between the endothelial cells and the hepatocytes (space of Disse), and even loss of vascular channels per se. This increased vascular resistance leads to an elevation of intrasinusoidal fluid pressure. When this intrahepatic (portal) hypertension reaches a critical threshold, the shunting of portal blood away from the liver (portosystemic shunting) contributes further to hepatic dysfunction. If the portal hypertension cannot be reduced, portal blood will continue to bypass the liver and return to the heart through the normally low-pressure esophageal veins. When this increasing intraesophageal venous pressure becomes severe enough, the walls of these veins thin dramatically and expand to form varices, which may burst suddenly, causing life-threatening esophageal variceal hemorrhage. This is a potentially fatal complication of cirrhosis of the liver.

Table 46.6   Diseases Discussed in Chapter 46

Disease or Disorder	Genetic or Environmental	Comments
Liver failure	Both, though primarily environmental	Destruction of hepatocyte function, leading to hyperammonemia, edema, and jaundice.
Amoebiasis	Environmental	Infection by amoeba, *Entamoeba histolytica*
Cirrhois	Environmental	Destruction of hepatocytes via inappropriate collagen and other fibrous protein deposition within the liver, usually in response to environmental insult.
Zellweger syndrome	Genetic	Lack of functional peroxisomes in all cells of the liver, kidney, and brain.
Reye's syndrome	Environmental	Both the brain and liver primarily affected, with progressive loss of nervous system function.

Key Concepts

- The liver consists of a variety of cell types, each with a different function.
  - Hepatocytes carry out the bulk of the metabolic pathways of the liver.
  - Endothelial cells line the sinusoids and release growth factors.
  - Kupffer cells are tissue macrophages that protect the liver from gut-derived particulate materials and bacterial products.
  - Stellate cells store vitamin A and regulate the contractility of the sinusoids.
  - Pit cells are liver-associated lymphocytes, which act as a defense mechanism against potentially toxic agents.
- The liver is the body's central receiving and recycling center:
  - Inactivation and detoxification of xenobiotic compounds and metabolites via cytochrome P450 systems
  - Regulation of blood glucose levels
  - Synthesis and export of cholesterol and triglyceride via VLDL
  - Synthesis and excretion of urea
  - Formation of ketone bodies from fatty acid oxidation
  - Nucleotide biosynthesis
  - Synthesis of blood proteins
- The liver highly coordinates its use of fuels versus that of the body. This is, in part, controlled by modulation of the activity of PPARα.
- Liver disease affects amino acid, carbohydrate, and lipid metabolism, leading to abnormalities in virtually all aspects of metabolism.
- Diseases discussed in this chapter are summarized in Table 46.6.

REVIEW QUESTIONS—CHAPTER 46

1. Drinking grapefruit juice while taking statins can lead to potentially devastating side effects. This is caused by a component of grapefruit juice doing which of the following?

   A. Interfering with hepatic uptake of statins
   B. Accelerating the conversion of the statin to a more toxic form
   C. Inhibiting the inactivation of statins
   D. Upregulating the HMG-CoA reductase
   E. Downregulating the HMG-CoA reductase

2. Which one of the following characteristics of cytochrome P450 enzymes is correct?

   A. They are all found in the Golgi apparatus and are referred to as microsomal enzymes.
   B. They all contain a flavin-containing reductase unit that uses NADH and not NADPH as a source of electrons.
   C. They are all inducible by oxygen, which binds to the iron of the cytochrome.
   D. They all oxidize the substrate on which they act.
   E. They all generate a free radical compound as a final product of the reaction.

3. Fairly predictable changes occur in the various metabolic pathways of lipid metabolism in patients with moderately advanced hepatocellular disease. Which one of the following changes would you expect to see under these conditions?

   A. The activity of plasma lecithin cholesterol acyltransferase (LCAT) is increased.

B. Serum cholesterol esters are increased.

C. Hepatic triglyceride lipase (HTGL) activity is increased.

D. Serum triacylglycerol levels are increased.

E. Serum nonesterified fatty acid levels are decreased.

4. After a 2-week alcoholic binge, **Jean Ann Tonich** ingested some Tylenol to help her with a severe headache. She took three times the suggested dose because of the severity of the pain. Within 24 hours, Jean Ann became very lethargic, vomited frequently, and developed severe abdominal pain. The symptoms Jean Ann is experiencing are attributable to a reaction to Tylenol because of which of the following?

A. The hypoglycemia experienced by the patient

B. Ethanol-induced inhibition of Tylenol metabolism

C. The hyperglycemia experienced by the patient

D. Ethanol-induced acceleration of Tylenol metabolism

E. Acetaminophen inhibition of VLDL secretion by the liver

5. An individual displays impaired glucose tolerance; blood glucose levels remain elevated after a meal for a longer time than is normal, although they do eventually go down to fasting levels. The patient has a normal release of insulin from the pancreas in response to elevated blood glucose levels. Hepatocytes obtained from the patient display normal levels of insulin binding to its receptor, and normal activation of the intrinsic tyrosine kinase activity associated with the insulin receptor. Analysis of glucose 6-phosphate formation within the hepatocytes, however, indicates a much slower rate of formation than in hepatocytes obtained from a normal control. A possible mutation that could lead to these results is which of the following?

A. A decrease in the K_m of glucokinase

B. An increase in the V_{max} of glucokinase

C. A nonfunctional glucokinase-regulatory protein

D. An increase in hexokinase activity

E. A decrease in hexokinase activity

There are three types of muscle cells: **smooth**, **skeletal**, and **cardiac**. In all types of muscle, contraction occurs via an actin/myosin sliding filament system, which is regulated by oscillations in **intracellular calcium levels**.

Muscle cells use stored glycogen and circulating glucose, fatty acids, and amino acids as energy sources. Muscle glycolysis is regulated differently from the liver, with the key difference being the regulation of **phosphofructokinase-2 (PFK-2)**. Muscle PFK-2 is not inhibited by phosphorylation; cardiac PFK-2 is actually activated by phosphorylation by a number of protein kinases. Thus, under conditions in which liver PFK-2 is inactive, and glycolysis is running slowly, muscle glycolysis is either unaffected, or even stimulated, depending on the isoform of PFK-2 being expressed.

Although muscle cells do not synthesize fatty acids, they do contain an isozyme of **acetyl-CoA carboxylase (ACC-2)** to regulate the **rate of fatty acid oxidation**. ACC-2 produces malonyl-CoA, which inhibits carnitine palmitoyl transferase I, thereby blocking fatty acid entry into the mitochondria. Muscle also contains **malonyl-CoA decarboxylase**, which catalyzes the conversion of malonyl-CoA to acetyl-CoA and carbon dioxide. Thus, both the synthesis and degradation of malonyl-CoA is carefully regulated in muscle cells to balance glucose and fatty acid oxidation. Both allosteric and covalent means of regulation are employed. Citrate activates ACC-2, and phosphorylation of ACC-2 by the adenosine monophosphate (AMP)-activated protein kinase inhibits ACC-2 activity. Phosphorylation of malonyl-CoA decarboxylase by the AMP-activated protein kinase activates the enzyme, further enhancing fatty acid oxidation when energy levels are low.

Muscles use **creatine phosphate** to store high-energy bonds. Creatine is derived from arginine and glycine in the kidney, and the guanidinoacetate formed is methylated (using S-adenosylmethionine) in the liver to form creatine. The enzyme **creatine phosphokinase (CPK)** then catalyzes the reversible transfer of a high-energy phosphate from adenosine triphosphate (ATP) to creatine, forming creatine phosphate and adenosine diphosphate (ADP). Creatine phosphate is unstable and spontaneously cyclizes to form **creatinine**, which is excreted in the urine. The spontaneous production of creatinine occurs at a constant rate and is proportional to body muscle mass. Thus, the amount of creatinine excreted each day (the creatinine clearance rate) is constant and can be used as an indicator of the normalcy of the excretory function of the kidneys.

Skeletal muscle cells can be subdivided into **type I** and **type II fibers**. Type I fibers are **slow-twitch** fibers that use primarily **oxidative metabolism** for energy, whereas the type II fibers (**fast-twitch**) use **glycolysis** as their primary energy-generating pathway.

Glucose transport into muscle cells can be stimulated during exercise because of the activity of the **AMP-activated protein kinase**. Fatty acid uptake into exercising muscle is dependent on the levels of circulating fatty acids, which are increased by **epinephrine** release.

A. Skeletal muscle   Nuclei

B. Smooth muscle

Nuclei

C. Cardiac muscle   Intercalated disks

FIG. 47.1. Structures of the three different muscle types. (Adapted from Junqueira LC, Carneiro J. *Basic Histology, Text and Atlas.* 10th ed. New York, NY: Lange, McGraw-Hill; 2003.)

THE WAITING ROOM

Rena Felya, a 9-year-old girl, complained of a severe pain in her throat and difficulty in swallowing. She had chills, sweats, headache, and a fever of 102.4°F. When her symptoms persisted for several days, her mother took her to her pediatrician, who found diffuse erythema (redness) in her posterior pharynx (throat), with yellow exudates (patches) on her tonsils. Large, tender lymph nodes were present under her jaw on both sides of her neck. A throat culture was taken, and therapy with penicillin was begun.

Although the sore throat and fever improved, 10 days after the onset of the original infection, Rena's eyes and legs became swollen and her urine suddenly turned the color of Coca-Cola. Her blood pressure was elevated. Protein and red blood cells were found in her urine. Her serum creatinine level (see Chapter 3 for how creatinine is measured) was elevated at 1.8 mg/dL (reference range, 0.3 to 0.7 mg/dL for a child). Because the throat culture grew group A β-hemolytic streptococci, the doctor ordered a Streptozyme test. This test was positive for antibodies to streptolysin O and several other streptococcal antigens. As a result, a diagnosis of acute poststreptococcal glomerulonephritis was made. Supportive therapy, including bed rest and treatment for hypertension, was initiated.

I. MUSCLE CELL TYPES

Muscle consists of three different types: skeletal, smooth, and cardiac (Fig. 47.1). The metabolism of each is similar, but the functions of the muscles are quite different.

A. Skeletal Muscle

Skeletal muscles are those muscles that are attached to bone and facilitate the movement of the skeleton. Skeletal muscles are found in pairs, which are responsible for opposing, coordinated directions of motion on the skeleton. The muscles appear striated under the microscope and are controlled voluntarily (you think about moving a specific muscle group, and then it happens).

Skeletal muscle cells are long, cylindrical fibers that run the length of the muscle. The fibers are multinucleated because of cell fusion during embryogenesis. The cell membrane surrounding the fibers is called the *sarcolemma*, and the *sarcoplasm* is the intracellular milieu, which contains the proteins, organelles, and contractile apparatus of the cell. The sarcoplasmic reticulum is analogous to the endoplasmic reticulum in other cell types and is an internal membrane system that runs throughout the length of the muscle fiber. Another membrane structure, the transverse tubules (T tubules), are thousands of invaginations of the sarcolemma that tunnel from the surface toward the center of the muscle fiber to make contact with the terminal cisterns of the sarcoplasmic reticulum. Because the T tubules are open to the outside of the muscle fiber and are filled with extracellular fluid, the muscle action potential that propagates along the surface of the muscle fiber's sarcolemma travels into the T tubules and to the sarcoplasmic reticulum.

The striations in skeletal muscle are attributable to the presence and organization of myofibrils in the cells. Myofibrils are threadlike structures consisting of thin and thick filaments. The contractile proteins actin and myosin are contained within the filaments—myosin in the thick filaments and actin in the thin filaments. The sliding of these filaments relative to each other, using myosin-catalyzed adenosine triphosphate (ATP) hydrolysis as an energy source, allows for the contraction and relaxation of the muscle (see Fig. 19.4).

 Damaged muscle cells release myoglobin, which can be observed clinically as a reddish tint to the urine. The primary measurement for myoglobin is via immunoassays. The primary antibody is linked to an insoluble support, whereas the second antibody is linked to alkaline phosphatase. Using a fluorescent substrate for the phosphatase allows low levels of myoglobin to be detected. If myoglobin is high in the sera, it could be a sign of a myocardial infarction. If high in the urine, muscle damage and potential renal failure could be the culprits.

Duchenne muscular dystrophy is caused by the absence of the protein dystrophin, which is a structural protein located in the sarcolemma. Dystrophin is required to maintain the integrity of the sarcolemma, and when it is absent, there is a loss of muscle function, caused by breakdown of the sarcolemma. The gene is X-linked, and mutations that lead to Duchenne's muscular dystrophy generally result from large deletions of the gene, such that dystrophin is absent from the membrane. Becker muscular dystrophy, a milder form of disease, is caused by point mutations in the dystrophin gene. In Becker muscular dystrophy, dystrophin is present in the sarcolemma, but in a mutated form.

Table 47.1   Properties of Muscle Fiber Types

| | Type II Fibers | |
Type I Fibers	**Type IIa**	**Type IIb**
Slow-twitch (slow speed of cont raction)	Intermediate-twitch (fast speed of contraction)	Fast-twitch (fast speed of contraction)
Slow-oxidative (low glycogen content)	Fast-oxidative glycolytic fibers (intermediate glycogen levels)	Fast-glycolytic (high glycogen content)
High myoglobin content (appear red)	Intermediate fiber diameter	Low myoglobin content (appear white)
Small fiber diameter	High myoglobin content (appear red)	Low mitochondrial content
Increased concentration of capillaries surrounding muscle (greater oxygen delivery)	Increased oxidative capacity on training	Limited aerobic metabolism
		Large fiber diameter
High capacity for aerobic metabolism	Intermediate resistance to fatigue	More sensitive to fatigue compared with other fiber types
High resistance to fatigue		Least efficient use of energy, primarily glycolytic
Used for prolonged, aerobic exercise		Used for sprinting and resistance tasks

Muscle fibers can be classified as either fast twitch or slow twitch. The slow-twitch fibers, or type I fibers (also called *slow-oxidative fibers*), contain large amounts of mitochondria and myoglobin (giving them a red color), use respiration and oxidative phosphorylation for energy, and are relatively resistant to fatigue. Compared with fast-twitch fibers, their glycogen content is low. The slow-twitch fibers develop force slowly but maintain contractions longer than fast-twitch muscles.

The fast-twitch fibers, or type II, can be subdivided as type IIa or type IIb. Type IIb fibers (also called *fast-glycolytic fibers*) have few mitochondria and low levels of myoglobin (hence, they appear white). They are rich in glycogen and use glycogenolysis and glycolysis as their primary energy source. These muscles are prone to fatigue because continued reliance on glycolysis to produce ATP leads to an increase in lactic acid levels, resulting in a drop in the intracellular pH. As the pH drops, the ability of the muscle to produce ATP also diminishes. However, fast-twitch muscle can develop greater force than slow-twitch muscle, so contractions occur more rapidly. Type IIa fibers (also called *fast-oxidative glycolytic fibers*) have properties of both type I and IIb fibers and thus display functional characteristics of both fiber types. The properties of types I, IIa, and IIb fibers are summarized in Table 47.1.

Muscles are a mixture of the different fiber types, but depending on the function, a muscle may have a preponderance of one fiber type over another. Type I fibers are found in postural muscles such as the psoas in the back musculature or the soleus in the leg. The ratio of type I to type II varies with the muscle. The triceps, which functions phasically, has 32.6% type I, whereas the soleus, which functions tonically, has 87.7% type I. Type II fibers are more prevalent in the large muscles of the limbs that are responsible for sudden, powerful movements. Extraocular muscles would also have more of these fibers than type I.

B. Smooth Muscle Cells

Smooth muscle cells are found in the digestive system, blood vessels, bladder, airways, and uterus. The cells have a spindle shape with a central nucleus (see Fig. 47.1B). The designation "smooth" refers to the fact that these cells, which contain a single nucleus, display no striations under the microscope. The contraction

of smooth muscle is controlled involuntarily (the cells contract and relax without any conscious attempt to have them do so; examples of smooth muscle activity include moving food along the digestive tract, altering the diameter of the blood vessels, and expelling urine from the bladder). In contrast to skeletal muscle, these cells have the ability to maintain tension for extended periods, and do so efficiently, with a low use of energy.

C. Cardiac Muscle Cells

The cardiac muscle cells are similar to skeletal muscle in that they are striated (contain fibers), but like smooth muscle cells, they are regulated involuntarily (we do not have to think about making our heart beat). The cells are quadrangular in shape (see Fig. 47.1C) and form a network with multiple other cells through tight membrane junctions and gap junctions. The multicellular contacts allow the cells to act as a common unit and to contract and relax synchronously. Cardiac muscle cells are designed for endurance and consistency. They depend on aerobic metabolism for their energy needs because they contain many mitochondria and very little glycogen. These cells thus generate only a small amount of their energy from glycolysis using glucose derived from glycogen. A reduced flow of oxygen-rich blood to the heart muscle may lead to a myocardial infarction (heart attack). The amount of ATP that can be generated by glycolysis alone is not sufficient to meet the energy requirements of the contracting heart.

II. NEURONAL SIGNALS TO MUSCLE

For an extensive review of how muscle contracts or a detailed view of the signaling to allow muscle contraction, consult a medical physiology book. Only a brief overview is presented here.

The nerve–muscle cell junction is called the *neuromuscular junction* (Fig. 47.2). When appropriately stimulated, the nerve cell releases acetylcholine at the junction, which binds to acetylcholine receptors on the muscle membrane. This binding stimulates the opening of sodium channels on the sarcolemma. The massive influx of sodium ions results in the generation of an action potential in the sarcolemma at the edges of the motor end plate of the neuromuscular junction. The action potential sweeps across the surface of the muscle fiber and down the transverse tubules to the sarcoplasmic reticulum, where it initiates the release of calcium

 The ryanodine receptors are calcium release channels found in the endoplasmic reticulum and sarcoplasmic reticulum of muscle cells. One type of receptor can be activated by a depolarization signal (depolarization-induced calcium release). Another receptor type is activated by calcium ions (calcium-induced calcium release). The proteins received their name because they bind ryanodine, a toxin obtained from the stem and roots of the plant *Ryania speciosa*. Ryanodine inhibits sarcoplasmic reticulum calcium release and acts as a paralytic agent. It was first used commercially in insecticides.

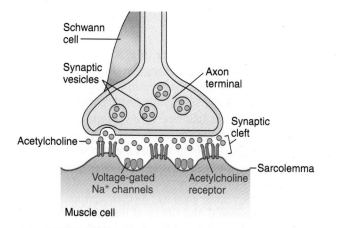

FIG. 47.2. The neuromuscular junction. When they are stimulated appropriately, the synaptic vesicles, containing acetylcholine, fuse with the axonal membrane and release acetylcholine into the synaptic cleft. The acetylcholine binds to its receptors on the muscle cells, which initiate signaling for muscle contraction.

FIG. 47.3. Events leading to sarcoplasmic reticulum calcium release in skeletal muscle. *(1)* Acetylcholine, released at the synaptic cleft, binds to acetylcholine receptors on the sarcolemma, leading to a change of conformation of the receptors so that they now act as an ion pore. This allows sodium to enter the cell and potassium to leave. *(2)* The membrane polarization that results from these ion movements is transmitted throughout the muscle fiber by the T-tubule system. *(3)* A receptor in the T tubules (the dihydropyridine receptor [DHPR]) is activated by membrane polarization (a voltage-gated activation) so that activated DHPR binds physically to and activates the ryanodine receptor in the sarcoplasmic reticulum (depolarization-induced calcium release). *(4)* The activation of the ryanodine receptor, which is a calcium channel, leads to calcium release from the sarcoplasmic reticulum (SR) into the sarcoplasm. In cardiac muscle, activation of DHPR leads to calcium release from the T tubules, and this small calcium release is responsible for the activation of the cardiac ryanodine receptor (calcium-induced calcium release) to release large amounts of calcium into the sarcoplasm.

 Acetylcholine levels in the neuromuscular junction are rapidly reduced by the enzyme acetylcholinesterase. A number of nerve gas poisons act to inhibit acetylcholinesterase (such as sarin and VX), so that muscles are continuously stimulated to contract. This leads to blurred vision, bronchoconstriction, seizures, respiratory arrest, and death. The poisons are covalent modifiers of acetylcholinesterase; therefore, recovery from exposure to such poisons requires the synthesis of new enzyme. A new generation of acetylcholinesterase inhibitors, which act reversibly (i.e., they do not form covalent bonds with the enzyme), is now being used to treat dementia, in particular dementia as brought about by Alzheimer disease.

from its lumen, via the ryanodine receptor (Fig. 47.3). The calcium ion binds to troponin, resulting in a conformational change in the troponin–tropomyosin complexes so that they move away from the myosin-binding sites on the actin. When the binding site becomes available, the myosin head attaches to the myosin-binding site on the actin. The binding is followed by a conformational change (pivoting) in the myosin head, which shortens the sarcomere. After the pivoting, ATP binds the myosin head, which detaches from the actin and is available to bind another myosin-binding site on the actin. As long as calcium ion and ATP remain available, the myosin heads will repeat this cycle of attachment, pivoting, and detachment (Fig. 47.4). This movement requires ATP, and when ATP levels are low (such as occurs during ischemia), the ability of the muscle to relax or contract is compromised. As the calcium release channel closes, the calcium is pumped back into the sarcoplasmic reticulum against its concentration gradient using the energy-requiring protein *SERCA* (sarcoplasmic reticulum Ca^{2+} ATPase), and contraction stops. This basic process occurs in all muscle cell types, with some slight variations between cell types.

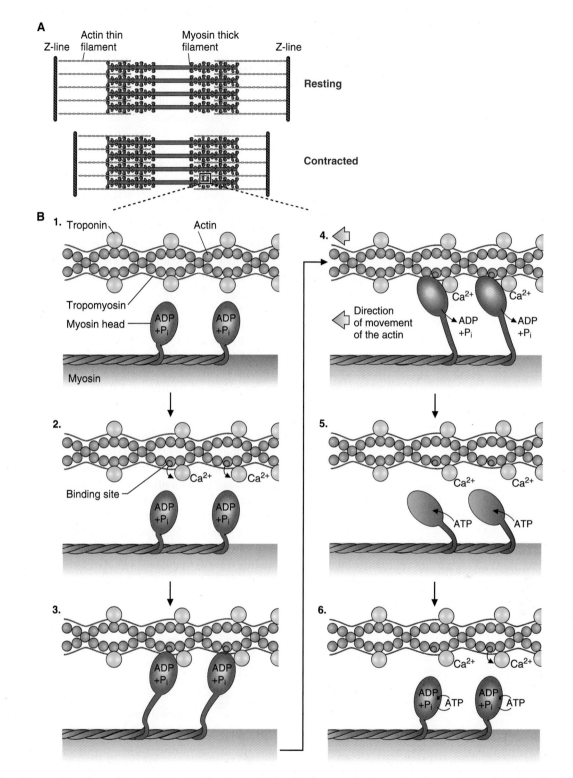

FIG. 47.4. An overview of muscle contraction. **A.** Muscle contraction. During muscle contraction, the myosin head binds to the actin thin filament. Pivoting of the myosin head toward the center of the sarcomere pulls the Z-lines closer together, with subsequent shortening of the sarcomere. **B.** A closer look at myosin–actin interactions. *(1)* A resting sarcomere. The troponin–tropomyosin complex is blocking the myosin-binding sites on the actin. The myosin head is already energized to power a contraction. *(2)* Exposure of the active site. After calcium binding to troponin, a conformational change in the troponin molecule pulls the troponin away from the binding site. *(3)* Cross-bridge attachment. Once the binding sites on the actin are exposed, the myosin head binds to it. *(4)* Myosin head pivoting. After cross-bridge attachment, the energy stored in the myosin head is released, and the myosin head pivots toward the center of the sarcomere (power stroke). Now the ADP and phosphate bound to the myosin head are released. *(5)* Detachment of the crossbridge. Now a molecule of ATP binds to the myosin head with simultaneous detachment of the myosin head from the binding site on the actin molecule. *(6)* Reactivation of the myosin head. The ATPase activity of the myosin head hydrolyzes the ATP into ADP and phosphate. The energy released from the hydrolysis of this high-energy bond is used to reenergize the myosin head, and the entire cycle can be repeated as long as calcium is present and there are sufficient ATP reserves.

III. GLYCOLYSIS AND FATTY ACID METABOLISM IN MUSCLE CELLS

The pathways of glycolysis and fatty acid oxidation in muscle are the same as has been previously described (see Chapters 22 and 23). The difference between muscles and other tissues is how these pathways are regulated.

Phosphofructokinase-2 (PFK-2) is negatively regulated by phosphorylation in the liver (the enzyme that catalyzes the phosphorylation is the cyclic adenosine monophosphate [cAMP]–dependent protein kinase). However, in skeletal muscle, PFK-2 is not regulated by phosphorylation. This is because the skeletal muscle isozyme of PFK-2 lacks the regulatory serine residue, which is phosphorylated in the liver. However, the cardiac isozyme of PFK-2 is phosphorylated and activated by a kinase cascade initiated by insulin. This allows the heart to activate glycolysis and to use blood glucose when blood glucose levels are elevated. The adenosine monophosphate (AMP)-activated protein kinase also activates cardiac PFK-2 (kinase activity) as a signal that energy is low.

Fatty acid uptake by muscle requires the participation of fatty acid–binding proteins and the usual enzymes of fatty acid oxidation. Fatty acyl-CoA uptake into the mitochondria is controlled by malonyl-CoA, which is produced by an isozyme of acetyl-CoA carboxylase (ACC-2; the ACC-1 isozyme is found in liver and adipose tissue cytosol and is used for fatty acid biosynthesis). ACC-2 (a mitochondrial protein, linked to carnitine palmitoyl transferase I [CPTI] in the outer mitochondrial membrane) is inhibited by phosphorylation by the AMP-activated protein kinase (AMP-PK) so that when energy levels are low, the levels of malonyl-CoA drop, allowing fatty acid oxidation by the mitochondria. In addition, muscle cells also contain the enzyme malonyl-CoA decarboxylase, which is activated by phosphorylation by the AMP-PK. Malonyl-CoA decarboxylase converts malonyl-CoA to acetyl-CoA, thereby relieving the inhibition of CPTI and stimulating fatty acid oxidation (Fig. 47.5). Muscle cells do not synthesize fatty acids; the presence of acetyl-CoA carboxylase in muscle is exclusively for regulatory purposes. Mice that have been bred to lack ACC-2 have a 50% reduction of fat stores compared with control mice. This was shown to be attributable to a 30% increase in skeletal muscle fatty acid oxidation resulting from dysregulation of CPTI, brought about by the lack of malonyl-CoA inhibition of CPTI.

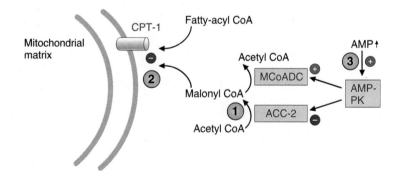

FIG. 47.5. Regulation of fatty acyl-CoA entry into muscle mitochondria. *(1)* Acetyl-CoA carboxylase-2 (ACC-2) converts acetyl-CoA to malonyl-CoA, which inhibits carnitine palmitoyl transferase I (CPTI), thereby blocking fatty acyl-CoA entry into the mitochondria. *(2)* However, as energy levels drop, AMP levels rise because of the activity of the adenylate kinase reaction. *(3)* The increase in AMP levels activates the AMP-activated protein kinase (AMP-PK), which phosphorylates and inactivates ACC-2, and also phosphorylates and activates malonyl-CoA decarboxylase (MCoADC). The decarboxylase converts malonyl-CoA to acetyl-CoA, thereby relieving the inhibition of CPTI and allowing fatty acyl-CoA entry into the mitochondria. This allows the muscle to generate ATP via the oxidation of fatty acids.

IV. FUEL USE IN CARDIAC MUSCLE

A. Normal Conditions

The heart uses primarily fatty acids (60% to 80%), lactate, and glucose (20% to 40%) as its energy sources. Ninety-eight percent of cardiac ATP is generated by oxidative means; 2% is derived from glycolysis. The lactate used by the heart is taken up by a monocarboxylate transporter in the cell membrane that is also used for the transport of ketone bodies. However, ketone bodies are not a preferred fuel for the heart; the heart prefers to use fatty acids.

Lactate is generated by red blood cells and working skeletal muscle. When the lactate is used by the heart, it is oxidized to carbon dioxide and water, following the pathway lactate to pyruvate, pyruvate to acetyl-CoA, acetyl-CoA oxidation in the tricarboxylic acid (TCA) cycle, and ATP synthesis through oxidative phosphorylation. An alternative fate for lactate is its use in the reactions of the Cori cycle in the liver.

Glucose transport into the cardiocyte occurs via both GLUT1 and GLUT4 transporters, although approximately 90% of the transporters are GLUT4. Insulin stimulates an increase in the number of GLUT4 transporters in the cardiac cell membrane, as does myocardial ischemia. This ischemia-induced increase in GLUT4 transporter number is additive to the effect of insulin on the translocation of GLUT4 transporters to the plasma membrane.

Fatty acid uptake into cardiac muscle is similar to that for other muscle cell types and requires fatty acid–binding proteins and carnitine palmitoyl transferase I for transfer into the mitochondria. Fatty acid oxidation in cardiac muscle cells is regulated by altering the activities of ACC-2 and malonyl-CoA decarboxylase. Under conditions in which ketone bodies are produced, fatty acid levels in the plasma are also elevated. Because the heart preferentially burns fatty acids as a fuel rather than the ketone bodies produced by the liver, the ketone bodies are spared for use by the nervous system.

B. Ischemic Conditions

When blood flow to the heart is interrupted, the heart switches to anaerobic metabolism. The rate of glycolysis increases, but the accumulation of protons (via lactate formation) is detrimental to the heart. Ischemia also increases the levels of free fatty acids in the blood and, surprisingly, when oxygen is reintroduced to the heart, the high rate of fatty acid oxidation in the heart is detrimental to the recovery of the damaged heart cells. Fatty acid oxidation occurs so rapidly that NADH accumulates in the mitochondria, leading to a reduced rate of NADH shuttle activity, an increased cytoplasmic NADH level, and lactate formation, which generates more protons. In addition, fatty acid oxidation increases the levels of mitochondrial acetyl-CoA, which inhibits pyruvate dehydrogenase, leading to cytoplasmic pyruvate accumulation and lactate production. As lactate production increases and the intracellular pH of the heart drops, it is more difficult to maintain ion gradients across the sarcolemma. ATP hydrolysis is required to repair these gradients, which are essential for heart function. However, the use of ATP for gradient repair reduces the amount of ATP available for the heart to use in contraction, which, in turn, compromises the ability of the heart to recover from the ischemic event.

V. FUEL USE IN SKELETAL MUSCLE

Skeletal muscles use many fuels to generate ATP. The most abundant immediate source of ATP is creatine phosphate. ATP also can be generated from glycogen stores, either anaerobically (generating lactate) or aerobically, in which case pyruvate is converted to acetyl-CoA for oxidation via the TCA cycle. All human skeletal muscles have some mitochondria and thus are capable of fatty acid and ketone body oxidation. Skeletal muscles are also capable of completely oxidizing the carbon skeletons of alanine, aspartate, glutamate, valine, leucine, and isoleucine, but not other amino acids. Each of these fuel oxidation pathways plays a particular role in skeletal muscle metabolism.

A new class of drugs, known as *partial fatty acid oxidation* (pFOX) inhibitors, is being developed to reduce the extensive fatty acid oxidation in heart after an ischemic episode. The reduction in fatty acid oxidation induced by the drug will allow glucose oxidation to occur and reduce lactate buildup in the damaged heart muscle. Other possible targets of such drugs, which have yet to be developed, include ACC-2, malonyl-CoA decarboxylase, and carnitine palmitoyl transferase I.

Creatine   **Creatine phosphate**

FIG. 47.6. The creatine phosphokinase reaction. The high-energy bond is the unusual nitrogen–phosphate bond, as indicated by the *red squiggle*.

A. Adenosine Triphosphate and Creatine Phosphate

ATP is not a good choice as a molecule to store in quantity for energy reserves. Many reactions are allosterically activated or inhibited by ATP levels, especially those that generate energy. Muscle cells solve this problem by storing high-energy phosphate bonds in the form of creatine phosphate. When energy is required, creatine phosphate donates a phosphate to adenosine diphosphate (ADP) to regenerate ATP for muscle contraction (Fig. 47.6).

Creatine synthesis begins in the kidney and is completed in the liver. In the kidney, glycine combines with arginine to form guanidinoacetate. In this reaction, the guanidinium group of arginine (the group that also forms urea) is transferred to glycine, and the remainder of the arginine molecule is released as ornithine. Guanidinoacetate then travels to the liver, where it is methylated by *S*-adenosylmethionine to form creatine (Fig. 47.7).

FIG. 47.7. The synthesis of creatine from arginine, glycine, and *S*-adenosylmethionine. Synthesis originates in the kidney and is completed in the liver.

Muscle and Brain

FIG. 47.8. The spontaneous production of creatinine from creatine phosphate.

The creatine formed is released from the liver and travels through the bloodstream to other tissues, particularly brain, heart, and skeletal muscle, where it reacts with ATP to form the high-energy compound creatine phosphate (see Fig. 47.6). This reaction, catalyzed by creatine phosphokinase (CK, also abbreviated as CPK), is reversible. Therefore, cells can use creatine phosphate to regenerate ATP.

Creatine phosphate serves as a small reservoir of high-energy phosphate that can readily regenerate ATP from ADP. As a result, it plays a particularly important role in muscle during exercise. It also carries high-energy phosphate from mitochondria, where ATP is synthesized, to myosin filaments, where ATP is used for muscle contraction.

Creatine phosphate is an unstable compound. It spontaneously cyclizes, forming creatinine (Fig. 47.8). Creatinine cannot be further metabolized and is excreted in the urine. The amount of creatinine excreted each day is constant and depends on body muscle mass. Therefore, it can be used as a gauge for determining the amounts of other compounds excreted in the urine and as an indicator of renal excretory function. The daily volume of urine is determined by such factors as the volume of blood reaching the renal glomeruli and the amount of renal tubular fluid reabsorbed from the tubular urine back into the interstitial space of the kidneys over time. At any given moment, the concentration of a compound in a single urine specimen does not give a good indication of the total amount that is being excreted on a daily basis. However, if the concentration of the compound is divided by the concentration of creatinine, the result provides a better indication of the true excretion rate.

B. Fuel Use at Rest

Muscle fuel use at rest is dependent on the serum levels of glucose, amino acids, and fatty acids. If blood glucose and amino acids are elevated, glucose will be converted to glycogen, and branched-chain amino acid metabolism will be high. Fatty acids will be used for acetyl-CoA production and will satisfy the energy needs of the muscle under these conditions.

There is a balance between glucose oxidation and fatty acid oxidation, which is regulated by citrate. When the muscle cell has adequate energy, citrate leaves the mitochondria and activates ACC-2, which produces malonyl-CoA. The malonyl-CoA inhibits carnitine palmitoyl transferase-1, thereby reducing fatty acid oxidation by the muscle. Malonyl-CoA decarboxylase is also inactive because the AMP-PK is not active in the fed state. Thus, the muscle regulates its oxidation of glucose and fatty acids in part through monitoring of cytoplasmic citrate levels.

C. Fuel Use during Starvation

As blood glucose levels drop, insulin levels drop. This reduces the levels of GLUT4 transporters in the muscle membrane, and glucose use by muscle drops significantly. This conserves glucose for use by the nervous system and red blood

Each kidney normally contains approximately 1 million glomerular units. Each unit is supplied by arterial blood via the renal arteries and acts as a "filter." Metabolites such as creatinine leave the blood by passing through pores or channels in the glomerular capillaries and enter the fluid within the proximal kidney tubule for eventual excretion in the urine. When they are functionally intact, these glomerular tissues are impermeable to all but the smallest of proteins. When they are acutely inflamed, however, this barrier function is lost to varying degrees, and albumin and other proteins may appear in the urine.

The marked inflammatory changes in the glomerular capillaries that accompany poststreptococcal glomerulonephritis significantly reduce the flow of blood to the filtering surfaces of these vessels. As a result, creatinine, urea, and other circulating metabolites that are filtered into the urine at a normal rate (the glomerular filtration rate [GFR]) in the absence of kidney disease now fail to reach the filters, and, therefore, they accumulate in the plasma. These changes explain **Rena Felya's** laboratory profile during her acute inflammatory glomerular disease (glomerulonephritis). In most patients, prognosis is excellent, although in some patients recovery may not occur. Such patients may progress to chronic renal insufficiency and even renal failure.

Muscle and brain cells contain large amounts of creatine phosphokinase (CK), and damage to these cells causes the enzyme to leak into the blood. Serum CK is measured to diagnose and evaluate patients who have had strokes and heart attacks. The presence of 5% or more of the CK in the blood as the muscle isoform is indicative of a heart attack (see Chapters 8 and 9).

cells. In cardiac muscle, PFK-2 is phosphorylated and activated by insulin. The lack of insulin results in a reduced use of glucose by these cells as well. Pyruvate dehydrogenase is inhibited by the high levels of acetyl-CoA and NADH being produced by fatty acid oxidation.

Fatty acids become the muscle's preferred fuel under starvation conditions. The AMP-PK is active because of lower than normal ATP levels, ACC-2 is inhibited, and malonyl-CoA decarboxylase is activated, thereby retaining full activity of CPTI. The lack of glucose reduces the glycolytic rate, and glycogen synthesis does not occur because of the inactivation of glycogen synthase by epinephrine-stimulated phosphorylation. Recall that in prolonged starvation, muscle proteolysis is induced (in part by cortisol release) for gluconeogenesis by the liver. This does not, however, alter the use of fatty acids by the muscle for its own energy needs under these conditions.

D. Fuel Use during Exercise

The rate of ATP use in skeletal muscle during exercise can be as much as 100 times greater than that in resting skeletal muscles; thus, the pathways of fuel oxidation must be rapidly activated during exercise to respond to the much greater demand for ATP. ATP and creatine phosphate would be rapidly used up if they were not continuously regenerated. The synthesis of ATP occurs from glycolysis (either aerobic or anaerobic) and oxidative phosphorylation (which requires a constant supply of oxygen).

Anaerobic glycolysis is especially important as a source of ATP in three conditions. The first is during the initial period of exercise, before exercise-stimulated increase in blood flow and substrate and oxygen delivery begin, allowing aerobic processes to occur. The second condition in which anaerobic glycolysis is important is exercise by muscle containing predominately fast-twitch glycolytic muscle fibers because these fibers have low oxidative capacity and generate most of their ATP through glycolysis. The third condition is during strenuous activity, when the ATP demand exceeds the oxidative capacity of the tissue, and the increased ATP demand is met by anaerobic glycolysis.

1. ANAEROBIC GLYCOLYSIS AT THE ONSET OF EXERCISE

During rest, most of the ATP required in all types of muscle fibers is obtained from aerobic metabolism. However, as soon as exercise begins, the demand for ATP increases. The amount of ATP present in skeletal muscle could sustain exercise for only 1.2 seconds if it were not regenerated, and the amount of phosphocreatine could sustain exercise for only 9 seconds if it were not regenerated. It takes longer than 1 minute for the blood supply to exercising muscle to increase significantly as a result of vasodilation and, therefore, oxidative metabolism of blood-borne glucose and fatty acids cannot increase rapidly at the onset of exercise. Thus, for the first few minutes of exercise, the conversion of glycogen to lactate provides a considerable portion of the ATP requirement.

2. ANAEROBIC GLYCOLYSIS IN TYPE IIB FAST-TWITCH GLYCOLYTIC FIBERS

Although humans have no muscles that consist entirely of fast-twitch fibers, many other animals do. Examples are white abdominal muscles of fish and the pectoral muscles of game birds (turkey white meat). These muscles contract rapidly and vigorously ("fast twitch" refers to the time to peak tension), but only for short periods. Thus, they are used for activities such as flight by birds and for sprinting and weight lifting by humans.

In such muscles, the glycolytic capacity is high because the enzymes of glycolysis are present in large amounts (thus, the overall V_{max} [maximum velocity] is large). The levels of hexokinase, however, are low, so very little circulating glucose is used. The low levels of hexokinase in fast-twitch glycolytic fibers prevent the muscle from drawing on blood glucose to meet this high demand for ATP, thus avoiding hypoglycemia. Glucose 6-phosphate, formed from glycogenolysis, further inhibits hexokinase. The tissues rely on endogenous fuel stores (glycogen and creatine phosphate) to generate ATP, following the pathway of glycogen breakdown to glucose 1-phosphate, the conversion of glucose 1-phosphate to glucose 6-phosphate, and the metabolism of glucose 6-phosphate to lactate. Thus, anaerobic glycolysis is the main source of ATP during exercise of these muscle fibers.

3. ANAEROBIC GLYCOLYSIS FROM GLYCOGEN

Glycogenolysis and glycolysis during exercise are activated together because both phosphofructokinase-1 (PFK-1) (the rate-limiting enzyme of glycolysis) and glycogen phosphorylase b (the inhibited form of glycogen phosphorylase) are allosterically activated by AMP.

AMP is an ideal activator because its concentration is normally kept low by the adenylate kinase (also called *myokinase in muscle*) equilibrium ($2ADP \leftrightarrow AMP + ATP$). Thus, whenever ATP levels decrease slightly, the AMP concentration increases manyfold (Fig. 47.9).

Starting from a molecule of glucose 1-phosphate derived from glycogenolysis, three ATP molecules are produced in anaerobic glycolysis, as compared with 31 to 33 molecules of ATP in aerobic glycolysis. To compensate for the low ATP yield of anaerobic glycolysis, fast-twitch glycolytic fibers have a much higher content of glycolytic enzymes, and the rate of glucose 6-phosphate use is more than 12 times as fast as in slow-twitch fibers.

Muscle fatigue during exercise generally results from a lowering of the pH of the tissue to approximately 6.4. Both aerobic and anaerobic metabolism lowers the pH. Both the lowering of pH and lactate production can cause pain.

Metabolic fatigue also can occur once muscle glycogen is depleted. Muscle glycogen stores are used up in <2 minutes of anaerobic exercise. If you do push-ups, you can prove this to yourself. The muscles used in push-ups, a high-strength exercise, are principally fast-twitch glycolytic fibers. Time yourself from the start of your push-ups. No matter how well you have trained, you probably cannot do push-ups for as long as 2 minutes. Furthermore, you will feel the pain as the muscle pH drops as lactate production continues.

The regulation of muscle glycogen metabolism is complex. Recall that glycogen degradation in muscle is not sensitive to glucagon (muscles lack glucagon receptors), so there is little change in muscle glycogen stores during overnight fasting or long-term fasting, if the individual remains at rest. Glycogen synthase is inhibited during exercise but can be activated in resting muscle by the release of insulin after a high-carbohydrate meal. Unlike the liver form of glycogen phosphorylase, the muscle isozyme contains an allosteric site for AMP binding. When AMP binds to

FIG. 47.9.   Activation of muscle glycogenolysis and glycolysis by AMP. As muscle contracts, ATP is converted to ADP and inorganic phosphate (P$_i$). In the adenylate kinase reaction, two ADP molecules react to form ATP and AMP. The ATP is used for contraction. As AMP accumulates, it activates glycogenolysis and glycolysis.

muscle glycogen phosphorylase b, the enzyme is activated even though it is not phosphorylated. Thus, as muscle begins to work and the myosin-ATPase hydrolyzes existing ATP stores to ADP, AMP begins to accumulate (because of the adenylate kinase reaction), and glycogen degradation is enhanced. The activation of muscle glycogen phosphorylase b is further enhanced by the release of Ca^{2+} from the sarcoplasmic reticulum, which occurs when muscles are stimulated to contract. The increase in sarcoplasmic Ca^{2+} also leads to the allosteric activation of glycogen phosphorylase kinase (through binding to the calmodulin subunit of the enzyme), which phosphorylates muscle glycogen phosphorylase b, fully activating it. And, finally, during intense exercise, epinephrine release stimulates the activation of adenylate cyclase in muscle cells, thereby activating the cAMP-dependent protein kinase (see Fig. 28.10). Protein kinase A phosphorylates and fully activates glycogen phosphorylase kinase so that continued activation of muscle glycogen phosphorylase can occur. The hormonal signal is slower than the initial activation events triggered by AMP and calcium (Fig. 47.10).

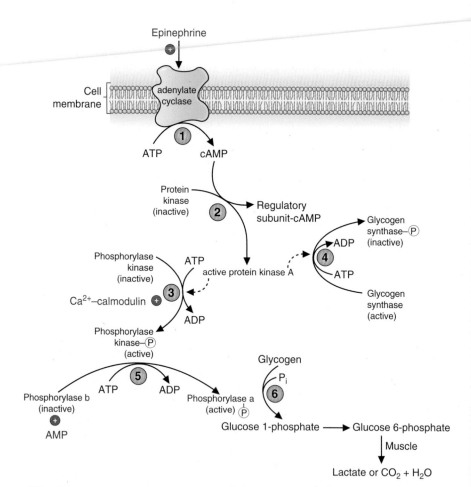

FIG. 47.10. Stimulation of glycogenolysis in muscle by epinephrine. *(1)* Epinephrine binding to its receptor leads to the activation of adenylate cyclase, which increases cAMP levels. *(2)* cAMP binds to the regulatory subunits of protein kinase A, thereby activating the catalytic subunits. *(3)* Active protein kinase A phosphorylates and activates phosphorylase kinase. Phosphorylase kinase also can be activated partially by the Ca^{2+}–calmodulin complex as Ca^{2+} levels increase as muscles contract. *(4)* Protein kinase A phosphorylates and inactivates glycogen synthase. *(5)* Active phosphorylase kinase converts glycogen phosphorylase b to glycogen phosphorylase a. *(6)* Glycogen degradation forms glucose 1-phosphate, which is converted to glucose 6-phosphate, which enters the glycolytic pathway for energy production.

4. ANAEROBIC GLYCOLYSIS DURING HIGH-INTENSITY EXERCISE

Once exercise begins, the electron-transport chain, the TCA cycle, and fatty acid oxidation are activated by the increase of ADP and the decrease of ATP. Pyruvate dehydrogenase remains in the active, nonphosphorylated state as long as NADH can be reoxidized in the electron-transport chain and acetyl-CoA can enter the TCA cycle. However, even though mitochondrial metabolism is working at its maximum capacity, additional ATP may be needed for very strenuous, high-intensity exercise. When this occurs, ATP is not being produced rapidly enough to meet the muscle's needs, and AMP begins to accumulate. Increased AMP levels activate PFK-1 and glycogenolysis, thereby providing additional ATP from anaerobic glycolysis (the additional pyruvate produced does not enter the mitochondria but rather is converted to lactate so that glycolysis can continue). Thus, under these conditions, most of the pyruvate formed by glycolysis enters the TCA cycle, whereas the remainder is reduced to lactate to regenerate NAD^+ for continued use in glycolysis.

5. FATE OF LACTATE RELEASED DURING EXERCISE

The lactate that is released from skeletal muscles during exercise can be used by resting skeletal muscles or by the heart, a muscle with a large amount of mitochondria and very high oxidative capacity. In such muscles, the $NADH/NAD^+$ ratio is lower than in exercising skeletal muscle, and the lactate dehydrogenase reaction proceeds in the direction of pyruvate formation. The pyruvate that is generated is then converted to acetyl-CoA and oxidized in the TCA cycle, producing energy by oxidative phosphorylation.

The second potential fate of lactate is that it will return to the liver through the Cori cycle, where it is converted to glucose (see Fig. 22.10).

VI. MILD- AND MODERATE-INTENSITY LONG-TERM EXERCISE

A. Lactate Release Decreases with Duration of Exercise

Mild-to-moderate intensity exercise can be performed for longer periods than can high-intensity exercise. This is because of the aerobic oxidation of glucose and fatty acids, which generates more energy per fuel molecule than anaerobic metabolism, and which also produces lactic acid at a slower rate than anaerobic metabolism. Thus, during mild- and moderate-intensity exercise, the release of lactate diminishes as the aerobic metabolism of glucose and fatty acids becomes predominant.

B. Blood Glucose as a Fuel

At any given time during fasting, the blood contains only approximately 5 g of glucose, enough to support a person running at a moderate pace for a few minutes. Therefore, the blood glucose supply must be constantly replenished. The liver performs this function by processes similar to those used during fasting. The liver produces glucose by breaking down its own glycogen stores and by gluconeogenesis. The major source of carbon for gluconeogenesis during exercise is, of course, lactate, produced by the exercising muscle, but amino acids and glycerol are also used (Fig. 47.11). Epinephrine released during exercise stimulates liver glycogenolysis and gluconeogenesis by causing cAMP levels to increase.

During long periods of exercise, blood glucose levels are maintained by the liver through hepatic glycogenolysis and gluconeogenesis. The amount of glucose that the liver must export is greatest at higher workloads, in which case the muscle is using a greater proportion of the glucose for anaerobic metabolism. With increasing duration of exercise, an increasing proportion of blood glucose is supplied by gluconeogenesis. For up to 40 minutes of mild exercise, glycogenolysis is mainly responsible for the glucose output of the liver. However, after 40 to 240 minutes of exercise, the total glucose output of the liver decreases. This is caused by the increased use of fatty acids, which are being released from adipose tissue triacylglycerols (stimulated by epinephrine release). Glucose uptake by the muscle is stimulated by the increase

Q: If **Otto Shape** runs at a pace at which his muscles require approximately 500 kcal/hour, how long could he run on the amount of glucose that is present in circulating blood? Assume that the blood volume is 5 L.

FIG. 47.11. Production of blood glucose by the liver from various precursors during rest and during prolonged exercise. The *green* area represents the contribution of liver glycogen to blood glucose, and the *lighter* area represents the contribution of gluconeogenesis. (From Wahren J, et al. In: Howald H, Poortmans JR, eds. *Metabolic Adaptation to Prolonged Physical Exercise.* Cambridge, MA: Birkhauser; 1973:148.)

Remember from Chapter 1 that a food calorie (cal) is equivalent to 1 kcal of energy. One gram of glucose can give rise to 4 kcal of energy, so at a rate of consumption of 500 kcal/hour we have

(500 kcal/h) × (1 g glucose/4 kcal energy)
× (1 h/60 min) = 2 g glucose/min

Thus, Otto must use 2 g of glucose per minute to run at his current pace. In the fasting state, blood glucose levels are approximately 90 mg/dL, or 900 mg/L. Because blood volume is estimated at 5 L, Otto has 4.5 g glucose available. If it is not replenished, that amount of glucose will support only 2.5 minutes of running at 2 g glucose per minute.

in AMP levels and the activation of the AMP-activated protein kinase, which stimulates the translocation of GLUT4 transporters to the muscle membrane.

The hormonal changes that direct the increased hepatic glycogenolysis, hepatic gluconeogenesis, and adipose tissue lipolysis include a decrease in insulin and an increase in glucagon, epinephrine, and norepinephrine. Plasma levels of growth hormone, cortisol, and thyroid-stimulating hormone (TSH) also increase and may contribute to fuel mobilization as well (see Chapter 43). The activation of hepatic glycogenolysis occurs through glucagon and epinephrine release. Hepatic gluconeogenesis is activated by the increased supply of precursors (lactate, glycerol, amino acids, and pyruvate), the induction of gluconeogenic enzymes by glucagon and cortisol (this occurs only during prolonged exercise), and the increased supply of fatty acids to provide the ATP and NADH needed for gluconeogenesis and the regulation of gluconeogenic enzymes.

C. Free Fatty Acids as a Source of Adenosine Triphosphate

The longer the duration of the exercise, the greater the reliance of the muscle on free fatty acids for the generation of ATP (Fig. 47.12). Because ATP generation from free fatty acids depends on mitochondria and oxidative phosphorylation, long-distance running uses muscles that are principally slow-twitch oxidative fibers, such as the gastrocnemius. It is also important to realize that resting skeletal muscle uses free fatty acids as a principal fuel. At almost anytime except the postprandial state (right after eating), free fatty acids are the preferred fuel for skeletal muscle.

The preferential use of fatty acids over glucose as a fuel in skeletal muscle depends on the following factors:

1. The availability of free fatty acids in the blood, which depends on their release from adipose tissue triacylglycerols by hormone-sensitive lipase. During prolonged exercise, the small decrease of insulin and increases of glucagon, epinephrine and norepinephrine, cortisol, and possibly growth hormone all activate adipocyte tissue lipolysis.

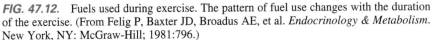

FIG. 47.12. Fuels used during exercise. The pattern of fuel use changes with the duration of the exercise. (From Felig P, Baxter JD, Broadus AE, et al. *Endocrinology & Metabolism.* New York, NY: McGraw-Hill; 1981:796.)

2. Inhibition of glycolysis by products of fatty acid oxidation. Pyruvate dehydrogenase activity is inhibited by acetyl-CoA, NADH, and ATP, all of which are elevated as fatty acid oxidation proceeds. As AMP levels drop and ATP levels rise, PFK-1 activity is decreased (see Chapter 22).

3. Glucose transport may be reduced during long-term exercise. Glucose transport into skeletal muscles via the GLUT4 transporter is greatly activated by either insulin or exercise. During long-term exercise, the effect of falling insulin levels or increased fatty acid levels may counteract the stimulation of glucose transport by the exercise itself.

4. Oxidation of ketone bodies also increases during exercise. Their use as a fuel is dependent on their rate of production by the liver. Ketone bodies are never, however, a major fuel for skeletal muscle (muscles prefer free fatty acids).

5. Acetyl-CoA carboxylase (isozyme ACC-2) must be inactivated for the muscle to use fatty acids. This occurs as the AMP-PK is activated and phosphorylates ACC-2, rendering it inactive, and activates malonyl-CoA decarboxylase, to reduce malonyl-CoA levels and allow full activity of CPTI.

D. Branched-Chain Amino Acids

Branched-chain amino acid oxidation has been estimated to supply a maximum of 20% of the ATP supply of resting muscle. Oxidation of branched-chain amino acids in muscle serves two functions. The first is the generation of ATP, and the second is the synthesis of glutamine, which effluxes from the muscle. The highest rates of branched-chain amino acid oxidation occur under conditions of acidosis, in which there is a higher demand for glutamine to transfer ammonia to the kidney and to buffer the urine as ammonium ion during proton excretion. Recall that glutamine synthesis occurs from the carbon skeletons of branched-chain amino acid oxidation (valine and isoleucine) after the initial five steps of the oxidative pathway.

E. The Purine Nucleotide Cycle

Exercise increases the activity of the purine nucleotide cycle, which converts aspartate to fumarate plus ammonia (see Fig. 41.13). The ammonia is used to buffer the proton production and lactate production from glycolysis, and the fumarate is recycled and can form glutamine.

F. Acetate

Acetate is an excellent fuel for skeletal muscle. It is treated by the muscle as a very short-chain fatty acid. It is activated to acetyl-CoA in the cytosol and then transferred into the mitochondria via acetylcarnitine transferase, an isozyme of carnitine palmitoyl transferase. Sources of acetate include the diet (vinegar is acetic acid) and acetate produced in the liver from alcohol metabolism. Certain commercial power bars for athletes contain acetate.

VII. METABOLIC EFFECTS OF TRAINING ON MUSCLE METABOLISM

The effect of training depends, to some extent, on the type of training. In general, training increases the muscle glycogen stores and increases the number and size of mitochondria. The fibers thus increase their capacity for generation of ATP from oxidative metabolism and their ability to use fatty acids as a fuel. The winners in marathon races seem to use muscle glycogen more efficiently than others.

Training to improve strength, power, and endurance of muscle performance is called *resistance training*. Its goal is to increase the size of the muscle fibers (hypertrophy of the muscle). Muscle fibers can develop a maximal force of 3 to 4 kg/cm^2 of muscle area. Thus, if we could increase our muscle size from 80 to 120 cm^2, the maximal resistance that could be lifted would increase from 240 to 360 kg. Hypertrophy occurs by increased protein synthesis in the muscle and a reduction in existing protein turnover.

CLINICAL COMMENTS

Rena Felya. Poststreptococcal glomerulonephritis (PSGN) may follow pharyngeal or cutaneous infection with one of a limited number of "nephritogenic" strains of group A β-hemolytic streptococci. The pathogenesis of PSGN involves a host immune (antibody) response to one or more of the enzymes secreted by the bacterial cells. The antigen–antibody complexes are deposited on the tissues of glomerular units, causing a local acute inflammatory response. Hypertension may occur as a consequence of sodium and water retention caused by an inability of the inflamed glomerular units to filter sodium and water into the urine. Proteinuria is usually mild if the immune response is self-limited.

Overall, one of the most useful clinical indicators of glomerular filtration rate in both health and disease is the serum creatinine concentration. The endogenous production of creatinine, which averages approximately 15 mg/kg of body weight per day, is correlated with muscle mass and, therefore, tends to be constant for a given individual if renal function is normal. Any rise in serum creatinine in a patient such as **Rena Felya**, therefore, can be assumed to result from decreased excretion of this metabolite into the urine. The extent of the rise in the blood is related directly to the severity of the pathologic process involving the glomerular units in the kidneys.

BIOCHEMICAL COMMENTS

The SERCA Pump. The *SERCA* pump is a transmembrane protein of 110 kDa that is present in several different isoforms throughout the body. Three genes encode *SERCA* proteins: designated *SERCA1*, *SERCA2*, and *SERCA3*. The *SERCA1* gene produces two alternatively spliced transcripts: *SERCA1a* and *SERCA1b*. *SERCA1b* is expressed in the fetal and neonatal fast-twitch skeletal muscles and is replaced by *SERCA1a* in adult fast-twitch muscles. The *SERCA2* gene also undergoes alternative splicing, producing the *SERCA2a* and *SERCA2b* isoforms. The *SERCA2b* isoform is expressed in all cell types and is associated with inositol trisphosphate (IP_3)-regulated calcium stores. *SERCA2a* is the primary isoform expressed in cardiac tissue. *SERCA3* produces at least five different alternatively spliced isoforms, which are specifically expressed in different tissues.

SERCA2a plays an important role in cardiac contraction and relaxation. Contraction is initiated by the release of calcium from intracellular stores, whereas relaxation occurs as the calcium is resequestered in the sarcoplasmic reticulum, in part mediated by the *SERCA2a* protein. The *SERCA2a* pump is regulated, in part, by its association with the protein phospholamban (PLN). PLN is a pentameric molecule consisting of five identical subunits of molecular weight 22,000 Da. PLN associates with *SERCA2a* in the sarcoplasmic reticulum and reduces its pumping activity. Because new contractions cannot occur until cytosolic calcium has been resequestered into the sarcoplasmic reticulum, a reduction in *SERCA2a* activity increases the relaxation time. However, when called on, the heart can increase its rate of contractions by inhibiting the activity of phospholamban. This is accomplished by phosphorylation of phospholamban by protein kinase A (PKA). Epinephrine release stimulates the heart to beat faster. This occurs through epinephrine binding to its receptor, activating a G protein, which leads to adenylate cyclase activation, elevation of cAMP levels, and activation of protein kinase A. PKA phosphorylates PLN, thereby reducing its association with *SERCA2a* and relieving the inhibition of pumping activity. This results in reduced relaxation times and more frequent contractions.

Mutations in PLN lead to cardiomyopathies, primarily an autosomal dominant form of dilated cardiomyopathy. This particular mutation substitutes an arginine in place of cysteine at position 9 in PLN, which forms an inactive complex with PKA and blocks PKA phosphorylation of PLN. Individuals with this form of PLN develop cardiomyopathy in their teens. In this condition, the cardiac muscle does not pump well (because of the constant inhibition of *SERCA2a*) and becomes enlarged (dilated). Because of the poor pumping action of the heart, fluid can build up in the lungs. The pulmonary congestion results in a sense of breathlessness (left heart failure). Eventually, progressive left heart failure leads to fluid accumulation in other tissues and organs of the body, such as the legs and ankles (right heart failure).

Key Concepts

- Muscle comprises three different types: skeletal, smooth, and cardiac.
  - Skeletal muscle facilitates movement of the skeleton.
    - Slow-twitch fibers contain large amounts of mitochondria and myoglobin, and generate energy primarily via oxidative means.
    - Fast-twitch fibers have few mitochondria, low levels of myoglobin, and are rich in glycogen. These fibers generate energy primarily via glycolysis.
  - Smooth muscle cells display no striations and aid in maintaining the shape and movement of the blood vessels, airways, uterus, and digestive systems.
  - Cardiac muscle cells contain striations but are regulated involuntarily. They use aerobic metabolism, oxidizing fatty acids, glucose, and lactate, and they contain many mitochondria, with very little glycogen.
- Acetylcholine release at the neuromuscular junction leads to muscle contraction.
- Fatty acid oxidation in muscle is controlled by the levels of malonyl-CoA produced by a muscle-specific isozyme of acetyl-CoA carboxylase (ACC-2).
- Skeletal muscle uses many fuels to generate ATP, storing excess high-energy phosphate bonds as creatine phosphate.
- Muscle fuel use is regulated carefully.
  - At rest, the muscle uses what is available in the blood (glucose, amino acids, fatty acids).
  - During starvation, fatty acids are the preferred energy source (even over ketone bodies).
  - During exercise, stored glycogen, blood glucose, and blood fatty acids are the primary sources of energy for the skeletal muscles.
- Diseases discussed in this chapter are summarized in Table 47.2.

Table 47.2   Diseases Discussed in Chapter 47

Disease or Disorder	Genetic or Environmental	Comments
Renal failure	Both	The lack of kidney function can lead to encephalopathy due to the buildup of toxic metabolites in the blood.
Duchenne muscular dystrophy	Genetic	The lack of dystrophin, due to deletions in the DMD gene on the X chromosome, lead to muscle dysfunction at an early age.

DMD, Duchenne muscular dystrophy.

1. The process of stretching before exercise has which of the following biochemical benefits?

    A. Stimulates the release of epinephrine
    B. Activates glycolysis in the liver
    C. Increases blood flow to the muscles
    D. Activates glycolysis in the muscles
    E. Stimulates glycogenolysis in the liver

2. The major metabolic fuel for participating in a prolonged aerobic exercise event is which of the following?

    A. Liver glycogen
    B. Muscle glycogen
    C. Brain glycogen
    D. Adipose triacylglycerol
    E. Red blood cell–produced lactate

3. A 24-hour urine collection showed that an individual's excretion of creatinine was much lower than normal. Decreased excretion of creatinine could be caused by which of the following?

    A. A decreased dietary intake of creatine
    B. A higher than normal muscle mass resulting from weight lifting
    C. A genetic defect in the enzyme that converts creatine phosphate to creatinine

    D. Kidney failure
    E. A vegetarian diet

4. In the biosynthetic pathways for the synthesis of heme, creatine, and guanine, which one of the following amino acids directly provides carbon atoms that appear in the final product?

    A. Serine
    B. Aspartate
    C. Cysteine
    D. Glutamate
    E. Glycine

5. In skeletal muscle, increased hydrolysis of ATP during muscular contraction leads to which of the following?

    A. A decrease in the rate of palmitate oxidation to acetyl-CoA
    B. A decrease in the rate of NADH oxidation by the electron-transport chain
    C. Activation of PFK-1
    D. An increase in the proton gradient across the inner mitochondrial membrane
    E. Activation of glycogen synthase

Metabolism of the Nervous System

The nervous system consists of various cell types. The most abundant cell in the nervous system is the **glial cell**, which consists of **astrocytes** and **oligodendrocytes** in the **central nervous system**, and **Schwann cells** in the **peripheral nervous system**. These cells provide support for the neurons and synthesize the protective **myelin sheath** that surrounds the axons emanating from the neurons. **Microglial cells** in the nervous system act as immune cells, destroying and ingesting foreign organisms that enter the nervous system. The interface between the brain parenchyma and the cerebrospinal fluid compartment is formed by the **ependymal cells**, which line the cavities of the brain and spinal cord. These cells use their cilia to allow for the circulation of the **cerebrospinal fluid (CSF)**, which bathes the cells of the central nervous system.

The cells of the brain are separated from free contact with the rest of the body by the **blood–brain barrier**. The capillaries of the brain exhibit features, such as tight endothelial cell junctions, that restrict their permeability to metabolites in the blood. This protects the brain from compounds that might be toxic or otherwise interfere with nerve impulse transmission. It also affects the entry of precursors for brain metabolic pathways such as fuel metabolism and neurotransmitter synthesis.

Neurotransmitters can be divided structurally into two categories: **small nitrogen-containing neurotransmitters** and **neuropeptides**. The small nitrogen-containing neurotransmitters are generally synthesized in the **presynaptic terminal** from amino acids and intermediates of glycolysis and the tricarboxylic acid (TCA) cycle. They are retained in storage vesicles until the neuron is depolarized. The **catecholamine** neurotransmitters (**dopamine, norepinephrine**, and **epinephrine**) are derived from tyrosine. **Serotonin** is synthesized from **tryptophan**. Acetylcholine is synthesized from **choline**, which can be supplied from the diet or is synthesized and stored as part of **phosphatidylcholine**. **Glutamate** and its neurotransmitter derivative, **γ-aminobutyric acid (GABA)**, are derived from **α-ketoglutarate** in the TCA cycle. **Glycine** is synthesized in the brain from **serine**. The synthesis of the neurotransmitters is regulated to correspond to the rate of depolarization of the individual neurons. Several cofactors are required for the synthesis of neurotransmitters, and deficiencies of **pyridoxal phosphate, thiamine pyrophosphate**, and **vitamin B_{12}** result in a variety of neurologic dysfunctions.

Brain metabolism has a high **requirement for glucose and oxygen. Deficiencies of either** (**hypoglycemia** or **hypoxia**) affect brain function because they influence adenosine triphosphate (ATP) production and the supply of precursors for neurotransmitter synthesis. **Ischemia** elicits a condition in which increased **calcium levels, swelling, glutamate excitotoxicity**, and **nitric oxide** generation affect brain function and can lead to a stroke. The generation of **free radicals** and abnormalities in nitric oxide production are important players in the pathogenesis of a variety of **neurodegenerative** diseases.

Because of the restrictions posed by the blood–brain barrier to the entry of a variety of substances into the central nervous system, the brain generally synthesizes and degrades its own lipids. Essential fatty acids can enter the brain but the *more common fatty acids do not. The turnover of lipids at the synaptic membrane is very rapid, and the neuron must replace those lipids lost during exocytosis. The glial cells produce the **myelin sheath**, which is composed primarily of lipids. These lipids are of a different composition than those of the neuronal cells. Because there is considerable lipid synthesis and turnover in the brain, this organ is sensitive to **disorders of peroxisomal function** (Refsum disease; interference in very long-chain fatty acid oxidation and α-oxidation) and **lysosomal diseases** (mucopolysaccharidoses; inability to degrade complex lipids and glycolipids).*

THE WAITING ROOM

Katie Colamin, a 34-year-old dress designer, developed alarming palpitations of her heart while bending forward to pick up her cat. She also developed a pounding headache and sweated profusely. After 5 to 10 minutes, these symptoms subsided. One week later, her aerobic exercise instructor, a registered nurse, noted that Katie grew very pale and was tremulous during exercise. The instructor took Katie's blood pressure, which was 220 mm Hg systolic (normal, up to 120 at rest) and 132 mm Hg diastolic (normal, up to 80 at rest). Within 15 minutes, Katie recovered, and her blood pressure returned to normal. The instructor told Katie to see her physician the next day.

The doctor told Katie that her symptom complex coupled with severe hypertension strongly suggested the presence of a tumor in the medulla of one of her adrenal glands (a pheochromocytoma) that was episodically secreting large amounts of catecholamines, such as norepinephrine (noradrenaline) and epinephrine (adrenaline). Her blood pressure was normal until moderate pressure to the left of her umbilicus caused Katie to suddenly develop a typical attack, and her blood pressure rose rapidly. In addition to ordering several biochemical tests, Katie also was immediately scheduled for a magnetic resonance imaging (MRI) study of her abdomen and pelvis. The MRI showed a 3.5 × 2.8 × 2.6 cm mass in the left adrenal gland, with imaging characteristics typical of a pheochromocytoma.

Ivan Applebod's brother, **Evan Applebod**, is 6 ft tall and weighed 425 lb (BMI = 57.6 kg/m²). He had only been successful in losing weight once in his life: in 1977, when he had lost 30 lb through a combination of diet and exercise with the support of a registered dietian. However, he quickly regained this weight over the next year. Evan's weight was not usually a concern for him, but in 1997, he became worried when it became difficult for him to take walks or go fishing because of joint pain in his knees. He was also suffering from symptoms suggestive of a peripheral neuropathy, manifesting primarily as tingling in his legs. In 1997, Evan approached his physician desperate for help to lose weight. The physician placed Evan on a new drug, Redux, which had just been approved for use as a weight-loss agent, and a low-fat, low-calorie diet along with physical therapy to help increase his activity level. In 4 months, Evan's weight dropped from 425 to 375 lb, his total cholesterol dropped from 250 to 185 mmol/L, and his serum triglycerides dropped from 375 to 130 mmol/L. However, Redux was withdrawn from the market by its manufacturer late in 1997 because of its toxicity. Evan was then placed on Prozac, a drug used primarily as an antidepressant and less commonly as an appetite suppressant.

I. CELL TYPES OF THE NERVOUS SYSTEM

The nervous system consists of neurons, the cells that transmit signals, and supporting cells, the neuroglia. The neuroglia consists of oligodendrocytes and astrocytes (known collectively as *glial cells*), microglial cells, ependymal cells, and Schwann cells. The neuroglia are designed to support and sustain the neurons and do so by surrounding neurons and holding them in place, supplying nutrients and oxygen to the neurons, insulating neurons so their electrical signals are more rapidly propagated, and cleaning up any debris that enters the nervous system. The central nervous system (CNS) consists of the brain and spinal cord. This system integrates all signals emanating from the peripheral nervous system (PNS). The PNS is composed of all neurons that lie outside the CNS.

A. Neurons

Neurons consist of a cell body (soma) from which long (axons) and short (dendrites) extensions protrude. Dendrites receive information from the axons of other neurons, whereas the axons transmit information to other neurons. The axon–dendrite connection is known as a *synapse* (Fig. 48.1). Most neurons contain multiple dendrites, each of which can receive signals from multiple axons. This configuration allows a single neuron to integrate information from multiple sources. Although neurons also contain just one axon, most axons branch extensively and distribute information to multiple targets (divergence). The neurons transmit signals by changes in the electrical potential across their membrane. Signaling across a synapse requires the release of neurotransmitters that, when bound to their specific receptors, initiate an electrical signal in the receiving or target cell. Neurons are terminally differentiated cells and, as such, have little capability for division. As a result, injured neurons have a limited capacity to repair themselves and frequently undergo apoptosis (programmed cell death) when damaged.

B. Neuroglial Cells

1. ASTROCYTES

The astrocytes are found in the CNS and are star-shaped cells that provide physical and nutritional support for neurons. During development of the CNS, the astrocytes guide neuronal migration to their final adult position and form a matrix that keeps neurons in place. These cells serve several functions, including phagocytosing debris left behind by cells, providing lactate (from glucose metabolism) as a carbon

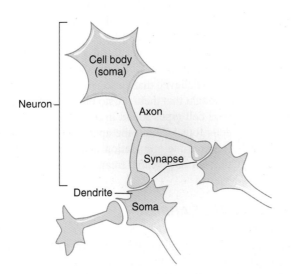

FIG. 48.1. A neuron consists of a cell body (soma) with short extensions (dendrites) and a long extension (axon). The axon–dendrite interface is the synapse. A soma may receive input from multiple axons.

source for the neurons, and controlling the brain extracellular ionic environment. Astrocytes help to regulate the content of the extracellular fluid (ECF) by taking up, processing, and metabolizing nutrients and waste products.

2. OLIGODENDROCYTES

Oligodendrocytes provide the myelin sheath that surrounds the axon, acting as "insulation" for many of the neurons in the CNS. The myelin sheath is the lipid–protein covering of the axons (see Section V.B for a description of the composition and synthesis of the myelin sheath). Oligodendrocytes can form myelin sheaths around multiple neurons in the CNS by sending out processes that bind to the axons on target neurons. The speed with which a neuron conducts its electric signal (action potential) is directly proportional to the degree of myelination. Oligodendrocytes, along with the astrocytes, form a supporting matrix for the neurons. Oligodendrocytes have a limited capacity for mitosis, and if damaged, do not replicate. If this occurs, demyelination of the axons may occur, resulting in abnormalities in signal conduction along that axon (see Biochemical Comments).

3. SCHWANN CELLS

Schwann cells are the supporting cells of the PNS. Like oligodendrocytes, Schwann cells form myelin sheaths around the axons, but unlike the oligodendrocytes, Schwann cells myelinate only one axon. Schwann cells also clean up cellular debris in the PNS. The Schwann cells also provide a means for peripheral axons to regenerate if damaged. There is a synergistic interaction among the Schwann cells, secreted growth factors, and the axon that allows damaged axons to reconnect to the appropriate target axon.

4. MICROGLIAL CELLS

The microglial cells are the smallest glial cells in the nervous system. They serve as immunologically responsive cells that function similarly to the action of macrophages in the circulation. Microglial cells destroy invading microorganisms and phagocytose cellular debris.

5. EPENDYMAL CELLS

The ependymal cells are ciliated cells that line the cavities (ventricles) of the CNS and the spinal cord. In some areas of the brain, the ependymal cells are functionally specialized to elaborate and secrete cerebrospinal fluid (CSF) into the ventricular system. The beating of the ependymal cilia allow for efficient circulation of the CSF throughout the CNS. The CSF acts as both a shock absorber protecting the CNS from mechanical trauma and as a system for the removal of metabolic wastes. The CSF can be aspirated from the spinal canal and analyzed to determine whether disorders of CNS function, with their characteristic CSF changes, are present.

For many years, it had been believed that damaged neurons in the CNS could not regenerate because it was thought that there are no pluripotent stem cells (cells that can differentiate into various cell types found in the CNS) in the CNS. However, recent data suggest that cells found within the ependymal layer can act as neural stem cells, which under appropriate stimulation can regenerate neurons. Such a finding opens up a large number of potential treatments for diseases that alter neuronal cell function.

II. THE BLOOD–BRAIN BARRIER
A. Capillary Structure

In the capillary beds of most organs, rapid passage of molecules occurs from the blood through the endothelial wall of the capillaries into the interstitial fluid. Thus, the composition of interstitial fluid resembles that of blood, and specific receptors or transporters in the plasma membrane of the cells being bathed by the interstitial fluid may interact directly with amino acids, hormones, or other compounds from the blood. In the brain, transcapillary movement of substrates in the peripheral circulation into the brain is highly restricted by the blood–brain barrier. This barrier limits the accessibility of blood-borne toxins and other potentially harmful compounds to the neurons of the CNS.

The blood–brain barrier begins with the endothelial cells that form the inner lining of the vessels supplying blood to the CNS (Fig. 48.2). Unlike the endothelial cells of other organs, these cells are joined by tight junctions that do not permit the movement of polar molecules from the blood into the interstitial fluid bathing the neurons. They also lack mechanisms for transendothelial transport that are present in other capillaries of the body. These mechanisms include fenestrations ("windows" or pores that span the endothelial lining and permit the rapid movement of molecules across membranes) or transpinocytosis (vesicular transport from one side of the endothelial cell to another).

The endothelial cells serve actively, as well as passively, to protect the brain. Because they contain a variety of drug-metabolizing enzyme systems similar to the drug-metabolizing enzymes found in the liver, the endothelial cells can metabolize neurotransmitters and toxic chemicals and, therefore, form an enzymatic barrier to entry of these potentially harmful substances into the brain. They actively pump hydrophobic molecules that diffuse into endothelial cells back into the blood (especially xenobiotics) with P-glycoproteins, which act as transmembranous, ATP-dependent efflux pumps. Although lipophilic substances, water, oxygen, and carbon dioxide can readily cross the blood–brain barrier by passive diffusion, other molecules depend on specific transport systems. Differential transporters on the luminal and abluminal endothelial membranes can transport compounds into, as well as out of, the brain.

Further protection against the free entry of blood-borne compounds into the CNS is provided by a continuous collagen-containing basement membrane that completely surrounds the capillaries. The basement membrane appears to be surrounded by the foot processes of astrocytes. Thus, compounds must pass through endothelial cell membranes, the enzymatic barrier in the endothelial cells, the basement membrane, and possibly additional cellular barriers formed by the astrocytes to reach the neurons in the brain.

B. Transport through the Blood–Brain Barrier

Many nonpolar substances, such as drugs and inert gases, probably diffuse through the endothelial cell membranes. A large number of other compounds are transported through the endothelial capillaries by facilitative transport, whereas others, such as nonessential fatty acids, cannot cross the blood–brain barrier. Essential fatty acids, however, are transported across the barrier.

1. FUELS

Glucose, which is the principal fuel of the brain, is transported through both endothelial membranes by facilitated diffusion via the GLUT-1 transporter (see Fig. 27.14). GLUT-3 transporters present on the neurons then allow the neurons to transport the glucose from the ECF. Glial cells express GLUT-1 transporters. Although the rate of glucose transport into the ECF normally exceeds the rate required for energy metabolism by the brain, glucose transport may become rate-limiting as blood glucose levels fall lower than the normal range. Thus, individuals begin to experience hypoglycemic symptoms at approximately 60 mg/dL, as the glucose levels are reduced to the K_m, or lower than the K_m values of the GLUT-1 transporters in the endothelial cells of the barrier.

Monocarboxylic acids, including L-lactate, acetate, pyruvate, and the ketone bodies acetoacetate and β-hydroxybutyrate, are transported by a separate stereospecific system that is slower than the transport system for glucose. During starvation, when the level of ketone bodies in the blood is elevated, this transporter is

Inside of capillary

1. Tight junctions between endothelial cells
2. Narrow intercellular spaces
3. Lack of pinocytosis
4. Continuous basement membrane
5. Astrocyte extension

FIG. 48.2. The blood–brain barrier. Compounds in the blood cannot pass freely into the brain; they must traverse the endothelial cells, basement membrane, and astrocytes using specific carriers to gain access to the brain. Very lipophilic molecules may pass through all of these membranes in the absence of a carrier.

 Several disorders of glucose transport across the blood–brain barrier are known. The most common of these is facilitated glucose transporter protein type 1 (GLUT-1) deficiency syndrome. In this disorder, GLUT-1 transporters are impaired, which results in a low glucose concentration in the CSF (a condition known as *hypoglycorrhachia*). A diagnostic indication of this disorder is that in normal blood glucose levels, the ratio of CSF glucose to blood glucose levels is <0.4. Clinical features are variable but include seizures, developmental delay, and a complex motor disorder. These symptoms are the result of inadequate glucose levels in the brain. The disorder can be treated by prescribing a ketogenic diet (high-fat, low-carbohydrate). This will force the patient to produce ketone bodies, which are easily transported into the CNS and can spare the brain's requirement for glucose as an energy source.

The finding that the large neutral amino acids (LNAAs) have a common carrier system across the blood–brain barrier suggests that if one amino acid is in excess, it can, by competitive inhibition, result in lower transport of the other amino acids. This suggests that the mental retardation that results from untreated phenylketonuria (PKU) and maple syrup urine disease (see Chapter 39) may be attributable to the high levels of either phenylalanine or branched-chain amino acids in the blood. These high levels overwhelm the LNAA carrier, so excessive levels of the damaging amino acid enter the central nervous system (CNS). In support of this theory is the finding that treatment of PKU patients with large doses of LNAAs that lack phenylalanine resulted in a decrease of phenylalanine levels in the cerebrospinal fluid (CSF) and brain, with an improvement in the patients' cognitive functions as well.

upregulated. Ketone bodies are important fuels for the brain of both adults and neonates during prolonged starvation (>48 hours).

2. AMINO ACIDS AND VITAMINS

Large neutral amino acids (LNAAs), such as phenylalanine, leucine, tyrosine, isoleucine, valine, tryptophan, methionine, and histidine, enter the CSF rapidly via a single amino acid transporter (L [leucine preferring]-system amino acid transporter). Many of these compounds are essential in the diet and must be imported for protein synthesis or as precursors of neurotransmitters. Because a single transporter is involved, these amino acids compete with each other for transport into the brain.

The entry of small neutral amino acids, such as alanine, glycine, proline, and γ-aminobutyric acid (GABA), is markedly restricted because their influx could dramatically change the content of neurotransmitters (see Section III). They are synthesized in the brain, and some are transported out of the CNS and into the blood via the A (alanine-preferring)-system carrier. Vitamins have specific transporters through the blood–brain barrier, just as they do in most tissues.

3. RECEPTOR-MEDIATED TRANSCYTOSIS

Certain proteins such as insulin, transferrin, and insulin-like growth factors cross the blood–brain barrier by receptor-mediated transcytosis. Once the protein binds to its membrane receptor, the membrane containing the receptor–protein complex is endocytosed into the endothelial cell to form a vesicle. It is released on the other side of the endothelial cell. Absorptive-mediated transcytosis also can occur. This differs from receptor-mediated transcytosis in that the protein binds nonspecifically to the membrane and not to a distinct receptor.

III. SYNTHESIS OF SMALL NITROGEN-CONTAINING NEUROTRANSMITTERS

Molecules that serve as neurotransmitters fall into two basic structural categories: (1) small nitrogen-containing molecules and (2) neuropeptides. The major small nitrogen-containing molecule neurotransmitters include glutamate, GABA, glycine, acetylcholine, dopamine, norepinephrine, serotonin, and histamine. Additional neurotransmitters that fall into this category include epinephrine, aspartate, and nitric oxide. In general, each neuron synthesizes only those neurotransmitters that it uses for transmission through a synapse or to another cell. The neuronal tracts are often identified by their neurotransmitter; for example, a dopaminergic tract synthesizes and releases the neurotransmitter dopamine.

Neuropeptides are usually small peptides that are synthesized and processed in the CNS. Some of these peptides have targets within the CNS (such as endorphins, which bind to opioid receptors and block pain signals), whereas others are released into the circulation to bind to receptors on other organs (such as growth hormone and thyroid-stimulating hormone). Many neuropeptides are synthesized as a larger precursor, which is then cleaved to produce the active peptides. Until recently, the assumption was that a neuron synthesized and released only a single neurotransmitter. More recent evidence suggests that a neuron may contain (1) more than one small-molecule neurotransmitter, (2) more than one neuropeptide neurotransmitter, or (3) both types of neurotransmitters. The differential release of the various neurotransmitters is the result of the neuron altering its frequency and pattern of firing.

A. General Features of Neurotransmitter Synthesis

Several features are common to the synthesis, secretion, and metabolism of most small nitrogen-containing neurotransmitters (Table 48.1). Most of these neurotransmitters are synthesized from amino acids, intermediates of glycolysis and the TCA cycle, and O_2 in the cytoplasm of the presynaptic terminal. The rate of synthesis is generally regulated to correspond to the rate of firing of the neuron. Once they are synthesized,

Table 48.1 Features Common to Neurotransmitters*a*

- Synthesis from amino acid and common metabolic precursors usually occurs in the cytoplasm of the presynaptic nerve terminal. The synthetic enzymes are transported by fast axonal transport from the cell body, where they are synthesized, to the presynaptic terminal.
- The synthesis of the neurotransmitter is regulated to correspond to the rate of firing of the neuron, both acutely and through long-term enhancement of synaptic transmission.
- The neurotransmitter is actively taken up into storage vesicles in the presynaptic terminal.
- The neurotransmitter acts at a receptor on the postsynaptic membrane.
- The action of the neurotransmitter is terminated through reuptake into the presynaptic terminal, diffusion away from the synapse, or enzymatic inactivation. The enzymatic inactivation may occur in the postsynaptic terminal, the presynaptic terminal, or an adjacent astrocyte or microglial cell.
- The blood–brain barrier affects the supply of precursors for neurotransmitter synthesis.

*a*Not all neurotransmitters exhibit all of these features. Nitric oxide is an exception to most of these generalities. Some neurotransmitters (epinephrine, serotonin, and histamine) are also secreted by cells other than neurons. Their synthesis and secretion by nonneuronal cells follow other principles.

the neurotransmitters are transported into storage vesicles by an ATP-requiring pump linked with the proton gradient. Release from the storage vesicle is triggered by the nerve impulse that depolarizes the postsynaptic membrane and causes an influx of Ca^{2+} ions through voltage-gated calcium channels. The influx of Ca^{2+} promotes fusion of the vesicle with the synaptic membrane and release of the neurotransmitter into the synaptic cleft. The transmission across the synapse is completed by binding of the neurotransmitter to a receptor on the postsynaptic membrane (Fig. 48.3).

The action of the neurotransmitter is terminated through reuptake into the presynaptic terminal, uptake into glial cells, diffusion away from the synapse, or enzymatic inactivation. The enzymatic inactivation may occur in the postsynaptic terminal, the presynaptic terminal, or an adjacent astrocyte microglia cell or in endothelial cells in the brain capillaries.

Not all neurotransmitters exhibit all of these features. Nitric oxide, because it is a gas, is an exception to most of these generalities. Some neurotransmitters are synthesized and secreted by both neurons and other cells (e.g., epinephrine, serotonin, histamine).

 Drugs have been developed that block neurotransmitter uptake into storage vesicles. Reserpine, which blocks catecholamine uptake into vesicles, had been used as an antihypertensive and antiepileptic drug for many years, but it was noted that a small percentage of patients on the drug became depressed and even suicidal. Animals treated with reserpine showed signs of lethargy and poor appetite, similar to depression in humans. Thus, a link was forged between monoamine release and depression in humans.

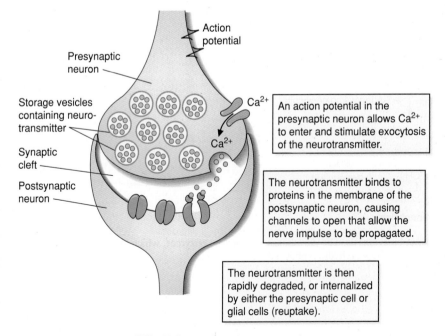

FIG. 48.3. Action of neurotransmitters.

FIG. 48.4. The pathways of catecholamine and melanin biosynthesis. The *dark* boxes indicate the enzymes, which, when defective, lead to albinism. *BH₄*, tetrahydrobiopterin; *PLP*, pyridoxal phosphate; *Dopa*, dihydroxyphenylalanine.

B. Dopamine, Norepinephrine, and Epinephrine

1. SYNTHESIS OF THE CATECHOLAMINE NEUROTRANSMITTERS

The three neurotransmitters dopamine, norepinephrine, and epinephrine are synthesized in a common pathway from the amino acid L-tyrosine. Tyrosine is supplied in the diet or is synthesized in the liver from the essential amino acid phenylalanine by phenylalanine hydroxylase (see Chapter 39). The pathway of catecholamine biosynthesis is shown in Figure 48.4.

The first and rate-limiting step in the synthesis of these neurotransmitters from tyrosine is the hydroxylation of the tyrosine ring by tyrosine hydroxylase, a tetrahydrobiopterin (BH_4)-requiring enzyme. The product formed is dihydroxyphenylalanine (Dopa). The phenyl ring with two adjacent –OH groups is a catechol, and hence dopamine, norepinephrine, and epinephrine are called catecholamines.

The second step in catecholamine synthesis is the decarboxylation of dopa to form dopamine. This reaction, like many decarboxylation reactions of amino acids, requires pyridoxal phosphate. Dopaminergic neurons (neurons that use dopamine as a neurotransmitter) stop the synthesis at this point because these neurons do not synthesize the enzymes required for the subsequent steps.

Neurons that secrete norepinephrine synthesize it from dopamine in a hydroxylation reaction catalyzed by dopamine β-hydroxylase (DBH). This enzyme is present only within the storage vesicles of these cells. Like tyrosine hydroxylase, it is a mixed-function oxidase that requires an electron donor. Ascorbic acid (vitamin C) serves as the electron donor and is oxidized in the reaction. Copper (Cu^{2+}) is a bound cofactor that is required for the electron transfer.

Although the adrenal medulla is the major site of epinephrine synthesis, epinephrine is also synthesized in a few neurons that use it as a neurotransmitter. These neurons contain the above pathway for norepinephrine synthesis and, in addition, contain the enzyme that transfers a methyl group from *S*-adenosylmethionine (SAM) to norepinephrine to form epinephrine. Thus, epinephrine synthesis is dependent on the presence of adequate levels of vitamin B_{12} and folate in order to produce the SAM (see Chapter 40).

2. STORAGE AND RELEASE OF CATECHOLAMINES

Ordinarily, only low concentrations of catecholamines are free in the cytosol, whereas high concentrations are found within the storage vesicles. Conversion of tyrosine to L-dopa and that of L-dopa to dopamine occurs in the cytosol. Dopamine is then taken up into the storage vesicles. In norepinephrine-containing neurons, the final β-hydroxylation reaction occurs in the vesicles.

The catecholamines are transported into vesicles by the protein VMAT2 (*vesicle monoamine transporter 2*) (Fig. 48.5). The vesicle transporters contain 12 transmembrane domains and are homologous to a family of bacterial drug-resistant transporters, including P-glycoprotein. The mechanism that concentrates the catecholamines in the storage vesicles is an ATP-dependent process linked to a proton pump (secondary active transport). Protons are pumped into the vesicles by a vesicular ATPase (V-ATPase). The protons then exchange for the positively charged catecholamine via the transporter VMAT2. The influx of the catecholamine is thus driven by the H^+ gradient across the vesicular membrane. The intravesicular concentration of catecholamines is approximately 0.5 M, roughly 100 times the cytosolic concentration. In the vesicles, the catecholamines exist in a complex with ATP and acidic proteins known as *chromogranins.*

The vesicles play a dual role: They maintain a ready supply of catecholamines at the nerve terminal that is available for immediate release, and they mediate the process of release. When an action potential reaches the nerve terminal, Ca^{2+} channels open, allowing an influx of Ca^{2+}, which promotes the fusion of vesicles with the neuronal membrane. The vesicles then discharge their soluble contents, including the neurotransmitters, ATP, chromogranins, and DBH, into the extraneuronal space

FIG. 48.5. Transport of catecholamines into storage vesicles. This is a secondary active transport based on the generation of a proton gradient across the vesicular membrane. *DBH,* dopamine β-hydroxylase; *NT+,* positively charged neurotransmitter (catecholamine); *V-ATPase,* vesicular ATPase; *VMAT2,* vesicle monoamine transporter 2.

 Chromogranins are required for the biogenesis of the secretory vesicles. When chromogranins are released from the vesicles, they can be proteolytically clipped to form bioactive peptides. Elevated levels of chromogranins in the circulation may be found in patients who have neuroendocrine tumors, such as pheochromocytomas.

In albinism, either the copper-dependent tyrosine hydroxylase of melanocytes (which is distinct from the tyrosine hydroxylase found in the adrenal medulla) or other enzymes that convert tyrosine to melanins may be defective. Individuals with albinism suffer from a lack of pigment in the skin, hair, and eyes, and they are sensitive to sunlight.

Tyramine is a degradation product of tyrosine that can lead to headaches, palpitations, nausea and vomiting, and elevated blood pressure if it is present in large quantities. Tyramine leads to norepinephrine release, which binds to its receptors, stimulating them. Tyramine is inactivated by MAO-A, but if a person is taking a MAO inhibitor, foods containing tyramine should be avoided.

by the process of exocytosis. In some cases, the catecholamines affect other neurons. In other cases, they circulate in the blood and initiate responses in peripheral tissues.

3. INACTIVATION AND DEGRADATION OF CATECHOLAMINE NEUROTRANSMITTERS

The action of catecholamines is terminated through reuptake into the presynaptic terminal and diffusion away from the synapse. Degradative enzymes are present in the presynaptic terminal and in adjacent cells, including glial cells and endothelial cells.

Two of the major reactions in the process of inactivation and degradation of catecholamines are catalyzed by monoamine oxidase (MAO) and catechol-*O*-methyltransferase (COMT). MAO is present on the outer mitochondrial membrane of many cells and oxidizes the carbon containing the amino group to an aldehyde, thereby releasing ammonium ion (Fig. 48.6). In the presynaptic terminal, MAO inactivates catecholamines that are not protected in storage vesicles. (Thus, drugs that deplete storage vesicles indirectly increase catecholamine degradation.) There are two isoforms of MAO with different specificities of action: MAO-A preferentially deaminates norepinephrine and serotonin, whereas MAO-B acts on a wide spectrum of phenylethylamines ("phenylethyl" refers to a –CH$_2$– group linked to a phenyl ring). MAO in the liver and other sites protects against the ingestion of dietary biogenic amines such as the tyramine found in many cheeses.

Katie Colamin's doctor ordered plasma fractionated metanephrine (methylated norepinephrine) levels and also had Katie collect a 24-hour urine specimen for the determination of catecholamines and their degradation products (in particular, metanephrine). All of these tests showed unequivocal elevations of these compounds in Katie's blood and urine. Katie was placed on phenoxybenzamine, an α_1- and α_2-adrenergic receptor antagonist that blocks the pharmacologic effect of the elevated catecholamines on these receptors. Once stable on the α-blockers, Katie was started on an agent that blocked β-adrenergic receptors (propranolol). After ruling out evidence to suggest metastatic disease to the liver or other organs (in case Katie's tumor was malignant), the doctor referred Katie to a surgeon with extensive experience in adrenal surgery. Katie's doctor also ordered diagnostic studies to rule out multiple endocrine neoplasm (MEN) syndrome. The tests for the presence of MEN were negative.

FIG. 48.6. Inactivation of catecholamines. Methylation and oxidation may occur in any order. Methylated and oxidized derivatives of norepinephrine and epinephrine are produced, and 3-methoxy-4-hydroxymandelic acid is the final product. These compounds are excreted in the urine. *COMT,* catechol-*O*-methyltransferase; *MAO,* monoamine oxidase; *SAH,* *S*-adenosylhomocysteine; *SAM,* *S*-adenosylmethionine.

COMT is also found in many cells, including erythrocytes. It works on a broad spectrum of extraneuronal catechols and those that have diffused away from the synapse. COMT transfers a methyl group from SAM to a hydroxyl group on the catecholamine or its degradation product (see Fig. 48.6). Because the inactivation reaction requires SAM, it is indirectly dependent on vitamin B_{12} and folate. The action of MAO and COMT can occur in almost any order, resulting in a large number of degradation products and intermediates, many of which appear in the urine. Cerebrospinal homovanillylmandelic acid (HVA) is an indicator of dopamine degradation. Its concentration is decreased in the brain of patients with Parkinson disease.

4. REGULATION OF TYROSINE HYDROXYLASE

Efficient regulatory mechanisms coordinate the synthesis of catecholamine neurotransmitters with the rate of firing. Tyrosine hydroxylase, the first committed step and rate-limiting enzyme in the pathway, is regulated by feedback inhibition that is coordinated with depolarization of the nerve terminal. Tyrosine hydroxylase is inhibited by free cytosolic catecholamines that compete at the binding site on the enzyme for the pterin cofactor (BH_4; see Chapter 39).

Depolarization of the nerve terminal activates tyrosine hydroxylase. Depolarization also activates several protein kinases (including protein kinase C, protein kinase A [the cAMP-dependent protein kinase], and CAM kinases [Ca^{2+}-calmodulin–dependent kinases]) that phosphorylate tyrosine hydroxylase. These activation steps result in an enzyme that binds BH_4 more tightly, making it less sensitive to end-product inhibition.

In addition to these short-term regulatory processes, a long-term process involves alterations in the amounts of tyrosine hydroxylase and dopamine β-hydroxylase present in nerve terminals. When sympathetic neuronal activity is increased for a prolonged period, the amounts of mRNA that code for tyrosine hydroxylase and dopamine β-hydroxylase are increased in the neuronal perikarya (the cell body of the neuron). The increased gene transcription may be the result of phosphorylation of CREB (*c*AMP *r*esponse *e*lement–*b*inding protein; see Chapter 26) by protein kinase A or by other protein kinases. CREB then binds to the CRE (*c*AMP *r*esponse *e*lement) in the promoter region of the gene (similar to the mechanism for the induction of gluconeogenic enzymes in the liver). The newly synthesized enzyme molecules are then transported down the axon to the nerve terminals. The concentration of dopamine decarboxylase in the terminal does not appear to change in response to neuronal activity.

C. Metabolism of Serotonin

The pathway for the synthesis of serotonin from tryptophan is very similar to the pathway for the synthesis of norepinephrine from tyrosine (Fig. 48.7). The first enzyme of the pathway, tryptophan hydroxylase, uses an enzymatic mechanism similar to that of tyrosine and phenylalanine hydroxylase and requires BH_4 to hydroxylate the ring structure of tryptophan. The second step of the pathway is a decarboxylation reaction catalyzed by the same enzyme that decarboxylates Dopa. Serotonin, like the catecholamine neurotransmitters, can be inactivated by MAO.

The neurotransmitter melatonin is also synthesized from tryptophan (see Fig. 48.7). Melatonin is produced in the pineal gland in response to the light–dark cycle, its level in the blood is rising in a dark environment. It is probably through melatonin that the pineal gland conveys information about light–dark cycles to the body, organizing seasonal and circadian rhythms. Melatonin also may be involved in regulating reproductive functions.

D. Metabolism of Histamine

Within the brain, histamine is produced both by mast cells and by certain neuronal fibers. Mast cells are a family of bone marrow–derived secretory cells that store and

 In addition to the catecholamines, serotonin is also inactivated by monoamine oxidase (MAO). The activity of several antipsychotic drugs is based on inhibiting MAO. The first generation of drugs (exemplified by iproniazid, which was originally developed as an antituberculosis drug and was found to induce mood swings in patients) were irreversible inhibitors of both the A and B forms of MAO. Although they did reduce the severity of depression (by maintaining higher levels of serotonin), these drugs suffered from the "cheese" effect. Cheese and other foods that are processed over long periods (such as red wine) contain tyramine, a degradation product of tyrosine. Usually, tyramine is inactivated by MAO-A, but if an individual is taking a MAO inhibitor, tyramine level increases. Tyramine induces the release of norepinephrine from storage vesicles, which leads to potentially life-threatening hypertensive episodes. When it was realized that MAO existed in two forms, selective irreversible inhibitors were developed; examples include clorgyline for MAO-A and deprenyl for MAO-B. Deprenyl has been used to treat Parkinson disease (which is caused by a lack of dopamine, which is also inactivated by MAO). Deprenyl, however, is not an antidepressant. Clorgyline is an antidepressant but suffers from the "cheese" effect. This led to the development of the third generation of MAO inhibitors, which are reversible inhibitors of the enzyme, as typified by moclobemide. *Moclobemide* is a specific, reversible inhibitor of MAO-A and is effective as an antidepressant. More important, because of the reversible nature of the drug, the "cheese" effect is not observed because as tyramine levels increase, they displace the drug from MAO, and the tyramine is safely inactivated.

Tyramine

A potential complication of using heparin as an anticoagulant is the generation of anti-heparin antibodies in the patients. The production of such antibodies leads to the patient developing heparin-induced thrombocytopenia (HIT). The anti-heparin antibodies bind to the heparin platelet factor 4 complex and also to the platelet surface. The antibody-induced binding leads to platelet activation, serotonin release, and thrombin activation. The platelet number drops (the thrombocytopenia), but thrombus formation (caused by thrombin activation) increases. To determine if a patient has developed HIT, the serotonin-release assay has emerged as the gold standard. Platelets store serotonin in granules, and release the serotonin upon activation. Anti-heparin antibody sensitive platelets are obtained from donors and incubated with radioactively labeled serotonin in order for the platelets to incorporate the serotonin. The treated platelets are then incubated with two samples of the patient's sera: one with a high level of exogenous heparin and the second with a low level of heparin. Serotonin release is then measured by determining the percentage of total radioactivity released by the platelets into the assay buffer. A positive result is obtained if, when using a low concentration of heparin, greater than 20% of the radioactivity incorporated into the platelets is released, and when using the high concentration of heparin, less than 20% of the incorporated radioactivity is released. The rationale behind the use of high heparin levels is to titrate out the antibody in the sera such that it cannot bind to the platelet cell surface, and to demonstrate that the release is caused by antibody binding to platelets.

The catecholamines exert their physiologic and pharmacologic effects by circulating in the bloodstream to target cells whose plasma membranes contain catecholamine receptors. This interaction initiates a biochemical cascade leading to responses that are specific for different types of cells. Patients such as **Katie Colamin** experience palpitations, excessive sweating, hypertensive headaches, and a host of other symptoms when a catecholamine-producing tumor of the adrenal medulla suddenly secretes supraphysiologic amounts of epinephrine and/or norepinephrine into the venous blood draining the neoplasm.

FIG. 48.7.   Synthesis and inactivation of serotonin.

release high concentrations of histamine. They are prevalent in the thalamus, hypothalamus, dura mater, leptomeninges, and choroid plexus. Histaminergic neuronal cell bodies in humans are found in the tuberomammillary nucleus of the posterior basal hypothalamus. The fibers project into nearly all areas of the CNS, including the cerebral cortex, the brainstem, and the spinal cord.

Histamine is synthesized from histidine in a single enzymatic step. The enzyme histidine decarboxylase requires pyridoxal phosphate, and its mechanism is very similar to that of dopa decarboxylase (Fig. 48.8).

Like other neurotransmitters, newly synthesized neuronal histamine is stored in the nerve terminal vesicles. Depolarization of nerve terminals activates the exocytotic release of histamine by a voltage-dependent as well as a calcium-dependent mechanism.

Once it is released from neurons, histamine is thought to activate both postsynaptic and presynaptic receptors. Unlike other neurotransmitters, histamine does

FIG. 48.8. Synthesis and inactivation of histamine; note the different pathways for brain and peripheral tissues. *SAH*, *S*-adenosylhomocysteine; *SAM*, *S*-adenosylmethionine.

not appear to be recycled into the presynaptic terminal to any great extent. However, astrocytes have a specific high-affinity uptake system for histamine and may be the major sites of the inactivation and degradation of this monoamine.

The first step in the inactivation of histamine in the brain is methylation (see Fig. 48.8). The enzyme histamine methyltransferase transfers a methyl group from SAM to a nitrogen ring of histamine to form methylhistamine. The second step is oxidation by MAO-B, followed by an additional oxidation step. In peripheral tissues, histamine undergoes deamination by diamine oxidase, followed by oxidation to a carboxylic acid (see Fig. 48.8).

E. Acetylcholine
1. SYNTHESIS

The synthesis of acetylcholine from acetyl coenzyme A (acetyl-CoA) and choline is catalyzed by the enzyme choline acetyltransferase (ChAT) (Fig. 48.9). This synthetic step occurs in the presynaptic terminal. The compound is stored in vesicles and later released through calcium-mediated exocytosis. Choline is taken up by the presynaptic terminal from the blood via a low-affinity transport system (high K_m) and from the synaptic cleft via a high-affinity transport mechanism (low K_m). It is also derived from the hydrolysis of phosphatidylcholine (and possibly sphingomyelin) in membrane lipids. Thus, membrane lipids may form a storage site for choline, and their hydrolysis, with the subsequent release of choline, is highly regulated.

Choline is a common component of the diet but also can be synthesized in the human as part of the pathway for the synthesis of phospholipids (see Chapter 33). The only route for choline synthesis is via the sequential addition of three methyl

Evan Applebod was placed on Redux, which increased the secretion of serotonin. Serotonin has been implicated in many processes, including mood control and appetite regulation. Serotonin agonists are thought to exert their hypophagic actions via stimulation of receptors located on proopiomelanocortin (POMC) containing neurons within the arcuate (ARC) nucleus of the hypothalamus. When serotonin levels are high, satiety results; when serotonin levels are low, increased appetite or depression or both can occur. Thus, drugs that can increase serotonin levels may be able to control appetite and depression. Redux was a second-generation drug developed from fenfluramine, a known appetite suppressant. When it was first used, fenfluramine could not be resolved between two distinct optical isomers (d versus l). The l-isomer induced sleepiness, so to counteract this effect; fenfluramine was often given with phentermine, which elevated norepinephrine levels to counteract the drowsiness (the combination of drugs was known as *fen/phen*). Once the two isomers of fenfluramine could be resolved, dexfenfluramine (Redux) was developed. Because levels of serotonin have been linked to mood, many antidepressant drugs were developed that affect serotonin levels. The first of these is the MAO inhibitors; the second class is the tricyclics; and the third class is known as selective serotonin reuptake inhibitors (SSRIs). The SSRIs block reuptake of serotonin from the synapse, leading to an elevated response to serotonin. Redux not only acted as an SSRI but also increased the secretion of serotonin, leading to elevated levels of this compound in the synapse. None of the other drugs that affect serotonin levels has this effect.

Histamine elicits several effects on different tissues. Histamine is the major mediator of the allergic response, and when it is released from mast cells (a type of white blood cell found in tissues), it leads to vasodilation and an increase in the permeability of blood vessel walls. This leads to the allergic symptoms of a runny nose and watery eyes. When histamine is released in the lungs, the airways constrict in an attempt to reduce the intake of the allergic material. The ultimate result of this, however, is bronchospasm, which can lead to difficulty in breathing. In the brain, histamine is an excitatory neurotransmitter. Antihistamines block histamine from binding to its receptor. In the tissues, this counteracts histamine's effect on vasodilation and blood vessel wall permeability, but in the brain, the effect is to cause drowsiness. The new generation of "nondrowsy" antihistamines have been modified so that they cannot pass through the blood–brain barrier. Thus, the effects on the peripheral tissues are retained, with no effect on CNS histamine response.

It is believed that the vitamin B_{12} requirement for choline synthesis contributes to the neurologic symptoms of vitamin B_{12} deficiency. The methyl groups for choline synthesis are donated by S-adenosylmethionine (SAM), which is converted to S-adenosylhomocysteine (SAH) in the reaction. Recall that formation of SAM through recycling of homocysteine requires both tetrahydrofolate and vitamin B_{12} (unless extraordinary amounts of methionine are available to bypass the B_{12}-dependent methionine synthase step).

FIG. 48.9.   Acetylcholine synthesis and degradation.

groups from SAM to the ethanolamine portion of phosphatidylethanolamine to form phosphatidylcholine. Phosphatidylcholine is subsequently hydrolyzed to release choline or phosphocholine. Conversion of phosphatidylethanolamine to phosphatidylcholine occurs in many tissues, including liver and brain. This conversion is folate-dependent and vitamin B_{12}–dependent.

The acetyl group used for acetylcholine synthesis is derived principally from glucose oxidation to pyruvate and decarboxylation of pyruvate to form acetyl-CoA via the pyruvate dehydrogenase reaction. This is because neuronal tissues have only a limited capacity to oxidize fatty acids to acetyl-CoA, so glucose oxidation is the major source of acetyl groups. Pyruvate dehydrogenase is found only in mitochondria. The acetyl group is probably transported to the cytoplasm as part of citrate, which is then cleaved in the cytosol to form acetyl-CoA and oxaloacetate.

2.   INACTIVATION OF ACETYLCHOLINE

Acetylcholine is inactivated by acetylcholinesterase, which is a serine esterase that forms a covalent bond with the acetyl group. The enzyme is inhibited by a wide range of compounds (pharmacologic agents and neurotoxins) that form a covalent bond with this reactive serine group. Neurotoxins such as Sarin (the gas used in Japanese subways by a terrorist group) and the nerve gas in the movie *The Rock* work through this mechanism. Acetylcholine is the major neurotransmitter at the neuromuscular junctions; inability to inactivate this molecule leads to constant activation of the nerve–muscle synapses, a condition that leads to varying degrees of paralysis.

F.   Glutamate and γ-Aminobutyric Acid
1.   SYNTHESIS OF GLUTAMATE

Glutamate functions as an excitatory neurotransmitter within the central nervous system, leading to the depolarization of neurons. Within nerve terminals, glutamate is generally synthesized de novo from glucose rather than taken up from the blood because its plasma concentration is low and it does not readily cross the blood–brain barrier.

Glutamate is synthesized primarily from the TCA cycle intermediate α-ketoglutarate (Fig. 48.10). This process can occur via either of two routes. The first is via the enzyme glutamate dehydrogenase, which reduces α-ketoglutarate to glutamate, thereby incorporating free ammonia into the carbon backbone. The ammonia pool is provided by amino acid/neurotransmitter degradation or by diffusion of ammonia across the blood–brain barrier. The second route is through transamination reactions

The supply of choline in the brain can become rate-limiting for acetylcholine synthesis, and supplementation of the diet with lecithin (phosphatidylcholine) has been used to increase brain acetylcholine in patients suffering from tardive dyskinesia (often persistent involuntary movements of the facial muscles and tongue). The neonate has a very high demand for choline, for both brain lipid synthesis (phosphatidylcholine and sphingomyelin) and acetylcholine biosynthesis. High levels of phosphatidylcholine in maternal milk and a high activity of a high-affinity transport system through the blood–brain barrier for choline in the neonate help to maintain brain choline concentrations. The fetus also has a high demand for choline, and there is a high-affinity transport system for choline across the placenta. The choline is derived from maternal stores, maternal diet, and synthesis primarily in the maternal liver. Because choline synthesis is dependent on folate and vitamin B_{12}, the high fetal demand may contribute to the increased maternal requirement for both vitamins during pregnancy.

An inherited pyruvate dehydrogenase deficiency, a thiamine deficiency, or hypoxia deprives the brain of a source of acetyl-CoA for acetylcholine synthesis as well as a source of acetyl-CoA for adenosine triphosphate (ATP) generation from the TCA cycle.

FIG. 48.10. Synthesis of glutamate and GABA and the GABA shunt. *α-KG*, α-ketoglutarate; *GDH*, glutamate dehydrogenase; *PLP*, pyridoxal phosphate.

in which an amino group is transferred from other amino acids to α-ketoglutarate to form glutamate. Glutamate also can be synthesized from glutamine, using glutaminase. The glutamine is derived from glial cells as described in Section III.F.2.

Like other neurotransmitters, glutamate is stored in vesicles, and its release is Ca^{2+}-dependent. It is removed from the synaptic cleft by high-affinity uptake systems in nerve terminals and glial cells.

2. γ-AMINOBUTYRIC ACID

GABA is the major inhibitory neurotransmitter in the central nervous system. Its functional significance is far-reaching, and altered GABAergic function plays a role in many neurologic and psychiatric disorders.

GABA is synthesized by the decarboxylation of glutamate (see Fig. 48.10) in a single step catalyzed by the enzyme glutamic acid decarboxylase (GAD). GABA is recycled in the central nervous system by a series of reactions called the *GABA shunt*, which conserves glutamate and GABA (see Fig. 48.10).

Much of the uptake of GABA occurs in glial cells. The GABA shunt in glial cells produces glutamate, which is converted to glutamine and transported out of the glial cells to neurons, where it is converted back to glutamate. Glutamine thus serves as a transporter of glutamate between cells in the CNS (see Chapter 42). Glial cells lack GAD and cannot synthesize GABA.

Tiagabine is a drug that inhibits the reuptake of GABA from the synapse, and it has been used to treat epilepsy as well as other convulsant disorders. Because GABA is an inhibitory neurotransmitter in the brain, its prolonged presence can block neurotransmission by other agents, thereby reducing the frequency of convulsions.

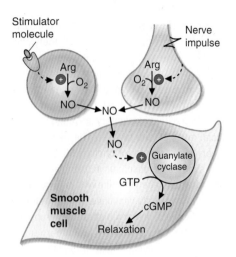

FIG. 48.11. Action of nitric oxide (NO) in vasodilation. The synthesis of NO occurs in response to a stimulator binding to a receptor on some cells or to a nerve impulse in neurons. NO enters smooth muscle cells, stimulating guanylate cyclase to produce cGMP, which causes smooth muscle cell relaxation. When the smooth muscle cells relax, blood vessels dilate.

FIG. 48.12. NO as a retrograde messenger. Cell A releases a neurotransmitter, which stimulates cell C to produce NO. NO, being a gas, can diffuse back and regulate cell A's production and release of neurotransmitters. NO can also diffuse to cell B and stimulate cell B to produce a different neurotransmitter to elicit a response from cell D. *NT*, neurotransmitter.

G. Other Amino Acid Neurotransmitters

1. ASPARTATE

Aspartate, like glutamate, is an excitatory neurotransmitter, but it functions in far fewer pathways. It is synthesized from the TCA cycle intermediate oxaloacetate via transamination reactions. Like glutamate synthesis, aspartate synthesis uses oxaloacetate that must be replaced through anaplerotic reactions. Aspartate cannot pass through the blood–brain barrier.

2. GLYCINE

Glycine is the major inhibitory neurotransmitter in the spinal cord. Most of the glycine in neurons is synthesized de novo within the nerve terminal from serine by the enzyme serine hydroxymethyltransferase, which requires folic acid. Serine, in turn, is synthesized from the intermediate 3-phosphoglycerate in the glycolytic pathway. The action of glycine is probably terminated via uptake by a high-affinity transporter.

3. CONVERSION OF ARGININE TO NITRIC OXIDE

Nitric oxide (NO) is a biologic messenger in a variety of physiologic responses, including vasodilation, neurotransmission, and the ability of the immune system to kill tumor cells and parasites. NO is synthesized from arginine in a reaction catalyzed by NO synthase (see Fig. 24.10).

NO synthase exists as tissue-specific forms of two families of enzymes. The form present in macrophages is responsible for overproduction of NO, leading to its cytotoxic actions on parasites and tumor cells. The enzyme present in nervous tissue, vascular endothelium, platelets, and other tissues is responsible for the physiologic responses to NO such as vasodilation and neural transmission. In target cells, NO activates a soluble guanylate cyclase, which results in increased cellular levels of cGMP (3′,5′-cyclic GMP) (Fig. 48.11). In smooth muscle cells, cGMP, like cAMP, activates one or more protein kinases, which are responsible for the relaxation of smooth muscle and the subsequent dilation of vessels. NO stimulates penile erection by acting as a neurotransmitter, stimulating smooth muscle relaxation that permits the corpus cavernosum to fill with blood. Nitric oxide can readily cross cell membranes because it is a gas. As a result, its effect may not necessarily be limited to the neuron that synthesizes it (Fig. 48.12). There is ample evidence that NO may function as a retrograde messenger that can influence neurotransmitter release from the presynaptic terminal after diffusing from the postsynaptic neuron (where it is synthesized). There is also evidence supporting retrograde messenger roles for both arachidonic acid and carbon monoxide in the CNS.

IV. METABOLIC ENCEPHALOPATHIES AND NEUROPATHIES

The brain has an absolute dependence on the blood for its supply of glucose and oxygen. It uses approximately 20% of the oxygen supply of the body. During the developmental period and during prolonged fasting, ketone bodies can be used as a fuel, but they cannot totally substitute for glucose. Glucose is converted to pyruvate in glycolysis, and the pyruvate is oxidized in the TCA cycle. Anaerobic glycolysis, with a yield of two molecules of ATP per molecule of glucose, cannot sustain the ATP requirement of the brain, which can be provided only by the complete oxidation of glucose to CO_2, which yields approximately 32 ATP per glucose. However, during periods of mild hypoglycemia or mild hypoxia, decreased neurotransmitter synthesis contributes as much, if not more, to the development of symptoms as does an absolute deficiency of ATP for energy needs.

A. Hypoglycemic Encephalopathy

Hypoglycemia is sometimes encountered in medical conditions such as malignancies producing insulin, insulin-like growth factors, or chronic alcoholism. Early clinical signs in hypoglycemia reflect the appearance of physiologic protective mechanisms initiated by hypothalamic sensory nuclei such as sweating, palpitations, anxiety, and hunger. If these symptoms are ignored, they proceed to a more serious CNS disorder, progressing through confusion and lethargy to seizures and eventually coma. Prolonged hypoglycemia can lead to irreversible brain damage.

During the progression of hypoglycemic encephalopathy, as blood glucose falls lower than 2.5 mM (45 mg/dL), the brain attempts to use internal substrates such as glutamate and TCA cycle intermediates as fuels. Because the pool size of these substrates is quite small, they are quickly depleted. If blood glucose levels continue to fall lower than 1 mM (18 mg/dL), ATP levels become depleted.

As the blood glucose drops from 2.5 to 2.0 mM (45 to 36 mg/dL, before electro-encephalographic [EEG] changes are observed), the symptoms appear to arise from decreased synthesis of neurotransmitters in particular regions of the brain rather than a global energy deficit. Figure 48.13 summarizes the relationship between the oxidation of glucose in glycolysis and the provision of precursors for the synthesis of neurotransmitters in different types of neurons.

As hypoglycemia progresses lower than 1 mM (18 mg/dL) and high-energy phosphate levels are depleted, the EEG becomes isoelectric, and neuronal cell death ensues. As is the case in some other metabolic encephalopathies, cell death is not global in distribution; rather, certain brain structures, in particular hippocampal and cortical structures, are selectively vulnerable to hypoglycemic insult. Pathophysiologic mechanisms responsible for neuronal cell death in hypoglycemia include the involvement of glutamate excitotoxicity. Glutamate excitotoxicity occurs when the cellular energy reserves are depleted. The failure of the energy-dependent reuptake pumps results in a buildup of glutamate in the synaptic cleft and overstimulation of the postsynaptic glutamate receptors. The prolonged glutamate receptor activation leads to prolonged opening of the receptor ion channel and the influx of lethal amounts of Ca^{2+} ion, which can activate cytotoxic intracellular pathways in the postsynaptic neuron.

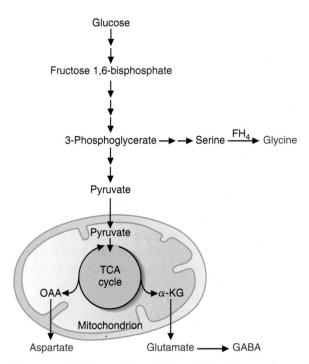

FIG. 48.13. Glucose metabolism leading to the synthesis of the neurotransmitters glycine, aspartate, glutamate, and GABA. As blood glucose levels drop and brain glucose levels diminish, synthesis of these neurotransmitters may be compromised. *α-KG*, α-ketoglutarate.

B. Hypoxic Encephalopathy

Experimental studies with human volunteers show that cerebral energy metabolism remains normal when mild to moderate hypoxia (partial pressure of oxygen, or $PaO_2 = 25$ to 40 mm Hg) results in severe cognitive dysfunction. The diminished cognitive function is believed to result from impaired neurotransmitter synthesis. In mild hypoxia, cerebral blood flow increases to maintain oxygen delivery to the brain. In addition, anaerobic glycolysis is accelerated, resulting in maintenance of ATP levels. This occurs, however, at the expense of an increase of lactate production and a fall of pH. Acute hypoxia ($PaO_2 \leq 20$ mm Hg) generally results in a coma.

Hypoxia can result from insufficient oxygen reaching the blood (e.g., at high altitudes), severe anemia (e.g., iron deficiency), or a direct insult to the oxygen-utilizing capacity of the brain (e.g., cyanide poisoning). All forms of hypoxia result in diminished neurotransmitter synthesis. Inhibition of pyruvate dehydrogenase diminishes acetylcholine synthesis, which is acutely sensitive to hypoxia. Glutamate and GABA synthesis, which depend on a functioning TCA cycle, are decreased as a result of elevated NADH levels, which inhibit TCA cycle enzymes. NADH levels are increased when oxygen is unavailable to accept electrons from the electron-transport chain and NADH cannot be readily converted back into NAD^+. Even the synthesis of catecholamine neurotransmitters may be decreased because the hydroxylase reactions require O_2.

C. Relationship between Glutamate Synthesis and the Anaplerotic Pathways of Pyruvate Carboxylase and Methylmalonyl-CoA Mutase

Synthesis of glutamate removes α-ketoglutarate from the TCA cycle, thereby decreasing the regeneration of oxaloacetate in the TCA cycle. Because oxaloacetate is necessary for the oxidation of acetyl-CoA, oxaloacetate must be replaced by anaplerotic reactions. There are two major types of anaplerotic reactions: (1) pyruvate carboxylase and (2) the degradative pathway of the branched-chain amino acids, valine and isoleucine, which contribute succinyl-CoA to the TCA cycle. This pathway uses vitamin B_{12} (but not folate) in the reaction catalyzed by methylmalonyl-CoA mutase.

V. LIPID SYNTHESIS IN THE BRAIN AND PERIPHERAL NERVOUS SYSTEM

Several features of lipid synthesis and degradation in the nervous system distinguish it from most other tissues. The first is that the portion of the neuronal cell membrane involved in synaptic transmission has a unique role and a unique composition. At the presynaptic terminal, the lipid composition changes rapidly as storage vesicles containing the neurotransmitter fuse with the cell membrane and release their contents. Portions of the membrane are also lost as endocytotic vesicles. On the postsynaptic terminal, the membrane contains the receptors for the neurotransmitter as well as a high concentration of membrane signaling components such as phosphatidylinositol. A second important feature of brain lipid metabolism is that the blood–brain barrier restricts the entry of nonessential fatty acids, such as palmitate, that are released from adipose tissue or present in the diet. Conversely, essential fatty acids are taken up by the brain. Because of these considerations, the brain is constantly synthesizing those lipids (cholesterol, fatty acids, glycosphingolipids, and phospholipids) which it needs for various neurologic functions. Neuronal signaling also requires that nonneuronal glial cells synthesize myelin, a multilayered membrane that surrounds the axons of many neurons. Myelin is lipid-rich and has a different lipid composition than the neuronal membranes. The white matter in the brain contains significantly more myelin than the gray matter; it is the presence of myelin sheaths that is responsible for the characteristic color differences that exist between the two types of brain tissue.

A. Brain Lipid Synthesis and Oxidation

Because the blood–brain barrier significantly inhibits the entry of certain fatty acids and lipids into the CNS, virtually all lipids found there must be synthesized within the CNS. The exceptions are the essential fatty acids (linoleic and linolenic acid) that do enter the brain where they are elongated or further desaturated. The uptake of fatty acids into the CNS is insufficient to meet the energy demands of the CNS—hence the requirement for aerobic glucose metabolism. Thus, cholesterol, glycerol, sphingolipids, glycosphingolipids, and cerebrosides are all synthesized using pathways discussed previously in this text. Of particular note is that very long-chain fatty acids are synthesized in the brain, where they play a major role in myelin formation.

Oxidation and turnover of brain lipids occurs as described previously (see Chapter 23). Peroxisomal fatty acid oxidation is important in the brain because the brain contains very long-chain fatty acids and phytanic acid (from the diet), both of which are oxidized in the peroxisomes by α-oxidation. Thus, disorders that affect peroxisome biogenesis (such as Refsum disease) severely affect brain cells because of the inability to metabolize both branched-chain and very long-chain fatty acids. If there is a disorder in which the degradation of glycosphingolipids or mucopolysaccharides is impaired, lysosomes in brain cells become engorged with partially digested glycolipids, leading to varying degrees of neurologic dysfunction.

B. Myelin Synthesis

A rapid rate of nerve conduction in the peripheral and central motor nerves depends on the formation of myelin, a multilayered lipid and protein structure that is formed from the plasma membrane of glial cells. In the peripheral nervous system, the Schwann cell is responsible for myelinating one portion of an axon of one nerve cell. The Schwann cell does this by wrapping itself around the axon multiple times so that a multilayered sheath of membrane surrounds the axon. In the central nervous system, the oligodendrocyte is responsible for myelination. Unlike the Schwann cell, oligodendrocytes can myelinate portions of numerous axons (up to 40) and do so by extending a thin process that wraps around the axon multiple times. Thus, CNS axons are surrounded only by the membranes of oligodendrocytes, whereas axons in the PNS are surrounded by the entire Schwann cell. A generalized view of myelination is depicted in Figure 48.14. To maintain the myelin structure, the oligodendrocyte synthesizes four times its own weight in lipids per day.

1. MYELIN LIPIDS

As the plasma membrane of the glial cell is converted into myelin, the lipid composition of the brain changes (Table 48.2). The lipid-to-protein ratio is greatly increased, as is the content of sphingolipids. The myelin is a tightly packed structure, and there are significant hydrophobic interactions between the lipids and proteins to allow this to occur. Cerebrosides constitute approximately 16% of total myelin lipid and are almost completely absent from other cell-type membrane lipids. The predominant cerebroside, galactosylcerebroside, has a single sugar attached to the hydroxyl group of the sphingosine. In contrast, sphingomyelin, which one might guess is the predominant lipid of myelin, is present in roughly the same low concentration in all membranes. Galactocerebrosides pack more tightly together than phosphatidylcholine; the sugar, although polar, carries no positively charged amino group or negatively charged phosphate. The brain synthesizes very long-chain fatty acids (>20 carbons long); these long uncharged side chains develop strong hydrophobic associations, allowing close packing of the myelin sheath. The high cholesterol content of the membrane also contributes to the tight packing, although the myelin proteins are also required to complete the tightness of the packing process.

FIG. 48.14. A composite diagram indicating a Schwann cell that has wrapped around a portion of an axon forming the myelin sheath. The expansion represents a portion of the myelin sheath. CNS myelin is shown, although it is similar to PNS myelin except that Po replaces proteolipid protein. Recall that there are multiple layers of membrane surrounding the axon; proteolipid protein protrudes into the extracellular space and aids in compaction of the membranes through hydrophobic interactions. MBPs help to stabilize the structure from within the membrane.

2. MYELIN STRUCTURAL PROTEINS

The layers of myelin are held together by protein–lipid and protein–protein interactions, and any disruption can lead to demyelination of the membrane (see Biochemical Comments). Although numerous proteins are found in both the CNS and PNS, only the major proteins are discussed here. The major proteins in the CNS and PNS are different. In the CNS, two proteins constitute between 60% and 80% of the total proteins—proteolipid protein and myelin basic proteins (MBPs). The proteolipid protein is a very hydrophobic protein that forms large aggregates in aqueous solution and is relatively resistant to proteolysis. Its molecular weight, based on sequence analysis, is 30,000 Da. Proteolipid protein is highly conserved in sequence among species. Its role is thought to be one of promoting the formation and stabilization of the multilayered myelin structure.

Table 48.2   Protein and Lipid Composition of CNS Myelin and Human Brain

Substance[a]	Myelin	White Matter	Gray Matter
Protein	30.0	39.0	55.3
Lipid	70.0	54.9	32.7
Cholesterol	27.7	27.5	22.0
Cerebroside	22.7	19.8	5.4
Sulfatide	3.8	5.4	1.7
Total galactolipid	27.5	26.4	7.3
Ethanolamine phosphatide	15.6	14.9	22.7
Phosphatidylcholine	11.2	12.8	26.7
Sphingomyelin	7.9	7.7	6.9
Phosphatidylserine	4.8	7.9	8.7
Phosphatidylinositol	0.6	0.9	2.7
Plasmalogen	12.3	11.2	8.8
Total phospholipids	43.1	45.9	69.5

[a]Protein and lipid figures in percentage dry weight; all others in percentage total lipid weight.
Data from Norton W. In: Siegel GJ, Albers RW, Agranoff BW, Katzman R, eds. *Basic Neurochemistry.* 3rd ed. Boston, MA: Little, Brown and Company; 1981:77.

The MBPs are a family of proteins. Unlike proteolipid protein, MBPs are easily extracted from the membrane and are soluble in aqueous solution. The major MBP has no tertiary structure and has a molecular weight of 15,000 Da. MBP is located on the cytoplasmic face of myelin membranes. Antibodies directed against MBPs elicit experimental allergic encephalomyelitis (EAE), which has become a model system for understanding multiple sclerosis—a demyelinating disease. A model of how proteolipid protein and MBPs aid in stabilizing myelin is shown in Figure 48.14.

In the PNS, the major myelin protein is Po, a glycoprotein that accounts for >50% of the PNS myelin protein content. The molecular weight of Po is 30,000 Da, the same as proteolipid protein. Po is thought to play a similar structural role in maintaining myelin structure as proteolipid protein does in the CNS. Myelin basic proteins are also found in the PNS, with some similarities and differences to the MBPs found in the CNS. The major PNS-specific MBP has been designated as P2.

CLINICAL COMMENTS

Katie Colamin. Catecholamines affect nearly every tissue and organ in the body. Their integrated release from nerve endings of the sympathetic (adrenergic) nervous system plays a critical role in the reflex responses we make to sudden changes in our internal and external environment. For example, under stress, catecholamines appropriately increase heart rate, blood pressure, myocardial (heart muscle) contractility, and conduction velocity of the heart.

Episodic, inappropriate secretion of catecholamines in supraphysiologic amounts, such as those occurs in patients with pheochromocytomas, like **Katie Colamin**, causes an often acute and alarming array of symptoms and signs of a hyperadrenergic state.

Most of the signs and symptoms related to catecholamine excess can be masked by phenoxybenzamine, a long-acting α_1- and α_2-adrenergic receptor antagonist, combined with a β_1- and β_2-adrenergic receptor blocker such as propranolol. Pharmacologic therapy alone is reserved for patients with inoperable pheochromocytomas (e.g., patients with malignant tumors with metastases and patients with severe heart disease). Because of the sudden, unpredictable, and sometimes life-threatening discharges of large amounts of catecholamines from these tumors, definitive therapy involves surgical resection of the neoplasm(s) after appropriate preoperative preparation of the patient with the agents mentioned previously. Katie's tumor was resected without intraoperative or postoperative complications. After surgery, she remained free of symptoms, and her blood pressure decreased to normal levels.

Evan Applebod. **Evan Applebod**, after stopping Redux, was placed on Prozac, an antidepressant that acts as a selective serotonin reuptake inhibitor (SSRI) but does not lead to increased synthesis or secretion of serotonin, as did dexfenfluramine in Redux. Thus, the mechanism of action of these two drugs is different, even if the end result (elevated levels of serotonin) is the same. Unfortunately, Prozac did not work as well for Mr. Applebod as did Redux, and he regained his 50 lb within 1 year after switching medications. Redux was withdrawn from the market by its manufacturer because of reports of heart valve abnormalities in a small percentage of patients who had taken either phen/fen (fenfluramine and phentermine) or Redux. Since then, the U.S. Food and Drug Administration (FDA) has banned the use of Redux for weight loss because of the undesirable side effects. Mr. Applebod now has several other options. Other medical treatments include orlistat, a partial inhibitor of dietary fatty acid absorption from the gastrointestinal tract; phentermine alone (described previously); and several medications used to treat other conditions, including diabetes, seizures, and depression, that also lead to weight loss. These latter agents are not FDA approved for weight loss, and thus Evan's physician did not want to try any more medications with him. Instead, the physician referred Evan for bariatric surgery.

BIOCHEMICAL COMMENTS

Demyelinating Diseases of the CNS. The importance of myelin in nerve transmission is underscored by the wide variety of demyelinating diseases, all of which lead to neurologic symptoms. The best known disease in this class is multiple sclerosis (MS). MS can be a progressive disease of the CNS in which demyelination of CNS neurons is the key anatomic and pathologic finding. The cause of MS has yet to be determined, although it is believed that an event occurs that triggers the formation of autoimmune antibodies directed against components of the nervous system. This event could be a bacterial or viral infection that stimulates the immune system to fight off the invaders. Unfortunately, this stimulus may also trigger the autoimmune response that leads to the antibody-mediated demyelinating process. The unusual geographic distribution of MS is of interest. Patients are concentrated in northern and southern latitudes, yet its incidence is almost nil at the equator. Clinical presentation of MS varies widely. Most commonly, it is a mild disease that has few or no obvious clinical manifestations. At the other end of the spectrum is a rapidly progressive and fatal disease. The most well-known presentation is the relapsing–remitting type. In this type, early in the course of the disease, the natural history is one of exacerbations followed by remission. Eventually, the CNS cannot repair the damage that has accumulated through the years, and remissions occur less and less frequently. Available treatments for MS target the relapsing–remitting type of disease.

The primary injury to the CNS in MS is the loss of myelin in the white matter, which interferes with nerve conduction along the demyelinated area (the insulator is lost). The CNS compensates by stimulating the oligodendrocyte to remyelinate the damaged axon, and when this occurs, remission is achieved. Often, remyelination leads to a slowing in conduction velocity because of a reduced myelin thickness (speed is proportional to myelin thickness) or a shortening of the internodal distances (the action potential has to be propagated more times). Eventually, when it becomes too difficult to remyelinate large areas of the CNS, the neuron adapts by upregulating and redistributing along its membrane ion pumps to allow nerve conductance along demyelinated axons. Eventually, this adaptation also fails and the disease progresses.

Treatment of MS is now based on blocking the action of the immune system. Because antibodies directed against cellular components appear to be responsible for the progression of the disease (regardless of how the autoantibodies were first generated), agents that interfere with immune responses have had various levels of success in keeping patients in remission for extended periods.

Other demyelinating diseases also exist, and their cause is much more straightforward. These are relatively rare disorders. In all of these diseases, there is no fully effective treatment for the patient. Inherited mutations in Po (the major PNS myelin protein) leads to a version of Charcot–Marie–Tooth polyneuropathy syndrome. The inheritance pattern for this disease is autosomal dominant, indicating that the expression of one mutated allele leads to expression of the disease. Mutations in proteolipid protein (the major myelin protein in the CNS) lead to Pelizaeus–Merzbacher disease and X-linked spastic paraplegia type 2 disease. These diseases display a wide range of phenotypes, from a lack of motor development and early death (most severe) to mild gait disturbances. The phenotype displayed depends on the precise location of the mutation within the protein. An altered function of either Po or proteolipid protein leads to demyelination and its subsequent clinical manifestations.

Key Concepts

- The nervous system consists of a variety of cell types with different functions.
  - Neurons transmit and receive signals from other neurons at synaptic junctions.
  - Astrocytes, found in the central nervous system, provide physical and nutritional support for the neurons.
  - Oligodendrocytes provide the myelin sheath that coats the axon, providing insulation for the electric signal that is propagated along the axon.
    - Myelin has a lipid composition that is distinct from that of cellular membranes.
    - A lack of myelin leads to demyelinating diseases as a result of impaired signal transmission across the axon.
  - Schwann cells are the supporting cells (and myelin-producing cells) of the peripheral nervous system.
  - Microglial cells destroy invading microorganisms and phagocytose cellular debris.
  - Ependymal cells line the cavities of the CNS and spinal cord.
- The brain is protected against blood-borne toxic agents by the blood–brain barrier.
  - Glucose, amino acids, vitamins, ketone bodies, and essential fatty acids (but not other fatty acids) can all be transported across the blood–brain barrier.
  - Proteins such as insulin can cross the blood–brain barrier by receptor-mediated transcytosis.
- Neurotransmitters are synthesized primarily from amino acids in the nervous system; others are derived from intermediates of glycolysis and the TCA cycle.
  - Neurotransmitters are synthesized in the cytoplasm of the presynaptic terminal, and then transported into storage vesicles for release upon receiving the appropriate signal.
  - Neurotransmitter action is terminated by reuptake into the presynaptic terminal or diffusion away from the synapse or by enzymatic inactivation.
  - Monoamine oxidase is a key enzyme for the inactivation of the catecholamines and serotonin.
- An encephalopathy will develop if the nervous system cannot generate sufficient ATP.
  - Hypoglycemic encephalopathy (lack of glucose to the brain)
  - Hypoxic encephalopathy (lack of oxygen to the brain)
- Diseases discussed in this chapter are summarized in Table 48.3.

Table 48.3 Diseases Discussed in Chapter 48

Disease or Disorder	Genetic or Environmental	Comments
Albinism	Genetic	A lack of melanoctye tyrosinase leads to the inability to produce Dopa, a required precursor to melanin production, such that pigment formation is inhibited.
Hypercholesterolemia	Both	Elevated cholesterol levels in the blood may be regulated by appropriate pharmacologic agents.
Multiple sclerosis	Environmental	An autoimmune induced loss of myelin sheath formation around neurons.
Pheochromocytoma	Environmental	Tumor of the adrenal gland leading to episodic and excessive epinephrine and norepinephrine release.
Facilitated glucose transporter protein type 1 deficiency syndrome	Genetic	Infantile seizures related to low glucose levels in the nervous system (low glucose in the cerebrospinal fluid).
Tyramine poisoning	Environmental	Tyramine, a compound found in aged cheeses, for example, is degraded by monoamine oxidase. In the presence of monoamine oxidase inhibitors, tyramine levels can accumulate triggering the release of high levels of norepinephrine, leading to a hypertensive crisis.
Depression	Both	Drugs used to elevate serotonin levels may alleviate depression and may also lead to appetite suppression
Appetite suppression	Both	A variety of drugs have been used to treat obesity, although many have side effects which need to be carefully monitored.

1. A patient with a tumor of the adrenal medulla experienced palpitations, excessive sweating, and hypertensive headaches. His urine contained increased amounts of vanillylmandelic acid. His symptoms are probably caused by an overproduction of which of the following?

    A. Acetylcholine
    B. Norepinephrine and epinephrine
    C. Dopa and serotonin
    D. Histamine
    E. Melatonin

2. The two lipids found in highest concentration in myelin are which of the following?

    A. Cholesterol and cerebrosides such as galactosylceramide
    B. Cholesterol and phosphatidylcholine
    C. Galactosylceramide sulfatide and sphingomyelin
    D. Plasmalogens and sphingomyelin
    E. Triacylglycerols and lecithin

3. Myelin basic protein can best be described by which of the following?

    A. It is synthesized in Schwann cells, but not in oligodendrocytes.
    B. It is a transmembrane protein found only in peripheral myelin.
    C. It attaches the two extracellular leaflets together in central myelin.
    D. It contains basic amino acid residues that bind the negatively charged extracellular sides of the myelin membrane together.

    E. It contains lysine and arginine residues that binds the negatively charged intracellular sides of the myelin membrane together.

4. A patient presented with dysmorphia and cerebellar degeneration. Analysis of his blood indicated elevated levels of phytanic acid and very long-chain fatty acids, but no elevation of palmitate. His symptoms are consistent with a defect in an enzyme involved in which of the following?

    A. α-Oxidation
    B. Mitochondrial β-oxidation
    C. Transport of enzymes into lysosomes
    D. Degradation of mucopolysaccharides
    E. Elongation of fatty acids

5. One of the presenting symptoms of vitamin B_6 deficiency is dementia. This may result from an inability to synthesize serotonin, norepinephrine, histamine, and γ-aminobutyric acid (GABA) from their respective amino acid precursors. This is because vitamin B_6 is required for which type of reaction?

    A. Hydroxylation
    B. Transamination
    C. Deamination
    D. Decarboxylation
    E. Oxidation

49 The Extracellular Matrix and Connective Tissue

Many of the cells in tissues are embedded in an **extracellular matrix** that fills the spaces between cells and binds cells and tissue together. In so doing, the extracellular matrix aids in determining the shape of tissues as well as the nature of the partitioning between tissue types. In the skin, loose connective tissue beneath epithelial cell layers consists of an extracellular matrix in which fibroblasts, blood vessels, and other components are distributed (Fig. 49.1). Other types of connective tissue, such as tendon and cartilage, consist largely of extracellular matrix, which is principally responsible for their structure and function. This matrix also forms the sheetlike **basal laminae**, or basement membranes, on which layers of epithelial cells rest, and which act as supportive tissue for muscle cells, adipose cells, and peripheral nerves.

Basic components of the extracellular matrix include fibrous structural proteins, such as **collagens**, **proteoglycans** containing long glycosaminoglycan chains attached to a protein backbone, and **adhesion proteins** linking components of the matrix to each other and to cells.

These **fibrous structural proteins** are composed of repeating elements that form a linear structure. **Collagens**, **elastin**, and **laminin** are the principal structural proteins of connective tissue.

Proteoglycans consist of a core protein covalently attached to many long, linear chains of **glycosaminoglycans**, which contain repeating disaccharide units. The repeating disaccharides usually contain a **hexosamine** and a **uronic acid**, and these sugars are frequently **sulfated**. Synthesis of the proteoglycans starts with the attachment of a sugar to a serine, threonine, or asparagine residue of the protein. Additional sugars, donated by **UDP-sugar precursors**, add sequentially to the nonreducing end of the molecule.

Proteoglycans, such as glycoproteins and glycolipids, are **synthesized in the endoplasmic reticulum (ER)** and the **Golgi complex**. The glycosaminoglycan chains of proteoglycans are **degraded** by **lysosomal enzymes** that cleave one sugar at a time from the nonreducing end of the chain. An inability to degrade proteoglycans leads to a set of diseases known as the **mucopolysaccharidoses**.

Adhesion proteins, such as **fibronectin** and **laminin**, are extracellular glycoproteins that contain separate distinct binding domains for proteoglycans, collagen, and fibrin. These domains allow these adhesion proteins to bind the various components of the extracellular matrix. They also contain specific binding domains for specific cell surface receptors known as **integrins**. These integrins bind to **fibronectin** on the external surface, span the plasma membrane of cells, and adhere to proteins, which in turn bind to the intracellular **actin** filaments of the **cytoskeleton**. Integrins also provide a mechanism for signaling between cells via both internal signals and through signals generated via the extracellular matrix.

Cell movement within the extracellular matrix requires remodeling of the various components of the matrix. This is accomplished by a variety

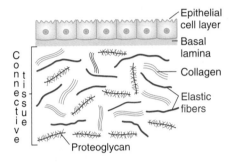

FIG. 49.1. An overview of connective tissue extracellular matrix. Supporting the epithelial cell layer is a basal lamina, beneath which are collagen, elastic fibers, and proteoglycans. The cell types present in connective tissue, such as fibroblasts and macrophages, have been removed from the diagram for clarity.

of **matrix metalloproteinases (MMPs)** *and regulators of the MMPs,* **tissue inhibitors of matrix metalloproteinases (TIMPs)**. *Dysregulation of this delicate balance of the regulators of cell movement allows cancer cells to travel to other parts of the body (***metastasize***) as well as to spread locally to contiguous tissues.*

THE WAITING ROOM

Sis Lupus (first introduced in Chapter 14) noted a moderate reduction in pain and swelling in the joints of her fingers while she was taking her immunosuppressant medication. At her next checkup, her rheumatologist described to Sis the underlying inflammatory tissue changes that her systemic lupus erythematosus (SLE) was causing in the joint tissues.

Ann Sulin complained of a declining appetite for food as well as severe weakness and fatigue. The reduction in her kidneys' ability to maintain normal daily total urinary net acid excretion contributed to her worsening metabolic acidosis. This, plus her declining ability to excrete nitrogenous waste products such as creatinine and urea into her urine ("azotemia") were responsible for many of her symptoms. Her serum creatinine level was rising steadily. As it approached a level of 5 mg/dL, she developed a litany of complaints caused by the multisystem dysfunction associated with her worsening metabolic acidosis and retention of nitrogenous waste products ("uremia"). Her physicians discussed the need to consider peritoneal dialysis or hemodialysis.

I.   COMPOSITION OF THE EXTRACELLULAR MATRIX
A. Fibrous Proteins
1.   COLLAGEN

Collagen, a family of fibrous proteins, is produced by a variety of cell types but principally by fibroblasts (cells found in interstitial connective tissue), muscle cells, and epithelial cells. Type I collagen, *collagen(I)*, the most abundant protein in mammals, is a fibrous protein that is the major component of connective tissue. It is found in the extracellular matrix (ECM) of loose connective tissue, bone, tendons, skin, blood vessels, and the cornea of the eye. Collagen(I) contains approximately 33% glycine and 21% proline and hydroxyproline. Hydroxyproline is an amino acid produced by posttranslational modification of peptidyl proline residues.

Procollagen(I), the precursor of collagen(I), is a triple helix composed of three polypeptide (pro-α) chains that are twisted around each other, forming a ropelike structure. Polymerization of collagen(I) molecules forms collagen fibrils, which provide great tensile strength to connective tissues (Fig. 49.2). The individual polypeptide chains each contain approximately 1,000 amino acid residues. The three polypeptide chains of the triple helix are linked by interchain hydrogen bonds. Each turn of the triple helix contains three amino acid residues, such that every third amino acid is in close contact with the other two strands in the center of the structure. Only glycine, which lacks a side chain, can fit in this position, and indeed, every third amino acid residue of collagen is glycine. Thus, collagen is a polymer of (Gly-X-Y) repeats, where Y is frequently proline or hydroxyproline and X is any other amino acid found in collagen.

FIG. 49.2.   The triple helix of collagen.

FIG. 49.3. Hydroxylation of proline and lysine residues in collagen. Proline and lysine residues within the collagen chains are hydroxylated by reactions that require vitamin C.

Procollagen(I) is an example of a protein that undergoes extensive posttranslational modifications. Hydroxylation reactions produce hydroxyproline residues from proline residues and hydroxylysine from lysine residues. These reactions occur after the protein has been synthesized (Fig. 49.3) and require vitamin C (ascorbic acid) as a cofactor of the enzymes prolyl hydroxylase and lysyl hydroxylase. Hydroxyproline residues are involved in hydrogen bond formation that helps to stabilize the triple helix, whereas hydroxylysine residues are the sites of attachment of disaccharide moieties (galactose–glucose). The role of carbohydrates in collagen structure is still controversial. In the absence of vitamin C (*scurvy*), the melting temperature of collagen drops from 42°C to 24°C because of the loss of interstrand hydrogen bond formation, which is in turn caused by the lack of hydroxyproline residues.

The side chains of lysine residues also may be oxidized to form the aldehyde—allysine. These aldehyde residues produce covalent cross-links between collagen molecules (Fig. 49.4). An allysine residue on one collagen molecule reacts with the amino group of a lysine residue on another molecule, forming a covalent Schiff base that is converted to more stable covalent cross-links. Aldol condensation also may occur between two allysine residues, which forms the structure lysinonorleucine.

i.   Types of Collagen

At least 28 different types of collagen have been characterized (Table 49.1). Although each type of collagen is found only in particular locations in the body, more than one type may be present in the ECM at a given location. The various types of collagen can be classified as fibril-forming (types I, II, III, V, XI, XXIV, and XXVII), network-forming (types IV, VIII, and X), those that associate with fibril surfaces (types IX, XII, XIV, XXI, and XXII), those that are transmembrane proteins (types XIII, XVII, XXIII, and XXV), endostatin-forming (types XV and XVIII), and those that form periodic beaded filaments (type VI).

All collagens contain three polypeptide chains with at least one stretch of triple helix. The non–triple helical domains can be short (as in the fibril-forming

Lysinonorleucine

FIG. 49.4. Formation of cross-links in collagen. **A.** Lysine residues are oxidized to allysine (an aldehyde). Allysine may react with an unmodified lysine residue to form a Schiff base (**B**), or two allysine residues may undergo an aldol condensation (**C**).

Table 49.1   Types of Collagen

Collagen Type	Gene	Structural Details	Localization
I	Col1A1–Col1A2	Fibrils	Skin, tendon, bone, cornea
II	Col2A1	Fibrils	Cartilage, vitreous humor
III	Col3A1	Fibrils	Skin, muscle, associates with type I collagen
IV	Col4A1–Col4A6	Nonfibrillar, mesh collagen	All basal laminae (basement membranes)
V	Col5A1–Col5A3	Small fibers, N-terminal globular domains	Associates with type I collagen in most interstitial tissues
VI	Col6A1–Col6A3	Microfibrils, with both N- and C-terminal globular domains	Associates with type I collagen in most interstitial tissues
VII	Col7A1	An anchoring collagen	Epithelial cells; dermal–epidermal junction
VIII	Col8A1–Col8A2	Nonfibrillar, mesh collagen	Cornea, some endothelial cells
IX	Col9A1–Col9A3	FACIT; N-terminal globular domain	Associates with type II collagen in cartilage and vitreous humor
X	Col10A1	Nonfibrillar, mesh collagen, with C-terminal globular domain	Growth plate, hypertrophic and mineralizing cartilage
XI	Col11A1–Col11A3	Small fibers	Cartilage, vitreous humor
XII	Col12A1	FACIT	Interacts with types I and II collagen in soft tissues
XIII	Col13A1	Transmembrane collagen	Cell surfaces, epithelial cells
XIV	Col14A1	FACIT	Soft tissue
XV	Col15A1	Endostatin-forming collagen	Endothelial cells
XVI	Col16A1	Other	Ubiquitous
XVII	Col17A1	Transmembrane collagen	Epidermal cell surface
XVIII	Col18A1	Endostatin forming	Endothelial cells
XIX	Col19A1	Other	Ubiquitous
XXI	Col21A1	FACIT	Heart, skeletal muscle, stomach, kidney, placenta
XXII	Col22A1	FACIT	Tissue junctions
XXIII	Col23A1	Transmembrane collagen	Lung, skin, cornea, brain, kidney, tendon
XXIV	Col24A1	Fibrils	Bone
XXV	Col25A1	Transmembrane collagen	Brain
XXVI	EMID2	Other	Mesenchymal cells
XXVII	Col27A1	Fibrils	Stomach, lung, gonads, skin, tooth
XXVIII	Col28A1	Other	Nervous system

See the text for descriptions of the differences in types of collagen. Type XX collagen is not present in humans. FACIT, fibril-associated collagens with interrupted triple helices.

collagens), or they can be rather large, such that the triple helix is actually a minor component of the overall structure (examples are collagen types XII and XIV). The fibril-associated collagens with interrupted triple helices (FACITs, collagen types IX, XII, and XIV) collagen types associate with fibrillar collagens, without themselves forming fibers. The endostatin-forming collagens are cleaved at their C-terminus to form endostatin, an inhibitor of angiogenesis. The network-forming collagens (type IV) form a meshlike structure because of large (approximately 230 amino acids) noncollagenous domains at the carboxy terminus (Fig. 49.5). And finally, several collagen types are actually transmembrane proteins (XIII, XVII, XXIII, and XXV) found on epithelial or epidermal cell surfaces, which play a role in several cellular processes, including adhesion of components of the ECM to cells embedded within it. Type XXV collagen has been associated with the neuronal plaques, which develop during Alzheimer disease.

Types I, II, and III collagens form fibrils that assemble into large insoluble fibers. The fibrils (see in the following text) are strengthened through covalent

A. Protomer

Carboxy terminus

Amino
terminus

B. Dimer

Carboxy-terminal hexamer
(NC1 domain)

C. Type IV collagen tetramer

Aggregation
at amino termini
(7S domain)

D. Suprastructure

NC1 hexamer

7S domain

FIG. 49.5. Type IV collagen contains a globular carboxy-terminal domain (**A**), which forms tropocollagen dimers (hexamers of collagen, **B**). Four dimers associate at the amino-terminal domains to form a 7S domain (**C**), and the tetramers form a lattice (**D**), which provides structural support to the basal lamina.

cross-links between lysine residues on adjacent fibrils. The arrangement of the fibrils gives individual tissues their distinct characteristics. Tendons, which attach muscles to bones, contain collagen fibrils aligned parallel to the long axis of the tendon, thus giving the tendon tremendous tensile strength.

The types of collagen that do not form fibrils perform a series of distinct roles. Fibril-associated collagens bind to the surface of collagen fibrils and link them to other matrix-forming components. The transmembrane collagens form anchoring fibrils that link components of the extracellular matrix to underlying connective tissue. The network-forming collagens (type IV) form a flexible collagen that is part of the basement membrane and basal lamina that surround many cells.

ii. Synthesis and Secretion of Collagen

Collagen is synthesized within the endoplasmic reticulum as a precursor known as *preprocollagen*. The presequence acts as the signal sequence for the protein and is

 Endostatins block angiogenesis (new blood vessel formation) by inhibiting endothelial cell migration. Because endothelial cell migration and proliferation are required to form new blood vessels, inhibiting this action blocks angiogenesis. Tumor growth is dependent on a blood supply, inhibiting angiogenesis can reduce tumor cell proliferation.

 One type of osteogenesis imperfecta (OI) is caused by a mutation in a gene that codes for collagen. The phenotype of affected individuals varies greatly, depending on the location and type of mutation. See the Biochemical Comments for more information concerning this type of OI.

Table 49.2   Steps in Collagen Biosynthesis

Location	Process
Rough endoplasmic reticulum	Synthesis of preprocollagen; insertion of the procollagen molecule into the lumen of the ER
Lumen of ER	Hydroxylation of proline and lysine residues; glycosylation of selected hydroxylysine residues
Lumen of ER and Golgi apparatus	Self-assembly of the tropocollagen molecule, initiated by disulfide bond formation in the carboxy-terminal extensions; triple helix formation
Secretory vesicle	Procollagen prepared for secretion from cell
Extracellular	Cleavage of the propeptides, removing the amino- and carboxy-terminal extensions, and self-assembly of the collagen molecules into fibrils and then fibers

ER, endoplasmic reticulum.

cleaved, forming procollagen within the endoplasmic reticulum. From there, it is transported to the Golgi apparatus (Table 49.2). Three procollagen molecules associate through formation of interstrand and intrastrand disulfide bonds at the carboxy terminus; once these disulfides are formed, the three molecules can align properly to initiate formation of the triple helix. The triple helix forms from the carboxy end toward the amino end, forming tropocollagen. The tropocollagen contains a triple helical segment between two globular ends: the amino- and carboxy-terminal extensions. The tropocollagen is secreted from the cell, the extensions are removed using extracellular proteases, and the mature collagen takes its place within the ECM. The individual fibrils of collagen line up in a highly ordered fashion to form the collagen fiber.

2. ELASTIN

Elastin is the major protein found in elastic fibers, which are located in the ECM of connective tissue of smooth muscle cells, endothelial and microvascular cells, chondrocytes, and fibroblasts. Elastic fibers allow tissues to expand and contract; this is of particular importance to blood vessels, which must deform and reform repeatedly in response to the changes in intravascular pressure that occur with the contraction of the left ventricle of the heart. It is also important for the lungs, which stretch each time a breath is inhaled and return to their original shape with each exhalation. In addition to elastin, the elastic fibers contain microfibrils, which are composed of several acidic glycoproteins, the major ones being fibrillin-1 and fibrillin-2.

i.   Tropoelastin

Elastin has a highly cross-linked, insoluble, amorphous structure. Its precursor, *tropoelastin*, is a molecule of high solubility, which is synthesized on the rough endoplasmic reticulum (RER) for eventual secretion. Tropoelastin contains two types of alternating domains. The first domain consists of a hydrophilic sequence that is rich in lysine and alanine residues. The second domain consists of a hydrophobic sequence that is rich in valine, proline, and glycine, which frequently occur in repeats of VPGVG or VGGVG. The protein contains approximately 16 regions of each domain, alternating throughout the protein (Fig. 49.6).

Upon secretion from the cell, the tropoelastin is aligned with the microfibrils, and lysyl oxidase initiates the reactions that cross-link elastin molecules, using lysine residues within the hydrophilic alternating domains in the proteins. This cross-linking reaction is the same as that which occurs in collagen. In this reaction, two, three, or four lysine residues are cross-linked to form a stable structure. The net result of the cross-linking is the generation of a fibrous mesh that encircles the cells.

 Supravalvular aortic stenosis (SVAS) results from an insufficiency of elastin in the vessel wall, leading to a narrowing of the large elastic arteries. Current theory suggests that the levels of elastin in the vessel walls may regulate the number of smooth muscle cell rings that encircle the vessel. If the levels of elastin are low, smooth muscle hypertrophy results, leading to a narrowing and stenosis of the artery.

FIG. 49.6. The cDNA structure of elastin, indicating the repeating cross-linking and hydrophobic domains.

ii.   Elastic Properties of Elastin

Elastic fibers have the ability to stretch and then to re-form without requiring an obvious energy source to do so. The mechanism by which this stretching and relaxing actively occurs is still controversial but does relate to the basic principles of protein folding described in Chapter 7. When the elastic fibers are stretched (such as when a breath is taken in and the lung fills up with air), the amorphous elastin structure is stretched. This stretching exposes the repeating hydrophobic regions of the molecule to the aqueous environment. This, in turn, leads to a decrease in the entropy of water because water molecules need to rearrange to form cages about each hydrophobic domain. When this stretching force within the lung is removed (e.g., when the subject exhales), the elastin takes on its original structure because of the increase in entropy that occurs because the water no longer needs to form cages about hydrophobic domains. Thus, the hydrophobic effect is the primary force that allows this stretched structure to re-form. Elastin is inherently stable, with a half-life of up to 70 years.

3.   LAMININ

After type IV collagen, *laminin* is the most abundant protein in basal laminae. Laminin provides additional structural support for the tissues through its ability to bind to type IV collagen, to other molecules present in the ECM, and to cell surface-associated proteins (the integrins; see Section I.D).

i.   Laminin Structure

Laminin is a heterotrimeric protein that is shaped, for the most part, like a cross (Fig. 49.7). The trimer is composed of α-, β-, and γ-subunits. There are five possible α-proteins (designated α_1 through α_5), three different versions of the β-subunit (β_1 through β_3), and three different γ-forms (γ_1 through γ_3). Thus, there is a potential for the formation of as many as 45 different combinations of these three subunits. However, only 18 have been discovered. Laminin 111, composed of $\alpha_1\beta_1\gamma_1$, is typical of this class of proteins. The major feature of the laminin structure is a coiled α-helix, which joins the three subunits together and forms a rigid rod. All three chains have extensions at the amino-terminal end. Only the α-chain has a significant carboxy-terminal extension past the rodlike structure. It is the laminin extensions that allow laminin to bind to other components within the ECM and to provide stability for the structure. Components of the ECM that are bound by laminin include collagen, sulfated lipids, and proteoglycans.

ii.   Laminin Biosynthesis

Like other secreted proteins, laminin is synthesized with a leader sequence that targets the three chains to the endoplasmic reticulum. Chain association occurs

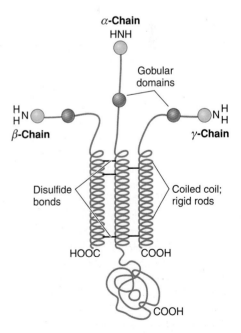

FIG. 49.7. The structure of laminin.

Defects in the structures of laminin 5 or laminin 6 (proteins that contribute to the cohesion of the dermis and epidermis) lead to the disorder referred to as junctional epidermolysis bullosa (JEB). In this disorder, there can be severe spontaneous blistering of the skin and mucous membranes. A severe form of the disease, JEB gravis, is often fatal early in life. Death occurs as a result of epithelial blistering of the respiratory, digestive, and genitourinary systems.

Congenital muscular dystrophy (CMD) results from a defect in laminin 2, which is a component of the bridge that links the muscle cell cytoskeleton to the extracellular matrix. Lack of this bridge triggers muscle cell apoptosis, which results in weakened muscles.

The ECM is not simply a glue that holds cells together; it also serves to keep cells from moving to other locations and to prevent large molecules and other particles, such as microorganisms, from reaching contiguous and distant cells. This confining property of the matrix is medically important. For example, infections spread, in part, because the infectious agent alters the "containing" capacity of the ECM. Cancer cells that metastasize (migrate to other tissues) can do so only by altering the integrity of the matrix. Diseases such as rheumatoid arthritis (an autoimmune destruction of articular and periarticular tissues) and osteoarthritis (degenerative joint disease often associated with aging) involve damage to the functional capacity of the matrix. Alterations in the structural characteristics of the matrix of the renal glomerulus may allow proteins to be excreted into the urine, an indication of inexorable decline in renal function. Genetic defects may cause components of the matrix to be structurally and functionally abnormal, resulting in connective tissue disorders such as the Ehlers–Danlos syndrome (caused by several mutations that affect specific collagen genes) and Marfan syndrome (a defect in the protein fibrillin, in which >330 different mutations, many of which give rise to different phenotypes, have been identified). Deficiencies of lysosomal enzymes involved in normal degradation of molecules of the matrix result in diseases such as the mucopolysaccharidoses.

within the Golgi apparatus before secretion from the cell. After laminin is secreted by the cell, the amino-terminal extensions promote self-association as well as the binding to other ECM components. Disulfide linkages are formed to stabilize the trimer, but there is much less posttranslational processing of laminin than there is of collagen and elastin.

B. Proteoglycans

The fibrous structural proteins of the ECM are embedded in gels formed from proteoglycans. Proteoglycans consist of polysaccharides called *glycosaminoglycans* (GAGs) linked to a core protein. The GAGs are composed of repeating units of disaccharides (Fig. 49.8). One sugar of the disaccharide is either *N*-acetylglucosamine or *N*-acetylgalactosamine, and the second is usually acidic (either glucuronic acid or iduronic acid). These sugars are modified by the addition of sulfate groups to the parent sugar. A proteoglycan may contain >100 GAG chains and consist of up to 95% carbohydrate by weight.

The negatively charged carboxylate and sulfate groups on the proteoglycan bind positively charged ions and form hydrogen bonds with trapped water molecules, thereby creating a hydrated gel. The gel provides a flexible mechanical support for the ECM. The gel also acts as a filter that allows the diffusion of ions (e.g., Ca^{2+}), H_2O, and other small molecules but slows diffusion of proteins and movement of cells. The gel also acts as a lubricant. Hyaluronan is the only GAG that occurs as a single long polysaccharide chain and is the only GAG that is not sulfated.

1. STRUCTURE AND FUNCTION OF THE PROTEOGLYCANS

Proteoglycans are found in interstitial connective tissues—for example, the synovial fluid of joints, the vitreous humor of the eye, arterial walls, bone, cartilage, and cornea. They are major components of the ECM in these tissues. The proteoglycans interact with a variety of proteins in the matrix, such as collagen and elastin, fibronectin (which is involved in cell adhesion and migration), and laminin.

Proteoglycans are proteins that contain many chains of GAGs (formerly called *mucopolysaccharides*). After synthesis, proteoglycans are secreted from cells; thus, they function extracellularly. Because the long, negatively charged glycosaminoglycan chains repel each other, the proteoglycans occupy a very large space and act as "molecular sieves," determining which substances enter or leave cells (Table 49.3). Their properties also give resilience and a degree of flexibility to substances such as cartilage, permitting compression and re-expansion of the molecule to occur.

At least seven types of glycosaminoglycans exist, which differ in the monosaccharides present in their repeating disaccharide units: chondroitin sulfate, dermatan sulfate, heparin, heparan sulfate, hyaluronic acid, and keratan sulfates I and II. Except for hyaluronic acid, the glycosaminoglycans are linked to proteins, usually attached covalently to serine or threonine residues (Fig. 49.9). Keratan sulfate I is attached to asparagine.

2. SYNTHESIS OF THE PROTEOGLYCANS

The protein component of the proteoglycans is synthesized on the ER. It enters the lumen of this organelle, where the initial glycosylations occur. UDP-sugars serve as the precursors that add sugar units, one at a time, first to the protein and then to the nonreducing end of the growing carbohydrate chain (Fig. 49.10). Glycosylation occurs initially in the lumen of the ER and subsequently in the Golgi complex. Glycosyltransferases, the enzymes that add sugars to the chain, are specific for the sugar being added, the type of linkage that is formed, and the sugars already present in the chain. Once the initial sugars are attached to the protein, the alternating action of two glycosyltransferases adds the sugars of the repeating disaccharide to the growing glycosaminoglycan chain. Sulfation occurs after addition of the sugar. The 3′-phosphoadenosine 5′-phosphosulfate (PAPS), also called *active sulfate*,

FIG. 49.8. Repeating disaccharides of some glycosaminoglycans. These repeating disaccharides usually contain an *N*-acetylated sugar and a uronic acid, which usually is glucuronic acid or iduronic acid. Sulfate groups are often present and are included in the sugar names in this figure. Iduronic acid and glucuronic acid are epimers at position 5 of the sugar.

Table 49.3   Some Specific Functions of the Glycosaminoglycans and Proteoglycans

Glycosaminoglycan	Function

Hyaluronic acid	Cell migration in:
	    Embryogenesis
	    Morphogenesis
	    Wound healing

Chondroitin sulfate proteoglycans	Formation of bone, cartilage, cornea
Keratan sulfate proteoglycans	Transparency of cornea
Dermatan sulfate proteoglycans	Transparency of cornea Binds LDL to plasma walls
Heparin	Anticoagulant (binds antithrombin III) Causes release of lipoprotein lipase from capillary walls
Heparan sulfate (syndecan)	Component of skin fibroblasts and aortic wall; commonly found on cell surfaces

LDL, low-density lipoprotein.

 The functional properties of a normal joint depend, in part, on the presence of a soft, well-lubricated, deformable, and compressible layer of cartilaginous tissue covering the ends of the long bones that constitute the joint.

In **Sis Lupus'** case, the pathologic process that characterizes SLE disrupted the structural and functional integrity of her articular (joint) cartilage.

provides the sulfate groups (see Fig. 33.33). An epimerase converts glucuronic acid residues to iduronic acid residues.

After synthesis, the proteoglycan is secreted from the cell. Its structure resembles a bottlebrush, with many glycosaminoglycan chains extending from the core protein (Fig. 49.11). The proteoglycans may form large aggregates, noncovalently attached by a "link" protein to hyaluronic acid (Fig. 49.12). The proteoglycans interact with the adhesion protein, fibronectin, which is attached to the cell membrane protein integrin. Cross-linked fibers of collagen also associate with this complex, forming the ECM (Fig. 49.13).

The long polysaccharide side chains of the proteoglycans in cartilage contain many anionic groups. This high concentration of negative charges attracts cations that create a high osmotic pressure within cartilage, drawing water into this specialized connective tissue and placing the collagen network under tension. At equilibrium, the resulting tension balances the swelling pressure caused by the proteoglycans. The complementary roles of this macromolecular organization give cartilage its resilience. Cartilage can thus withstand the compressive load of weight bearing and then re-expand to its previous dimensions when that load is relieved.

3.   DEGRADATION OF PROTEOGLYCANS

Lysosomal enzymes degrade proteoglycans, glycoproteins, and glycolipids, which are brought into the cell by the process of endocytosis. Lysosomes fuse with the

FIG. 49.9. Attachment of glycosaminoglycans to proteins. The sugars are linked to a serine or threonine residue of the protein. **A** and **B** represent the sugars of the repeating disaccharide.

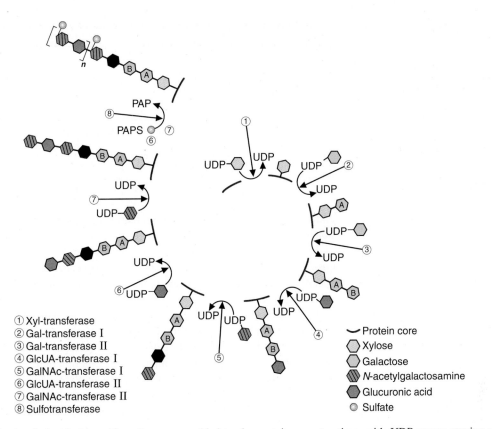

① Xyl-transferase
② Gal-transferase I
③ Gal-transferase II
④ GlcUA-transferase I
⑤ GalNAc-transferase I
⑥ GlcUA-transferase II
⑦ GalNAc-transferase II
⑧ Sulfotransferase

◝ Protein core
⬡ Xylose
⬡ Galactose
▨ N-acetylgalactosamine
⬣ Glucuronic acid
○ Sulfate

FIG. 49.10.   Synthesis of chondroitin sulfate. Sugars are added to the protein one at a time, with UDP-sugars serving as the precursors. Initially, a xylose residue is added to a serine in the protein. Then two galactose residues are added, followed by a glucuronic acid (GlcUA) and an N-acetylglucosamine (GalNAc). Subsequent additions occur by the alternating action of two enzymes that produce the repeating disaccharide units. One enzyme ⑥ adds GlcUA residues, and the other ⑦ adds GalNAc. As the chain grows, sulfate groups are added by phosphoadenosine phosphosulfate (PAPS). (Modified from Roden L. In: Fishman WH, ed. *Metabolic Conjugation and Metabolic Hydrolysis*. Vol. II. Orlando, FL: Academic Press; 1970:401.)

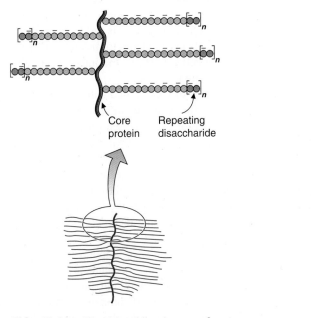

FIG. 49.11.   "Bottlebrush" structure of a proteoglycan with a magnified segment.

FIG. 49.12.   Proteoglycan aggregate.

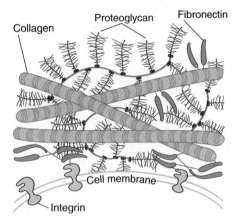

FIG. 49.13. Interactions between the cell membrane and the components of the extracellular matrix.

Table 49.4 Defective Enzymes in the Mucopolysaccharidoses

Disease	Enzyme Deficiency	Accumulated Products
Hunter	Iduronate sulfatase	Heparan sulfate, dermatan sulfate
Hurler + Scheie	α-L-iduronidase	Heparan sulfate, dermatan sulfate
Maroteaux–Lamy	N-acetylgalactosamine sulfatase	Dermatan sulfate
Mucolipidosis VII	β-Glucuronidase	Heparan sulfate, dermatan sulfate
Sanfilippo A	Heparan sulfamidase	Heparan sulfate
Sanfilippo B	N-acetylglucosaminidase	Heparan sulfate
Sanfilippo D	N-acetylglucosamine 6-sulfatase	Heparin sulfate

These disorders share many clinical features, although there are significant variations between disorders, and even within a single disorder, based on the amount of residual activity remaining. In most cases, multiple organ systems are affected (with bone and cartilage being a primary target). For some disorders, there is significant neuronal involvement, leading to mental retardation.

endocytic vesicles, and lysosomal proteases digest the protein component. The carbohydrate component is degraded by lysosomal glycosidases.

Lysosomes contain both endoglycosidases and exoglycosidases. The endoglycosidases cleave the chains into shorter oligosaccharides. Then exoglycosidases, specific for each type of linkage, remove the sugar residues one at a time from the nonreducing ends.

Deficiencies of lysosomal glycosidases cause partially degraded carbohydrates from proteoglycans, glycoproteins, and glycolipids to accumulate within membrane-enclosed vesicles inside cells. These "residual bodies" can cause marked enlargement of the organ, with impairment of its function.

In the clinical disorders known as the *mucopolysaccharidoses* (caused by accumulation of partially degraded glycosaminoglycans), deformities of the skeleton may occur (Table 49.4). Mental retardation often accompanies these skeletal changes.

II. INTEGRINS

Integrins are the major cellular receptors for ECM proteins and provide a link between the internal cytoskeleton of cells (primarily the actin microfilament system) and extracellular proteins, such as fibronectin, collagen, and laminin. Integrins consist of an α- and a β-subunit. There are 18 distinct α- and 10 distinct β-gene products. Twenty-four unique α-/β-dimers have been discovered. Mice have been genetically engineered to be unable to express many of the integrin genes (one gene at a time), and the phenotypes of these knockout mice vary from embryonic lethality (the α_5 gene is an example) to virtually no observable defects (as exemplified by the α_1 gene). In addition to anchoring the cell's cytoskeleton to the ECM, thereby providing a stable environment in which the cell can reside, the integrins are also involved in a wide variety of cell signaling options.

Certain integrins, such as those associated with white blood cells, are normally inactive because the white cell must circulate freely in the bloodstream. However, if an infection occurs, cells located in the area of the infection release cytokines, which activate the integrins on the white blood cells, allowing them to bind to vascular endothelial cells (leukocyte adhesion) at the site of infection. *Leukocyte adhesion deficiency* (LAD) is a genetic disorder that results from mutations in the β_2-integrin such that leukocytes cannot be recruited to the sites of infection. Conversely, drugs are now being developed to block either the β_2- or α_4-integrins (on lymphocytes) to treat inflammatory and autoimmune disorders by interfering with the normal white cell response to cytokines.

Integrins can be activated by "inside-out" mechanisms, whereby intracellular signaling events activate the molecule, or by "outside-in" mechanisms, in which a binding event with the extracellular portion of the molecule initiates intracellular signaling events. For those integrins that bind cells to ECM components, activation of specific integrins can result in migration of the affected cell through the ECM. This mechanism is operative during growth, during cellular differentiation, and in the process of metastasis of malignant cells to neighboring tissues.

III. ADHESION PROTEINS

Adhesion proteins are found in the ECM and link integrins to ECM components. *Adhesion proteins*, of which fibronectin is a prime example, are large multidomain proteins that allow binding to many different components simultaneously. In addition to integrin-binding sites, fibronectin contains binding sites for collagen and glycosaminoglycans. As the integrin molecule is bound to intracellular cytoskeletal proteins, the adhesion proteins provide a bridge between the actin cytoskeleton of the cell and the cells' position within the ECM. Loss of adhesion protein capability can lead to either physiologic or abnormal cell movement. Alternative splicing of fibronectin allows many different forms of this adhesion protein to be expressed, including a soluble form (versus cell-associated forms), which is found in the plasma. The metabolic significance of these products remains to be determined.

Fibronectin was first discovered as a large, external transformation-sensitive (LETS) protein, which was lost when fibroblasts were transformed into tumor cells. Many tumor cells secrete less than normal amounts of adhesion protein material, which allows for more movement within the extracellular milieu. This, in turn, increases the potential for the tumor cells to leave their original location and take root at another location within the body (metastasis).

IV. MATRIX METALLOPROTEINASES

The ECM contains a series of proteases known as the *matrix metalloproteinases* or MMPs. These are zinc-containing proteases that use the zinc to appropriately position water to participate in the proteolytic reaction. Over 20 different types of human MMPs exist, and they cleave all proteins found in the ECM, including collagen and laminin.

Because MMPs degrade ECM components, their expression is important to allow cell migration and tissue remodeling during growth and differentiation. In addition, many growth factors bind to ECM components and, as bound components, do not exhibit their normal growth-promoting activity. Destruction of the ECM by the MMPs releases these growth factors, allowing them to bind to cell surface receptors to initiate growth of tissues. Thus, coordinated expression of the MMPs is required for appropriate cell movement and growth. Cancer cells that metastasize require extensive ECM remodeling and usually use MMP activity to spread throughout the body.

A propeptide is present in newly synthesized MMPs that contains a critical cysteine residue. The cysteine residue in the propeptide binds to the zinc atom at the active site of the protease and prevents the propeptide from exhibiting proteolytic activity. Removal of the propeptide is required to activate the MMPs. Once they are activated, certain MMPs can activate other forms of MMP.

Regulation of MMP activity is quite complex. These regulatory processes include transcriptional regulation, proteolytic activation, inhibition by the circulating protein α_2-macroglobulin, and regulation by a class of inhibitors known as *tissue inhibitors of metalloproteinases* or TIMPs. It is important that the synthesis of TIMPs and MMPs be coordinately regulated because dissociation of their expression can facilitate various clinical disorders, such as certain forms of cancer and atherosclerosis.

CLINICAL COMMENTS

Sis Lupus. Articular cartilage is a living tissue with a turnover time determined by a balance between the rate of its synthesis and that of its degradation (Fig. 49.14). The chondrocytes that are embedded in the matrix of intra-articular cartilage participate in both its synthesis and its enzymatic degradation. The latter occurs as a result of cleavage of proteoglycan aggregates by enzymes produced and secreted by the chondrocytes.

The movement of tumor cells from its tissue of origin (metastasis) through the blood or lymph system, and colonization of a target tissue, requires degradation of the extracellular matrix to allow for cell movement. This is accomplished by a family of proteins known as matrix metalloproteinases (MMPs). The MMPs degrade specific extracellular matrix components (such as collagen or elastin), thereby allowing cells access through this compartment. One assay for determining if MMPs are present in a biological sample is the gelatin zymography assay; a newer, more sensitive assay is based on fluorescence resonance energy transfer (FRET). In the zymography assay polyacrylamide gels containing the protein gelatin are prepared, and the enzyme samples are run through the gel, in the presence of SDS. After the gel has run, enzyme activity is reconstituted by substituting Triton X-100 for the SDS. An assay buffer is then placed over the gel, which is left overnight. During this part of the procedure, if a lane on the gel contained MMP activity, the MMP would be digesting the gelatin in the area of the gel where the MMP resided. After the activity phase is complete, the gel is developed with Coomassie stain, which binds to the proteins in the gel, including the gelatin. A positive result would appear as white bands on a blue background. The white bands are caused by the absence of gelatin in that region of the gel, as the MMPs present at that region have digested the gelatin such that Coomassie stain has nothing to bind to in that area of the gel. The FRET assay uses a peptide substrate that contains both a fluorophore and a quencher in close proximity. When excited, the quencher blocks fluorescence emittance from the fluorophore because of the close proximity of the two molecules on the peptide. After MMP treatment, however, the peptide is cleaved between the flurophore and quencher, such that the quencher is no longer in close proximity to the fluorophore. This results in a strong fluorescence emittance. Thus, fluorescence intensity will increase as the peptide is cleaved in the presence of the MMP. This is a very sensitive assay, detecting subnanogram levels of a wide variety of members of the MMP family.

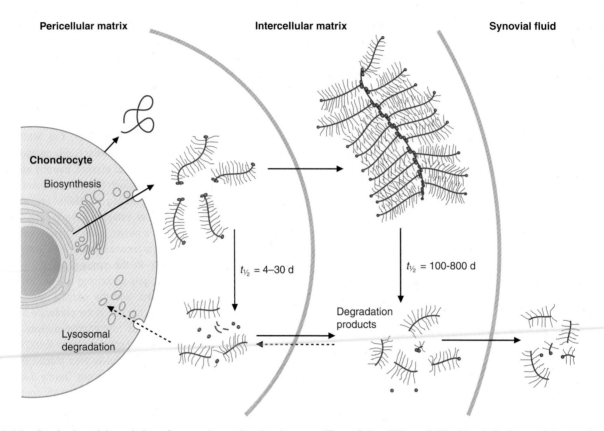

FIG. 49.14.   Synthesis and degradation of proteoglycans by chondrocytes. (From Cohen RD, et al. *The Metabolic Basis of Acquired Disease*. Vol. 2. London: Bailliere Tindall; 1990:1859.)

In systemic lupus erythematosus (SLE), the condition that affects **Sis Lupus**, this delicate balance is disrupted in favor of enzymatic degradation, leading to dissolution of articular cartilage and, with it, the loss of its critical cushioning functions. The underlying mechanisms responsible for this process in SLE involves an autoimmune induced inflammation. In this sense, SLE is an "autoimmune" disease because antibodies are produced by the host that attack "self" proteins. This process excites the local release of cytokines such as interleukin-1 (IL-1), which increases the proteolytic activity of the chondrocytes, causing further loss of articular proteins such as the proteoglycans. The associated inflammatory cascade is responsible for **Sis Lupus'** joint pain.

 Ann Sulin. The microvascular complications of both type 1 and type 2 diabetes mellitus involve the small vessels of the retina (diabetic retinopathy), the renal glomerular capillaries (diabetic nephropathy), and the vessels that supply blood to the peripheral nerves (autonomic neuropathy). The lack of adequate control of **Ann Sulin's** diabetic state over many years caused a progressive loss of the filtering function of the approximately 1.5 million glomerular capillary-mesangial units that are present in her kidneys.

Chronic hyperglycemia is postulated to be a major metabolic initiator or inducer of diabetic microvascular disease, including those renal glomerular changes that often lead to end-stage renal disease ("glucose toxicity").

For a comprehensive review of the four postulated molecular mechanisms by which chronic hyperglycemia causes these vascular derangements, the reader is referred to an excellent review by Sheetz and King (see the online Suggested Readings).

Regardless of which of the postulated mechanisms (increased flux through the aldose reductase or polyol pathway [see Chapter 30], the generation of advanced glycosylation end products [AGEs], the generation of reactive oxygen intermediates [see Chapter 24], or excessive activation of protein kinase C [see Chapter 18]) will eventually be shown to be the predominant causative mechanism, each can lead to the production of critical intracellular and extracellular signaling molecules (e.g., cytokines). These, in turn, can cause pathologic changes within the glomerular filtration apparatus that reduces renal function. These changes include increased synthesis of type IV collagen, fibronectin, and some of the proteoglycans, causing the glomerular basement membrane (GBM) (Fig. 49.15) to become diffusely thickened throughout the glomerular capillary network. This membrane thickening alters certain specific filtration properties of the GBM, preventing some of the metabolites that normally enter the urine from the glomerular capillary blood (via the fenestrated capillary endothelium) from doing so (a decline in glomerular filtration rate [GFR]). As a result, these potentially toxic substances accumulate in the blood and contribute to the overall clinical presentation of advancing uremia. In spite of the thickening of the GBM, this membrane becomes "leaky" for some macromolecules (e.g., albumin) that normally do not enter the urine from the glomerular capillaries (microalbuminuria). Suggested mechanisms for this increased permeability or leakiness include reduced synthesis of the specific proteoglycan, heparan sulfate, as well as increased basement membrane production of vascular endothelium growth factor (VEGF), a known angiogenic and permeability factor, and expansion of the extracellular matrix in the mesangium. The mesangium consists of specialized tissue containing collagen, proteoglycans, and other macromolecules that surround the glomerular capillaries and that, through its gel-like and sieving properties, determine, in part, the glomerular capillary hydraulic filtration pressure as well as the functional status of the capillary endothelium–mesangial glomerular basement membrane filtration apparatus (see Fig. 49.15). As the mesangial tissue expands, the efficiency of glomerular filtration diminishes proportionately. The cause of these mesangial changes is, in part, the consequence of increased expression of certain growth factors, especially transforming growth

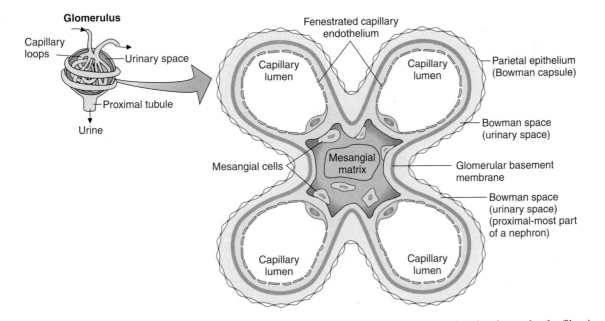

FIG. 49.15.   A cross section of a normal renal glomerulus showing four capillary tufts delivering blood to the glomerulus for filtration across the fenestrated capillary endothelium, then through the glomerular basement membrane into the Bowman space to form urine. The urine then enters the proximal tubule of the nephron. This filtration removes potentially toxic metabolic end products from the blood. The mesangium, by contracting and expanding, controls the efficiency of these filtering and excretory functions by regulating the hydraulic filtration pressures in the glomerulus. An intact basement membrane must be present to maintain the integrity of the filtering process.

factor β (TGF-β) and connective tissue growth factor (CTGF). Future therapeutic approaches in patients with early diabetic nephropathy may include the use of antibodies that neutralize TGF-β.

BIOCHEMICAL COMMENTS

 Osteogenesis Imperfecta. *Osteogenesis imperfecta* (OI) is a heterogenous group of diseases that have in common a defect in collagen production. This defect can be either of two types: the first type is associated with a reduction in the synthesis of normal collagen (resulting from a gene deletion or splice-site mutation). The second type is associated with the synthesis of a mutated form of collagen. Most of the mutations have a dominant-negative effect, leading to an autosomal dominant mode of transmission.

In the second type of OI, many of the known mutations involve substitutions of another amino acid for glycine. This results in an unstable collagen molecule because glycine is the only amino acid that can fit between the other two chains within the triple helix of collagen. If the mutation is near the carboxy-terminal end of the molecule, the phenotype of the disease is usually more severe than if the mutation is near the amino-terminal end (recall that triple helix formation proceeds from the carboxy- to the amino-terminal end of the molecule). Of interest are mutations that replace glycine with either serine or cysteine. Such mutations are more stable than expected because of the hydrogen bonding capabilities of serine and the ability of cysteine to form disulfide bonds. Both would aid in preventing the strands of the triple helix from unwinding.

Children with OI can be treated with a class of compounds known as *bisphosphonates*, which consist of two phosphates linked by a carbon or nitrogen bridge (thus, they are analogs of pyrophosphate, in which the two phosphates are linked by oxygen). Normal bone remodeling is the result of a coordinated "coupling" between osteoclast activity (cells that resorb bone) and osteoblast activity (cells that form bone). In OI, bone resorption outpaces bone formation because osteoclast activity is enhanced (perhaps because of the reduced levels of normal collagen present to act as nucleating sites for bone formation). This leads to a net loss of bone mass and fragility of the skeleton. Bisphosphonates inhibit osteoclast action with the potential to increase bone mass and its tensile strength.

 Osteogenesis imperfecta (OI) can occur due to mutations in genes other than collagen. Mutations in CRTAP (cartilage associated protein) or LEPRE1 (prolyl 3-hydroxylase 1, or PH3-1) lead to defective collagen fibers being produced. CRTAP forms a complex with PH3-1 and cyclophilin to hydroxylate a specific proline residue in types I and II collagen. Failure to hydroxylate this proline residue leads to unstable collagen and moderate to severe forms of OI. The pattern of inheritance for both CRTAP and LEPRE1 mutations is autosomal recessive.

Key Concepts

- The extracellular matrix (ECM) consists of fibrous structural proteins, proteoglycans, and adhesion proteins.
- The ECM provides support to the tissues and restricts movement of cells.
- Collagen is the most abundant fibrous protein, and it consists of a triple helix stabilized by hydrogen bonds and intramolecular cross-links. There are more than 25 different types of collagen.
- Elastin is the major protein found in elastic fibers, and it is responsible for the contractility exhibited by these fibers.
- Laminin provides structural support to tissues via binding to various components of the ECM.
- Proteoglycans consist of polysaccharides (glycosaminoglycans) bound to a core protein.
  - The polysaccharides are usually a repeating disaccharide unit containing negative charges.
  - Because of charge repulsion, the proteoglycans form a hydrated gel that provides flexible mechanical support to the ECM.
- Integrins are cellular membrane receptors for ECM proteins, and they link the cellular cytoskeleton to extracellular proteins.
- Integrins are also signaling proteins when they are bound to appropriate components.
- Adhesion proteins link the integrins to ECM components.
- Matrix metalloproteinases are the only proteases that can degrade ECM components, and they are carefully regulated by the tissue inhibitors of matrix metalloproteinases (TIMPS).
- Diseases discussed in this chapter are summarized in Table 49.5.

Table 49.5   Diseases Discussed in Chapter 49

Disease or Disorder	Genetic or Environmental	Comments
Lupus	Environmental	Alterations in cell matrix components caused by an autoimmune induced trigger
Type 2 diabetes	Both	Cell matrix interactions can be altered because of elevated glucose levels and nonenzymatic glycosylation
Osteogenesis imperfecta	Genetic	Inherited mutations in collagen genes that disrupt the function of the altered collagen
Supravalvular aortic stenosis (Williams syndrome)	Genetic	An inherited mutation in the elastin gene leading to abnormal heart function
Junctional epidermolysis bullosa	Genetic	A blistering skin condition caused by a mutation in either one form of collagen or laminin
Mucopolysaccharidoses	Genetic	Defects in the breakdown of mucopolysaccharides, found primarily in the extracellular matrix. See Table 49.4 for more details on these diseases.

REVIEW QUESTIONS—CHAPTER 49

1. Individuals who develop scurvy suffer from sore and bleeding gums and loss of teeth. This is a result, in part, of the synthesis of a defective collagen molecule. The step that is affected in collagen biosynthesis attributable to scurvy is which of the following?

   A. The formation of disulfide bonds, which initiates tropocollagen formation
   B. The formation of lysyl cross-links between collagen molecules
   C. Secretion of tropocollagen into the extracellular matrix
   D. The formation of collagen fibrils
   E. The hydroxylation of proline residues, which stabilizes the collagen structure

2. The underlying mechanism that allows elastin to exhibit elastic properties (expand and contract) is which of the following?

   A. Proteolysis during expansion, and resynthesis during contraction
   B. Breaking of disulfide bonds during expansion, and re-formation of these bonds during contraction
   C. A decrease in entropy during expansion, and an increase in entropy during contraction
   D. The breaking of salt bridges during expansion, and re-formation of the salt bridges during contraction
   E. Hydroxylation of elastin during expansion, and decarboxylation of elastin during contraction

3. The underlying mechanism by which glycosaminoglycans allow for the formation of a gel-like substance in the extracellular matrix occur by which of the following?

   A. Charge attraction between glycosaminoglycan chains
   B. Charge repulsion between glycosaminoglycan chains
   C. Hydrogen bonding between glycosaminoglycan chains
   D. Covalent cross-linking between glycosaminoglycan chains
   E. Hydroxylation of adjacent glycosaminoglycan chains

4. The movement of tumor cells from their site of origin to other locations within the body requires the activity of which of the following proteins?

   A. Collagen
   B. Laminin
   C. Proteoglycans
   D. Elastin
   E. Matrix metalloproteinases

5. Fibronectin is frequently absent in malignant fibroblast cells. One of the major functions of fibronectin is which of the following?

   A. To inhibit the action of matrix metalloproteinases
   B. To coordinate collagen deposition within the extracellular matrix
   C. To fix the position of cells within the extracellular matrix
   D. To regulate glycosaminoglycan production
   E. To extend glycosaminoglycan chains using nucleotide sugars

Answers to Review Questions

CHAPTER 1

1. **The answer is B.** In the process of respiration, O_2 is consumed and fuels are oxidized to CO_2 and H_2O. The energy from the oxidation reactions is used to generate ATP from ADP and P_i. However, a small amount of energy is also released as heat (thus, C is incorrect). Although fuels can be stored as triacylglycerols, this is not part of respiration (thus, A is incorrect). Respiration is a catabolic pathway (fuels are degraded), as opposed to an anabolic pathway (compounds combine to make larger molecules) (thus, E is incorrect).

2. **The answer is A.** Mrs. Jones's diet lacks grain products, fruits, and vegetables, all of which are good sources of vitamin C. Her diet is adequate in protein, as eggs, milk, cheese, and cream contain significant levels of protein. Her calcium levels should be fine because of the milk, cream, and cheese in her diet. Vitamin B_{12} is derived from foods of animal origin such as eggs, milk, and cheese. As the patient's weight has been stable for a year, her diet contains sufficient calories to allow her to maintain this weight, which is in the normal range for a patient who is 5 ft 4 in tall, as her BMI is 21.5.

3. **The answer is A.** The resting metabolic rate (RMR) is the calories being expended by a recently awakened resting person who has fasted for 12 to 18 hours and whose body temperature is at 20°C. It is equivalent to the energy expenditure of our major organs and resting skeletal muscle. Women generally have a lower RMR per kilogram body weight because more of their body weight is usually metabolically less active adipose tissue. Children have a higher RMR per kilogram body weight because more of their body weight is metabolically active organs such as brain. The RMR increases in a cold environment because more energy is being expended to generate heat. The RMR is not equivalent to our daily energy expenditure (DEE), which includes RMR, physical activity, and diet-induced thermogenesis.

4. **The answer is D.** The Recommended Daily Allowance (RDA) of a nutrient is determined from the Estimated Average Requirement (EAR) + 2 standard deviations (SD) of the mean, and should meet the needs for 97% to 98% of the healthy population. It is, therefore, a reasonable goal for the intake of a healthy individual. The EAR is the amount that prevents development of established signs of deficiency in 50% of the healthy population. Although data with laboratory animals have been used to establish deficiency symptoms, RDAs are based on data collected on nutrient ingestion by humans.

5. **The answer is B.** The recommended total fat intake is less than 30% of total calories. His total caloric consumption was 4,110 kcal/day (carbohydrate, $4 \times 585 = 2,340$ kcal; protein, $150 \times 4 = 600$ kcal; fat, $95 \times 9 = 855$ kcal; alcohol, $45 \times 7 = 315$ kcal) (thus, A is incorrect). His fat intake was 21% ($855 \div 4,110$) of his total caloric intake. His alcohol intake was 7.7% ($315 \div 4,110$) (thus, C is incorrect). His protein intake was well above the RDA of 0.8 g/kg body weight (thus, D is incorrect). His RMR is roughly 24 kcal/day/kg body weight or 2,880 kcal/day (it will actually be less because he is obese and has a greater proportion of metabolically less active tissue than the average 70-kg man). His daily energy expenditure is about 3,744 kcal/day ($1.3 \times 2,880$) or less. Thus, his intake is greater than his expenditure, and he is in positive caloric balance and is gaining weight (thus, E is incorrect).

CHAPTER 2

1. **The answer is E.** During digestion of a mixed meal, starch and other carbohydrates, proteins, and dietary triacylglycerols are broken into their monomeric units (carbohydrates into simple monosaccharides, protein into amino acids, triacylglycerols into fatty acids and glycerol). Glucose is the principal sugar in dietary carbohydrates, and thus it increases in the blood. Amino acids and monosaccharides enter the portal vein and go to the liver first. After digestion of fats and absorption of the fatty acids, most fatty acids are converted back into triacylglycerols and subsequently into chylomicrons by intestinal cells. Chylomicrons go through lymphatic vessels and then blood, principally to adipose tissue.

2. **The answer is C.** After a high-carbohydrate meal, glucose is the major fuel for most tissues, including skeletal muscle, adipose tissue, and liver. The increase in blood glucose levels stimulates the release of insulin, not glucagon. Insulin stimulates the transport of glucose in skeletal muscle and adipose tissue, not brain. Liver, not skeletal muscle, converts glucose to fatty acids. Although the red blood cell uses glucose as its only fuel at all times, it generates ATP from conversion of glucose to lactate, not CO_2.

3. **The answer is C.** In the fed state, insulin will be released because of the increase in blood glucose levels. Insulin will act on muscle cells to increase glucose uptake in the muscle. Insulin will also stimulate the liver to synthesize both glycogen and fatty acids, which leads to enhanced triglyceride synthesis and very low-density lipoprotein (VLDL) production to deliver the fatty acids to other tissues of the body. Insulin will stimulate glucose uptake in fat cells, but does not stimulate fatty acid synthesis in the fat cells (i.e., unique to the liver), but will lead to enhanced triglyceride synthesis in the fat cells.

4. Answer is B. Chylomicrons are the lipoprotein particles formed in intestinal epithelial cells from dietary fats, and they contain principally triacylglycerols formed from components of dietary triacylglycerols. A decreased intake of calories in general would include a decreased consumption of fat, carbohydrate, and protein, which might not lower chylomicron levels. Dietary cholesterol, although found in chylomicrons, is not their principal component.

5. The answer is A. The patient's BMI is in the obese range, with large abdominal fat deposits. He needs to decrease his intake of total calories because an excess of calories ingested as carbohydrate, fat, or protein results in deposition of triacylglycerols in adipose tissue. If he keeps his total caloric intake the same, substitution of one type of food for another will help very little with weight loss. (However, a decreased intake of fat may be advisable for other reasons). Limited food diets, such as the ice cream and sherry diet, or a high protein diet of shrimp, work if they decrease appetite and, therefore, ingestion of total calories.

CHAPTER 3

1. The answer is A. By 24 hours after a meal, hepatic (liver) gluconeogenesis is the major source of blood glucose because hepatic glycogen stores have been nearly depleted. Muscle and other tissues lack an enzyme necessary to convert glycogen or amino acids to glucose (thus, B is incorrect). The liver is the only significant source of blood glucose. Glucose is synthesized in the liver from amino acids (provided by protein degradation), from glycerol (provided by hydrolysis of triacylglycerols in adipose tissue), and from lactate (provided by anaerobic glycolysis in red blood cells and other tissues). Glucose cannot be synthesized from fatty acids or ketone bodies (thus, D and E are incorrect).

2. The answer is A. The liver will produce ketone bodies when fatty acid oxidation is increased, which occurs when glucagon is the predominant hormone (glucagon leads to fatty acid release from the fat cells, for oxidation in the liver and muscle). This would be the case in an individual who cannot produce insulin and is not taking insulin injections. However, in this situation, the ketone bodies are not being used by the nervous system (brain) because of the high levels of glucose in the circulation. This leads to severely elevated ketone levels due to nonuse. The glucose is high because, in the absence of insulin, muscle and fat cells are not using the glucose in circulation as an energy source. Recall, although the liver produces ketone bodies, it lacks a necessary enzyme to use ketone bodies as an energy source. There is no relation between blood urea nitrogen levels and the rate of ketone body

production. The muscle reduces its use of ketone bodies under these conditions, but not of fatty acids.

3. The answer is C. The major change during prolonged fasting is that as muscles decrease their use of ketone bodies, ketone bodies increase enormously in the blood and are used by brain as a fuel. However, even during starvation, glucose is still required by the brain, which cannot oxidize fatty acids to an appreciable extent (thus, D is incorrect). Red blood cells can use only glucose as a fuel (thus, B is incorrect). Because the brain, red blood cells, and certain other tissues are glucose dependent, the liver continues to synthesize glucose, and blood glucose levels are maintained at only slightly less than fasting levels (thus, A is incorrect). Adipose tissue stores (approximately 135,000 kcal) are not depleted in a well-nourished individual after 1 week of fasting (thus, E is incorrect).

4. The answer is A. Decreased serum albumin could have several causes, including hepatic disease that decreases the ability of the liver to synthesize serum proteins, protein malnutrition, marasmus, or diseases that affect the ability of the intestine to digest protein and absorb the amino acids. However, his BMI is in the healthy weight range (thus, B and D are incorrect). His normal CHI indicates that he has not lost muscle mass and is, therefore, not suffering from protein malnutrition (thus, B, C, D, and E are incorrect).

5. The answer is C. His protein intake of 150 kcal is about 37 g protein (150 kcal ÷ 4 kcal/g = 37 g) below the Recommended Dietary Allowance (RDA) of 0.8 g protein per kilogram body weight (thus, A is incorrect, as Otto weighs approximately 88 kg). His carbohydrate intake of 150 kcal is below the glucose requirements of his brain and red blood cells (about 150 g/day; see Chapter 2) (thus, B is incorrect). Therefore, he will be breaking down muscle protein to synthesize glucose for the brain and other glucose-dependent tissues and adipose tissue mass to supply fatty acids for muscle and tissues able to oxidize fatty acids. Because he will be breaking down muscle protein to amino acids and converting the nitrogen from both these amino acids and his dietary amino acids to urea, his nitrogen excretion will be greater than his intake and he will be in negative nitrogen balance (thus, D is incorrect). It is unlikely that he will develop hypoglycemia while he is able to supply gluconeogenic precursors.

CHAPTER 4

1. The answer is A. The pH is the negative log of the hydrogen ion concentration, $[H^+]$. Thus, at a pH of 7.5, $[H^+]$ is $10^{-7.5}$; and at pH 6.5, it is $10^{-6.5}$. The $[H^+]$ has changed by a factor of $10^{-6.5}/10^{-7.5}$, which is 10^1 or 10. Any decrease of 1 pH unit is a 10-fold increase of $[H^+]$ or a 10-fold decrease of $[OH^-]$. A shift in the concentration of buffer anions has definitely occurred, but the change in pH reflects the increase in hydrogen ion concentration in excess of that absorbed by buffers.

2. **The answer is C.** To solve this problem, one first needs to calculate the concentration of the conjugate base and acid of the buffer at pH 7.4. Using the Henderson-Hasselbalch equation, one can calculate that the concentration of the conjugate base is 0.061 M and that of the acid is 0.039 M. At this point, the reaction occurs, generating 0.01 M protons (10 μmol/mL is a concentration of 10 mM, or 0.01 M). As the protons are generated, they will combine with the conjugate base, producing the acid. This will change the concentration of conjugate base to 0.051 M, and the concentration of the acid to 0.049 M. Plugging those values into the Henderson-Hasselbalch equation leads to a pH value of 7.22. Recall, if the concentration of the conjugate base equaled the concentration of the acid, the pH would be the pK value (in this case 7.2). Because protons are being generated, the pH will drop, not rise, so answer (A) cannot be correct.

3. **The answer is B.** NH_3 is a weak base, which associates with a proton to produce the ammonium ion ($NH_3 + H^+ \rightarrow NH_4^+$), which has a p$K_a$ of 9.5. Thus, at pH 7.4, most of the ammonia will be present as ammonium ion. The absorption of hydrogen ions will tend to increase, not decrease, the pH of the blood (thus, A is incorrect). With the decrease of hydrogen ions, carbonic acid will dissociate to produce more bicarbonate ($H_2CO_3 \rightarrow HCO_3^- + H^+$) and more CO_2 will go toward carbonic acid (thus, C is incorrect). Kussmaul respiration, an increased expiration of CO_2, occurs under an acidosis, the opposite condition.

4. **The answer is C.** Vomiting expels the strong acid gastric acid (HCl). As cells in the stomach secrete more HCl, they draw on H^+ ions in interstitial fluid and blood, thereby tending to increase blood pH and cause an alkalosis. The other conditions tend to produce an acidosis (thus, A, B, D, and E are incorrect). Lactic acid is a weak acid secreted into the blood by muscles during exercise. A patient with increased ketone body production can exhibit a fall of pH because the ketone bodies acetoacetate and β-hydroxybutyrate are dissociated acids. As bicarbonate in the intestinal lumen is lost in the watery diarrhea, more bicarbonate is secreted by intestinal cells. As intestinal cells produce bicarbonate, more H^+ is also generated ($H_2CO_3 \rightarrow HCO_3^- + H^+$). While the bicarbonate produced by these cells is released into the intestinal lumen, the protons accumulate in blood, resulting in an acidosis. Hypercatabolism (see E), an increased rate of catabolism, generates additional CO_2, which produces more acid ($CO_2 + H_2O \rightarrow H_2CO_3 \rightarrow HCO_3^- + H^+$).

5. **The answer is B.** Methylmalonic acid contains two carboxylic acid groups and is, therefore, a weak acid. According to the Henderson-Hasselbalch equation, the carboxylic acid groups are 50% dissociated at their pK_a (thus, C is incorrect). Carboxylic acid groups usually have a pK_a between 2 and 5, so this acid would be nearly fully dissociated at a blood pH of 7.4 and cannot buffer intracellularly at neutral pH (thus, D and E are incorrect). (Although you do not need to know anything about methylmalonate to answer this question, methylmalonate is an organic acid generated in patients with a problem in metabolism of methylmalonyl coenzyme A, such as a deficiency in vitamin B_{12}. Its acidity may contribute to the development of symptoms involving the nervous system. Its appearance in the urine can be classified as an organic aciduria.)

CHAPTER 5

1. **The answer is D.** Water-soluble compounds are polar (contain an uneven distribution of charge) so that the more positive portion of the molecule hydrogen-bonds (shares electrons) with the oxygen of water, and the more negative portion of the molecule hydrogen-bonds with the hydrogens of water. Water-soluble compounds need not contain a full negative or positive charge (thus, B and C are incorrect) and generally contain oxygen or nitrogen, in addition to carbon and hydrogen (see A). Large C–H portions of a molecule, such as an aromatic ring, are nonpolar and contribute to the insolubility of the molecule in water (see E).

2. **The answer is E.** The compound contains an $-OH$ group, which should appear in the name as an "-ol" or a "hydroxyl-" group. All answers fit this criterion. The structure also contains a carboxylate group ($-COO^-$), which should appear in the name as an "-ate" or "acid." Only D and E fit this criterion. Counting backward from the carboxylate group (carbon 1), the second carbon is α, the third carbon is β, and the fourth carbon, containing the hydroxyl group, is γ. Thus, the compound is γ-hydroxybutyrate. A, B, and C can also be eliminated because "meth-" denotes a single carbon, "eth-" denotes two carbons, and the "-ene" in ethylene denotes a double bond.

3. **The answer is B.** The term "glycosidic bond" refers to a *covalent* bond formed between the anomeric carbon of one sugar, when it is in a ring form, and a hydroxyl group or nitrogen of another compound (see Fig. 5.16) (thus, A, D, and E are incorrect). Disaccharides can be linked through their anomeric carbons, but not polysaccharides, because there would be no anomeric carbon left to form a link with the next sugar in the chain (thus, C is incorrect).

4. **The answer is A.** Triglycerides (triacylglycerols) are composed of a glycerol backbone to which three fatty acids ("tri-") are attached (see Fig. 5.18). The carboxylic acid group of each fatty acid forms an ester with one of the three $-OH$ groups on glycerol; thus, the fatty acid is an "acyl" group. Sphingolipids, in contrast, contain one fatty acyl group and one group derived from a fatty acid, attached to a group derived from serine (see Fig. 5.20).

5. **The answer is B.** Sphingolipids contain a ceramide group, which is sphingosine with an attached fatty acid. They do not contain a glycerol moiety (thus, A is incorrect). However, different sphingolipids have different substituents on the $-CH_2OH$ group of ceramide. For example, sphingomyelin contains phosphorylcholine, and gangliosides contain NANA (thus, C and D are incorrect). No known sphingolipids contain a steroid (E).

CHAPTER 6

1. **The answer is D.** In hydrogen bonds, a hydrogen atom is shared between two electron-rich groups, such as oxygen or nitrogen. Thus, the nitrogen in the peptide bond may share its hydrogen with the oxygen in an aspartate carboxyl group, which will be negatively charged at a pH of 7.4. Leucine is nonpolar and cannot participate in hydrogen bonding (thus, A is incorrect), and aspartyl and glutamyl residues are both negatively charged (thus, B is incorrect). Bonds between two fully charged groups are electrostatic bonds, not hydrogen bonds (thus, C is incorrect). Sulfhydryl groups do not participate in hydrogen bonding.

2. **The answer is A.** The peptide backbone contains only carbon and nitrogen atoms linked covalently in a chain. The amide nitrogen of one amino acid (N) is covalently attached to the α-carbon of the same amino acid (C), which is covalently linked to the carboxyl carbon (C) of that amino acid, which forms a peptide bond with the nitrogen of the next amino acid (N).

3. **The answer is A.** Arginine is a basic amino acid that has a positively charged side chain at neutral pH. It can, therefore, form tight electrostatic bonds with negatively charged asp and glu side chains in insulin. The α-carboxylic acid groups at the N-terminals of proteins are bound through peptide bonds (thus, B is incorrect). The arginine side chain is not hydrophobic, and it cannot form disulfide bonds because it has no sulfhydryl group (thus, C and D are incorrect). Its basic group is an ureido group that cannot form peptide bonds (see E).

4. **The answer is B.** Only these amino acids have side chain hydroxyl groups. As a general rule, serine–threonine protein kinases form one group of protein kinases, and tyrosine protein kinases form another.

5. **The answer is A.** Adding a phosphate group to the serine side chain adds negative charges to the side chain, allowing ionic interactions to develop. These new ionic interactions allow the protein to change shape and to alter its activity. Substituting a glutamate for the serine adds a negative charge to this location within the protein, which may participate in ionic interactions and lead to a shape change in the protein. None of the other suggested mutations (serine to either threonine [which adds a hydroxyl group, just as serine has], to tyrosine [again, another hydroxyl containing amino acid side chain], to lysine [adding a positive charge rather than a negative charge], or to leucine [a totally hydrophobic side chain]) will lead to the insertion of negative charges at this location in the protein.

CHAPTER 7

1. **The answer is B.** The regular repeating structure of an α-helix is possible because it is formed by hydrogen bonds within the peptide backbone of a single strand. Thus, α-helices can be formed from a variety of primary structures. However, proline cannot accommodate the bends for an α-helix because the atoms involved in the peptide backbone are part of a ring structure, and glycine cannot provide the space filling required for a stable structure.

2. **The answer is C.** Globular proteins fold into a spherelike structure with their hydrophilic residues on the outside to interact with water (hence, A is incorrect) and their hydrophobic residues on the inside away from water (thus, B is incorrect). Secondary structures are formed by hydrogen bonding, not hydrophobic bonding (thus, D is incorrect). Disulfide bonds are rare in globular proteins and are not needed to maintain a stable structure (thus, E is incorrect).

3. **The answer is D.** When an α-helix is formed, all side chains face the outside of the helix, which is the hydrophobic environment of the lipid membrane. Thus, the side chains should be hydrophobic. Of the amino acids listed, only leucine fits the bill (see Chapter 6). Proline interrupts helical structure because the imino bond of its ring structure does not allow the polypeptide backbone to form the angles required for α-helical formation.

4. **The answer is A.** The characteristic staining of amyloid arises from fibrils of β-pleated sheet structure perpendicular to the axis of the fiber (thus, B, C, and D are incorrect). The native conformation of a protein is generally the most stable and lowest energy conformation, and the lower its energy state, the more readily a protein folds into its native conformation and the less likely it will assume the insoluble β-pleated sheet structure of amyloid (thus, E is incorrect).

5. **The answer is A.** The protein hydrolyzes ATP, which is a characteristic of the actin fold. None of the other folds described will hydrolyze ATP.

CHAPTER 8

1. **The answer is B.** In most reactions, the substrate binds to the enzyme before its reaction with the coenzyme occurs. Thus, the substrate may bind but it cannot react with the coenzyme to form the transition-state complex.

Each coenzyme carries out a single type of reaction, so no other coenzyme can substitute (thus, C is incorrect). The three-dimensional geometry of the reaction is so specific that functional groups on amino acid side chains cannot substitute (thus, D is incorrect). Free coenzymes are not very reactive because amino acid side chains in the active site are required to activate the coenzyme or the reactants (thus, E is incorrect). However, increasing the supply of vitamins to increase the amount of coenzyme bound to the enzyme can sometimes help.

2. **The answer is D.** The patient was diagnosed with maturity-onset diabetes of the young (MODY) caused by this mutation. In glucokinase, binding of glucose normally causes a huge conformational change in the actin fold that creates the binding site for ATP. Although proline and leucine are both nonpolar amino acids, B is incorrect—proline creates kinks in helices and thus would be expected to disturb the large conformational change required (see Chapter 7). In general, binding of the first substrate to an enzyme creates conformational changes that increases the binding of the second substrate or brings functional groups into position for further steps in the reaction. Thus, a mutation need not be in the active site to impair the reaction, and A is incorrect. It would probably take more energy to fold the enzyme into the form required for the transition-state complex, and fewer molecules would acquire the energy necessary (thus, C is incorrect). The active site lacks the functional groups required for an alternate mechanism (thus, E is incorrect).

3. **The answer is A.** When the pK_a of an ionizable group is below the pH value, the group will be deprotonated. When the pK_a of an ionizable group is above the pH value, the group will be protonated. Thus, at pH 5.2, glutamate 35 (with a pK_a of 5.9, which is greater than 5.2) will remain protonated, and aspartate 52 (with a pK_a of 4.5, which is less than 5.2) will be ionized (because the side chain carries a negative charge when deprotonated). Therefore, E35 is protonated, and D52 is ionized. There is sufficient information presented to answer this question.

4. **The answer is A.** The glucose residue from UDP-glucose is being transferred to the alcohol group of another compound. In isomerization reactions, groups are transferred within the same molecule (thus, B is incorrect). There is no cleavage or synthesis of carbon–carbon bonds (thus, C and D are incorrect). Oxidation–reduction has not occurred because no hydrogens or oxygen atoms have been removed or added in the conversion of substrate to product.

5. **The answer is C.** Transfer of a carbohydrate residue from one molecule to another is a glycosyltransferase reaction. Kinases transfer phosphate groups, dehydrogenases transfer electrons as hydrogen atoms or hydride ions, transaminases transfer amino groups, and isomerases transfer atoms within the same molecule.

CHAPTER 9

1. **The answer is B.** The rate of the reaction is directly proportional to the proportion of enzyme molecules that contain bound substrate. Thus, it is at 50% of its maximal rate when 50% of the molecules contain bound substrate (thus, A, C, and D are incorrect). The rate of the reaction is directly proportional to the amount of enzyme present, which is incorporated into the term V_{max} (where $V_{max} = k$[total enzyme]) (thus, E is incorrect).

2. **The answer is A.** The patient's enzyme has a lower K_m than the normal enzyme and, therefore, requires a lower glucose concentration to reach ½V_{max}. Thus, the mutation may have increased the affinity of the enzyme for glucose, but it has greatly decreased the subsequent steps of the reaction leading to formation of the transition-state complex, and thus V_{max} is much slower. The difference in V_{max} is so great that the patient's enzyme is much slower whether you are above or below its K_m for glucose. You can test this by substituting 2 mM glucose and 4 mM glucose into the Michaelis-Menten equation, $v = V_{max} S/(K_m + S)$ for the patient's enzyme and for the normal enzyme. The values are 0.0095 U/mg and 0.0129 U/mg for the patient's enzyme versus 23.2 U/mg and 37.2 U/mg for the normal enzyme, respectively (thus, B and C are incorrect). At near-saturating glucose concentrations, both enzymes will be near V_{max}, which is equal to k_{cat} times the enzyme concentration. Thus, it will take nearly 500 times as much of the patient's enzyme to achieve the normal rate (93 ÷ 0.2), and so C is incorrect. E is incorrect because rates change most as you decrease substrate concentration below the K_m. Thus, the enzyme with the highest K_m will show the largest changes in rate.

3. **The answer is B.** Ethanol has a structure very similar to methanol (a structural analog) and thus can be expected to compete with methanol at its substrate-binding site. This inhibition is competitive with respect to methanol and, therefore, V_{max} for methanol will not be altered and ethanol inhibition can be overcome by high concentrations of methanol (thus, A, C, and D are incorrect). E is illogical because the substrate methanol stays in the same binding site as it is converted to its product, formaldehyde.

4. **The answer is A.** Allosteric activators will shift the sigmoidal kinetic curve for the enzyme to the left, thereby reducing the $K_{m,app}$ (so one-half maximal velocity will be reached at a lower substrate concentration), without affecting the maximal velocity (although in some cases V_{max} can also be increased). Allosteric inhibitors will shift the curve to the right, increasing the $K_{m,app}$ and, sometimes, also decreasing the V_{max}.

5. **The answer is C.** The most effective regulation should be a feed-forward type of regulation in which the toxin activates the pathway. One of the most common ways this occurs is through the toxin acting to increase the amount

of enzyme by increasing transcription of its gene. A and B describe mechanisms of feedback regulation, in which the end product of the pathway decreases its own rate of synthesis and are, therefore, incorrect. D is incorrect because a high K_m for the toxin might prevent the enzyme from working effectively at low toxin concentrations, although it would allow the enzyme to respond to increases of toxin concentration. It would do little good for the toxin to allosterically activate any enzyme but the rate-limiting enzyme (thus, E is incorrect).

CHAPTER 10

1. **The answer is D.** Phosphatidylserine, the only lipid with a net negative charge at neutral pH, is located in the inner leaflet, where it contributes to the more negatively charged intracellular side of the membrane. The membrane is composed principally of phospholipids and cholesterol (thus, A is incorrect). Phospholipids are amphipathic (contain polar and nonpolar ends, see Chapter 5), with their polar head groups extending into the aqueous medium inside and outside of the cell. The fatty acyl groups of the two layers face each other on the inside of the bilayer, and the polar oligosaccharides groups of glycoproteins and glycolipids extend into the aqueous medium (thus, B, C, and E are incorrect).

2. **The answer is E.** The transmembrane regions are α-helices with hydrophobic amino acid side chains binding to membrane lipids. The hydrophobic interactions hinder their extraction (thus, A and D are incorrect). Because they are not easily extracted, they are classified as integral proteins (thus, B is incorrect). The carboxy and amino terminals of transmembrane proteins extend into the aqueous intracellular and extracellular medium and thus need to contain many hydrophilic residues (thus, C is incorrect).

3. **The answer is A.** Most of fuel oxidation and ATP generation occurs in the mitochondrion. Although some may also occur in the cytosol, the amount is much smaller in most cells.

4. **The answer is A.** Channels that open in response to a change in ion concentration across the membrane (which results in a change in membrane potential, or voltage, across the membrane) are known as *voltage-gated channels*. The calcium influx is not passive diffusion, as a carrier is required (the channel). This is not an active transport process, as calcium is flowing down its concentration gradient, and the cell is not concentrating calcium within it. A ligand-gated channel opens when a particular ligand binds to it, not when the membrane potential changes. There is no phosphorylation event described in the opening of this calcium channel, so it is not an example of a phosphorylation-gated channel.

5. **The answer is A.** ATP is required by the vesicular ATPase, which uses the energy of ATP hydrolysis to concentrate protons within the lysosome, which generates the acidic environment required for enzyme activity. Answer B is, therefore, incorrect because lysosomes are acidic compared to the cytoplasm, not basic. ATP is not required to activate, regulate, or as a cofactor, for any lysosomal hydrolase.

CHAPTER 11

1. **The answer is C.** Each chemical messenger has a specific protein receptor in a target cell that will generally bind only that messenger, and only that cell responds to the message. Only endocrine messengers reach their target cells through the blood (thus, A is incorrect). Many chemical messengers have paracrine actions. Messengers are secreted by only one type of cell (thus, B is incorrect). Many messengers bind to extracellular domains of plasma membrane receptors and do not enter the cells (thus, D is incorrect). No chemical messengers are metabolized to intracellular second messengers (thus, E is incorrect).

2. **The answer is D.** Only lipophilic chemical messengers are able to diffuse into cells and bind to transcription-factor receptors. Because they are water insoluble, they must be transported in the blood bound to a protein. Cytokines, polypeptide hormones, and small-molecule neurotransmitters are not lipophilic (thus, A and B are incorrect). Because they work through regulation of gene transcription, their effects are relatively slow (thus, C is incorrect). Like all messengers, they are secreted in response to a specific stimulus (thus, E is incorrect).

3. **The answer is D.** Parathyroid hormone is a polypeptide hormone and thus must bind to a plasma membrane receptor instead of an intracellular receptor (thus, A and B are incorrect). Hormones that bind to plasma membrane receptors do not need to enter the cell to transmit their signals (thus, C is incorrect). Heptahelical receptors work through heterotrimeric G proteins that have an α-subunit, and tyrosine kinase receptors work through monomeric G proteins that have no subunits (thus, D is correct and E is incorrect).

4. **The answer is C.** $G\alpha_s$ normally activates adenylyl cyclase to generate cyclic adenosine monophosphate (cAMP) in response to parathyroid hormone. Because the patient has end-organ unresponsiveness, he or she must have a deficiency in the signaling pathway (thus, A is incorrect) and cAMP will be decreased. Decreased GTPase activity will increase binding to adenylyl cyclase and increase responsiveness (thus, B is incorrect). Neither IP_3 nor phosphatidylinositol 3,4,5-trisphosphate are involved in signal transduction by the $G\alpha_s$ subunit.

5. **The answer is A.** *GRB2* binding to the receptor requires phosphotyrosine residues on the receptor. *GRB2* normally binds to the receptor through its SH2 domains, which

recognize phosphotyrosine residues on the receptor. In the absence of these phosphotyrosine residues, *GRB2* would not be able to bind to the receptor. Growth factor binding to the receptor does not require phosphotyrosine residues. It is the binding of the growth factor to the receptor, through a conformational change in the receptor that activates the intrinsic tyrosine kinase of the receptor, which then leads to autophosphorylation of the receptor. The lack of intracellular tyrosine residues on the receptor will not alter the events initiated by the conformational change of the receptor. Dimerization of receptors occurs upon binding growth factor and is not dependent on the activation of the tyrosine kinase activity, nor of autophosphorylation of the receptor.

CHAPTER 12

1. **The answer is D.** The complementary strand must run in the opposite direction, so the 5′-end must base-pair with the G at the 3′-end of the given strand. Therefore, the 5′-end of the complementary strand must be C. G would then base-pair to C, A to T, and T to A. B is incorrect because the bases do not base-pair with each other with the sequences indicated, C is incorrect because U is not found in DNA, and E is incorrect because it has the wrong polarity (the 5′-T in answer E would not base-pair with the 3′-G in the given sequence).

2. **The answer is C.** The RNA strand must be complementary to the DNA strand, and A in DNA base-pairs with U in RNA, whereas T in DNA base-pairs with A in RNA, G in DNA base-pairs with C in RNA, and C in DNA base-pairs with G in RNA. A and E are incorrect because they contain T, which is found in DNA, not RNA. B is incorrect because the base-pairing rules are broken when the strands are aligned in antiparallel fashion. D is incorrect because the polarity of the strand is incorrect (if one were to switch the 5′- and 3′-ends, the answer would be correct).

3. **The answer is D.** The phosphate is in an ester bond to two ribose groups, generating the phosphodiester bond in the DNA backbone. None of the other interactions is correct.

4. **The answer is E.** There are four possible bases at each position in the molecule, so as a total there are 4^8 possibilities. This comes out to 65,536 possible DNA sequences for a molecule that is only 8 bases long. Because the sequence of one strand in double-stranded DNA dictates the sequence of the other strand, we do not need to consider the second strand in this calculation.

5. **The answer is B.** The backbone is composed of the phosphates and deoxyribose in phosphodiester linkages. The bases are internal to the backbone, base-paired to bases in the complementary strand, and forming stacking interactions within the double helix.

CHAPTER 13

1. **The answer is B.** The 3′-to-5′ exonuclease activity is required for proofreading (check the base just inserted, and if it is incorrect, remove it), and reverse transcriptase does not have this activity, whereas pol δ does. Both reverse transcriptase and pol δ synthesize DNA in the 5′-to-3′ directions (all DNA polymerases do this), and both follow standard Watson–Crick base-pairing rules (A with T or U, G with C). Neither polymerase can synthesize DNA in the wrong direction (3′-to-5′) nor insert inosine into a growing DNA chain. Thus, the only difference between the two polymerases is answer B.

2. **The answer is D.** In 50 seconds, each replication origin will have synthesized 100 kb of DNA (50 in each direction). Because there are 10 origins, 10 × 100 will yield the 1,000 kb needed to replicate the DNA. The first origin will be 50 kb from one end, and the remaining nine origins will each be 100 kb apart.

3. **The answer is E.** The role of the primer is to provide a free 3′-OH group for DNA polymerase to add the next nucleotide and form a phosphodiester bond. When DNA repair occurs, one of the remaining bases in the DNA will have a free 3′-OH, which DNA polymerase I will use to begin extension of the DNA.

4. **The answer is A.** Helicase aids in unwinding DNA strands, along with DNA gyrase, so that the replication fork can keep moving. The 3′-to-5′ exonuclease activity is required for proofreading by DNA polymerases, DNA ligase connects a 3′-OH with an adjacent 5′-phosphate, primase lays down the RNA primer, and AP endonuclease looks for apurinic or apyrimidinic sites (without a purine or pyrimidine base, respectively) to remove them from the DNA strand.

5. **The answer is B.** Xeroderma pigmentosum is a set of diseases all related to an inability to repair thymine dimers, leading to an inability to excise UV-damaged DNA. It does not affect bypass polymerases, which can synthesize across the damaged region, sometimes making mutations in its path. The primase gene, or mismatch repair, is not involved in excising thymine dimers. Proofreading ability of DNA polymerases is likewise not involved in this process.

CHAPTER 14

1. **The answer is B.** The transcript that is produced is copied from the DNA template strand, which must be of the opposite orientation from the transcript. So the 5′-end of the template strand should base-pair with the 3′-end of the transcript, or the G. Thus, CGTACGGAT would base-pair with the transcript and would represent the template strand.

2. **The answer is A. Amanda Tin** weighs 50 kg, and if 1 mg/kg body weight is the LD$_{50}$, then for Amanda, 5 mg of toxin would bring her to the LD$_{50}$. Because one mushroom contains 7 mg of the toxin, ingesting just one mushroom could be fatal.

3. **The answer is C.** Enhancer sequences can be thousands of bases away from the basal promoter and still stimulate transcription of the gene. This is accomplished by looping of the DNA so that the proteins binding to the enhancer sequence (transactivators) can also bind to proteins bound to the promoter (coactivators). A promoter-proximal element is a DNA sequence nearby the promoter that can bind transcription factors that aid in recruiting RNA polymerase to the promoter region.

4. **The answer is D.** Both prokaryotes and eukaryotes require RNA polymerase binding to an upstream promoter element. Answer A applies only to eukaryotes; prokaryote mRNA is not capped, nor does it contain a poly(A) tail. Prokaryotes have no nucleus, thus the 5′-end of an mRNA is immediately available for ribosome binding and initiation of translation (thus, B is incorrect). Answer C is incorrect overall; RNA synthesis, like DNA synthesis, is always in the 5′-to-3′ direction. Answer E is incorrect because introns are present only in eukaryotic genes.

5. **The answer is A.** A β-thalassemia refers to a condition in which the α-chain of globin is produced in excess of the β-chain. The greater the ratio of α- to β-chain, the more severe the disease. Patients are usually asymptomatic at a ratio of 2:1, but once the ratio is greater than 2:1, symptoms will become evident. The reduction in β-globin synthesis can come about because of splicing mutations, promoter mutations, or point mutations within the coding regions of the β-globin gene.

CHAPTER 15

1. **The answer is A.** It is important to note that the question is asking about prokaryotic mechanisms. In prokaryotes, there is no nucleus (thus, E cannot be correct), and translation begins before transcription is terminated (coupled translation–transcription, thus B is incorrect). Therefore, before the ribosome can move from one codon to the next (translocation), or the protein synthesis machinery terminates (via termination factors), the initiating tRNA must bind and align with the mRNA to initiate translation, indicating that answer A is the first step of the choices listed that must occur.

2. **The answer is C.** Because the extract contains all normal components, the Cys-tRNA charged with alanine will compete with Cys-tRNA charged with cysteine for binding to the cysteine codons. Thus, the protein will have some alanines put in the place of cysteine, leading to a deficiency of cysteine residues. Answer A is incorrect

because the tRNA recognizes the cysteine codon, not the alanine codon. Answer B is incorrect because of the competition mentioned previously.

3. **The answer is C.** There are 64 triplet codes, and only 20 amino acids, so some amino acids have more than one codon that codes for them. The other answers do not address this issue.

4. **The answer is A.** In order to answer this question, one first needs to find the start codon: AUG in mRNA, ATG in DNA. Bases 3 to 5 in the sequence contain this element. Next, the sequence needs to specify a phenylalanine residue near the amino terminus, which is UUU or UUC in mRNA or TTT or TTG in DNA, but these sequences need to be in frame with the initiating methionine codon. The last element to look for is the absence of a premature stop codon, as this protein is 300 amino acids long. There is no stop sequence in the remaining bases of this piece of DNA. For answer B, the last three bases of this sequence are TGA, which in mRNA would be UGA, and this is an in-frame stop signal. This sequence would not give rise to a protein that contained 300 amino acids. For answer C, the TTT in that sequence (bases 10 to 12) are not in frame with the initiating methionine, indicating that there is no phenylalanine near the amino terminus in the protein encoded by this sequence. For answers D and E, there are no ATG sequences, indicating that the initiating methionine is absent, and that this stretch of DNA cannot code for the amino terminal end of a protein.

5. **The answer is D.** Because each codon is three bases long, there are four possible bases that can fill each codon position (A, T, C, or G). That means there are $4 \times 4 \times 4$ possible combinations of bases for a total of 64 codons. There are fewer than 64 aminoacyl tRNA synthetases because one tRNA recognizes more than one codon (as a result of wobble); thus, A is incorrect. Not all bases participate in wobble (G can base-pair with U, and C, A, or U can base-pair with I, but those are the only combinations possible), and only one reading frame is used for each message produced (thus, B and C are incorrect). The rate of protein synthesis is not dependent on the number of codons, but rather on how rapidly the components required to synthesize proteins can be brought to the ribosomes and how much RNA is present to be translated.

CHAPTER 16

1. **The answer is E.** Many prokaryotic genes are organized into operons, in which one polycistronic mRNA contains the translational start and stop sites for several related genes. Although each gene within the mRNA can be read from a different reading frame, the reading frame is always consistent within each gene (thus, A is incorrect). Redundancy in codon/tRNA interactions has nothing

to do with multiple cistrons within an mRNA (thus, B is incorrect). Operator sequences are in DNA and initiate transcription, not translation (thus, C is incorrect). Alternative splicing occurs only in eukaryotes (which have introns), not in prokaryotes (thus, D is incorrect).

2. **The answer is D.** In order to transcribe the *lac* operon, the repressor protein (*lac I* gene product) must bind allolactose and leave the operator region, and the cAMP–CRP complex must bind to the promoter in order for RNA polymerase to bind. Of the choices offered, only raising cAMP levels can allow transcription of the operon when both lactose and glucose are high. Raising cAMP, even though glucose is present, will allow the cAMP–CRP complex to bind and recruit RNA polymerase. Answers that call for mutations in the repressor (answers A and E) will not affect binding of cAMP–CRP. Mutations in the DNA (answers B and C) do not allow CRP binding in the absence of cAMP.

3. **The answer is A.** The repressor will bind to the operator and block transcription of all genes in the operon unless prevented by the inducer allolactose. If the repressor has lost its affinity for the inducer, it cannot dissociate from the operator and the genes in the operon will not be expressed (thus, E is incorrect). If the repressor has lost its affinity for the operator (answer B), then the operon would be expressed constitutively. Because the question states that there is a mutation in the *I* (repressor) gene, answer D is incorrect, and mutations in the *I* gene do not affect *trans*acting factors from binding to the promoter, although the only other one for the *lac* operon is the CRP.

4. **The answer is B.** The sequence, if read 5′ to 3′, is identical to the complementary sequence read 5′ to 3′. None of the other sequences fits this pattern.

5. **The answer is A.** All DNA-binding proteins contain an α-helix that binds to the major or minor groove in DNA. These proteins do not recognize RNA molecules (thus, B is incorrect), nor do they form bonds between the peptide backbone and the DNA backbone (thus, C is incorrect; if this was correct, how could there be any specificity in protein binding to DNA?). Only zinc fingers contain zinc, and dimers are formed by hydrogen bonding—not by disulfide linkages.

CHAPTER 17

1. **The answer is B.** All DNA fragments are negatively charged and will migrate toward the positive charge. The only difference between the fragments is their size, and the smaller fragments will move faster than the larger fragments because of their ability to squeeze through the gel at a faster rate.

2. **The answer is E.** The enzyme recognizes six bases, and the probability that the correct base is in each position is 1 in 4, so the overall probability is $(¼)^6$, or 1 in 4,096 bases.

3. **The answer is B.** The Sanger technique requires both deoxyribonucleotides and dideoxyribonucleotides, and a template DNA. It does not use Taq polymerase (which is for PCR), nor does it need reverse transcriptase (which is required for producing DNA from RNA).

4. **The answer is A.** PCR experiments, using primers that flank the repeat area, can determine the number of repeats in a gene as compared to a gene with no or few repeats (the PCR product would be larger for a region containing multiple repeats as compared to a region with few repeats). Similarly, using restriction endonuclease recognition sites, which flank the repeat, one will see restriction fragment length polymorphisms, the length of the restriction fragment being dependent on the number of repeats in the gene. SNP analysis, however, examines single nucleotide polymorphisms, not multiple triplet repeats, and would not be a suitable method for determining a region of the genome, which contained multiple triplet nucleotide repeats. Most individuals will have a certain number of repeats, and PCR and RFLP will enable expanded repeat regions to be distinguished from small repeat regions relatively easily.

5. **The answer is C.** A Northern blot allows one to determine which genes are being transcribed in a tissue at the time of mRNA isolation. The mRNA is run on a gel, transferred to filter paper, and then analyzed with a probe. If albumin is being transcribed, then a probe for albumin should give a positive result in the Northern blot. A library screening will not indicate if a particular gene is being transcribed, nor will a Southern blot. Those techniques will only allow one to determine that the gene is present in the genome. A Western blot analyzes protein content, not mRNA content. Analysis of VNTRs does not provide information about whether a gene is transcribed.

CHAPTER 18

1. **The answer is C.** The *ras* oncogene has a point mutation in codon 12 (position 35 of the DNA chain) in which T replaces G. This changes the codon from one that specifies glycine to one that specifies valine. Thus, there is a single amino acid change in the proto-oncogene (a valine for a glycine) that changes *ras* to an oncogene.

2. **The answer is C.** Ras, when it is oncogenic, has lost its GTPase activity and thus remains active for a longer time. Answer A is incorrect because GAP proteins activate the GTPase activity of Ras, and this mutation would make Ras less active. cAMP does not interact directly with Ras (thus, B is incorrect), and if Ras could no longer bind GTP, it would not be active (hence, D is also incorrect). Ras is not phosphorylated by the MAP kinase (thus, E is incorrect).

3. **The answer is B.** Retroviral oncogenes were originally obtained from genes on a host's chromosome. All retroviruses do not contain oncogenes (thus, A is incorrect); proto-oncogenes are found in host cells, not viruses (thus, C is incorrect); the oncogenes that lead to human disease are very similar to those that are mutated in animals (thus, D is incorrect); and oncogenes are a misexpressed or mutated version of normal cellular genes, not viral genes (thus, E is incorrect).

4. **The answer is D.** When p53 increases in response to DNA damage, it acts as a transcription factor and induces the transcription of p21, which blocks phosphorylation of Rb. Rb then stays bound to transcription factor E2F, and E2F cannot induce the genes required for the G_1-to-S transition. p53 does not induce transcription of either cyclin D or cdk4 (thus, A and B are incorrect), nor does p53 bind to E2F (thus, C is incorrect), nor does p53 contain kinase activity (thus, E is incorrect).

5. **The answer is B.** Tumor-suppressor genes balance cell growth and quiescence. When they are not expressed (via loss-of-function mutations), the balance shifts to cell proliferation and tumorigenesis (thus, A is incorrect). Answer C is incorrect because tumor-suppressor genes do not act on viral genes, answer D is incorrect because tumor-suppressor genes are not specifically targeted to just one aspect of the cell cycle, and answer E is incorrect because a loss of expression of tumor-suppressor genes leads to tumor formation, not expression of these genes.

CHAPTER 19

1. **The answer is E.** Both of the high-energy phosphate bonds in ATP are located between phosphate groups (both the α- and β-phosphates, and the β- and γ-phosphates). The phosphate bond between the α-phosphate and ribose (or adenosine) is not a high-energy bond (thus, A and B are incorrect), and there is no phosphate between the ribose and adenine, or two hydroxyl groups in the ribose ring; therefore, answers C and D are incorrect.

2. **The answer is C.** The change in enthalpy, ΔH, is the total amount of heat that can be released in a reaction. The first law of thermodynamics states that the total energy of a system remains constant, and the second law of thermodynamics states the universe tends toward a state of disorder (thus, A and B are incorrect). Answer D is incorrect because $\Delta G^{0'}$ is the standard free energy change measured at 25°C and a pH of 7. Answer E is incorrect because a high-energy bond releases more than about 7 kcal/mol of heat when it is hydrolyzed. The definition of a high-energy bond is based on the hydrolysis of one of the high-energy bonds of ATP.

3. **The answer is A.** The concentration of the substrates and products influence the direction of a reaction. Answer B is incorrect because reactions with a positive free energy, at 1 M concentrations of substrate and product, will proceed in the reverse direction. Answer C is incorrect because substrate and product concentrations do influence the free energy of a reaction. Answer D is incorrect because the free energy must be considered (in addition to the substrate and product concentrations) to determine the direction of a reaction. Answer E is false; an enzyme's efficiency does not influence the direction of a reaction.

4. **The answer is C.** A heart attack results in decreased pumping of blood and thus a decreased oxygen supply to the heart (thus, A is incorrect). The lack of oxygen leads to a lack of ATP (thus, B is incorrect) because of an inability to perform oxidative phosphorylation. The lack of ATP impairs the working of Na^+, K^+-ATPase, which pumps sodium out of the cell in exchange for potassium. Therefore, intracellular levels of sodium will increase as Na^+ enters the cell through other transport mechanisms (thus, E is incorrect). The high intracellular sodium concentration then blocks the functioning of the Na^+/H^+ antiporter (which sends protons out of the cell in exchange for sodium. Because intracellular sodium is high, the driving force for this reaction is lost), which leads to increased intracellular H^+ or a lower intracellular pH (thus, C is correct). The intracellular pH also decreases because of glycolysis in the absence of oxygen, which produces lactic acid. The loss of the sodium gradient, coupled with the lack of ATP, leads to increased calcium in the cell (thus, D is incorrect) because of an inability to pump calcium out.

5. **The answer is C.** NAD^+ accepts two electrons as hydride ions to form NADH (thus, A and B are incorrect). Answers D and E are incorrect because FAD can accept two single electrons from separate atoms, together with protons, or can accept a pair of electrons.

CHAPTER 20

1. **The answer is E.** The α-keto acid dehydrogenase complex uses thiamine pyrophosphate, lipoic acid, FAD, NAD^+, and CoASH. Of these, only lipoate is used by no other enzyme and is unique to the α-keto acid dehydrogenase complexes. Many dehydrogenases use NAD^+ as a coenzyme (such as malate dehydrogenase) or FAD (such as succinate dehydrogenase) (thus, A and B are incorrect). Answer C is incorrect because GDP is not a coenzyme for α-keto acid dehydrogenase complexes. Answer D is incorrect because H_2O is not a coenzyme.

2. **The answer is B.** Thiamine pyrophosphate is the coenzyme for the α-ketoglutarate dehydrogenase and pyruvate dehydrogenase complexes. With these complexes inactive, pyruvic acid and α-ketoglutaric acid accumulate and dissociate to generate the anion and H^+. As α-ketoglutarate is not listed as an answer, the only possible answer is pyruvate.

3. The answer is A. Succinate dehydrogenase is the only TCA cycle enzyme located in the inner mitochondrial membrane. The other enzymes are in the mitochondrial matrix. Answer B is incorrect because succinate dehydrogenase is not regulated by NADH. Answer C is incorrect because α-ketoglutarate dehydrogenase also contains a bound FAD (the difference is that the FAD[2H] in α-ketoglutarate dehydrogenase donates its electrons to NAD^+, whereas the FAD[2H] in succinate dehydrogenase donates its electrons directly to the electron-transfer chain). Answer D is incorrect because both succinate dehydrogenase and aconitase have Fe–S centers. Answer E is incorrect because succinate dehydrogenase is not regulated by a kinase. Kinases regulate enzymes by phosphorylation (e.g., the regulation of pyruvate dehydrogenase occurs through reversible phosphorylation).

4. The answer is E. NADH decreases during exercise to generate energy for the exercise (if it were increased, it would inhibit the cycle and slow it down); thus the NADH/NAD$^+$ ratio is decreased; and the lack of NADH activates flux through isocitrate dehydrogenase, α-ketoglutarate dehydrogenase, and malate dehydrogenase. Isocitrate dehydrogenase is inhibited by NADH; so, answer A is not correct. Fumarase is not regulated, thus answer B is incorrect. The four-carbon intermediates of the cycle are regenerated during each turn of the cycle, so their concentrations do not decrease (thus, C is incorrect). Product inhibition of citrate synthase would slow the cycle and not generate more energy; hence, D is incorrect.

5. The answer is D. Pantothenate is the vitamin precursor of coenzyme A. Niacin is the vitamin precursor of NAD, and riboflavin is the vitamin precursor of FAD and FMN. Vitamins A and C are used with only minor modifications, if any.

CHAPTER 21

1. The answer is B. For a component to be in the oxidized state, it must have donated, or never received, electrons. Complex II will metabolize succinate to produce fumarate (generating FAD[2H]), but no succinate is available in this experiment. Thus, complex II never sees any electrons and is always in an oxidized state. The substrate malate is oxidized to oxaloacetate, generating NADH, which donates electrons to complex I of the electron-transport chain. These electrons are transferred to coenzyme Q, which donates electrons to complex III, to cytochrome c, and then to complex IV. Cyanide will block the transfer of electrons from complex IV to oxygen, so all previous complexes containing electrons will be backed up and the electrons will be "stuck" in the complexes, making these components reduced. Thus, answers A and C through E must be incorrect.

2. The answer is D. The proton motive force consists of two components: a ΔpH and a $\Delta\psi$ (electrical component). The addition of valinomycin and potassium will destroy the electrical component but not the pH component. Thus, the proton motive force will decrease but will still be greater than zero. Thus, the other answers are all incorrect.

3. The answer is D. Dinitrophenol equilibrates the proton concentration across the inner mitochondrial membrane, thereby destroying the proton motive force. Thus, none of the other answers is correct.

4. The answer is A. A deficiency of Fe–S centers in the electron-transport chain would impair the transfer of electrons down the chain and reduce ATP production by oxidative phosphorylation. Answer B is incorrect because the decreased production of water from the electron-transport chain is not of sufficient magnitude to cause her to become dehydrated. Answer C is incorrect because iron does not form a chelate with NADH and FAD(2H). Answer D is incorrect because iron is not a cofactor for α-ketoglutarate dehydrogenase. Answer E is incorrect because iron does not accompany the protons that make up the proton gradient.

5. The answer is B. NADH would not be reoxidized as efficiently by the electron-transport chain, and the NADH/NAD$^+$ ratio would increase. Answer A is incorrect because ATP would not be produced at a high rate. Therefore, ADP would build up, and the ATP:ADP ratio would be low. Answer C is incorrect because OXPHOS diseases can be caused by mutations in nuclear or mitochondrial DNA, and not all OXPHOS proteins are encoded by the X chromosome. Answer D is incorrect because, depending on the nature of the mutation, the activity of complex II of the electron-transport chain might be normal or decreased, but there is no reason to expect increased activity. Answer E is incorrect because the integrity of the inner mitochondrial membrane would not necessarily be affected. It could be, but it would not be expected for all patients with OXPHOS disorders.

CHAPTER 22

1. The answer is B. The major roles of glycolysis are to generate energy and to produce precursors for other biosynthetic pathways. Gluconeogenesis is the pathway that generates glucose (thus, A is incorrect), FAD(2H) is produced in the mitochondria by a variety of reactions but not glycolysis (thus, C is incorrect), glycogen synthesis occurs under conditions in which glycolysis is inhibited (thus, D is incorrect), and glycolysis does not hydrolyze ATP to generate heat (i.e., nonshivering thermogenesis; thus, E is incorrect).

2. The answer is D. By starting with glyceraldehyde 3-phosphate, the energy-requiring steps of glycolysis are bypassed. Thus, as glyceraldehyde 3-phosphate is converted to pyruvate, two molecules of ATP will be produced (at the phosphoglycerate kinase and pyruvate kinase steps) and one molecule of NADH will be produced (at the glyceraldehyde-3-phosphate dehydrogenase step).

3. **The answer is H.** Glucose 1-phosphate is isomerized to glucose 6-phosphate, which then enters glycolysis. This skips the hexokinase step, which uses 1 ATP. Thus, starting from glucose 1-phosphate, one would get the normal 2 ATP and 2 NADH, but with one less ATP used, for a total yield of 3 ATP and 2 NADH.

4. **The answer is B.** The pathway consumes 2 ATP at the beginning of the pathway and produces 4 ATP at the end of the pathway for each molecule of glucose. Therefore, the net energy production is 2 ATP for each molecule of glucose. Glycolysis synthesizes ATP via substrate-level phosphorylation, not oxidative phosphorylation (thus, A is incorrect) and synthesizes two molecules of pyruvate in the process (thus, D is incorrect). The pathway is cytosolic (thus, D is incorrect), and the rate-limiting step is the one catalyzed by PFK-1 (thus, C is incorrect).

5. **The answer is D.** Each mole of glucose produces 2 mol of pyruvate, 2 mol of ATP, and 2 mol of NADH during glycolysis. As each pyruvate is converted to acetyl-CoA, 1 NADH is produced. Each acetyl-CoA enters the TCA cycle to produce 1 GTP, 3 NADH, and 1 FAD(2H). Therefore, the oxidation of 1 mol of glucose would yield a total of 2 mol of ATP and 2 mol of NADH from glycolytic reactions; 2 mol of NADH from the conversion of 2 mol of pyruvate to 2 mol of acetyl-CoA; and 6 mol of NADH, 2 mol of GTP, and 2 mol of FAD(2H) from the oxidation of 2 mol of acetyl-CoA in the TCA cycle. Each GTP has the same energy as 1 ATP. Each mitochondrial NADH is oxidized to produce 2.5 ATP. Each cytoplasmic NADH can generate either 1.5 ATP (using the glycerol phosphate shuttle) or 2.5 ATP (using the malate–aspartate shuttle). Each mitochondrial FAD(2H) is oxidized to produce 1.5 ATP. Therefore, the total ATP yield from the oxidation of 1 mol of glucose is 30 to 32 mol of ATP (30 mol if the glycerol phosphate shuttle is used; 32 mol if the malate–aspartate shuttle is used).

CHAPTER 23

1. **The answer is D.** The ETF:CoQ oxidoreductase is required to transfer the electrons from the FAD(2H) of the acyl-CoA dehydrogenase to coenzyme Q. When the oxidoreductase is missing, the electrons cannot be transferred, and the acyl-CoA dehydrogenase cannot continue to oxidize fatty acids because it has a reduced cofactor instead of an oxidized cofactor. During times of fasting, when fatty acids are the primary energy source, no energy will be forthcoming, gluconeogenesis is shut down, and death may result. The lack of this enzyme does not affect the other pathways listed as potential answers.

2. **The answer is C.** An 18-carbon saturated fatty acid would require eight spirals of fatty acid oxidation, which yields 8 NADH, 8 FAD(2H), and 9 acyl-CoA. As each NADH gives rise to 2.5 ATP, and each FAD(2H) gives rise to 1.5 ATP, the reduced cofactors will give rise to 32 ATP. Each acyl-CoA gives rise to 10 ATP, for a total of 90 ATP. This then yields 122 ATP, but we must subtract 2 ATP for the activation step, at which two high-energy bonds are broken. Thus, the net yield is 120 ATPs for each molecule of fatty acid oxidized.

3. **The answer is A.** Fatty acid oxidation is initiated by the acyl-CoA dehydrogenase (an oxidation step), followed by hydration of the double bond formed in the first step, followed by the hydroxyacyl-CoA dehydrogenase step (another oxidation), and then attack of the β-carbonyl by CoA, breaking a carbon–carbon bond (the thiolase step).

4. **The answer is D.** A lack of carnitine would lead to an inability to transport fatty acyl-CoAs into the mitochondria. This would lead to a decrease in fatty acid oxidation (thus, A is incorrect), a decrease in ketone body production because fatty acids cannot be oxidized (thus, B is incorrect), a decrease in blood glucose levels because gluconeogenesis is impaired as a result of a lack of energy (thus, C is incorrect), and no increase in the levels of very long-chain fatty acids because these are initially oxidized in the peroxisomes and do not require carnitine for entry into that organelle (thus, E is incorrect). The ω-oxidation system, which creates dicarboxylic acids, is found in the endoplasmic reticulum, and as the concentration of fatty acyl-CoAs increase in tissues, they will be oxidized by this alternative pathway.

5. **The answer is E.** Fatty acids are the major fuel for the body during prolonged exercise and fasting. Answers A, B, and C are incorrect because glucose would be the major fuel after eating. Answer D is incorrect because, at the start of exercise, muscle glycogen and gluconeogenesis are being used as the major source of fuel.

CHAPTER 24

1. **The answer is D.** Vitamin B6 is a water-soluble vitamin that is important for amino acid and glycogen metabolism but has no role in protecting against free radical damage. Ascorbate (vitamin C), vitamin E, and β-carotene can all react with free radicals to terminate chain propagation, whereas superoxide dismutase uses the superoxide radical as a substrate and converts it to hydrogen peroxide, and glutathione peroxidase removes hydrogen peroxide from the cell, converting it to water.

2. **The answer is B.** Superoxide dismutase combines two superoxide radicals to produce hydrogen peroxide and molecular oxygen. None of the other reactions is correct.

3. **The answer is C.** Vitamin E donates an electron and proton to the radical, thereby converting the radical to a stable form (LOO• → LOOH). The vitamin thus prevents the free radical from oxidizing another compound by extracting an H from that compound and propagating a free radical chain reaction. The radical form of vitamin E generated is relatively stable and actually donates another electron and proton to a second free radical, forming oxidized vitamin E.

4. **The answer is B.** The Fenton reaction is the nonenzymatic donation of an electron from Fe^{2+} to H_2O_2 to produce Fe^{3+}, the hydroxyl radical, and hydroxide ion. Only Fe^{2+} or Cu^{1+} can be used in this reaction; thus, the other answers are incorrect.

5. **The answer is E.** Histones coat nuclear DNA and protect it from damage by radicals. Mitochondrial DNA lacks histones, so when radicals are formed, the DNA can be easily oxidized. Answers A and B are nonsensical; superoxide dismutase reduces radical concentrations, so the fact that it is present in the mitochondria should help to protect the DNA from damage, not enhance it; and glutathione also protects against radical damage, and if the nucleus lacks it, then one would expect higher levels of nuclear DNA damage, not reduced levels. Reactive oxygen species can diffuse across membranes, so answers C and D are incorrect. Other factors that increase mitochondrial DNA damage relative to nuclear DNA are the proximity of mitochondrial DNA to the membrane, and the fact that most radical species are formed from coenzyme Q, which is found within the mitochondria.

CHAPTER 25

1. **The answer is A.** Acetate is converted to acetyl-CoA by other tissues so that it can enter the TCA cycle to generate ATP. Answer B is incorrect because acetaldehyde, not acetate, is toxic to cells. Answer C is incorrect because acetate is excreted by the lung and kidney, and not in the bile. Answer D is incorrect because acetate cannot enter the TCA cycle directly. It must be converted to acetyl-CoA first. Answer E is incorrect because alcohol dehydrogenase converts ethanol into acetaldehyde. It does not convert acetate into NADH.

2. **The answer is B.** There is an increase in the NADH/NAD^+ ratio because NADH is produced by the conversion of ethanol to acetate (thus, D is incorrect). The increased ratio of NADH/NAD^+ favors the conversion of gluconeogenic precursors (such as lactate and oxaloacetate) to their reduced counterparts (lactate and malate, respectively), in order to generate NAD^+ for ethanol metabolism. This reduces the concentration of gluconeogenic precursors, slows down gluconeogenesis (thus, E is incorrect), and can lead to lactic acidosis. Answer A

is incorrect because the increase of NADH inhibits fatty acid oxidation. Answer C is incorrect because ketogenesis increases as a result of the increase of NADH. NADH inhibits key enzymes of the TCA cycle, thereby diverting acetyl-CoA from the TCA cycle and toward ketone body synthesis.

3. **The answer is C.** Disulfiram blocks the conversion of acetaldehyde to acetate. The accumulation of acetaldehyde is toxic and causes vomiting and nausea. Answers A and B are incorrect because disulfiram would not interfere with the absorption of ethanol or the first step of its metabolism. Answer D is incorrect because an acetaldehyde dehydrogenase inhibitor (such as disulfiram) would inhibit the conversion of ethanol to acetate, not increase the rate of the conversion. Answer E is incorrect because disulfiram does not interfere with the excretion of acetate, nor does acetate accumulation lead to nausea and vomiting.

4. **The answer is E.** An increase in the concentration of *CYP2E1* (the MEOS system) would result in an increase of ethanol metabolism and clearance from the blood (thus, A is incorrect). An increased rate of acetaldehyde production would result (thus, B is incorrect). The increase in *CYP2E1* would cause an increase in the probability of producing free radicals (thus, C is incorrect). Answer D is incorrect because hepatic damage would be more likely to occur because there is an increase of free radical production. Answer E is correct because the increased clearance rate of ethanol from the blood results in a higher alcohol tolerance level.

5. **The answer is E.** Liver cirrhosis is irreversible. It is an end-stage process of liver fibrosis. Answers A, B, C, and D are all consequences of liver disease, but they are all reversible. Therefore, E is the only answer that is correct.

CHAPTER 26

1. **The answer is D.** Once insulin is injected, glucose transport into the peripheral tissues will be enhanced. If the patient does not eat, the normal fasting level of glucose will drop even further because of the injection of insulin, which increases the movement of glucose into muscle and fat cells. The patient becomes hypoglycemic, as a result of which epinephrine is released from the adrenal medulla. This, in turn, leads to the signs and symptoms associated with high levels of epinephrine in the blood. Answers A and B are incorrect because as glucose levels drop, glucagon will be released from the pancreas to raise blood glucose levels, which would alleviate the symptoms. Answer E is incorrect because ketone body production does not produce hypoglycemic symptoms, nor would they be significantly elevated only a few hours after the insulin shock the patient is experiencing.

2. **The answer is B.** When glucagon binds to its receptor, the enzyme adenylate cyclase is eventually activated (through the action of G proteins), which raises cAMP levels in the cell. The cAMP phosphodiesterase opposes this rise in cAMP, and hydrolyzes cAMP to 5′-AMP. If the phosphodiesterase is inhibited by caffeine, cAMP levels would stay elevated for an extended period, enhancing the glucagon response. The glucagon response in liver is to export glucose (thus, E is incorrect) and to inhibit glycolysis (thus, D is incorrect). cAMP activates protein kinase A, making answer C incorrect as well. The effect of insulin is to reduce cAMP levels (thus, A is incorrect).

3. **The answer is B.** Insulin release is dependent on an increase in the [ATP]/[ADP] ratio within the pancreatic β-cell. In MODY, the mutation in glucokinase results in a less active glucokinase at glucose concentrations that normally stimulate insulin release. Thus, higher concentrations of glucose are required to stimulate glycolysis and the tricarboxylic acid (TCA) cycle to effectively raise the ratio of ATP to ADP. Answer A is incorrect because cAMP levels are not related to the mechanism of insulin release. Answer C is incorrect because, initially, transcription is not involved, as insulin release is caused by exocytosis of preformed insulin in secretory vesicles. Answer D is incorrect because the pancreas will not degrade glycogen under conditions of high blood glucose, and answer E is incorrect because lactate does not play in role in stimulating insulin release.

4. **The answer is A.** The brain requires glucose because fatty acids cannot readily cross the blood–brain barrier to enter neuronal cells. Thus, glucose production is maintained at an adequate level to allow the brain to continue to burn glucose for its energy needs. The other organs listed as possible answers can switch to the use of alternative fuel sources (lactate, fatty acids, amino acids) and are not as dependent on glucose for their energy requirements as is the brain.

5. **The answer is E.** Muscle does not express glucagon receptors, so they are refractory to glucagons' actions. Muscle does, however, contain GTP (made via the TCA cycle), G proteins, protein kinase A, and adenylate cyclase (epinephrine stimulation of muscle cells raises cAMP levels and activates protein kinase A).

CHAPTER 27

1. **The answer is E.** The GLUT 5 transporter has a much higher affinity for fructose than glucose and is the facilitator of choice for fructose uptake by cells. The other GLUT transporters do not transport fructose to any significant extent.

2. **The answer is A.** The pancreas produces α-amylase, which digests starch in the intestinal lumen. If pancreatic α-amylase cannot enter the lumen because of pancreatitis, the starch will not be digested to a significant extent. (The salivary α-amylase begins the process, but only for the time during which the food is in the mouth, as the acidic conditions of the stomach destroy the salivary activity.) The discomfort arises from the bacteria in the intestine, digesting the starch and producing acids and gases. Lactose, sucrose, and maltose are all disaccharides that would be cleaved by the intestinal disaccharidases located on the brush border of the intestinal epithelial cells (thus, B, D, and E are incorrect). These activities might be slightly reduced, as the pancreas would also have difficulty excreting bicarbonate to the intestine, and the low pH of the stomach contents might reduce the activity of these enzymes. However, these enzymes are present in excess and will eventually digest the disaccharides. Fiber cannot be digested by human enzymes, so answer C is incorrect.

3. **The answer is C.** Insulin is required to stimulate glucose transport into muscle and fat cells but not into brain, liver, pancreas, or red blood cells. Thus, muscle would be feeling the effects of glucose deprivation and would be unable to replenish its own glycogen supplies as a result of its inability to extract blood glucose, even though blood glucose levels would be high.

4. **The answer is E.** Flour contains starch, which will lead to glucose production in the intestine. Milk contains lactose, a disaccharide of glucose and galactose, which will be split by lactase in the small intestine. Sucrose is a disaccharide of glucose and fructose, which is split by sucrase in the small intestine. Thus, glucose, galactose, and fructose will all be available in the lumen of the small intestine for transport through the intestinal epithelial cells and into the circulation.

5. **The answer is A.** Salivary and pancreatic α-amylase will partially digest starch to glucose, but maltose and disaccharides will pass through the intestine and exit with the stool, as a result of the limited activity of the brush border enzymes. Because the amylase enzymes are working, there will only be normal levels of starch in the stool (thus, B is incorrect). Not all available glucose is entering the blood, so less insulin will be released by the pancreas (thus, E is incorrect), which will lead to less glucose uptake by the muscles and less glycogen production (thus, D is incorrect). Because neither lactose nor sucrose can be digested to a large extent in the intestinal lumen under these conditions, it would be difficult to have elevated levels of galactose or fructose in the blood (thus, C is incorrect).

CHAPTER 28

1. **The answer is B.** Glycogen phosphorylase produces glucose 1-phosphate; the debranching enzyme hydrolyzes branch points and thus releases free glucose. Ninety

percent of the glycogen contains α-1,4-bonds and only 10% are α-1,6-bonds, so more glucose 1-phosphate will be produced than glucose.

2. **The answer is D.** If, after fasting, the branches were shorter than normal, glycogen phosphorylase must be functional and capable of being activated by glucagon (thus, A and B are incorrect). The branching enzyme (amylo-4,6-transferase) is also normal because branch points are present within the glycogen (thus, E is incorrect). Because glycogen is also present, glycogenin is present in order to build the carbohydrate chains, indicating that C is incorrect. If the debranching activity is abnormal (the amylo-1,6-glucosidase), glycogen phosphorylase would break the glycogen down up to four residues from branch points and would then stop. With no debranching activity, the resultant glycogen would contain the normal number of branches, but the branched chains would be shorter than normal.

3. **The answer is C.** The patient has McArdle disease, a glycogen storage disease caused by a deficiency of muscle glycogen phosphorylase. Because he or she cannot degrade glycogen to produce energy for muscle contraction, he or she becomes fatigued more readily than a normal person (thus, A is incorrect), the glycogen levels in her muscle will be higher than normal as a result of the inability to degrade them (thus, D is incorrect), and his or her blood lactate levels will be lower because of the lack of glucose for entry into glycolysis. He or she will, however, draw on the glucose in his or her circulation for energy, so his or her forearm blood glucose levels will be decreased (thus, B is incorrect), and because the liver is not affected, blood glucose levels can be maintained by liver glycogenolysis (thus, E is incorrect).

4. **The answer is A.** After ingestion of glucose, insulin levels rise, cAMP levels within the cell drop (thus, E is incorrect), and protein-phosphatase-I is activated (thus, D is incorrect). Glycogen phosphorylase a is converted to glycogen phosphorylase b by the phosphatase (thus, B is incorrect), and glycogen synthase is activated by the phosphatase. Red blood cells continue to use glucose at their normal rate, thus lactate formation will remain the same (thus, C is incorrect).

5. **The answer is F.** In the absence of insulin, glucagon-stimulated activities predominate. This leads to the activation of protein kinase A, the phosphorylation and inactivation of glycogen synthase, the phosphorylation and activation of phosphorylase kinase, and the phosphorylation and activation of glycogen phosphorylase.

CHAPTER 29

1. **The answer is D.** The aldolase B gene has two alleles. One or both may have mutations. Because HFI is recessive, both alleles must be mutated for the disease to be expressed. Examination of the gel shows that the normal gene is cleaved by ahaII to produce a 306-bp (base pair) restriction fragment. When a mutation creates a new ahaII site within the gene, this 306-bp fragment is cleaved into two fragments of 183 and 123 bp (which together contain 306 bp). The husband and Jill, thus, are carriers. They have one normal allele that produces the 306-bp fragment and one that has an additional ahaII site, which is cleaved to yield the two fragments of 183 and 123 bp. The wife and Jack have the disease. Both of their alleles have the additional ahaII site and produce only 183- and 123-bp fragments.

2. **The answer is C.** This man could be the father of both children. He could provide either a normal gene (which produces a 306-bp ahaII fragment) or a mutant gene (which produces 183- and 123-bp ahaII fragments) to his offspring. This mother could provide only the mutant gene (of which she has two copies). Jill is a carrier. She received the mutant gene from her mother and could have received the normal gene from this man. Jack has the disease. He received one mutant gene from his mother and another from his father.

3. **The answer is C.** Transketolase requires thiamine pyrophosphate as a cofactor, whereas none of the other enzymes listed does. Thus, if an individual has a thiamine deficiency, transketolase activity as isolated from a patient's blood cells will be enhanced by the addition of thiamine; in well-nourished individuals, the addition of thiamine will not enhance transketolase activity.

4. **The answer is B.** Fructose is converted to fructose 1-phosphate by fructokinase, and aldolase B in the liver splits the fructose 1-P into glyceraldehyde and dihydroxyacetone phosphate. Thus, the major regulated step of glycolysis, PFK-1, is bypassed and PEP is rapidly produced. As the [PEP] increases, pyruvate kinase produces pyruvate. As the glyceraldehyde-3-phosphate dehydrogenase reaction is proceeding rapidly (remember that fructokinase is a high V_{max} enzyme, so there is a lot of substrate proceeding through the glycolytic pathway), the intracellular [NADH]/[NAD$^+$] ratio is high, and the pyruvate produced is converted to lactate in order to regenerate NAD$^+$. Thus, the pyruvate kinase step is not bypassed (thus, A is incorrect). Neither aldolase B nor lactate dehydrogenase is allosterically regulated (thus, C and D are incorrect), and even though the [ATP]:[ADP] ratio is high in the liver under these conditions, the ratio does not affect lactate formation (thus, E is incorrect).

5. **The answer is B.** Reduction of sugar aldehydes to alcohols requires NADPH, which is generated primarily by the pentose phosphate pathway. 6-Phosphogluconate is not a polyol (thus, A is incorrect; 6-phosphogluconate is glucose oxidized at position 1 to form a carboxylic acid); ribitol is not a product of the pentose phosphate pathway (thus, B is incorrect; ribulose 5-phosphate is a product of

the pentose phosphate pathway); the HMP shunt uses glucose 6-phosphate as the starting material, not free glucose as in the sorbitol pathway (thus, D and E are incorrect).

CHAPTER 30

1. **The answer is B.** Galactose metabolism requires the phosphorylation of galactose to galactose 1-phosphate, which is then converted to UDP-galactose (which is the step that is defective in the patient), and then epimerized to UDP-glucose. Although the mother cannot convert galactose to lactose because of the enzyme deficiency, she can make UDP-glucose from glucose 6-phosphate, and once she has made UDP-glucose, she can epimerize it to form UDP-galactose and can synthesize lactose (thus, A is incorrect). However, because of her enzyme deficiency, the mother cannot convert galactose 1-phosphate to UDP-galactose or UDP-glucose, so the dietary galactose cannot be used for glycogen synthesis or glucose production (thus, C and D are incorrect). After ingesting milk, the galactose levels will be elevated in the serum because of the metabolic block in the cells (thus, E is incorrect).

2. **The answer is D.** Nucleotide sugars, such as UDP-glucose, UDP-galactose, and CMP-sialic acid, donate sugars to the growing carbohydrate chain. The other activated sugars listed do not contribute to this synthesis.

3. **The answer is C.** Bilirubin is conjugated with glucuronic acid residues to enhance its solubility. Glucuronic acid is glucose oxidized at position 6; gluconic acid is glucose oxidized at position 1 and is generated by the HMP shunt pathway.

4. **The answer is C.** Glutamine donates the amide nitrogen to fructose 6-phosphate to form glucosamine 6-phosphate. None of the other nitrogen-containing compounds (A, B, and D) donate their nitrogen to carbohydrates. Dolichol contains no nitrogens and is the carrier for carbohydrate chain synthesis of *N*-linked glycoproteins.

5. **The answer is C.** Sandhoff disease is a deficiency of both hexosaminidase A and B activity, resulting from loss of the β-subunit activity of these enzymes. The degradative step at which amino sugars need to be removed from the glycolipids would be defective, such that globoside and GM2 accumulate in this disease. The other answers are incorrect; GM1 does contain an amino sugar, but it is converted to GM2 before the block is apparent.

CHAPTER 31

1. **The answer is D.** Glycerol is converted to glycerol 3-phosphate, which is oxidized to form glyceraldehyde 3-phosphate. The glyceraldehyde 3-phosphate formed then follows the gluconeogenic pathway to glucose. Lactate is converted to pyruvate, which is then carboxylated to form oxaloacetate. The oxaloacetate is decarboxylated to form phosphoenolpyruvate and then run through gluconeogenesis to glucose. Because glycerol enters the gluconeogenic pathway at the glyceraldehyde 3-phosphate step and lactate at the PEP step, the only compounds in common between these two starting points are the steps from glyceraldehyde 3-phosphate to glucose. Of the choices listed in the question, only glucose 6-phosphate is in that part of the pathway.

2. **The answer is A.** PEPCK converts oxaloacetate to phosphoenolpyruvate. In combination with pyruvate carboxylase, it is used to bypass the pyruvate kinase reaction. Thus, compounds that enter gluconeogenesis between PEP and OAA (such as lactate, alanine, or any TCA cycle intermediate) must use PEPCK to produce PEP. Glycerol enters gluconeogenesis as glyceraldehyde 3-phosphate, bypassing the PEPCK step. Galactose is converted to glucose 1-phosphate, then glucose 6-phosphate, also bypassing the PEPCK step. Even-chain fatty acids can only give rise to acetyl-CoA, which cannot be used to synthesize glucose.

3. **The answer is C.** Glucagon counteracts insulin's action, in that it is a catabolic hormone (thus, A is incorrect), and its levels decrease when insulin levels increase (thus, E is incorrect). As insulin levels rise after a meal, glucagon levels will decrease, so D is incorrect. The muscle lacks glucagon receptors and cannot respond to glucagon, hence B is incorrect.

4. **The answer is B.** High blood glucose levels signal the release of insulin from the pancreas; glucagon levels either stay the same or decrease slightly.

5. **The answer is D.** The hyperglycemia in an untreated diabetic creates osmotic diuresis, which means that excessive water is lost through urination. This can lead to a contraction of blood volume, leading to low blood pressure and a rapid heart beat. It also leads to dehydration. The rapid respirations result from acidosis-induced stimulation of the respiratory center of the brain, in order to reduce the amount of acid in the blood. Ketone bodies have accumulated, leading to diabetic ketoacidosis (thus, B is incorrect). A patient in a hypoglycemic coma (which can be caused by excessive insulin administration) does not exhibit dehydration, low blood pressure, or rapid respirations; in fact, the patient will sweat profusely as a result of epinephrine release (thus, C and E are incorrect). Answer A is incorrect because lack of a pancreas would be fatal.

CHAPTER 32

1. **The answer is B.** Chylomicrons transport dietary lipids, and >80% of the chylomicron is triglyceride. All other components are present at <10%, hence all other answers are incorrect.

2. The answer is D. High-density lipoproteins transfer apoproteins CII and E to nascent chylomicrons to convert them to mature chylomicrons. Bile salts are required to emulsify dietary lipid, 2-monoacylglycerol is a digestion product of pancreatic lipase, lipoprotein lipase digests triglyceride from mature chylomicrons, and the lymphatic system delivers the nascent chylomicrons to the bloodstream.

3. The answer is A. Both apoB-48 and apoB-100 are derived from the same gene and from the same mRNA (there is no difference in splicing between the two, thus B is incorrect). However, RNA editing introduces a stop codon in the message such that B-48 stops protein synthesis approximately 48% along the message. Thus, proteolytic cleavage is not correct. B-48 is found only in chylomicrons, and B-100 is found only in VLDL particles.

4. The answer is B. The bile salts must be above their critical micelle concentration to form micelles with the components of lipase digestion, fatty acids, and 2-monoacylgycerol. In the absence of micelle formation, lipid absorption would not occur. The critical micelle concentration is independent of triglyceride concentration (thus, A is incorrect). Bile salts do not bind or activate lipase (thus, C and E are incorrect). The absorption of bile salts in the ileum is not related to digestion (thus, D is incorrect).

5. The answer is D. Nascent chylomicrons would be synthesized, which can only acquire apo CII from HDL (thus, A is incorrect). The chylomicrons would be degraded in part by lipoprotein lipase, leading to chylomicron remnant formation. However, the chylomicron remnants would remain in circulation because of the lack of apo E (thus, B is incorrect). Because these remnant particles still contain a fair amount of triglyceride, serum triglyceride levels will be elevated (thus, C and E are incorrect).

CHAPTER 33

1. The answer is A. Fatty acids, cleaved from the triacylglycerols of blood lipoproteins by the action of lipoprotein lipase, are taken up by adipose cells and react with coenzyme A to form fatty acyl-CoA. Glucose is converted via dihydroxyacetone phosphate to glycerol 3-phosphate, which reacts with fatty acyl-CoA to form phosphatidic acid (adipose tissue lacks glycerol kinase, so it cannot use glycerol directly). After inorganic phosphate is released from phosphatidic acid, the resulting diacylglycerol reacts with another fatty acyl-CoA to form a triacylglycerol, which is stored in adipose cells (2-monoacylglycerol is an intermediate of triglyceride synthesis only in the intestine, not in adipose tissue).

2. The answer is D. The triacylglycerol is degraded by pancreatic lipase, which releases the fatty acids at positions 1 and 3. The fatty acids released are then transported to

the cell surface in a bile salt micelle. The only exception is short-chain fatty acids (shorter than palmitic acid), which can diffuse to the cell surface and enter the intestinal cell in the absence of micelle formation.

3. The answer is B. Dietary carbohydrate is converted to lipid in the liver and exported via VLDL. Thus, a low-carbohydrate diet will reduce VLDL formation and reduce the hyperlipoproteinemia.

4. The answer is C. Sphingosine is derived from the condensation of palmitoyl-CoA and serine. It is converted to ceramide via reaction with a fatty acyl-CoA, not a UDP-sugar. There is no glycerol in this structure, and cardiolipin is derived from phosphatidic acid and phosphatidylglycerol. All cells synthesize sphingosine; its synthesis is not restricted to neuronal cells.

5. The answer is E. When fatty acids are being synthesized, malonyl-CoA accumulates, which inhibits carnitine palmitoyl transferase I. This blocks fatty acid entry into the mitochondrion for oxidation. Many tissues both synthesize and degrade fatty acids (such as liver and muscle; thus, A is incorrect). NADPH blocks the glucose-6-phosphate dehydrogenase reaction but not fatty acid oxidation (thus, B is incorrect). Insulin has no effect on the synthesis of the enzymes involved in fatty acid degradation (unlike the effect of insulin on the induction of enzymes involved in fatty acid synthesis; thus, C is incorrect). Finally, newly synthesized fatty acids are converted to their CoA derivatives for elongation and desaturation (thus, D is incorrect).

CHAPTER 34

1. The answer is B. The reduction of HMG-CoA to mevalonate is catalyzed by HMG-CoA reductase, which is an integral enzyme in the smooth endoplasmic reticulum. The activity of HMG-CoA reductase is carefully controlled and is the rate-limiting step for de novo cholesterol biosynthesis. The other steps listed, although they are on the pathway to cholesterol, are not catalyzed by regulated enzymes.

2. The answer is C. The squalene monooxygenase reaction uses one of the oxygen atoms of O_2 to form an epoxide at one end of the squalene molecule, which requires NADPH as a cosubstrate of the reaction. All sterols have four fused rings (thus, A is incorrect). Because the epoxide is formed at one end of the squalene molecule, answer B is incorrect. Answer D is incorrect because NADPH provides the reducing power, not FAD(2H); and answer E is incorrect because carbons 1 and 30 remain independent during the cyclization of squalene.

3. The answer is C. The presence of chronic hyperglycemia (usually accompanied by high levels of free fatty acids in the blood) causes diffuse multiorgan toxic effects ("glucose toxicity" and "lipotoxicity"), to the extent that it raises the risk for a future atherosclerotic event to a level equal to that posed by a history of the patient having already suffered such an event in the past. The other risk factors, in the absence of a previous myocardial infarction, do not require the suggested lower limits for circulating cholesterol levels.

4. **The answer is B.** ApoCIII appears to inhibit the activation of LPL. ApoE acts as a ligand in binding several lipoproteins to the LDL receptor, the LDL receptor-related protein (LRP), and possibly to a separate apoE receptor. ApoB$_{48}$ is required for the normal assembly and secretion of chylomicrons from the small bowel, whereas apoB$_{100}$ is required in the liver for the assembly and secretion of VLDL. ApoCII is the activator of LPL.

5. **The answer is B.** Because chylomicrons contain the most triacylglycerol, they are the least dense of the blood lipoproteins. Because VLDL contains more protein, it is denser than chylomicrons. Because LDL is produced by degradation of the triacylglycerol in VLDL, LDL is denser than VLDL. HDL is the densest of the blood lipoproteins. It has the most protein and the least triacylglycerol.

CHAPTER 35

1. **The answer is C.** Most prostaglandins are synthesized from arachidonic acid (*cis*-Δ5,8,11,14 C$_{20:4}$), which is derived from the essential fatty acid, linoleic acid (*cis*-Δ9,12 C$_{18:2}$). Glucose, oleic acid, or acetyl-CoA cannot give rise to linoleic or arachidonic acid, as mammals cannot introduce double bonds six carbons from the ω-end of a fatty acid. Leukotrienes are also derived from arachidonic acid, but they are not precursors of prostaglandins; they follow a different pathway.

2. **The answer is A.** Arachidonic acid is produced from linoleic acid (an essential fatty acid) by a series of elongation and desaturation reactions. Arachidonic acid is stored in membrane phospholipids, released, and oxidized by a cyclooxygenase (which is inhibited by aspirin) in the first step of the biosynthesis of prostaglandins, prostacyclins, and thromboxanes. Leukotrienes require the enzyme lipoxygenase, rather than cyclooxygenase, for their synthesis from arachidonic acid.

3. **The answer is A.** Aspirin leads to the acetylation of COX-1 and COX-2, which inhibits the enzymes. Tylenol contains acetaminophen, which is a competitive inhibitor of both COX-1 and COX-2, but acetaminophen does not attach covalently to the enzymes. Advil contains ibuprofen, which is another competitive inhibitor of the COX enzymes. Vioxx and Celebrex contain inhibitors that are specific for COX-2, which is the form of cyclooxygenase that is induced during inflammation. Vioxx and Celebrex do not inhibit COX-1 activity.

4. **The answer is C.** Release of TXA$_2$ by platelets at wounds, while enhancing platelet aggregation (see Chapter 45), also induces vasoconstriction, reducing blood flow to the wounded area. TXA$_2$ has no effect on either COX-1 or COX-2 activity and does induce bronchial constriction, but not bronchial dilation.

5. **The answer is B.** Phospholipase C is activated by a G$_q$ protein, which is coupled to the prostaglandin receptor. Activation of phospholipase C leads to the hydrolysis of phosphatidylinositol bisphosphate (PIP$_2$) to produce diacylglycerol and inositol trisphosphate (IP$_3$). The IP$_3$ leads to the increase in intracellular calcium levels (see Chapter 11). Activation of the protein kinase A pathway, via a G protein and adenylate cyclase, does not lead to a rise in intracellular calcium levels. Protein kinase C is activated by diacylglycerol, one of the products of PIP$_2$ hydrolysis, but protein kinase C is not involved in the increase in intracellular calcium levels. Phospholipase A2 releases arachidonic acid from phospholipids, but this response is not required when prostaglandins bind to their receptors.

CHAPTER 36

1. **The answer is B.** The acetone on the woman's breath (which is produced by decarboxylation of acetoacetate; thus, E is incorrect) and the ketones in her urine indicate that she is in diabetic ketoacidosis. This is caused by low insulin levels, so her blood glucose levels are high because the glucose is not being taken up by the peripheral tissues (thus, A and C are incorrect). An insulin injection will reduce her blood glucose levels and decrease the release of fatty acids from adipose triglycerides. Consequently, ketone body production will decrease. Glucagon injections would just exacerbate the woman's current condition (thus, D is incorrect).

2. **The answer is D.** Chylomicrons are blood lipoproteins produced from dietary fat. VLDL is produced mainly from dietary carbohydrate. IDL and LDL are produced from VLDL. HDL does not transport triacylglycerol to the tissues.

3. **The answer is B.** Consider the energy required to convert dietary carbohydrates to triacylglycerol. Some ATP is generated from glycolysis and the pyruvate dehydrogenase reaction, but energy is also lost as the fatty acids are synthesized (the synthesis of each malonyl-CoA requires ATP, and the reduction steps require two molecules of NADPH). Dietary fat, however, only requires activation and attachment to glycerol; the fatty acid chain does not need to be synthesized. Therefore, it requires less energy to package dietary fat into chylomicrons than it does to convert dietary carbohydrate into fatty acids for incorporation into VLDL. Thus, weight gain will be more rapid if

all the excess calories are derived from fat as opposed to carbohydrates.

4. **The answer is B.** Metabolism of ethanol leads to production of NADH in the liver, which will inhibit fatty acid oxidation in the liver. Because the patient has not eaten for 5 days, the insulin/glucagon ratio is low, hormone-sensitive lipase is activated, and fatty acids are being released by the adipocyte and taken up by the muscle and liver. However, because the liver NADH levels are high as a result of ethanol metabolism, the fatty acids received from the adipocyte are repackaged into triacylglycerol (the high NADH promotes the conversion of dihydroxyacetone phosphate to glycerol 3-phosphate as well) and secreted from the liver in the form of VLDL. None of the other answers is a correct statement.

5. **The answer is A.** The clotting problems are caused by a lack of vitamin K, a lipid-soluble vitamin. Vitamin K is absorbed from the diet in mixed micelles and packaged with chylomicrons for delivery to the other tissues. Individuals with abetalipoproteinemia lack the microsomal triglyceride transfer protein and cannot produce chylomicrons effectively, thus vitamin K deficiency can result. Such patients also cannot produce VLDL, but lipid-soluble vitamin distribution does not depend on VLDL particles, only on chylomicrons. The other answers are all incorrect statements.

CHAPTER 37

1. **The answer is C.** Trypsinogen, which is secreted by the intestine, is activated by enteropeptidase, a protein found in the intestine (thus, D is backward and incorrect). Once trypsin is formed, it activates all of the other zymogens secreted by the pancreas. Trypsin does not activate pepsinogen (thus, B is incorrect) because pepsinogen is found in the stomach and autocatalyzes its own activation when the pH drops as a result of acid secretion. Trypsin has no effect on intestinal motility (hence, E is incorrect) and also does not have a much broader base of substrates than any other protease (trypsin cleaves on the carboxy side of basic side chains, lysine, and arginine; thus, A is incorrect).

2. **The answer is C.** Leucine can be transported by several different amino acid systems. Leucine is an essential amino acid, so the body cannot synthesize it (thus, A is incorrect). If the intestine cannot absorb leucine, then the kidneys do not have a chance to reabsorb it, so B is incorrect. Leucine and isoleucine have different structures and cannot substitute for each other in all positions within a protein, thus D is incorrect. Leucine is an important component of proteins and is required for protein synthesis; hence, E is incorrect.

3. **The answer is D.** Kwashiorkor is a disease that results from eating a calorie-adequate diet that lacks protein. None of the other answers is correct.

4. **The answer is C.** Pepsinogen, under acidic conditions, autocatalyzes its conversion to pepsin in the stomach. Both enteropeptidase and aminopeptidases are synthesized in active form by the intestine (thus, A and D are incorrect). Enteropeptidase activates trypsinogen (thus, B is incorrect), which then activates proelastase (thus, E is incorrect).

5. **The answer is E.** Because of the lack of protein in the diet, protein synthesis in the liver is impaired (lack of essential amino acids). The liver can still synthesize fatty acids from carbohydrate or fat sources, but very low-density lipoprotein (VLDL) particles cannot be assembled because of the shortage of apoprotein B-100. Thus, the fatty acids remain in the liver, leading to a fatty liver. None of the other answers explains this finding.

CHAPTER 38

1. Infant I has a defect in carbamoyl phosphate synthetase I (CPSI; answer A), and infant IV has a defect in ornithine transcarbamoylase (OTC; answer B). Infants with high ammonia, low arginine, and low citrulline levels must have a defect in a urea-cycle enzyme before the step that produces citrulline, that is, CPSI or OTC. If CPSI is functional and carbamoyl phosphate is produced but cannot be further metabolized, more than the normal amount is diverted to the pathway for pyrimidine synthesis and the intermediate orotate appears in the urine. Therefore, infant I has a defect in CPSI (citrulline is low and less than the normal amount of orotate is in the urine). Infant IV has an OTC defect; carbamoyl phosphate is produced, but it cannot be converted to citrulline, so citrulline is low and orotate is present in the urine.

Infants II and V have high levels of citrulline but low levels of arginine. Therefore, they cannot produce arginine from citrulline. Argininosuccinate synthetase or argininosuccinate lyase is defective. The very elevated citrulline levels in infant II suggest that the block is in argininosuccinate synthetase (answer C). In infant V, citrulline levels are more moderately elevated, suggesting that citrulline can be converted to argininosuccinate and that the defect is in argininosuccinate lyase (answer D). Thus, the accumulated intermediates of the urea cycle are distributed between argininosuccinate and citrulline (both of which can be excreted in the urine). The high levels of arginine and more moderate hyperammonemia in infant III suggest that, in this case, the defect is in arginase (answer E).

2. **The answer is D.** The nitrogens in urea are derived from carbamoyl phosphate and aspartate directly during one turn of the cycle. The nitrogen in the side chain of

ornithine is never incorporated into urea because it stays with ornithine (thus, A, B, and C are incorrect). Glutamine does not donate a nitrogen directly during the urea cycle, so E and F are also incorrect.

3. **The answer is C.** Glutamate dehydrogenase fixes ammonia into α-ketoglutarate, generating glutamate, in a reversible reaction that also requires NAD(P)H. Alanine-pyruvate aminotransferase catalyzes the transfer of nitrogen from alanine to an α-keto acid acceptor but does not use ammonia as a substrate. Glutaminase converts glutamine to glutamate and ammonia, but the reaction is not reversible. Arginase splits arginine into urea and ornithine, and argininosuccinate synthetase forms argininosuccinate from citrulline and aspirate. The only other two enzymes that can fix ammonia into an organic compound are carbamoyl phosphate synthetase I and glutamine synthetase.

4. **The answer is C.** Glycogen phosphorylase requires pyridoxal phosphate to break the α-1,4-linkages in glycogen. None of the other pathways listed contains an enzyme that requires this cofactor.

5. **The answer is A.** CPSI is the major regulated step, being activated by *N*-acetylglutamate, the synthesis of which is stimulated by arginine. None of the other urea-cycle enzymes is regulated allosterically.

CHAPTER 39

1. **The answer is A.** Tyrosine is derived from phenylalanine, which requires BH_4 but not vitamin B_6. Vitamin B_6 is required in the synthesis of serine (transamination), alanine (another transamination), cysteine (β-elimination, β-addition, β-elimination), and aspartate (transamination).

2. **The answer is E.** The other end products are acetoacetate, acetyl-CoA, fumarate, oxaloacetate, α-ketoglutarate, and pyruvate.

3. **The answer is C.** The classical form of PKU, a deficiency of phenylalanine hydroxylase, results in elevations of phenylalanine and phenylpyruvate. However, this enzyme is not a choice. In the nonclassical variant of PKU, there is a problem in either synthesizing or regenerating BH_4. The enzyme that converts BH_2 to BH_4 is dihydropteridine reductase.

4. **The answer is B.** The reaction pathway in which methionine goes to cysteine and α-ketobutyrate requires pyridoxal phosphate at two steps: the cystathionine β-synthase reaction and the cystathionase reaction. Phenylalanine to tyrosine requires BH_4; propionyl-CoA to succinyl-CoA requires B_{12}; pyruvate to acetyl-CoA requires thiamine pyrophosphate, lipoic acid, NAD, FAD, and coenzyme A; and glucose to glycogen does not require a cofactor.

5. **The answer is C.** Folic acid is required for the conversion of serine to glycine and the serine is produced from 3-phosphoglycerate and alanine. Folic acid is not needed to synthesize aspartate (from oxaloacetate by transamination), glutamate (from α-ketoglutarate by transamination), proline (from glutamate by a series of steps that do not require folic acid), or serine (from 3-phosphoglycerate, with no one-carbon metabolism needed).

CHAPTER 40

1. **The answer is D.** The homocysteine-to-methionine reaction requires N^5-methyl-FH_4; serine to glycine requires free FH_4 and generates N^5,N^{10}-methylene-FH_4; betaine donates a methyl group to homocysteine to form methionine without the participation of FH_4; and the purine ring requires N^{10}-formyl-FH_4 in its biosynthesis.

2. **The answer is B.** Propionic acid is derived from an accumulation of propionyl-CoA. The normal pathway for the degradation of propionyl-CoA is, first, a biotin-dependent carboxylation to D-methylmalonyl-CoA, racemization to L-methylmalonyl-CoA, and then, the B_{12}-dependent rearrangement to succinyl-CoA.

3. **The answer is C.** An inability to hydrolyze dietary protein and release bound B_{12} will lead to a deficiency. Pancreatic insufficiency will result in reduction of proteases in the pancreas and reduced ability to release B_{12} from protein. Both R-binders and intrinsic factor are required for appropriate B_{12} absorption; animal protein contains high levels of B_{12}, and glutamic acid is conjugated to folic acid, not to B_{12}. Folic acid absorption does not affect B_{12} absorption.

4. **The answer is B.** The only three forms of folate that transfer carbons are the N^5-methyl-FH_4 form, the N^5,N^{10}-methylene-FH_4 form, and the N^{10}-formyl form. None of the other forms participates in reactions in which the carbon is transferred. It is the N^5-methyl form that transfers the methyl group to form methionine from homocysteine.

5. **The answer is E.** Choline, derived from phosphatidylcholine, is converted to betaine (trimethylglycine). Betaine can donate a methyl group to homocysteine to form methionine plus dimethylglycine. Sarcosine is *N*-methylglycine, which is formed when excess SAM methylates glycine, but it is not used as a methyl donor in this reaction.

CHAPTER 41

1. **The answer is A.** Both carbamoyl phosphate synthetase (CPS) I and II use carbon dioxide as the carbon source in the production of carbamoyl phosphate. CPSI is located in the mitochondria, whereas CPSII is in the cytoplasm (thus, B is incorrect). CPSI can fix ammonia; CPSII requires glutamine as the nitrogen source (thus, C is incorrect).

N-acetylglutamate activates CPSI; CPSII is activated by PRPP (thus, D is incorrect). UMP inhibits CPSII, but has no effect on CPSI (thus, E is also incorrect).

2. **The answer is B.** A lack of glucose 6-phosphatase activity (von Gierke disease) leads to an accumulation of glucose 6-phosphate, which leads to an increase in ribose 5-phosphate levels, and then an increase in PRPP levels. As PRPP levels rise, purine synthesis is stimulated, leading to excessive levels of purines in the blood. The degradation of the extra purines leads to uric acid production and gout. A loss of either PRPP synthetase activity or glutamine phosphoribosyl aminotransferase activity would lead to reduced purine synthesis and hypouricemia (thus, A and D are incorrect). A lack of glucose-6-phosphate dehydrogenase would hinder ribose 5-phosphate production and thus would not lead to excessive purine synthesis. A lack of purine nucleoside phosphorylase would hinder the salvage pathway, leading to an accumulation of nucleosides. Purine nucleoside phosphorylase activity is required to synthesize uric acid, so in the absence of this enzyme, less uric acid would be produced (thus, E is incorrect).

3. **The answer is C.** The enzyme defect in Lesch–Nyhan syndrome involves hypoxanthine-guanine phosphoribosyltransferase (HGPRT). This enzyme converts the free base to a nucleotide—specifically, guanine to GMP and hypoxanthine to IMP. Adenine phosphoribosyltransferase (APRT) converts adenine to AMP (thus, A is incorrect). Adenosine kinase converts adenosine to AMP (thus, B is incorrect). There are no enzymes to convert guanosine to GMP or thymine to TMP (thus, D and E are incorrect). Pyrimidine nucleoside phosphorylase will convert thymine to thymidine but not to the nucleotide level. Thymidine kinase converts thymidine to TMP (thus, F is incorrect).

4. **The answer is B.** Allopurinol inhibits the conversion of both hypoxanthine to xanthine and xanthine to uric acid. This occurs because both of those reactions are catalyzed by xanthine oxidase, the target of allopurinol. Answer A is incorrect because AMP is not converted directly to XMP (AMP, when degraded, is deaminated to form IMP, which loses its phosphate to become inosine, which undergoes phosphorolysis to generate hypoxanthine and ribose 1-phosphate). Answer C is incorrect because the inosine-to-hypoxanthine conversion, catalyzed by nucleoside phosphorylase, is not inhibited by allopurinol. Answer D is incorrect because the conversion of hypoxanthine to xanthine occurs at the free base level, not at the nucleotide level. Answer E is incorrect because GMP is converted first to guanosine (loss of phosphate), the guanosine is converted to guanine and ribose 1-phosphate, and the guanine is then converted to xanthine by guanase.

5. **The answer is B.** If dGTP were to accumulate in cells, the dGTP would bind to the substrate specificity site of ribonucleotide reductase and direct the synthesis of dADP.

This would lead to elevations of dATP levels, which would inhibit the activity of ribonucleotide reductase. The inhibition of ribonucleotide reductase leads to a cessation of cell proliferation, as the supply of deoxyribonucleotides for DNA synthesis become limiting. Answer A is incorrect because ATP would need to bind to the substrate specificity site to direct the synthesis of dCDP. That would not occur under these conditions of elevated dGTP levels. Answer C is incorrect because the enzyme works only on diphosphates; AMP would never be a substrate for this enzyme. Answer D is incorrect because the thioredoxin is always regenerated and does not become rate limiting for the reductase reaction. Answer E is incorrect because dGTP does not bind to the activity site of the reductase; only ATP (activator) or dATP (inhibitor) is capable of binding to the activity site.

CHAPTER 42

1. **The answer is D.** High levels of amino acids in the blood stimulate the pancreas to release glucagon (thus, A, C, E, and G are incorrect). Insulin is also released, but the glucagon/insulin ratio is such that the liver still uses the carbons of amino acids to synthesize glucose (thus, A, E, and F are incorrect). However, the insulin levels are high enough to stimulate BCAA uptake into the muscle for oxidation (thus, E, F, G, and H are incorrect).

2. **The answer is C.** The pathway followed is glutamine to glutamate, to glutamate semialdehyde, to ornithine, and then, after condensation with carbamoyl phosphate, to citrulline. Aspartate, succinyl-CoA, serine, and fumarate are not part of this pathway.

3. **The answer is D.** Cortisol is released during fasting and times of stress and signals muscle cells to initiate ubiquitin-mediated protein degradation. The other hormones listed do not have this effect on muscle protein metabolism. Insulin stimulates protein synthesis; glucagon has no effect on muscle because muscle has no glucagon receptors. Epinephrine initiates glycogen degradation but not protein degradation, and glucose is not a signaling molecule for muscle as it can be for the pancreas.

4. **The answer is D.** Glutamine is derived from glutamate, which is formed from α-ketoglutarate. Only isoleucine and valine can give rise to glutamine because leucine is strictly ketogenic. These amino acids give rise to succinyl-CoA, which goes around the TCA cycle to form citrate (after condensing with acetyl-CoA), which then forms isocitrate (the correct answer), and the isocitrate is converted to α-ketoglutarate. Urea, pyruvate, phosphoenolpyruvate, and lactate are not required intermediates in the conversion of BCAA carbons to glutamine carbons.

5. **The answer is B.** An individual in sepsis will be catabolic; protein degradation exceeds protein intake (leading to negative nitrogen balance; thus, A, C, and E are incorrect). The liver is synthesizing glucose from amino acid precursors to raise blood glucose levels for the immune cells and the nervous system (thus, gluconeogenesis is active, and E and F are incorrect). Fatty acid release and oxidation has also been stimulated to provide an energy source for the liver and skeletal muscle (indicating that C, D, and F are incorrect).

CHAPTER 43

1. **The answer is E.** A tumor of the adrenal cortex is secreting excessive amounts of cortisol into the blood, which adversely affects glucose tolerance, suppresses pituitary secretion of ACTH, and, through chronic hypercortisolemia, causes the physical changes described in this patient. Uncomplicated non–insulin-dependent and insulin-dependent diabetes mellitus can be eliminated as possible diagnoses because they are not associated with elevated plasma cortisol levels and low plasma ACTH levels. In this patient, hyperglycemia resulted from the diabetogenic effects of chronic hypercortisolemia. An ACTH-secreting tumor of the anterior pituitary gland would cause hypercortisolemia, which, in turn, could adversely affect glucose tolerance, but in this case, the plasma ACTH levels would have been high rather than 0 pg/mL. The posterior pituitary gland secretes oxytocin and vasopressin, neither of which influences blood glucose, cortisol, nor ACTH levels.

2. **The answer is A.** High blood glucose levels cause a decrease in growth hormone levels in the blood. This fact serves as the basis for the glucose suppression test for growth hormone. Answers B, C, and D all would cause growth hormone levels to increase, whereas answer E would have no effect on the test.

3. **The answer is B.** When iodine is deficient in the diet, the thyroid does not make normal amounts of T_3 and T_4. Consequently, there is less feedback inhibition of TSH production and release; hence, an increased secretion of TSH would be observed. There is no direct effect on thyroglobulin synthesis (thus, A is incorrect). TRH is released by the hypothalamus to release TSH from the pituitary; a lack of thyroid hormone would increase production of TRH, not decrease it (thus, C is incorrect). An overproduction of thyroid hormone leads to increased heat production and weight loss; lack of thyroid hormone does not lead to these symptoms (thus, D and E are incorrect).

4. **The answer is A.** The woman is experiencing hypothyroidism; TSH is elevated in an attempt to secrete more thyroid hormone, as the existing dose is too low to suppress TSH release.

5. **The answer is C.** If 15% of the radioactive T_4 is bound to antibody, the amount of T_4 in 0.1 mL of the patient's serum is 0.015 μg/0.1 mL or 15 μg/dL (1.0 dL = 100 mL).

CHAPTER 44

1. **The answer is A.** Increased 2,3-bisphosphoglycerate in the red cell will favor the deoxy conformation of hemoglobin and thus allow more oxygen to be released in the tissues. This is useful because the hemoglobin is not as saturated at high altitudes as at low elevations because of the lower concentration of oxygen at high altitudes. Answers C and D are incorrect because the red cells do not synthesize proteins. Answer E is incorrect because reducing the blood pH will not aid in oxygen delivery; the Bohr effect works best when tissue pH is lower than blood pH, in order to stabilize the deoxy form of hemoglobin. If the pH of both the blood and the tissue are the same, the Bohr effect will not be able to occur.

2. **The answer is D.** The boy is suffering from lead poisoning, which interrupts heme synthesis at the ALA-dehydratase and ferrochelatase steps. Without heme, the oxygen-carrying capability of blood is reduced, and the flow of electrons through the electron-transfer chain is reduced because of the lack of functional cytochromes. Together, these lead to an inability to generate energy, and fatigue results. Answer A is incorrect because although an iron deficiency would lead to the same symptoms, this would not be expected in the patient because of his daily vitamin uptake. Lead ingestion will not lead to an iron loss. Answers B and C are incorrect because vitamin B_{12} and folate deficiencies will lead to macrocytic anemia due to disruption of DNA synthesis. Answer E is incorrect because the ingestion of paint chips is unlikely to lead to a vitamin B_6 deficiency in a child, particularly one who is taking daily vitamins.

3. **The answer is C.** Turning on a gene that would provide a functional alternative to the β-gene would enable the defective β-protein to be bypassed. Only the γ-chain can do this, but it is normally only found in fetal hemoglobin. The δ-chain is also a β-replacement globin, but it was not listed as a potential answer. Answer D is incorrect because it is the β-chain that is mutated, and it is already being expressed. Unlike the α-gene, of which there are two copies per chromosome, there is only one copy of the β-gene per chromosome. The other genes listed (answers A, B, and E) are α-chain replacements, and expression of these genes will not alleviate the problem inherent in the β-gene.

4. **The answer is D.** The only two types of blood cells that lack nuclei are the mature red blood cell and the platelet. Platelets arise from membrane budding from megakaryocytes and are essentially membrane sacs containing the

cytoplasmic contents of their precursor cell. All of the other cell types listed contain a nucleus.

5. **The answer is D.** Thalassemias result from an imbalance in the synthesis of α- and β-chains. Excessive synthesis of α-chains results in their precipitation in developing red cells, which often kills the developing cell. The more severely affected child has an α/β ratio of 1:5, whereas the less severely affected child has a ratio of 1:2½. When β-chains are in excess, they form stable tetramers that bind but do not release oxygen, thus reducing the red cell's ability to deliver oxygen. Thus, this difference in chain ratio makes an important difference in the functioning of the red cell.

CHAPTER 45

1. **The answer is D.** Under conditions of reduced protein ingestion, essential amino acids are scarce and the liver reduces protein synthesis, including circulating plasma proteins. The reduction of protein in the plasma results in a lower osmotic pressure, so excess fluid in the extravascular spaces cannot return to the blood and remains outside of the circulation, collecting in tissues.

2. **The answer is C.** Warfarin inhibits the reduction of vitamin K epoxide, so active vitamin K levels decrease. The reduction in active vitamin K levels reduces the γ-carboxylation of clotting factors. In the absence of γ-carboxylation, the clotting factors cannot bind to calcium to form membrane-associated complexes with other clotting factors. Warfarin has no effect on the liver's ability to synthesize the clotting factor (the synthesized factor is not modified), nor does warfarin specifically inhibit the activation of factor XIII. The inhibition is more global than just attacking one step in the coagulation cascade. Plasma calcium levels are not altered by warfarin, and protein C activity is actually decreased in the presence of warfarin because protein C is one of the proteins that is γ-carboxylated in a vitamin K–dependent reaction.

3. **The answer is C.** Activated protein C turns off the clotting cascade; in the absence of protein C, regulation of clotting is impaired, and clots can develop when not required. Mutations in any of the other answers listed would lead to excessive bleeding, as an essential component of the clotting cascade would be inactivated.

4. **The answer is C.** Classical hemophilia is the absence of factor VIII, which is a necessary cofactor for the activation of factor X by factor IXa. Factor II is directly activated by factor Xa, and factor IX is directly activated by factor XIa. Proteins C and S are directly activated by thrombin, factor IIa.

5. **The answer is B.** Hemophilia B is an inactivating mutation in factor IX, such that factor IXa cannot be formed. Factor XIa is formed but its substrate, factor IX, is defective, and a nonactive protein results.

CHAPTER 46

1. **The answer is C.** Grapefruit juice contains a component that blocks *CYP3A4* activity, which is the cytochrome P450 isozyme that converts statins to an inactive form. If the degradative enzyme is inhibited, statin levels rise above normal, accelerating their damage of muscle cells. Grapefruit juice does not affect hepatic uptake of the drug (thus, A is incorrect), nor is it accelerating statin metabolism (thus, B is also incorrect). Although HMG-CoA reductase is the target of the statins, grapefruit juice neither upregulates nor downregulates the amount of enzyme present in the cell (thus, D and E are incorrect).

2. **The answer is D.** Cytochrome P450 enzymes oxidize their substrates, transferring the electrons to molecular oxygen to form water and a hydroxylated product. The enzymes require NADPH (thus, B is incorrect) and are located in the endoplasmic reticulum membrane (thus, A is incorrect). Oxygen does not induce all cytochrome P450 members (although it is a substrate for all these isozymes; thus, C is incorrect), and although these enzymes proceed through a free radical mechanism, the final products are not radicals (thus, E is incorrect).

3. **The answer is D.** Hepatocellular disease reduces protein synthesis in the liver, which leads to reduced levels of both LCAT and hepatic triglyceride lipase being produced (thus, A and C are incorrect). Because LCAT activity is reduced, cholesterol ester formation in circulating particles is reduced (thus, B is incorrect). Because a diseased liver has trouble synthesizing glucose, fatty acid release from adipocytes is increased to provide energy (thus, E is incorrect). Serum triacylglycerol levels are increased as a result of the reduced hepatic triglyceride lipase activity; LPL activity is also reduced in liver disease.

4. **The answer is D.** Ethanol induces the *CYP2E1* system, which converts acetaminophen to NAPQI, a toxic intermediate. Under normal conditions (noninduced levels of *CYP2E1*), the conversion of acetaminophen to NAPQI results in low levels of NAPQI being produced, which can easily be detoxified. However, when *CYP2E1* is induced, the excessive levels of NAPQI being produced when Tylenol is taken in greater than recommended amounts cannot be readily detoxified, and NAPQI binds to proteins and inactivates them, leading to hepatocyte death. The toxicity is neither related to blood glucose levels (thus, A and C are incorrect), nor to secretion of VLDL (thus, E is incorrect). Ethanol does not inhibit the detoxification of Tylenol per se, but rather accelerates one of its potential metabolic fates (thus, B is also incorrect).

5. **The answer is C.** The glucokinase-regulatory protein regulates glucokinase expression at a posttranscriptional level. A lack of regulatory protein activity results in less glucokinase being present in the cell and a reduced overall rate of glucose phosphorylation by the liver. This results

in less circulating glucose being removed by the liver, and a longer clearance time for glucose levels to return to fasting levels. A decrease in the glucokinase K_m, or an increase in the V_{max} for glucokinase, would lead to the opposite effect, enhanced glucose phosphorylation by the liver, and an accelerated clearance from the circulation (thus, A and B are incorrect). The liver does not express hexokinase, so D and E are also incorrect.

CHAPTER 47

1. **The answer is C.** Stretching aids in stimulating blood flow to the muscles, which enhances oxidative muscle metabolism (by allowing for better oxygen delivery). Stretching, per se, does not stimulate epinephrine release (thus, A is incorrect), nor does it activate glycolysis in either the liver or muscle.

2. **The answer is D.** Adipose triacylglycerol is the largest energy store in the body and is the predominant fuel in long-term aerobic exercise. During exercise, muscle glycogen is used for bursts of speed but not for long-term energy requirements. Liver glycogen is used to maintain blood glucose levels for use by the nervous system and as a supplement for use by the muscle when rapid speed is required; however, it is not designed to be a long-term energy source. The brain does not contain significant levels of glycogen, and lactic acid produced by the red blood cells is used as a gluconeogenic precursor by liver, but not as a fuel for muscle.

3. **The answer is D.** Creatine is synthesized from glycine, arginine, and *S*-adenosylmethionine (thus, intake of dietary creatine is not relevant). In muscle, creatine is converted to creatine phosphate, which is nonenzymatically cyclized to form creatinine (thus, C is incorrect). The amount of creatinine excreted by the kidneys each day depends on body muscle mass but is constant for each individual (therefore, if there is an increase in body muscle mass, there would be an increase in creatinine excretion). In kidney failure, the excretion of creatinine into the urine is low, and an elevation of serum creatinine would be observed.

4. **The answer is E.** Glycine is required for the synthesis of heme (combining with succinyl-CoA in the initial step), for the synthesis of purine rings (the entire glycine molecule is incorporated into adenine and guanine), and for creatine, where glycine reacts with arginine in the first step.

5. **The answer is C.** A decrease in the concentration of ATP (which occurs as muscle contracts) stimulates processes that generate ATP. The proton gradient across the inner mitochondrial membrane decreases as protons enter the matrix via the ATPase to synthesize ATP; NADH oxidation by the electron-transport chain increases to reestablish the proton gradient; fuel use also increases to generate more ATP. Glycogen synthesis is inhibited because of phosphorylation of glycogen synthase as induced by epinephrine. Palmitate is oxidized and glycolysis increases because of the activation of PFK-1 by AMP. As ATP decreases, AMP rises as a result of the myokinase reaction (2ADP → ATP + AMP).

CHAPTER 48

1. **The answer is B.** The symptoms exhibited by the patient are caused by excessive release of epinephrine or norepinephrine. Vanillylmandelic acid is also the degradation product of norepinephrine; thus, these hormones are being overproduced. Acetylcholine degradation leads to the formation of acetic acid and choline, which are not observed (thus, A is incorrect). Although dopa degradation could lead to vanillylmandelic acid production, serotonin degradation does not (it leads to 5-hydroxyindoleacetic acid), and the symptoms exhibited by the patient are not consistent with dopa or serotonin overproduction (thus, C is incorrect). Histamine and melatonin also do not produce the symptoms exhibited by the patient (thus, D and E are incorrect).

2. **The answer is A.** Myelin contains very high levels of cholesterol and cerebrosides, particularly galactosylcerebrosides.

3. **The answer is E.** Myelin basic protein is a basic protein, indicating that it must contain a significant number of lysine and arginine residues. MBP is found on the intracellular side of the myelin membrane, and its role is to compact the membrane by binding to negative charges on both sides of it, thereby reducing the "width" of the membrane. Both Schwann cells and oligodendrocytes synthesize myelin (thus, A is incorrect). MBP is not a transmembrane protein (proteolipid protein in the CNS and Po in the PNS are, so B is incorrect), and because MBP is found intracellularly, answers C and D cannot be correct.

4. **The answer is A.** The accumulation of both phytanic acid and very long-chain fatty acids indicates a problem in peroxisomal fatty acid oxidation, which is where α-oxidation occurs. Lysosomal transport is, therefore, not required to metabolize these fatty acids (thus, C is incorrect). The finding that palmitate levels are low indicates that β-oxidation is occurring; therefore, answer B is incorrect. The compounds that accumulate are not mucopolysaccharides nor is fatty acid elongation required in the metabolism of these compounds (thus, D and E are incorrect).

5. **The answer is D.** Vitamin B_6 participates in transamination and decarboxylation reactions (and indirectly in deamination reactions). The one common feature in the synthesis of serotonin, GABA, norepinephrine, and histamine is decarboxylation of an amino acid, which requires vitamin B_6. The other reactions are not required in the biosynthesis of these neurotransmitters.

CHAPTER 49

1. **The answer is E.** Scurvy is caused by a deficiency of vitamin C. Vitamin C is a required cofactor for the hydroxylation of both proline and lysine residues in collagen. The hydroxyproline residues that are formed stabilize the triple helix through the formation of hydrogen bonds with other collagen molecules within the helix. The loss of this stabilizing force greatly reduces the strength of the collagen fibers. The hydroxylation of lysine allows carbohydrates to be attached to collagen, although the role of the carbohydrates is still unknown. Vitamin C is not required for disulfide bond formation, the formation of lysyl cross-links (that enzyme is lysyl oxidase), secretion of tropocollagen, or the formation of collagen fibrils. Thus, all the other choices are incorrect.

2. **The answer is C.** When elastin expands as a result of outside forces (such as the respiratory muscles causing the lungs to expand with air), hydrophobic regions of elastin are exposed to the aqueous environment, resulting in a decrease in the entropy of water. When the outside force is removed (by relaxation of the respiratory muscles), the driving force for contraction of elastin is an increase in the entropy of water, so that the hydrophobic residues of elastin are again shielded from the environment. The expansion and contraction of elastin does not involve covalent modifications (thus, A, B, and E are incorrect), nor does it involve extensive changes in salt bridge formation (thus, D is also incorrect).

3. **The answer is B.** Glycosaminoglycan chains contain negative charges, resulting from the presence of acidic sugars and the sulfated sugars in the molecule. Thus, in their characteristic bottleneck structure, the chains repel each other (thus, A is incorrect), yet they also attract positively charged cations and water into the spaces between the chains. The water forms hydrogen bonds with the sugars and a gel-like space is created. This gel acts as a diffusion sieve for materials that leave, or enter, this space. Hydroxylation and cross-linking of chains does not occur (thus, D and E are incorrect), nor does hydrogen bonding between chains (they are too far apart because of the charge repulsion, but they do form hydrogen bonds with water).

4. **The answer is E.** In order for cells to migrate, they must free themselves from the extracellular matrix material, which requires remodeling of the matrix components. Because of the unique structural aspects of these components, only a small subset of proteases, the metalloproteinases, is capable of doing this. The other answers listed are all components of the matrix, which must be remodeled in order for cell migration to occur.

5. **The answer is C.** Fibronectin binds to integrins on the cell surface, as well as to various extracellular matrix components (collagen and glycosaminoglycans). This binding fixes the position of the cell within the matrix. Loss of these binding components can lead to undesirable cell movement. Fibronectin plays no role in any of the other functions listed as possible answers.

Patient Index

Note: Page numbers followed by *f* denote figures.

Index

Note: Page numbers followed by *f* denote figures; page numbers followed by *t* denote tables.

Mammalian target of rapamycin (TOR), 791
Mammary gland, 587
Mannose, 549, 550
  interconversion of, 549, 550*f*
  structure and functions of, 549
Mannose-6-phosphate synthesis, 553*f*
MAP kinase, in oncogenesis, 315–316, 317*f*
MAPKKK, 180
Maple syrup urine disease, 736, 741*t*, 742*t*, 908
Marasmus, 13, 19*t*, 31
Marfan syndrome, 934
Markers, polymorphic, 299
Mast cells, histamine synthesis by, 913–914
Matrix metalloproteinases (MMP), 881, 939
Maturity-onset diabetes of the young (MODY), 485, 492*t*
MCAD deficiency, 422, 423, 432–433, 435*t*
McArdle disease, 517–518, 518*t*
mdm2 gene, 320
Mean corpuscular hemoglobin concentration (MCHC), 826
Mean corpuscular volume (MCV), 826
Mechanical work, energy transformations for, 341, 341*f*
Medium-chain acyl CoA dehydrogenase (MCAD) deficiency, 422, 423, 432–433, 435*t*
Medium-chain-length fatty acid–activating enzyme (MMFAE), 876, 877
Medium-chain-length fatty acid oxidation, 415*f*, 423
Medium-chain-length triacylglycerols (triglycerides), 876
Megakaryocytes, 850
Megaloblast, 745, 750
Megaloblastic anemia, 13*t*, 745
  alcohol-induced, 745–746, 750, 758*t*
  pathophysiology of, 750
  treatment of, 750
  from vitamin B₁₂ deficiency, 745, 839
Megaloblastic madness, 753
Melanin synthesis, 910*f*
Melanocyte
  function of, 312
  tyrosine hydroxylase of, in albinism, 912
Melanoma, 218, 225*t*, 312
  hereditary risk factors in, 319
  incidence of, 223
  malignant, 225*t*, 331*t*
    hereditary risk factors in, 319
    incidence of, 223
    mutations in, 329
    risk factors in, 319
MELAS, 387*t*
Melatonin, as antioxidant, 452, 452*f*
Melting, DNA, 200
Membrane attack, by free radicals, 442, 442*f*, 443*f*
Membrane, plasma, 154–161. *See also* Plasma membrane
Membranes, 153–154
Menadione, 853*f*, 855*f*
Menaquinone, 853*f*, 855*f*
MEOS. *See* Microsomal ethanol oxidizing system (MEOS)
MERRF, 387, 387*t*
Mesangium, 941, 941*f*
Messenger, chemical, 172–176. *See also* Chemical messengers; *specific messengers*
Messenger RNA (mRNA), 145, 191
  degradation of, regulation of, 284, 284*f*
  in *E. coli*, 267, 267*f*
  promoter regions of genes for, 231–233, 231*f*, 232*f*

reading frame of, 251, 251*f*
stabilization of, 145
structure of, 204, 204*f*
synthesis of, 235–237, 235*f*–238*f*
  intron removal in, 235*f*, 237, 237*f*, 238*f*
  overview of, 235, 235*f*
  poly(A) tail addition in, 236–237, 236*f*
  transcription and capping in, 235–236, 236*f*
transport and stability of, 284, 284*f*
Metabolic acid, 41
  buffers and, 47–50
    bicarbonate and hemoglobin in red blood cells in, 45*t*, 48–49, 49*f*
    bicarbonate buffer system in, 48, 48*f*, 49*f*
    hydrochloric acid in, 50
    intracellular pH in, 45*t*, 49–50, 49*f*
    principles of, 47
    sources of, 47
    urinary hydrogen, ammonium, and phosphate ions in, 45*t*, 46*f*, 50
Metabolic acidosis, 46, 410, 458
Metabolic capacities, by tissue, 34*t*
Metabolic diseases, 39. *See also specific diseases*
Metabolic encephalopathies, 918–920
  glutamine synthesis and anaplerotic pathways of pyruvate carboxylase and methylmalonyl-CoA mutase in, 920
  hypoglycemic, 918–919, 919*f*
  hypoxic, 920
Metabolic fatigue, in exercise, 895
Metabolic homeostasis, 478–480, 479*f*
Metabolic homeostasis hormones, 480–482. *See also specific hormones*
  glucagon in, 480–481, 481*f*
  glucose, insulin, and glucagon levels in, blood, 481, 481*f*
  insulin counterregulatory hormones in, 477, 478*f*, 481, 482*t*
  insulin in, 477, 478*f*, 480, 480*f*
  metabolites in, circulating levels of, 481
Metabolic rate, resting, 8, 9*t*, 390
Metabolic syndrome, 27, 490, 622–624, 623*f*
  drugs for, 659
    fibrates, 660
    metformin, 659–660, 660*f*
    thiazolidinediones, 660–661
  insulin resistance in, 484*f*, 623
  NADPH from islet cell pyruvate cycling in, 623–624, 623*f*
  signs and symptoms of, 627–628
Metabolism. *See also specific types*
  energy from, 4
  fuel, 1–2, 2*f*, 24, 333–334, 333*f*, 334*f* (*See also specific fuels*)
  oxygen in, 3
  thermodynamics of, 342
Metabolites. *See also specific reactions and types*
  blood and urine measurements of, 36
  circulating, on metabolic homeostasis, 481
Metachromatic leukodystrophy, 554*t*
Metal ions, in catalysis, 122*f*, 126, 126*f*
Metanephrine, plasma fractionated, 912
Metaphase, 192
Metastasis, 192, 194, 312, 939
Metathyroid diabetes mellitus, 813
Metformin, 659–660, 660*f*
Methanol toxicity, 54
Methemoglobinemia, congenital, 828, 845*t*
Methionine
  chemical structure of, 74*f*, 75*t*, 76
  degradation of, 734, 734*f*
  from homocysteine, 752*f*

in homocystinuria, 731–732
in *S*-adenosylmethionine synthesis, 752–753, 753*f*
sulfur in, 74*f*, 75*t*, 76
Methotrexate, 274
  mechanism of action of, 750, 750*f*
  structure of, 749–750, 749*f*
Methylated norepinephrine, 912
Methylation
  DNA, 273
  in genomic imprinting, 273
Methyl-B₁₂ deficiency, 734
Methyl caps
  synthesis of, 235–236, 236*f*
  types of, 235, 235*f*
Methylmalonyl-CoA mutase, 920
Methylprednisolone
  for asthma, 561
  muscle weakness from, 561, 564
Methyltetrahydrofolate deficiency, 734
Methyl-trap hypothesis, 753
Methylxanthines, on fuel metabolism, 487–488
Metronidazole, 867
Mevalonate, from acetyl-CoA, 630–632, 630*f*, 631*f*
Micelles, 64, 588, 588*f*
Michaelis–Menten equation, 137–138, 137*f*
Microarrays, 300
Microfilaments, 166, 168*f*
Microglial cells, 906
Micronodular cirrhosis, 879
MicroRNAs (miRNAs), 303
  apoptosis and, 326
  definition and function of, 206, 229–230
  gene expression regulation by, 283–284, 283*f*
  in non-Hodgkin's lymphomas, 283
  as proto-oncogenes, 315
Microsomal enzymes, 868
Microsomal ethanol oxidizing system (MEOS), 136, 459*f*, 868
  alcoholism on, 148, 165, 463
  compartmentation in, 147
  cytochrome P450 enzymes in CYPE2E1 in, 459, 461–462
    induction of, 462
    structure and function of, 459, 461, 461*f*
  function of, 136
Microsomal triglyceride transfer protein (MTP), 594–595, 595*f*, 608
Microsomal triglyceride transfer protein (MTP) inhibitors, 595
Microsomes, 165, 461
Microtubules, 165–166, 165*f*
Microvascular complications, of diabetes mellitus, 480, 578–579, 940–942, 941*f*
Midarm anthropometry, 27
Midarm arm muscle circumference (MUAMC), 27–28
Milk, human breast, 587
Mineralocorticoid synthesis, 651, 652, 653*f*
Minerals. *See also specific minerals*
  dietary, 14–15, 15*t*
  dietary guidelines for, 16–17
Minor grooves, in DNA, 198, 199*f*
Mismatch repair, 220, 221*f*
Missense mutations, 251*t*, 252
Mitochondria, 163–164, 163*f*
  apoptosis and, 393
  compartmentation of enzymes of, 374
  cyanide poisoning on, 386
  DNA in, 194–195
  doxorubicin on, 379
  glutathione and glutathione peroxidase in, 450
  oxidative metabolism in, 333–334, 334*f*